Date Due

DEC 3 68	MAR 3 0 2005	
FE. 4 70		
MR 18 71		
MY 29 73		
DEC 10 74		
MAY 27 75		
DEC 15 78		
DEC 10 85		
MAY 12 1992		
APR 29 1994		

REAGENT CHEMICALS AND STANDARDS

WITH

METHODS OF TESTING AND ASSAYING

REAGENT
CHEMICALS AND STANDARDS

WITH

METHODS OF TESTING AND ASSAYING THEM; ALSO
THE PREPARATION AND STANDARDIZATION OF
VOLUMETRIC SOLUTIONS AND EXTENSIVE
TABLES OF EQUIVALENTS

by

JOSEPH ROSIN

Member American Chemical Society; the U. S. Pharmacopoeia Revision Committee
Formerly Chief Chemist and Chemical Director Merck & Co., Inc.

FIFTH EDITION

D. VAN NOSTRAND COMPANY, INC.

PRINCETON, NEW JERSEY

TORONTO   LONDON

PREFACE

A fifth edition of a book, one might think, needs no introduction or preface. Even so, the users of the book are indeed entitled to a survey of the progress in the new edition, and to a presentation of the new features and improvements. This objective, the author believes, is realized, necessarily in a condensed form, in the following paragraphs.

About 30 new reagents have been incorporated in the new edition. Among them are: Dianthrimide—for boron; Dimethylsulfoxide—a solvent miscible with water and organic liquids; Furildioxime—a very sensitive reagent for nickel, more sensitive than dimethylglyoxime; L-Glutamic Acid, Nicotinamide and Pyridoxine Hydrochloride—as standards for the evaluation of the substances in commercial preparations of these products; Osmium Tetroxide—a powerful catalyst for chemical interactions; Propionic Acid; Silver Chloride; Titanium Dioxide—a standard for titanium; and Uranyl-Zinc Acetate Crystals.

A special chapter on flame photometry is included in the new edition. It presents a procedure for the determination of small amounts (0.01% or less) or alkali or alkaline-earth impurities in the presence of large amounts of other elements of their groups, as is the case with reagents of these elements, e.g., sodium in reagents of lithium, potassium, magnesium, etc.

Assays have been added to over 15 of the reagents in the preceding edition, and many of the new reagents are provided with assays. It is the author's conviction that a reasonably accurate assay is a *positive* evaluation of quality.

The proper composition of the complex-inorganic reagents, such as Phosphotungstic Acid or Sodium Cobaltinitrite, is now proven by assays. The quality of Potassium and Sodium Perchlorates is also attested in this way.

If so desired, such small amounts of nitrate as may occur as an impurity in reagent chemicals (0.01% or less) may be readily determined quantitatively.

Several of the tests for impurities have been revised or refined. Quantities of less than 0.1 gram are expressed in milligrams, thus eliminating small decimal quantities.

JOSEPH ROSIN

December 1966

CONTENTS

TABLE OF ATOMIC WEIGHTS, 1961

(Based on Carbon-12)

Element	Symbol	Atomic Number	Atomic Weight
Actinium	Ac	89	
Aluminum	Al	13	26.9815
Americium	Am	95	
Antimony	Sb	51	121.75
Argon	Ar	18	39.948
Arsenic	As	33	74.9216
Astatine	At	85	
Barium	Ba	56	137.34
Berkelium	Bk	97	
Beryllium	Be	4	9.0122
Bismuth	Bi	83	208.980
Boron	B	5	10.811 ($\pm$0.003, nat.)
Bromine	Br	35	79.909 ($\pm$0.002, exp.)
Cadmium	Cd	48	112.40
Calcium	Ca	20	40.08
Californium	Cf	98	
Carbon	C	6	12.01115 ($\pm$0.00005, nat.)
Cerium	Ce	58	140.12
Cesium	Cs	55	132.905
Chlorine	Cl	17	35.453 ($\pm$0.001, exp.)
Chromium	Cr	24	51.996 ($\pm$0.001, exp.)
Cobalt	Co	27	58.9332
Copper	Cu	29	63.54
Curium	Cm	96	
Dysprosium	Dy	66	162.50
Einsteinium	Es	99	
Erbium	Er	68	167.26
Europium	Eu	63	151.96
Fermium	Fm	100	
Fluorine	F	9	18.9984
Francium	Fr	87	
Gadolinium	Gd	64	157.25
Gallium	Ga	31	69.72
Germanium	Ge	32	72.59
Gold	Au	79	196.967
Hafnium	Hf	72	178.49
Helium	He	2	4.0026
Holmium	Ho	67	164.930
Hydrogen	H	1	1.00797 ($\pm$0.00001, nat.)
Indium	In	49	114.82
Iodine	I	53	126.9044
Iridium	Ir	77	192.2
Iron	Fe	26	55.847 ($\pm$0.003, exp.)
Krypton	Kr	36	83.80
Lanthanum	La	57	138.91
Lead	Pb	82	207.19
Lithium	Li	3	6.939
Lutetium	Lu	71	174.97
Magnesium	Mg	12	24.312
Manganese	Mn	25	54.9380
Mendelevium	Md	101	
Mercury	Hg	80	200.59
Molybdenum	Mo	42	95.94
Neodymium	Nd	60	144.24

TABLE OF ATOMIC WEIGHTS, 1961 *(Continued)*

Element	Symbol	Atomic Number	Atomic Weight
Neon	Ne	10	20.183
Neptunium	Np	93	
Nickel	Ni	28	58.71
Niobium	Nb	41	92.906
Nitrogen	N	7	14.0067
Nobelium	No	102	
Osmium	Os	76	190.2
Oxygen	O	8	15.9994 (±0.0001, nat.)
Palladium	Pd	46	106.4
Phosphorus	P	15	30.9738
Platinum	Pt	78	195.09
Plutonium	Pu	94	
Polonium	Po	84	
Potassium	K	19	39.102
Praseodymium	Pr	59	140.907
Promethium	Pm	61	
Protactinium	Pa	91	
Radium	Ra	88	
Radon	Rn	86	
Rhenium	Re	75	186.2
Rhodium	Rh	45	102.905
Rubidium	Rb	37	85.47
Ruthenium	Ru	44	101.07
Samarium	Sm	62	150.35
Scandium	Sc	21	44.956
Selenium	Se	34	78.96
Silicon	Si	14	28.086 (±0.001, nat.)
Silver	Ag	47	107.870 (±0.003, exp.)
Sodium	Na	11	22.9898
Strontium	Sr	38	87.62
Sulfur	S	16	32.064 (±0.003, nat.)
Tantalum	Ta	73	180.948
Technetium	Tc	43	
Tellurium	Te	52	127.60
Terbium	Tb	65	158.924
Thallium	Tl	81	204.37
Thorium	Th	90	232.038
Thulium	Tm	69	168.934
Tin	Sn	50	118.69
Titanium	Ti	22	47.90
Tungsten	W	74	183.85
Uranium	U	92	238.03
Vanadium	V	23	50.942
Xenon	Xe	54	131.30
Ytterbium	Yb	70	173.04
Yttrium	Y	39	88.905
Zinc	Zn	30	65.37
Zirconium	Zr	40	91.22

nat. = Variation in atomic weight due to
natural variation in the isotopic composition.
exp. = Experimental uncertainty of magnitude given.

Adopted 1961 by the International Union of Pure and Applied Chemistry.

EXPLANATORY NOTES

The reagents used in making the tests should be of the grade herein described.

Acids (HCl, HNO_3, H_2SO_4) and **Ammonium Hydroxide** (NH_4OH): Wherever these reagents are specified by their names or by their symbols with no qualification as to strength or dilution, the full-strength reagent acid or ammonium hydroxide is to be used.

Dilution indicated for instance by "(1+9)" means that one volume of the acid or other liquid reagent is to be diluted with nine volumes of water unless otherwise specified.

Percentage is understood to mean percentage of weight.

Alcohol: Alcohol means 95% ethyl alcohol, by volume, unless otherwise stated.

Ammonia Water is synonymous with Ammonium Hydroxide.

Ammonia Tests (Colorimetric): The "NH_3" added to the blank or control is in the form of a solution of ammonium chloride. The standard ammonium chloride solution for this purpose is described on page 8. If the solution in the test for ammonia has to be filtered, the filter should first be thoroughly washed with water to remove from it any ammonium compounds. After the Nessler solution has been added, the solutions are stirred and the colors compared immediately.

Arsenic (Per Cent vs. Parts per Million (ppm)): In view of the fact that the amount (per cent) of arsenic in reagents as an impurity is minute, it is more convenient to express it in terms of parts per million—usually abbreviated as ppm. This term is widely used for stating small amounts of many other substances and we have adopted it in this edition. One part per million = 0.0001%.

Blanks and Controls: A blank differs from the test made on the sample only in that the sample is omitted. The same quantities of the same reagents and water are to be used, and the same procedure followed, including filtration, heating, cooling, etc. When a portion of a solution is used in making a test, it is understood that proportionate quantities of the reagents are to be used in making the blank.

Wherever the use of a **control** is directed, the quantities of the reagents to be used are specified in each instance.

In either case, the final volume of the test with the sample, and that of the blank or control, is adjusted to the same volume with water. Also the solutions are to be at the same temperature, before adding the reagent producing the color or turbidity. This reagent is added to the two solutions in immediate sequence.

Colorimetric and Turbidimetric Tests: The substances used for comparisons in blanks or controls, Cl, N, SO_4, Pb, Fe, etc., are ionized salts. They are added in the form of standard solutions described on pages 8–10.

The solution to be tested turbidimetrically must be perfectly clear before the precipitating reagent is added. If not clear it must be filtered through filter paper, previously well washed with water or with water slightly acidulated with the acid used in the test—nitric acid for chloride, and hydrochloric acid for sulfate.

Chloride Tests: The "Cl" added to the control or blank refers to ionic chloride. The standard chloride solution for this purpose is described on page 8.

Before adding the silver nitrate, the solutions are filtered if not perfectly clear. The turbidities are compared 5 minutes after the silver nitrate has been added.

Controls: See **Blanks and Controls.**

Dilutions: Where the diluent is not specified, dilution is made with water.

Heavy Metals Test: For the observation or comparison of the color in this test Nessler tubes are preferably to be used. The solutions are viewed downwards while held over a white surface. The tubes used for the sample and the blank or control should be of practically colorless glass, and of the same internal diameter.

The color is observed or compared 5 minutes after the addition of the hydrogen sulfide water.

The "Pb" or other metal added to the blank or control is used in the form of standard solutions, described on page 9.

Hydrogen Sulfide: When the directions specify the use of a volume (ml) of H_2S, it is understood that that volume of a freshly prepared, saturated aqueous solution of hydrogen sulfide is to be used.

Ignition Residue: The sample is ignited to constant weight at the lowest temperature at which it will be volatilized; or, in the case of organic compounds, at the lowest temperature at which the carbon formed is completely burned away.

Insoluble: Where the solution is required to be heated, it is to be contained in a covered beaker, and any loss, due to evaporation, is to be restored by the addition of water.

If an insoluble residue remains, it is collected by filtration of the solution through a filtering crucible or a Gooch crucible with an asbestos pad, which has been thoroughly washed with the same solvents used with the sample, dried to constant weight at the temperature directed for drying the residue, and tared. The undissolved residue is then washed thoroughly with water or the special solution or solvent specified, then dried and weighed.

Iron, Tests for: The "Fe" added to the blank or control is to be in the form of ferric ions. The standard iron solution for this purpose is described on page 9. Two minutes is to be allowed for development of the color, before comparison.

Nitrogen Tests (Colorimetric): The "N" added to the blank or control is in the form of ammonium chloride. The standard nitrogen solution for this purpose is described on page 9. After the Nessler solution has been added, the solutions are stirred and the colors compared immediately.

Phosphate Tests: The "PO_4" added to the control or blank is to be in the form of ionic ortho-phosphate. The standard phosphate solution for this purpose is described on page 9.

Solutions Used as Reagents: See pages 3–7.

Specific Gravity (Sp. gr.): Unless otherwise indicated, the specific gravities of liquids in this book refer to the ratio of the weight of the liquid, in air, at 25° to that of an equal volume of water at the same temperature.

Sulfate Tests (Turbidimetric): The "SO_4" directed to be added to the control or blank refers to ionic sulfate. The standard sulfate solution for this purpose is described on page 10.

Before making the test, the solution should be filtered if not perfectly clear. The turbidities are compared 10 to 20 minutes after the barium chloride solution has been added.

Temperatures given in this book refer to centigrade scale.

Turbidimetric Tests: See **Colorimetric and Turbidimetric Tests.**

Washing: Unless the use of another solvent is directed, washing is to be done with water.

Water: The water used in the tests and assays as well as in the preparation of reagent and standard solutions is water distilled from a glass (enamel) lined still, preferably in the laboratory or plant where it is used. In addition to being "free" from anionic and cathionic impurities, it should also comply with the following test for oxidizable impurities: To 200 ml of the water add 1.5 ml of H_2SO_4, heat to boiling, add 0.05 ml of 0.1 N $KMnO_4$ and continue boiling for 10 minutes. At the end of this time the pink color should not have completely disappeared.

SOLUTIONS USED AS REAGENTS

When the directions call for a volume (ml) of the reagents, the solution, prepared as described below, is to be used.

When dilution is indicated by " $(1+x)$ " it means that one volume of the solution is to be diluted with x volumes of water.

Acetic Acid: When a test calls for acetic acid the glacial acid is to be used, unless otherwise qualified.

Acetic Acid 1 N: Dilute 57.5 ml of the glacial acid with water to 1 liter.

Acetic Acid 36% (6 N): Dilute 345 ml of glacial acetic acid with water to 1 liter.

Acids and Ammonia: See **Acids and Ammonium Hydroxide,** page 1.

Alcohol: Alcohol means 95% of ethyl alcohol, by volume, unless otherwise stated.

Alcohol 50% (by volume): Dilute 100 volumes of alcohol with 95 volumes of water.

Alcohol 70% (by volume): Dilute 100 volumes of alcohol with 39 volumes of water.

Aluminon: Dissolve 100 mg of aurintricarboxylic acid or its ammonium salt in a mixture of 10 ml of water and 1 ml of ammonium hydroxide and dilute to 100 ml.

Ammonia, 10% NH_3: Dilute 400 ml of ammonium hydroxide with water to 1 liter.

Ammonia, 2.5% NH_3: Dilute 10 ml of ammonium hydroxide with water to 100 ml.

Ammonium Acetate: Dissolve 10 g of ammonium acetate in water to make 100 ml.

Ammonium Carbonate: Dissolve 20 g of ammonium carbonate and 20 ml of 10% ammonia (NH_3) in water to make 100 ml.

Ammonium Citrate Deleaded: Dissolve 40 g of ammonium citrate (dibasic) in water to make about 90 ml. Add 2 drops of phenol red solution, then make the solution slightly alkaline with ammonia and dilute to 100 ml. To remove any lead, etc., that it may contain, shake the solution with 2 or more 30-ml portions of a solution of 25 mg of dithizone per liter of chloroform until the original color of the dithizone solution remains unchanged.

Ammonia-Cyanide: Dissolve 2 g of potassium cyanide in 15 ml of ammonium hydroxide, and dilute with water to 100 ml.

Ammonium Molybdate-Nitric Acid (for the gravimetric or volumetric determination of phosphorus): Dissolve 100 g of 85% molybdic acid in a mixture of 240 ml of water and 140 ml of ammonium hydroxide. Filter, add 60 ml of nitric acid, and cool. Add the solution, with constant stirring, to a cooled mixture of 400 ml of nitric acid and 960 ml of water. Then add a solution of 0.1 g of ammonium phosphate, let stand for 24 to 48 hours, and filter. Filter or decant the clear solution, if necessary, before use.

Ammonium Molybdate (for the colorimetric determination of phosphate): Dissolve 5 g of ammonium molybdate in 100 ml of 1 N H_2SO_4.

Ammonium Oxalate: Dissolve 4 g of ammonium oxalate in water to make 100 ml.

Ammonium Phosphate: Dissolve 13 g of dibasic ammonium phosphate in water to make 100 ml.

Ammonium Thiocyanate: Dissolve 25 g of ammonium thiocyanate in water to make 100 ml.

Barium Chloride: Dissolve 100 g of barium chloride in water to make 1 liter.

Bromocresol Green Indicator (acid-base): Dissolve 100 mg in 100 ml of alcohol.

Bromocresol Purple Indicator (acid-base): Dissolve 100 mg in 100 ml of alcohol.

Bromine Water: A saturated aqueous solution of bromine. Keep in tightly closed, glass-stoppered bottles protected from light.

Bromophenol Blue Indicator (acid-base): Dissolve 100 mg in 100 ml of 50% alcohol.

Bromothymol Blue Indicator (acid-base): Dissolve 100 mg in 100 ml of 50% alcohol.

Brucine Sulfate: Dissolve 1.0 g of brucine sulfate in water to make 100 ml.

Butanolic Potassium Thiocyanate: Dissolve 10 g of potassium thiocyanate in 10 ml of water. Warm the solution to 25°–30°, add n-butanol to measure 100 ml and shake vigorously until clear.

Calcium Chloride: Dissolve 10 g of calcium dihydrate in water to make 100 ml.

Calcium Sulfate: A saturated aqueous solution of calcium sulfate.

Chlorine Water: A saturated aqueous solution of chlorine. It can also be prepared by adding some hydrochloric acid (35% to 38%) to a 5% aqueous solution of potassium chlorate. It must be freshly prepared.

Clayton Yellow: See **Thiazole Yellow.**

Dimethylglyoxime: Dissolve 1.0 g of dimethylglyoxime in alcohol to make 100 ml.

Diphenylamine: Dissolve 100 mg of diphenylamine in a mixture of 25 ml of H_2SO_4 and 25 ml of water, add 2 ml of HCl and sufficient H_2SO_4 to make 100 ml.

Diphenylbenzidine: Dissolve 100 mg of diphenylbenzidine in a mixture of 20 ml of H_2SO_4 and 10 ml of water, then add H_2SO_4 to make 100 ml.

Dithizone Extraction Solutions:

In **Carbon Tetrachloride,** or in **Chloroform:** Dissolve 30 mg of dithizone in 1 liter of carbon tetrachloride, or in 1 liter of chloroform.

Dithizone Standard Solutions:

In **Carbon Tetrachloride,** or in **Chloroform:** Dissolve 10 mg of dithizone in 1 liter of carbon tetrachloride or in 1 liter of chloroform. Keep all dithizone solution in glass-stoppered lead-free bottles protected from light and in a refrigerator.

Eosin Solution (adsorption indicator): Dissolve 500 mg in 100 ml of water.

Ferric Ammonium Sulfate Indicator Solution: Dissolve 10 g of ferric ammonium sulfate in freshly boiled and cooled water containing a few drops of H_2SO_4 and dilute to 100 ml.

Ferric Chloride: Dissolve 100 g of ferric chloride in water, and add 2 ml of HCl and water to make 1 liter.

Ferric Nitrate: Dissolve 10 g in water, add 1 ml of nitric acid and dilute to 100 ml.

Ferrous Sulphate: Dissolve 10 g of uneffloresced crystals of ferrous sulfate in 100 ml of recently boiled and cooled water containing 5 drops of H_2SO_4. It must be freshly prepared when required for use.

Fuchsine-Sulfurous Acid: Dissolve 200 mg of fuchsine in 120 ml of hot water, cool and add a solution of 2 g sodium sulfite in 20 ml of water. Follow with 2 ml of hydrochloric acid, dilute to 200 ml and let stand for 1 hour. It must be quite fresh when used.

Hydrochloric Acid, 20% HCl: Dilute 470 ml of hydrochloric acid with water to 1 liter.

Hydrochloric Acid, 10% HCl: Dilute 235 ml of hydrochloric acid with water to 1 liter.

Hydrogen Sulfide: A freshly prepared, saturated, aqueous solution of H_2S.

Hydroxylamine Hydrochloride (for use in the dithizone determination of heavy metals): Dissolve 10 g in 30 ml of water, add a few drops of thymol blue indicator solution, and follow with 10% NH_3 until the solution is yellow. Add 10 ml of a 5% solution of sodium diethyldithiocarbamate and allow to stand for 5 minutes. Then extract with small portions of chloroform until the chloroform does not become yellow when shaken with a dilute cupric sulfate solution. Now add 10% HCl until the solution is pink, and dilute to 50 ml.

8-Hydroxyquinoline: Dissolve 12.5 g of 8-hydroxyquinoline in 12.5 ml of glacial acetic acid and dilute with water to 1 liter.

Indigo Carmine: Dry indigo carmine of reagent quality or "certified" FD&C Blue No. 2 at 105° for 2 hours. Dissolve 100 mg of the dried reagent in a mixture of 12 ml of H_2SO_4 and 80 ml of water and dilute to 100 ml. This solution is subject to deterioration indicated by paling of the blue color, and it should not be used when it is more than 3 months old.

Lead Acetate: Dissolve 10 g of lead acetate in 100 ml of recently boiled and cooled water. Keep in tightly closed bottles.

Magnesium Uranyl Acetate (Uranium Magnesium Acetate): See page 558.

p-**Methylaminophenol Solution:** Dissolve 100 mg of *p*-methylaminophenol sulfate and 20 g of sodium bisulfite in 100 ml of water.

Methyl Orange Indicator: Dissolve 100 mg of methyl orange in 100 ml of water.

Methyl Red Indicator: Dissolve 100 mg of methyl red in 100 ml of alcohol.

Methylrosaniline Chloride (Crystal Violet, Methyl Violet) **Indicator** for titrations in nonaqueous solvents: Dissolve 1.0 g of the dye in 100 ml of glacial acetic acid.

Nessler Solution: Dissolve 14.5 g of sodium hydroxide in 75 ml of water. Dissolve 5 g of red mercuric iodide and 4 g of potassium iodide in 20 ml of water. Pour the iodide solution into the NaOH solution and dilute to 100 ml. Allow to settle and use the clear supernatant liquid.

Nitric Acid, 10% HNO$_3$: Dilute 105 ml of HNO$_3$ (70%) with water to 1 liter.

Nitric Acid 1%: Dilute 10.5 ml of HNO$_3$ (70%) with water to 1 liter.

o-**Phenanthroline, Redox Indicator Solution:** Freshly prepare a solution of 500 mg of ferrous ammonium sulfate in 100 ml of water containing 1 ml of H$_2$SO$_4$, and in this solution dissolve 500 mg of *o*-phenanthroline.

o-**Phenanthroline, Reagent for Iron:** Dissolve 100 mg of *o*-phenanthroline in 100 ml of water containing 0.3 ml of 1 *N* HCl.

Phenoldisulfonic Acid: Dissolve 10 g of phenol in 60 ml of sulfuric acid. Add 30 ml of fuming sulfuric acid (15–20%), stir well, and heat for 2 hours at 100°. Transfer while still fluid to a glass-stoppered bottle and stopper. When required for use, warm until liquefied.

Phenolphthalein Indicator: Dissolve 1.0 g in 100 ml of alcohol.

Phenol Red Indicator: Dissolve 100 mg of phenol red in 100 ml of alcohol.

m-**Phenylenediamine:** Dissolve 1 g of *m*-phenylenediamine hydrochloride in 200 ml of water. The solution must be colorless before use; if not, it can be decolorized by shaking with charcoal or activated carbon and filtering.

Phosphate Reagent—A: Dissolve 5 g of ammonium molybdate in 100 ml of 1 *N* H$_2$SO$_4$.

Phosphate Reagent—B: Dissolve 500 mg of *p*-methylaminophenol sulfate in 100 ml of water, and add 20 g of sodium bisulfite. Keep in well-filled, tightly closed bottles. Reagent **B** should not be kept longer than 2 weeks.

Potassium Chromate: Dissolve 10 g of potassium chromate in water to make 100 ml.

Potassium Cyanide (for the test for heavy metals with dithizone): Dissolve 10 g of potassium cyanide in water to make 20 ml. Extract the solution with several 10-ml portions of dithizone solution, then extract with several 5-ml portions of chloroform and dilute with water to 100 ml.

Potassium Dichromate: Dissolve 5.0 g in water to make 100 ml.

Potassium Ferricyanide: Dissolve 1 g of potassium ferricyanide in 20 ml of water. It must be freshly prepared.

Potassium Ferrocyanide: Dissolve 1 g of potassium ferrocyanide in 20 ml of water. It must be freshly prepared.

Potassium Hydroxide in Alcohol—Approximately 0.5 *N*: Cautiously add

34 g of KOH in 25 ml of cold water, and when the solution has cooled to room temperature add ethanol or methanol to make 1 liter. Mix and allow to stand for 1 or 2 days, then decant the clear solution and preserve it in a tightly stoppered bottle.

Potassium Hydroxide, 10%: Dissolve 13 g of potassium hydroxide in water to make 100 ml.

Potassium Iodide: Dissolve 10 g of potassium iodide in water to make 100 ml. Keep this solution in amber-colored bottles.

Potassium Plumbite (for detection of sulfidic sulfur in organic compounds): Dissolve 1.7 g of lead acetate, 3.4 g of potassium citrate, and 50 g of KOH in water to make 100 ml.

Silver Nitrate (approximately 0.1 N): Dissolve 1.7 g of silver nitrate in 100 ml of H_2O.

Sodium Alizarin Sulfonate: Dissolve 1.0 g of sodium alizarine sulfonate (Alizarin S) in water to make 100 ml.

Sodium Carbonate (approximately 1 N): Dissolve 5.3 g of anhydrous Na_2CO_3 or 6.2 g of $Na_2CO_3 \cdot H_2O$ in water to make 100 ml.

Sodium Cobaltinitrite: Dissolve 20 g of sodium cobaltinitrite in water to make 100 ml, allow to stand overnight, and filter if not clear.

A more sensitive solution of sodium cobaltinitrite for the detection or determination of potassium may be prepared as described on page 559.

Sodium Hydroxide, 30%: Dissolve 300 g of sodium hydroxide in water and dilute to 1 liter.

Sodium Hydroxide, 20%: Dissolve 200 g of sodium hydroxide in water and dilute to 1 liter.

Stannous Chloride Solution: Dissolve 40 g of stannous chloride in 60 ml of hydrochloric acid.

Starch Indicator Solution: Triturate 500 mg of starch, preferably arrowroot, with 10 ml of cold water and slowly pour it, with constant stirring, into 100 ml of boiling water. Boil gently until the liquid is thin and translucent. Allow to settle and use only the clear supernatant liquid. Keep in the refrigerator.

Sulfuric Acid, 25%: Cautiously add 150 ml of sulfuric acid to 800 ml of water, cool and dilute to 1 liter.

Sulfuric Acid, 10%: Cautiously add 60 ml of sulfuric acid to 800 ml of water, cool and dilute to 1 liter.

Thiazole Yellow: Dissolve 10 mg of thiazole yellow (Clayton yellow, Titan yellow) in 100 ml of water.

Titan Yellow: See **Thiazole Yellow.**

Thymol Blue Indicator: Dissolve 100 mg of thymol blue in 100 ml of alcohol.

Thymolphthalein Indicator: Dissolve 100 mg of the thymolphthalein in 100 ml of alcohol.

Zinc Uranyl Acetate (Uranium Zinc Acetate): See page 560.

STANDARD SOLUTIONS

For Use in Blanks and Controls

Aluminum (1 ml = 0.1 mg of Al): Dissolve 1.760 g of clear uneffloresced crystals of aluminum potassium sulfate in water, add 5 ml of HCl and dilute to 1 liter.

Ammonia (1 ml = 0.1 mg NH_3): Dissolve 314 mg of ammonium chloride in water to make 1 liter.

Antimony (1 ml = 0.1 mg Sb): Dissolve 275 mg of antimony potassium tartrate and about 1 g of potassium bitartrate in water to make 1 liter. It may also be prepared by dissolving 188 mg of antimony trichloride in a mixture of 20 volumes of hydrochloric acid and 80 volumes of water to make 1 liter.

Arsenic (1 ml = 0.001 mg or 1 microgram As): Dissolve 132 mg of arsenic trioxide in 15 ml of 10% NaOH. Neutralize the solution with 10% H_2SO_4, add 10 ml excess of the acid and dilute with water to 1 liter. To 10 ml of this solution add 10 ml of 10% H_2SO_4 and dilute with water to 1 liter.

Barium (1 ml = 0.1 mg Ba): Dissolve 178 mg of barium chloride, $BaCl_2 \cdot 2H_2O$, in water to make 1 liter.

Bismuth (1 ml = 0.1 mg Bi): Dissolve 2.320 g of clear crystals of bismuth nitrate in a mixture of 25 ml of HNO_3 and 50 ml of water and dilute with water to 100.0 ml. To 10.0 ml of this solution add 5 ml of HNO_3 and dilute with water to 1 liter.

Boron: (1 ml = 0.01 mg B): Dissolve 57.2 mg of boric acid in water to make 100.0 ml. Dilute 10.0 ml of the solution to 100.0 ml.

Cadmium (1 ml = 0.1 mg Cd): Dissolve 228 mg of cadmium sulfate, $3CdSO_4 \cdot 8H_2O$, in 10 ml of 10% H_2SO_4 and make up with water to 100.0 ml. Dilute 10.0 ml of this solution to 100.0 ml.

Calcium (1 ml = 0.1 mg Ca): Dissolve 250 mg of dried (at 200°) calcium carbonate in 10 ml of water and 1 ml of HCl, then dilute with water to 1 liter.

Carbon Dioxide (1 ml = 0.1 mg CO_2): Dissolve 241 mg of dried anhydrous sodium carbonate in water to make 1 liter.

Chloride (1 ml = 0.1 mg Cl): Dissolve 165 mg of sodium chloride in water to make 1 liter.

Chromate (1 ml = 0.1 mg CrO_3): Dissolve 147 mg of dried reagent potassium dichromate in water to make 1 liter.

Chromium (1 ml = 0.1 mg Cr): Dissolve 283 mg of dried potassium dichromate in 25 ml of water, add 2 ml of HCl and 2 ml of alcohol, and evaporate on the steam bath to dryness. Moisten the residue with a few drops of HCl and a few ml of water, warm, if necessary, to dissolve and dilute to 1 liter.

Copper (1 ml = 0.1 mg Cu): Dissolve 393 mg of cupric sulfate, $CuSO_4 \cdot 5H_2O$, in water to make 1 liter.

Copper Standard for Dithizone Test (0.001 mg Cu in 1 ml): Dilute 1.0 ml of the preceding **Copper** solution with water to 100 ml.

Fluoride (1 ml = 0.01 mg F): Dissolve 223 mg of dried sodium fluoride in water to make 100 ml, then dilute 10 ml of this solution with water to 100 ml. This solution must be freshly prepared. Keep in a plastic container.

Iron (1 ml = 0.1 mg Fe): Dissolve 863 mg clear, violet crystals of ferric ammonium sulfate, $FeNH_4(SO_4)_2 \cdot 12H_2O$, in 20 ml of 10% H_2SO_4 and dilute with water to 1 liter.

Lead Stock Solution (1 ml = 0.1 mg Pb): Dissolve 160 mg of lead nitrate in 100 ml of water to which has been added 1 ml of HNO_3, and dilute to 1 liter. Keep this solution in lead-free, stoppered bottles.

Lead Standard Solution (1 ml = 0.01 mg Pb): Dilute 10 ml of the lead stock solution with water to 100 ml.

Lead Standard for Dithizone Test (0.001 mg Pb in 1 ml): Dilute 1.0 ml of the **lead stock solution** to 100 ml with water containing 0.5 ml of HNO_3 per 100 ml.

Magnesium (1 ml = 0.1 mg Mg): Dissolve 1.014 g of uneffloresced crystals of magnesium sulfate, $MgSO_4 \cdot 7H_2O$, in water to make 1 liter.

Manganese (1 ml = 0.1 mg Mn): To 9.1 ml of 0.1 N potassium permanganate, or its equivalent, add 2 ml of HCl and 1 ml of alcohol and cautiously evaporate to dryness on the steam bath. Dissolve the residue in water to 100.0 ml.

Molybdenum (1 ml = 0.1 mg Mo): Dissolve 150 mg of molybdenum trioxide in 5 ml of 10% NH_3 and 10 ml of water by warming in a covered beaker until dissolved, and after cooling dilute to 100.0 ml.

Mercury (1 ml = 0.1 mg Hg): Dissolve 135 mg of mercuric chloride in water, add 2 ml of HCl and dilute to 1 liter.

Nickel (1 ml = 0.1 mg Ni): Dissolve 673 mg of nickel ammonium sulfate, $NiSO_4 \cdot (NH_4)_2SO_4 \cdot 6H_2O$, in water to make 1 liter.

Nitrate (1 ml = 0.01 mg NO_3): Dissolve 16.3 mg of potassium nitrate, KNO_3, previously heated at 120° for 2 hours, in freshly boiled out and cooled water to make 1 liter. This solution is slowly deteriorated by action of molds and it should therefore be distributed immediately after preparation into small, sterilized, well-filled and well-closed bottles. It should be inspected for molds before use if it is older than 4 months.

Nitrogen (1 ml = 0.1 mg N): Dissolve 382 mg of ammonium chloride, NH_4Cl, in water to 1 liter.

Phosphate (1 ml = 0.01 mg PO_4): Dissolve 143 mg of potassium biphosphate, KH_2PO_4, in water to make 100 ml. Dilute 10 ml of this solution with water to make 1 liter.

Potassium (1 ml = 0.1 mg K): Dissolve 191 mg of potassium chloride, KCl, in water to make 1 liter.

Silver (1 ml = 0.1 mg Ag): Dissolve 157 mg of silver nitrate, $AgNO_3$, in water to make 1 liter.

Sodium (1 ml = 0.1 mg Na): Dissolve 254 mg of dried sodium chloride, HaCl, in water to make 1 liter.

Sodium Carbonate (1 ml = 1.0 mg Na_2CO_3): Dissolve 1.000 g of dried anhydrous sodium carbonate in water to make 1 liter.

Strontium (1 ml = 0.1 mg Sr): Dissolve 242 mg of anhydrous strontium nitrate, $Sr(NO_3)_2$, or 181 mg of anhydrous strontium chloride, $SrCl_2$ (made by drying the hydrous at 150°), in water to make 1 liter.

Sulfate (1 ml = 0.1 mg SO_4): Dissolve 182 mg of potassium sulfate, K_2SO_4, in water to make 1 liter.

Sulfide (1 ml = 0.1 mg S): Dissolve 750 mg of crystals of sodium sulfide, $Na_2SO_3 \cdot 9H_2O$, in water to make 1 liter.   It must be freshly prepared.

Tin (1 ml = 0.1 mg Sn): Dissolve 500 mg of metallic tin (Sn) in $1+1$ HCl, warming to aid solution if necessary, and dilute to 250.0 ml.   When required for use dilute 5.0 ml of this solution with diluted $(1+9)$ HCl to 100.0 ml.

Titanium: Dry about 200 mg of reagent titanium dioxide (TiO_2) at 110° for 2 hours.   Weigh accurately 100.5 mg of the dried reagent and transfer it completely into a 200-ml beaker.   Add 15 ml of H_2SO_4, stir well, then add 4 g of ammonium sulfate and heat on a hot plate to evolution of sulfuric fumes.   Raise the temperature and continue heating until all, or practically all, is dissolved.   Allow to cool, then completely transfer the solution to a 1-liter volumetric flask containing 300 ml of water, cool again to room temperature, dilute to volume and mix thoroughly.

Zinc (1 ml = 0.1 mg Zn): Dissolve 124 mg of zinc oxide in a mixture of 10 ml of water and 1 ml of sulfuric acid, and dilute with water to 1 liter.

Zinc Standard for the Dithizone Test (0.001 mg Zn in 1 ml): Dilute 1.0 ml of the **Zinc** standard solution to 100 ml with water containing 0.5 ml of HNO_3 per 100 ml.

ACETIC ACID, GLACIAL

CH_3CO_2H; mol. wt. 60.05.

Clear, colorless liquid, irritating, characteristic odor. Miscible with water, alcohol, ether. Boils at 118°. Spr. gr. 1.048 at 25°. Glacial acetic acid freezes at 16°, and when the congealed acid melts the container may break due to sudden expansion of the acid. *It should therefore be kept at a temperature above 16° to prevent freezing of the acid.*

Standards

Assay............min 99.7% CH_3COOH
Evaporation residue.........max 0.001%
Miscibility with water.........to pass test
Dichromate-reducing
  substances ....to pass test
  (limit as formic acid about 0.01%)

Acetic anhydride.............to pass test
Chloride (Cl)...............max 0.0001%
Sulfate (SO_4)...............max 0.0001%
Heavy metals (as Pb).......max 0.0001%
Iron (Fe)..................max 0.0001%

Assay: Determine the freezing temperature of the acid, page 581. It should not be below 16.0°. See table and note on next page.

Evaporation residue: Evaporate 100 ml on the steam bath and dry the residue at 105° for 1 hour. The weight of the residue does not exceed 1.0 mg (retain).

Miscibility with water: Mix 10 ml with 25 ml of H_2O. No turbidity is produced in 1 hour.

Dichromate-reducing substances: Dissolve 30 mg of potassium dichromate in 20 ml of H_2SO_4.

To 5 ml of the acetic acid add 0.5 ml of water, then add 5 ml of the dichromate solution, mix gently and allow to stand for 10 minutes. Any resulting greenish color is not substantially darker than that of a blank made by slowly mixing 5.5 ml of ice-cooled water with 5 ml of ice-cooled dichromate solution and standing the same time as the sample.

Acetic Anhydride: Transfer 25 ml into a small flask, add 50 mg of selenous acid, cover the flask, and heat it on the steam bath for 1 hour. The acid has no more color than a similar portion of the same acetic acid heated in the same manner, but without selenous acid.

Chloride: Dilute 10 ml with 25 ml of H_2O, and add 2 ml of HNO_3 and 12 ml of silver nitrate. If a turbidity is produced, it is not greater than that in a blank to which 0.01 mg of Cl has been added.

Sulfate: To 50 ml add 10 mg of sodium carbonate and evaporate to dryness on the steam bath. Dissolve the residue in 5 ml of H_2O and 0.5 ml of 1 N HCl, filter if necessary, dilute to 10 ml, add 2 ml of $BaCl_2$ and allow to stand for 10 minutes. Any turbidity produced is not greater than that in a blank with 0.05 mg of SO_4 added.

Solution R: Warm the residue obtained in the test for *Evaporation residue* with 2 ml of 1 N HCl and 5 ml of H_2O, and dilute to 100 ml.

Heavy metals: Dilute 20 ml of *Solution R* to 40 ml, and add 10 ml of H_2S. Any darkening produced is not greater than that in a control made with 0.02 mg of Pb, 0.2 ml of 1 N HCl and 10 ml of H_2S in the same final volume as with the sample.

Iron: To 20 ml of *Solution R* add 2 ml of hydrochloric acid, 30 mg of ammonium persulfate, dilute to 50 ml and add 3 ml of ammonium thiocyanate solution. Any resulting red color is not darker than that in a control made with 0.02 mg of Fe, the same quantities of the reagents and in the same final volume as with the sample.

Note: The water content of acetic acid may be determined by the iodine (Fischer) method.

The freezing temperatures of several concentrations of acetic acid are:

Freezing Temperature (degrees C.)	Per Cent CH_3COOH	Freezing Temperature (degrees C.)	Per Cent CH_3COOH
11.80	97.0	15.1	99.2
12.5	97.5	15.65	99.5
13.25	98.0	16.05	99.7
14.0	98.5	16.57	99.9
14.8	99.0	16.75	100.0

ACETIC ANHYDRIDE

$(CH_3CO)_2O$; mol. wt. 102.09.

Colorless, clear liquid, pungent odor. Sp. gr. 1.08. The anhydride of commerce contains some acetic acid. Absolute acetic anhydride boils at 139°. Slowly soluble in water, forming acetic acid; miscible with alcohol, ether, chloroform or benzene. *Keep protected from moisture.*

Standards

Assay.............min 97% $(CH_3CO)_2O$
Evaporation residue.........max 0.003%
Permanganate-reducing
  substances.................to pass test
Chloride (Cl)..............max 0.0005%

Phosphate (PO_4)...........max 0.001%
Sulfate (SO_4)..............max 0.0005%
Heavy metals (as Pb).......max 0.0002%
Iron (Fe).................max 0.0004%

Assay: Weigh accurately about 2 ml in a glass-stoppered flask, and add 100 ml of CO_2-free water. Allow to stand for 30 minutes, then titrate with 1 N NaOH, using phenolphthalein as indicator. Calculate the percentage of $(CH_3CO)_2O$ from the equation:

$$A = \frac{34.03V}{W} - 566.7,$$

where A is the percentage of $(CH_3CO)_2O$, V is the volume (in ml) of 1 N NaOH consumed, and W is the weight (in grams) of the sample taken.

Evaporation residue: Evaporate 28 ml on the steam bath and dry at 105° for 1 hour. The weight of the residue does not exceed 1.0 mg (retain).

Permanganate-reducing substances: Dissolve 2 ml in 10 ml of water and add 0.3 ml of 0.1 N potassium permanganate. The pink color is not entirely discharged in 10 minutes.

Solution S: Dilute 18.0 ml (20 g) of sample with water to 100 ml.

Chloride: To 20 ml of *Solution S* add 2 ml of HNO_3 and 1 ml of $AgNO_3$. Any turbidity produced is not greater than that in a blank to which 0.02 mg of Cl has been added.

Phosphate: To 10 ml of *Solution S* add 1 ml of HNO_3 and evaporate to dryness on the steam bath. Take up the residue with 2 ml of 25% H_2SO_4 and 20 ml of water. Add 1 ml each of phosphate reagents **A** and **B** and heat at 60° for 10 minutes. Any blue color produced is not darker than that in a control made with 0.02 mg of PO_4, 2 ml of 25% H_2SO_4, the same volumes of the phosphate reagents and in the same volume as used with the sample.

Sulfate: To 50 ml of *Solution S* add 10 mg of sodium carbonate and evaporate to dryness on the steam bath. Dissolve the residue in 5 ml of water, filter if not clear through a small filter paper and wash with water to 10 ml. Add 0.5 ml of 1 N HCl and 2 ml of barium chloride solution, and allow to stand for 10 minutes. Any resulting turbidity is not greater than that in a blank with 0.05 mg of SO_4 added.

Solution R: Warm the residue obtained in the test for *Evaporation residue* with 2 ml of 1 N HCl and 5 ml of water, and dilute to 60 ml.

Heavy metals: Dilute 20 ml of *Solution R* to 40 ml, and add 10 ml of H_2S. Any darkening produced is not greater than that in a control made with 0.02 mg of Pb, 0.3 ml of 1 N HCl and 10 ml of H_2S in the same final volume as with the sample.

Iron: To 10 ml of *Solution R* add 2 ml of HCl, 30 mg of ammonium persulfate, dilute to 50 ml, and add 3 ml of ammonium thiocyanate. Any resulting red color is not darker than that in a control made with 0.02 mg of Fe, the same quantities of the reagents and in the same final volume as with the sample.

ACETONE

$(CH_3)_2CO$; mol. wt. 58.08.

Clear, colorless liquid, characteristic odor. Miscible with water, alcohol, ether and most organic liquids. Boils at 56.5°. *Keep in tightly closed containers, in a cool place, away from fire.*

Standards

Assay......................min 99.5%	Aldehyde....................to pass test
Boiling range................55.5°–56.5°	Methanol....................max 0.05%
Evaporation residue.........max 0.001%	Permanganate-reducing	
Miscibility with water........to pass test	substances.................to pass test
Acid (as CH_3COOH).........max 0.003%	Water.......................max 0.4%
Alkalinity (as NH_3).........max 0.001%	

Assay: Determine the specific gravity at 25°/25°. It should not be above 0.7880.

Boiling range: Distill 100 ml. After the first 20 drops, all distills between 55.5° and 56.5°, correction being made in the observed temperature reading for any variation in the barometric pressure from 760 mm by the formula given on page 581.

Evaporation residue: Evaporate 125 ml on the steam bath and dry at 105° for 30 minutes. The weight of the residue is not more than 1.0 mg.

Miscibility with water: A mixture of 25 ml of the acetone with 25 ml of water remains clear for 30 minutes.

Acid: Dilute 25 ml with 25 ml of CO_2-free water and add 2 drops of phenol-phthalein. Not more than 0.1 ml of 0.1 N NaOH is required to produce a pink color.

Alkalinity: Mix 20 ml with 25 ml of H_2O and add 1 drop of methyl red. Any yellow color produced is changed to pink by not more than 0.1 ml of 0.1 N HCl.

Aldehyde: Mix 10 ml with 5 ml of silver ammonium nitrate solution, page 559, and allow to stand, protected from light, at 15° for 15 minutes. No brown color or turbidity is produced.

Methanol: Dilute 1 ml of the acetone with water to 10 ml. To 1 ml of the dilution add 0.2 ml of diluted phosphoric acid (1 + 9 by volume) and 0.2 ml of 5% potassium permanganate. Allow to stand for 10 minutes, then add dropwise a 10% solution of sodium bisulfite until the solution is colorless. If a brown color persists, add a drop or two more of the diluted phosphoric acid and more of the sodium bisulfite if necessary. To the colorless solution add slowly 5 ml of ice-cold 80% H_2SO_4 (made by adding 3 volumes of H_2SO_4 to 1 volume of H_2O), then add 0.1 ml of a 1% water solution of chromotropic acid and heat at 70°–80° for 15 minutes. No violet color is produced.

Permanganate-reducing substances: To 10 ml add 0.05 ml of 0.1 N $KMnO_4$ and allow to stand at about 25° for 30 minutes. The pink color is not entirely discharged.

Water: Water in acetone may be determined by the iodine (Fischer) method, using 5 ml of sample and 25 ml of pyridine as solvent. About 0.4% of water is usually found.

ACETONITRILE

Methyl Cyanide

CH_3CN; mol. wt. 41.05.

Clear, colorless liquid; slight but characteristic odor. Miscible with water, alcohol, ether. Sp. gr. 0.780. It is a good solvent for many inorganic compounds, and is used in nonaqueous titrations and for spectrophotometry.

Standards

Boiling range....................81°–82°	Evaporation residue..........max 0.01%
Miscibility with water.........to pass test	Permanganate-reducing
Neutrality....................to pass test	substances................to pass test
Hydrogen cyanide (HCN).....max 0.005%	Water........................max 0.2%

Boiling range: Distill 50 ml. After the first 10 drops, all distills between 81° and 82°, correction being made for barometric pressure, page 581.

Miscibility with water: Mix 5 ml of sample with 15 ml of H_2O. A clear solution results and it remains clear after 30 minutes.

Neutrality: Blue and red litmus papers soaked in the sample show neither acid nor alkaline reaction.

Hydrogen cyanide: Mix 2 ml with 2 ml of H_2O, add 2 drops of 10% ferrous sulfate solution and 4 drops of 10% NaOH. Heat to boiling, cool and acidify with 10% H_2SO_4. No green or blue color is produced.

Evaporation residue: Evaporate 13 ml (10 g) on the steam bath, and dry at 105° for 30 minutes. Not more than 1.0 mg of residue remains.

Permanganate-reducing substances: To 5 ml of sample add 0.05 ml of 0.1 N potassium permanganate and shake for 1 minute. The pink color persists for 30 minutes.

Water: Water in acetonitrile may be determined by the iodine (Fischer) method.

ACETYLACETONE

2,4-Pentanedione

$CH_3COCH_2COCH_3$; mol. wt. 100.11.

Colorless or only slightly yellow, flammable liquid. Soluble in about 10 parts of water; miscible with alcohol, benzene, chloroform, ether, glacial acetic acid; soluble in HCl.

Standards

Specific gravity (25°/25°).......0.974–0.976	Solubility in H_2O, benzene.....to pass test
Boiling range.................139°–141°	Evaporation residue...........max 0.01%
Refractive index.........1.4512 ± 0.0005	Acid (as acetic)...............max 0.03%

Boiling range: Distill 50 ml. After 20 drops (1 ml) has come over into the receiver, all distills between 139° and 141°, correction being made for the barometric pressure (page 581).

Refractive index: Determine at 20°.

Solubility in H_2O and in benzene: Shake 2.0 ml of the sample with 25 ml of water. It dissolves completely without any turbidity. A 2.0-ml portion of the sample yields a clear solution with 10 ml of benzene.

Evaporation residue: Evaporate 10.0 ml on the steam bath and dry at 110° for 2 hours. The residue does not exceed 1.0 mg.

Acid: To 20 ml of alcohol add 0.15 ml of phenolphthalein solution, then add dropwise 0.1 N NaOH until a pink color is produced which persists after shaking. Add 10 ml of water and 5.0 ml of the sample. If the pink color disappears it is restored upon the addition of 0.25 ml of 0.1 N NaOH.

ACETYL CHLORIDE

$CH_3 \cdot CO \cdot Cl$; mol. wt. 78.50; Cl—45.17%; CH_3CO—54.83%.

Clear, colorless, flammable liquid; strong, pungent odor. Decomposed by water and alcohols; miscible with chloroform or benzene. Sp. gr. about 1.1. *Keep in tightly closed, glass-stoppered bottles or in sealed ampuls.*

Standards

Assay......................min 98%	Solubility in water............to pass test
Boiling range....................50°–53°	Phospho*rous* compounds.......to pass test
Evaporation residue..........max 0.010%	Phosphorus compound, as P...max 0.002%
Miscibility with chloroform	Sulphur compound, as SO_4...max 0.002%
and benzene................to pass test	Heavy metals (as Pb)........max 0.002%

Assay: Weight accurately a 100-ml volumetric flask containing 30 ml of H_2O. Add from a pipette about 2.0 ml of sample, stopper immediately, shake, allow to cool and reweigh.   Dilute with H_2O to exactly 100 ml and mix well.

(*a*) Titrate 50 ml of the solution with 0.5 N NaOH, using phenolphthalein indicator, to the production of a pink color.   One ml of 0.5 N NaOH = 0.01962 g CH_3COCl, log 29270.

(*b*) Dilute 20 ml of the solution with 30 ml of water and determine the chloride (Cl) by Method 1, page 565.   One ml of 0.1 N $AgNO_3$ = 0.007850 g CH_3COCl, log 89487.

Neither (*a*) nor (*b*) shows less than 98%, and should not differ by more than 0.5%.

Boiling range: Not less than 95% distills between 50° and 53°, after correcting for barometric pressure, page 581.

Evaporation residue: Evaporate 10 ml on the steam bath and dry at 105° for 1 hour.   Not more than 1.0 mg of residue remains.

Miscibility with chloroform and benzene: Separate, 5-ml portions of the acetyl chloride give a clear solution with 20 ml of benzene or chloroform.

Solubility in water: Place 9 ml in a 100-ml graduated cylinder, add dropwise and cautiously about 5 ml H_2O, shaking after each addition of the H_2O until the reaction is complete, then dilute to 50 ml.   The solution is clear (*Solution S*).

Phosphorous compounds: To 10 ml of *Solution S* add 5 ml of 5% aqueous mercuric chloride solution and heat for 2 minutes.   Not more than a slight turbidity is produced.

Phosphorus compounds: To 5.0 ml of *Solution S* add 2 ml of HNO_3 and evaporate to dryness on the steam bath.   Take up the residue with 2 ml of 25% H_2SO_4 and 20 ml of water, add 1 ml each of phosphate reagents **A** and **B** and heat at 60° for 10 minutes.   Any blue color produced is not darker than that in a control made with 0.06 mg of PO_4, 2 ml of 25% H_2SO_4 and 1 ml each of phosphate reagents **A** and **B** in the same final volume as used with the sample.

Sulfur compounds (as SO_4)**:** To 25 ml of *Solution S* add 1 ml of bromine water, and evaporate to about 5 ml.   Dilute to 10 ml and add 1 ml of 0.1 HCl and 2 ml of $BaCl_2$.   Mix well and allow to stand for 10 minutes.   If a turbidity results it is not greater than that produced by treating a solution of 0.1 mg of SO_4 in 25 ml of water exactly in the same manner as the solution of the sample.

Heavy metals: Evaporate 5 ml of *Solution S* with 5 drops of HCl to dryness on the steam bath.   Take up the residue with 1 ml of 1 N acetic acid and 10 ml of hot water, cool, dilute to 40 ml, and add 10 ml of H_2S.   Any darkening produced is not greater than that in a control made with 0.02 mg of Pb, 1 ml of 1 N acetic acid and 10 ml of H_2S in the same final volume as with the sample.

AGAR

Agar–Agar

Yellowish powder; slight odor.   Insoluble in cold water, soluble in boiling water.   A 1% solution in hot water forms a stiff jelly on cooling.

Standards

Drying loss....................max 18%	Starch...................max about 1%
Water-absorption	Ignition residue (ash),
capacity...........min 5 × its weight	dried basis.................max 6.0%
Insoluble in hot H_2O..........max 0.5%	Acid insoluble ash.............max 0.5%
Gelatin max about 0.1%	Heavy metals (as Pb).........max 0.003%

Drying loss: Weigh accurately about 1 g in a tared dish, spread out evenly, and dry at 105° for 4 hours.   The loss in weight corresponds to not more than 18%.

Note: The drying loss (water) may be determined by the iodine (Fischer) method.

Water-absorption capacity: Place 5.0 g, cut into small pieces if in strips, in a cylinder or flask, add 100.0 ml of water at about 25°, and allow stand at 22°–28° for 24 hours.   Pour the contents of the cylinder (or flask) through a funnel provided with a plug of moistened glass wool into a graduated 100-ml cylinder, allowing to drain completely.   Not more than 75 ml of water is obtained.

Insoluble in hot H_2O: Add 2.0 g to 250 ml of boiling water and boil until no more dissolves.   Filter the hot solution through a tared filtering crucible (retain the filtrate).   Rinse the beaker several times with hot water into the filtering crucible to recover all the insoluble, and dry at 105° to constant weight.   The dried insoluble matter amounts to not more than 0.5%.

Gelatin: To 10 ml of the first filtrate, liquefied by warming if not fluid, obtained in the test for *Insoluble in hot H_2O*, add 5 ml of approximately 1% picric acid solution.   No turbidity is produced.

Starch: Dilute 20 ml of the filtrate obtained in the test for *Insoluble in hot H_2O*, liquefied, if necessary, by warming to 60°–70°, with 80 ml of water, allow to cool and add 2 drops of 0.1 N iodine.   No blue color is produced.

Ignition residue (ash): Slowly heat in a small, tared dish 1.0 g until thoroughly charred; then place the dish in an electric muffle furnace at about 700°–800° and ignite to constant weight.   The residue amounts to not more than 6.0% on dried basis (retain).

Acid insoluble ash: To the residue from the preceding test add 20 ml of 10% HCl and 2 ml of HNO_3 and gently boil for 5 minutes.   If an insoluble residue remains, filter on a tared, fritted-glass crucible, wash with 20 ml of hot water and ignite. This insoluble residue corresponds to not more than 0.5% of the agar taken.

Heavy metals: Evaporate the filtrate from the preceding test to dryness on the steam bath. Add to the residue 1 ml of HCl and 20 ml of hot water and digest for 5 minutes. Now add a slight excess of NH_4OH, bring to a boil and filter. Dilute the filtrate to 40 ml and add 10 ml of H_2S. Any dark color produced is not more intense than that produced by making 3.0 ml of standard lead solution (= 0.03 mg Pb) alkaline with NH_3, diluting to 40 ml and treating with 10 ml H_2S.

ALCOHOL, 95%

Ethanol; Ethyl Alcohol

CH_3CH_2OH; mol. wt. 46.07.

Colorless liquid; slight characteristic odor. Miscible with water, chloroform, ether, and many other organic liquids. Boils at 78°. *Keep in tightly closed containers.*

Standards

Assay......min 95% C_2H_5OH by volume	Fusel oil.....................to pass test
Miscibility with water.........to pass test	Methanol.....................max 0.1%
Evaporation residue.........max 0.001%	Substances darkened by
Acid (as $HC_2H_3O_2$)..........max 0.003%	sulfuric acid................to pass test
Alkalinity (as NH_3).........max 0.0003%	Permanganate-reducing
Acetone; Isopropyl alcohol....max 0.005%	substances.................to pass test

Assay: The sp. gr. at 25°/25° is not higher than 0.810.

Miscibility with water: Dilute 15 ml with 45 ml of H_2O. At the end of 1 hour the dilution is as clear as an equal volume of the H_2O.

Evaporation residue: Evaporate 120 ml on a steam bath and dry at 105° for 30 minutes. The weight of the residue does not exceed 1.0 mg.

Acid: Mix 10 ml with 25 ml of H_2O and 0.5 ml of phenolphthalein. Add 0.02 N NaOH until a slight pink color persists after shaking for one-half minute. Disregard the quantity of the alkali used. Then add 25 ml of sample, mix, and titrate with 0.02 N NaOH until the pink color is reproduced. Not more than 0.5 ml of the NaOH is required.

Alkalinity: Dilute 25 ml with 25 ml of H_2O and add 1 drop of methyl red indicator. If the solution is yellow, it requires not more than 0.2 ml of 0.02 N H_2SO_4 to produce a pink color.

Acetone; Isopropyl alcohol: Dilute 1.0 ml with 1 ml of H_2O, add 1 ml of a saturated solution of disodium phosphate and 3 ml of a saturated solution of potassium permanganate. Warm the mixture to 45°–50°, and allow to stand until the permanganate color is discharged. Add 3 ml of 10% NaOH, filter through glass or asbestos, and add to the filtrate 1 ml of 1% furfural. Allow to stand for 10 minutes, then add 3 ml of well-cooled HCl to 1 ml of the mixture. No pink color is produced.

Fusel oil: Mix 10 ml with 5 ml of H_2O and 1 ml of glycerol and allow to evaporate spontaneously from a piece of clean blotting paper. When the last traces of the alcohol leave the paper, no disagreeable odor is perceptible.

Methanol: Dilute 1.0 ml of the ethanol with water to 20 ml. To 1 ml of the dilution add 0.2 ml of diluted phosphoric acid $(1+9$ volume) and 0.2 ml of 5% potassium permanganate. Allow to stand for 10 minutes, then add dropwise a 10% solution of sodium bisulfite until the solution is colorless. If a brown color persists, add a drop or two more of the diluted phosphoric acid and more of the sodium bisulfite if necessary. To the colorless solution add slowly 5 ml of ice-cold 80% H_2SO_4 (made by adding 3 volumes of H_2SO_4 to 1 volume of H_2O), then add 0.1 ml of a 1% water solution of chromotropic acid and heat at 70°–80° for 15 minutes. No violet color is produced.

Substances darkened by sulfuric acid: Cool 10 ml of H_2SO_4 in a small flask to 10°, and add dropwise, with agitation, 10 ml of the sample, keeping the temperature of the mixture below 20°. The resulting mixture should not have more than a slight brown color.

Permanganate-reducing substances: Cool 20 ml to 15°, add 0.1 ml of 0.1 N potassium permanganate, and allow to stand at 15° for 5 minutes. The pink color should not entirely disappear.

Note: The water in alcohol may be determined by the iodine (Fischer) method.

ALCOHOL, ABSOLUTE

Absolute Ethanol; Absolute Ethyl Alcohol

Absolute alcohol has the same physical properties as Alcohol, 95%, but its sp. gr. at 25°/25° is not above 0.7900, corresponding to not less than 99.5% of C_2H_5OH by volume, or to 99.2% by weight. It is very hygroscopic and should be kept well protected from access of moisture.

The limits for impurities and methods of testing are also the same as for Alcohol, 95%.

Note: The actual H_2O content may be determined by the iodine (Fischer) method, page 579, and it should not exceed 0.3%.

ALIZARIN, *see* SODIUM ALIZARINSULFONATE

ALUMINON

Ammonium Aurintricarboxylate

;mol. wt. 473.43.

Yellow-brown or brown-red powder. Freely soluble in water, soluble in alcohol.

Aurintricarboxylic acid, which is also used for the same determination as aluminon, is a red-brown powder insoluble in water, but readily soluble in dilute ammonia or alkali hydroxide. For use, it is brought in solution by the addition of just sufficient ammonium hydroxide to dissolve.

Standards

Sensitiveness................to pass test	Ignition residue.............max 0.20%
Solubility...................to pass test	

Sensitiveness: (a) Dissolve 25 mg of the reagent in 25 ml of water containing 2 drops of 10% NH_3.

(b) Dilute 1 ml of standard aluminum solution with water to 100 ml (1 ml = 0.001 mg Al).

Dilute 1 ml of (b) to 10 ml, add 0.1 ml of glacial acetic acid and 0.1 ml of (a) and let stand for 15 minutes. A distinct pink color is produced.

Solubility: Two-tenths gram dissolves completely in 20 ml of water containing 2 drops of 10% NH_3.

Ignition residue: Char well 0.5 g. Allow to cool, add 0.5 ml H_2SO_4 and ignite at first gently to evaporate the acid, then strongly to constant weight. Not more than 1.0 mg of residue remains.

ALUMINUM

Al; at. wt. 26.98.

Sheets, wire or granules. Soluble, with evolution of hydrogen, in dilute hydrochloric or sulfuric acids and in solutions of the fixed alkali hydroxides.

Standards

HCl—Insoluble.............max 0.050%	Copper (Cu)................max 0.020%
Nitrogen (N)...............max 0.001%	Iron (Fe)...................max 0.10%
Arsenic (As)................max 1 ppm	Other metals (Mn, Ti, Zn
Silicon (Si)..................max 0.10%	and Fe)...................max 0.3%

HCl—Insoluble: Dissolve 5 g in 100 ml of a mixture of equal volumes of HCl and water. Filter through a tared filtering crucible, wash well with water containing 1 ml of HCl per 100 ml and dry at 105°. The weight of the insoluble residue is not more than 2.5 mg.

Nitrogen: In a distillation flask connected through a trap to a condenser, the end of which dips 10 ml of water containing 1 drop of 10% HCl, dissolve 1.25 g of sample in 30 ml 20% NaOH. Add 40 ml of water and distill over about 40 ml into 5 ml of water containing 1 drop of 10% HCl. Dilute to 50 ml, and add 1 ml of 10% NaOH and 2 ml of Nessler solution. The resulting color is not more intense than that produced by treating 0.25 g of sample with 0.01 mg of N (0.04 mg NH_4Cl) exactly as the 1.25 g sample.

Arsenic: Place 1.25 g of the sample in the generator described on page 563, omitting the pledget of cotton. Add 10 ml of water and 15 ml of 30% NaOH and allow the reaction to proceed for 30 minutes. The stain produced on the mercuric bromide paper is not greater than that resulting from the treatment of 0.25 g of the aluminum and 0.001 mg of As exactly as the 1.25 g sample.

Silicon: Treat 2 g of the metal contained in a flask with 70 ml of a mixture composed of: water 485 ml, sulfuric acid 115 ml, hydrochloric acid 200 ml, nitric acid 200 ml. When the metal has dissolved, evaporate until heavy sulfuric fumes have been evolved for 10 minutes. Cool somewhat, add 20 ml of diluted sulfuric acid $(1+5)$, follow with 80 ml of hot water, and boil until the aluminum sulfate is dissolved. Add 50 ml of H_2S water and remove from the hot plate as soon as the solution begins to boil. Filter through a paper filter in which some paper pulp has been placed and wash 4 times with hot water. Retain the filtrate and the first two washings as *Solution A*.

Treat the precipitate on the filter with sufficient (about 5 ml) hot diluted $(1+1)$ nitric acid to decompose all the metallic sulfides on the filter, receiving the filtrate in the dissolving flask, and wash 4 times with hot water. Retain the filtrate as *Solution B*. Then wash the precipitate with hot water until practically free from acid, dry and ignite in a platinum crucible and weigh. Add to the residue in the crucible 2 drops of water, then add 3 drops of H_2SO_4 and 2 ml of hydrofluoric acid, evaporate to dryness and ignite. Re-evaporate with 2 ml of hydrofluoric acid, ignite sharply, cool and weigh. The difference between the first weight and that after treatment with HF represents SiO_2. This difference multiplied by 0.4672 represents silicon (Si).

Copper: To *Solution B* add 1 ml of H_2SO_4 and evaporate on the hot plate to the copious evolution of sulfuric fumes. Cool, add 20 ml of water and a few drops of H_2SO_4, and boil until the residue is dissolved. Cool and dilute to 200 ml. To 10 ml of the solution add 10 ml of 20% ammonium citrate solution and sufficient ammonium hydroxide to produce a pH of about 9. Add 2 ml of a 0.1% solution of sodium diethyldithiocarbamate and 10 ml of isoamyl alcohol and shake well. The yellow color of the alcohol layer is not darker than that of a control made with 0.02 mg of Cu and the same quantities of the ammonium citrate solution, ammonium hydroxide, sodium diethyldithiocarbamate, and isoamyl alcohol as in the test with the sample.

Iron: To 1 ml of solution prepared in the preceding test add 2 ml of HCl and dilute to 50 ml. Add about 30 mg of ammonium persulfate and 3 ml of ammonium thiocyanate, and mix. Any red color produced is not darker than that of a control made with 0.01 mg Fe, 2 ml of HCl, the same quantities of ammonium persulfate and thiocyanate and in the same final volume as with the sample.

Other metals: To *Solution A* add 2 drops of methyl red indicator and neutralize with sodium hydroxide solution. Then add sufficient 20% sodium sulfide solution to redissolve the precipitated aluminum hydroxide. Allow to stand until the undissolved precipitate has coagulated, filter and wash a few times with a 2% solution of sodium sulfide. Dissolve the precipitate from off the filter first with a few ml of warm dilute hydrochloric acid $(2+3)$, then with 2 ml of warm dilute $(1+2)$ HNO_3, neutralize with sodium hydroxide, and add 3 ml of 10% sodium sulfide solution. Filter, wash with water containing some H_2S, dry and ignite to constant weight.

This weight, multiplied by 0.7, approximately represents the iron and other sodium sulfide insoluble metals.

ALUMINUM AMMONIUM SULFATE

Ammonia Alum

$AlNH_4(SO_4)_2 \cdot 12H_2O$; mol. wt. 453.33; anhydrous—52.31%; H_2O—47.69%; Al—5.95%; NH_3—3.76%; SO_4—42.38%; Al_2O_3—11.24%.

Colorless crystals or crystalline fragments. Soluble in about 6 parts of water, 0.5 part of boiling water; insoluble in alcohol.

Standards

Insoluble....................max 0.005%	Arsenic (As)..................max 2 ppm
Chloride (Cl)................max 0.001%	Heavy metals (as Pb)........max 0.001%
Alkalies, Earths, etc...........max 0.25%	Iron (Fe)....................max 0.001%

Insoluble: Dissolve 20 g in 100 ml of water and 0.5 ml of H_2SO_4 and heat on a steam bath for 30 minutes. Filter any undissolved matter, wash it with hot H_2O and dry at 105°. The weight of the undissolved matter does not exceed 1.0 mg.

Chloride: Dissolve 2 g in 20 ml of water, add 2 ml of HNO_3 and 1 ml of $AgNO_3$. Any resulting turbidity is not greater than that in a blank with 0.02 mg of Cl added.

Alkalies, Earths, etc.: Dissolve 2 g in 130 ml of water and add a slight excess of ammonium hydroxide. Boil until nearly free from ammonia odor, dilute to 150 ml and filter. Evaporate 75 ml of the filtrate and ignite. The ignited residue weighs not more than 2.5 mg.

Arsenic: Determine in 1 g by the method on page 563. The stain is not greater than that from 0.002 mg of As.

Heavy metals: Dissolve 4 g in H_2O to make 40 ml. To 10 ml add 0.02 mg of Pb, and dilute to 40 ml (A). Dilute the remaining 30 to 40 ml (B). Then to each add 10 ml of H_2S; B is not darker than A.

Iron: Dissolve 1 g in 10 ml of water, add 2 ml of HCl, boil for 30 seconds, cool and dilute to 50 ml. Add about 30 mg of ammonium persulfate and 3 ml of ammonium thiocyanate, and mix. Any red color produced is not darker than that of a blank to which 0.01 mg of Fe has been added.

ALUMINUM CHLORIDE, ANHYDROUS

$AlCl_3$; mol. wt. 133.34; Al—20.23%; Cl—79.77%.

Slightly grayish or yellowish powder, or granules, with a strong odor of HCl. It is very hygroscopic and fumes in air. *Unites with water with explosive violence. Keep in tightly closed containers, protected from moisture.*

Standards

Sulfate (SO_4)................max 0.005%	Heavy metals (as Pb)........max 0.002%
Alkalies, Earths, etc...........max 0.20%	Iron (Fe)....................max 0.005%

Exercise caution when dissolving in water!

Sulfate: *Cautiously* dissolve 3 g in about 60 ml H_2O and slowly pour the solution, with stirring, into a mixture of 20 ml of ammonium hydroxide and 80 ml of H_2O. Boil until nearly free from ammonia odor, then adjust the volume to 150 ml and filter. Evaporate 50 ml of the filtrate to about 10 ml, refilter if necessary, add 1 ml of 0.1 N HCl and 2 ml of $BaCl_2$ and allow to stand for 20 minutes. Any resulting turbidity is not greater than that in a control made with 0.05 mg of SO_4 1 ml of 0.1 N HCl and 2 ml $BaCl_2$ in the same final volume as with the sample.

Alkalies, Earths, etc.: Test as described for Aluminum Chloride, Hydrated, using 25 ml of the filtrate obtained in the test for *Sulfate.*

Heavy metals: Cautiously dissolve 2 g in 40 ml of H_2O. To 10 ml add 0.02 mg of Pb and dilute to 40 ml (*A*). Dilute the remaining 30 ml to 40 ml (*B*). Then to each add 10 ml of H_2S. *B* is not darker than *A*.

Iron: Test 0.20 g as described for Aluminum Chloride, Hydrated. The results should be as there stated.

ALUMINUM CHLORIDE, HYDRATED

$AlCl_3 \cdot 6H_2O$; mol. wt. 241.44; anhydrous—55.23%; H_2O—44.77%; Al—11.17%; Cl—44.06%.

White or slightly yellowish crystals or granules; deliquescent. Very soluble in water, soluble in alcohol or ether. *Keep in tightly closed containers.*

Standards

Insoluble....................max 0.010%	Arsenic (As).................max 2 ppm
Free acid (as HCl)............max 0.10%	Heavy metals (as Pb)........max 0.002%
Sulfate (SO_4)................max 0.010%	Iron (Fe)....................max 0.002%
Alkalies, Earths, etc...........max 0.10%	*Assay*.........................min 99%
Ammonia (NH_3).............max 0.030%	

Insoluble: Dissolve 10 g in 100 ml of water and 1 ml hydrochloric acid, and heat on the steam bath for 30 minutes. Filter any undissolved matter, wash it with water, and dry at 105°. Its weight is not more than 1.0 mg.

Free acid: Dissolve 3 g of sodium fluoride in 50 ml of hot H_2O and add 3 drops of phenolphthalein. If no pink color is produced, add 0.1 N NaOH until the pink color persists for 30 seconds. If a pink color is immediately produced, discharge it in the hot solution with 0.1 N HCl and just reproduce the color with 0.1 N NaOH. Cool the solution, add it to a solution of 2 g of the sample in 25 ml of water and dilute to 80 ml. Allow to stand for 3 hours, then filter through a dry filter and titrate 40 ml of the filtrate with 0.1 N NaOH to a slight pink color. Not more than 0.3 ml of 0.1 N NaOH is required to produce a pink color.

Sulfate: Dissolve 3 g in about 40 ml of H_2O and slowly pour the solution, with stirring, into a mixture of 15 ml of ammonium hydroxide and 75 ml of H_2O. Boil until nearly free from NH_3 odor, adjust the volume to 150 ml, and filter. Evaporate 50 ml of the filtrate to 10 ml, filter, add to the filtrate 1 ml of 0.1 N HCl and 2 ml of $BaCl_2$. Any resulting turbidity is not greater than that in a control made with

0.1 mg of SO_4, 1 ml of 0.1 N HCl and 2 ml of $BaCl_2$ in the same final volume as with the sample.

Alkalies, Earths, etc.: Evaporate 50 ml of the filtrate from the *Sulfate* test to 20 ml and filter. Add to filtrate 5 drops of H_2SO_4, evaporate and ignite. The residue does not exceed 1.0 mg.

Ammonia: Dissolve 0.1 g in 20 ml of H_2O, add 5 ml of 10% NaOH, dilute to 50 ml, and add 2 ml of Nessler solution. The color is not darker than that in a blank with 0.03 mg of NH_3 added.

Arsenic: Test 1.0 g by method on page 563. The stain is not greater than that from 0.003 mg of As.

Heavy metals: Dissolve 2 g in H_2O to make 40 ml. To 10 ml add 0.02 mg of Pb and 1 ml of 1 N acetic acid, and dilute to 40 ml (A). To the remaining 30 ml add 1 ml of 1 N acetic acid and dilute to 40 ml (B). Then to each add 10 ml of H_2S; B is not darker than A.

Iron: Dissolve 0.5 g in 10 ml of H_2O, add 2 ml of HCl, boil for 30 seconds, cool, and dilute to 50 ml. Add 30 mg of ammonium persulfate and 3 ml of ammonium thiocyanate, and mix. Any red color produced is not darker than that of a blank to which 0.01 mg of Fe has been added.

Assay: Aluminum chloride may be assayed by the following method. Other soluble aluminum salts may equally be assayed by this method.

Weigh accurately a quantity of the sample equivalent to 50–60 mg of Al, or use an accurately measured volume of a stock solution corresponding to this quantity of Al. Dissolve in 100 ml of water, add 2 drops of HCl, heat to about 70° and add 120 ml of 8-hydroxyquinoline solution. Slowly add, with stirring, 20% ammonium acetate solution until a permanent precipitate is produced, and then add 15–20 ml more. Allow the precipitate to cool and to settle, filter through a tared filtering crucible or other suitable filter, wash with cold water, then dry at 120°–130° to constant weight. The precipitate, $Al(C_9H_6NO)$, contains 5.87% Al. The weight of the aluminum hydroxyquinolinate $\times$ 0.5255 represents $AlCl_3 \cdot 6H_2O$.

ALUMINUM NITRATE

$Al(NO_3)_3 \cdot 9H_2O$; mol. wt. 375.13; anhydrous—56.78%; H_2O—43.22%; Al—7.19%; NO_3—49.59%; Al_2O_3—13.59%.

Colorless, deliquescent crystals. Soluble in water or alcohol. *Keep in well-closed containers.*

Standards

Insoluble...................max 0.010%	Alkalies, Earths, etc...........max 0.10%	
Free acid (as HNO_3)..........max 0.15%	Ammonia (NH_3).............max 0.030%	
Chloride (Cl)................max 0.002%	Heavy metals (as Pb)........0.001% max	
Sulfate (SO_4)...............max 0.010%	Iron (Fe)...................max 0.002%	

Insoluble: Dissolve 10 g in 100 ml of water and 0.5 ml of HNO_3 and heat on steam bath for 30 minutes. Filter any undissolved residue, wash it with water and dry at 105°. The weight of the insoluble matter is not more than 1.0 mg.

Free acid: Determine as described for Aluminum Chloride, Hydrated. Not more than 0.25 ml of 0.1 N NaOH is required to produce a pink color.

Chloride: To a solution of 1 g in 20 ml of H_2O, add 1 ml of HNO_3 and 1 ml of silver nitrate. Any resulting turbidity is not greater than that in the blank to which 0.02 mg of Cl has been added.

Solution S: Evaporate 2 g with 7 ml of HCl on the steam bath. Dissolve the residue in 50 ml of hot water and pour the solution into a mixture of 10 ml of ammonium hydroxide and 50 ml of water. Boil until nearly free from NH_3 odor, filter and wash to 100 ml.

Sulfate: Evaporate 50 ml of *Solution S* to about 10 ml, then add 1 ml of 0.1 N HCl and 2 ml of $BaCl_2$. Any resulting turbidity in 15 minutes is not greater than that in a control made with 0.1 mg of SO_4, 1 ml of 0.1 N HCl and 2 ml of $BaCl_2$ in the same final volume as with the sample.

Alkalies, Earths, etc.: Evaporate 50 ml of *Solution S* to 20 ml, filter, add 5 drops of sulfuric acid, evaporate and ignite. The residue does not exceed 1.0 mg.

Ammonia: Dissolve 0.1 g in 20 ml of H_2O, add 5 ml of 10% NaOH, dilute to 50 ml, and add 2 ml of Nessler solution. The color is not darker than that in a blank with 0.03 mg NH_3 added.

Heavy metals: Evaporate 4 g with 10 ml of hydrochloric acid to dryness on steam bath, re-evaporate with 10 ml of water and dissolve the residue in 40 ml of water. To 10 ml add 0.02 mg of Pb and 1 ml of 1 N acetic acid and dilute to 40 ml (A). To the remaining 30 ml add 1 ml of 1 N acetic acid and dilute to 40 ml (B). Then to each add 10 ml of H_2S; B is not darker than A.

Iron: Dissolve 1 g in 15 ml of H_2O, add 2 ml of 10% HCl, about 30 mg of ammonium persulfate and 15 ml of butanolic potassium thiocyanate. Shake vigorously for about 30 seconds, then allow to separate. Any red color in the clear butanol layer is not darker than that of a blank to which 0.02 mg of Fe has been added.

ALUMINUM OXIDE

Ignited Aluminum Oxide, "Neutral" Aluminum Oxide

Al_2O_3; mol. wt. 101.94, Al—52.91%.

White, amorphous powder. Insoluble in water or acids. Absorbs water on exposure to air. *Keep in tightly closed containers.*

Standards

Chloride (Cl) ....max 0.005%	Iron (Fe) ....max 0.010%	
Silica, etc........................trace	Ignition loss.................max 5.0%	
Sulfate (SO_4)...............max 0.050%	Water-soluble substances.......max 0.5%	
Alkalies, Earths, etc..........max 0.50%	pH............................5.7–8.0	
Heavy metals (as Pb)........max 0.005%		

Chloride: Digest 1 g with 45 ml of H_2O and 5 ml of HNO_3 for 30 minutes, filter, and make up to 50 ml. To 10 ml of the filtrate add 1 ml of silver nitrate. Any resulting turbidity is not greater than that in the blank to which 0.01 mg Cl has been added.

Silica, etc.: Fuse 0.5 g of the finely powdered Al_2O_3 with 10 g of potassium bisulfate for 1 hour in platinum, cool and dissolve in 100 ml of hot H_2O. Not more than a small amount of insoluble matter remains.

Sulfate: Boil 2 g with 5 ml of HCl and 50 ml of H_2O for 30 minutes, dilute with 130 ml of H_2O and add an excess of NH_4OH. Boil until nearly free from NH_3 odor, cool, dilute to 200 ml and filter. Evaporate 20 ml of the filtrate to about 10 ml, then add 1 ml of 0.1 N HCl and 2 ml of $BaCl_2$. Any turbidity produced in 15 minutes is not greater than that in a control made with 0.1 mg of SO_4, 1 ml of 0.1 N HCl and 2 ml of $BaCl_2$ in the same final volume as with the sample.

Alkalies, Earths, etc.: Evaporate 50 ml of the filtrate from the test for *Sulfate* with 5 drops of H_2SO_4 and ignite. The weight of the residue does not exceed 2.5 mg.

Solution S: To 2 g add 5 ml of HCl and 5 ml of H_2O, and evaporate to dryness on steam bath. Heat the residue with 30 ml of H_2O, filter and wash with water to 50 ml.

Heavy metals: To 5 ml of *Solution S* add 0.02 mg of Pb, 1 ml of 1 N acetic acid and dilute to 40 ml (A). To 15 ml of *Solution S* add 1 ml of 1 N acetic acid and dilute to 40 ml (B). Then to each add 10 ml of H_2S; B is not darker than A.

Iron: Dilute 10 ml of *Solution S* with H_2O to 40 ml. To 10 ml of the dilution add 2 ml of HCl and dilute to 50 ml. Add 30 mg of ammonium persulfate and 3 ml of ammonium thiocyanate, and mix. Any red color produced is not darker than that of a blank to which 0.01 mg of Fe has been added.

Ignition loss: Ignite 1 g strongly. The loss in weight corresponds to not more than 5%.

Water-soluble substances: Digest 2 g with 100 ml of H_2O on the steam bath for 30 minutes, cool, dilute to 100 ml and filter. Evaporate 50 ml of the filtrate and ignite gently. The residue weighs not more than 5.0 mg.

pH: Prepare an aqueous slurry of the aluminum oxide by mixing well in an Erlenmeyer flask 5 g with about 150 ml of H_2O. Allow to stand for 10 minutes; then determine the pH electrometrically. It should be between 5.7 and 8.0.

ALUMINUM OXIDE, pH 4

Acid Washed, for Chromatography

White or nearly white powder, or fine granules. It is very hygroscopic. *Keep tightly closed.*

Standards

Adsorptive power............to pass test	Ignition loss....................max 5%
pH...........................3.5–4.5	Silica, etc.........................trace

Adsorptive power: Dissolve 50 mg of *o*-nitroaniline in benzene to make 50.0 ml. (*a*) Dilute 10 ml of the solution with benzene to 100 ml.

Weigh quickly about 2 g (± 0.005 g) of sample in a glass-stoppered weighing bottle and rapidly transfer it into a dry, glass-stoppered test tube. Add 20.0 ml of (*a*), stopper, shake vigorously for 3 minutes, and allow to settle.

(*b*) Pipette 10.0 ml of the clear supernatant liquid into a 100-ml volumetric flask, dilute to mark with benzene, and mix.

Determine the absorbancies of *a* and of *b* at 395 mμ, using the benzene as reference. Calculate by the following formula:

$$2\left(1 - \frac{Ab}{Aa}\right) \div W$$

where Aa and Ab are the absorbancies of the respective solutions *a* and *b*, and W is the weight of the aluminum oxide. Not less than 0.4 mg of the nitroaniline is adsorbed per 1 g of the aluminum oxide.

pH: Prepare an aqueous slurry of the aluminum oxide by mixing well in an Erlenmeyer flask 5 g with about 150 ml of H_2O. Allow to stand for 10 minutes, then determine the *p*H electrometrically. It should be between 3.5 and 4.5.

Ignition loss: Strongly ignite about 1 g, accurately weighed, to constant weight. The loss in weight corresponds to not more than 5%.

Silica, etc.: Fuse 0.5 g of the finely powdered aluminum oxide with 10 g of potassium bisulfate for 1 hour in platinum, cool and dissolve in 100 ml of hot H_2O. Not more than a small amount of insoluble matter remains.

ALUMINUM OXIDE, *p*H 10

For Chromatography

White or nearly white powder or fine granules. It is very hygroscopic. *Keep tightly closed.*

Standards

Adsorptive power............to pass test	Ignition loss....................max 8%
*p*H............................9.5–10.5	Silica, etc........................trace

Adsorptive power: Test as described under Aluminum Oxide *p*H-4. Not less than 0.7 mg of the nitroaniline is adsorbed per 1 g of the aluminum oxide.

pH: Proceed as described under Aluminum Oxide *p*H-4. The *p*H should be between 9.5 and 10.5.

Ignition loss: Determine as described under Aluminum Oxide *p*H-4. The loss does not exceed 8%.

Silica, etc.: Test as described under Aluminum Oxide *p*H-4. The result should be as there stated.

ALUMINUM POTASSIUM SULFATE

Potassium Alum

$AlK(SO_4)_2 \cdot 12H_2O$; mol. wt. 474.39; anhydrous—54.43%; H_2O—45.47%; Al—5.69%; K—8.24%; SO_4—40.50%; Al_2O_3—10.74%.

Colorless crystals or crystalline fragments. Soluble in 8 parts of water, in 0.5 part of boiling water; insoluble in alcohol.

Standards

Insoluble..................max 0.005%	Heavy Metals (as Pb)..........max 0.001%
Chloride (Cl)...............max 0.0005%	Iron (Fe)...................max 0.001%
Ammonia (NH_3)............max 0.010%	Sodium (Na)...........max about 0.02%
Arsenic (As)................max 2 ppm	

Insoluble: Dissolve 20 g in 150 ml of hot H_2O and heat on the steam bath for 30 minutes. Filter any undissolved residue, wash it with hot water and dry at 105°. The weight of the undissolved matter does not exceed 1.0 mg.

Chloride: Dissolve 2 g in 20 ml of warm water, cool, and add 2 ml of HNO_3 and 1 ml of $AgNO_3$. Any resulting turbidity is not greater than that in a blank to which 0.01 mg of Cl has been added.

Ammonia: To a solution of 0.2 g in 10 ml of H_2O add 5 ml of 10% NaOH, dilute to 50 ml, and add 2 ml of Nessler solution. The resulting color is not darker than that of a blank to which 0.02 mg of NH_3 has been added.

Arsenic: Determine in 1 g by the method on page 563. The stain is not greater than that from 0.002 mg of As.

Heavy metals: Dissolve 4 g in H_2O to make 40 ml. To 10 ml add 0.02 mg of Pb and dilute to 40 ml (*A*). Dilute the remaining 30 ml to 40 ml (*B*). Then to each add 10 ml of H_2S. *B* is not darker than *A*.

Iron: Dissolve 1 g in 10 ml of H_2O, add 2 ml of HCl, boil for 30 seconds, cool, and dilute to 50 ml. Add about 30 mg of ammonium persulfate and 3 ml of ammonium thiocyanate, and mix. Any red color produced is not darker than that of a blank to which 0.01 mg of Ge has been added.

Sodium: A 10% solution, tested on a platinum wire, imparts no pronounced yellow color to a colorless flame.

ALUMINUM SULFATE

$Al_2(SO_4)_3 \cdot 18H_2O$; mol. wt. 666.41; anhydrous—51.34%; H_2O—48.66%; Al—8.09%; SO_4—43.24%; Al_2O_3—15.30%.

White, lustrous crystals or granules. Soluble in 1 part of water; insoluble in alcohol.

Note: The water in aluminum sulfate may be determined by the iodine (Fischer) method.

Standards

Insoluble..................max 0.010%	Arsenic (As)................max 2 ppm
Free acid (as H_2SO_4)..........max 0.10%	Heavy metals (as Pb)........max 0.001%
Chloride (Cl)...............max 0.001%	Iron (Fe)...................max 0.002%
Alkalies, Earths, etc...........max 0.20%	*Assay*
Ammonia (NH_3)............max 0.020%	

Insoluble: Dissolve 10 g in 100 ml of water and 0.5 ml of H_2SO_4 and heat on steam bath for 30 minutes. Filter any undissolved matter, wash it with hot H_2O and dry at 105°. The weight of the undissolved matter does not exceed 1.0 mg.

Free acid: Dissolve 3 g of sodium fluoride in 50 ml of hot H_2O and add 3 drops of phenolphthalein. If no pink color is produced, add 0.1 N NaOH until the pink color persists for 30 seconds.   If a pink color is immediately produced, discharge it in the hot solution with 0.1 N HCl and just reproduce the color with 0.1 N NaOH. Cool the solution and add it to a solution of 2 g of the sample in 30 ml of water. Allow to stand for 3 hours, then filter through a dry filter and titrate 40 ml of the filtrate with 0.1 N NaOH to a slight pink color.   Not more than 0.2 ml of the NaOH is required.

Chloride: To a solution of 2 g in 20 ml of H_2O add 2 ml of HNO_3 and 1 ml of silver nitrate.   Any resulting turbidity is not greater than that in the blank to which 0.02 mg of Cl has been added.

Alkalies, Earths, etc.: Dissolve 2 g in 130 ml of H_2O and add a slight excess of ammonium hydroxide.   Boil until nearly free from NH_3 odor, filter, and wash to 150 ml.   Evaporate 75 ml and ignite.   The ignited residue weighs not more than 2.0 mg.

Ammonia: Dissolve 0.1 g in 20 ml H_2O, add 5 ml of 10% NaOH, dilute to 50 ml, and add 1 ml of Nessler solution.   The color is not darker than that in a blank with 0.02 mg NH_3 (0.1 mg NH_4Cl) added.

Arsenic: Test 1 g by method on page 563.   The stain is not greater than that from 0.002 mg of As.

Heavy metals: Dissolve 4 g in H_2O to make 40 ml.   To 10 ml add 0.02 mg of Pb and 1 ml of 1 N acetic acid, and dilute to 40 ml (A).   To the remaining 30 ml add 1 ml of 1 N acetic acid and dilute to 40 ml (B).   Then to each add 10 ml of H_2S; B is not darker than A.

Iron: Dissolve 0.5 g in 10 ml of H_2O, add 2 ml of HCl, boil for 30 seconds, cool, and dilute to 50 ml.   Add 30 mg of ammonium persulfate and 3 ml of ammonium thiocyanate, and mix.   Any red color produced is not darker than that of a blank to which 0.01 mg of Fe has been added.

Assay: Aluminum sulfate may be assayed as described under Aluminum Chloride, Hydrated.   The weight of the aluminum hydroxyquinolate × 7.7253 represents $Al_2(SO_4)_3 \cdot 18H_2O$.

AMINOACETIC ACID

Glycocoll; Glycine

$NH_2CH_2CO_2H$; mol. wt. 75.05; N—18.66%.

White, crystalline powder.   Soluble in water; slightly soluble in alcohol.

Standards

Assay....................99%–100.5%	Chloride (Cl)................max 0.005%
Insoluble...................to pass test	Sulfate (SO_4)...............max 0.005%
Ignition residue.............max 0.03%	Heavy metals (as Pb).......max 0.0005%
pH...........................4 to 4.5	Iron (Fe).................max 0.0005%

Assay: Weigh accurately about 0.20 g of the aminoacetic acid, previously dried at 100° for 1 hour, and dissolve it in 25 ml of water in a small beaker.   Add 6 ml of neutral formaldehyde solution—prepared by shaking formaldehyde frequently during several hours with small chips of iceland spar or marble—and titrate with

0.1 N NaOH, using a calomel and glass electroder, to an equivalent point of pH 9.2. One ml of 0.1 N NaOH = 0.007507 g of H_2NCH_2COOH, log 3.8755.

Insoluble: A solution of 2 g in 10 ml of water is complete and clear.

Ignition residue: Add 1 ml of H_2SO_4 to 3.0 g of sample and ignite to constant weight. The weight of the residue does not exceed 1.0 mg.

pH: The pH of 0.2 mol solution is 4 to 4.5.

Chloride: Dissolve 0.5 g in 25 ml of H_2O and add 1 ml of nitric acid and 1 ml of silver nitrate. Any turbidity produced is not greater than that in a blank to which 0.025 mg of Cl has been added.

Sulfate: Dissolve 2 g in 10 ml of H_2O and add 1 ml of 1 N HCl and 1 ml of $BaCl_2$. If a turbidity is produced it is not greater than that in a blank to which 0.1 mg of SO_4 has been added.

Heavy metals: Dissolve 8 g in water to make 40 ml. To 10 ml of the solution add 0.02 mg of Pb and 2 ml of 1 N acetic acid, and dilute to 40 ml (A). To the remaining 30 ml add 2 ml of 1 N acetic acid, and dilute to 40 ml (B). Then to each add 10 ml of H_2S. B is not darker than A.

Iron: To a solution of 2 g in 10 ml of H_2O, add 3 ml of HCl and dilute to 50 ml. Add about 30 mg of ammonium persulfate and 3 ml of ammonium thiocyanate, and mix. Any red color produced is not darker than that of a blank to which 0.01 mg of Fe has been added.

p-AMINOACETOPHENONE

$H_2N \cdot C_6H_4 \cdot CO \cdot CH_3$; mol. wt. 135.16; N—10.36%.

Pale yellow crystals or powder; characteristic odor. Slightly soluble in cold water; soluble in hot water or in alcohol; also soluble in diluted HCl or H_2SO_4.

It is used as a chromophor group, yielding colored reaction products with a number of organic chemicals, e.g., thiamine, sulfa drugs, etc., which can then be determined colorimetrically.

Standards

Melting range....................104°–106°	Solubility in alcohol...........to pass test
Ignition residue..............max 0.10%	Solubility in HCl.............to pass test

Ignition residue: To 1 g add 0.5 ml of H_2SO_4 and ignite gently at first, then strongly to constant weight. The weight of the residue does not exceed 1.0 mg.

Solubility in alcohol: A solution of 1 g in 20 ml of alcohol is complete and clear.

Solubility in HCl: Dissolve 0.5 in 10 ml of 10% HCl, warming if necessary; the cooled solution is complete and clear.

p-AMINOBENZOIC ACID

H_2N⟨ ⟩$COOH$; mol. wt. 137.13; N—10.21%.

Colorless or slightly yellow crystals. Soluble in about 200 parts of H_2O, more soluble in alcohol; soluble in solutions of alkali hydroxides or carbonates. Gradually darkens on exposure to light.

Standards

Melting range.................187°–189°	Chlorine compounds (as Cl)...max 0.004%
Assay..................99.5%–100.2%	Sulfate (SO₄)................max 0.010%
Ignition residue............max 0.030%	Heavy metals (as Pb).......max 0.001%
Solution in Na₂CO₃..........to pass test	Iron (Fe).................max 0.002%

Assay: Dissolve 0.4 to 0.5 g of the dried and accurately weighed sample in 15 to 20 ml of previously neutralized alcohol, and titrate with 0.1 N sodium hydroxide, using phenolphthalein indicator.   One ml of 0.1 N NaOH = 0.01371 g of $C_7H_7NO_2$, log 13704.

Ignition residue: To 3 g add 1 ml of H_2SO_4 and ignite gently to constant weight.   The weight of the residue does not exceed 1.0 mg (retain).

Solution in sodium carbonate: Slowly add 10 ml of Na_2CO_3 solution to 1 g of the sample and warm gently.   The resulting solution is clear and not darker than pale yellow.

Chlorine compounds: Mix 0.5 g with 0.25 g of sodium carbonate in a crucible or small dish, add 10 ml of water, evaporate to dryness, then ignite gently until thoroughly carbonized.   Add to the charred mass 10 ml of hot H_2O and 1 ml of HNO_3, filter, wash with water to 20 ml.   Add to the filtrate 1 ml of HNO_3 and 1 ml of $AgNO_3$.   Any turbidity produced is not greater than that in a control made with 0.02 mg of Cl ion, 0.25 g Na_2CO_3, 1 ml of HNO_3, 1 ml of $AgNO_3$, and in the same volume as with the sample.

Sulfate: Warm 0.75 g of sample with 0.4 g of Na_2CO_3 and 10 ml of water until dissolved.   Cool, add 4 ml of 10% HCl, and dilute to 15 ml.   Filter, and to 10 ml of the filtrate add 2 ml of $BaCl_2$.   Any turbidity produced in 10 minutes is not greater than in a control made with 0.05 mg of SO_4, 0.2 g of the Na_2CO_3, and 2 ml of the HCl.

Solution R: To the residue obtained in the test for *Ignition residue*, add 2 ml of HCl and 1 ml of HNO_3, and slowly evaporate to dryness on the steam bath. Treat the residue with 2 ml of 1 N HCl and 10 ml of hot H_2O, digest for 2–3 minutes, cool and dilute to 30 ml.

Heavy metals: To 20 ml of *Solution R*, add 1 ml of 1 N acetic acid, dilute to 40 ml and add 10 ml of H_2S.   Any color produced is not darker than that of a blank to which 0.02 mg of Pb has been added.

Iron: To the remaining 10 ml of *Solution R* add 2 ml of HCl and dilute to 50 ml. Add about 30 mg of ammonium persulfate and 3 ml of ammonium thiocyanate. Any resulting red color is not darker than that of a blank to which 0.02 mg of Fe has been added.

1,2,4-AMINONAPHTHOLSULFONIC ACID

; mol. wt. 239.25; N—5.86%; S—13.4%.

White to slightly brownish-pink powder.   Sparingly soluble in water; soluble in solutions of alkali hydroxides or carbonates.

Standards

Sensitiveness................to pass test	Ignition residue..............max 0.10%
Solubility in Na_2CO_3.........to pass test	Sulfate (SO_4).................max 0.2%

Sensitiveness: Dissolve 100 mg of the sample in a mixture of 50 ml of H_2O and 10 g of sodium bisulfite, warming, if necessary, to aid solution, and filter.

To 20 ml of H_2O add 0.02 mg of PO_4 and 2 ml of 25% H_2SO_4; then add 1 ml of phosphate reagent **A** and 1 ml of the solution of the sample prepared as in the preceding paragraph.   A distinct blue color should be produced in 5 minutes.

Solubility in sodium carbonate: Dissolve 100 mg in 3 ml of sodium carbonate solution and dilute with water to 10 ml.   The solution is clear and complete or practically so.

Ignition residue: Char 1.0 g, allow to cool, add 0.5 ml H_2SO_4 and ignite strongly to constant weight.   Any residue does not exceed 1.0 mg.

Sulfate: Heat 0.5 g with 25 ml of H_2O and 2 drops of HCl on the steam bath for 10 minutes.   Cool, dilute to 50 ml, and filter.   To 20 ml of the filtrate add 1 ml of 1 N HCl and 2 ml $BaCl_2$.   Any turbidity produced is not greater than that in a blank to which 0.20 mg of SO_4 has been added.

AMMONIUM ACETATE

$NH_4C_2H_3O_2$; mol. wt. 77.08; NH_3—22.11%; acetic—77.89%.

Colorless crystals or crystalline masses, usually with a slight acetous odor.   It is very hygroscopic and very soluble in water or alcohol.   *Keep in tightly closed container*, in a cool place.

Standards

Assay...................98% to 100.5%	Nitrate (NO_3)...............max 0.001%
Insoluble...................max 0.005%	Sulfate (SO_4)...............max 0.001%
pH of 4% solution.............6.7 to 7.3	Permanganate reducing.......to pass test
Ignition residue.............max 0.010%	Heavy metals (as Pb).......max 0.0005%
Chloride (Cl)...............max 0.0005%	Iron (Fe).................max 0.0005%

Assay: Weigh accurately about 3 g and dissolve it in 40 ml of water.   Add 40 ml of diluted formaldehyde $(1+1)$, previously neutralized to phenolphthalein with 0.1 N NaOH, mix and allow to stand for 30 minutes.   Then titrate with 1 N NaOH until the pink color persists for 5 minutes.   One ml of 1 N NaOH = 0.07708 g $NH_4C_2H_3O_2$, log 88694.

Insoluble: Dissolve 20 g in 100 ml of H_2O.   Filter any undissolved residue, wash it with water and dry at 105°.   The weight of the insoluble residue is not more than 1.0 mg.

***p*H:** Determine in a 4% solution in CO_2-free water, using bromothymol blue or phenol red indicator (see page 583), or preferably potentiometrically.

Ignition residue: Slowly ignite 10 g to constant weight. Not more than 1.0 mg of residue remains (retain).

Chloride: To a solution of 2 g in 20 ml H_2O add 1 ml of HNO_3 and 1 ml of silver nitrate. Any resulting turbidity is not greater than that in a blank to which 0.01 mg of Cl has been added.

Nitrate: Dissolve 0.5 g in 10 ml of water. Add to the solution 20 mg of NaCl and 0.2 ml diphenylamine solution, and follow slowly with 10 ml of H_2SO_4. No blue color appears after 30 minutes.

Sulfate: To a solution of 10 g in 10 ml of hot H_2O add 20 mg of sodium carbonate, evaporate to dryness on the steam bath and heat at 120° until all the ammonium acetate is volatilized. Treat the residue with 1 ml of 1 N HCl and 5 ml of H_2O, filter, wash to 10 ml, and add 2 ml of $BaCl_2$. Any resulting turbidity is not greater than that in a blank with 0.1 mg of SO_4 added.

Permanganate reducing substances: Dissolve 5 g in 50 ml of water, add 5 ml of 25% H_2SO_4 and 0.10 ml of 0.1 N $KMnO_4$. The pink color should not entirely disappear in 1 hour. Run a blank with the same volumes of the water and H_2SO_4.

Heavy metals: Dissolve 6 g in 10 ml of H_2O, add 5 ml of HCl and dilute to 30 ml. To 5 ml of the solution add 0.02 mg of Pb and dilute to 40 ml (A). Dilute the remaining 25 ml of the solution to 40 ml (B). Then add to each 10 ml H_2S. B is not darker than A.

Iron: To the ignition residue add 2 ml of HCl and 2 ml of H_2O and slowly evaporate to dryness on the steam bath. Take up the residue with 1 ml of HCl and sufficient H_2O to make 50 ml. To 10 ml of the solution add 2 ml of HCl and dilute to 50 ml. Add about 30 mg of ammonium persulfate and 3 ml of ammonium thiocyanate, and mix. Any resulting red color is not darker than that of a control made with 0.01 mg of Fe, 2 ml of HCl, the same quantities of the reagents and in the same final volume as with the sample.

AMMONIUM AURINTRICARBOXYLATE, *see* ALUMINON

AMMONIUM BICARBONATE

NH_4HCO_3; mol. wt. 79.06; NH_3—21.54%; CO_2—55.67%.

White crystals or crystalline powder, with relatively slight odor of NH_3. At ordinary room temperature it is quite stable and volatilizes only slightly. At about 60° it rapidly volatilizes, dissociating into NH_3, CO_2, and H_2O. It is similarly decomposed by hot water. Soluble in about 5–6 parts of water, insoluble in alcohol.

Because of its greater stability and constancy of composition ammonium bicarbonate is preferred by some to ammonium carbonate.

Standards

Assay....................21%–22% NH_3	Sulfur compounds (as SO_4)....max 0.002%
Insoluble...................max 0.005%	Heavy metals (as Pb).......max 0.0005%
Nonvolatile.................max 0.010%	Iron (Fe)..................max 0.0005%
Chloride (Cl)..............max 0.0005%	

Assay: Accurately weigh a glass-stoppered flask containing about 20 ml of water. Add about 2.5 g of sample and reweigh. Slowly add 40 ml of 1 N H_2SO_4, then gently boil the solution for 1–2 minutes. Cool and titrate the excess of acid with 1 N NaOH, using methyl red indicator. One ml of 1 N acid = 0.01703 g NH_3, log 23121.

Insoluble: Nonvolatile; Chloride; Sulfur compounds; Heavy metals; Iron: Apply the tests as under Ammonium Carbonate. The results should be as there stated.

AMMONIUM BROMIDE

NH_4Br; mol. wt. 97.96; NH_3—17.38%; HBr—82.62%; Br—81.58%.

Colorless, small crystals or white granules; somewhat hygroscopic. Soluble in 1.5 parts of water, in 15 parts of alcohol.

Standards

Insoluble.................max 0.005%	Iodide (I)...................to pass test
Ignition residue............max 0.010%	(limit about.................0.005%)
Free acid...................to pass test	Sulfate (SO_4)...............max 0.010%
Bromate (BrO_3)............max 0.002%	Barium....................max 0.001%
Chloride (Cl)................max 0.2%	Heavy metals (as Pb).......max 0.0005%
	Iron (Fe).................max 0.0005%

Insoluble: Dissolve 20 g in 100 ml of H_2O and heat on the steam bath 1 hour. Filter any undissolved matter, wash it with water and dry at 105°. The weight of the insoluble residue is not over 0.5 mg.

Ignition residue: To 10 g add 1 ml of H_2SO_4, heat slowly to volatilize, then ignite to constant weight. The residue does not exceed 1.0 mg (retain).

Free acid: Dissolve 3 g in 30 ml of H_2O, and add 1 drop of methyl red. If a red color is produced it is changed to yellow by 0.10 ml of 0.1 N NaOH.

Bromate: Dissolve 0.5 g in 10 ml of oxygen-free H_2O, add 2 drops of 10% potassium iodide, 1 ml starch, and 5 drops of 1 N H_2SO_4, and allow to stand for 1 minute. No blue or violet color is produced.

Chloride: Dissolve 0.5 g of sample in a mixture of 5 ml of HNO_3 and 15 ml of water in a 100-ml Erlenmyer flask. Add 3 ml of 30% H_2O_2 and gently heat on the steam bath until the solution is colorless. Do not heat any longer than necessary to decolorize the solution. Wash down the inside of the flask with a little water, add 1 ml of 30% H_2O_2 and digest on the steam bath for an additional 15 minutes, washing down the sides of the flask, once or twice, with a little water during this digestion. Cool and dilute to 200 ml. Dilute 5 ml of this solution to 20 ml, and add 1 ml of HNO_3 and 1 ml of $AgNO_3$ solution. The turbidity so produced is not greater than that produced by treating 1.0 mg Cl^- (as NaCl) in the same manner as the sample.

Iodide: Dissolve 3 g in 20 ml of H_2O, add 1 ml chloroform, 2 drops of ferric chloride and 5 drops of 10% H_2SO_4, and shake. No violet tint is produced in the chloroform.

Sulfate: Dissolve 1 g in 10 ml of water, add 1 ml of 0.1 N HCl and 2 ml of $BaCl_2$. Any turbidity produced is not greater than that in the blank to which 0.1 mg of SO_4 has been added.

Barium: Dissolve 2.0 g in 15 ml of water, add 5 drops of glacial acetic acid, and filter if not clear. Add to the solution 1.0 ml of potassium chromate solution and sufficient 10% NH_3 to make the color clear yellow. Treat 15 ml of the water exactly as the solution of the reagent including filtration if the solution was filtered. After 5 minutes both are equally clear.

Heavy metals: Dissolve 6 g in water to make 30 ml. To 5 ml add 0.02 mg of Pb and 1 ml of 1 N acetic acid, and dilute to 40 ml (A). To the remaining 25 ml add 1 ml of 1 N acetic acid (B) and dilute to 40 ml. Then add to each 10 ml of H_2S. B is not darker than A.

Iron: To the *Ignition residue* add 2 ml of HCl and 2 ml of H_2O, and slowly evaporate to dryness on the steam bath. Warm the residue with 1 ml of HCl and dilute to 50 ml. To 10 ml of the solution add 2 ml of HCl and dilute to 50 ml. Add about 30 mg of ammonium persulfate and 3 ml of ammonium thiocyanate, and mix. Any resulting red color is not darker than that of a blank to which 0.01 mg of Fe has been added.

AMMONIUM CARBONATE

A mixture of about equal parts of ammonium bicarbonate (NH_4HCO_3) and ammonium carbamate ($NH_4NH_2CO_2$).

White, hard translucent lumps, or $\frac{3}{8}$-inch cubes, having a strong odor of ammonia. Loses NH_3 on exposure to the air, becoming opaque and powdery. Entirely volatilizes at about 60°. Very slowly soluble in 5 parts of water; alcohol dissolves the carbamate. *Keep in tightly closed containers in a cool place.*

Standards

Assay.....................min 30% NH_3	Sulfur compounds	
Insoluble....................max 0.005%	(as SO_4)..................max 0.002%	
Nonvolatile.................max 0.010%	Heavy metals (as Pb).......max 0.0005%	
Chloride (Cl)...............max 0.0005%	Iron (Fe)..................max 0.0005%	

Assay: Accurately weigh a glass-stoppered flask with 25 ml of water, add about 2 g of sample and reweigh. Add slowly 40 ml of 1 N H_2SO_4, boil for 1–2 minutes, cool, and titrate the excess of acid with 1 N NaOH, using methyl red indicator. One ml of 1 N HCl = 0.01703 g NH_3, log 23121.

Insoluble: Dissolve 20 g in 100 ml of hot H_2O. Filter any undissolved matter, wash with water and dry at 105°. The insoluble residue does not exceed 1.0 mg.

Nonvolatile: Volatilize 10 g on the steam bath and dry at 105°. The residue is not more than 1.0 mg (retain).

Chloride: Dissolve 2 g in 20 ml of hot H_2O, add 10 mg of sodium carbonate and evaporate on the steam bath. Add to the residue 10 ml of water, filter and add to the filtrate 0.5 ml of HNO_3 and 0.5 ml of $AgNO_3$. Any resulting turbidity is not greater than that in a blank to which 0.01 mg of Cl has been added.

Sulfur compounds: Dissolve 5 g in 20 ml hot H_2O, add 20 mg of sodium carbonate and evaporate to 5 ml. Add a few drops of bromine water and evaporate to dryness. Take up the residue with 5 ml of H_2O and 2 ml of 1 N HCl and evaporate to dryness on the steam bath. Dissolve the residue in 1 ml of 0.1 N HCl and 5 ml of H_2O, filter if necessary, wash to 10 ml with H_2O, add to the filtrate 2 ml of $BaCl_2$, and allow to stand for 10 minutes. Any turbidity produced is not greater than that in a blank to which 0.1 mg of SO_4 has been added.

Solution R: Add 2 ml of HCl to the residue from *Nonvolatile* and slowly evaporate to dryness on the steam bath. Warm the residue with 0.5 ml of 1 N HCl and dilute with water to 50 ml.

Heavy metals: Dilute 20 ml of *Solution R* to 40 ml and add 10 ml of H_2S. Any darkening is not more than is produced in a control made with 0.02 mg of Pb, 0.2 ml in 1 N HCl and 10 ml of H_2S in the same volume as with the sample.

Iron: To 10 ml of *Solution R* add 2 ml of HCl and dilute to 50 ml. Add about 30 mg of ammonium persulfate and 3 ml of ammonium thiocyanate, and mix. Any resulting red color is not darker than that of a blank to which 0.01 mg of Fe has been added.

AMMONIUM CHLORIDE

NH_4Cl; mol. wt. 53.50; NH_3—31.83%; HCl—68.17%; N—26.18%; Cl—66.28%.

Colorless, small crystals or white granules; odorless. Soluble in 3 parts of water, 80 parts of alcohol.

Standards

Insoluble....................max 0.005%	Arsenic (As).................max 1 ppm	
Ignition residue.............max 0.010%	Calcium and magnesium	
Free acid.....................to pass test	precipitate................max 0.005%	
Nitrate (NO_3)...............max 0.001%	Heavy metals (as Pb).......max 0.0005%	
Phosphate (PO_4)...........max 0.0002%	Iron (Fe).................max 0.0002%	
Sulfate (SO_4)...............max 0.001%		

Insoluble: Dissolve 20 g in 150 ml of H_2O and heat on the steam bath for 1 hour. Filter any undissolved matter, wash it with water and dry at 105°. The weight of the insoluble residue is not over 1.0 mg.

Ignition residue: To 10 g of sample in a porcelain or silica dish add 2 ml of H_2SO_4, heat at a temperature requiring about 1 hour to volatilize, then ignite at low red heat for 5 minutes. The weight of the residue does not exceed 1.0 mg (retain).

Free acid: To a solution of 5 g in 50 ml of CO_2-free water add 1 drop of methyl red. If a red color is produced it is changed to yellow by 0.10 ml of 0.1 N NaOH.

Nitrate: Dissolve 0.5 g in 10 ml of water and add 0.2 ml of diphenylamine solution. Cool in ice water for 1 minute, then withdraw from the cooling bath, and, holding the beaker at an angle of about 45°, add slowly 10 ml of H_2SO_4 without agitation. Allow to stand for 10 minutes, then mix the liquids by gentle swirling and allow to stand for 1 hour. No blue color appears.

Phosphate: Place 5 g of sample in a platinum crucible, add 0.25 g of Na_2CO_3 and a few ml of H_2O, evaporate to dryness and ignite gently. Add to the residue 2 ml of 25% H_2SO_4 and 15 ml of water, and filter, if necessary. Add to filtrate 1 ml each of phosphate reagents **A** and **B** and heat at 60° for 10 minutes. If a blue color is produced, it is not deeper than that of a blank to which 0.01 mg of PO_4 has been added.

Sulfate: Dissolve 10 g in 100 ml of H_2O, add 1 ml of 1 N HCl, bring to a boil, add 5 ml of $BaCl_2$ and allow to stand overnight. No precipitate or turbidity is produced.

Arsenic: Test 2 g by method on page 563. The stain is not greater than that from 0.002 mg of As.

Calcium and magnesium precipitate: Warm the residue from *Ignition residue* with 1 ml of HCl and 3 ml of H_2O, then add 2 ml of ammonium hydroxide, filter and wash with a few ml of water. Add to the filtrate 2 ml of ammonium oxalate and 2 ml of ammonium phosphate and allow to stand overnight. Filter any precipitate present, wash it with 2.5% NH_3 and ignite. The ignited precipitate does not weigh more than 0.5 mg.

Heavy metals: Dissolve 6 g in H_2O to make 30 ml. To 5 ml add 0.02 mg of Pb, and 1 ml of 1 N acetic acid and dilute to 40 ml (A). To the remaining 25 ml add 1 ml of 1 N acetic acid and dilute to 40 ml (B). Then to each add 10 ml of H_2S. B is not darker than A.

Iron: Dissolve 5 g in 30 ml of H_2O, add 2 ml of HCl and dilute to 50 ml. Add 30 mg of ammonium persulfate and 3 ml of ammonium thiocyanate, and mix. Any resulting red color is not darker than that of a blank to which 0.01 mg of Fe has been added.

AMMONIUM CHROMATE

$(NH_4)_2CrO_4$; mol. wt. 152.09; NH_3—22.40%; CrO_3—65.75%.

Yellow crystals or granular. Soluble in 3 parts of water.

Standards

Assay..........99%–100.5% $(NH_4)_2CrO_4$	Sulfate (SO_4)................max 0.010%	
Insoluble...................max 0.010%	Alkali salts...................max 0.20%	
Chloride (Cl)...............max 0.002%	Calcium (Ca)...............max 0.005%	

Assay: As for Ammonium Dichromate. One ml of 0.1 N thiosulfate = 0.005070 g $(NH_4)_2CrO_4$, log 70501.

Insoluble: Dissolve 10 g in 100 ml of water and heat for 30 minutes on the steam bath. Filter any undissolved residue on a tared, sintered glass crucible, wash it with water until the washings are colorless, and dry at 105°. The weight of the insoluble residue does not exceed 1.0 mg.

Chloride: Dissolve 2 g in 40 ml of water, add 20 ml of HNO_3 and divide into two equal portions. Heat both portions to 50°, and to one portion add 1 ml of $AgNO_3$, and to the other portion add 1 ml of water. At the end of 5 minutes both portions are equally clear.

Sulfate: Dissolve 2 g in 75 ml of water, add 2 ml of HCl, heat to about 80° and add 10 ml of a solution containing 1 g of $BaCl_2$ and 2 ml of HCl in 100 ml. No turbidity or precipitate is produced in 1 hour.

Alkali salts: Ignite 1 g strongly, cool and digest the residue with 15 ml of hot H_2O. Filter, evaporate the filtrate and ignite. Treat the residue again with 15 ml of hot H_2O, filter, evaporate and ignite. The final residue weighs not more than 2.0 mg.

Calcium: To a solution of 2 g in 20 ml of H_2O add a few drops of NH_4OH and 2 ml of ammonium oxalate and let stand overnight. Any precipitate formed is not more than is formed in a blank to which 0.1 mg of Ca has been added.

AMMONIUM CITRATE DIBASIC

$(NH_4)_2HC_6H_5O_7$; mol. wt. 226.19; NH_3—15.06%; anhydrous citric acid = 84.94%.

Colorless, small crystals, or white granules. Very soluble in water, slightly soluble in alcohol.

Standards

Assay......................98%–102%	Sulfate (SO_4)................max 0.005%
Insoluble...................max 0.005%	Tartrate, etc., substances dark-
Ignition residue.............max 0.010%	ened by H_2SO_4 (as tartaric
Chloride (Cl)................max 0.001%	acid).................max about 0.2%
Oxalate (C_2O_4).........max about 0.03%	Heavy metals (as Pb).......max 0.0005%
Phosphate (PO_4)...........max 0.001%	Iron (Fe)..................max 0.001%

Assay: Weigh accurately about 3 g and dissolve it in 40 ml of water. Add 40 ml of diluted formaldehyde (1+1), previously neutralized to phenolphthalein with 1 N NaOH, mix and allow to stand for 30 minutes; then titrate with 1 N NaOH until the pink color persists for 5 minutes. One ml of 1 N NaOH = 0.0754 g of $(NH_4)_2HC_6H_5O_7$, log 87737. The reaction of the reagent with formaldehyde is as follows:

$$2(NH_4)_2HC_6H_5O_7 + 6HCHO \rightarrow 2H_3C_6H_5O_7 + (CH_2)_6N_4 + 6H_2O$$
$$\text{citric acid} \qquad \text{hexamethylene-tetramime}$$

Insoluble: Dissolve 20 g in 100 ml of H_2O and heat on the steam bath for 1 hour. Filter any undissolved residue, wash it with water and dry at 105°. The weight of the insoluble residue is not more than 1.0 mg.

Ignition residue: Char well 10 g, cool, add 0.5 ml H_2SO_4 and ignite gently at first, then strongly to constant weight. Not more than 1.0 mg of residue remains.

Chloride: Dissolve 1 g in 10 ml of water, add 1 ml of nitric acid and 1 ml of silver nitrate. Any turbidity produced is not greater than that in a blank with 0.01 mg of Cl added.

Oxalate: Dissolve 3 g in 25 ml of H_2O, add 3 ml of glacial acetic acid and 2 ml of 10% calcium acetate solution. No turbidity or precipitate is produced in 2 hours.

Phosphate: Dissolve 2 g in 5 ml of H_2O in a platinum crucible, add 0.5 g of magnesium nitrate, evaporate and ignite. Warm the residue with 3 ml of 25% H_2SO_4 and 5 ml of H_2O, then add 15 ml of H_2O and filter. Add to filtrate 1 ml each of phosphate reagents **A** and **B** and heat at 60° for 10 minutes.   Any resulting blue color is not darker than that in a control made with 0.02 mg of PO_4, 2 ml of 25% H_2SO_4, 0.5 g of ignited magnesium nitrate and the same quantities of the phosphate reagents and in the same final volume as with the sample.

Sulfate: Dissolve in a crucible or small dish 2 g in a few ml of water, add 0.5 g of sodium carbonate, evaporate to dryness, and ignite the residue, protecting from access of sulfur, until nearly free of carbon.   Add to the residue 15 ml of water and 1 ml of 30% hydrogen peroxide, boil for a few minutes, then add 2 ml of HCl and evaporate to dryness on the steam bath.   Dissolve the residue in 5 ml of hot water, filter, wash with water to 10 ml and add 1 ml of 0.1 N HCl and 2 ml of $BaCl_2$. Any turbidity produced is not greater than that in a control made as follows: Evaporate 0.5 g sodium carbonate with 2 ml of HCl and 1 ml of 30% hydrogen peroxide on the steam bath, add to the residue 0.1 mg of SO_4 and sufficient water to make 10 ml, filter if necessary, and add 1 ml of 0.1 N HCl and 2 ml of $BaCl_2$.

Tartrate: Carefully powder 1 g of the sample, then mix 0.5 g of the powder with 10 ml of H_2SO_4 in a test tube previously rinsed with H_2SO_4, cover and heat at 110° for 30 minutes.   The color of the solution is not darker than pale yellow.

Heavy metals: Dissolve 6 g in water, add 7 ml of 10% HCl and dilute to 30 ml. To 5 ml of the solution add 0.02 mg of Pb, and dilute to 10 ml (A).   Dilute the remaining 25 ml of the solution to 40 ml (B).   Then add to each 10 ml of H_2S. B is not darker than A.

Iron: Dissolve 1 g in 20 ml of H_2O, add 2 ml of HCl and dilute to 50 ml.   Add about 50 mg of ammonium persulfate and 3 ml of ammonium thiocyanate and mix. Any resulting red color is not darker than that of a blank to which 0.01 mg of Fe has been added.

AMMONIUM DICHROMATE

$(NH_4)_2Cr_2O_7$; mol. wt. 252.10; NH_3—13.51%; CrO_3—79.34%.

Orange-red crystals or granules.   Soluble in 3 parts of water; insoluble in alcohol.

Standards

Assay.........99%–100.5% $(NH_4)_2Cr_2O_7$		Sulfate (SO_4).................max 0.01%	
Insoluble....................max 0.005%		Alkali salts......................0.10%	
Chloride (Cl)...............max 0.002%		Calcium (Ca)...................0.002%	

Assay: Weigh accurately about 1.2 g, dissolve in H_2O and dilute to exactly 200 ml.   Transfer 20 ml into a glass-stoppered flask, dilute with 130 ml of water and add 7 ml of HCl and 3 g of potassium iodide.   Allow to stand for 15 minutes, then titrate the liberated iodine with 0.1 N sodium thiosulfate, using starch toward the end.   Correct for a blank.   One ml of 0.1 N thiosulfate = 0.004202 g $(NH_4)_2Cr_2O_7$, log 62346.

$$(NH_4)_2Cr_2O_7 + 6KI + 14HCl \rightarrow 2CrCl_3 + 6I + 2NH_4Cl + 6KCl + 7H_2O$$

and: $$2I + 2Na_2S_2O_3 \rightarrow Na_2S_4O_6 + 2NaI$$

Insoluble: Dissolve 20 g in 100 ml H_2O and heat on the steam bath for 1 hour. Filter any undissolved residue on a tared, sintered glass crucible, wash with hot water and dry at 105°. The insoluble residue weighs not more than 1.0 mg.

Chloride: Dissolve 2 g in 40 ml of water, add 20 ml of HNO_3 and divide into two equal portions. Heat both portions to 50°, and to one portion add 1 ml of $AgNO_3$, and to the other portion add 1 ml of water. At the end of 5 minutes both portions are equally clear.

Sulfate: Dissolve 2 g in 75 ml of water, heat to about 80° and add 10 ml of a solution containing 1 g of $BaCl_2$ and 2 ml of HCl in 100 ml. No turbidity or precipitate is produced in 1 hour.

Alkali salts: Ignite 1 g strongly, cool and digest the residue with 15 ml of hot H_2O. Filter, evaporate the filtrate and ignite. Treat the residue again with 15 ml of hot H_2O, filter, evaporate and ignite. The final residue weighs not more than 1.0 mg.

Calcium: To a solution of 5 g in 50 ml of H_2O add a slight excess of NH_4OH and 5 ml of ammonium oxalate, and allow to stand overnight. Any precipitate formed is not more than that in a blank to which 0.1 mg of Ca has been added.

AMMONIUM FLUORIDE

NH_4F; mol. wt. 37.04; NH_3—45.98%; F—51.30%.

Moist, white crystals; corrodes glass. Freely soluble in water; sparingly soluble in alcohol. Usually contains some acid ammonium fluoride.

Standards

Ignition residue............max 0.020%	Sulfate (SO_4)...............max 0.020%
Acid fluoride (NH_4HF_2)........max 0.5%	Heavy metals (as Pb)........max 0.001%
Chloride (Cl)...............max 0.002%	Iron (Fe)...................max 0.003%
Nitrate (NO_3)..............max 0.002%	*Assay*.......................min 98%
Silicofluoride (H_2SiF_6).........max 0.3%.	

Ignition residue: Weigh quickly 5 g in a platinum crucible, add 1 ml of H_2SO_4 and ignite gently, under the hood, to constant weight. The residue weighs not more than 1.0 mg.

Acid fluoride: Weigh accurately about 5 g, dissolve it in 50 ml of cold H_2O in a platinum dish, and titrate with 1 N NaOH, using methyl red indicator. One ml of 1 N NaOH = 0.05705 g NH_4HF_2, log 75626. Not more than 0.5 ml of the NaOH is required.

Chloride: Dissolve 1 g of the sample in 10 ml of water and 1 ml of HNO_3 in platinum. Mix in a beaker 20 ml of water and 1 ml of $AgNO_3$, then add to it the solution of the sample. If a turbidity is produced it is not greater than that in a blank to which 0.02 mg of Cl has been added.

Nitrate: Mix 0.2 g of sample with 10 ml of water, add 20 mg of NaCl and 0.2 ml of diphenylamine solution and slowly run in 10 ml of H_2SO_4. Mix gently and let stand for 1 hour. No blue color appears.

Silicofluoride: Dissolve 3 g in 15 ml of H_2O in platinum, add 3 ml of a 20% aqueous solution of potassium chloride and 15 ml of alcohol. After 5 minutes transfer the solution to a test tube and examine at once.   At most only a slight turbidity is apparent.

Sulfate: Place 0.5 g of the sample in a platinum dish, add 0.1 g of sodium carbonate and a few ml of H_2O.   When the effervescence ceases, add 5 ml of HCl and evaporate to dryness on the steam bath.   Re-evaporate 3 times to dryness with 5-ml portions of HCl.   Take up the residue with 10 ml of H_2O and 1 ml of 0.1 N HCl, filter if not clear and add 2 ml of $BaCl_2$.   If a turbidity is produced, it does not exceed that of a control made as follows: Evaporate 0.1 g of sodium carbonate and 20 ml of HCl to dryness on the steam bath, dissolve the residue and 0.1 mg of SO_4 in H_2O to make 10 ml, then add 1 ml of 0.1 N HCl and 2 ml of $BaCl_2$.

Heavy metals: Dissolve 2 g in water to 40 ml.   To 10 ml of the solution add 0.01 mg of Pb and 2 g of sodium acetate and dilute to 40 ml (A).   To the remaining 30 ml add 2 g of sodium acetate and dilute to 40 ml (B).   Then to each add 10 ml of H_2S. B is not darker than A.

Iron: Dissolve 1 g in 20 ml of water in platinum, add 3 ml of HCl and boil for 2 minutes.   Cool and make up to 30 ml.   To 10 ml add 50 mg of ammonium persulfate and 15 ml of butanolic potassium thiocyanate, shake well and allow to separate.   Any resulting red color in the butanol layer is not darker than that of a control made with 0.01 mg of Fe and 1 ml of HCl, and the same quantities of the reagent and in same volume as with the sample.

Assay: Ammonium fluoride may be assayed by the method given for Potassium Fluoride.   One ml of 0.1 N thorium nitrate = 0.003704 g NH_4F, log 56867.

AMMONIUM HYDROXIDE

Ammonia Water; Aqua Ammonia

An aqueous solution of NH_3.   (NH_3; mol. wt. 17.03; N—82.25%; H—17.75%.)

Colorless liquid; extremely pungent odor.   Absorbs carbon dioxide from the air.   Mixed with acids, much heat is produced.   Sp. gr. about 0.89 at 25°.   *Keep in tightly stoppered bottles, in a cold place.*

Standards

Assay.................28%–30% NH_3	Sulfur, total as SO_4.........max 0.0002%
Nonvolatile.................max 0.002%	Heavy metals (as Pb)......max 0.00005%
Carbon dioxide..............max 0.002%	Iron (Fe).................max 0.00002%
Chloride (Cl).............max 0.00005%	Pyridine....................to pass test
Phosphate (PO_4)..........max 0.0002%	Permanganate-reducing
Sulfide.....................to pass test	substances.................to pass test

Assay: Accurately weigh a glass-stoppered flask with 15 ml of water, add about 2 ml of the sample and reweigh.   Dilute with 40 ml of H_2O and titrate with 1 N acid, using methyl red as indicator.   One ml of 1 N acid = 0.01703 g NH_3, log 23121.

Nonvolatile: Evaporate 55 ml (50 g) and ignite at cherry redness for 5 minutes.   The residue does not exceed 1.0 mg (retain).

Carbon Dioxide: Dilute 11 ml with 10 ml of H_2O and add 5 ml of saturated

barium hydroxide solution.   Any resulting turbidity is not greater than that produced by the same volume of barium hydroxide in a solution of 0.5 mg of anhydrous
sodium carbonate in 20 ml of CO_2-free water.

Chloride: To 22 ml (20 g) add 10 mg of sodium carbonate and evaporate to
dryness on the steam bath.   Take up the residue with 8 ml of H_2O and 1 ml of 10%
HNO_3, and add 1 ml of $AgNO_3$.   Any turbidity produced is not greater than that
in a blank to which 0.01 mg of Cl has been added.

Phosphate: Evaporate 11 ml to dryness on the steam bath.   Warm the
residue with 2 ml of 25% H_2SO_4, add 20 ml of H_2O and filter.   Add to the filtrate
1 ml each of phosphate reagents **A** and **B** and heat at 60° for 10 minutes.   If a
blue color is produced it is not deeper than that of a blank with 0.02 mg of PO_4
added.

Sulfide: Dilute 10 ml with 10 ml of H_2O and add 5 drops of sodium plumbite
solution (made by adding 10% NaOH to lead acetate solution until the precipitate
redissolves).   No darkening is produced.

Sulfur, total: To 33 ml (30 g) add 10 mg of sodium carbonate and evaporate
to 5 ml.   Add 1 ml of 30% hydrogen peroxide, evaporate to dryness on the steam
bath, then add a few drops of HCl and re-evaporate to dryness.   Take up the
residue with 5 ml of H_2O, filter, wash with water to 10 ml, add to the filtrate 0.5 ml
of 1 N HCl and 2 ml of $BaCl_2$, and allow to stand for 15 minutes.   Any resulting
turbidity does not exceed that of a blank to which 0.06 mg of SO_4 has been added.

Heavy metals: To 44 ml add 10 mg of NaCl, and evaporate to dryness on the
steam bath.   Take up the residue in 20 ml of 1 N acetic acid, dilute to 40 ml, and
add 10 ml of H_2S.   Any darkening produced is not greater than that in a blank to
which 0.02 mg of Pb has been added.

Iron: To the residue from the test for *Nonvolatile* add 2 ml of HCl and 2 ml of
H_2O, and slowly evaporate on the steam bath to dryness.   Take up the residue in
2 ml of HCl and a few ml of H_2O, and dilute to 50 ml.   Add to the solution about
30 mg of ammonium persulfate and 3 ml ammonium thiocyanate, and mix.   Any
resulting red color is not darker than that in a control made with 0.01 mg of Fe,
2 ml of HCl, the same quantities of the reagents and in the same final volume as
with the sample.

Pyridine: Mix 25 ml with 25 ml of H_2O, nearly neutralize the mixture with
25% H_2SO_4, using methyl orange indicator, and stir briskly.   Not more than a
very faint odor of pyridine is perceptible.

Permanganate-reducing substances: Dilute 3 ml with 5 ml of H_2O, add
50 ml of 10% H_2SO_4 and 0.05 ml of 0.1 N potassium permanganate.   The pink
color remains after boiling for 5 minutes.   Run a blank with the acid and the
water.

AMMONIUM IODIDE

NH_4I; mol. wt. 144.96; NH_3—11.75%; I—87.56%.

White, or slightly yellow, hygroscopic crystals or granules.   It darkens with
age due to liberation of iodine.   Very soluble in water; soluble in alcohol.

Standards

Assay...................min 99% NH_4I	Phosphorus compounds
Insoluble....................to pass test	(as PO_4).................max 0.001%
Ignition residue.............max 0.05%	Sulfate (SO_4)................max 0.03%
Chloride and Bromide (as Cl)...max 0.01%	Barium (Ba)...............max 0.003%
	Heavy metals (as Pb).......max 0.001%

Assay: Dry about 1 g in a vacuum over sulfuric acid overnight, and assay about 0.4 g of the dried sample, accurately weighed, by the assay method given for Potassium Iodide.   One ml of 0.05 molar potassium iodate = 0.01450 g NH_4I, log 16137.

Insoluble: Dissolve 5 g in 50 ml of H_2O.   The solution is clear and no insoluble residue remains.

Ignition residue: To 2 g add 1 ml of H_2SO_4, heat slowly to volatilize, then ignite to constant weight.   The residue does not exceed 1.0 mg.

Chloride and Bromide: Dissolve 2 g in a mixture of 8 ml of NH_4OH and 7 ml of H_2O, and add to it slowly, with constant agitation, 50 ml of 5% $AgNO_3$.   Filter, and to 30 ml of the filtrate add 6 ml of HNO_3.   The turbidity produced is not more than that produced by treating 0.5 g of the sample and 0.15 mg of Cl (as NaCl) in the same manner.

Phosphorus compounds: Add 5 ml of HNO_3 to a solution of 2 g in 10 ml of H_2O.   Evaporate on the steam bath to dryness and until all the iodine has completely volatilized, aiding the volatilization by addition of a little water and re-evaporating.   Add to the residue 0.1 g of anhydrous sodium carbonate and a few ml of water, evaporate and ignite gently.   Dissolve the residue in 40 ml of water and filter if necessary.   To 20 ml of the filtrate add 2 ml of 25% H_2SO_4, 1 ml each of phosphate reagents **A** and **B** and heat at 60° for 10 minutes.   Any blue color produced is not darker than that in a control made with 0.02 mg of PO_4, 50 mg of Na_2CO_3 and the same quantity of the other reagents and in the same final volume as with the sample.

Sulfate: Dissolve 1 g in 30 ml of H_2O.   To 20 ml of the solution add 1 ml of 0.1 N HCl and 2 ml of $BaCl_2$.   Any turbidity produced is not greater than that in a blank to which 0.2 mg of SO_4 has been added.

Barium: Dissolve 2.0 g in 10 ml of water, add 3 drops of glacial acetic acid and filter if necessary.   Add to the filtrate 3 ml of a clear 10% solution of anhydrous Na_2SO_4, shake well and allow to stand for 15 minutes.   No turbidity is visible.

Note: The solution may be yellow due to free iodine liberated by oxygen in the water, but this does not interfere with seeing any barium sulfate turbidity.   If desired, however, the yellow color may be discharged by the addition of 10–20 mg of ascorbic acid or sodium sulfite.

Heavy metals: To a solution of 4 g in 10 ml of H_2O, add 5 ml of HCl and follow with 5 ml of 30% hydrogen peroxide.   Evaporate to dryness on the steam bath.   Re-evaporate with several small volumes of water until the iodine is completely volatilized.   Dissolve the residue in 40 ml of H_2O.   To 10 ml of the solution add 0.02 mg of Pb, 1 ml of 1 N acetic acid, and dilute to 40 ml (A).   To the remaining 30 ml add 1 ml of 1 N acetic acid and dilute to 40 ml (B).   Then to each add 10 ml of H_2S. B is not darker than A.

AMMONIUM MOLYBDATE

$(NH_4)_6Mo_7O_{24} \cdot 4H_2O$; mol. wt. 1235.95; anhydrous—94.17%; H_2O—5.83%; NH_3—7.27%; Mo—54.34%; MoO_3—81.52%.

Colorless, or slightly green or yellow crystals. Soluble in water; insoluble in alcohol.

Standards

Assay....................min 81% MoO_3	Phosphate etc. (as PO_4).....max 0.0005%
Insoluble....................max 0.010%	Sulfate (SO_4)................max 0.020%
Chloride (Cl)................max 0.002%	Heavy metals (as Pb)........max 0.001%
Nitrate (NO_3)...............max 0.003%	

Assay: Determine the molybdenum trioxide by the assay method described for Molybdic Acid, 85%.

Insoluble: Dissolve 10 g in 100 ml of hot H_2O and heat on the steam bath for 1 hour. Filter any undissolved matter (retain filtrate), wash it with water and dry at 105°. The insoluble residue is not more than 1.0 mg.

Chloride: Dissolve 1 g in 20 ml of H_2O, add the solution gradually to 5 ml of nitric acid, then add 1 ml of $AgNO_3$. Any turbidity produced is not greater than that in a blank to which 0.02 mg of Cl has been added.

Nitrate: To a solution of 0.5 g in 10 ml of H_2O add 0.1 ml of indigo carmine, 10 mg NaCl, and 10 ml of H_2SO_4. The blue color persists for 5 minutes.

Phosphate: To the filtrate from *Insoluble* add 10 ml of ammonium hydroxide and pour it into a mixture of 50 ml of HNO_3 and 25 ml of H_2O. Shake at 40° for 5 minutes and let stand for 1 hour. Any yellow precipitate formed is no more than that in a control made by treating 2 g of the sample and 0.04 mg of PO_4 with the same quantities of reagents and in the same manner.

Sulfate: Dissolve 1 g in 5 ml of hot H_2O, add 5 ml of HNO_3 and evaporate to dryness. Digest the residue with 1 ml of 10% HCl and 10 ml of water, dilute to 40 ml and filter. To 20 ml of the filtrate add 2 ml of $BaCl_2$ and allow to stand for 20 minutes. Any resulting turbidity is not greater than that in a control made with 0.10 mg of SO_4, 1 ml of 1 N HCl and 2 ml of $BaCl_2$ in the same volume as with the sample.

Heavy metals: Dissolve 3 g in 15 ml of H_2O, and add 10 ml of 10% NaOH, 3 ml of ammonium hydroxide, and dilute to 30 ml. To 5 ml of the solution add 0.02 mg of Pb and dilute to 40 ml (A). Dilute the remaining 25 ml of the solution to 40 ml (B). Then add to each 10 ml of H_2S. B is not darker than A.

AMMONIUM NITRATE

NH_4NO_3; mol. wt. 80.05; NH_3—21.28%; HNO_3—78.72%; total N—35.00%.

Colorless crystals or white granules; slightly hygroscopic. Melts at about 158°. When dissolved in water a lowering of the temperature takes place. Soluble in 1 part of water, in 25 parts of alcohol. *Keep in well-closed containers.*

Standards

Insoluble	max 0.005%	Phosphate (PO₄)	max 0.0005%
Ignition residue	max 0.010%	Sulfate (SO₄)	max 0.002%
Free acid	to pass test	Heavy metals (as Pb)	max 0.0005%
Chloride (Cl)	max 0.0005%	Iron (Fe)	max 0.0002%
Nitrite (NO₂)	max 0.0005%		

Insoluble .... max 0.005% Phosphate (PO_4) .... max 0.0005%
Ignition residue .... max 0.010% Sulfate (SO_4) .... max 0.002%
Free acid .... to pass test Heavy metals (as Pb) .... max 0.0005%
Chloride (Cl) .... max 0.0005% Iron (Fe) .... max 0.0002%
Nitrite (NO_2) .... max 0.0005%

Insoluble: Dissolve 20 g in 100 ml of H_2O and heat on the steam bath for 1 hour. Filter any undissolved residue, wash it with water and dry at 105°. The insoluble matter does not exceed 1.0 mg.

Ignition residue: Heat 10 g until volatilized, then ignite for 5 minutes. The residue is not more than 1.0 mg.

Free acid: Dissolve 5 g in 50 ml H_2O, and add a drop of methyl red. If a red color is produced it is changed to yellow by 0.10 ml of 0.1 N NaOH.

Chloride: To a solution of 2 g in 20 ml of H_2O, add 1 ml of HNO_3 and 1 ml of silver nitrate. Any resulting turbidity is not greater than that in a blank with 0.01 mg of Cl added.

Nitrite: Dissolve 1 g in 10 ml of H_2O, add 1 ml of 10% H_2SO_4 and 0.5 ml of colorless metaphenylenediamine hydrochloride solution. No yellowish or brownish color is produced in 5 minutes. (*Note:* The metaphenylenediamine hydrochloride solution can be decolorized by treating with a little decolorizing charcoal and filtering.)

Phosphate: Dissolve 4 g in 20 ml H_2O. Add 2 ml of 25% H_2SO_4 and 1 ml each of phosphate reagents **A** and **B** and heat at 60° for 10 minutes. If a blue color is produced it is not deeper than in a blank to which 0.02 mg of PO_4 has been added.

Sulfate: Dissolve 5 g in 10 ml of warm H_2O, add 50 mg of sodium carbonate, evaporate and ignite gently until the ammonium nitrate is volatilized. Add to the residue 10 ml of H_2O, 2 ml of 1 N HCl and a few drops of bromine water, and boil for 1 minute. Filter if necessary, wash with water to 10 ml, add 2 ml of $BaCl_2$ and allow to stand for 10 minutes. Any resulting turbidity is not greater than that in a blank to which 0.1 mg of SO_4 has been added.

Heavy metals: Dissolve 6 g in water to make 30 ml. To 5 ml of the solution add 0.02 mg of the Pb, 1 ml of 1 N acetic acid, and dilute to 40 ml (A). To the remaining 25 ml add 1 ml of 1 N acetic acid, and dilute to 40 ml (B). Then to each add 10 ml of H_2S. B is not darker than A.

Iron: Dissolve 2.5 g in 15 ml of water. Add 3 ml of 10% HCl and 10 ml of butanolic potassium thiocyanate, shake well, and allow to separate. Any red color in the butanol layer is not darker than that of a blank to which 0.005 mg of Fe has been added.

AMMONIUM OXALATE

$(NH_4)_2C_2O_4 \cdot H_2O$; mol. wt. 142.12; anhydrous—87.32%; H_2O—12.68%; NH_3—23.97%; anhydrous oxalic acid = 63.35%.

Colorless crystals. Soluble in 20 parts of water, in 3 parts of boiling water; insoluble in alcohol.

Standards

Insoluble.....................max 0.005%	Sulfate (SO_4)................max 0.003%
Ignition residue.............max 0.010%	Heavy metals (as Pb).......max 0.0005%
Chloride (Cl)................max 0.001%	Iron (Fe).................max 0.0005%
Nitrate (NO_3)..............max 0.001%	*Assay*........................min 99.5%

Insoluble: Dissolve 20 g in 200 ml of hot H_2O and heat on steam bath for 1 hour. Filter any undissolved residue, wash it with water and dry at 105°. The insoluble residue is not more than 1.0 mg.

Ignition residue: Ignite 10 g at low temperature to constant weight. The weight of the residue does not exceed 1.0 mg (retain).

Chloride: To a solution of 1 g in 20 ml H_2O add 3 ml of HNO_3 and 1 ml of $AgNO_3$. Any resulting turbidity is not more than that in a blank with 0.01 mg of Cl added.

Nitrate: Dissolve 0.5 g in 10 ml of H_2O and add 20 mg of NaCl; then add 0.2 ml of diphenylamine solution, mix, and slowly run in, without agitation, 10 ml of H_2SO_4. After a few minutes mix gently and allow to stand for 30 minutes. No blue color is produced.

Sulfate: To 3.0 g of sample in a beaker, add 5 ml of water and 5 ml of HNO_3, mix, then add 5 ml of 30% H_2O_2, cover the beaker and digest on steam bath until the reaction ceases, then remove the cover and evaporate to dryness. Add 5 ml of water and 5 ml of HCl, and re-evaporate to dryness. Dissolve the residue in 10 ml of water, add 1 ml of 1 N HCl, filter if necessary, add 2 ml of $BaCl_2$ and mix well. Any resulting turbidity in 15 minutes is not greater than that produced when 0.1 mg of SO_4 is treated exactly as the sample.

Solution R: Evaporate the *Ignition residue* with 2 ml of HCl and 2 ml of H_2O to dryness on a steam bath. Warm the residue with 1 ml of 1 N HCl and dilute with water to 50 ml.

Heavy metals: Dilute 20 ml of *Solution R* to 40 ml, and add 10 ml of H_2S. Any resulting color is not darker than that of a control made with 0.02 mg of Pb, 0.5 ml of 1 N HCl and 10 ml of H_2S in the same volume as with the sample.

Iron: To 20 ml of *Solution R* add 2 ml of HCl and dilute to 50 ml. Add about 30 mg of ammonium persulfate and 3 ml of ammonium thiocyanate, and mix. Any resulting red color is not darker than that produced in a blank to which 0.01 mg of Fe has been added.

Assay: Weigh accurately about 1.0 g, dissolve in H_2O and dilute to exactly 100 ml. Dilute 25 ml of the solution with 70 ml of H_2O, add 5 ml of H_2SO_4 and titrate slowly with 0.1 N potassium permanganate until about 25 ml has been added. Then heat to 70° and complete the titration with the permanganate. One ml of 0.1 N permanganate = 0.007106 g $(NH_4)_2C_2O_4 \cdot H_2O$, log 85163.

$$5(NH_4)_2C_2O_4 + 2KMnO_4 + 8H_2SO_4$$
$$\rightarrow 10CO_2 + 2MnSO_4 + K_2SO_4 + 5(NH_4)_2SO_4 + 8H_2O$$

AMMONIUM PERSULFATE

$(NH_4)_2S_2O_8$; mol. wt. 228.20; active oxygen—7.01%.

Colorless crystals or white granules. Soluble in 2 parts of water. It is slowly decomposed by moisture, losing available oxygen. *Keep in a cool, dry place.*

Standards

Assay............min 98% $(NH_4)_2S_2O_8$	Nitrate and Chlorate (as NO_3) max 0.003%
Insoluble...................max 0.010%	Heavy metals (as Pb)........max 0.003%
Ignition residue.............max 0.05%	Iron (Fe)...................max 0.001%
Chlorate and Chloride (as Cl)..max 0.001%	Manganese (Mn)..........max 0.00005%

Assay: Weigh accurately about 0.3 g and dissolve it in 25 ml of 10% potassium iodide in a gloss-stoppered flask. Add 10 ml of 10% H_2SO_4, stopper and allow to stand for 30 minutes; then titrate the liberated iodine with 0.1 N sodium thiosulfate. One ml of 0.1 N thiosulfate $= 0.01141$ g $(NH_4)_2S_2O_8$, log 05729.

$$(NH_4)_2S_2O_8 + 2H_2O \rightarrow 2NH_4HSO_4 + H_2O_2,$$
and
$$H_2O_2 + 2KI + 2NH_4HSO_4 \rightarrow 2NH_4KSO_4 + 2I + 2H_2O$$

Insoluble: Dissolve 10 g in 100 ml of H_2O and heat on the steam bath for 1 hour. Filter any undissolved matter, wash it with water and dry at 105°. The weight of the insoluble residue is not more than 1.0 mg.

Ignition residue: Ignite 4 g in porcelain, gently at first, then sharply, to constant weight. The weight of the residue is not more than 2.0 mg. (retain).

Chlorate and Chloride: Mix 1 g with 1 g of sodium carbonate and heat until no more gas is evolved. Dissolve the residue in 20 ml of water, neutralize with HNO_3 and add 1 ml excess acid, then add 1 ml of silver nitrate. The resulting turbidity is not greater than that in a blank to which 0.01 mg of Cl has been added.

Nitrate and Chlorate: Dissolve 0.1 g in 10 ml of water, add 2 ml of 10% NaOH and evaporate to dryness on the steam bath. Re-evaporate on the steam bath to dryness with 10 ml of water. Dissolve the cooled residue in 8 ml of water and neutralize with 25% H_2SO_4. Add 0.2 ml of diphenylamine solution, 10 mg NaCl, mix, then add 10 ml of H_2SO_4 and allow to stand for 30 minutes. No blue color results.

Solution R: To the *Ignition residue* add 2 ml of HCl and 1 ml of HNO_3 and slowly evaporate to dryness on the steam bath. Take up the residue in 0.5 ml of 1 N HCl and 10 ml of water, filter, if necessary, and wash with H_2O to 20 ml.

Heavy metals: Dilute 5 ml of *Solution R* to 40 ml and add 10 ml of H_2S. Any color produced is not darker than that produced in a control made with 0.03 mg of Pb, 0.1 ml of 1 N HCl, and 10 ml of H_2S in the same final volume as with the sample.

Iron: To 5 ml of *Solution R* add 2 ml of HCl and dilute to 50 ml. Add about 30 mg of ammonium persulfate and 3 ml of ammonium thiocyanate, and mix. Any red color produced is not darker than that of a blank to which 0.01 mg of Fe has been added.

Manganese: Gently ignite 20 g in porcelain. Take up the residue in 40 ml of H_2O, 10 ml of nitric acid, 5 ml of H_2SO_4 and 5 ml of phosphoric acid, and boil the solution for 5 minutes. Cool, add 0.25 g of potassium periodate, and again boil for 5 minutes. Any pink color produced is not deeper than that resulting from treating 0.01 mg of Mn in the same manner as the residue from the ignition of the sample for this test.

AMMONIUM PHOSPHATE, DIBASIC
Diammonium Hydrogen Phosphate

$(NH_4)_2HPO_4$; mol. wt. 132.07; NH_3—25.78%; H_3PO_4—74.22%; P—23.48%.

Small, colorless crystals or white granules. Loses NH_3 on exposure to air. Soluble in 4 parts of water; insoluble in alcohol. *Keep in well-closed containers in a cool place.*

Standards

Insoluble....................max 0.005%	Alkali salts...................max 0.10%
Reaction....................to pass test	Arsenic (As).................max 1 ppm
Chloride (Cl)................max 0.001%	Heavy metals (as Pb)........max 0.001%
Nitrate (NO_3)..............max 0.002%	Iron (Fe)....................max 0.001%
Sulfate (SO_4)...............max 0.005%	

Insoluble: Dissolve 20 g in 100 ml of H_2O and heat on the steam bath for 1 hour. Filter any undissolved matter, wash it with water and dry at 105°. The insoluble residue is not more than 1.0 mg.

Reaction: Dissolve 2 g in 20 ml of H_2O and add 0.1 ml of phenolphthalein solution. If no pink color is produced, it should require the addition of not more than 0.1 ml of 1 N NaOH to produce a pink color. The pH of an 0.2 M solution is 7.5 to 8.1.

Chloride: Dissolve 1 g in 10 ml of H_2O, add 3 ml of HNO_3 and 1 ml of silver nitrate. Any resulting turbidity is not greater than that in a blank to which 0.01 mg of Cl has been added.

Nitrate: Dissolve 0.5 g in 10 ml of H_2O and add 50 mg of NaCl. When the latter has dissolved, add 0.2 ml of diphenylamine solution, mix, and slowly run in, without agitation, 10 ml of H_2SO_4. After a few minutes mix gently and allow to stand for 1 hour. No blue color is produced.

Sulfate: Dissolve 10 g in 100 ml of H_2O, add 10 ml of HCl, bring to a boil, then add 5 ml of $BaCl_2$ and let stand overnight. If a precipitate is formed, filter, wash it with small portions of hot water until free of chloride, ignite and weigh. The weight of the $BaSO_4$ does not exceed 1.3 mg.

Alkali salts: Dissolve 3 g in 100 ml of water, add a solution of 15 g of lead acetate in 50 ml of H_2O and filter. Precipitate the lead from 100 ml of the filtrate with H_2S, filter without washing, evaporate filtrate and ignite. The weight of the residue is not over 2.0 mg. Run a blank by precipitating a solution of 10 g of lead acetate in 150 ml H_2O with H_2S, filter, evaporate and filtrate and ignite. If a weighable residue is found, test it for substances precipitated by ammonium phosphate and apply a further correction.

Arsenic: Test 2 g by method on page 563. The stain is not more than that from 0.002 mg of As.

Heavy metals: Dissolve 4 g in 20 ml of H_2O, add 10 ml of 10% HCl and dilute to 40 ml. To 10 ml of the solution add 0.02 mg of Pb and dilute to 40 ml (A). Dilute the remaining 30 ml of the solution to 40 ml (B). Then to each add 10 ml of H_2S. B is not darker than A.

Iron: Dissolve 1 g in 15 ml of H_2O, add 2 ml of HCl and boil for 2 minutes. Cool, add about 30 mg of ammonium persulfate and 15 ml of butanolic potassium thiocyanate, shake well for 30 seconds and allow to separate. Any red color in the butanolic (upper) layer is not darker than that of a blank to which 0.01 mg of Fe has been added.

AMMONIUM PHOSPHATE, MONOBASIC

Ammonium Dihydrogen Phosphate; Primary Ammonium Phosphate

$NH_4H_2PO_4$; mol. wt. 115.03; NH_3—14.80%; H_3PO_4—85.20%; P—26.96%.

Colorless crystals or white granules. Soluble in 0.5 part H_2O.

Standards

Assay...................98.0%–100.5%	Sulfate (SO_4)...............max 0.005%
Insoluble and Ammonium hydroxide	Alkali salts..................max 0.10%
precipitate................max 0.010%	Arsenic (As)................max 1 ppm
Chloride (Cl)...............max 0.001%	Heavy metals (as Pb)........max 0.001%
Nitrate (NO_3)..............max 0.002%	Iron (Fe)...................max 0.001%

Assay: Accurately weigh about 3 g and dissolve in 75 ml of water. Add 0.5 ml of thymolphthalein solution and titrate with 1 N NaOH to the first appearance of a blue color. One ml of 1 N NaOH = 0.1150 g $NH_4H_2PO_4$, log 06070.

$$NH_4H_2PO_4 + NaOH \rightarrow NH_4NaHPO_4 + H_2O$$

Note: The assay is preferably performed by titrating the solution to pH 8.8 electrometrically with a pH meter, etc.

Insoluble and Ammonium hydroxide precipitate: Dissolve 10 g in 100 ml of water, add 3 ml of ammonium hydroxide and heat on the steam bath for 30 minutes. Filter any undissolved matter, wash it with water and dry at 105°. The weight of the undissolved matter does not exceed 1.0 mg.

Chloride, Nitrate, Sulfate, Alkali Salts, Arsenic, Iron: Perform these tests as described under the preceding.

Heavy metals: Dissolve 4 g in water to 40 ml. To 10 ml of the solution add 1 ml of N acetic acid and 0.02 mg of Pb and dilute to 40 ml (A). To the remaining 30 ml of the solution add 1 ml of 1 N acetic acid and dilute to 40 ml (B). Then to each add 10 ml of H_2S. B is not darker than A.

AMMONIUM REINECKATE, see REINECKE SALT

AMMONIUM SULFAMATE

$NH_4 \cdot SO_3NH_2$; mol. wt. 114.13; N—24.55%; SO_3—70.15%.

Colorless or white crystals. Freely soluble in water; sparingly in alcohol.

Standards

Melting range.................131°–133°	Sulfate (SO_4)...............max 0.10%
Insoluble, etc...............max 0.010%	Heavy metals (as Pb).......max 0.0005%
Ignition residue.............max 0.010%	Iron (Fe)...................max 0.0005%
Chloride (Cl)...............max 0.001%	*Assay*........................min 98%
Nitrate (NO_3)..............max 0.002%	

Insoluble: Dissolve 10 g in 100 ml of H_2O, add 1 ml of ammonium hydroxide, and heat on the steam bath for 1 hour. If a precipitate is present, filter, wash with water and dry at 105° for 2 hours. The weight of the insoluble residue and precipitate does not exceed 1.0 mg.

Ignition residue: Ignite 10 g to constant weight. The weight of the residue does not exceed 1.0 mg.

Chloride: To a solution of 2 g in 20 ml of H_2O add 2 ml of HNO_3 and 1 ml of $AgNO_3$. Any resulting turbidity is not greater than that in a blank to which 0.02 mg of Cl has been added.

Nitrate: Dissolve 0.5 g in 10 ml of water, add 20 mg of NaCl and 0.2 ml of diphenylamine solution, and slowly run in 10 ml of H_2SO_4. Mix gently and allow to stand for 1 hour. No blue color results.

Sulfate: Dissolve 1 g in 100 ml of H_2O. To 20 ml of the solution add 1 ml of 1 N HCl and 2 ml of $BaCl_2$. Any resulting turbidity is not greater than that in a blank to which 0.2 mg of SO_4 has been added.

Heavy metals: Dissolve 6 g in H_2O to make 30 ml. To 5 ml add 0.02 mg of Pb, and 1 ml of 1 N acetic acid, and dilute to 40 ml (A). To the remaining 25 ml add 1 ml of 1 N acetic acid and dilute to 40 ml (B). Then to each add 10 ml of H_2S. B is not darker than A.

Iron: Dissolve 2 g in 20 ml of H_2O, add 2 ml of HCl and dilute to 50 ml. Add about 30 mg of ammonium persulfate and 3 ml of ammonium thiocyanate, and mix. Any resulting red color is not darker than that of a blank to which 0.01 mg of Fe has been added.

Assay: Dissolve 1.2 to 1.4 g of sample, previously dried over a suitable desiccant for 2 hours, and accurately weighed in water to 100.0 ml. Transfer 25.0 ml of the solution to a conical flask, add 75 ml of water and 5 ml of H_2SO_4 and titrate slowly, at room temperature, with 0.1 M sodium nitrite:

$$NH_4SO_3 \cdot NH_2 + NaNO_2 + H_2SO_4 \rightarrow N_2 + NaNH_4SO_4 + H_2O$$

After the addition of each 5 ml or so of the nitrite solution the flask is stoppered and vigorously shaken to aid in the removal of nitrogen. Near the end point the titration must be dropwise with shaking after each drop. The end point is reached when a drop of the titrated solution added to starch-iodide solution on a spot plate produces a blue color which persists for 30 seconds. One ml of 0.1 M $NaNO_2$ = 0.01142 g of $NH_4SO_3 \cdot NH_2$.

AMMONIUM SULFATE

$(NH_4)_2SO_4$; mol. wt. 132.14; NH_3—25.78%; H_2SO_4—74.22%; N—21.20%.

Colorless crystals or white granules. Soluble in 2 parts of water; insoluble in alcohol.

Standards

Insoluble	max 0.005%	Phosphate (PO_4) .... max 0.0005%
Ignition residue	max 0.010%	Arsenic (As) .... max 0.2 ppm
Free acid	to pass test	Heavy metals (as Pb) .... max 0.0005%
Chloride (Cl)	max 0.0005%	Iron (Fe) .... max 0.0005%
Nitrate (NO_3)	max 0.001%	*Assay*

Insoluble: Dissolve 20 g in 100 ml of water and heat for 1 hour on the steam bath. Filter any undissolved residue, wash it with water and dry at 105°. The weight of the insoluble residue does not exceed 1.0 mg.

Ignition residue: To 10 g add 1 ml of H_2SO_4, ignite at a temperature requiring at least 30 minutes to volatilize, then at a red heat for 5 minutes. Not more than 1.0 mg of residue remains.

Free acid: Dissolve 5 g in 50 ml of freshly boiled and cooled water and add 1 drop of methyl red. If a red color is produced it is changed to yellow by not more than 0.10 ml of 0.1 N NaOH. pH of 0.2 M solution is 5.4.

Chloride: To a solution of 2 g in 20 ml of H_2O add 1 ml of HNO_3 and 1 ml of silver nitrate. Any resulting turbidity is not greater than in a blank to which 0.01 mg Cl has been added.

Nitrate: Dissolve 0.5 g in 10 ml of H_2O and add 50 mg of NaCl. When the latter has dissolved, add 0.2 ml of diphenylamine solution, mix, and slowly run in, without agitation, 12 ml of H_2SO_4. After a few minutes mix gently and allow to stand for 30 minutes. No blue color is produced.

Phosphate: Dissolve 4 g in 20 ml of H_2O. Add 2 ml of 25% H_2SO_4 and 1 ml each of phosphate reagents **A** and **B** and heat at 60° for 10 minutes. If a blue color is produced it is not deeper than that of a blank to which 0.02 mg of PO_4 has been added.

Arsenic: Test 10 g by method on page 563. The stain is not more than that from 0.002 mg of As.

Heavy metals: Dissolve 6 g in H_2O to make 30 ml. To 5 ml add 0.02 mg of Pb and 1 ml of 1 N acetic acid, and dilute to 40 ml (A). To the remaining 25 ml add 1 ml of 1 N acetic acid and dilute to 40 ml (B). Then to each add 10 ml of H_2S; B is not darker than A.

Iron: Dissolve 2 g in H_2O, add 2 ml of HCl, and dilute to 50 ml. Add about 30 mg of ammonium persulfate and 3 ml of ammonium thiocyanate, and mix. Any resulting red color is not darker than that of a blank to which 0.01 mg of Fe has been added.

Assay: Ammonium sulfate may be assayed as follows: Weigh accurately about 2 g and dissolve in 40 ml of H_2O in a flask. Add 20 ml of formaldehyde previously mixed with 20 ml of H_2O and neutralized with 1 N NaOH, using 3 drops of phenolphthalein solution. Mix, allow to stand for 30 minutes, then titrate with 1 N NaOH to a pink color which persists for 5 minutes. One ml of 1 N NaOH = 0.06607 g $(NH_4)_2SO_4$, log 82000. When so assayed not less than 99.5% and not more than 100.2% $(NH_4)_2SO_4$ should be found.

AMMONIUM SULFIDE SOLUTION

Yellow liquid; odor of ammonia and hydrogen sulfide, becoming darker with age, due to the formation of polysulfide. It usually contains an amount of sulfidic sulfur equivalent to about 20% $(NH_4)_2S$.

Standards

Assay—Sulfidic sulfur . . . . min 9%	Ignition residue . . . . max 0.020%
corresponding to $(NH_4)_2S$ 19.7%	Carbonate . . . . to pass test
Chloride (Cl) . . . . max 0.005%	Arsenic (As) . . . . .max 1 ppm

Solution S: Measure exactly 10 ml and dilute it with oxygen-free water to exactly 100 ml.   Use this solution for the *Assay* and *Chloride.*

Assay: Place exactly 50 ml of 0.1 N $AgNO_3$ in a 100-ml volumetric flask and add 7 ml of ammonium hydroxide; then add, in small portions with agitation, exactly 5 ml of *Solution S.*   Add H_2O to the 100-ml mark, mix well and filter through a dry filter into a dry flask, rejecting the first 10 ml of the filtrate.   To 50 ml of the subsequent filtrate add 7 ml of nitric acid, 2 ml of ferric ammonium sulfate and titrate the excess of silver with 0.1 N thiocyanate.   One ml 0.1 N $AgNO_3$ = 0.001603 g of S, log 20495, or 0.003404 g of $(NH_4)_2S$, log 53148.

Chloride: Dilute 5 ml of *Solution S* with 20 ml of water, add 5 ml of NH_4OH and follow with a solution of 1 g silver nitrate in 10 ml of water.   Filter and acidify 20 ml of the filtrate with nitric acid.   The solution is not more than slightly opalescent.

Ignition residue: Evaporate 5 ml to dryness and ignite to constant weight. Not more than 1.0 mg of residue remains.

Carbonate: To 10 ml add 3 ml of calcium chloride solution and warm.   No precipitate is formed.

Arsenic: Evaporate 2 ml of the sample to dryness on the steam bath, add to the residue 2 ml of HNO_3 and 2 ml of H_2SO_4 and evaporate to strong sulfuric fumes, but not dryness.   This residue tested for arsenic by the method on page 563 gives no greater stain that 0.002 mg of As.

AMMONIUM TARTRATE

$(NH_4)_2C_4H_4O_6$; mol. wt. 184.15; NH_3—18.50%; tartaric acid = 81.50%.

Colorless crystals.   Very soluble in water; moderately soluble in alcohol. Loses some NH_3 on exposure to air.   *Keep in well-closed containers in a cool place.*

Standards

Assay.........99%–102% $(NH_4)_2C_4H_4O_6$	Phosphate (PO_4)............max 0.001%
pH..................................6–7	Sulfate (SO_4)...............max 0.005%
Insoluble....................max 0.01%	Heavy metals (as Pb).......max 0.0005%
Ignition residue.............max 0.040%	Iron (Fe)...................max 0.001%
Chloride (Cl)................max 0.001%	

Assay: Weigh accurately about 2 g and dissolve in 20 ml of water.   Add 40 ml of dilute formaldehyde (1+1), previously neutralized to phenolphthalein with 1 N NaOH, and let stand for 30 minutes; then titrate with 1 N NaOH to a pink color which persists for 5 minutes.   One ml of 1 N NaOH = 0.09208 g $(NH_4)_2C_4H_4O_6$, log 96417.

For the course of the reaction underlying this assay see under Ammonium Citrate, Dibasic.

*p*H: The *p*H of ammonium tartrate in 2% solution is between 6 and 7.

Insoluble: Dissolve 10 g in 100 ml of H_2O and heat on the steam bath for 1 hour.   Filter any undissolved residue (retain filtrate), wash it with water and dry at 105°.   The weight of the insoluble residue is not more than 1.0 mg.

Ignition residue: Char well 10 g. Cool, add 0.5 ml of H_2SO_4 and ignite at first gently, then strongly to constant weight. Any remaining residue does not exceed 1.0 mg.

Chloride: Dissolve 1 g in 10 ml of water, add 1 ml of nitric acid and 1 ml of silver nitrate. Any turbidity produced is not greater than that in a blank with 0.01 mg of Cl added.

Phosphate, Sulfate: Proceed as described under Ammonium Citrate, Dibasic. The results should be as there stated.

Heavy metals: Dissolve 6 g in water, add 6 ml of 10% HCl and dilute to 30 ml. To 5 ml of the solution add 0.02 mg of Pb, and dilute to 40 ml (A). Dilute the remaining 25 ml of the solution to 40 ml (B). Then add to each 10 ml of H_2S. B is not darker than A.

Iron: Dissolve 1 g in water, add 2 ml of HCl and dilute to 50 ml. Add about 50 mg of ammonium persulfate and 3 ml of ammonium thiocyanate, and mix. Any resulting red color is not darker than that of a blank to which 0.01 mg of Fe has been added.

AMMONIUM THIOCYANATE

Ammonium Sulfocyanide

NH_4SCN; mol. wt. 76.12; NH_3—22.37%; SCN—76.30%; CN—34.17%.

Colorless, rapidly deliquescent crystals. Soluble in 1 part of water; freely soluble in alcohol. Melts at about 160°. *Keep in well-closed containers.*

Standards

Insoluble	max 0.005%	Chloride (Cl)	max 0.005%
Solubility in alcohol	to pass test	Sulfate (SO_4)	max 0.005%
Ignition residue	max 0.025%	Heavy metals (as Pb)	max 0.0005%
Iodine-consuming substances		Iron (Fe)	max 0.0003%
(cyanide, sulfide, etc.)	to pass test	Assay	min. 99.5%

Insoluble: Dissolve 20 g in 75 ml of H_2O and heat on the steam bath for 1 hour. Filter any insoluble residue, wash it with H_2O, and dry at 105°. Its weight is not over 1.0 mg.

Solubility in alcohol: One gram dissolves in 10 ml of alcohol, giving a clear solution with no insoluble residue remaining.

Ignition residue: Ignite 4 g at the lowest possible temperature to constant weight. The weight of the residue does not exceed 1.0 mg.

Iodine-consuming substances: Dissolve 2 g in a mixture of 20 ml of water and 1 ml of 10% H_2SO_4. Add 0.5 g of KI and 0.5 ml of starch solution and titrate with 0.1 N iodine. Not more than 0.3 ml of the iodine is required to produce a blue or reddish-blue color.

Chloride: Dissolve 1 g in 20 ml H_2O in a small flask, add 10 ml of 25% H_2SO_4 and 7 ml of 30% hydrogen peroxide, and boil down gently *under hood* to 20 ml. Restore the volume with H_2O and again evaporate to 20 ml. Repeat this operation until all the cyanide has volatilized. Cool, dilute to 50 ml and mix well. To

20 ml of this solution add 1 ml of nitric acid and 1 ml of silver nitrate. The turbidity produced is not greater than that in a control made with 0.02 mg of Cl, 1 ml of HNO_3 and 1 ml of silver nitrate in the same final volume as with the sample.

Sulfate: To a solution of 2 g in 20 ml of water add 1 ml of 0.1 N HCl and 2 ml of $BaCl_2$. Any turbidity produced in 15 minutes is not greater than that in a blank to which 0.1 mg of SO_4 has been added.

Heavy metals: Dissolve 5 g in water to make 50 ml. To 10 ml of the solution add 0.015 mg of Pb, dilute to 40 ml and add 1 ml of 1 N acetic acid (A). To the remaining 40 ml add 1 ml of 1 N acetic acid (B). Then to each add 10 ml of H_2S. B is not darker than A.

Iron: Dissolve 4 g in water to make 40 ml. To 10 ml of the solution add 0.006 mg of Fe and dilute to 50 ml (A). Dilute the remaining 30 ml of the solution to 50 ml (B). Then to each add 2 ml of HCl and 50 mg of ammonium persulfate and mix well. Any red color in B is not darker than that in A.

Assay: Ammonium thiocyanate may be assayed by the adsorption indicator method for *Chloride and Thiocyanate*, page 565, using about 0.3 g, accurately weighed, of the sample previously dried over H_2SO_4. One ml of 0.1 N $AgNO_3$ = 0.007612 g NH_4SCN, log 88093.

AMMONIUM VANADATE

Ammonium Metavanadate

NH_4VO_3; mol. wt. 117.00; V—43.55%; VO_3—77.74%.

White, crystalline powder. Slightly soluble in cold water; soluble in hot water, also in dilute ammonium hydroxide.

Standards

Assay...............min 98% NH_4VO_3	Carbonate (CO_3).........max about 0.3%
Solubility in ammonium	Chloride (Cl).................max 0.05%
hydroxide.................to pass test	Sulfate (SO_4)...........max about 0.02%

Assay: Weigh accurately about 0.4 g and dissolve it in 50 ml of warm water. Add 1 ml of H_2SO_4 and 30 ml of sulfurous acid, and boil gently until the odor of SO_2 is no longer perceptible, then boil for 5 minutes longer. Cool, dilute to about 100 ml and titrate with 0.1 N potassium permanganate to a pink color. One ml of 0.1 N permanganate = 0.01170 g NH_4VO_3, log 06819.

Solubility in ammonium hydroxide: Dissolve 1 g in a mixture of 3 ml of ammonium hydroxide and 50 ml of warm water. A clear and colorless solution results.

Carbonate: To 0.5 g add 1 ml H_2O and 2 ml 10% HCl. No effervescence is produced.

Chloride: Dissolve 0.5 g in 40 ml of hot H_2O, add 2 ml of nitric acid and let stand for 1 hour. Filter, wash with a few ml of H_2O and dilute to 100 ml. To 20 ml add 0.5 ml of silver nitrate. The turbidity is not greater than that in the blank to which 0.05 mg of Cl has been added.

Sulfate: Dissolve 0.7 g in 40 ml of hot H_2O, add 2 ml of 10% HCl and 1.5 g of hydroxylamine hydrochloride, and heat at 60° for 3 minutes.   Filter, cool, add to the filtrate 2 ml of $BaCl_2$ and let stand for 30 minutes.   No greater turbidity or precipitate results than that produced by treating 0.2 g of sample and 1.5 g of the hydroxylamine hydrochloride in the same manner as the sample.

AMYL ACETATE, *see* ISOAMYL ACETATE

n-AMYL ALCOHOL

n-Pentanol

CH_3CH_2—CH_2—CH_2—CH_2OH; mol. wt. 88.13.

Colorless, clear liquid, characteristic, rather disagreeable odor.   Sp. gr. about 0.81; boils at 138°.   Slightly and very slowly soluble in water (1 in about 75); miscible with alcohol, benzene, etc., organic liquids.

Standards

Boiling range.................136°–139°	Pyridine, etc...........max about 0.003%
Evaporation residue.........max 0.003%	Substances darkened by
Acids and Esters	H_2SO_4.....................to pass test
(as amyl acetate)...........max 0.06%	Water........................max 0.5%
Aldehyde....................to pass test	

Boiling range: Distill 50 ml.   After the first 10 drops not less than 48 ml between 136° and 139°, correction being made for barometric pressure (page 581).

Evaporation residue: Evaporate 40 ml on the steam bath and dry at 105° for 2 hours.   The residue is not more than 1.0 mg.

Acids and Esters: Mix 20 ml with 20 ml of neutral alcohol, add 5 ml of 0.1 *N* NaOH and reflux for 10 minutes.   Cool, add 0.2 ml of phenolphthalein and titrate the excess of alkali with 0.1 *N* HCl.   The volume of the NaOH consumed is not more than 0.75 ml greater than the volume consumed in a complete blank.

Aldehyde: Shake 5 ml with 5 ml of 30% potassium hydroxide in a glass-stoppered cylinder for 5 minutes and allow to separate.   No color appears in either layer.

Pyridine: Mix 2 ml with 5 ml of H_2O and acidify to litmus with dilute H_2SO_4. Evaporate on the steam bath until no odor remains, then make alkaline with sodium hydroxide.   No distinct odor of pyridine is noticeable.

Substances darkened by H_2SO_4: Cool 10 ml to 10°, add in small portions 10 ml of sulfuric acid, also cooled to 10°, and shake for 2 minutes.   The color is not darker than that of a mixture of 5 ml of 1% cobalt chloride solution, 0.4 ml of a 1% potassium dichromate solution and 15 ml of H_2O.

Water: Water in Isoamyl Alcohol may be determined by the iodine (Fischer) method.

ANILINE

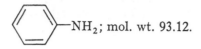—NH$_2$; mol. wt. 93.12.

Colorless or pale yellow, oily liquid;ch aracteristic odor. Becomes dark in air and light. Soluble in 30 parts of water; miscible with alcohol, benzene, ether. Sp. gr. about 1.021. *Keep in well-closed containers, protected from light, redistilling for use if too dark.*

Standards

Boiling range................183° to 186°
Ignition residue.............max 0.005%

Hydrocarbons and
    Nitrobenzene...............to pass test

Boiling range: Distill 100 ml. After the first 20 drops (1 ml), not less than 97 ml distills between 183°–186°, correction being made for barometric pressure (page 581).

Ignition residue: Evaporate 20 ml and ignite to constant weight. The residue does not exceed 1.0 mg.

Hydrocarbons and Nitrobenzene: Mix 5 ml with 10 ml of HCl and warm on a steam bath. The resulting solution is clear while hot and remains clear when mixed with 15 ml of H$_2$O.

ANILINE CHLORIDE

Aniline Hydrochloride

$C_6H_5NH_2 \cdot HCl$; mol. wt. 129.59; aniline—71.86%; HCl—28.14%.

White or nearly white crystals. Soluble in water or in alcohol. Discolors in air and light. *Keep protected from light.*

Standards

Melting range.................197°–199°
Assay...........min 99% $C_6H_5NH_2 \cdot HCl$
Solubility....................to pass test

Ignition residue.............max 0.05%
Sulfate (SO$_4$)................max 0.010%
Heavy metals (as Pb)........max 0.002%

Assay: Weight accurately about 2 g of sample, and dissolve it in a mixture of 150 ml of water and 15 ml of hydrochloric acid. Cool the solution to about 10° and run in very slowly, with constant stirring, 0.5 M sodium nitrite until 2 drops of the solution placed on starch iodide paper produce a blue color. One ml of 0.5 M sodium nitrite = 0.06477 g $C_6H_5NH_2 \cdot HCl$, log 81137.

$$C_6H_5NH_2 + NaNO_2 + 2HCl \rightarrow C_6H_5N{=\!=}NCl + 2H_2O + NaCl$$
benzene diazonium chloride

Solubility: One gram dissolves completely in 50 ml of water, and the solution is colorless.

Ignition residue: Ignite 2 g with 0.5 ml g sulfuric acid to constant weight. The residue does not exceed 1.0 mg.

Sulfate: Dissolve 1 g in 10 ml of warm water, add 1 ml of 1 N HCl and 1 ml of barium chloride. Any turbidity produced is not greater than that in a blank to which 0.10 mg of SO_4 has been added.

Heavy metals: Dissolve 2 g in 40 ml of water. To 10 ml of the solution add 0.02 mg of Pb and 1 ml of 1 N acetic acid, and dilute to 40 ml (A). To the remaining 30 ml of the solution add 1 ml of 1 N acetic acid and dilute to 40 ml (B). Then to each add 10 ml of H_2S. B is not darker than A.

ANILINE SULFATE

$(C_6H_5NH_2)_2 \cdot H_2SO_4$; mol. wt. 284.32; aniline—65.50%; H_2SO_4—34.50%.

White or nearly white crystals, or a crystalline powder. Discolors in light and air. Very soluble in water; slightly soluble in alcohol. *Keep protected from light.*

Standards

Assay......min 99% $(C_6H_5NH_2)_2 \cdot H_2SO_4$	Chloride (Cl)........ max 0.002%
Solubility..................to pass test	Heavy metals (as Pb)........max 0.002%
Ignition residue.............max 0.05%	

Assay: Proceed as described for Aniline Chloride. One ml of 0.5 M sodium nitrite = 0.07108 g $(C_6H_5NH_2)_2 \cdot H_2SO_4$, log 85175.

Solubility: One gram dissolves completely in 50 ml of water and the solution is colorless or nearly so.

Ignition residue: Ignite 2 g to constant weight. The residue does not exceed 1.0 mg.

Chloride: Dissolve 1 g in 20 ml of cold water, add 2 ml of cold nitric acid and 1 ml of silver nitrate. If a turbidity is produced it is not greater than that in a blank to which 0.02 mg of Cl has been added.

Heavy metals: Dissolve 2 g in 40 ml of water. To 10 ml of the solution add 0.02 mg of Pb and 1 ml of 1 N acetic acid and dilute to 40 ml (A). To the remaining 30 ml of the solution add 1 ml of 1 N acetic acid and dilute to 40 ml (B). Then to each add 10 ml of H_2S; B is not darker than A.

ANTHRONE

; mol. wt. 194.22.

Pale yellow crystals. Insoluble in water. One gram dissolves in about 140 ml of alcohol, 5 ml of chloroform, 10 ml of carbon tetrachloride, and 50 ml of ether.

Anthrone is used for the determination of sugars, starches, carboxymethyl-celluloses, etc., carbohydrates.

Standards

Melting range.................154°–156°	Solubility in carbon tetra-
Sensitiveness.................to pass test	chloride...................to pass test
Ignition residue...............max 0.1%	Anthranol...................to pass test

Sensitiveness: (*a*) Mix (*caution*) 25 ml of H_2SO_4 with 1 ml of water and dissolve 15 mg of the anthrone in this mixture.   (*b*) Dissolve 10 mg of sucrose in 100 ml of water.

To 1.0 ml of (*b*) add 3 ml of (*a*).   A clear bluish-green color is produced.

Anthranol: Dissolve 0.1 g in 10 ml of warm alcohol.   The solution is free from fluorescence.

Solubility in carbon tetrachloride: 0.5 g of anthrone dissolves completely in 10 ml of carbon tetrachloride, forming a clear nonfluorescent solution.

Ignition residue: Char well 1.0 g, cool, add 0.5 ml of H_2SO_4, evaporate and ignite to constant weight.   Any remaining residue does not exceed 1.0 mg.

ANTIMONY POTASSIUM TARTRATE

Antimonyl Potassium Tartrate

$KOOC \cdot CHOH \cdot CHOH \cdot COO(SbO) \cdot \frac{1}{2}H_2O$.   Mol. wt. 333.94.   Anhydrous—97.3%. H_2O—2.7%; Sb—36.47%; Sb_2O_3—43.65%.

Colorless, transparent crystals or white, crystalline powder.   Slowly effloresces in air.   Soluble in 15 parts of water, in 20 of glycerol; insoluble in alcohol.

Standards

Assay (anhydrous basis).....99.5–100.3%	Chloride (Cl)................max 0.005%
Insoluble....................to pass test	Sulfate (SO_4)................max 0.010%
Free acid (as tartaric)........max 0.15%	Arsenic (As)................max 20 ppm
Free alkali (as Na_2CO_3)........max 0.1%	Lead (Pb).................max 0.001%

Assay: Dry about 1 g of the powdered sample at 105° for 3 hours.   Weigh accurately about 0.5 g of the dried material, and dissolve it in 30 ml of water.   Add 20 ml of cold saturated solution of sodium bicarbonate (1 in 15) and a few drops of starch and immediately titrate with 0.1 N iodine to a persistent blue color.   One ml of 0.1 N iodine = 0.01630 g of anhydrous antimony potassium tartrate, log 21669.

Solubility: A solution of 2 g in 40 ml of warm water is clear and complete.

Free acid, Free alkali: A solution of 1.00 g in 40 ml of water requires not more than 0.2 ml of either 0.1 N HCl or of 0.1 NaOH for neutralization to the green or green-blue color of bromocresol green.

Chloride: Dissolve 0.5 g in 23 ml of water, add 2 ml of HNO_3, and filter.   To 10 ml of the filtrate add 1 ml of $AgNO_3$ solution.   Any resulting turbidity is not greater than that in a blank to which 0.01 mg of Cl has been added.

Sulfate: Dissolve 2.00 g in 15 ml of hot water, add 4.5 ml of 10% HCl, allow to cool, dilute to 20 ml, and filter. Heat 10 ml of the filtrate to about 70°, add 2 ml of $BaCl_2$ and allow to stand for 15 minutes. If a turbidity is produced it is not greater than that in control made with 0.1 mg of SO_4 and 0.2 ml of 1 N HCl, the same quantities of the reagents and in the same volume as with the sample.

Arsenic: Dissolve 0.50 g in 10 ml of 1 + 2 HCl in a suitable test tube, add 10 ml of a freshly prepared solution of 20 g of stannous chloride in 30 ml of HCl, mix, warm to 50°, and allow to stand for 30 minutes. The color of the solution, if any, is not darker than that of a blank to which 0.01 mg of As has been added.

Lead: Dissolve 3.0 g in 60 ml of warm water. To 20 ml of the solution add 1 ml of standard lead solution (0.01 mg Pb) 7 ml of 20% NaOH, 1 ml of 10% KCN, and dilute to 50 ml (A). To the remaining 40 ml of the solution add 7 ml of 20% NaOH, 1 ml of 10% KCN, and dilute to 50 ml (B). Then to each add 3 drops of freshly prepared 10% sodium sulfide solution. B is not darker than A.

ANTIMONY TRICHLORIDE

Antimonous Chloride

$SbCl_3$; mol. wt. 228.13; Sb—53.38%; Cl—46.62%.

Colorless crystals or translucent crystalline masses; very deliquescent. Soluble in a small quantity of water, decomposed by larger amounts to insoluble oxychloride. Tartaric acid dissolves the oxychloride. Soluble in hydrochloric acid, in alcohol, and in chloroform. Melts at 72°, boils at 230°. *Keep in well-closed containers.*

Standards

Assay..................min 99% $SbCl_3$	Not precipitated by H_2S......max 0.20%
Solubility in chloroform.......to pass test	Iron (Fe)...................max 0.005%
Sulfate (SO_4)..........max about 0.02%	Other heavy metals...........to pass test
Arsenic (As)................max 0.01%	

Assay: Weigh accurately about 0.5 g and dissolve it in 5 ml of 10% HCl. Add a solution of 4 g of potassium sodium tartrate in 30 ml of H_2O, follow with 40 ml of a cold, saturated solution of sodium bicarbonate, and titrate immediately with 0.1 N iodine, using starch as indicator. One ml of 0.1 N iodine = 0.01141 g $SbCl_3$, log 05729.

$$SbCl_3 + 2I + 2NaHCO_3 \rightarrow SbCl_3O + 2NaI + 2CO_2 + H_2O$$

Solubility in chloroform: A solution of 5 g in 10 ml of chloroform is clear, or not more than slightly turbid.

Sulfate: To a solution of 0.5 g in 10 ml of 10% HCl add 1 ml of $BaCl_2$. No turbidity is produced in 5 minutes.

Arsenic: Dissolve 0.5 g in 10 ml of stannous chloride solution and allow to stand for 1 hour. Not more than a faint color develops.

Not precipitated by H_2S: Dissolve 2 g in 5 ml of hydrochloric acid and dilute with 95 ml of water. Precipitate the antimony with H_2S and filter (retain precipitate).   To 50 ml of the filtrate add a few drops of H_2SO_4, evaporate and ignite.   The residue does not exceed 2.0 mg.

Iron: To the residue from *Not precipitated by H_2S* add 2 ml of HCl, 2 ml of H_2O and 5 drops of HNO_3, and slowly evaporate to dryness on the steam bath. Take up the residue with 5 drops of HCl and sufficient water to make 50 ml.   To 10 ml of the dilution add 2 ml of HCl, dilute to 50 ml, add 30 mg of ammonium persulfate and 3 ml of ammonium thiocyanate, and mix.   Any resulting red color is not darker than that of a control made with 0.01 mg of Fe, 2 ml of HCl, and the same quantities of the other reagents and in the same final volume as with the sample.

Other heavy metals: The precipitate resulting from *Not precipitated by H_2S* is completely soluble in red ammonium sulfide solution.

L-ARABINOSE

$C_5H_{10}O_5$; mol. wt. 150.13.

Colorless crystals or white crystalline powder.   Soluble in water; almost insoluble in alcohol.

Standards

Melting range . . . . 157°–160°	Acid (as acetic) . . . . max 0.015%
Drying loss . . . . max 0.50%	Chloride (Cl) . . . . max 0.004%
Specific rotation . . . . +104° to +105.5°	Sulfate (SO_4) . . . . max 0.005%
Solubility . . . . to pass test	Heavy metals (as Pb) . . . . max 0.001%
Ignition residue . . . . max 0.10%	Iron (Fe) . . . . max 0.001%

Drying loss: Dry about 1.5 g, accurately weighed, at 105° for 3 hours.   The loss in weight corresponds to not more than 0.50%.

Specific rotation: Dissolve 1.000 g of the dried sample obtained in the test for *Drying loss* in about 15 ml H_2O, add 0.1 ml of ammonium hydroxide and sufficient H_2O to make exactly 25 ml.   Determine the rotation of this solution in a 200-mm tube at 25°, using sodium light.   The observed rotation multiplied by $12.5 = [\alpha]_{DI}^{25}$.

Solubility: A solution of 1 g in 10 ml H_2O is complete and colorless.

Ignition residue: Moisten 1 g with 0.5 ml of H_2SO_4 and ignite to constant weight.   Not more than 1.0 mg of residue remains (retain).

Acid: To 20 ml of CO_2-free water add 1 drop of phenolphthalein, then add dropwise 0.02 N NaOH until a pink color is produced.   Dissolve 2 g of the sample in this solution and titrate with 0.02 N NaOH until the pink color is restored.   Not more than 0.25 ml of the NaOH is required.

Chloride: Dissolve 0.5 g in 20 ml of H_2O, add 2 ml of 10% HNO_3 and 0.5 ml of $AgNO_3$.   Any resulting turbidity is not greater than that in a blank to which 0.02 mg of Cl has been added.

Sulfate: Dissolve 1 g in 10 ml of warm H_2O, add 1 ml of 1 N HCl and 2 ml of $BaCl_2$, and allow to stand for 15 minutes.   If a turbidity is produced it is not greater than that in a blank to which 0.05 mg of SO_4 has been added.

Heavy metals: Dissolve 2.5 g in 25 ml of water. To 5 ml of the solution add 0.015 mg of Pb, dilute to 20 ml and add 1 ml of 1 N acetic acid (A). To the remaining 20 ml add 1 ml of 1 N acetic acid (B). Then to each add 5 ml of H_2S. B is not darker than A.

Iron: To the *Ignition residue* add 2 ml of HCl and 2 ml of H_2O, and slowly evaporate to dryness on the steam bath. Take up the residue in 2 ml of HCl and dilute with H_2O to 50 ml. Add 30 mg of ammonium persulfate and 3 ml of ammonium thiocyanate. Any red color produced is not darker than that in a control made with 0.01 mg of Fe, 2 ml of HCl and the same quantities of the other reagents.

L-ARGININE MONOHYDROCHLORIDE

Arginine Hydrochloride

HN
‖
$C \cdot NH(CH_2)_3 \cdot CHNH_2 \cdot COOH$; mol. wt. 210.67; N—26.60%; HCl—17.5%.
|
$NH_2 \cdot HCl$

Colorless or white crystals. Soluble in water, sparingly in alcohol.

Standards

Nitrogen (N) dried basis.....26.6% ± 0.2°	Drying loss..................max 0.3%
HCl dried basis..........17.3% ± 0.2%	Phosphate................max 0.002%
Specific rotation	Sulfate (SO_4)..............max 0.010%
(in 1 N HCl)...........+21.5° ± 0.5°	Ammonium Salts (as NH_3)....max 0.020%
Solubility..................to pass test	Heavy metals (as Pb)........max 0.001%
Ignition residue.............max 0.05%	Iron (Fe)..................max 0.001%

Nitrogen: Determine by the Kjeldahl method, using 0.18–0.22 g of the dried sample accurately weighed.

HCl Content: Using an accurately weighed quantity of about 0.5 g of the dried (at 105°) sample determine the HCl by either of the methods for Assay for Chlorides and Thiocyanates, page 565. One ml of 0.1 N AgNO$_3$ = 0.003646 g HCl, log 56182.

Specific rotation and **Drying loss:** Dry about 1 g, accurately weighed, at 105° for 2 hours: the loss in weight corresponds to not more than 0.3%. Dissolve 0.75 g of the dried sample in 1 N HCl to make exactly 25 ml, observe the rotation of the solution in a 200-mm tube at 25° ± 2° and calculate the specific rotation.

Solubility: A solution of 1.0 g in 10 ml of water is complete, clear and colorless.

Ignition residue: To 2.0 g add 1 ml of H_2SO_4 and ignite to constant weight. Not more than 1.0 mg of residue remains (retain residue).

Phosphate: Place 0.5 g of sample in a platinum crucible, add an equal quantity of magnesium nitrate and 5 ml of H_2O. Evaporate to dryness and ignite at a low temperature until the residue is nearly white. Add to the residue 5 ml of water and 3 ml of 25% H_2SO_4, heat for 5 minutes, then add 10 ml of hot water, filter and wash to 20 ml.   Add to the filtrate 1 ml each of phosphate reagents **A** and **B** and heat at 60° for 10 minutes.   Any resulting blue color is not darker than that in a blank to which 0.01 mg of PO_4 has been added.

Sulfate: To a solution of 0.5 g in 10 ml of water add 1 ml of 0.1 N HCl and 2 ml of $BaCl_2$.   If a turbidity is produced in 10 minutes it does not exceed that of a blank to which 0.1 mg of SO_4 has been added.

Ammonium Salts: Dissolve 0.5 g in 60 ml of water in a small distilling flask, add 1.0 g of magnesium oxide, and distill about 40 ml into 5 ml of water containing 1 drop of diluted $(1+3)$ HCl.   Dilute the distillate to 50 ml.   Dilute 10 ml of this solution to 50 ml, and add 2 ml of 10% NaOH and 2 ml of Nessler solution.   Any color produced is not darker than that of a control made with 0.10 mg of NH_3 (0.30 mg NH_4Cl) and treated as the sample.

Heavy metals: To the *Ignition residue* add 2 ml of HCl, 2 ml of H_2O, and 0.5 ml of HNO_3 and evaporate to dryness on the steam bath.   Digest the residue with 0.5 ml of 1 N HCl and 10 ml of hot water for 5 minutes, cool and dilute to 30 ml. To 15 ml add 5 ml of H_2S.   Any resulting coloration is not darker than that of a control made with 0.01 mg Pb, 0.2 ml of 1 N HCl and 5 ml H_2S in the same final volume as with the sample.

Iron: To the remaining 15 ml of solution from the preceding test add 2 ml of HCl, dilute to 50 ml, add 30 mg of ammonium persulfate and 3 ml of ammonium thiocyanate solution and mix.   Any resulting red coloration is not darker than that in a blank to which 0.01 mg of Fe has been added.

ARSENIC PENTOXIDE

Arsenic Acid Anhydride

As_2O_5; mol. wt. 229.8; As—65.2%.

White to faintly yellow powder.   Slowly soluble in water, forming arsenic acid.

Standards

Assay................min 98.5% As_2O_5	Alkalies, Earths, etc..........max 0.20%
Insoluble..................max 0.020%	Trivalent arsenic (as As_2O_3)....max 0.10%
Chloride (Cl)...............max 0.005%	Heavy metals (as Pb)........max 0.010%
Nitrate (NO_3)...............max 0.03%	Iron (Fe)..................max 0.010%
Sulfate (SO_4)...............max 0.030%	

Assay: Weigh accurately 0.5–0.70 g and dissolve it in sufficient water to measure exactly 100 ml.   Transfer 25 ml of the solution into an iodine flask, add 25 ml of water and 10 ml of HCl and warm to about 50°.   Add 3 g of potassium iodide, immediately stopper the flask and allow to stand for 20 minutes.   Cool, dilute with 25 ml of water and titrate with 0.1 N thiosulfate, using starch toward the end.   Correct for a blank.   One ml of 0.1 N thiosulfate = 0.005748 g As_2O_5, log 75952.

Insoluble: Dissolve 5 g in 100 ml of H_2O and heat on the steam bath for 1 hour.   Filter any undissolved residue, wash it well with H_2O and dry at 105°. Its weight does not exceed 1.0 mg.

Chloride: To a solution of 0.4 g in 20 ml of H_2O add 1 ml of HNO_3 and 1 ml of $AgNO_3$. Any resulting turbidity is not greater than that in a blank to which 0.02 mg of Cl has been added.

Nitrate: Dissolve 0.20 g in 10 ml of H_2O, add 10 mg of NaCl and 0.2 ml of indigo carmine, and follow with 10 ml of H_2SO_4. The blue color is not entirely discharged in 10 minutes.

Sulfate: Dissolve 3 g in 75 ml of H_2O, add 2 ml of HCl and filter if necessary. Heat to boiling, add 5 ml $BaCl_2$ and allow to stand overnight. If a precipitate is present, filter, wash with H_2O and ignite. The weight of the precipitate ($BaSO_4$) does not exceed 2.5 mg.

Alkalies, Earths, etc.: Dissolve 0.5 g in 5 ml of hot H_2O in a small porcelain dish, add 10 ml of hydrobromic acid and evaporate to dryness on a steam bath *under hood!* Warm the residue with 2 ml of HCl until dissolved, dilute with 25 ml of H_2O, saturate the solution with H_2S, filter and wash with about 10 ml H_2O containing 3 drops of H_2SO_4 and some H_2S. Evaporate the filtrate to dryness and ignite. The weight of the residue does not exceed 1.0 mg (retain), correcting for any residue derived from 10 ml of the hydrobromic acid.

Trivalent arsenic: To a solution of 2 g in 25 ml of H_2O add 10% sodium hydroxide until the solution is slightly alkaline to litmus. Add 2 drops of HCl, dissolve in the solution 1 g of sodium bicarbonate and titrate with 0.1 N iodine using starch as the indicator. One ml of 0.1 N iodine = 0.00495 ml As_2O_3. Not more than 0.45 ml is required.

Heavy metals: Dissolve 0.2 g in 5 ml of hot H_2O in a small porcelain crucible, add 10 mg of Na_2CO_3, 5 ml of hydrobromic acid and evaporate to dryness on a steam bath *under hood*. Re-evaporate with 5 ml of H_2O and 5 ml of hydrobromic acid. Warm the residue with 1.0 ml of 1 N HCl, dilute to 40 ml with H_2O and add 10 ml of H_2S. Any color produced is not darker than that of a control made as follows: Place in a small porcelain dish 0.02 mg Pb and 10 mg of Na_2CO_3, add 10 ml of hydrobromic acid and evaporate to dryness on the steam bath; then proceed as before described for the sample beginning with "Warm the residue. . . ."

Iron: To the residue obtained in the test for *Alkalies, Earths, etc.*, add 2 ml of HCl, 2 ml of H_2O and a few drops of HNO_3, and slowly evaporate to dryness on the steam bath. Take up with 1 ml of HCl and water to make 50 ml. To 20 ml of the solution add 2 ml of HCl and dilute to 50 ml. Add 30 mg of ammonium persulfate and 3 ml of ammonium thiocyanate, and mix. Any resulting red color is not darker than that of a control made with 0.02 mg of Fe, 2 ml of HCl, the same quantities of the other reagents and in the same final volume as with the sample.

ARSENIC TRIOXIDE, PRIMARY STANDARD

As_2O_3; mol. wt. 197.82; As—75.74%.

White, amorphous, glassy or opaque pieces, or white powder. Very slowly soluble in water; slightly soluble in alcohol or ether; readily soluble in solution of alkali carbonates of hydroxides.

Standards

Insoluble in NH_4OH	max 0.010%	Sulfide (S)	max 0.001%
Ignition residue	max 0.020%	Antimony (Sb)	max 0.002%
Organic matter	no reaction	Iron (Fe)	max 0.001%
Chloride (Cl)	max 0.005%	Lead, etc., metals	max 0.001%

Insoluble in NH_4OH: Heat 10 g with 65 ml of water and 33 ml of ammonium hydroxide under reflux until dissolved. Filter any undissolved residue, wash it with warm dilute ammonium hydroxide and dry at 105°. The insoluble residue is not more than 1.0 mg.

Ignition residue: Slowly ignite 5 g in a platinum or silica dish *under hood*. The residue does not exceed 1.0 mg (retain residue).

Organic matter: During ignition there is no darkening in color.

Chloride: Heat 0.5 g with 5 ml of 10% NH_3 and 15 ml of H_2O until dissolved. Cool, add 5 ml of HNO_3, dilute to 50 ml and filter if necessary. To 20 ml add 1 ml of silver nitrate. Any resulting turbidity does not exceed that of a control made with 0.01 mg of Cl and 1 ml each of the NH_3, HNO_3 and silver nitrate in the same volume as with the sample.

Sulfide: Dissolve 1 g in 10 ml of 1 N NaOH and add 1 drop of lead acetate solution. The color is the same as that of 10 ml of the NaOH with 1 drop of lead acetate solution added.

Antimony: Place in a small separatory funnel 5 ml of a mixture of 10 volumes of HCl and 5 volumes of H_2O, then add 0.10 g of sample, shake gently until the sample has dissolved. In a similar separatory funnel place 4 ml of the HCl–H_2O mixture, add a volume of a standard antimony solution, corresponding to 0.002 mg of Sb, and dilute with HCl to 5 ml.

To each separator add 0.2 ml of a 10% solution of sodium nitrite and mix. Add 5 ml of H_2O, 5 ml of a solution of 10 mg of rhodamine B in 100 ml of water and 15 ml of toluene (or benzene). Shake for 1 minute, allow to separate and discard the aqueous (lower) layer. Add 10 ml of 10% HCl, shake for about 1 minute, allow to separate and discard the aqueous layer.

Transfer the toluene layers to glass-stoppered cylinders of the same diameter, rinse the separatory funnels each with 5 ml of toluene and add the rinsings to the respective cylinders. Add to the cylinders 1 g of anhydrous Na_2SO_4 and sufficient toluene to make 25 ml, and shake until the liquid is clear. Any violet red color in the cylinder with the sample is not deeper than that made with the antimony standard.

Iron: To the *Ignition residue* add 2 ml of HCl and 2 ml of H_2O, and slowly evaporate to dryness on the steam bath. Dissolve the residue in 2 ml of HCl and sufficient H_2O to make 50 ml. Dilute 20 ml of the solution to 50 ml, add 30 mg of ammonium persulfate and 3 ml of ammonium thiocyanate, and mix. Any resulting red color is not darker than that of a control made with 0.02 mg of Fe, 2 ml of HCl, the same quantities of the other reagents and in the same final volume as with the sample.

Lead, etc., metals: To 1.0 g of sample in a small porcelain dish add 25 mg of sodium carbonate, 10 ml of water, 10 ml of HCl, and evaporate *under hood* on a steam bath to dryness. Wash down the sides of the dish with 3 ml of HCl and 3 ml of water and re-evaporate on the steam bath.   Take up the residue with 1 ml of 1 N acetic acid and digest well with 10 ml of hot water.   Transfer completely to a 50-ml Nessler tube, dilute to 40 ml and add 10 ml of H_2S.   Any color produced is not darker than that of a control made as follows: In a porcelain dish place 0.01 mg of Pb, 25 mg of sodium carbonate, 10 ml of water, and 13 ml of HCl, and evaporate to dryness on the steam bath; then treat this residue as that of the sample.

ARSENIC TRIOXIDE

Arsenous Acid

This grade of arsenic trioxide is suitable for the preparation of volumetric arsenic solutions and standardized with 0.1 N iodine, etc.

Standards

Assay......................min 99.5%	Sulfide (as S)...............max 0.003%
Insoluble in NH_4OH.........max 0.03%	Antimony (Sb)...............max 0.02%
Ignition residue.............max 0.10%	Lead, etc., metals (as Pb).....max 0.003%
Chloride (Cl)................max 0.010%	

Assay: Dry about 0.5 g of the powdered sample over H_2SO_4 for 18 hours, then weigh accurately about 0.20 g and dissolve it in a mixture of 25 ml of H_2O and 5 ml of 1 N NaOH, warming, if necessary, to aid solution.   Cool, render slightly acid with dilute H_2SO_4, then add 40 ml of a cold saturated solution of sodium bicarbonate and titrate with 0.1 N iodine, using starch indicator.   One ml 0.1 N iodine = 0.004947 g As_2O_3, log 69434.

$$As_2O_3 + 4I + 4NaHCO_3 \rightarrow As_2O_5 + 4NaI + 4CO_2 + 2H_2O$$

Insoluble in NH_4OH: Heat 5 g with 30 ml of H_2O and 20 ml of ammonium hydroxide under reflux until dissolved.   Filter, wash with warm dilute ammonium hydroxide and dry at 105°.   The insoluble residue is not more than 1.5 mg.

Ignition residue: Ignite 1 g in a platinum or silica crucible *under the hood*. The residue does not exceed 1.0 mg.

Chloride: Heat 0.5 g with 5 ml of 10% NH_3 and 15 ml of H_2O until dissolved. Cool, add 5 ml of HNO_3, dilute to 50 ml and filter if necessary.   To 20 ml add 1 ml of silver nitrate.   Any resulting turbidity does not exceed that of a control made with 0.02 mg of Cl, 1 ml each of the NH_3, HNO_3 and silver nitrate in the same volume as with the sample.

Sulfide: Dissolve 0.3 g in 10 ml of 1 N NaOH and add 1 drop of lead acetate solution.   The color is the same as that of 10 ml of the NaOH with 1 drop of lead acetate solution.

Antimony: Dissolve 0.10 g of the sample in 20 ml of a mixture of 12 volumes of HCl and 8 volumes of H_2O.   Place 5 ml of the solution in a small separatory funnel and add 1 ml of water, then proceed with the test as described under the preceding reagent, beginning with "In a similar separatory funnel...", but using for the control 0.005 mg of Sb.   The result should be as there stated.

Lead, etc., metals: Using 0.3 g of the sample make the test as directed under the preceding reagent. The result should be as there stated.

ASBESTOS

Acid Washed

Asbestos is essentially a calcium magnesium *o*-silicate, approximately $CaMg_3(SiO_4)_3$ in the form of white to grayish white or slightly greenish, fine, smooth, and soft fibers. It is used as a filtering medium and is available in several fiber lengths. The fiber lengths used in chemical analytical work are: (1) Long fibers of 0.75 to 1 cm, and (2) medium fibers of 0.4 to 0.75 cm.

Standards

Hydrochloric acid—soluble. . . . max 0.50%   Water soluble. . . . . max 0.20%
Acid; Alkalinity. . . . . to pass test

Hydrochloric acid—soluble: Place 3 g in a flask, add 75 ml of a mixture of 1 volume HCl (35%–38%) and 6 volumes of H_2O, and bring to a boil. Cool, dilute with H_2O to 75 ml and filter. To 50 ml of the filtrate add 5 drops of H_2SO_4, evaporate to dryness and ignite. The weight of the residue is not more than 10.0 mg.

Acid; Alkalinity: Digest 2 g with 50 ml of hot H_2O on the steam bath for 15 minutes, add H_2O to make 60 ml and filter. The filtrate is neutral to litmus paper.

Water soluble: Evaporate 30 ml of the filtrate from the preceding test to dryness on the steam bath, and dry at 105° for 1 hour. The weight of the residue is not more than 2.0 mg.

ASCORBIC ACID

L-Ascorbic Acid; Vitamin C; L-Xyloascorbic Acid

$$O=C-C=C-C-C-C \; ; \; C_6H_8C_6 \; ; \; \text{mol. wt. } 176.13$$

Colorless or white crystals, or white crystalline powder. Melts at about 190° with some decomposition. Stable in air when dry; in aqueous solution it rapidly oxidizes in presence of air, forming dehydroascorbic acid $(C_6H_6O_6)$. Oxidation in solution is retarded by presence of mineral acids, but accelerated by alkalies, copper, iron. Ascorbic acid is a relatively strong reducing agent. Soluble in 3 parts water, in 30 parts alcohol, in 50 parts absolute alcohol; insoluble in benzene, chloroform, ether, or in petroleum benzin.

Ascorbic acid is used as a reference standard for the standardization of dichlorophenol-indophenol solution which is used for the determination of ascorbic acid in foods, pharmaceuticals, etc., and as a reducing agent in chemical analysis.

Standards

Assay....................min 99.7%	Ignition residue.............max 0.050%
Specific rotation...........+21° to +22°	Heavy metals (as Pb).......max 0.001%
Sensitiveness................to pass test	

Assays: Weigh accurately about 0.3 g of the sample previously dried for 2 hours over H_2SO_4, dissolve it in a mixture of 100 ml of oxygen-free water and 10 ml of 10% H_2SO_4, and titrate at once with 0.1 N iodine, adding a few drops of starch indicator as the end point is neared. One ml of 0.1 N iodine = 0.008806 g of $C_6H_8O_6$, log 94478.

$$C_6H_8O_6 + I_2 \rightarrow C_6H_6O_6 + 2HI$$
$$\text{dehydroascorbic acid}$$

Specific rotation: Dissolve 1.000 g of the dried sample in sufficient oxygen-free water to make exactly 10 ml, and, without delay, determine the rotation of this solution at 25° in a 100-mm tube, using sodium light. The observed rotation multiplied by 10 = αD.

Sensitiveness: *Solution* (a) Dissolve 25 mg of sample in 25 ml of a solution composed of 15 g of metaphosphoric acid, 1 ml of glacial acetic acid, and H_2O to make 50 ml. *Solution* (b) Dissolve 25 mg of dichlorophenol-indophenol sodium and 20 mg of sodium bicarbonate in water to make 100 ml. Filter through a dry filter into a dry flask, rejecting the first 10 ml of the filtrate.

To exactly 15 ml of *solution* (b) add exactly 2.5 ml of *solution* (a). The resulting mixture is colorless.

Ignition residue: Char 2.0 g, cool, add 0.5 ml of H_2SO_4 and 1 ml of HNO_3, and ignite to constant weight. The weight of the residue does not exceed 1.0 mg (retain residue).

Heavy metals: To the *Ignition residue* add 1 ml of HNO_3 and 0.5 ml of HCl and slowly evaporate to dryness on the steam bath. Add to the residue 1 ml of 1 N acetic acid and 10 ml of hot H_2O and digest for 2 minutes. Cool, dilute to 40 ml, and add 10 ml of H_2S. Any brown color produced is not darker than that of a control made with 0.02 mg of Pb, 1 ml of 1 N acetic acid and 10 ml of H_2S in the same final volume as with the sample.

ASPARAGINE

L-Aminosuccinamic Acid

$COOH \cdot CH(NH_2) \cdot CH_2 \cdot CONH_2 \cdot H_2O$; mol. wt. 150.13; N—18.66%.

Colorless, or white odorless crystals. Soluble in 50 parts of water; soluble in acids and in alkalies; insoluble in alcohol or ether. Its neutral or alkaline solutions are levorotatory; the acid solutions are dextrorotatory.

Standards

Specific rotation	+31° to +33°	Chloride (Cl)	max 0.003%
Nitrogen	18.5%–18.8%	Sulfate (SO$_4$)	max 0.005%
Solubility	to pass test	Heavy metals (as Pb)	max 0.001%
Ignition residue	max 0.050%	Iron (Fe)	max 0.002%

Specific rotation: Determine the rotation of a solution in 10% HCl, containing 0.50 g of sample in 10 ml of the solution, using a 200-mm tube. From the observed angular rotation calculate the specific rotation by formula on page 582.

Nitrogen: Determine the nitrogen by the Kjeldahl method. One ml of 0.1 N HCl = 0.001401 g N, log 14644, or to 0.007505 g $C_4H_8O_3N_2 \cdot H_2O$, log 87535.

Solubility: One gram dissolves completely in 50 ml warm water and the solution is colorless.

Ignition residue: Char 2 g, then add 1 ml of sulfuric acid and ignite to constant weight. Not more than 1.0 mg of residue remains (retain residue).

Chloride: Dissolve 0.5 g in 20 ml of water and 1 ml of HNO$_3$, and add 1 ml of silver nitrate. If a turbidity is produced it is not greater than that in a blank to which 0.015 mg of Cl has been added.

Sulfate: Dissolve 2 g in a mixture of 15 ml of warm water and 5 ml of 10% HCl, cool and add 2 ml of BaCl$_2$. Any turbidity produced is not greater than that in a control made with 0.1 mg of SO$_4$, 1 ml of 1 N HCl and 2 ml of BaCl$_2$ in the same final volume as with the sample.

Solution R: To the *Ignition residue* add 2 ml of HCl, 2 ml of H$_2$O, and a few drops of HNO$_3$, and slowly evaporate to dryness on the steam bath. Take up the residue in 0.5 ml of 1 N HCl and 10 ml of hot H$_2$O, cool and dilute to 20 ml.

Heavy metals: Dilute 10 ml of *Solution R* to 20 ml and add 5 ml of H$_2$S. Any color produced is not darker than that in a control made with 0.01 mg of Pb, 0.2 ml of 1 N HCl, and 5 ml of H$_2$S in the same volume as with the sample.

Iron: To 5 ml of *Solution R* add 2 ml of HCl, dilute to 50 ml and add about 30 mg of ammonium persulfate and 3 ml of ammonium thiocyanate. Any red color produced is not darker than that in a blank to which 0.01 mg of Fe has been added.

AURINTRICARBOXYLIC ACID, *see* ALUMINON

AZOLITMIN

Dark violet scales, or a red powder. Slightly soluble in water, insoluble in alcohol and dilute acids; very soluble in dilute alkalies. pH range: 4.5 red; 8.3 blue. It is usually used in 0.5% aqueous solution.

Azolitmin solutions should be kept in partly filled bottles plugged with cotton to permit access of air.

Sensitiveness: Dissolve 0.1 g in 8 ml of hot water and 2 ml of alcohol. Add 0.1 ml of this solution to 50 ml of CO$_2$-free water and follow with 0.05 ml of 0.1 N NaOH. A bluish-violet color is produced. Another 0.1 ml of the solution added to 50 ml of CO$_2$-free water is colored red by 0.05 ml of 0.1 N HCl.

BARIUM ACETATE

$Ba(CH_3 \cdot CO_2)_2$; mol. wt. 255.4; Ba—53.77%; acetic acid = 47.02%.

White, crystalline powder.   Soluble in about 2 parts of water; slightly soluble in alcohol.

Standards

Insoluble................... max 0.010%	Alkalies and Calcium (as Ca)... max 0.10%
Free acid (as acetic)........... max 0.2%	Calcium and Strontium
Alkalinity.................... to pass test	(as Sr).................... max 0.20%
Chloride (Cl)................ max 0.001%	Heavy metals (as Pb)........ max 0.001%
Nitrate (NO_3).............. max 0.003%	Iron (Fe).................. max 0.001%

Insoluble: Dissolve 10 g in 100 ml of hot water, and heat on the steam bath for 1 hour.   Filter any undissolved residue, wash with hot water and dry at 105°. The weight of the insoluble residue does not exceed 1.0 mg.

Free acid; Alkalinity: Dissolve 3 g in 30 ml of water, and add 3 drops of phenolphthalein; at most only a faint pink color is produced.   If no pink color is produced it requires not more than 1 ml of 0.1 N NaOH to produce a pink color.

Chloride: To a solution of 1 g in 10 ml of water add 1 ml of HNO_3 and 1 ml of silver nitrate.   Any resulting turbidity is not greater than that in a blank with 0.01 mg of Cl added.

Nitrate: Dissolve 0.5 g in 5 ml of water and add the solution in small portions and with continuous stirring to 8 ml of hot Na_2CO_3 solution previously diluted with 7 ml of water.   Boil for 1–2 minutes and filter.   Cool the filtrate, neutralize it with 25% H_2SO_4 and dilute to 25 ml.   To 5 ml of this solution add 20 mg of NaCl, 5 ml of water, 0.2 ml diphenylamine solution, mix and slowly run in, without agitation, 10 ml of H_2SO_4.   After a few minutes mix by gently swirling the liquid and allow to stand for 1 hour.   No blue color appears.

Alkalies and Calcium: Dissolve 3 g in 130 ml of H_2O, add 1 ml of HCl, heat to boiling and add 20 ml of 10% H_2SO_4.   Cool, dilute with H_2O to 150 ml and allow to stand overnight.   Filter, evaporate 100 ml of the filtrate and ignite.   The residue is not over 5.0 mg.

Calcium and Strontium: Dissolve 2 g in 15 ml of hot water, add 10 ml of HCl and evaporate to dryness.   Add to the residue 10 ml of hot water and 10 ml of HCl, re-evaporate on steam bath and dry for 2 hours at 105°.   Finely powder the residue, transfer it to a small flask, and add 20 ml of alcohol.   Stopper, shake for a few minutes, and let stand for 1 hour with occasional shaking.   Filter, and to 10 ml of the filtrate add a few drops of H_2SO_4, evaporate and ignite.   The residue does not exceed 4.0 mg.

Note: The calcium and strontium may be determined separately by Flame Photometry.

Heavy metals.   Dissolve 6 g in 5 ml of 10% HCl and H_2O to make 30 ml.   To 5 ml add 0.02 mg of Pb, dilute to 40 ml (A).   Dilute the remaining 25 ml to 40 ml (B).   Then to each add 10 ml of H_2S. B is not darker than A.

Iron: Dissolve 1 g in 10 ml of H_2O, add 2 ml of HCl and 3 drops of HNO_3. Bring to a boil, cool, dilute to 50 ml and add 3 ml of ammonium thiocyanate.   Any resulting red color is not darker than that of a blank to which 0.01 mg of Fe has been added.

BARIUM CARBONATE

$BaCO_3$; mol. wt. 197.37; Ba—69.59%; CO_2—22.30%.

White powder. Almost insoluble in water, soluble in dilute hydrochloric or nitric acid, and in acetic acid.

Standards

Hydrochloric acid—insoluble..max 0.015%	Sulfide (S)....................to pass test
Chloride (Cl)...............max 0.002%	Alkalies and Calcium (as Ca)...max 0.20%
Hydroxide and Alkali carbonate	Calcium and Strontium
(as Na_2CO_3)...............max 0.10%	(as Sr)....................max 0.25%
Nitrate (NO_3)...............max 0.003%	Heavy metals (as Pb)........max 0.001%
Phosphate (PO_4)............max 0.002%	Iron (Fe)..................max 0.001%

Hydrochloric acid—insoluble: Mix 10 g with 100 ml of water and add slowly 10 ml of HCl. Dilute with water to 200 ml and heat on the steam bath for 30 minutes. Filter any undissolved residue, wash with water slightly acidified with HCl and dry at 105°. The insoluble weighs not more than 1.5 mg.

Chloride: Dissolve 0.5 g in 20 ml of H_2O and 1 ml of HNO_3. Filter, if necessary, and add to the filtrate 1 ml of $AgNO_3$. Any turbidity produced is not greater than in a blank with 0.01 mg of Cl added.

Hydroxide and Alkali carbonate: Shake 5 g with 50 ml of CO_2-free water for 10 minutes and filter. To 30 ml of the filtrate add 2 drops of phenolphthalein. If a pink color is produced it is discharged by 0.15 ml of 0.02 N HCl.

Nitrate: Mix 0.50 g of sample with a few ml of water, add dropwise glacial acetic acid until all is dissolved and dilute to 10 ml. Slowly add this solution and with constant stirring to 10 ml of hot sodium carbonate solution, previously diluted with 5 ml of water, and gently boil for 1–2 minutes. Filter, neutralize the cooled filtrate with 25% H_2SO_4 and dilute to 25 ml. To 5 ml add 5 ml of water, 20 mg NaCl, and 0.2 ml of diphenylamine solution. Mix, and slowly run in, without agitation, 10 ml of H_2SO_4. After 5 minutes mix the liquid by swirling gently and allow to stand for 1 hour. No blue color appears.

Phosphate: To 1 g add 20 ml of H_2O, then add HCl dropwise until dissolved. Dilute with about 30 ml of H_2O, heat to boiling, add 4 ml of 25% H_2SO_4 and allow to stand for 30 minutes. Filter and wash to 50 ml. To 25 ml of the filtrate add 1 ml of each of phosphate reagents **A** and **B** and heat at 60° for 10 minutes. Any blue color produced is not darker than that of a control made with 0.01 mg of PO_4, 2 ml of 25% H_2SO_4, the same amounts of the reagents **A** and **B** in the same volume of solution and heated as the sample.

Sulfide: Dissolve 1 g in 8 ml of H_2O and 2 ml of glacial acetic acid, and add immediately 1 ml of $AgNO_3$. No darkening is produced in 5 minutes.

Alkalies and Calcium: Dissolve 2 g in 30 ml of H_2O and 3 ml of HCl, and dilute with water to 80 ml. Boil, add 15 ml of 10% H_2SO_4, cool, make up to 100 ml, mix and allow to stand overnight. Filter, evaporate 50 ml of the filtrate and ignite. The residue does not exceed 6.0 mg.

Calcium and Strontium: To 2 g add 20 ml of H_2O and 3 ml of HCl, evaporate to dryness on the steam bath and dry at 105° for 2 hours. Transfer the finely powdered residue to a small flask, add 20 ml of alcohol, shake for 5 minutes and allow to stand for 1 hour, shaking a few times. Filter, and to 10 ml of the filtrate add a few drops of H_2SO_4, evaporate and ignite. No more than 5.0 mg of residue is obtained.

Note: The individual amounts of calcium and of strontium may be determined by Flame Photometry.

Solution S: Mix 5 g with 30 ml of H_2O, cautiously add 7 ml of HCl, and evaporate to dryness on the steam bath. Add to the residue 15 ml of hot H_2O and re-evaporate to dryness on the steam bath. Dissolve the residue in water to make 50 ml and filter if necessary.

Heavy metals: To 10 ml of *Solution S* add 0.02 mg of Pb and 1 ml of 1 *N* acetic acid, and dilute to 40 ml (*A*). To 30 ml add 1 ml of 1 *N* acetic acid and dilute to 40 ml (*B*). Then to each add 10 ml of H_2S. *B* is not darker than *A*.

Iron: To 10 ml of *Solution S* add 2 ml of HCl and 3 drops of HNO_3. Bring to a boil, cool, dilute to 50 ml and add 3 ml of ammonium thiocyanate. Any resulting red color is not darker than that of a blank to which 0.01 mg of Fe has been added.

BARIUM CHLORIDE

$BaCl_2 \cdot 2H_2O$; mol. wt. 244.31; anhydrous—85.25%; H_2O—14.75%; Ba—56.22%; Cl—29.03%.

Colorless or white crystals. Soluble in about 2.5 parts of water; insoluble in alcohol. Its solubility in water is decreased by the presence of hydrochloric acid, and it is almost insoluble in the concentrated acid.

Standards

Insoluble . . . . max 0.010%	Calcium and Strontium
Neutrality . . . . to pass test	(as Sr) . . . . max 0.10%
Chlorate and Nitrate	Heavy metals (as Pb) . . . . max 0.0005%
(as NO_3) . . . . max 0.003%	Iron (Fe) . . . . max 0.0003%
Alkalies and Calcium (as Ca) . . max 0.050%	

Insoluble: Dissolve 20 g in 200 ml of water and heat on steam bath for 1 hour. Filter any undissolved residue, wash it with water and dry at 105°. Not more than 2.0 mg of insoluble is found.

Neutrality: Dissolve 2 g in 30 ml of water and add 2 drops of phenolphthalein; no pink color is produced. On the subsequent addition of 0.1 ml and 0.02 *N* NaOH a pink color is produced.

Chlorate and Nitrate: Dissolve 0.5 g in 5 ml of water and add the solution in small portions and with continuous stirring to 8 ml of hot Na_2CO_3 solution previously diluted with 7 ml of water. Boil for 1–2 minutes and filter. Cool the filtrate, neutralize it with 25% H_2SO_4 and dilute to 25 ml. To 5 ml of this solution add 5 ml of water, 0.2 ml diphenylamine solution, mix and slowly run in, without agitation, 10 ml of H_2SO_4. After a few minutes mix by gently swirling the liquid and allow to stand for 1 hour. No blue color appears.

Alkalies and Calcium: Dissolve 5 g in 150 ml of water, add 1 ml of hydrochloric acid, heat to boiling, and add 25 ml of 10% H_2SO_4. Cool, dilute with water to 250 ml, and allow to stand overnight. Filter, evaporate 100 ml of the filtrate, and ignite. The residue is not over 3.0 mg.

Calcium and Strontium: Reduce 2 g of the sample to a fine powder. Transfer to a small flask, add 20 ml of alcohol, stopper the flask, shake for 5 minutes and let stand for 1 hour with occasional shaking. Filter, and to 10 ml of the filtrate add a few drops of H_2SO_4, evaporate to dryness and ignite. The residue does not exceed 2.0 mg.

Note: The individual amounts of calcium (Ca) and of strontium in this reagent are best determined by Flame Photometry.

Heavy metals: Dissolve 6 g in water to make 40 ml. To 10 ml add 0.015 mg of Pb, 1 ml of 1 N acetic acid and dilute to 40 ml (A). To the remaining 30 ml add 1 ml of 1 N acetic acid and dilute to 40 ml (B). Then add to each 10 ml of H_2S; B is not darker than A.

Iron: To a solution of 3 g in 20 ml of H_2O, add 2 ml of HCl and 5 drops of nitric acid and bring to a boil. Cool, dilute to 50 ml, and add 3 ml of ammonium thiocyanate. Any resulting red color is not darker than that of a blank to which 0.01 mg of Fe has been added.

BARIUM CHROMATE

$BaCrO_4$; mol. wt. 253.37; Ba—54.21%; CrO_3—39.47%; Cr—20.53%.

Yellow, crystalline powder. Insoluble in water; soluble in dilute hydrochloric or nitric acids.

Standards

Assay.................min 99% $BaCrO_4$	Alkali chromate..............to pass test
Hydrochloric acid—insoluble...max 0.05%	Moisture....................max 1.0%
Chloride (Cl)...............max 0.005%	Water soluble...............max 0.20%

Assay; Moisture: Dry about 1 g, accurately weighed, for 18 hours over H_2SO_4. The loss in weight corresponds to not more than 1.0%. Weigh accurately about 0.30 g of the dried sample, and transfer it to a glass-stoppered flask. Add 50 ml of H_2O, 3 g of potassium iodide and follow with 7 ml of HCl. Allow to stand for 15 minutes in the dark with frequent shaking, then dilute with 75 ml of H_2O and titrate the liberated iodine with 0.1 N sodium thiosulfate, using starch toward the end. Correct for any iodine liberated by the reagents. One ml of 0.1 N thiosulfate = 0.008446 g $BaCrO_4$, log 92665.

$$BaCrO_4 + 3KI + 8HCl \rightarrow 3I + BaCl_2 + CrCl_3 + 3KCl + 4H_2O$$
and
$$2I + 2Na_2S_2O_3 \rightarrow Na_2S_4O_6 + 2NaI$$

Hydrochloric acid—insoluble: Warm 2 g with a mixture of 50 ml of water and 10 ml of HCl until no more dissolves. Filter any undissolved residue, wash it with hot H_2O until the washings are colorless, and dry to constant weight at 105°. The insoluble does not exceed 1.0 mg.

Chloride: Dissolve 1 g in 30 ml of water and 10 ml of HNO_3, and divide into two equal portions. Heat both portions to 50°, and to one portion add 1 ml of $AgNO_3$; to the other portion add 1 ml of water. At the end of 5 minutes both portions are equally clear.

Alkali chromate: Boil 1.0 g with 25 ml of water for 3 minutes, cool and filter. The filtrate is colorless (retain).

Water soluble: Wash the barium chromate on the filter from the test for *Alkali Chromate* with 5 ml of water. Combine the washings with the filtrate from the preceding test and evaporate in a tared beaker or dish to dryness on the steam bath. Dry any remaining residue at 105° for 1 hour and weigh. Its weight should not exceed 2.0 mg.

BARIUM HYDROXIDE

$Ba(OH)_2 \cdot 8H_2O$; mol. wt. 315.50; anhydrous—54.32%, H_2O—45.68%; Ba—43.54%; BaO—48.61%.

Colorless or white crystals. Soluble in about 20 parts of water; slightly soluble in alcohol. Absorbs CO_2 from the air, becoming converted into carbonate. *Keep in tightly closed containers.*

Standards

Assay..........min 97% $Ba(OH)_2 \cdot 8H_2O$	Alkalies and Calcium (as Ca)...max 0.15%
Carbonate ($BaCO_3$)............max 3.0%	Calcium and Strontium (as Sr) max 0.50%
Hydrochloric acid—insoluble..max 0.010%	Heavy metals (as Pb).......max 0.0005%
Chloride (Cl)...............max 0.001%	Iron (Fe)..................max 0.001%
Sulfide (S) to pass test; limit about 0.001%	

Assay and Carbonate: Weigh accurately about 5 g, add 200 ml CO_2-free water and 3 drops of phenolphthalein, and titrate with 1 N HCl to the disappearance of the red color. Then add methyl orange and continue titration to a pink color. The acid consumed in the titration with phenolphthalein as indicator represents the barium hydroxide, and the acid consumed with the methyl orange represents the barium carbonate. One ml of 1 N HCl = 0.1578 g $Ba(OH)_2 \cdot 8H_2O$, log 19811, or 0.09858 g $BaCO_3$, log 99423.

Hydrochloric acid—insoluble: To 10 g add 100 ml of water and 10 ml of hydrochloric acid. Heat on steam bath for 1 hour, filter any undissolved residue, wash it with hot water and dry at 105°. The weight of the undissolved residue does not exceed 1.0 mg.

Chloride: To 1 g add 20 ml of H_2O, and cautiously follow with 2 ml of HNO_3. Cool, filter and add to filtrate 1 ml of $AgNO_3$. Any turbidity produced is not greater than that in a blank to which 0.02 mg of Cl has been added.

Sulfide: Dissolve 1 g in 8 ml of warm H_2O, add 5 drops of alkaline lead solution (made by adding NaOH solution to 10% lead acetate solution until the precipitate is redissolved) and 2 ml of glacial acetic acid. No darkening is produced.

Alkalies and Calcium: To 5 g add 150 ml of H_2O and 5 ml of HCl, heat to boiling and add 20 ml of 10% H_2SO_4. Cool, dilute to 250 ml with water, mix and allow to stand overnight.   Filter, evaporate 100 ml of the filtrate, and ignite. The residue is not more than 4.5 mg.

Calcium and Strontium: Treat 2 g with 15 ml of H_2O and 2 ml of HCl. Evaporate to dryness on the steam bath and dry at 105° for 2 hours.   Transfer the finely powdered residue to a small flask, add 20 ml of alcohol, stopper, shake well for 5 minutes, and let stand for 1 hour with occasional shaking.   Filter, and to 10 ml of the filtrate add a few drops of H_2SO_4, evaporate to dryness, and ignite. The residue is not over 10.0 mg.

Note: The individual amounts of calcium (Ca) and of strontium in this reagent are best determined by Flame Photometry.

Solution S: To 6 g add 30 ml of H_2O and, in small portions, 6 ml of HCl, and evaporate to dryness on the steam bath.   Add 20 ml of hot H_2O, and re-evaporate to dryness.   Dissolve the residue in H_2O to make 60 ml.

Heavy metals: To 10 ml of *Solution S* add 0.01 mg of Pb and 1 ml of 1 N acetic acid, and dilute to 40 ml (A).   To 30 ml add 1 ml of 1 N acetic acid and dilute to 40 ml (B).   Then to each add 10 ml of H_2S; B is not darker than A.

Iron: To 10 ml *Solution S* add 3 drops of nitric acid, bring to a boil, cool, add 2 ml of HCl and dilute to 50 ml.   Add 3 ml of ammonium thiocyanate and mix. Any resulting red color is not darker than that of a blank to which 0.01 mg of Fe has been added.

BARIUM HYDROXIDE, ANHYDROUS

$Ba(OH)_2$; mol. wt. 171.4; Ba—80.15%; BaO—89.49%.

White powder, soluble in water, a few per cent of $BaCO_3$ usually remaining undissolved.

Standards

Assay...............min 94% $Ba(OH)_2$	Sulfide (S).to pass test; limit about 0.001%
Hydrochloric acid—insoluble..max 0.020%	Alkalies and Calcium (as Ca)...max 0.20%
Chloride (Cl)................max 0.005%	Heavy metals (as Pb)........max 0.002%

Assay: Weigh accurately about 3 g, add 150 ml of CO_2-free H_2O and 3 drops phenolphthalein, and titrate with 1 N HCl to the disappearance of the red color. One ml of 1 N HCl is equivalent to 0.1714 g Ba $(OH)_2$, log 23401.

Hydrochloric acid—insoluble: To 5 g add 100 ml of H_2O and follow slowly with 10 ml of HCl, then heat on a steam bath for 1 hour.   If any insoluble residue remains, filter, wash it with hot H_2O and dry at 105°.   Its weight does not exceed 1.0 mg.

Chloride: To 0.5 g add 20 ml of H_2O and cautiously follow with 2 ml of HNO_3. Cool, filter, if necessary, and add to the filtrate 1 ml of $AgNO_3$.   Any turbidity produced is not greater than that in a blank to which 0.025 mg of Cl has been added.

Sulfide: Cautiously dissolve 1.0 g in 10 ml of warm H_2O, add 5 drops of alkaline lead solution (made by adding 10% NaOH to 10% solution of lead acetate until the precipitate is redissolved) and 2 ml of glacial acetic acid.   No darkening is produced.

Alkalies and Calcium: Dissolve 2 g in 100 ml of H_2O and 5 ml of HCl. Heat the solution to boiling and add 15 ml of 10% H_2SO_4. Cool, dilute to 150 ml with H_2O, mix, and allow to stand overnight. Filter, evaporate 75 ml of the filtrate, and ignite. The weight of the residue does not exceed 6.0 mg.

Heavy metals: To 2 g add 20 ml of H_2O and 3 ml of HCl, and evaporate to dryness on a steam bath. Add 15 ml of hot H_2O, re-evaporate to dryness, and dissolve the residue in water to 40 ml. To 10 ml of the solution add 0.02 mg of Pb and 1 ml of 1 N acetic acid, and dilute to 40 ml (A). To the remaining 30 ml add 1 ml of 1 N acetic acid and dilute to 40 ml (B). Then to each add 1 ml of H_2S. B is not darker than A.

BARIUM NITRATE

$Ba(NO_3)_2$; mol. wt. 261.38; Ba—52.55%; NO_3—47.45%.

Colorless or white crystals. Soluble in about 12 parts of water; insoluble in alcohol. Hydrochloric or nitric acid decreases its solubility in water. It is almost insoluble in the concentrated acids.

Standards

Insoluble....................max 0.010%	Calcium and Strontium (as Sr) max 0.10%
Neutrality...................to pass test	Heavy metals (as Pb).......max 0.0005%
Chloride (Cl).... max 0.0005%	Iron (Fe)...................max 0.0002%
Alkalies and Calcium (as Ca)..max 0.050%	

Insoluble: Dissolve 10 g in 150 ml of hot H_2O and heat on steam bath for 1 hour. Filter any undissolved residue, wash with hot water and dry at 105°. The weight of the insoluble residue does not exceed 1.0 mg.

Neutrality: Dissolve 2 g in 30 ml of hot water and add 2 drops of phenolphthalein; no pink color is produced. On the subsequent addition of 0.1 ml of 0.02 N NaOH, a pink color is produced.

Chloride: To 2 g dissolved in 30 ml of warm H_2O add 2 drops of HNO_3 and 1 ml of $AgNO_3$. Any resulting turbidity is not greater than that in a blank with 0.01 mg of Cl added.

Alkalies and Calcium: Dissolve 5 g in 150 ml of water, heat the solution to boiling and add 25 ml of 10% H_2SO_4. Cool, dilute to 250 ml, mix and let stand overnight. Filter, evaporate 100 ml of the filtrate and ignite. The weight of the residue is not more than 3.0 mg.

Calcium and Strontium: Proceed as directed under Barium Chloride. The result should be as there stated.

Note: The individual amounts of calcium and of strontium may be determined by Flame Photometry.

Heavy metals: Dissolve 4 g in 60 ml of warm H_2O. To 15 ml add 0.01 mg of Pb, dilute to 45 ml and add 1 ml of 1 N acetic acid (A). To the remaining 45 ml add 1 ml of 1 N acetic acid (B). Then to each add 10 ml of H_2S. B is not darker than A.

Iron: Dissolve 2.5 g in 20 ml of hot H_2O, cool, add 1 ml of HCl, dilute to 30 ml, and add 2 ml of ammonium thiocyanate. Any resulting red color is not darker than that of a blank to which 0.005 mg of Fe has been added.

BARIUM PEROXIDE

Barium Dioxide

BaO_2; mol. wt. 169.36; BaO—90.55%; active oxygen—9.45%.

White or grayish-white powder. Usually contains some barium monoxide. Decomposes on contact with moisture. Insoluble in water; soluble in dilute acids with formation of hydrogen peroxide. In presence of water it is transposed by carbon dioxide into hydrogen peroxide and barium carbonate. *Keep in well-closed containers.*

Standards

Assay....................min 88% BaO_2	Alkalies and Calcium (as
Hydrochloric acid—insoluble....max 1.0%	sulfates)..................max 0.75%
Chloride (Cl)...............max 0.010%	Heavy metals (as Pb)........max 0.003%
Nitrogen compounds (as N)...max 0.010%	Iron (Fe)...................max 0.010%

Assay: Weigh accurately about 0.3 g, add 30 ml of water and 25 ml of 10% HCl and titrate with 0.1 N potassium permanganate. One ml of 0.1 N permanganate = 0.008468 g BaO_2, log 92778.

Hydrochloric acid—insoluble: To 1 g add 50 ml of H_2O and 5 ml of HCl, and heat for 1 hour on the steam bath. Filter the undissolved residue, wash with water and dry at 105°. Not more than 10 mg of insoluble matter is found.

Chloride: Dissolve 0.5 g in 30 ml of H_2O and 2 ml of HNO_3, filter and dilute the filtrate to 50 ml. To 10 ml of filtrate add 1 ml of $AgNO_3$. The resulting turbidity is not greater than that in the blank to which 0.01 mg of Cl has been added.

Nitrogen compounds: Dissolve 1 g in 50 ml of H_2O and 2 ml of glacial acetic acid in a distilling flask. Add 0.5 g of powdered Devarda metal and 30 ml of 10% NaOH, digest for 2 hours, then distill 40 ml into 5 ml of H_2O containing 3 drops of 1 N HCl and dilute the distillate to 50 ml. To 20 ml add 1 ml of 10% NaOH, dilute to 50 ml, and add 2 ml of Nessler solution. The color produced is not darker than that produced by treating 0.1 mg of nitrogen (0.4 mg NH_4Cl) in the same manner as the sample.

Alkalies and Calcium: Dissolve 2 g in 120 ml of H_2O and 5 ml of HCl. Heat the solution to boiling, add 25 ml of 10% H_2SO_4 and allow to stand overnight. Dilute with water to 150 ml, mix and filter. Evaporate 75 ml of the filtrate and ignite. The residue does not exceed 7.5 mg.

Solution S: Evaporate 2.5 g with 20 ml of H_2O and 5 ml of HCl to dryness on the steam bath. Add 20 ml of hot H_2O and re-evaporate to dryness. Dissolve the residue in H_2O to make 50 ml and filter.

Heavy metals: To 10 ml of *Solution S* add 0.03 mg of Pb, 1 ml of 1 N acetic acid, and dilute to 40 ml (*A*). To 30 ml of the filtrate add 1 ml of 1 N acetic acid and dilute to 40 ml (*B*). Then to each add 10 ml of H_2S. *B* is not darker than *A*.

Iron: To 4.0 ml of *Solution S* add 2 ml of HCl, dilute to 50 ml, and add 3 ml of ammonium thiocyanate. Any resulting red color is not darker than that of a blank to which 0.02 mg of Fe has been added.

BARIUM SULFATE

$BaSO_4$; mol. wt. 233.43; Ba—58.84%; SO_4—41.15%; S—13.74%.

White, heavy powder. Insoluble in water, almost insoluble in acids; soluble in hot concentrated sulfuric acid.

Standards

Neutrality....................to pass test	Arsenic (As)..................max 1 ppm
Ignition loss...................max 1.5%	Soluble salts..................max 0.25%
Organic matter...............no reaction	Soluble barium salts.........max 0.001%
Chloride (Cl)...............max 0.001%	Heavy metals (as Pb)........max 0.001%
Phosphate (PO_4)............max 0.001%	Iron (Fe)....................max 0.003%
Silicate, etc.................to pass test	

Neutrality: Shake 2 g with 25 ml of hot water for a few minutes, filter and add to filtrate 2 drops of phenolphthalein; no red color is produced. On the subsequent addition of 0.4 ml of 0.02 N NaOH a red color is produced.

Ignition loss: Weigh accurately about 2 g and ignite. The loss corresponds to not more than 1.5%.

Organic matter: Heat 1 g in a recently ignited test tube. No white fumes appear and no appreciable darkening is produced.

Chloride: Boil 2 g with 50 ml of H_2O for 10 minutes, cool, dilute to 50 ml and filter. To 25 ml of the filtrate add 1 ml of HNO_3 and 1 ml of $AgNO_3$. Any resulting turbidity is not greater than that in the blank to which 0.01 mg of Cl has been added.

Phosphate: Boil 4 g with 30 ml of H_2O and 5 ml of HNO_3 for 10 minutes. Dilute with water to 40 ml, filter and evaporate 20 ml of the filtrate to dryness on the steam bath. Take up the residue with 2 ml of 25% H_2SO_4 and 20 ml of warm water, add 1 ml each of phosphate reagents **A** and **B** and heat at 60° for 10 minutes. Any blue color produced is not darker than that produced by treating 0.02 mg of PO_4 with the same volumes of H_2SO_4, water, and phosphate reagents in the same manner as the sample.

Silicate, etc.: Mix 0.5 g with 4 g of sodium carbonate and fuse in a platinum crucible. Cool, disintegrate and boil with 50 ml of water. Filter and add to the filtrate a slight excess of hydrochloric acid; no precipitate forms. Now boil the solution and then make it alkaline with NH_4OH: at most only a slight precipitate is produced.

Arsenic: Test 2 g by method on page 563. The stain is not greater than that from 0.002 mg As.

Soluble salts: Boil 10 g with 90 ml of water and 5 ml of HCl for 10 minutes, cool, dilute with water to 100 ml and filter. Evaporate 50 ml of the filtrate on the steam bath to dryness, add to the residue 10 ml of hot water and 2 drops of HCl, filter and wash with 5 ml of hot water. Evaporate the filtrate on the steam bath to dryness and dry at 105° for 2 hours.   The weight of the residue does not exceed 12.5 mg (retain).

Soluble barium salts: Heat the residue from the preceding test with 5 ml of H_2O, filter, and add to the filtrate 0.3 ml of 10% H_2SO_4.   No turbidity is produced in 30 minutes.

Solution S: Boil 4 g with 30 ml of H_2O, 2 ml of HNO_3 and 1 ml of HCl for 10 minutes, filter, wash with 10–20 ml of hot H_2O and evaporate the filtrate to dryness on the steam bath.   Take up the residue in 1 ml of 1 N HCl and 15 ml of hot water, filter, if necessary, and dilute to 40 ml.

Heavy metals: Dilute 20 ml of *Solution S* to 40 ml and add 10 ml of H_2S. Any color produced is not darker than that of a control made with 0.02 mg of Pb, 0.2 ml of 1 N HCl and 10 ml of H_2S in the same final volume as with the sample.

Iron: To 5 ml of *Solution S* add 2 ml of HCl, dilute to 50 ml and add 3 ml of ammonium thiocyanate.   Any resulting red color is not darker than that of a blank to which 0.015 mg of Fe has been added.

BENZALDEHYDE

—CHO; mol. wt. 106.12.

Colorless or yellowish, strongly refractive liquid; characteristic odor.   Sp. gr. about 1.05.   Boils at 179°.   Volatile with steam.   Gradually oxidized by air to benzoic acid.   Soluble in 300 parts of water; miscible with alcohol and ether. *Keep protected from air and light.*

Standards

Assay......................min 98%	Chlorine (Cl) to pass test (limit about 0.01%)
Refractive index...........1.5445–1.5465	Nitrobenzene.................no reaction

Assay: Prepare a hydroxylamine hydrochloride solution by dissolving 10 g of hydroxylamine HCl in 30 ml of water and diluting with ethanol or methanol to 200 ml.   Accurately weigh in a weighing bottle about 3 ml of the benzaldehyde and transfer it into a 250-ml conical flask containing 30 ml of the hydroxylamine-HCl solution, using 40 ml of the latter solution to transfer completely the contents of the weighing bottle in the flask.   Mix well and allow to stand 10–15 minutes; then add 1 ml of bromophenol blue indicator solution and titrate with 1 N NaOH to a pale green color.   To a volume of the hydroxylamine-HCl solution equal to the volume used in preparing the solution of the sample, add 1 ml of the bromophenol blue solution and titrate with the 1 N NaOH to match the green color of the titrated solution of the benzaldehyde.   The difference between the two volumes represents the HCl liberated through the interaction between the benzaldehyde and the hydroxylamine hydrochloride.   One ml of 1 N NaOH = 0.1061 g C_6H_5CHO, log 02572.

$$C_6H_5CHO + NH_2OH \cdot HCl \rightarrow HCl + C_6H_5CH{:}N \cdot OH + H_2O$$
benzaldoxime

Refractive index: Determine at 20°. It should not be less than 1.5445 and not more than 1.5465.

Chlorine compounds: Moisten a clean, ignited copper spiral with the sample and heat in a colorless flame. No greenish tint is produced.

Nitrobenzene: Dissolve 1 ml in 20 ml of alcohol and add water until a slight turbidity forms. Add 2 g zinc and sufficient 10% H_2SO_4 to maintain a brisk evolution of hydrogen for 1 hour. Filter and evaporate the filtrate on the steam bath to 20 ml. Boil 10 ml with 0.5 ml of 0.1 N potassium dichromate. No violet color is produced.

BENZENE

Benzol

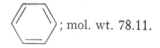 ; mol. wt. 78.11.

Colorless, clear liquid; characteristic odor. Insoluble in water; miscible with absolute alcohol or ether. Highly flammable. Sp. gr. about 0.87 at 25°. *Keep in well-closed containers in a cool place, remote from fire.*

Standards

Boiling range................79.5°–80.5°	Substances darkened by H_2SO_4 to pass test
Freezing temperature.......not below 5.2°	Sulfur compounds (as S)......max 0.002%
Evaporation residue........max 0.001%	Thiophene......................0.000%
Neutrality.................to pass test	Water................max about 0.03%

Boiling range: Distill 100 ml. After 10 drops has come over, all distills between 79.5° and 80.5°, correction being made for barometric pressure, page 581.

Freezing temperature: Determine as described on page 581.

Evaporation residue: Evaporate 115 ml on the steam bath and dry at 105° for 30 minutes. The weight of the residue does not exceed 1.0 mg.

Neutrality: Shake 20 ml with 10 ml of CO_2-free water, draw off the aqueous layer and add to it 1 drop of methyl red. If a red color is produced, it is changed to yellow by 0.1 ml of 0.02 N NaOH. If a yellow color is produced, it is changed to red by 0.1 ml of 0.02 N HCl.

Substances darkened by sulfuric acid: Shake 25 ml with 15 ml of sulfuric acid for 15 to 20 seconds. On separation there is no darkening in either layer.

Sulfur compounds: To 10 ml of the sample add 1 ml of absolute alcohol and 3 ml of potassium plumbite solution. Gently boil the mixture under a reflux condenser for 15 minutes, agitating well the contents of the flask several times during the heating, and then set aside for 5 minutes. The aqueous layer is colorless.

Note: The sulfur may be quantitatively determined by the method for Sulfur in Volatile Hydrocarbon, using 5 ml of the sample, page 579.

Thiophene: Dissolve about 3 mg of isatin in 10 ml of sulfuric acid, add to the solution 20 ml of the benzene, shake well and allow to stand for 1 hour. The acid layer is not blue or green.

Water: Introduce 10 ml of the benzene into a dry test tube, stopper immediately and cool in crushed ice for 5 minutes. No cloudiness appears. Care must be exercised to avoid absorption to moisture from the air.

Note: The actual amount of water in benzene may be determined by the iodine (Fischer) method.

BENZIDINE

Suitable for Detecting Blood

H_2N—⟨benzene ring⟩—⟨benzene ring⟩—NH_2; mol. wt. 184.23.

White or slightly reddish, crystalline powder. It discolors on exposure to air and light. Almost insoluble in cold water, soluble in 100 parts of boiling water; soluble in ethanol, ether or acetic acid. *Keep protected from light.*

Standards

Melting range anhydrous,.......127°–129°	Sulfate (SO_4)...........max about 0.03%
Sensitiveness for detecting	Substances affected by H_2O_2...to pass test
blood..................min 1:500,000	Ignition residue.............max 0.050%
Solubility to glacial acetic acid.to pass test	

Sensitiveness for detecting blood: Measure exactly 4.3 ml of glacial acetic acid, heat it to 50° in a water bath, and add 0.50 g of the benzidine. Maintain at 50° for 10 minutes, then add 19 ml of H_2O. Introduce 1.4 ml of this solution into a perfectly clean, dry test tube, add 0.2 ml of glacial acetic acid, then 1 ml of blood solution (see note) and finally 0.4 ml of 3% hydrogen peroxide (made by diluting 1 volume of 30% hydrogen peroxide with 9 volumes of water). A bluish or greenish color develops within 5 minutes. A blank test, made in the same manner but omitting the blood solution, shows no distinct bluish or greenish color within 5 minutes.

Note: The blood solution is made by diluting 0.10 ml of blood to 100 ml with water and diluting 1.0 ml of this solution with water to 500 ml. It must be freshly prepared before use.

Solubility in glacial acetic acid; Sulfate: Dissolve 0.2 g in 5 ml of glacial acetic acid. The solution is clear and not more than faintly colored.

Substances affected by H_2O_2: To the solution from the preceding test add 5 ml of a mixture of 1 volume of 30% hydrogen peroxide and 9 volumes of water. No darkening is produced.

Ignition residue: Char 2.0 g, cool, add 0.5 ml of H_2SO_4, evaporate the acid and ignite to constant weight. The residue does not exceed 1.0 mg.

BENZIDINE DIHYDROCHLORIDE

$(C_6H_4)_2(NH_2)_2 \cdot 2HCl$; mol. wt. 257.16; HCl—28.36%; Benzidine—71.64%.

White or nearly white crystalline powder; soluble in about 50 parts of water; in about 300 parts 95% ethanol.

It is used for detection of blood, the estimation of hemoglobin, and the determination of sulfate, acetaldehyde and furfural.

Standards

Sensitiveness for detecting
blood.................min 1:500,000
Solubility and sulfate.........to pass test

Substances affected by H_2O_2...to pass test
Ignition residue.............max 0.050%

Sensitiveness for detecting blood: Prepare a 1% aqueous solution of the sample without the application of heat. Dilute 0.1 ml of blood with H_2O to 100 ml, then dilute 1.0 ml of this with H_2O to 500 ml. This solution must be freshly prepared before use.

Place 1 ml of the final blood dilution in a test tube and add, in the order named, 1 ml of the benzidine dihydrochloride solution, 1 ml of 3% hydrogen peroxide solution and 1 ml of 1% sodium acetate solution. A distinct blue color develops within about 1 minute.

Solubility and Sulfate: A solution of 1 g in 50 ml of warm H_2O is clear and complete.

Substances affected by H_2O_2: To the solution from the preceding test add 5 ml of a mixture of 1 volume of 30% hydrogen peroxide and 9 volumes of water. No darkening is produced.

Ignition residue: Char 2.0 g, cool, add 0.5 ml of H_2SO_4, evaporate the acid and ignite to constant weight. The residue does not exceed 1.0 mg.

BENZOIC ACID, PRIMARY STANDARD

$C_6H_5 \cdot COOH$; mol. wt. 122.12; C—68.84%; H—4.95%.

Colorless, glistening needles or scales. Soluble in 300 parts of water, more soluble in hot water; soluble in alcohol, ether, chloroform, benzene. Volatile with steam.

Standards

Melting range.................122°–123°
Ignition residue.............max 0.010%
Ammonium hydroxide—
  insoluble..................to pass test
Chlorine compounds (as Cl)...max 0.002%

Sulfur compounds (as S)......max 0.002%
Heavy metals..............max 0.0005%
Oxygen absorption (as O)......max 0.02%
Substances darkened by
  H_2SO_4....................to pass test

Ignition residue: Heat 10 g slowly until nearly all is volatilized, cool, add 0.5 ml of H_2SO_4 and ignite. Not more than 1.0 mg of residue remains.

Ammonium hydroxide—insoluble: Five grams dissolve completely in a mixture of 40 ml warm water and 10 ml of ammonium hydroxide (retain solution).

Chlorine compounds: Mix 1 g with 0.5 g of sodium carbonate and add in small portions 20 ml of H_2O. Evaporate, then ignite until thoroughly charred. Cool, triturate the charred mass with 15 ml of H_2O and 2 ml of HNO_3, filter, wash the char with water to 25 ml and add to the filtrate 1 ml $AgNO_3$. If a turbidity is produced, it is not greater than that in a blank to which 0.02 mg of Cl has been added.

Sulfur compounds: Mix 2.0 g with 1 g of Na_2CO_3 in a crucible or dish, and add, in small portions, 10 ml of water. Evaporate to dryness and ignite, protected from access of sulfur, preferably in an electric muffle furnace, until nearly white. Add to the cooled ignited mass 20 ml of hot water, and allow the mass to disintegrate. Now add 3 ml of 30% H_2O_2 and boil for a few minutes, then add 4 ml of HCl and evaporate to dryness on the steam bath. Prepare a control by evaporating 1 g of the Na_2CO_3, 3 ml of the H_2O_2 and 0.12 mg of SO_4 with 4 ml of HCl to dryness on the steam bath and treat each residue as follows: Dissolve the residue in 10 ml of hot water, filter and wash with water to 15 ml. Add to filtrate 0.5 ml of 0.1 N HCl and 2 ml of $BaCl_2$. If a turbidity is produced in the test with the sample it is not greater than that of the control.

Heavy metals: To 30 ml of the solution from the test for *Ammonium hydroxide —insoluble* add 10 ml H_2S. No darkening is produced.

Oxygen absorption: Mix 100 ml of H_2O with 1.5 ml of H_2SO_4, heat to boiling and add 0.1 N potassium permanganate until the pink color persists for 30 seconds. Dissolve in the hot solution 1.0 g of the sample and titrate with 0.1 N potassium permanganate until a pink color persists for 15 seconds. Not more than 0.25 ml of the potassium permanganate is required.

Substances darkened by sulfuric acid: Heat 0.1 g with 2 ml H_2SO_4 at 50° for 5 minutes. No darkening is produced.

BENZOIC ACID

This grade of benzoic acid is for general laboratory use as, for instance, when a reasonably pure, solid organic compound high in carbon is required. It conforms to the description given under Benzoic Acid, Primary Standard.

Standards

Melting range . . . . 121°–123°	Chlorine compounds (as Cl) . . . max 0.005%
Assay 99.5%–100.2%	Sulfur compounds (as S) . . . . . . max 0.002%
Ignition residue . . . . max 0.010%	Heavy metals . . . . max 0.0005%
Ammonium hydroxide—	Substances darkened by
insoluble . . . . to pass test	H_2SO_4 . . . . to pass test

Assay: Weigh accurately about 0.4 g of sample, previously dried for 2 hours over H_2SO_4, and dissolve it in 5 ml of ethanol. Add 30 ml of H_2O and 3 drops of phenolphthalein, and titrate with 0.1 N NaOH to a pink color. Correct for a blank. One ml of 0.1 N NaOH = 0.01221 g of C_6H_5COOH, log 08672.

Ignition residue: Heat 10 g slowly until nearly all is volatilized, cool, add 0.4 ml of H_2SO_4 and ignite. Not more than 1.0 mg of residue remains.

Ammonium hydroxide—insoluble: Three grams dissolve completely in a mixture of 20 ml warm H_2O and 5 ml of ammonium hydroxide (retain solution).

Chlorine compounds: Mix 0.6 g with 0.3 g of sodium carbonate and add, in small portions, 10 ml of H_2O. Evaporate, then ignite until thoroughly charred. Cool, triturate the char with 15 ml of H_2O and 2 ml of HNO_3, filter, and wash with water to 30 ml. To 20 ml of the filtrate add 1 ml of silver nitrate. Any turbidity produced is not greater than that in a blank made with 0.02 mg of Cl, 0.15 g of Na_2CO_3 and 1 ml of HNO_3.

Sulfur compounds: Test as Benzoic Acid, Primary Standard. The result should be as there stated.

Heavy Metals: To the solution from the test for *Ammonium hydroxide—insoluble* add 10 ml of H_2S. No darkening is produced.

Substances darkened by sulfuric acid: Heat 0.1 g with 2 ml of sulfuric acid for 5 minutes at 50°. No darkening is produced.

α-BENZOINOXIME

"Cupron"

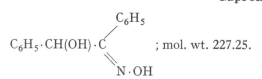

$C_6H_5 \cdot CH(OH) \cdot C$; mol. wt. 227.25.

White crystalline powder. Darkens in light. Practically insoluble in water; soluble in about 45 parts of alcohol, 100 of ether, 200 of chloroform. Soluble in aqueous solutions of alkali hydroxides. Used in alcoholic solutions as a specific reagent for copper,[1,2] also for molybdenum in sulfuric acid solutions.[3,4] *Keep protected from light.*

Standards

Melting range...............153°–155°	Solubility...................to pass test
Sensitiveness................to pass test	Ignition residue..............max 0.10%

Sensitiveness: (*a*) Dissolve 50 mg of the reagent in 1 ml of alcohol by gently warming. (*b*) Dissolve 10 mg of cupric sulfate and 3 ml of acetic acid and water to make 250 ml (1 ml = 10 micrograms Cu).

Place 1 drop (0.05 ml) of solution (*b*) on a filter paper, add 1 drop of solution (*a*), then hold over ammonia. A distinct yellowish-green color is produced.

Solubility: To 0.1 g, add 10 ml of H_2O and 1 ml of ammonium hydroxide. A complete or practically complete solution results. A solution of 0.1 g in 20 ml of alcohol is clear and colorless.

Ignition residue: Char 1.0 g, cool, add 0.5 ml of H_2SO_4, evaporate the acid and ignite to constant weight. The residue does not exceed 1.0 mg.

[1] Feigl, I. F., *Ber.* **56**, 2083 (1923).
[2] Azzalin, E., *Ann. chim. appl.* **15**, 373 (1925).
[3] Mitchell and Ward, *Modern Methods in Quantitative Chemical Analysis*, Longmans, Green & Co., New York, 1st ed., 66 (1932).
[4] Knowles, H. B., *Bur. Standards J. Research*, **9**, 1 (1932).

BENZOYL CHLORIDE

$C_6H_5 \cdot COCl$; mol. wt. 140.57.

Colorless, clear, fuming liquid; pungent odor. It is decomposed by water or alcohol; soluble in benzene or ether. Sp. gr. about 1.20; boils at 197°; congeals at about −5°. *Keep in glass-stoppered bottles.*

Standards

Boiling range.................195°–198°	Phosphorus compounds (as P).max 0.002%
Assay...............min 98% C_6H_5COCl	Heavy metals (as Pb)........max 0.001%
Evaporation residue.........max 0.050%	Iron (Fe)...................max 0.001%

Boiling range: Distill 50 ml.   Not less than 48 ml distills between 195° and 198°, making correction for barometric pressure, page 581.

Assay: (*a*) Weigh accurately about 2 ml in a glass-stoppered flask, add 50 ml of 1 N NaOH, stopper and allow to stand with frequent agitation until dissolved. Titrate the excess of NaOH with 1 N H_2SO_4, using phenolphthalein indicator. One ml of 1 N NaOH = 0.07028 g $C_6H_5 \cdot COCl$, log 84665.

(*b*) Dilute the titrated solution from the preceding test to exactly 250 ml and mix.   Dilute 25 ml of this solution to about 50 ml and determine the chloride (Cl) by Method 1, page 565.   One ml of 0.1 N $AgNO_3$ = 0.01406 g C_6H_5COCl, log 14798. Correct for any chloride (Cl) in the proportionate volume of the 1 N NaOH.

Neither (*a*) nor (*b*) shows less than 98%, and should not differ by more than 0.5%.

Evaporation residue: Evaporate 4 ml (5 g) in porcelain and dry at 200° for 2 hours.   The residue does not exceed 2.5 mg (retain residue).

Phosphorus compounds: Boil 1.0 ml with 7 ml of H_2O and 3 ml of HNO_3 for 2 minutes, cool, dilute with water to 20 ml and filter.   To 10 ml of the filtrate add 3 ml of 25% sulfuric acid and evaporate in a platinum dish to incipient evolution of sulfuric fumes.   Cool, dilute to 20 ml and add 1 ml each of phosphate reagents **A** and **B** and heat at 60° for 10 minutes.   Any blue color produced is not darker than that of a control made with 0.03 mg of PO_4 and 2 ml of 25% H_2SO_4, and treated with the same quantities of phosphate reagents and in the same volume as the sample.

Solution R: To the evaporation residue add 2 ml of HCl and 2 ml of water and slowly evaporate to dryness on a steam bath.   Take up the residue with 1 ml of 1 N HCl and 10 ml of hot water and dilute with water to 50 ml.

Heavy Metals: Dilute 20 ml of *Solution R* to 40 ml, and add 10 ml of H_2S.   Any resulting brown color is not darker than that of a control made with 0.02 mg of Pb, 0.3 ml of 1 N HCl, and 10 ml of H_2S in the same volume as with the sample.

Iron: To 10 ml of *Solution R* add 2 ml of HCl and dilute to 50 ml.   Add about 30 mg of ammonium persulfate and 3 ml of ammonium thiocyanate, and mix. Any resulting red color is not darker than that produced in a blank to which 0.01 mg of Fe has been added.

BENZYL ALCOHOL

$C_6H_5 \cdot CH_2OH$; mol. wt. 108.13.

Colorless, clear liquid; faint, aromatic odor.   Soluble in 25 parts of water; miscible with alcohol, ether or chloroform.   Sp. gr. 1.04; boils at 205°.

Standards

Boiling range.................202°–206°	Solubility in H_2O.............to pass test
Refractive index...........1.5385–1.5405	Chlorine (Cl)................to pass test
Evaporation residue.........max 0.050%	(limit about 0.01%)
Acid (as benzoic)............max 0.03%	Water......................to pass test

Boiling range: Distill 50 ml. After 10 drops has distilled not less than 48 ml distills between 202° and 206°, correction being made for barometric pressure, page 581.

Refractive index: The refractive index of benzyl alcohol at 20° is 1.5385 to 1.5405.

Evaporation residue: Evaporate 5 ml on the steam bath and dry at 200° for 2 hours. Not more than 2.5 mg of residue remains.

Acid: To 20 ml of alcohol add 2 drops of phenolphthalein and sufficient 0.02 N NaOH to produce a pink color which persists after shaking. Disregard the volume of the alkali consumed. Then add 5 ml of the sample and titrate with 0.02 N NaOH to the reproduction of the pink color. Not more than 0.6 ml of the NaOH is required.

Solubility in H_2O: Shake 2.0 ml with 60 ml of H_2O. A clear solution results.

Chlorine: Moisten a clean, freshly ignited, copper spiral with the sample and heat it in a nonluminous flame. The flame is not colored green.

Water: Water in benzyl alcohol may be determined by the iodine (Fischer) method.

BENZYL CHLORIDE

$C_6H_5 \cdot CH_2Cl$; mol. wt. 126.58.

Colorless, clear refractive liquid; irritating odor. Insoluble in water; miscible with alcohol, chloroform, ether. Sp. gr. about 1.10; boils at 179°. Volatile with steam.

Standards

Boiling range.................178°–181°   Acid (as HCl)..............max 0.030%
Evaporation residue.........max 0.050%

Boiling range: Distill 50 ml. After 10 drops has distilled, not less than 48 ml distills between 178° and 181°, correction being made for barometric pressure, page 581.

Evaporation residue: Evaporate 4.5 ml on the steam bath, then dry at 180° for 2 hours. The residue does not exceed 2.5 mg.

Acid: Shake 5 ml for one-half minute with 20 ml of water at 25°, then immediately draw off the benzyl chloride (lower layer). To the aqueous layer add a drop of phenolphthalein and titrate with 0.1 N NaOH to a pink color. Not more than 0.5 ml of the NaOH is required.

BISMUTH CHLORIDE

Bismuth Trichloride

$BiCl_3$; mol. wt. 315.37; Bi—66.27%; Cl—33.73%

White, or yellowish-white, hygroscopic crystals or crystalline masses. Melts at 227°, volatilizes at about 430°. Insoluble in water, being hydrolyzed by it into bismuth oxychloride and free HCl; soluble in nitric or hydrochloric acid, in acetone, and in absolute alcohol. *Keep in well-closed containers.*

Standards

Hydrochloric acid—insoluble and Silver...............max 0.010%	Alkalies, Earths, etc...........max 0.10%	
Nitrate (NO_3)...............max 0.010%	Copper (Cu)................max 0.003%	
Sulfate (SO_4)...............max 0.010%	Iron (Fe)...................max 0.003%	
	Lead (Pb).................max 0.010%	

Hydrochloric acid—insoluble and Silver: Heat 10 g with 15 ml of HCl and 35 ml of H_2O on the steam bath for 30 minutes. If an insoluble residue remains, filter on asbestos, wash it with 10% HCl and dry at 105°. Not more than 1.0 mg of insoluble residue is obtained.

Nitrate: To 200 mg of sample add 3 ml of water and 2 ml of brucine sulfate solution (S). For a control add 2.0 ml of standard nitrate solution (= 0.02 mg NO_3) to 2 ml of brucine sulfate solution and dilute to 5.0 ml (C). Slowly add to each with stirring 25 ml of H_2SO_4. Allow to stand until any transient red color changes to yellow (about 1 minute), then immediately cool in ice water to room temperature. The yellow color in S is not darker than in C.

The color intensities of S and C are preferably measured by determining their absorbencies at 410 mμ, using as a blank 2 ml of brucine sulfate solution + 3 ml of water and mixed with 25 ml of H_2SO_4 (see Nitrate—Estimation of Small Amounts, page 575).

Sulfate: Test as described for Bismuth Nitrate. The turbidity produced is not greater than that in the control made with 0.2 mg of SO_4.

Alkalies, Earths, etc.: Dissolve 2 g in 3 ml of warm HCl and dilute with water to 100 ml. Precipitate the bismuth completely with H_2S and filter. To 50 ml of the filtrate add 5 drops of H_2SO_4, evaporate and ignite. The residue does not exceed 1.0 mg (retain).

Copper: Test as described for Bismuth Nitrate, dissolving the sample in 3 ml of HCl instead of HNO_3. Any red color produced is not darker than that produced by 0.03 mg of Cu in the control.

Iron: To the residue from *Alkalies, Earths, etc.* add 2 ml of HCl and 2 ml of H_2O, and slowly evaporate to dryness on the steam bath. Take up in a few drops of HCl and sufficient H_2O to make 50 ml. To 15 ml of the dilution add 2 ml of HCl and dilute to 50 ml. Add about 30 mg of ammonium persulfate and 3 ml of ammonium thiocyanate, and mix. Any resulting red color is not darker than that of a blank to which 0.01 mg of Fe has been added.

Lead: To 0.6 g of sample add 10 ml of water and with stirring just sufficient (about 1 ml) HNO_3 to dissolve. Slowly and while stirring add the solution to 15 ml of 10% NaOH. Heat on the steam bath for 10 minutes, cool, dilute to 25 ml and filter. To 20 ml of the filtrate add 1 drop of methyl red and diluted (1 + 1) HNO_3 to distinct acid (red) reaction, then make just alkaline (yellow) with diluted ammonia. For a control add 0.03 mg of Pb to 10 ml of 10% NaOH, make slightly acid to methyl red with the same HNO_3 as used for the sample solution and then just alkaline with diluted ammonia. Transfer the solution from the sample and from the control to similar separatory funnels, dilute to approximately the same volume and treat each as described in the test for lead in Bismuth Nitrate beginning with "Add 1 ml of potassium cyanide solution. . . ." Any red or bluish-red color of the extract from the sample is not darker than that of the extract from the control.

BISMUTH NITRATE

Bismuth Trinitrate

$Bi(NO_3)_3 \cdot 5H_2O$; mol. wt. 483.10; anhydrous—81.43%; H_2O—18.57%; Bi—43.08%; NO_3—38.35%.

Colorless crystals, with an odor of nitric acid. Decomposed by water with formation of an insoluble basic salt; soluble in dilute nitric acid. *Keep in glass-stoppered bottles.*

Standards

Nitric acid—insoluble........max 0.005%	Copper (Cu)................max 0.003%
Chloride (Cl)...............max 0.002%	Iron (Fe)..................max 0.003%
Sulfate (SO₄)...............max 0.005%	Lead (Pb)..................max 0.002%
Alkalies, Earths, etc.........max 0.10%	Silver........to pass test (about 0.002%)
Arsenic....................max 5 ppm	

Nitric acid—insoluble: Dissolve 20 g in a mixture of 20 ml of HNO_3 and 80 ml of water. Filter any undissolved residue on asbestos or sintered glass filtering crucible, wash it with 10% HNO_3 and dry at 105°. Not more than 0.5 mg of insoluble residue is found.

Chloride: Dissolve 1 g in a warm mixture of 18 ml of H_2O and 2 ml of HNO_3, cool and add 1 ml $AgNO_3$. Any resulting turbidity is not greater than that in a blank to which 0.02 mg of Cl has been added.

Sulfate: Dissolve 3 g in 5 ml of warm HCl, dilute with water to 100 ml and nearly neutralize with 10% ammonia. Filter and wash with hot water to 150 ml. Evaporate 100 ml of the filtrate to 15 ml, add 0.5 g of sodium carbonate, evaporate to dryness and ignite gently. Treat the residue with 15 ml of hot water, neutralize with dilute HCl, filter and wash with water to 20 ml. Add to the filtrate 1 ml of 1 N HCl and 2 ml of barium chloride. Any turbidity produced in 15 minutes is not greater than that in a control made as follows: Evaporate 0.1 mg of SO_4, 0.5 g sodium carbonate, and 2 ml of HCl to dryness on the steam bath. Dissolve the residue in 20 ml of H_2O and add 1 ml of 1 N HCl and 2 ml of barium chloride.

Alkalies, Earths, etc.: Dissolve 2 g in 3 ml of warm HNO_3 and dilute with water to 100 ml. Precipitate the bismuth completely with H_2S and filter. To 50 ml of the filtrate add 5 drops of H_2SO_4, evaporate and ignite. The weight of the residue does not exceed 1.0 mg (retain).

Arsenic: To 0.6 g add 5 ml of H_2O and 5 ml of H_2SO_4 and evaporate to strong sulfuric fumes. Cautiously add to the cooled residue 5 ml of H_2O and 1 ml of H_2SO_4, and re-evaporate to strong sulfuric fumes. Test the residue for arsenic by the method on page 563. The stain produced is not greater than that from 0.003 mg of As.

Copper: Dissolve 2 g in a mixture of 3 ml of HNO_3 and 15 ml of water. Add the solution slowly and with stirring to 8 ml of ammonium hydroxide, previously diluted with 10 ml of water, then dilute with water to 40 ml and filter. Slightly acidify 20 ml of the filtrate with acetic acid and add 5 drops of fresh potassium ferrocyanide solution. Any red color produced is not darker than that of a control made with 0.03 mg of Cu, 1.5 ml of HNO_3, 4 ml of ammonium hydroxide, sufficient acetic acid to acidify, and in the same final volume of solution as with the sample.

Iron: To the residue from *Alkalies, Earths, etc.*, add 2 ml of HCl and 2 ml of H_2O, and slowly evaporate to dryness on the steam bath. Take up in 4 ml of HCl and H_2O to make 50 ml. Dilute 25 ml to 50 ml, add about 30 mg of ammonium persulfate and 3 ml of ammonium thiocyanate, and mix. Any resulting red color is not darker than that of a blank to which 0.015 mg of Fe has been added.

Lead: To 1.0 g of sample add 20 ml of water and just sufficient HNO_3 to dissolve. Add 1–2 drops of methyl red, then add slowly and with stirring 10% NH_3 until the supernatant liquid is just yellow (*p*H 6), although the precipitate may be pink, and on the addition of 2 drops of phenol red the supernatant liquid must remain yellow— not red. Now heat on the steam bath for a few minutes, cool, filter into a separatory funnel, wash the precipitate with 10–20 ml of water and discard it. For a control place in a similar separatory funnel 0.02 mg of Pb (2.0 ml standard lead solution), add approximately the same volume of HNO_3 as used to dissolve the sample, 30 ml of water and sufficient of the same 10% NH_3 to make the liquid just yellow to methyl red. Dilute to about the same volume as in the funnel containing the solution of the sample, and treat each solution as follows: Add 1 ml of potassium cyanide solution, 3 ml of ammonium citrate solution and 1 ml of 10% hydroxylamine hydrochloride solution, and make alkaline (red) to phenol red with dilute $(1+10)$ ammonium hydroxide. Extract the liquids with three or more 5-ml portions of dithizone-chloroform extraction solution until the last extract remains pure green. Wash each combined extract with 50 ml of water and drain off the water into another funnel. Extract the water with 5 ml of chloroform and add the latter to the main extracts. Shake the dithizone extract with 20 ml of 1% HNO_3 to extract the metals (Bi and Pb), allow to separate and discard the dithizone layer. Add to the aqueous layers dilute (2.5% NH_3) ammonia until *p*H 2 is reached (orange color of metacresol purple) and extract the bismuth with 5-ml portions of the dithizone extraction solution referred to above until the color of the extract remains pure green. Drain off the dithizone solutions and discard them. Shake the aqueous layers with 5 ml of chloroform, allow to separate well and discard the chloroform layer. Now add to the aqueous layers in the funnels 5 ml of dithizone-chloroform standard solution, 3 ml of ammonia-cyanide solution, shake vigorously for 1 minute, allow to separate and completely drain off the dithizone extract. Repeat the extraction of the aqueous layers with 3-ml portions of the dithizone standard solution until the last extract remains unchanged in color. Combine, separately, the extracts from sample and control, and dilute to the smallest equal volume with chloroform. Any red or bluish-red color of the extract from the sample is not darker than that of the extract from the control.

Silver: To a solution of 1 g in 5 ml of HNO_3 add 15 ml of water and 1 drop of HCl. No opalescence is produced.

BISMUTH SUBCARBONATE

Basic Bismuth Carbonate; Bismuth Oxycarbonate

Approximately 2 $(BiO)_2CO_3 \cdot H_2O$; mol. wt. 1038; Bi—80.54%; Bi_2O_3—89.78%.

White or faintly yellowish-white powder. Insoluble in water or alcohol; soluble in nitric or hydrochloric acids.

Standards

Nitric acid—insoluble........max 0.005%	Copper (Cu)................max 0.005%
Chloride (Cl)...............max 0.010%	Iron (Fe)..................max 0.005%
Nitrate (NO_3)................max 0.1%	Lead (Pb)..................max 0.003%
Sulfate (SO_4)................max 0.01%	Silver (Ag)....to pass test (about 0.002%)
Alkalies, Earths, etc..........max 0.30%	*Assay*
Arsenic (As)................max 5 ppm	

Nitric acid—insoluble: Dissolve 10 g in a mixture of 25 ml of HNO_3 and 25 ml of water. Filter any undissolved residue on asbestos or tared glass crucible, wash it with 10% HNO_3, and dry at 105°. Not more than 0.5 mg of insoluble residue is found.

Chloride: Dissolve 0.5 g in 3 ml of HNO_3 and 25 ml of H_2O and add 1 ml of $AgNO_3$. Any turbidity produced is not greater than that in a blank to which 0.05 mg of Cl has been added.

Nitrate: To 50.0 mg add 2 ml of brucine sulfate solution and dilute to 10 ml. For a control add 5.0 ml of standard nitrate solution (= 0.05 mg NO_3) to 2 ml of brucine sulfate solution and dilute to 10 ml. Prepare a blank by diluting 2 ml of brucine solution to 10 ml; then proceed as described in *Procedure* under Nitrate—Estimation of Small Amounts, page 575.

Alkalies, Earths, etc.: Dissolve 2 g by heating with a mixture of 4 ml of HNO_3 and 5 ml of water. Dilute with water to 100 ml, precipitate the bismuth completely with H_2S and filter. To 50 ml of the filtrate add 5 drops of H_2SO_4, evaporate and ignite. Not more than 3.0 mg of residue remains (retain).

Arsenic: Dissolve 0.6 g of the sample by heating with a mixture of 3 ml of sulfuric acid and 7 ml of water, then test the resulting solution for arsenic by the method on page 563. The stain obtained is not greater than that obtained from 0.003 mg of As.

Copper: Dissolve 2 g by heating with 3 ml of HNO_3 and 5 ml of water, then dilute with 10 ml of water and proceed as for Bismuth Nitrate beginning with "Add the solution. . . ." Any red color produced is not darker than that of the control made with 0.05 mg of Cu.

Iron: To the residue from *Alkalies, Earths, etc.*, add 2 ml HCl and 2 ml of H_2O, and slowly evaporate to dryness on the steam bath. Take up the residue with a few drops of HCl and water to make 50 ml. To 10 ml of the dilution add 2 ml of HCl, and dilute to 50 ml. Add about 30 mg of ammonium persulfate and 3 ml of ammonium thiocyanate, and mix. Any resulting red color is not darker than that of a blank to which 0.01 mg of Fe has been added.

Lead: Heat 0.7 g of sample with 20 ml of water and add just sufficient HNO_3 to dissolve.   Add 1–2 drops of methyl red, then add slowly and with stirring 10% NH_3 until the supernatant liquid is just yellow (pH 6) (although the precipitate may be pink) and on the addition of 2 drops of phenol red the supernatant liquid must remain yellow; then proceed as directed in the test for Lead in Bismuth Nitrate beginning with "Now heat on the steam bath. . . ." The results should be as there stated.

Silver: Dissolve 1 g by heating with a mixture of 5 ml HNO_3 and 15 ml H_2O, then add 1 drop HCl.   No opalescence is produced.

Assay: Bismuth subcarbonate may be assayed for its bismuth content by either one of the following methods.   (*a*) A weighed sample of 0.5 g to 1 g is ignited, preferably in a muffle furnace, at 550°–650°.   From the weight of the residue is deducted a proportionate quantity of residue found in the test for *Alkalies, Earths, etc.* described before.   The difference represents Bi_2O_3.   The weight of the Bi_2O_3 multiplied by 0.897 represents Bi.

(*b*) Weigh accurately about 1 g and dissolve it in a mixture of 3 ml of HNO_3 and 15 ml of H_2O.   Dilute to 400 ml with water and add, with stirring, 1 ml of HCl; then add 10% ammonia to neutralize most of the free acid and let stand for several hours or overnight.   Filter through a tared Gooch, previously dried at 105°, wash with H_2O and dry at 105° to constant weight.   The weight of the bismuth oxychloride so obtained, multiplied by 0.8024 = Bi, log 90439.

BORIC ACID

H_3BO_3; mol. wt. 61.84; B—17.50%; B_2O_3—56.29%.

Colorless, transparent crystals or a white, smooth powder.   Soluble in 20 parts of water or alcohol; slowly but freely soluble in glycerin.   It volatilizes with water vapors.

Standards

Solubility in alcohol . . . . to pass test	Sulfate (SO_4) . . . . max 0.010%
Nonvolatile with methanol	Arsenic (As) . . . . max 1 ppm
and HCl . . . . max 0.05%	Calcium (Ca) . . . . max 0.003%
Chloride (Cl) . . . . max 0.001%	Heavy metals (as Pb) . . . . max 0.001%
Phosphate (PO_4) . . . . max 0.001%	Iron (Fe) . . . . max 0.001%

Solubility in alcohol: Reflux 2 g with 25 ml of alcohol.   The acid dissolves completely and no undissolved residues remain while the solution is hot.

Nonvolatile with methanol: Add 25 ml of methanol and 5 drops of HCl to 2 g of the acid, and evaporate to dryness in a platinum dish on the steam bath. Re-evaporate with 15 ml of methanol and 3 drops of HCl, then add 3 drops of H_2SO_4 and ignite.   Not more than 1.0 mg of residue remains.

Chloride: Dissolve 1 g in 15 ml of warm H_2O, add 1 ml of HNO_3 and 1 ml of silver nitrate.   Any resulting turbidity is not greater than in a blank to which 0.01 mg of Cl has been added.

Solution S: Place in a beaker 10 g of the boric acid and 20 mg of sodium carbonate.   Add 100 ml of methanol and 5 ml of HCl, cover the beaker and digest on steam bath until solution is effected. Now remove the cover and evaporate to dryness. Again add 100 ml of methanol and 5 ml of HCl and re-evaporate to dryness on the steam bath. Add 5 drops of HCl and 10 ml of water, digest on the steam bath for 10 minutes, filter if necessary, and dilute to 100 ml.

Phosphate: To 10 ml of *Solution S* add 2 ml of 25% H_2SO_4, dilute to 20 ml, add 1 ml each of phosphate reagents **A** and **B** and heat at 60° for 10 minutes. Any blue color produced is not darker than that of a control made with 0.01 mg of PO_4 and the same volumes of 25% H_2SO_4 and phosphate reagents **A** and **B** and in the same final volume.

Sulfate: To 10 ml of *Solution S* add 1 ml of 0.1 N HCl and 2 ml of $BaCl_2$. If a turbidity is produced in 10 minutes, it is not greater than that in a control made with 0.1 mg of SO_4.

Arsenic: Test 2 g by the Arsenic Test (page 563). The stain is not greater than that from 0.002 mg of As.

Calcium: Evaporate 20 ml of *Solution S* to 10 ml. Cool, add 0.2 ml of acetic acid and 2 ml of ammonium oxalate and allow to stand for 20 minutes. Any ensuing turbidity is not greater than that in a control made with 0.06 mg of calcium (Ca).

Heavy metals: Dilute 20 ml of *Solution S* to 40 ml and add 10 ml of H_2S. Any darkening produced is not greater than that in a control made with 0.02 mg of Pb 0.5 ml of 0.1 N HCl and in the same final volume.

Iron: To 10 ml of *Solution S* add 2 ml of HCl and dilute to 50 ml. Add about 30 mg of ammonium persulfate and 3 ml of ammonium thiocyanate. Any red color should not be darker than that of a control made with 0.01 mg of Fe, the same quantities of the reagents, and in the same final volume.

BORIC ANHYDRIDE

Boron Trioxide

B_2O_3; mol. wt. 69.64; B—31.07%.

Colorless, brittle, vitreous pieces. Slowly soluble in water forming boric acid; soluble in alcohol. Contains, theoretically, 31.07% boron.

Standards

Assay...................min 98% B_2O_3	Sulfate (SO_4).................max 0.02%
Silica, Alkalies, etc............max 0.10%	Heavy metals (as Pb)........max 0.003%

Assay: Weigh accurately 1.0 g and dissolve it by gently warming with a mixture of 30 ml of H_2O and 60 ml of glycerol, previously neutralized to phenolphthalein. Cool, and titrate with 1 N NaOH until the pink color produced is not appreciably diminished on the further addition of 10 ml of the neutralized glycerin. One ml of 1 N NaOH = 0.03482 g B_2O_3, log 54183.

Silica and Alkalies: Powder 3 g of the sample in an agate mortar, transfer 2 g to a weighed platinum dish, add 50 ml methanol and 1 ml of HCl, and evaporate to dryness on the steam bath. Re-evaporate the residue with 25 ml of methanol and 1 ml of HCl, repeating if necessary. Finally add a few drops of H_2SO_4 and ignite. The residue does not exceed 2.0 mg.

Sulfate: Boil 2 g with 50 ml of H_2O until dissolved, dilute to 50 ml, cool on ice, and filter. To 25 ml of the filtrate add 1 ml of 1 N HCl and 2 ml of $BaCl_2$. Any turbidity produced is not more than that in a blank to which 0.2 mg of SO_4 has been added.

Heavy metals: To the residue obtained in the test for *Silica, Alkalies, etc.* add 2 ml of HCl and 2 ml of water, and slowly evaporate to dryness on the steam bath. Moisten the residue with 3 drops of HCl, then add 10 ml of hot water, digest for 10 minutes, filter and dilute to 20 ml. Dilute 10 ml of this solution to 40 ml and add 10 ml of H_2S. Any dark color produced is not darker than that of a control made with 0.03 mg of Pb.

BROMINE

Br; at. wt. 79.92.

Dark, reddish-brown, fuming liquid; highly irritating odor. Solidifies at about $-7°$. Boils at $63°$. Sp. gr. 3.14 at $25°$. Soluble in about 30 parts of water; freely soluble in carbon disulfide, chloroform, carbon tetrachloride, also in concentrated hydrochloric acid. *Keep in well-closed, glass-stoppered bottles or in sealed ampuls, in a cool place.*

Standards

Evaporation residue.........max 0.015%	Organic bromine compounds...to pass test	
Chlorine (Cl)..................max 0.3%	Sulfur compounds (as S)......max 0.002%	
Iodine (I)....................max 0.05%	Heavy metals (as Pb).......max 0.0002%	

Evaporation residue: Volatilize 3 ml on the steam bath *under hood*, and dry at $105°$ for 1 hour. The residue does not exceed 1.5 mg (retain).

Chlorine: Weigh a 100-ml glass-stoppered flask with 15 ml of $1+2$ nitric acid, quickly add about 1 ml of the bromine, stopper immediately, and reweigh. Add 5 ml of 30% H_2O_2, and digest on the steam bath until the solution is colorless. Add 1 ml of the H_2O_2, wash down the sides of the flask with a little water, and digest for 20 minutes longer. Cool, and dilute to such a volume as corresponds to 1.00 g of the bromine in 100 ml of the solution. Dilute 5 ml of the solution to 100 ml and to 20 ml of this dilution add 1 ml of HNO_3 and 1 ml of $AgNO_3$. Any turbidity produced is not greater than that in a control made with 0.03 mg of Cl, 1.5 ml HNO_3 and 0.5 ml of the H_2O_2 in the same volume as with the sample.

Iodine: Shake 1 ml with 50 ml of H_2O and 3 g of granulated zinc until all the bromine is decolorized. Filter, add to the filtrate 1 ml of ferric chloride and 5 ml of chloroform, and shake. No pink or violet color is produced in the chloroform.

Organic bromine compounds: Add 1 ml of the bromine to 25 ml of 10% NaOH, dilute with an equal volume of H_2O, stopper, and let stand overnight. No oily drops or film separate.

Sulfur compounds: Weigh about 5 g, add 10 ml of H_2O and allow to evaporate on the steam bath.   Add to the residue a few drops of HCl and re-evaporate on the steam bath.   Take up the residue in 1 ml of 1 N HCl and 10 ml of H_2O, filter and add to the filtrate 2 ml of $BaCl_2$.   Any turbidity produced is not more than that in a control made with 0.09 mg of SO_4 for each gram of bromine used for the test, 1 ml of 1 N HCl and 2 ml of $BaCl_2$ in the same final volume as with the sample.

Heavy metals: To the *Evaporation residue* add 2 ml of HNO_3 and 1 ml of H_2O, and evaporate to dryness on the steam bath.   Treat the residue with 1 ml of 1 N acetic acid and 15 ml of hot H_2O and digest for 2 minutes.   Cool, dilute to 40 ml and add 10 ml of H_2S.   Any color produced is not darker than that of a control made with 0.02 mg of Pb, 1 ml of 1 N acetic acid and 10 ml of H_2S in the same final volume as with the sample.

BROMOCRESOL GREEN

Tetrabromo-*m*-cresolsulfonphthalein; Bromocresol Blue

Br; mol. wt. 698.05.

White or slightly buff-colored powder.   Slightly soluble in water; soluble in alcohol or in dilute aqueous alkali hydroxide solutions. pH range: 4.0 yellow; 5.4 blue.

Standards

Solubility.....................to pass test   Ignition residue..............max 0.20%
Sensitiveness.................to pass test

Solubility: Dissolve 0.1 g in 50 ml of alcohol and dilute with water to 100 ml. The solution is clear and complete.

Sensitiveness: To 100 ml of CO_2-free water, add 0.3 ml of the solution obtained in the preceding test and follow with 0.2 ml of 0.01 N NaOH.   The water should become yellow with not more than a slight greenish hue (pH 4).   Now add 1.0 ml of 0.1 N NaOH.   The color changes to blue (pH 5.4).

Ignition residue: Char 0.5 g, cool, add 0.5 ml of H_2SO_4, evaporate the acid and ignite to constant weight.   The residue does not exceed 1.0 mg.

BROMOCRESOL PURPLE

Dibromo-*o*-cresolsulfonphthalein

Br; mol. wt. 540.24.

Slightly yellow or pink crystalline powder. Insoluble in water; soluble in alcohol or in dilute alkalies. pH range: 5.2 yellow; 6.8 purple.

Standards

Solubility....................to pass test   Ignition residue.............max 0.20%
Sensitiveness.................to pass test

Solubility: Dissolve 0.1 g in a mixture of 50 ml of alcohol and 50 ml of water; the solution is clear and complete.

Sensitiveness: To 100 ml of CO_2-free water, add 0.3 ml of the solution obtained in the preceding test.   The water is colored greenish-yellow by the addition of 0.2 ml of 0.01 N HCl.   On the subsequent addition of 0.5 ml of 0.01 N NaOH the color is changed to purple (pH 6.8).

Ignition residue: Char well 0.5 g, cool, add 0.5 ml of H_2SO_4, and ignite gently at first, then strongly to constant weight.   Not more than 1.0 mg of residue remains.

BROMOPHENOL BLUE

Tetrabromophenolsulfonphthalein

$$SO_3H \cdot C_6H_4 \cdot C \Big\langle \begin{array}{l} C_6H_2 : O \cdot Br_2 \\ C_6H_2 \cdot OH \cdot Br_2 \end{array}$$; mol. wt. 670.02

Pale, orange-colored, crystalline powder.   Slightly soluble in water or in ether; soluble in alcohol or in dilute aqueous alkali hydroxide solutions. pH range: 3.0 yellow; 4.6 blue.

Standards

Solubility....................to pass test   Ignition residue.............max 0.20%
Sensitiveness.................to pass test

Solubility: Dissolve 0.1 g in 50 ml of alcohol and dilute with water to 100 ml. The solution is complete and clear.

Sensitiveness: To 100 ml of CO_2-free water add 0.3 ml of the solution obtained in the preceding test. A yellowish color is produced. Now follow with 0.3 ml of 0.01 N NaOH. A distinct blue color is produced.

Ignition residue: Char 0.5 g of sample, cool, add 0.5 ml of H_2SO_4 and ignite to constant weight. Not more than 1.0 mg of residue remains.

BROMOTHYMOL BLUE

Dibromothymolsulfonphthalein

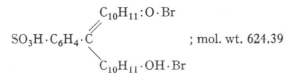

Buff-colored, crystalline powder. Insoluble in water; soluble in alcohol and in dilute solutions of hydroxide alkalies. pH range: 6.0 yellow; 7.6 blue.

Standards

Solubility....................to pass test   Ignition residue..............max 0.20%
Sensitiveness................to pass test

Solubility: Dissolve 0.1 g in 50 ml of alcohol and dilute with water to 100 ml. The solution is complete and clear.

Sensitiveness: To 100 ml of CO_2-free water add 0.3 ml of the solution obtained in the preceding test. A yellowish color is produced which is changed to blue-green by 0.3 ml of 0.01 N NaOH.

Ignition residue: Char 0.5 g, cool, add 0.5 ml of H_2SO_4 and ignite to constant weight. Not more than 1.0 mg of residue remains.

BRUCINE SULFATE

$(C_{23}H_{26}N_2O_4)_2 \cdot H_2SO_4 \cdot 7H_2O$: mol. wt. 1013.15; H_2O—12.45%.

Small, colorless, or white crystals. Soluble in 80 parts of water, 35 parts of hot H_2O, 100 parts of alcohol.

Standards

Sensitiveness and nitrate......to pass test   Ignition residue..............max 0.1%
Solubility and free acid........to pass test   Strychnine..................no reaction

Nitrate: To 10 ml of NO_3-free H_2SO_4 add 10 mg of sample and stir for 1 minute. Neither the acid nor the brucine sulfate show any more than a transient pink color which rapidly disappears.

Sensitiveness: To the solution from the test for Nitrate cautiously add 1.0 ml of standard nitrate solution (= 0.01 mg NO_3) and mix.   A distinct pink color is produced, changing to yellow.

Solubility and free acid: 1.0 g dissolves completely in 50 ml of hot water. Upon adding 2 drops of methyl red to the cooled solution, the color is orange but not pink or red.

Ignition residue: Char 1 g, cool, add 0.5 ml of H_2SO_4, heat slowly to volatilize the H_2SO_4, then ignite to constant weight.   The residue weighs not more than 1.0 mg.

Strychnine: Heat 0.5 g with 2.5 ml of water until dissolved.   Cool to about 25° and add 5 ml of $1+1$ HNO_3, stir well, and allow to stand for 10 minutes stirring a few times.   At the expiration of the 10 minutes, transfer the solution to a separatory funnel containing 30 ml of 10% NaOH cooled to 20°, and extract at once with 20 ml of chloroform, then with 3 10-ml portions.   Pass the chloroform extract through a filter paper moistened with chloroform, collecting the filtrate in a porcelain dish. Evaporate to 3–4 ml, wash down the sides of the dish with a few ml of chloroform and evaporate on the steam bath to dryness.   Cool, dissolve the residue in 2 ml of H_2SO_4, rotating to collect any residue adhering to the sides of the dish, then add a small crystal of potassium dichromate.   No violet color should be produced.

n-BUTYL ALCOHOL

n-Butanol

$CH_3(CH_2)_2CH_2OH$; mol. wt. 74.12.

Clear, colorless liquid; characteristic odor.   Slightly soluble in water; miscible with alcohol or ether.   Sp. gr about 0.81.

Standards

Boiling range..................116°–118°	Acid (as butyric).............max 0.01%	
Evaporation residue.........max 0.005%	Aldehyde....................to pass test	
Fluorescence.................to pass test	Alkalinity (as NH_3)..........max 0.001%	

Boiling range: Distill 100 ml.   After 20 drops has come over, all distills between 116° and 118°, correction being made for the difference in the barometric pressure from 760 mm, page 581.

Evaporation residue: Evaporate 25 ml (20 g) on the steam bath and dry at 105° for 1 hour.   Not more than 1.0 mg of residue remains.

Fluorescence: The fluorescence of *n*-butyl alcohol measured in a suitable fluorophotometer is not greater than that of a solution of quinine sulfate in 0.1 N H_2SO_4 containing 0.0005 mg of quinine sulfate per ml.

Acid: To 25 ml of alcohol add 0.2 ml of phenolphthalein and sufficient 0.02 N NaOH to produce a slight pink color which persists after shaking.   Disregard the volume of the alkali consumed.   Then add 10 ml of the sample and titrate with 0.02 N NaOH to the reproduction of the pink color.   Not more than 0.5 ml of the NaOH is required for this titration.

Aldehyde: Dilute 0.5 ml of sample with 20 ml of water, add 2 ml of fuchsine-sulfurous acid solution, and mix. At the end of 10 minutes the mixture has no more color than a mixture of 20 ml of H_2O and 2 ml of the fuchsine-sulfurous acid.

Alkalinity: Mix 10 ml with 40 ml of water and add 2 drops of methyl red. If the mixture is yellow, it requires not more than 0.25 ml of 0.02 N H_2SO_4 to change it to pink.

BUTYL ALCOHOL, TERTIARY, see TERTIARY BUTYL ALCOHOL

CACOTHELINE

Approximately $C_{21}H_{21}N_3O_7$; mol. wt. 427.

Cacotheline is a nitro derivative of brucine made by heating brucine with 10% HNO_3 at 60°–70°.

Yellow crystals. Soluble in about 400 parts of water.

Cacotheline reacts with stannous tin to give a lilac or violet color even in very dilute aqueous solutions.[1,2,3] In presence of free HCl it is sensitive to about 2 ppm.

Standards

Sensitiveness..................to pass test   Ignition residue...............max 0.2%

Sensitiveness: (a) Shake about 10 mg of the reagent with 2 ml of H_2O until saturated.

(b) Dissolve 100 mg of stannous chloride in 2 ml of HCl and dilute with water to 100 ml. To 1.0 ml of this solution add about 50 mg of hydroxylamine hydrochloride and dilute to 10 ml.

Place 0.1 ml of (b) in a small test tube and add 0.1 ml of (a). A violet color is produced.

Ignition residue: To 0.5 g of sample add 0.5 ml of H_2SO_4 and ignite to constant weight. Not more than 1.0 mg of residue remains.

[1] Leuchs, H., and Leuch, F., *Ber.* **43**, 1042 (1910).
[2] Newell, L., Ficklen, J. B., and Maxwell, L. S., *Ind. Eng. Chem. Anal.* **7**, 26 (1935).
[3] Beck, G., *Mikrochim, Acta*, **2**, 287 (1937).

CADMIUM ACETATE

$Cd(CH_3CO_2)_2 \cdot 2H_2O$; mol. wt. 266.53; anhydrous—86.48%; Cd—42.18%; CdO—48.18%.

Colorless crystals; freely soluble in water; soluble in alcohol.

Standards

H_2O—insoluble.............max 0.010%	Copper (Cu)................max 0.001%
NH_4OH—insoluble...........to pass test	Iron (Fe)..................max 0.001%
Chloride (Cl)................max 0.002%	Lead (Pb).................max 0.003%
Nitrate (NO_3)...............max 0.01%	Zinc (Zn)...................max 0.05%
Sulfate (SO_4)...............max 0.010%	*Assay*
Alkalies, Earths, etc..........max 0.15%	

H_2O—insoluble: Dissolve 20 g in 100 ml of H_2O and 1 ml of glacial acetic acid, and heat on the steam bath for 30 minutes.　Filter any undissolved matter, wash it with water acidulated with acetic acid and dry at 105°.　The weight of the insoluble residue does not exceed 1.0 mg.

NH_4OH—insoluble: To a clear solution of 1.0 g in 10 ml of H_2O add slowly and with continuous stirring 10% NH_3 solution (about 3 ml) until the precipitate formed just redissolves.　The solution remains clear.

Chloride: To 1 g dissolved in 20 ml of H_2O add 1 ml of HNO_3 and 1 ml of $AgNO_3$. Any turbidity produced is not greater than that in a blank to which 0.02 mg of Cl has been added.

Nitrate: Dissolve 0.20 g of cadmium acetate in 5 ml of water, add 2 ml of brucine sulfate solution and dilute to 10 ml (S).　For the control, dilute 2.0 ml of standard nitrate solution (0.02 mg NO_3) with a few ml of water, add 2 ml of brucine sulfate solution, and dilute to 10 ml (C); then proceed with the test as directed under Nitrate—Estimation of Small Amounts, page 575.

Sulfate; Alkalies and Earths; Copper; Iron; Lead; Zinc: Apply the tests described for Cadmium Chloride, using 1 g in test for sulfate.　The results conform to the requirements there given.

Assay: Cadmium acetate may be assayed for its cadmium content by the electrolytic method given under Cadmium Chloride.　The weight of the cadmium × 2.371 = Cd $(C_2H_3O_2)_2 \cdot 2H_2O$, log 37493.

CADMIUM CHLORIDE

$CdCl_2 \cdot 2\frac{1}{2}H_2O$; mol. wt. 228.36; anhydrous—80.28%; H_2O—19.72%; CD—49.22%; Cl—31.05%.

Colorless crystals or white granules.　Somewhat efflorescent.　Soluble in 1 part of water; slightly soluble in alcohol.　*Keep in well-closed containers.*

Standards

H_2O—insoluble............max 0.005%	Ammonia (NH_3)............max 0.005%
NH_4OH—insoluble...........to pass test	Copper (Cu)................max 0.001%
Free acid....................to pass test	Iron (Fe)...................max 0.001%
Nitrate (NO_3)..............max 0.002%	Lead (Pb).................max 0.003%
Sulfate (SO_4)...............max 0.005%	Zinc (Zn)...................max 0.05%
Alkalies, Earths, etc..........max 0.15%	*Assay*

H_2O—insoluble: Dissolve 20 g in 100 ml of H_2O and heat on the steam bath for 1 hour.　Filter any undissolved residue, wash and dry at 105°.　The insoluble is not more than 1.0 mg.

NH_4OH—insoluble: To a clear solution of 1.0 g in 10 ml of H_2O add slowly and with continuous stirring 10% NH_3 solution (about 3 ml) until the precipitate formed just redissolves.　The solution remains clear.

Free acid: To a solution of 1 g in 30 ml of H_2O add 2 drops of methyl orange; the color is yellow to orange-yellow but not red.

Nitrate: Dissolve 0.20 g in 10 ml of water, and add 0.2 ml of diphenylamine solution.　Mix and slowly add, without agitation, 10 ml of H_2SO_4.　After 5–10 minutes mix by swirling and allow to stand for 1 hour.　No blue color appears.

Sulfate: Dissolve 2 g in 10 ml of H_2O, add 1 ml of 0.1 N HCl and 2 ml of $BaCl_2$. Any resulting turbidity is not greater than that in a blank to which 0.1 mg of SO_4 has been added.

Alkalies, Earths, etc.: Dissolve 2 g in 145 ml of water and add 5 ml of 10% H_2SO_4. Heat to boiling and precipitate the cadmium with H_2S. Filter, evaporate 75 ml of the filtrate with 5 drops of sulfuric acid and ignite. Not more than 1.5 mg of residue remains.

Ammonia: Dissolve 1 g in 80 ml of water and add, with stirring, 20 ml of 10% NaOH. Decant 20 ml of the clear liquid, dilute to 50 ml and add 2 ml of Nessler solution. The color produced is not darker than that produced by treating 0.01 mg of NH_3 with 4 ml of the NaOH and 2 ml of Nessler solution in the same final volume as the sample.

Copper: Dissolve 1.0 g in 10 ml of H_2O, add 10 ml of ammonium citrate deleaded solution and sufficient ammonium hydroxide (about 5–8 drops) to produce a pH of about 9. Add 1 ml of an 0.1% solution of sodium diethylthiocarbamate and shake well. Add 5 ml of isoamyl alcohol, shake well for about 1 minute and allow to separate. The color (yellow) of the isoamyl alcohol is not darker than that of a blank to which 0.01 mg of Cu has been added.

Iron: Dissolve 1 g in water, add 2 ml of HCl and dilute to 50 ml. Add 30 mg of ammonium persulfate and 3 ml of ammonium thiocyanate solution, and mix. Any red color produced is not darker than that of a blank to which 0.01 mg of Fe has been added.

Lead: Dissolve 1.0 g in 10 ml of water, add 0.2 ml of glacial acetic acid and filter if necessary (A). To 10 ml of the same water add 0.2 ml of glacial acetic acid (blank). Then to each add 1.0 ml of potassium chromate solution and mix. After 5 minutes A is no more turbid than the blank.

Zinc: Dissolve 1.0 g of sample in 25 ml of diluted (1+10) HCl. For a control add 0.5 mg of zinc (Zn) to 25 ml of the same acid. Transfer the solutions to separatory funnels and treat them as follows: Add to each 25 ml of ammonium thiocyanate and 25 ml of ether and shake vigorously for 1 minute. Allow the liquids to separate, draw off the aqueous layer into another funnel and reserve the ether. Repeat the extraction with ether of the aqueous phase three times. Combine, separately, the ether extracts from each, add 1 ml of 10% H_2SO_4 and heat on the steam bath until all the ether has evaporated. Add 50 ml of water, filter and wash the undissolved matter thoroughly with H_2O. Transfer the filtrate and washings to a 500-ml volumetric flask, dilute to volume and mix. To 20.0-ml portions of each solution add approximately 0.5 N sodium acetate to bring the pH to 5 = 0.5, then add 1 ml of 0.1 N sodium thiosulfate. Transfer the solutions to small separatory funnels, add to each 5 ml of dithizone-carbon tetrachloride standard solution, shake vigorously for 1 minute, allow to separate, and draw off the carbon tetrachloride layer. Repeat the extraction of the aqueous layer with 3-ml volumes of the dithizone solution until the extract remains unchanged in color. Combine, separately, the extracts from each and make the volumes alike, if necessary, by adding carbon tetrachloride to the smaller. The red color in the extract from the sample is not darker than that from the control.

Assay: To determine its degree of hydration, cadmium chloride may be assayed by determining the chloride content with $AgNO_3$, volumetrically (see page 565), or gravimetrically.   A more specific assay method which determines the cadmium and is applicable to other cadmium salts is the electrolytic method as follows:

Weigh accurately about 0.7 g and dissolve in 20 ml of H_2O.   Add 2 drops of phenolphthalein and sufficient NaOH solution to produce a permanent red color. Now add 10% sodium cyanide solution with stirring until the precipitate of cadmium hydroxide is just completely dissolved.   Dilute with water to about 125 ml and electrolyze at room temperature, using a platinum gauze electrode, for 4 to 6 hours with a current of 0.5–0.7 ampere.   When all the cadmium has been deposited, evidenced by the failure of 10 drops of the clear mother liquor to produce a yellow coloration with a few drops of colorless sodium sulfide solution, wash with water by siphonation until the current nearly ceases to flow, then wash the deposited metal with alcohol, finally with ether, and dry at 100°.   The weight of the cadmium × 1.631 = $CdCl_2$, log 21245, or × 2.031 = $CdCl_2 \cdot 2\frac{1}{2}H_2O$, log 30771.

CADMIUM IODIDE

CdI_2; mol. wt. 366.25; Cd—30.69%; I—69.31%.

White, lustrous scales.   Soluble in 1 part of water, soluble in alcohol or acetone. *Keep protected from light.*

Standards

Assay.......................min 99.5%	Sulfate (SO_4)................max 0.005%
H_2O—insoluble...............max 0.01%	Alkali, Earths, etc............max 0.15%
NH_4OH—insoluble...........to pass test	Zinc (Zn)....................max 0.05%
Chloride and Bromide (as Cl)...max 0.01%	

Assay: Weigh accurately about 0.5 g and dissolve it in 20 ml of water in a glass-stoppered flask.   Add 30 ml of hydrochloric acid and 5 ml of chloroform, cool if necessary, and titrate with 0.05 M potassium iodate until the iodine color disappears from the aqueous layer.   Stopper the flask, shake vigorously and continue the titration, shaking vigorously after each addition of the iodate, until the iodine color in the chloroform is discharged.   One ml of 0.05 M potassium iodate = 0.01831 g CdI_2, log 26269.

$$CdI_2 + KIO_3 + 6HCl \rightarrow CdCl_2 + KCl + 3ICl + 3H_2O$$

H_2O—insoluble: Dissolve 10 g in 100 ml of H_2O and heat on the steam bath for 1 hour.   Filter any undissolved residue, wash and dry at 105°.   Not more than 1.0 mg of insoluble is found.

NH_4OH—insoluble: To a clear solution of 1.0 g in 10 ml of H_2O add slowly and with continuous stirring 10% NH_3 solution (about 3 ml) until the precipitate formed just redissolves.   The solution remains clear.

Chloride and Bromide: Dissolve 0.6 g in 10 ml of water, pour the solution into a mixture of 5 ml of ammonium hydroxide and 40 ml of water, then add slowly, with vigorous agitation, 25 ml of 5% silver nitrate.   Filter, and to 40 ml of the filtrate add 5 ml HNO_3.   The turbidity produced is not greater than that produced in a control made by treating 0.1 g of the sample and 0.05 mg of Cl in the same manner.

Sulfate: Dissolve 1 g in 10 ml of H_2O, add 1 ml of 0.1 N HCl and 2 ml of $BaCl_2$, and allow to stand for 15 minutes. Any resulting turbidity is not greater than that in a blank to which 0.05 mg of SO_4 has been added.

Alkalies, Earths, etc.: Dissolve 2 g in 145 ml of water and add 5 ml of 10% H_2SO_4. Heat to boiling and precipitate the cadmium with H_2S. Filter, evaporate 75 ml of the filtrate with 5 drops of sulfuric acid and ignite. The residue is not more than 1.5 mg.

Zinc: Apply the test described under Cadmium Chloride. The results should be as there stated.

CADMIUM NITRATE

$Cd(NO_3)_2 \cdot 4H_2O$; mol. wt. 308.49; anhydrous—76.64%; H_2O—23.36%; Cd—36.44%; NO_3—40.20%.

White, deliquescent crystals. Soluble in 1 part of water; soluble in alcohol.

Standards

H_2O—insoluble............max 0.005%	Ammonia (NH_3)............max 0.010%
NH_4OH—insoluble...........to pass test	Copper (Cu)................max 0.001%
Free acid....................to pass test	Iron (Fe)..................max 0.001%
Chloride (Cl)...............max 0.001%	Lead (Pb)................ max 0.003%
Sulfate (SO_4)...............max 0.005%	Zinc (Zn)...................max 0.05%
Alkalies, Earths, etc..........max 0.10%	*Assay*

Chloride: Dissolve 1 g in 20 ml of H_2O, add 1 ml of HNO_3, and 1 ml of silver nitrate. Any turbidity produced is not greater than that in a blank to which 0.01 mg of Cl has been added.

Sulfate: Evaporate 1 g with 5 ml of HCl to dryness on the steam bath. Dissolve the residue in 10 ml of H_2O, add 1 ml of 0.1 N HCl and 2 ml of $BaCl_2$, and allow to stand for 15 minutes. Any resulting turbidity is not greater than that in a control made with 0.05 mg of SO_4, 1 ml of 0.1 N HCl and 2 ml of $BaCl_2$ in the same volume as with the sample.

Alkalies, Earths, etc.: Dissolve 2 g in 145 ml of water and add 5 ml of 10% H_2SO_4. Heat to boiling and precipitate the cadmium with H_2S. Filter, evaporate 75 ml of the filtrate with 5 drops of sulfuric acid and ignite. The residue is not more than 1.0 mg.

Ammonia: Dissolve 1 g in 80 ml of water and add, with stirring, 20 ml of 10% NaOH. Decant 20 ml of the clear liquid, dilute to 50 ml and add 2 ml of Nessler solution. The color produced is not darker than that produced by treating 0.02 mg of NH_3 with 4 ml of the NaOH and 2 ml of Nessler solution in the same final volume as with the sample.

H_2O—insoluble; NH_4OH—insoluble; Free acid; Copper; Lead; Zinc: Apply the tests described for Cadmium Chloride, but using only 0.5 g in the test for Cu. The results conform to the requirements there stated.

Iron: Dissolve 1 g in 15 ml of H_2O, add 2 ml of HCl, and boil for 2 minutes. Cool, add about 30 mg of ammonium persulfate and 15 ml of butanolic potassium thiocyanate, shake well for 30 seconds and allow to separate. Any red color in the clear butanolic (upper) layer is not darker than that of a blank to which 0.01 mg of Fe has been added.

Assay: Cadmium nitrate may be assayed electrolytically as described under Cadmium Chloride. The weight of the cadmium × 2.745 = $Cd(NO_3)_2 \cdot 4H_2O$, log 43854.

CADMIUM SULFATE

$3CdSO_4 \cdot 8H_2O$; mol. wt. 769.56; anhydrous—81.31%; H_2O—18.69%; Cd—43.82%; SO_4—37.45%.

Colorless crystals, somewhat efflorescent. Soluble in 1.5 parts of water; insoluble in alcohol.

Standards

H_2O—insoluble............max 0.005%	Arsenic (As)................max 2 ppm
NH_4OH—insoluble..........to pass test	Copper (Cu)................max 0.002%
Free acid...................to pass test	Iron (Fe)..................max 0.001%
Chloride (Cl)...............max 0.001%	Zinc (Zn)..................max 0.05%
Nitrate (NO_3)..............max 0.002%	Lead (Pb).................max 0.003%
Alkalies, Earths, etc..........max 0.10%	*Assay*
Ammonia (NH_3)............max 0.010%	

H_2O—insoluble: Dissolve 20 g in 200 ml of H_2O and heat on steam bath for 1 hour. Filter any undissolved residue, wash, and dry at 105°. The insoluble residue is not more than 1.0 g.

NH_4OH—insoluble: To a clear solution of 1.0 g in 10 ml of H_2O add slowly and with continuous stirring 10% NH_3 solution (about 3 ml) until the precipitate formed just redissolves. The solution remains clear.

Free acid: To a solution of 1 g in 30 ml of H_2O add 2 drops of methyl orange; the color is yellow to orange-yellow, but not red.

Chloride: Dissolve 1 g in 10 ml of water and add 1 ml of HNO_3 and 1 ml of silver nitrate. Any turbidity produced is not greater than that in the blank to which 0.01 mg of Cl has been added.

Nitrate: Dissolve 0.20 g in 10 ml of water, and add about 20 mg of NaCl and 0.2 ml of diphenylamine solution. Mix and slowly add, without agitation, 10 ml of H_2SO_4. After 5 minutes, mix by swirling and allow to stand for 1 hour. No blue color appears.

Alkalies, Earths, etc.: Dissolve 2 g in 145 ml of water and add 5 ml of 10% H_2SO_4. Heat to boiling and precipitate the cadmium with H_2S. Filter, evaporate 75 ml of the filtrate with 5 drops of sulfuric acid and ignite. Not more than 1.0 mg of residue remains.

Ammonia: Dissolve 1 g in 80 ml of water and add, with stirring, 20 ml of 10% NaOH. Decant 20 ml of the clear liquid, dilute to 50 ml, and add 2 ml of

Nessler solution.   The color produced is not darker than that produced by treating 0.02 mg of NH_3 with 4 ml of the NaOH and 2 ml of Nessler solution in the same final volume as the sample.

Arsenic: Test 1 g by the method on page 563.   The stain is not greater than that from 0.002 mg of As.

Copper: Dissolve 0.5 g in 10 ml of H_2O, add 5 ml of ammonium citrate deleaded solution and sufficient ammonium hydroxide (about 5–8 drops) to produce a pH of about 9.   Add 1 ml of a 0.1% solution of sodium diethylthiocarbamate and shake well.   Add 5 ml of isoamyl alcohol, shake well for about 1 minute and allow to separate.   The color (yellow) of the isoamyl alcohol is not darker than that of a blank to which 0.01 mg of Cu has been added.

Iron: Dissolve 1 g in H_2O, add 2 ml of HCl, and dilute to 50 ml.   Add about 30 mg of ammonium persulfate and 15 ml of ammonium thiocyanate.   Any resulting red color is not darker than that of a blank to which 0.01 mg of Fe has been added.

Zinc: Dissolve 1.0 g of sample in 25 ml of diluted $(1 + 10)$ HCl.   For a control add 0.5 mg of zinc (Zn) to 25 ml of the same acid.   Transfer the solutions to separatory funnels and treat them as follows: Add to each 25 ml of ammonium thiocyanate and 25 ml of ether and shake vigorously for 1 minute.   Allow the liquids to separate, draw off the aqueous layer into another funnel and reserve the ether.   Repeat the extraction with ether of the aqueous phase three times.   Combine, separately, the ether extracts from each, add 10 ml of 10% H_2SO_4, and heat on the steam bath until all the ether has evaporated.   Add 50 ml of water, filter, and wash the undissolved matter thoroughly with H_2O.   Transfer the filtrate and washings to a 500-ml volumetric flask, dilute to volume and mix.   To 20.0-ml portions of each solution add approximately 0.5 N (7%) sodium acetate to bring the pH to 5 = 0.5 and 1 ml of 0.1 N sodium thiosulfate.   Transfer the solutions to small separatory funnels. Add to each 5 ml of dithizone-carbon tetrachloride standard solution, shake vigorously for 1 minute, allow to separate and draw off the carbon tetrachloride layer. Repeat the extraction of the aqueous layer with 3-ml volumes of the dithizone solution until the extract remains unchanged in color.   Combine separately the extracts from each and make the volumes alike, if necessary, by adding carbon tetrachloride to the smaller.   The red color in the extract from the sample is not darker than that from the control.

Lead: Dissolve 1.0 g in 10 ml of water, add 5 drops of glacial acetic acid and 0.2 ml of potassium chromate solution.   No turbidity is produced in 5 minutes.

Assay: Cadmium sulfate may be assayed electrolytically as described under Cadmium Chloride.   The weight of the cadmium $\times$ 2.282 = cadmium sulfate of above formula.

CALCIUM ACETATE

$Ca(CH_3CO_2)_2 \cdot H_2O$; mol. wt. 176.18; anhydrous 89.77%; H_2O—10.23%; Ca— 22.75%; CaO—31.83% acetic acid—68.17%.

White, crystalline powder, or granules.   Soluble in 3 parts of water, slightly soluble in alcohol.

Standards

Insoluble and Ammonium	Sulfate (SO$_4$)................max 0.040%
hydroxide precipitate......max 0.015%	Barium (Ba)................max 0.003%
Free acid (as CH$_3$COOH)......max 0.20%	Heavy metals (as Pb)........max 0.001%
Alkalinity........................none	Iron (Fe)....................max 0.002%
Chloride (Cl)................max 0.005%	Magnesium and Alkalies
Nitrate (NO$_3$)...............max 0.002%	(Mg + Na)................max 0.10%
Phosphate (PO$_4$)............max 0.001%	

Insoluble and Ammonium hydroxide precipitate: Dissolve 10 g in 100 ml of water, heat the solution to boiling and render slightly alkaline with NH$_4$OH. Filter and wash with a little water.   Pour on the filter, dropwise, a few ml of hot 10% HCl and wash well with water.   Make the second filtrate slightly alkaline with NH$_4$OH and heat it to boiling.   Filter any precipitate through the same filter as before, wash it with water, ignite and weigh.   The weight does not exceed 1.0 mg.

Free Acid; Alkalinity: Dissolve 2 g in 25 ml of water and add 2 drops of phenolphthalein; no pink color is produced.   Now add 0.1 N NaOH to the production of a pink color; not more than 0.7 ml of the NaOH is required.

Chloride: Dissolve 1 g in 20 ml of water, add 2 ml of HNO$_3$ and dilute to 50 ml. To 20 ml add 1 ml of silver nitrate.   Any resulting turbidity is not greater than that in a blank to which 0.02 mg of Cl has been added.

Nitrate: Dissolve 0.50 g in 20 ml of water and add 5 ml of 25% H$_2$SO$_4$.   Shake well and allow to stand for 20 minutes, shaking several times during this period. Filter or centrifuge and decant.   To 10 ml of the filtrate add 20 mg of NaCl, 0.2 ml of diphenylamine solution, mix, then run in slowly 10 ml of H$_2$SO$_4$.   Mix gently and allow to stand for 1 hour.   No blue color results.

Phosphate: Dissolve 2 g in 20 ml of water.   Add 1 ml of HCl and 1 ml each of phosphate reagents **A** and **B**, and heat at 60° for 10 minutes.   Any blue color produced is not darker than that of a control made with 0.02 mg of PO$_4$, 1 ml of HCl and the same quantities of the other reagents and in the same volume as with the sample.

Sulfate: Dissolve 1 g in 40 ml of water.   To 10 ml of the solution add 1 ml of 0.1 N HCl and 2 ml of BaCl$_2$.   If a turbidity is produced it is not greater than that in a blank to which 0.1 mg of SO$_4$ has been added.

Barium: Dissolve 2 g in 15 ml of H$_2$O and add 1 drop of glacial acetic acid. Filter, if necessary, and add to the filtrate 0.5 ml of potassium chromate.   No turbidity is produced in 10 minutes.

Heavy metals: Dissolve 4 g in 30 ml of water, add 2 ml of 10% HCl and dilute to 40 ml.   To 10 ml of the solution add 0.02 mg of Pb and dilute to 40 ml (A). Dilute the remaining 30 ml of the solution to 40 ml (B).   Then to each add 10 ml of H$_2$S; B is not darker than A.

Iron: Dissolve 1 g in 10 ml of water, add 2 ml of HCl and dilute to 50 ml.   Add about 30 mg of ammonium persulfate and 3 ml of ammonium thiocyanate solution, and mix.   Any resulting red color is not darker than that of a blank to which 0.02 mg of Fe has been added.

Magnesium and Alkalies: Dissolve 2.0 g in 75 ml of water and add 5 ml of HCl.   Heat to boiling and add 60 ml of ammonium oxalate solution.   Slowly neutralize the solution with NH_4OH while the solution is cooling, then dilute to 200.0 ml and let stand for 4 hours or overnight.   Filter, and to 100 ml of the filtrate add a few drops of H_2SO_4, evaporate to dryness and gently ignite to constant weight. Not more than 4.5 mg of residue remains.

CALCIUM CARBONATE, PRECIPITATED

$CaCO_3$; mol. wt. 100.09; Ca—40.04%; CaO—56.03%; CO_2—43.97%; C—12.00%.

White, fine powder.   Insoluble in water, but dissolves appreciably in the presence of carbon dioxide; soluble in dilute acid with effervescence.

Standards

Hydrochloric acid—insoluble, and NH_4OH precipitate....max 0.015%	Ammonia (NH_3)..............max 0.003%
Alkalinity...................to pass test	Barium (Ba)................max 0.003%
Chloride (Cl)................max 0.002%	Heavy metals (as Pb)........max 0.001%
Nitrate (NO_3)..............max 0.003%	Iron (Fe)...................max 0.003%
Phosphate (PO_4)...........max 0.001%	Magnesium and Alkalies
Sulfate (SO_4)...............max 0.010%	(Mg + Na)...............max 0.15%
	Assay.......................min 99%

Hydrochloric acid—insoluble, and NH_4OH precipitate: Mix 10 g with 100 ml of water and add, portionwise, hydrochloric acid until dissolved (do not filter). Boil, dilute to 100 ml and add 2 drops of methyl red and make slightly alkaline with NH_4OH Filter and wash with a little hot water.   Pour on the filter, dropwise, a little hot diluted (1 + 1) HCl and wash well with water.   Make the second filtrate slightly alkaline with ammonium hydroxide and bring it to a boil.   Filter any precipitate through the same filter as before, wash it with water, ignite and weigh. The weight does not exceed 1.5 mg.

Alkalinity: Shake 3 g for 5 minutes with 30 ml of warm, CO_2-free water, cool, and filter.   To 20 ml of the filtrate add 0.1 ml of phenolphthalein.   Any pink color produced is discharged by 0.25 ml of 0.02 N HCl.

Chloride: Dissolve 1 g in a mixture of 20 ml of H_2O and 3 ml of HNO_3, and add 1 ml of $AgNO_3$.   Any resulting turbidity is not greater than that in a blank to which 0.02 mg of Cl has been added.

Nitrate: Suspend 0.50 g of sample in 5 ml of water and add glacial acetic acid, 2–3 drops at a time, shaking after each addition, until the sample is dissolved. Dilute to 20 ml and add 5 ml of 25% H_2SO_4.   Shake well and allow to stand for 15 minutes, shaking several times during this period.   Filter, or, preferably, centrifuge and decant.   To 10 ml of the filtrate add 20 mg of NaCl, 0.2 ml of diphenylamine solution, then run in slowly without agitation 10 ml of H_2SO_4.   Mix gently by swirling and allow to stand for 30 minutes.   No blue color results.

Phosphate: Dissolve 1 g in 10 ml of H_2O and 10 ml of 10% HCl.   Boil for 1 minute, cool, and dilute with H_2O to 20 ml.   Add to the solution 1 ml each of phosphate reagents **A** and **B** and heat at 60° for 10 minutes.   Any blue color produced is not darker than that produced in a control made with 0.01 mg of PO_4, 2 ml of 10% HCl and 1 ml each of the phosphate reagents and in the same volume as with the sample.

Sulfate: Heat 1 g with 10 ml of water, add just sufficient glacial acetic acid to dissolve and evaporate on the steam bath.   Dissolve the residue in 10 ml of water, filter if necessary and add 2 ml of $BaCl_2$.   Any turbidity produced in 15 minutes is not greater than that of a control made with 0.1 mg of SO_4, 2 drops of glacial acid and 2 ml of $BaCl_2$ in the same volume as with the sample.

Ammonia: Dissolve 1 g in 20 ml of H_2O and a slight excess of HCl, and dilute to 80 ml.   Add 20 ml of 10% NaOH, mix well and let stand for 1 hour.   Decant 50 ml through an asbestos filter previously washed with 10% NaOH, and add to the filtrate 2 ml of Nessler solution.   The resulting color is not darker than that of a control made with 0.015 mg of NH_3, 10 ml of the NaOH and 2 ml of Nessler solution in the same final volume as with the sample.

Barium: Dissolve 1.0 g in 10 ml of water with a slight excess of HCl (about 2 ml) and boil the solution for 1 minute.   Now make it slightly alkaline with NH_4OH, bring to a boil and filter.   Dilute the filtrate to 10 ml, and add 1.0 ml of potassium chromate solution and sufficient 10% NH_3 to produce a clear yellow color.   No turbidity is produced in 5 minutes.   If preferred the solution may be viewed by comparing with a blank made with 10 ml of water, 1 ml of the potassium chromate and alkalinized with NH_4OH.

Heavy metals: Mix 4 g with 20 ml of H_2O, add 10 ml of HCl and evaporate to dryness on the steam bath.   Dissolve the residue in 30 ml of water, add 1 drop of phenolphthalein, neutralize with 0.1 N sodium hydroxide and dilute to 40 ml. To 10 ml add 0.02 mg of Pb, 1 ml of 1 N acetic acid and dilute to 40 ml (A).   To the remaining 30 ml add 1 ml of 1 N acetic acid and dilute to 40 ml (B).   Then to each add 10 ml of H_2S. B is not darker than A.

Iron: To 0.5 g add 20 ml of water and 3 ml of HCl, and dilute to 50 ml.   Add 50 mg of ammonium persulfate and 3 ml of ammonium thiocyanate, and mix. Any resulting red color is not darker than that of a blank to which 0.015 mg of Fe has been added.

Magnesium and Alkalies: Dissolve 2.0 g in 75 ml of water and add 5 ml of HCl.   Heat to boiling and add 75 ml of ammonium oxalate solution.   Slowly neutralize the solution with NH_4OH while the solution is cooling; then dilute to 200.0 ml and let stand for 4 hours or overnight.   Filter, and to 100 ml of the filtrate add a few drops of H_2SO_4, evaporate to dryness and gently ignite to constant weight. Not more than 4.5 mg of residue remains.

Assay: Calcium carbonate may be assayed by the following method:

Dry about 1 g of sample at 200° for 3 hours.   Weigh accurately about 0.7 g of the dried sample and transfer it completely into a 200-ml volumetric flask with about 50 ml of water.   Add in several portions 20 ml of 10% HCl, heat gently for a few minutes, cool, dilute to the 200-ml volume and mix well.

Withdraw 50 ml of the solution into a 400–500 ml beaker and dilute to about 100 ml.   Add 10 ml of ammonium oxalate solution and 2 drops of methyl red solution, heat nearly to boiling and add dropwise with constant stirring 10% NH_3 until the color of the solution just changes to yellow.   Add 25 ml more of the ammonium oxalate solution and digest on the steam bath for 30 minutes.   Cool to room temperature, allowing the precipitate to settle, and decant the supernatant liquid through a filtering glass crucible.   Wash the precipitate in the beaker three times by decantation with 30-ml portions of cold 1% ammonium oxalate solution, completely transfer the precipitate onto the filter with the aid of the 1% ammonium oxalate solution, and finally wash the beaker and precipitate three times with 10-ml portions of cold water.

Place the crucible with the precipitate in the beaker, add 100 ml of water and 50 ml of 25% H_2SO_3 (1+5), then add from a burette 30 ml of 0.1 N potassium permanganate and stir until the color disappears. Heat to about 75° and complete titration with the permanganate. One ml of 0.1 N permanganate = 0.005005 g of $CaCO_3$, log 69940.

CALCIUM CARBONATE, PRECIPITATED

Low in Alkalies and Chloride

This reagent of commerce, dried at 200°, is about 99.8% pure.

Standards

Hydrochloric acid—insoluble, and NH₄OH precipitate........max 0.015%	Alkalies total (K and Na).....max 0.020%
Alkalinity...................to pass test	Ammonia (NH_3)............max 0.003%
Chloride (Cl).... max 0.001%	Barium (Ba)...............max 0.003%
Nitrate (NO_3)..............max 0.003%	Heavy metals (as Pb)........max 0.001%
Phosphate (PO_4)...........max 0.001%	Iron (Fe)..................max 0.002%
Sulfate (SO_4)...............max 0.010%	Magnesium (Mg).............max 0.02%
	Strontium (Sr)..............max 0.05%

Chloride: Dissolve 1 g in a mixture of 10 ml of H_2O and 2 ml of HNO_3, and add 1 ml of $AgNO_3$. Any resulting turbidity is not greater than that in a blank to which 0.01 mg of Cl has been added.

Alkalies, total: Mix 10 g with 40 ml of H_2O, heat and add portionwise 20 ml of HCl. Neutralize the solution with dilute NH_4OH, add 65 ml of ammonium carbonate solution, heat to boiling, filter and wash the precipitate with 30 ml of hot H_2O (*filtrate A*). Wash the precipitate into a 250-ml beaker with about 40 ml of H_2O and dissolve it in 20 ml of HCl. Make the solution slightly alkaline with NH_4OH, boil, and reprecipitate with 50 ml of ammonium carbonate solution. Filter and wash with 25 ml of hot H_2O. Combine the filtrate with *filtrate A*, evaporate to dryness in a platinum dish, and ignite gently. Dissolve the residue in 5 ml of hot H_2O, make alkaline with NH_4OH, add 3 ml of ammonium oxalate and let stand overnight. Filter through a small filter paper and wash with 5 ml of H_2O. Evaporate the filtrate and washings with 3 drops of H_2SO_4 and ignite. The weight of the residue does not exceed 6.0 mg. Run a blank on the reagents and deduct.

Iron: Test 1 g as the preceding grade of calcium carbonate, and make the control with 0.02 mg of Fe.

Magnesium: Dissolve 1.00 g in 20 ml of water and 2 ml of HCl and boil the solution for 2 minutes to expel CO_2. Cool and dilute to 100 ml. To 10 ml of the solution add 0.05 mg of magnesium (Mg) and dilute to 45 ml (*A*). Dilute 35 ml of the solution to 45 ml (*B*). To each of the dilutions add 0.3 ml of thiazol yellow (Clayton Yellow) solution and 5 ml of 5% NaOH solution, mix and allow to stand for 10 minutes. The pink color of *B* is not darker than that of *A*.

Hydrochloric acid—insoluble, and NH₄OH precipitate; Alkalinity; Nitrate; Phosphate; Sulfate; Ammonia; Barium; Heavy metals: Apply the tests described for the preceding grade.   The results conform to the requirements there stated.

Strontium may be quantitatively determined by Flame Photometry, page 566.

CALCIUM CHLORIDE, ANHYDROUS

$CaCl_2$; mol. wt. 110.99; Ca—36.11%; Cl—63.89%.

White, very hygroscopic granules.   Very soluble in water, or in alcohol.   When dissolved in water much heat is liberated.   *Keep in tightly closed containers.*

Standards

Assay..................min 96% $CaCl_2$	Barium (Ba)...............max 0.005%
Insoluble and ammonium	Heavy metals (as Pb)........max 0.001%
hydroxide precipitate......max 0.015%	Iron (Fe)...................max 0.001%
Alkalinity (as Ca(OH)₂)......max 0.020%	Zinc (Zn)...................max 0.01%
Nitrate (NO₃)...............max 0.003%	Magnesium and Alkalies
Phosphate (PO₄)............max 0.001%	(Mg + Na)...............max 0.15%
Sulfate (SO₄)...............max 0.020%	

Assay: Weigh accurately about 1.5 g and dissolve it in water to exactly 50 ml. Using 5.0 ml of the solution determine the chloride (Cl—) by the Volhard or the adsorption indicator assay method for chloride, page 565. One ml of $0.1\ N$ $AgNO_3$ = 0.005550 g $CaCl_2$, log 74429.

Insoluble and Ammonium hydroxide precipitate: Determine as in Calcium Chloride Dehydrate.   The weight of the ignited precipitate does not exceed 1.5 mg.

Alkalinity: Dissolve 5 g in 50 ml H_2O and add 2 drops of phenolphthalein.   The pink color produced is discharged by 0.3 ml of $0.1\ N$ HCl.

Phosphate: Dissolve 1 g in 20 ml of H_2O, add 2 ml of 10% HCl and 1 ml each of phosphate reagents **A** and **B**, and heat at 60° for 10 minutes.   Any blue color is not darker than that of a blank to which 0.01 mg of PO_4 has been added.

Sulfate: Dissolve 1 g in 20 ml H_2O, and add 1 ml of $0.1\ N$ HCl and 2 ml $BaCl_2$. Any turbidity produced is not greater than that in a blank to which 0.2 mg of SO_4 has been added.

Nitrate; Barium; Iron: Apply the test described under Calcium Chloride, Dihydrate; the results conform to the requirements there stated.   Use 0.3 g in the test for nitrate.

Heavy metals: Dissolve 4 g in 40 ml H_2O.   To 10 ml add 0.02 mg Pb, 2 ml of $1\ N$ acetic acid, and dilute to 40 ml (A).   To the remaining 30 ml add 2 ml $1\ N$ acetic acid, and dilute to 40 ml (B).   Then to each add 10 ml H_2S; B is not darker than A.

Zinc: Dissolve 2 g in 40 ml of H_2O.   To 10 ml of the solution add 0.10 mg of Zn, dilute to 30 ml and add 1 ml of 10% HCl (A).   To the remaining 30 ml add 1 ml of 10% HCl (B).   Then to each add 1 ml of potassium ferrocyanide solution and allow to stand for 10 minutes. B shows no greater turbidity than A.

Magnesium and Alkalies: Determine as described under Calcium Chloride, Dihydrate.   The weight of the residue does not exceed 4.5 mg.

CALCIUM CHLORIDE, ANHYDROUS, FOR DRYING

White, porous, hygroscopic granules. *Keep in tightly closed containers.*

Standards

Assay................min 96% as $CaCl_2$
Alkalinity [as $Ca(OH)_2$]......max 0.020%

Magnesium and Alkalies
(as sulfates)................max 2.0%

Assay: Apply the assay method described for Calcium Chloride, Anhydrous. One ml of 0.1 N $AgNO_3$ = 0.005550 g $CaCl_2$, log 74429.

Alkalinity: Dissolve 5 g in 50 ml of water and add 2 drops of phenolphthalein. The pink color produced is discharged by 0.3 ml of 0.1 N HCl.

Magnesium and Alkalies: Test as described under Calcium Chloride, Dihydrate; the residue is not more than 20 mg.

CALCIUM CHLORIDE, DIHYDRATE

$CaCl_2 \cdot 2H_2O$; mol. wt. 147.03; anhydrous—75.49%; H_2O—24.51%; Ca—27.25%; Cl 48.23%.

White, small crystals or granules. Very soluble in water, soluble in the lower (C_1–C_5) aliphatic alcohols. Loses its water of hydration at about 150°. The water may also be determined by the iodine (Fischer) method.

Standards

Assay...............74.0%–78.0% $CaCl_2$
Insoluble and NH_4OH
  precipitate...............max 0.010%
Neutrality...................to pass test
Nitrate (NO_3)...............max 0.003%
Phosphate (PO_4)............max 0.001%
Sulfate (SO_4)................max 0.010%

Ammonia (NH_3)............max 0.005%
Barium (Ba)................max 0.003%
Heavy metals (as Pb).......max 0.0005%
Iron (Fe)...................max 0.001%
Magnesium and Alkalies
  (Mg + Na)................max 0.10%

Assay: Weigh accurately about 2 g of sample and dissolve it in water to make exactly 50.0 ml. Using exactly 5.0 ml of the solution, determine the chloride (Cl—) by the Volhard or adsorption indicator method, page 565. One ml of 0.1 N $AgNO_3$ = 0.005550 g $CaCl_2$, log 74429.

Insoluble and Ammonium hydroxide precipitate: Dissolve 10 g in 100 ml of water, heat to boiling, render slightly alkaline with NH_4OH, and boil for 5 minutes. If a precipitate is formed, filter through a small filter paper and wash with a little hot H_2O. Redissolve the precipitate in hot 10% HCl, boil for 1 minute, then make alkaline with NH_4OH. Filter through the same filter paper as before, wash and ignite. The ignited precipitate does not exceed 1.0 mg.

Neutrality: Dissolve 5 g in 50 ml of water and add 2 drops of phenolphthalein. If a pink color is produced it is discharged by 0.1 ml of 0.1 N HCl. If no pink color is produced, the solution becomes pink on the addition of 0.1 ml of 0.1 N NaOH.

Nitrate: Dissolve 0.5 g in 22 ml of water, add 3 ml of 25% H_2SO_4, shake well, and let stand for 15 minutes, shaking a few times during this period. Filter or centrifuge and decant. To 10 ml of the filtrate add 0.2 ml of diphenylamine solution, then run in slowly, without agitation, 10 ml of H_2SO_4. After 10 minutes mix the contents of the beaker by gently swirling it and allow to stand for 1 hour. No blue color appears.

Phosphate: Dissolve 1 g in 20 ml of H_2O, add 2 ml of 10% HCl and 1 ml each of phosphate reagents **A** and **B**, and heat at 60° for 10 minutes. Any blue color produced is not deeper than that of a blank to which 0.01 mg of PO_4 has been added.

Sulfate: Dissolve 2 g in 20 ml of water, and add 1 ml of 0.1 N HCl and 2 ml of $BaCl_2$. Any turbidity produced is not greater than that in a blank to which 0.2 mg of SO_4 has been added.

Ammonia: Dissolve 1 g in 40 ml of water, add 10 ml of 10% NaOH, mix well and let stand for 30 minutes protected from access of ammonia. Decant 20 ml through an asbestos filter previously washed with 10% NaOH, dilute to 50 ml and add 2 ml of Nessler solution. The color produced is not darker than that of a control made with 0.02 mg of NH_3, 4 ml of the NaOH, and 2 ml of Nessler solution in the same volume as with the sample.

Barium: Dissolve 2 g of the sample and 2 g of sodium acetate in 15 ml of water. Filter, if necessary, and add to the filtrate 1 drop of glacial acetic acid and 2.0 ml of potassium dichromate solution. No turbidity is produced in 10 minutes.

Heavy metals: Dissolve 6 g in water to make 30 ml. To 5 ml add 0.02 mg of Pb, 1 ml of 1 N acetic acid, and dilute to 40 ml (A). To the remaining 25 ml add 1 ml of 1 N acetic acid and dilute to 40 ml (B). Then to each add 10 ml of H_2S. B is not darker than A.

Iron: Dissolve 1 g in 30 ml of water, add 2 ml of HCl and about 30 mg of ammonium persulfate. Dilute to 50 ml and add 3 ml of ammonium thiocyanate. Any resulting red color is not darker than that of a blank to which 0.01 mg of Fe has been added.

Magnesium and Alkalies: Dissolve 2.0 g in 75 ml of water, and add 2 ml of HCl. Heat to boiling and add 50 ml of ammonium oxalate solution. Slowly neutralize the solution with NH_4OH while the solution is cooling, then dilute to 200.0 ml and let stand for 4 hours or overnight. Filter, and to 100 ml of the filtrate add a few drops of H_2SO_4, evaporate to dryness and gently ignite to constant weight. Not more than 3.0 mg of residue remains.

CALCIUM HYDROXIDE

$Ca(OH)_2$; mol. wt. 74.10; Ca—54.09%; CaO—75.69%.

White powder; slowly absorbing CO_2 from air. *Keep tightly closed.*

Standards

Assay.............min 93% $Ca(OH)_2$	Sulfur compounds (as SO_4).....max 0.20%
Hydrochloric acid—	Heavy metals (as Pb)........max 0.003%
insoluble.................max 0.10%	Iron (Fe)...................max 0.02%
Ammonium hydroxide	Magnesium and Alkalies
precipitate................max 0.50%	(as MgO).................max 0.75%

Assay: Place in a 500-ml volumetric flask about 2 g of the sample, accurately weighed, add 10 ml of neutral alcohol, shake gently, then add 350 ml of a 10% sucrose solution, previously neutralized with 0.1 N NaOH to phenolphthalein. Stopper the flask and shake vigorously for 5 minutes and then at frequent intervals during 4 hours. Add CO_2-free water to the 500-ml volume, mix well, filter and titrate 200 ml of the filtrate with 1 N HCl, using phenolphthalein solution as indicator. One ml of 1 N HCl = 0.03705 g $Ca(OH)_2$, log 56879.

Hydrochloric acid—insoluble: To 2.0 g of sample add 50 ml of H_2O and follow, in small portions, with 10 ml of HCl. Boil the solution for 5 minutes, and if undissolved matter is present, filter, wash with hot water (retain filtrate), dry and ignite. The ignited residue does not exceed 2.0 mg.

Ammonium hydroxide precipitate: To the filtrate from the preceding test add 2 drops of methyl orange solution, bring to a boil and add NH_4OH until the solution just turns yellow. Filter hot, wash with hot water, dry and ignite. The ignited residue does not exceed 10.0 mg.

Sulfur compounds: Mix 2 g with 100 ml of H_2O, add 5 ml of bromine water and heat the mixture for 5 minutes. Add 6 ml of HCl, boil to expel bromine, filter, and wash any undissolved matter with water. Heat the filtrate to boiling, add 5 ml of $BaCl_2$ and heat on steam bath for 2 hours. Filter, wash the precipitate well with hot water and ignite. The weight of the ignited $BaSO_4$ does not exceed 10.0 mg.

Solution S: Mix 2.5 g with 40 ml of H_2O, *cautiously* add 10 ml of HCl, then 3 ml of HNO_3, and evaporate to dryness on the steam bath. Take up the residue with 1 ml of 10% HCl and 30 ml of hot water, filter and wash with a few ml of H_2O. Add to the filtrate 2 drops of phenolphthalein and just enough 1 N NaOH to produce a permanent pink color. Discharge the pink color with 1 or 2 drops of 1 N HCl and dilute to 50 ml.

Heavy metals: To 10 ml of *Solution S* add 0.03 mg of Pb, 1 ml of 1 N acetic acid, and dilute to 40 ml (A). To 30 ml of *Solution S* add 1 ml of 1 N acetic acid and dilute to 40 ml (B). Then to each add 10 ml of H_2S. B is not darker than A.

Iron: To 2.0 ml of *Solution S* add 2 ml of HCl and dilute to 50 ml. Add about 30 mg ammonium persulfate and 3 ml of ammonium thiocyanate, and mix. Any resulting red color is not darker than that of a control made with 0.02 mg of Fe, 2 ml of HCl, the same quantities of the other reagents and in the same final volume as with the sample.

Magnesium and Alkalies: Mix 1.0 g with 30 ml of H_2O, slowly add 5 ml of HCl and boil for a few minutes. Dilute to about 75 ml and add 60 ml of ammonium oxalate solution. Add 2 drops of methyl red and neutralize with NH_4OH. Cool, dilute to 150 ml and allow to stand for 4 hours or overnight. Filter, and to 75 ml of the filtrate add 0.5 ml of H_2SO_4, evaporate and ignite. The weight of the ignited residue does not exceed 12.0 mg.

CALCIUM NITRATE

$Ca(NO_3)_2 \cdot H_2O$; mol. wt. 236.16; anhydrous—69.5%; H_2O—30.5%; Ca—16.97%; NO_3—52.5%; CaO—23.3%.

Calcium nitrate is also available as a monohydrate: $Ca(NO_3)_2 \cdot H_2O$; mol. wt. 182.11; anhydrous salt—90.11%; Ca—22.01%; NO_3—68.1%.

White, deliquescent granules. Soluble in 1 part of water; soluble in alcohol. *Keep in tightly closed containers.*

Standards

Insoluble and NH_4OH precipitate................max 0.010%	Ammonia (NH_3)............max 0.005%
Neutrality.....................to pass test	Barium (Ba)................max 0.003%
Chloride (Cl).................max 0.003%	Heavy metals (as Pb)........max 0.001%
Phosphate (PO_4)............max 0.001%	Iron (Fe)...................max 0.001%
Sulfate (SO_4)................max 0.010%	Magnesium and Alkalies (Mg and Na)...............max 0.10%

Neutrality: Dissolve 2 g in 30 ml of H_2O, and add 2 drops of phenolphthalein. No pink color is produced, but the solution becomes pink on the addition of 0.2 ml of 0.02 N NaOH.

Chloride: To a solution of 1 g in 20 ml of H_2O add 1 ml of HNO_3 and 1 ml of $AgNO_3$. Any resulting turbidity is not greater than that in a blank to which 0.03 mg of Cl has been added.

Phosphate: Dissolve 1 g in a few ml of H_2O, add 5 ml and evaporate to dryness on the steam bath. Dissolve the residue in 20 ml of water and proceed as described for Calcium Chloride, Dihydrate, beginning with "add 2 ml of 10% HCl. . . ."

Sulfate: Evaporate 1.0 g with 5 ml of HCl to dryness on the steam bath. Dissolve the residue in 10 ml of H_2O and add 1 ml of 0.1 N HCl and 2 ml of $BaCl_2$. Any resulting turbidity is not greater than that in a control made with 0.10 mg of SO_4, 1 ml of 0.1 N HCl, and 2 ml of $BaCl_2$ in the same volume as with the sample.

Heavy metals: Dissolve 4 g in water to make 40 ml. To 10 ml add 0.02 mg of Pb, 1 ml of 1 N acetic acid and dilute to 40 ml (A). To the remaining 30 ml add 1 ml of 1 N acetic acid and dilute to 40 ml (B). Then to each add 10 ml of H_2S; B is not darker than A.

Iron: Dissolve 1 g in 30 ml of water, add 5 ml of 10% HCl and dilute to 50 ml. Add about 30 mg of ammonium persulfate and 3 ml of ammonium thiocyanate. Any resulting red color is not darker than that of a blank to which 0.01 mg of Fe has been added.

Insoluble and NH_4OH precipitate; Ammonia; Barium; Magnesium and Alkalies: Make these tests as described for Calcium Chloride, Dihydrate. The results conform to the requirements there stated.

CALCIUM OXIDE

CaO; mol. wt. 56.08; Ca—71.47%; O—28.53%.

White or slightly yellowish, or brownish-tinted irregular pieces, or a granular powder. Readily absorbs carbon dioxide and moisture from the air. Soluble in 850 parts of water, less soluble in hot water; insoluble in alcohol. When mixed with a little water much heat is generated. Much heat is also generated when it is treated with acids. *Keep in tightly closed containers.*

Standards

Acetic acid—insoluble and		Sulfate (SO$_4$)................max 0.20%	
NH$_4$OH precipitate........max 0.30%		Heavy metals (as Pb)........max 0.005%	
Ignition loss.................max 10.0%		Iron (Fe)....................max 0.015%	
Chloride (Cl)................max 0.005%		Magnesium and Alkalies	
Nitrate (NO$_3$)..............max 0.010%		(as MgO)...................max 1.0%	

Acetic acid—insoluble and NH$_4$OH precipitate: Mix 3 g with 50 ml of water, *cautiously* add 10 ml of glacial acetic acid, and evaporate to dryness on the steam bath. Dissolve the residue in 100 ml of water (do not filter), heat the solution to boiling and make it slightly alkaline with ammonium hydroxide. Filter and wash with a little H$_2$O. Pour on the filter, dropwise, a few ml of warm 10% HCl and wash well with H$_2$O. Make the second filtrate slightly alkaline with NH$_4$OH, boil and filter through the same filter as before, then wash with water, ignite and weigh. The weight does not exceed 9.0 mg.

Ignition loss: Weigh accurately about 1 g and ignite strongly to constant weight. The loss in weight corresponds to not more than 10%.

Chloride: Mix 1 g with 40 ml of H$_2$O and *cautiously* add 4 ml of HNO$_3$. Filter and add to the filtrate 1 ml of AgNO$_3$. Any resulting turbidity is not greater than that in a blank to which 0.05 mg of Cl has been added.

Nitrate: Mix 0.5 g of sample with 10 ml of cold water and allow to "slack." Add a few drops at a time glacial acetic acid (about 0.5 ml) until no more dissolves, dilute to 25 ml and add 5 ml of 25% H$_2$SO$_4$. Shake well, allow to stand for 15–20 minutes, shaking a few times, then filter or centrifuge and decant. To 6 ml (= 0.1 g of sample) add 2 ml of brucine sulfate solution and dilute to 10 ml (*S*). For control, dilute 3 ml of standard nitrate solution (= 0.03 mg NO$_3$) with water to 8 ml and add 2 ml of brucine sulfate solution (*C*); then proceed as directed under Nitrate—Estimation of Small Amounts.

Sulfate: To 2.5 g add 75 ml of H$_2$O, then add dropwise HCl until dissolved and add 1 ml excess of the acid. Filter, heat the filtrate to boiling, add 5 ml of BaCl$_2$, and allow to stand overnight. Filter any precipitate formed, wash it with H$_2$O, and ignite. The weight of the BaSO$_4$ so obtained is not more than 12.0 mg.

Solution S: Mix 2 g with 25 ml of H$_2$O, *cautiously* add 7 ml of HCl, then 3 ml of HNO$_3$, and evaporate to dryness on the steam bath. Take up the residue with 1 ml of 10% HCl and 25 ml of hot water, filter and wash with a few ml of H$_2$O. Add to the filtrate 2 drops of phenolphthalein and just enough 1 *N* NaOH to produce a permanent pink color. Discharge the pink color with 1 or 2 drops of 1 *N* HCl and dilute to 100 ml.

Heavy metals: To 10 ml of *Solution S* add 0.02 mg of Pb, 1 ml of 1 *N* acetic acid, and dilute to 40 ml (*A*). To 30 ml of *Solution S* add 1 ml of 1 *N* acetic acid and dilute to 40 ml (*B*). Then to each add 10 ml of H$_2$S. *B* is not darker than *A*.

Iron: To 5 ml of *Solution S*, add 2 ml of HCl and dilute to 50 ml. Add 30 mg ammonium persulfate and 3 ml of ammonium thiocyanate and mix. Any resulting red color is not darker than that of a control made with 0.015 mg of Fe, 2 ml of HCl and the same quantities of the other reagents and in the same final volume as with the sample.

Magnesium and Alkalies: Mix 1 g with 50 ml of H_2O, *cautiously* add 6 ml of HCl, heat to boiling and add 75 ml of ammonium oxalate solution. Slowly neutralize with NH_4OH while the solution is cooling. Dilute to 150 ml and let stand for 4 hours or overnight. Filter, and to 75 ml of the filtrate add 0.5 ml of H_2SO_4, evaporate, ignite and weigh. The weight of the residue is not more than 15.0 mg.

CALCIUM PHOSPHATE, DIBASIC

Secondary Calcium Phosphate

$CaHPO_4 \cdot 2H_2O$; mol. wt. 172.10%; anhydrous—79.06%; H_2O—20.94%; Ca—23.29%; PO_4—55.19%; CaO—32.59%; P—18.00%.

White, crystalline powder. Almost insoluble in water, readily soluble in dilute hydrochloric or nitric acid, difficultly soluble in acetic acid. On ignition it is converted into pyrophosphate, $Ca_2P_2O_7$. Its H_2O of hydration may be determined by the iodine (Fischer) method.

Standards

Hydrochloric acid—insoluble..max 0.010%	Nitrogen compounds
Assay.......................min 98%	(NH₃, NO₃ as N)..........max 0.02%
Monobasic...................max 1.0%	Sulfate (SO₄)...............max 0.010%
Tribasic.....................max 1.5%	Arsenic (As)................max 2 ppm
Carbonate...................to pass test	Barium (Ba)................max 0.01%
Chloride (Cl)...............max 0.005%	Heavy metals (as Pb).......max 0.002%
Fluoride (F)...............max 0.001%	Iron (Fe)...................max 0.005%
	Magnesium (Mg)..............max 0.2%

Hydrochloric acid—insoluble: Heat 10 g of sample with 90 ml of H_2O and 10 ml of HCl until dissolved. Filter any undissolved matter (retain filtrate), wash it well with water and dry at 105°. Its weight does not exceed 1.0 mg.

Assay: Dry about 5 g in a shallow layer at 110° to constant weight. Weigh accurately about 3 g of the dried sample into a beaker, add 30.0 ml of 1 N HCl and 25 ml of water, and warm, if necessary, to dissolve. Add a neutralized (to phenolphthalein) solution of 4 g of potassium oxalate in 75 ml of water. Stir well for a few minutes, and allow to stand for 30 minutes, stirring a few times. Then using a pH meter and glass electrodes titrate with 1 N NaOH to pH 4.0. The difference between the volume of the 1 N HCl added and the volume of 1 N NaOH used for the back titration divided by the weight of the dried sample represents the volume of 1 N HCl consumed by 1 g of sample. Designate this volume as V. Theoretically 7.35 ml of 1 N HCl is required. If more has been consumed, tribasic is present; the per cent of $CaHPO_4$ is $V - (V - 7.35) \times 0.1361 \times 100$, and that of tribasic is $V - 7.35 \times 0.07755 \times 100$. If V is less than 7.35, monobasic is present; the per cent of $CaHPO_4$ is $V \times 0.1361 \times 100$, and that of monobasic $7.35 - V \times 0.1260 \times 100$. Not less than 7.20 ml and not more than 7.45 ml should be consumed by 1 g of the dried sample.

Carbonate: Mix 1 g with 5 ml of H_2O and 2 ml HCl. No bubbles of carbon dioxide are evolved.

Chloride: Digest 2 g with 40 ml of H_2O and 3 ml of HNO_3 for 15 minutes, filter and wash to 50 ml. To 10 ml of the filtrate add 1 ml of $AgNO_3$. Any resulting turbidity is not greater than that of a control made with 0.02 mg of Cl, 1 ml of NHO_3, and 1 ml of $AgNO_3$ in the same final volume as the sample.

Fluoride: Place 4 g of sample, 5 ml of 70% perchloric acid, 15 ml of H_2O, and a few glass beads in a 50-ml distilling flask connected with a condenser and carrying a thermometer and a capillary tube, both of which extend into the liquid. Connect a small dropping funnel, filled with H_2O, to the capillary tube. Support the flask on an asbestos mat with a hole which exposes about one-third of the flash to the flame. Distill until the temperature reaches 135°, receiving the distillate under the surface of a few ml of H_2O. Maintain at from 135° to 140° by adding H_2O from the funnel and continue the distillation until about 70 ml has been collected. Dilute the distillate to 80 ml and mix well. Transfer 40 ml of the solution into a Nessler tube. In a similar Nessler tube, place 40 ml of H_2O as a control. Add to each tube 0.1 ml of sodium alizarin-sulfonate solution and mix well. To the tube containing the distillate add, drop by drop, and with stirring, 0.05 N NaOH until its color just matches that of the control which is faintly pink, then add to each tube exactly 1 ml of 0.1 N HCl and mix well. From a burette, add slowly to the tube containing the distillate enough thorium nitrate solution (made by dissolving 0.25 g of thorium nitrate in 1000 ml of H_2O) so that, after mixing, the color of the liquid just changes to a faint pink. Note the volume of thorium nitrate solution added, add exactly the same volume to the control, and mix. Now add to the control standard fluoride solution from a burette to make the colors of the two tubes match after dilution to the same volume. Mix well and allow all air bubbles to escape. Check the end point by adding 1 or 2 drops of sodium fluoride to the control. A distinct change in color should take place. Not more than 2 ml of the fluoride solution is required for the tube containing the distillate. Each ml of sodium fluoride is equivalent to 0.01 mg of fluorine.

Nitrogen compounds (NH_3, NO_3): Place 0.5 g of sample in a distilling flask connected through a spray trap to a condenser and a receiver containing 10 ml of water and 5 drops of 10% HCl. Add to the flask 10 ml of water and just sufficient HCl to dissolve the calcium phosphate and dilute to about 75 ml. Add 1 g of fine aluminum wire in small pieces and follow with 20 ml of 10% NaOH. Stopper the flask, allow to stand for 2 hours, mixing the contents a few times during this period. Then slowly distill about 50 ml and dilute the distillate with ammonia-free water to 100 ml. Dilute 20 ml of this solution with ammonia-free water to 50 ml and add 2 ml of 10% NaOH and 2 ml of Nessler solution. Any color produced is not darker than that produced by treating 0.1 mg of nitrogen (0.4 mg NH_4Cl) in the same manner as the sample.

Sulfate: Heat the filtrate from the *Hydrochloric acid—insoluble* to boiling, add 5 ml of $BaCl_2$ solution and allow to stand overnight. If a precipitate is present, filter, wash with hot water, dry and ignite, and weigh. The weight of the $BaSO_4$ so obtained does not exceed 2.5 mg.

Arsenic: Test 1.0 g by the method on page 563. The stain produced is not greater than that from 0.002 mg of As.

Barium: Heat 1.0 g with 10 ml of water and add HCl, a few drops at a time, until just dissolved. Filter if not clear, add to the filtrate 2 ml of a 1% solution of K_2SD_4, shake well and allow to stand. No turbidity develops in 30 minutes.

Heavy metals: To 2 g add 25 ml of water, heat to boiling and add at first 1.0 ml of HCl, then a drop at a time until the sample just dissolves. Add to the hot solution 10% NH_3, a drop at a time, until a slight precipitate forms, which no longer dissolves on stirring. Now add HCl, dropwise, while stirring the liquid until the precipitate just dissolves. Cool and dilute to 40 ml. To 10 ml add 0.02 mg of Pb and dilute to 40 ml (A). Dilute the remaining 30 ml of the solution to 40 ml (B). Then to each add 10 ml of H_2S. B is not darker than A.

Iron: To 1 g add 25 ml of water, heat and add HCl in small portions at a time, until the sample is just dissolved. Cool and dilute with H_2O to 100 ml. To 20 ml of the solution add 1 ml of HCl, 50 mg of ammonium persulfate and 20 ml of butanolic potassium thiocyanate, shake well and allow to separate. Any red color in the butanol layer is not darker than that of a control made with 0.01 mg of Fe, 1 ml of HCl, 10 ml of H_2O, and the same quantities of the other reagents as used with the sample.

Magnesium: Mix 1 g with 15 ml of water, heat and add HCl dropwise until dissolved. Cool, and dilute with water to 250 ml. Dilute 7 ml of the solution with H_2O to 40 ml (A). To 2 ml of the solution add 0.04 mg of Mg and dilute with water to 40 ml (B). Add 0.3 ml of Clayton Yellow (thiazole yellow) solution to A and 0.2 ml to B, and follow with 20 ml of 10% NaOH to each. The pink color in A is not darker than that in B.

CALCIUM PHOSPHATE, MONOBASIC

Calcium Biphosphate; Primary Calcium Phosphate

$Ca(H_2PO_4)_2 \cdot H_2O$; mol. wt. 252.09; anhydrous—92.85%; Ca—15.90%; PO_4—75.35%; CaO—22.24%; P—24.58%.

White crystals, or a crystalline powder; deliquescent. Sparingly soluble in water; insoluble in alcohol. When boiled with water a more basic salt and free phosphoric acid are formed (pH about 3.5). *Keep in well-closed containers.*

Standards

Hydrochloric acid—insoluble..max 0.010%	Arsenic (As)................max 2 ppm
Assay........................min 98%	Barium (Ba)................max 0.01%
Dibasic ($CaHPO_4$).............max 2.0%	Heavy metals (as Pb)........max 0.002%
Free H_3PO_4................max 1.5%	Iron (Fe)...................max 0.005%
Chloride (Cl)...............max 0.005%	Magnesium (Mg)..............max 0.2%
Sulfate (SO_4)...............max 0.010%	
Nitrogen compounds	
(NH_3, NO_3) as N..........max 0.02%	

Dilute Hydrochloric acid—insoluble: Heat 10 g with a mixture of 5 ml of HCl and 100 ml of water until no more dissolves. Filter any undissolved matter (retain filtrate), wash it well with water, and dry at 105°. Its weight does not exceed 1.0 mg.

Assay: Dissolve about 2.5 g of sample, accurately weighed, in 15.0 ml of 1 N HCl and 25 ml of water. Dilute with 50 ml of water and add a solution of 2 g of neutral potassium oxalate in 50 ml of water. Stir vigorously and allow to stand for 20 minutes; then using a standardized pH meter and glass electrodes titrate with 1 N NaOH to pH 3.8. Observe the volume of the NaOH used. Theoretically it should be equal or practically so to the volume of 1 N HCl added. If it is greater, excess of H_3PO_4 is indicated and it should not be more than 0.15 ml for each 1 g of sample. If the volume of the HCl exceeds that of the NaOH, dibasic ($CaHPO_4$) is present and it corresponds to not more than 0.15 ml for each 1 g of sample. Now resume titration with the NaOH, stirring the solution vigorously, to pH 9.2. This titration represents $Ca(H_2PO_4)_2$. Not less than 7.8 ml nor more than 8.1 ml should be consumed for each 1 g of sample.

Sulfate: Using the filtrate from the test for *Hydrochloric acid—insoluble*, determine the SO_4 as directed under *Calcium Phosphate, Dibasic*. The weight of the $BaSO_4$ does not exceed 2.5 mg.

Barium; Chloride; Nitrogen Compounds; Arsenic; Heavy Metals; Iron; Magnesium: Test as described under Calcium Phosphate, Dibasic. The results conform to the requirements there stipulated.

Heavy metals: To 2 g add 25 ml of water, heat to boiling and add HCl, a drop at a time, until the sample just dissolves. Add to the hot solution 10% NH_3, a drop at a time, until a slight precipitate is produced, which no longer dissolves on stirring. Now add HCl, dropwise, while stirring the liquid, until the precipitate just dissolves. Cool and dilute to 40 ml. To 10 ml add 0.02 mg of Pb and dilute to 40 ml (A). Dilute the remaining 30 ml of the solution to 40 ml (B). Then to each add 10 ml of H_2S. B is not darker than A.

CALCIUM PHOSPHATE, TRIBASIC

Tertiary Calcium Phosphate

$Ca_3(PO_4)_2$; mol. wt. 310.20; Ca—38.76%; PO_4—61.24%; P—19.97.

White powder. Insoluble in water, acetic acid, or in organic solvents; soluble in HCl, HHO_3, and H_3PO_4.

Standards

Hydrochloric acid—insoluble..max 0.020%	Sulfate (SO_4)................max 0.030%
Assay, $Ca_3(PO_4)_2$..............min 97%	Arsenic (As).................max 2 ppm
Dibasic.....................max 0.70%	Barium (Ba).................max 0.01%
Excess (free) CaO.............max 2.0%	Heavy metals (as Pb)........max 0.002%
Carbonate (CO_3).............to pass test	Iron (Fe)....................max 0.01%
Chloride (Cl)................max 0.005%	Magnesium (Mg).............max 0.2%
Fluoride (F)...............max 0.002%	
Nitrogen compounds	
(NH_3, NO_3) as N..........max 0.04%	

Hydrochloric acid—insoluble: Heat 10 g with a mixture of 20 ml of HCl and 80 ml of water until solution is effected. Filter any undissolved matter (retain filtrate) wash well with water, and dry at 105°. Its weight does not exceed 2.0 mg.

Assay: Ignite about 2.5 g at 700°–800° to constant weight. Weigh accurately 2.0 g of the ignited sample and dissolve it in 30.0 1 N HCl + 20 ml of water, warming if necessary. Add a neutralized (to phenolphthalein) solution of 3.5 g of potassium oxalate in 100 ml of water, stir well for a few minutes, and allow to stand for 30 minutes, stirring a few times.   Now using a pH meter and glass electrode system titrate with 1 N NaOH to pH 4.0.   The difference between the volume of the HCl added and the volume of the NaOH required for back titration divided by the weight of sample is the volume of 1 N HCl consumed for each 1 gram.   Designate this volume as V.   Theoretically 1 gram of $Ca_3(PO_4)_2$ should consume 12.90 ml.   If the volume consumed by sample is less, dibasic ($CaHPO_4$) is present, and its amount is $(12.90 - V) \times 0.1361 \times 100$, and the percentage of tribasic is $V \times 0.07755 \times 100$. If the volume of the 1 N HCl is greater, excess (free) CaO is present, and its amount is $V - 12.90 \times 0.028 \times 100$.

Not less than 12.65 ml and not more than 13.60 ml of 1 N HCl should be consumed per gram of the ignited sample.

Carbonate: Mix 1 g with 5 ml of water and add dropwise diluted HCl $(1+1)$. No bubbles (of CO_2) are evoked.

Chloride: Mix 0.50 g with 10 ml of water and add just sufficient HNO_3 to effect solution.   Filter if necessary, dilute to 50, and add 1 ml of HNO and 2 ml of $AgNO_3$. Any resulting turbidity is not greater than that in a blank to which 0.1 mg of Cl has been added.

Fluoride; Nitrogen: Determine as in Calcium Phosphate, Dibasic using one-half the quantity of sample there directed.   The results should be as there stated.

Sulfate: Determine as in Calcium Phosphate, Dibasic.   The weight of $BaSO_4$ does not exceed 7.5 mg.

Arsenic; Barium; Heavy metals; Iron; Nitrogen Compounds; Magnesium: Test as in Calcium Phosphate, Dibasic, using for the nitrogen and iron tests one half of the quantities there used.

CALCIUM SULFATE

$CaSO_4 \cdot 2H_2O$; mol. wt. 172.18; anhydrous—79.07%; H_2O—20.93%; Ca—23.27%; SO_4—55.79%; CaO—32.57%; SO_3—46.5%; S—18.62%.

White powder, or pulverulent pieces.   Soluble in 400 parts of water, less soluble in hot water; insoluble in alcohol.

Standards

Hydrochloric acid—insoluble...max 0.20%	Magnesium and Alkalies
Organic substances, etc........to pass test	(as sulfates)...............max 0.20%
Neutrality...................to pass test	Heavy metals (as Pb)........max 0.002%
Carbonate (CO_3).........max about 0.2%	Iron (Fe)...................max 0.002%
Chloride (Cl)................max 0.002%	

Hydrochloric acid—insoluble: Reflux 2 g with a mixture of 100 ml of H_2O and 15 ml of HCl.   If an undissolved residue remains, filter it while hot, wash with hot 10% HCl and ignite.   Its weight does not exceed 4.0 mg.

Organic substances, etc.: Ignite 1 g in a test tube.   No white fumes are evolved and no darkening occurs.

Neutrality: Digest 3 g in 50 ml of hot H_2O for 5 mintues and add 2 drops of phenolphthalein.   No pink color is discerned.   Now titrate with 0.02 N NaOH to production of a pink color.   Not more than 0.3 ml of the NaOH is required.

Carbonate: Mix 1 g with 5 ml of H_2O and follow with 2 ml HCl.   No bubbles of carbon dioxide are evolved.

Chloride: Digest 2 g with 30 ml of H_2O and 3 ml of HNO_3 for 15 minutes, filter and dilute to 40 ml.   To 10 ml of the filtrate add 1 ml of $AgNO_3$.   Any resulting turbidity is not greater than that in a control made with 0.01 mg of Cl, 1 ml of HNO_3, and 1 ml of $AgNO_3$ in the same final volume as with the sample.

Magnesium and Alkalies: Heat to boiling 20 ml of the filtrate obtained in the test for *Chloride*, add 40 ml of ammonium oxalate and make just alkaline with NH_4OH.   Heat on the steam bath for 2 hours, cool, dilute to 100 ml, mix well and filter.   Evaporate 50 ml of the filtrate and ignite.   Not more than 2.0 mg of residue remains.

Solution S: To 5 g of the sample add 5 ml HCl, follow with 30 ml of H_2O and heat to boiling.   Filter, wash with 20 ml of hot H_2O and evaporate the filtrate to dryness on the steam bath.   Take up the residue with 30 ml of H_2O, add 2 drops of phenolphthalein and just enough 1 N NaOH to produce a pink color.   Then add 1 or 2 drops of 1 N HCl to discharge the pink color and dilute to 50 ml; filter if not clear.

Heavy metals: To 5 ml of *Solution S* add 0.02 mg of Pb with 1 ml of 1 N acetic acid and dilute to 40 ml (*A*).   To 15 ml of *Solution S*, add 1 ml of 1 N acetic acid and dilute to 40 ml (*B*).   Then add to each 10 ml of H_2S; *B* is not darker than *A*.

Iron: To 5 ml of *Solution S* add 2 ml of HCl and dilute to 50 ml.   Add about 30 mg of ammonium persulfate and 3 ml of ammonium thiocyanate, and mix.   Any resulting red color is not darker than that of a control made with 0.01 mg of Fe, 2 ml of HCl, and the same quantities of the reagents and in the same final volume as with the sample.

α-CAMPHORIC ACID

$C_8H_{14}(COOH)_2$; mol. wt. 200.23.

Colorless or white, odorless crystals.   Soluble in 125 parts of water, in 10 parts of boiling water; soluble in alcohol, in ether and in chloroform.

Standards

Melting range..................185°–188°	Ignition residue..............max 0.05%
Specific rotation...........+47° to +48°	Nitrate (NO_3)................max 0.01%
Solubility in alcohol...........to pass test	

Specific rotation: Determine at 25° the rotation of an ethanol solution containing the equivalent of 10 g of the acid in 100 ml of solution, using a 200-mm tube. The observed rotation in degrees multiplied by 5 = $[\alpha]_{25}$.

Solubility in alcohol: Two grams dissolve without residue in 20 ml of ethanol, forming a colorless solution.

Ignition residue: Moisten 2 g with 1 ml of H_2SO_4 and ignite to constant weight. Not more than 1.0 mg of residue remains.

Nitrate: Add 0.5 g to a mixture of 10 ml of H_2SO_4, 10 ml of water containing 0.2 ml of indigo carmine and heat in boiling H_2O for 2 minutes.   The blue color persists for 5 minutes.

CAPRYLIC ALCOHOL, SECONDARY

2-Octanol

$$CH_3$$
$$|$$
$CH_3(CH_2)_5CHOH$; mol. wt. 130.22.

Clear, colorless, oily, refractive liquid, pungent, aromatic odor.   Insoluble in water; miscible with alcohol, benzene or ether.   Sp. gr. 0.825 at 15°/15°.

Standards

Boiling range..................177°–180°	Acid (as $C_7H_{15}COOH$).........max 0.02%
Refractive index...........1.4200–1.4205	Water......................to pass test
Evaporation residue.........max 0.005%	

Boiling range: Distill 50 ml.   After the first 10 drops have come over, all distills between 177° and 180°, correction being made for barometric pressure, page 581.

Refractive index: Determine at 20°.

Evaporation residue: Evaporate 25 ml and dry at 150° for 1 hour.   Not more than 1.0 mg of residue remains.

Acid: To 20 ml of alcohol add 5 drops of phenolphthalein and 0.02 N NaOH until a pink color persists after shaking for 30 seconds.   Disregard this quantity of the NaOH.   Now add 10 ml of the sample and titrate with 0.02 N NaOH until the pink color is reproduced.   Not more than 0.6 ml of the NaOH is required.

Water: Mix 5 ml with 20 ml of petroleum ether.   The mixture is clear.

CARBON, DECOLORIZING

Activated Charcoal

Fine, black, odorless powder.   It has a high capacity for adsorbing organic coloring substances, as well as nitrogenous bases.

Standards

Adsorptive power............to pass test	Alcohol-soluble substances......max 0.2%
Decolorizing power...........to pass test	Completeness of
Substances volatile at 120°......max 15%	carbonization..............to pass test
Ignition residue...............max 3.5%	Chloride (Cl)................max 0.10%
Neutrality...................to pass test	Sulfate (SO_4)................max 0.15%
Acid-soluble substances.........max 3.0%	Sulfide (S)..................no reaction

Adsorptive power: Dissolve 0.15 g of strychnine sulfate in 50 ml of water, add 1 g of the sample, shake for 5 minutes, then filter through a dry filter, rejecting the first 20 ml.   To a 10-ml portion of the subsequent filtrate add 1 drop of HCl and 5 drops of mercuric potassium iodide solution (Mayers Reagent).   No turbidity is produced.

Decolorizing power: Prepare a solution of 10.0 mg of bromophenol blue in a mixture of 25 ml of alcohol + 75 ml of water. To 75 ml of this solution contained in a flask add 100 mg of sample and rotate the flask for several minutes. Allow to stand for 5 minutes, swirling the contents 2–3 times and filter. The color of the filtrate is not deeper than that of a mixture of 1.0 ml of the bromophenol blue solution + 75 ml of alcohol of the same concentration.

Substances volatile at 120°: Dry 1 g to constant weight at 120°. The loss corresponds to not more than 15% (see Note below).

Ignition residue: Ignite 1 g to constant weight. Not more than 35 mg of residue remains.

Neutrality: Boil 2 g with 50 ml H_2O for 5 minutes, cool, dilute to 50 ml, and filter. The filtrate is colorless and neutral to litmus paper (retain).

Acid-soluble substances: Boil 1 g with 20 ml of H_2O and 5 ml of HCl for 5 minutes, filter into a tared dish, and wash with 10 ml of hot H_2O. Add to the filtrate 1 ml of H_2SO_4, evaporate, and ignite to constant weight. The weight of the residue does not exceed 30 mg.

Alcohol-soluble substances: Boil 2 g with 40 ml of alcohol under a reflux condenser for 5 minutes and filter. Evaporate 20 ml of the filtrate to dryness on the steam bath and dry for 1 hour at 105°. The residue does not exceed 2.0 mg.

Completeness of carbonization: To 0.25 g add 5 ml of 10% NaOH and 5 ml of H_2O, heat to boiling and filter. The filtrate is colorless.

Chloride: Dilute 2 ml of the filtrate from the test for *Neutrality* to 50 ml and add 2 ml of HNO_3 and 2 ml of $AgNO_3$. The turbidity is not greater than that in a blank to which 0.08 mg of Cl has been added.

Sulfate: Dilute 5 ml of the filtrate from the test for *Neutrality* to 25 ml and add 1 ml of 1 N HCl and 2 ml of $BaCl_2$. The turbidity is not greater than that in a blank to which 0.3 mg of SO_4 has been added.

Sulfide: Place 1 g in a small flask with a narrow neck, add 35 ml of H_2O and 5 ml of HCl and boil gently. The escaping vapors do not darken moist lead acetate paper.

Note: The water content of decolorizing carbon may be determined by the iodine (Fischer) method (page 579).

CARBON DISULFIDE

CS_2; mol. wt. 76.14; S—84.23%.

Clear, colorless or faintly yellowish liquid. *Very flammable.* Insoluble in water; miscible with absolute ethanol or ether. Sp. gr. 1.272. *Keep in tightly stoppered containers, in a cool place, remote from flames.*

Standards

Boiling range....................46°–47°	Sulfite and Sulfate.....max about 0.002%
Evaporation residue.........max 0.002%	Water......................max 0.05%
Foreign sulfides and dissolved	
sulfur.....................to pass test	

Boiling range: Distil 50 ml, immersing the bulb of the distilling flask in water heated to about 60° and keeping the level of the liquid in the flask above the level of the water in the bath during the distillation. All distills between 46° and 47°, correction being made for barometric pressure, page 581.

Evaporation residue: Evaporation 40 ml at about 50°; the residue has no disagreeable odor. Dry the residue at 60° for 1 hour; its weight does not exceed 1.0 mg.

Foreign sulfides: Shake 2 ml with a globule of mercury in a dry test tube for 2 minutes. The mercury remains bright.

Sulfite and Sulfate: Shake 10 ml with 10 ml of H_2O in a separatory funnel for 5 minutes, then separate the layers and add 1 drop 0.1 N iodine to the aqueous layer. A yellow or violet color is produced. Now add 1 ml of $BaCl_2$; no turbidity is produced in 15 minutes.

Water: Cool 10 ml in test tube to 0°. No turbidity or drops of water appear.

Note: The water may be quantitatively determined by the iodine (Fischer) method, using 20 ml of sample and 25 ml of methanol as solvent.

CARBON TETRACHLORIDE

CCl_4; mol. wt. 153.84; Cl—92.2%.

Clear, colorless, nonflammable liquid. Boils at 77°; solidifies at about —20°. Very slightly soluble in water; miscible with ethanol, ether, benzene. Sp. gr. 1.589 at 25°.

Standards

Specific gravity (25°/25°) 1.588–1.590	Free chlorine.................no reaction
Boiling range.................76.5°–77.5°	Iodine consuming substances........none
Evaporation residue.........max 0.001%	Substances darkened
Acid (as HCl)...............max 0.002%	by H_2SO_4.................to pass test
Aldehyde....................to pass test	Sulfur compounds (CS_2, etc.)...to pass test
Chloride (Cl)...............max 0.0002%	(max about 0.002% as S)

Specific gravity: Determine at 25° with a pycnometer of at least 10 ml capacity.

Boiling range: Distill 100 ml. Not less than 98 ml distill between 76.5° and 77.5°, correcting for the difference of the barometric pressure from 760 mm (page 581).

Evaporation residue: Evaporate 60 ml on the steam bath and dry at 105° for 30 minutes. The weight of the residue does not exceed 1.0 mg.

Acid: Shake 13 ml with 20 ml of H_2O for 5 minutes, separate, and reject the lower layer. To 10 ml of the aqueous layer add 2 drops of phenolphthalein and 0.05 ml of 0.1 N NaOH. A pink color is produced.

Aldehyde: Shake 10 ml with 10 ml of water and 0.05 ml of 0.1 N potassium permanganate. The pink color persists for 5 minutes.

Chloride: To the remaining 10 ml of the aqueous layer from the test for *Acid* add 2 drops of HNO_3 and 1 ml of 0.1 N AgNO₃. Any resulting turbidity is not more than that in a blank to which 0.02 mg of Cl has been added.

Free chlorine: Shake 10 ml with 10 ml of H_2O and add 2 drops of potassium iodide. No violet tint is produced in the carbon tetrachloride layer.

Iodine consuming substances: To 25 ml add 1 drop of 0.1 N iodine and shake well. The violet color persists for 30 minutes.

Substances darkened by sulfuric acid: Shake 20 ml with 5 ml of H_2SO_4 for 5 minutes in a glass-stoppered cylinder previously rinsed with H_2SO_4. The carbon tetrachloride is colorless and the acid layer acquires not more than a slight color.

Sulfur compounds: To 10 ml of the sample add 2 ml of absolute alcohol and 3 ml of potassium plumbite solution. Gently boil the mixture under a reflux condenser for 15 minutes, agitating well the contents of the flask several times during the heating, and then set aside for 5 minutes. The aqueous layer is colorless.

Note: The sulfur may be quantitatively determined by the method for Sulfur in Volatile Hydrocarbon (page 579) using 5 ml of the sample.

CARMINIC ACID

$CO(CHOH)_4CH_3$; mol. wt. 492.38.

Dark, reddish-brown powder. Freely soluble in water, in alcohol, or in solutions of alkali hydroxides. pH range: 4.8 yellow; 6.2 violet. It is usually used in a 0.1% aqueous solution.

Standards

Solubility....................to pass test   Ignition residue.............max 0.20%
Sensitiveness................to pass test

Solubility: One gram dissolves completely or practically so in 5 ml of water, and the solution does not become turbid upon the addition of 20 ml of alcohol.

Sensitiveness: Dissolve 5 g of ammonium chloride in 50 ml of water and add 0.05 ml of a 1% aqueous solution of the sample. It requires not more than 0.05 ml of 0.1 N NaOH to change the yellowish-red color of the solution to violet-red.

Ignition residue: Cautiously char 0.5 g of sample, cool, add 1 ml of HNO_3 and 1 ml of H_2SO_4, evaporate, and ignite to constant weight. The weight of the residue does not exceed 1.0 mg.

CASEIN

White or slightly yellow, odorless, granular powder. Insoluble in water or organic solvents; readily soluble in solutions of alkali hydroxides, usually forming a cloudy solution; also soluble in dilute mineral acids.

Standards

Nitrogen, anhydrous basis...15.2%–16.0%	Alkalinity...................to pass test
Ignition residue..............max 1.00%	Soluble substances...........max 0.10%
Water......................max 10.0%	Fats......................max 0.20%

Nitrogen; Water: Dry 1 g to constant weight at 105°. The loss in weight corresponds to not more than 10%. Weigh accurately about 0.30 g of the dried sample and determine the nitrogen by the Kjeldahl method, page 576. One ml of 0.1 N HCl = 0.001401 g N, log 14644.

Ignition residue: Gently ignite 1 g in porcelain until thoroughly charred. Cool, add to the char 1 ml of HNO_3 and 1 ml of sulfuric acid and ignite to constant weight. Not more than 0.010 g of residue remains.

Alkalinity: Shake 1 g with 20 ml of H_2O for 10 minutes and filter. The filtrate is not alkaline to litmus paper (*retain filtrate*).

Soluble substances: Evaporate the filtrate from the test for *Alkalinity* on the steam bath and dry at 105°. The residue does not exceed 1.0 mg.

Fats: Dissolve 1 g in a mixture of 5 ml each of alcohol, 10% NH_3 and water, and shake out with two 20-ml portions of petroleum ether. Evaporate the petroleum ether and dry at 70°. The residue does not exceed 2.0 mg.

CELLOSOLVE

2-Ethoxyethanol; Ethylene Glycol Monoethyl Ether

$HO \cdot CH_2 = CH_2 \cdot OC_2H_5$; mol. wt. 90.12.

Colorless liquid, slight characteristic odor. Sp. gr. 0.930. Boils at 135°. Flash point 44°. Miscible with water, alcohol, ether, liquid esters and many other organic liquids. It is a solvent for oils, resins, and waxes. Being an ether, it is subject to peroxidation in the air.

Standards

Specific gravity (25°/25°).....0.929–0.9310	Evaporation residue.........max 0.005%
Boiling range.................134°–135°	Aldehyde....................to pass test
Acid (as acetic)..............max 0.02%	Peroxide (as H_2O_2).........max 0.010%
Miscibility with H_2O, benzene..to pass test	Substances darkened by
	H_2SO_4.....................to pass test

Boiling range: Distill 50 ml. After the first 10 drops, not less than 48 ml distills between 134° and 135°, correction being made for barometric pressure, page 581.

Acid: Mix 10 ml with 15 ml of water, add 2 drops of phenolphthalein and titrate with 0.1 N NaOH. Not more than 0.3 ml of the NaOH is required to produce a pink color.

Miscibility: Mixed with 2 volumes of water and, separately, with 2 volumes of benzene: perfectly clear mixtures result.

Evaporation residue: Evaporate 20 ml on the steam bath and dry at 120° for 1 hour. Not more than 1.0 mg of residue remains.

Aldehyde: Shake 5 ml with 5 ml of 30% KOH in a glass-stoppered cylinder and allow to stand for 5 minutes.   The mixture is colorless.

Peroxide: Place 10 ml in a 50-ml glass-stoppered flask, add 10 ml of water, 0.5 ml of glacial acetic acid, 5 ml of chloroform and 1 ml of 10% KI solution.   Mix, let stand for 2 minutes and titrate any liberated iodine with 0.1 N thiosulfate until the liquid remains colorless for 2 minutes.   One ml of 0.1 N thiosulfate = 0.0017 g H_2O_2.   Not more than 0.5 ml of the thiosulfate is required.   Correct for a blank.

Substances darkened by H_2SO_4: Cool 10 ml of H_2SO_4 to 10°–12° and add to it dropwise and with stirring 10 ml of the sample.   The resulting mixture is not darker than a water solution of 5 mg of K_2CrO_4 per liter.

Note: The water content of Cellosolve may be determined by the iodine (Fischer) method.   It is usually not more than 0.1%.

CERIC AMMONIUM NITRATE

$Ce(NO_3)_4 \cdot 2NH_4NO_3 \cdot 2H_2O$; mol. wt. 584.29; anhydrous—93.83%. Ce—23.98%; H_2O—6.17%.   It is also available in anhydrous form.

Orange-red crystals, slowly soluble in water; insoluble in alcohol; in dioxane; almost insoluble in concentrated HNO_3.

Standards

Assay, anhydrous basis.........min 99%	Aluminium, etc...............max 0.08%
Dilute H_2SO_4—insoluble.......max 0.05%	Not precipitated by NH_4OH...max 0.25%
Chloride (Cl).................max 0.01%	Heavy metals (as Pb)........max 0.003%
Sulfate (SO_4)................max 0.02%	Iron (Fe)..................max 0.005%

Assay:

Ceric Solution: Dry about 3.0 g of sample in a shallow layer at 105° for 3 hours, then weigh accurately and dissolve it in 25 ml of 25% H_2SO_4, warming if necessary. Transfer the solution to a 100-ml volumetric flask, dilute with water to volume and mix well.

Procedure: Weigh accurately about 200 mg of arsenic trioxide primary standard, previously dried at 105° for 2 hours, transfer to a 300-ml conical flask with the aid of 15–20 ml of water, add 10 ml of 10% NaOH, rotate the contents of the flask and warm *gently* until the As_2O_3 is completely dissolved.   Cool, add 25 ml of water, 40 ml of hydrochloric acid, 5 ml of iodine monochloride solution (or, preferably, 0.1 ml of a 1 in 100 solution of osmium tetroxide in 10% H_2SO_4), and 0.1 ml of o-phenanthroline indicator solution and titrate with the Ceric Solution added from a burette until the red color remains discharged for 30 seconds and the solution acquires a bluish color.   Toward the end the reaction is somewhat sluggish, and the last 2–3 ml of the Ceric Solution should be added in small portions, each portion being allowed to react before the next one is added.   Correct for a blank with the same volume of the reagents and indicator.   One gram As_2O_3 = 5.548 g anhydrous ceric ammonium nitrate.

$$4Ce(NO_3)_4 + As_2O_3 + 2H_2O \rightarrow As_2O_5 + 4Ce(NO_3)_3 + 4HNO_3$$

Dilute H_2SO_4—insoluble: To 5.0 g of sample in a beaker add 10 ml of H_2SO_4, stir and *cautiously* add 90 ml of water.   Heat to boiling, cover the beaker and digest on the steam bath for 1 hour. If an undissolved residue is present, filter through a tared, filtering crucible (retain filtrate but not the washings). Wash well until the washings are colorless, and dry at 105°. The weight of the residue does not exceed 2.5 mg.

Chloride: To 0.50 g add 5 ml of H_2O and 5 ml of HNO_3, stir, add water to 50 ml and mix. Filter if not clear and divide filtrate into 2 equal portions. To one portion add 1 ml of $AgNO_3$, heat to boiling, allow to stand for 10 minutes, filter until clear and use for the control. To the other portion add 1 ml of $AgNO_3$. The ensuing turbidity, if any, is not greater than that produced by adding 0.025 mg of Cl to the control and diluting both to the same volume.

Sulfate: To 1.0 g add 5 ml of HCl and 2 ml of 30% hydrogen peroxide and slowly evaporate on the steam bath to dryness. Add 1 ml of 10% HCl, 20 ml of hot water, and 200 mg of hydroxylamine hydrochloride, stir to dissolve, and filter if necessary. Dilute to 25 ml and add 3 ml of $BaCl_2$. Prepare a control by treating 0.2 mg of SO_4 exactly as the sample. Any turbidity ensuing in the solution of the sample in 15 minutes is not greater than that of the control.

Solution S: Dilute the filtrate from the test for *Dilute H_2SO_4—insoluble* with water to 125 ml.

Not precipitated by NH_4OH: Dilute 50 ml of *Solution S* with 40 ml of water, add a moderate excess of NH_4OH, dilute to 100 ml, and filter. Evaporate 50 ml of the filtrate to dryness, refiltering if a turbidity appears during evaporation, and ignite. The weight of the residue does not exceed 2.5 mg.

Aluminium, etc.: Add 50 ml of *Solution S* with continuous stirring to 25 ml of 10% NaOH, dilute to 100 ml and filter. Acidify 50 ml of the filtrate with HCl, then make just alkaline (yellow) with NH_3 to methyl red and bring to a boil. If a turbidity is present, filter, wash with water, ignite, and weigh. Its weight does not exceed 1.5 mg.

Heavy metals: To 1.2 g of sample add 10 ml of HCl and a few drops of 3% H_2O_2 to discharge the yellow color of the solution and evaporate to dryness on the steam bath. Dissolve the residue in 3 drops of HCl and 10 ml of water, add 0.3 g of hydroxylamine hydrochloride and dilute to 40 ml (A). Prepare a control as follows: To 0.20 g of sample add 0.03 mg of Pb, and treat it exactly as (A) beginning with "add 10 ml of HCl ..." (B). Then add to each solution 10 ml of H_2S. A is not darker than B.

Iron: Dissolve 0.50 g in 20 ml of 10% HCl, and add dropwise 3% H_2O_2 until the yellow color of the solution is discharged. Prepare a control by adding 0.05 mg of Fe to 20 ml of the 10% HCl and the same volume of the 3% H_2O_2 as added to the sample. Dilute each solution to 50 ml. To 10 ml of each solution add 1 ml of HCl, 5 ml of H_2O, and 15 ml of butanolic potassium thiocyanate solution. Shake vigorously for 30 seconds and allow to separate. Any red color in the butanol layer of the sample is not darker than that of the control.

CERIC AMMONIUM SULFATE

$Ce(SO_4)_2 \cdot 2(NH_4)_2SO_4 \cdot 2H_2O$; mol. wt. 632.59; $Ce(SO_4)_2$—52.5%; Ce—22.15%.

Yellow to orange-yellow crystals. Slowly soluble in water, more readily in presence of mineral acids.

Standards

Assay......................min 98.5%	Heavy metals (as Pb).......max 0.003%
Acid—insoluble..............max 0.05%	Iron (Fe)...................max 0.005%
Chloride (Cl)...............max 0.005%	Not precipitated by NH_4OH
Aluminum (Al)...............max 0.08%	(Alkalies, Alk. earths, etc.)...max 0.20%

Assay: Weigh accurately about 0.5 g transfer to a flask, add 10 ml of water, then add *cautiously* 3 ml of H_2SO_4. Dilute with 20 ml of water and warm until dissolved. Cool, add 60 ml of diluted phosphoric acid $(1+20)$ and 25 ml of 10% potassium iodide. Allow to stand for 15 minutes and, while passing CO_2 into the flask, titrate the liberated iodine with 0.1 N sodium thiosulfate, adding starch indicator solution toward the end. One ml of 0.1 N thiosulfate $= 0.06326$ g of $Ce(SO_4)_2 \cdot 2(NH_4)_2SO_4 \cdot 2H_2O$, log 82518.

Acid—insoluble: To 5.0 g of the sample in a glass mortar add 5 ml of H_2SO_4 and triturate well; then *cautiously* add 50 ml of water and transfer to 200-ml beaker with the aid of 25 ml of water. Cover and heat on the steam bath until no more dissolves. If an insoluble residue remains filter through a tared filtering crucible (retain filtrate). Wash with hot water, and dry at 120°. The weight of the un-dissolved matter does not exceed 2.5 mg.

Chloride: Dissolve 1.0 g in 5 ml of HNO_3 and 45 ml of water and dilute to 80 ml. Filter if not clear and divide the filtrate into two equal portions. To one portion (A) add 1 ml of $AgNO_3$ solution, bring to a boil and filter after 10 minutes until clear. To the other portion (B) add 1 ml of the $AgNO_3$ solution. The resulting tur-bidity in (B), if any, is not greater than is produced by adding 0.025 mg of Cl to (A).

Solution S: Dilute the filtrate from the test for *Acid—insoluble* with water to 200 ml.

Aluminum: To 80 ml of *Solution S* add an excess of 20% NaOH, dilute to 100 ml and filter. Acidify 50 ml of the filtrate with HCl; then make just alkaline with NH_4OH and boil to remove the excess of NH_3. If a precipitate is present, filter, wash it well with water and ignite. Its weight does not exceed 1.5 mg.

Heavy metals: To 1.2 g of sample add 10 ml of HCl and a few drops of 3% H_2O_2 to discharge the yellow color of the solution and evaporate to dryness on the steam bath. Dissolve the residue in 3 drops of HCl and 10 ml of water, add 0.3 g of hydroxylamine hydrochloride, and dilute to 40 ml (A). Prepare a control as follows: To 0.20 g of sample add 0.03 mg of Pb, and treat it exactly as (A) beginning with "add 10 ml of HCl. . . ." (B). Then add to each solution 10 ml of H_2S. A is not darker than B.

Iron: Dissolve 0.50 g in 20 ml of 10% HCl, and add dropwise 3% H_2O_2 until the yellow color of the solution is discharged. Prepare a control by adding 0.05 mg of Fe to 20 ml of the 10% HCl and the same volume of the 3% H_2O_2 as added to the sample. Dilute each solution to 50 ml. To 10 ml of each solution add 1 ml of HCl, 5 ml of H_2O, and 15 ml of butanolic potassium thiocyanate solution. Shake vigorously for 30 seconds and allow to separate. Any red color in the butanol layer of the sample is not darker than that of the control.

Not precipitated by NH_4OH: To 80 ml of *Solution S* add a slight excess of NH_4OH, dilute to 100 ml and filter. Evaporate 50 ml of the filtrate to dryness and ignite. The weight of the residue is not more than 2.0 mg. Correct for a blank.

CERIC SULFATE

$Ce(SO_4)_2 \cdot 4H_2O$; mol. wt. 404.33; anhydrous—82.18%; Ce—34.66%.

Deep yellow crystal or more commonly a yellow powder. Decomposed by water forming an insoluble basic salt. Slowly soluble in cold mineral acids; more readily soluble in the hot acids.

Standards

Assay........................min 98%
Acid—insoluble..............max 0.10%
Chloride (Cl)...............max 0.005%
Not precipitated by NH$_4$OH
  (Alkalies, etc., Earths)......max 0.26%

Aluminum (Al)..............max 0.08%
Heavy metals (as Pb)........max 0.003%
Iron (Fe)..................max 0.015%

Assay: Proceed as directed under Ceric Ammonium Sulfate.   One ml of 0.1 N thiosulfate = 0.04043 g of $Ce(SO_4)_2 \cdot 4H_2O$, log 60670.

Chloride: Test as Ceric Ammonium Sulfate.   The result should be as there stated.

Solution S: Dilute the filtrate from the test for *Acid—insoluble* with water to 100 ml.

Not precipitated by NH$_4$OH; Aluminum; Heavy metals; Iron: Apply the tests described for Ceric Ammonium Sulfate. The results should be as there required.

CHLORAL HYDRATE

$CCl_3 \cdot CHO \cdot H_2O$; mol. wt. 165.42; Cl—64.3%.

Colorless, transparent crystals of a penetrating odor.   Generally becomes yellow with age.   Soluble in 0.3 part of water, in 1.5 parts of alcohol or ether, in 2 parts of chloroform.   *Keep in tightly closed containers.*

Standards

Ignition residue.............max 0.05%
Substances darkened by
  H$_2$SO$_4$.................to pass test

Chloride (Cl).........max about 0.002%
Assay.......................min 99%

Ignition residue: Moisten 2 g with 1 ml of sulfuric acid and ignite to constant weight.   Not more than 1.0 mg of residue remains.

Substances darkened by sulfuric acid: Shake 0.5 g with 5 ml of sulfuric acid frequently during one-half hour.   The mixture is colorless or practically so.

Chloride: Dissolve 1 g in 20 ml of alcohol and add 0.5 of silver nitrate.   No immediate turbidity is produced.

Assay: Chloral hydrate may be assayed as follows, and when so assayed not less than 99.0% should be found:

Weigh accurately about 5 g and dissolve in 10 ml of water. Add 50 ml of 1 N NaOH, allow the mixture to stand for 2 minutes, then titrate the excess of NaOH with 1 N H$_2$SO$_4$, using phenolphthalein indicator. One ml of 1 N NaOH = 0.1654 g CCl$_3$·CHO·H$_2$O, log 21854.

$$CCl_3 \cdot CHO \cdot H_2O + NaOH \rightarrow \underset{\text{chloroform}}{CHCl_3} + \underset{\text{sodium formate}}{H \cdot CO_2Na} + H_2O$$

CHLORAMINE-T

Sodium p-Toluenesulfonchloramide

CH$_3$·C$_6$H$_4$·SO$_2$NClNa·3H$_2$O; mol. wt. 281.70; active Cl—12.6%.

White, crystalline powder having a slight odor of chlorine. It slowly decomposes on exposure to air. Soluble in about 8 parts of water; insoluble in most organic solvents. Its aqueous solution is alkaline. When treated with an acid it yields free chlorine and oxygen. It should assay the equivalent of from 12% to 13% as "active chlorine."

Chloramine-T is a useful laboratory reagent for furnishing chlorine. A standardized solution of it has been recommended for use as a volumetric solution in place of iodine.

Assay: Weigh accurately about 0.5 g of Chloramine-T and dissolve it in 50 ml of water in a glass-stoppered flask. Add 5 ml of 20% potassium iodide solution and 3 ml of glacial acetic acid and allow to stand for 10 minutes; then titrate the liberated iodine with 0.1 N sodium thiosulfate, using starch indicator. One ml of 0.1 N sodium thiosulfate = 0.001773 g active chlorine.

$$CH_3 \cdot C_6H_4 \cdot SO_2 \cdot NClNa + 2KI + 2CH_3CO_2H$$
$$\rightarrow \underset{\text{toluenesulfonamide}}{CH_3C_6H_4SO_2NH_2} + 2I + 2CH_3CO_2K + NaCl$$

CHLOROFORM

CHCl$_3$; mol. wt. 119.39; Cl—89.1%.

Colorless, clear liquid, characteristic odor. Soluble in 300 parts of water; miscible with alcohol or ether. Contains about 0.7% of alcohol added as a preservative. *Keep in tightly closed containers, protected from light, in a cool place.*

Standards

Specific gravity (25%/25%)....1.475–1.478	Free chlorine...............max 0.0001%
Evaporation residue.........max 0.001%	Phosgene....................to pass test
Acetone; Aldehydes..........max 0.005%	Substances darkened by
Acid.......................no reaction	H$_2$SO$_4$....................to pass test
Chloride....................max 0.0001%	

Evaporation residue: Evaporate 70 ml on the steam bath and dry at 105° for 30 minutes. The residue does not exceed 1.0 mg.

Acetone; Aldehydes: Shake 5 ml with 10 ml of ammonia-free water for 5 minutes in a small glass-stoppered separatory funnel. To 5 ml of the aqueous layer add 40 ml of ammonia-free water and 5 ml of Nessler solution.   No turbidity or precipitate is produced within 1 minute.

Acid; Chloride: Shake 17 ml (25 g) with 25 ml of water for 5 minutes and discard the chloroform layer.   A 10-ml portion of the aqueous layer does not redden blue litmus paper.   To another 10-ml portion add 5 drops of $AgNO_3$.   No turbidity is produced in 1 minute.

Free chlorine: Shake 10 ml with 10 ml of H_2O for 2 minutes, separate the aqueous layer and add to it 2 drops of 10% potassium iodide and 2 drops of starch solution.   No blue color is produced.

Phosgene: Overlay 10 ml with a clear, saturated barium hydroxide solution. No white film forms at the interface.

Substances darkened by sulfuric acid: In a glass-stoppered cylinder, previously rinsed with sulfuric acid, shake 20 ml of the sample with 5 ml of sulfuric acid for 5 minutes and allow to separate.   The chloroform is colorless and the acid is colorless or practically so.

CHOLESTEROL

$C_{27}H_{45} \cdot OH$; mol. wt. 386.64.

White, pearly leaflets.   Insoluble in water; slowly soluble in 80 parts of alcohol; soluble in acetone, benzene, chloroform, ether, ethyl acetate, petroleum benzin; also in vegetable oils.

Characteristic reactions: On adding 1 ml of H_2SO_4 to a solution of about 20 mg in 1 ml of chloroform the latter acquires a blood-red color and the sulfuric acid shows a green fluorescence.   To a solution of a few mg of cholesterol in 2 ml of chloroform, 1 ml of acetic anhydride is added, followed by a drop of sulfuric acid.   A pink color is produced which rapidly changes to red, then to blue, and finally to a brilliant green.

Standards

Melting range..................148°–150°	Alcohol—insoluble............to pass test	
Specific rotation in	Acid........................to pass test	
absolute alcohol.............. −30°–31°	Ignition residue.............max 0.05%	

Specific rotation: Prepare a solution in absolute ethanol, containing the equivalent of 1 g of the sample in 50 ml, determine the rotation of the solution at 25°, preferably in a 200-mm. tube, and calculate the specific rotation.

Alcohol—insoluble: Dissolve 0.5 g in 50 ml warm alcohol in a small flask, cover, and allow to stand for 3 hours at 20°–25°.   No deposit or turbidity is formed.

Acid: Dissolve 1 g in 10 ml of ether in a small flask, add 10 ml of 0.1 N NaOH and shake well for about 1 minute.   Heat gently to expel the ether, then boil gently for 5 minutes.   Cool, dilute with H_2O to 10 ml and titrate excess alkali with 0.1 N acid, using 2 drops of phenolphthalein as indicator.   Run a blank.   Not more than 0.2 ml of the 0.1 N NaOH is consumed.

Ignition residue: To 2 g add 1 ml of H_2SO_4 and ignite gently at first, then strongly to constant weight.   The residue does not exceed 1.0 mg.

CHOLINE CHLORIDE

Cl
|
$(CH_3)_3N \cdot (CH_2 \cdot CH_2OH)$; mol. wt. 139.63; choline—86.8%; Cl—25.4%; N—10.03%.

Colorless or white crystals or crystalline powder, usually having a slightly fishy odor. It is hygroscopic and very soluble in water or alcohol.

Standards

Chloride content (Cl)........25.2%–25.6%	Ammonium salts (as NH_3).....max 0.10%
Nitrogen content (N).......9.80%–10.10%	Heavy metals (as Pb)........max 0.002%
Solubility....................to pass test	Ignition residue..............max 0.05%
Trimethylamine..............to pass test	

Chlorine content: Using about 0.3 g, accurately weighed, of the sample previously dried for 24 hours over H_2SO_4, or for 4 hours in a vacuum over a suitable dehydrating agent (P_2O_5, silica gel, H_2SO_4), determine the chloride (Cl^-) by either the Volhard method or the adsorption indicator method. One ml of 0.1 $NagNO_3$ = 0.003546 g Cl, log 54934.

Nitrogen content: Determine the nitrogen in the sample previously dried over H_2SO_4 for 24 hours by the Kjedahl method. One ml of 0.1 N acid = 0.001408 g N, log 14644.

Solubility: A solution of 1 g in 5 ml of H_2O or in 5 ml of alcohol is clear, complete and colorless.

Trimethylamine: Dissolve 0.1 g in 10 ml of H_2O saturated with sodium bicarbonate and boil for 1 minute. The odor of trimethylamine is not evolved.

Ammonium salts: Dissolve 0.1 g in 10 ml of water, and immediately add one drop of phenolphthalein solution and 1 ml of neutralized formaldehyde. Not more than 0.3 ml of 0.02 N NaOH is required to produce a pink color.

Heavy metals: Dissolve 2 g in 40 ml of H_2O. To 10 ml of the solution add 0.02 mg of Pb and 1 ml of 1 N acetic acid, and dilute to 40 ml (A). To the remaining 30 ml add 1 ml of 1 N acetic acid and dilute to 40 ml (B). Then to each add 10 ml of H_2S. B is not darker than A.

Ignition residue: Char 2.0 g. Cool, add 0.5 ml of H_2SO_4 and ignite gently at first, then strongly (600°–800°) to constant weight. Any residue present is not more than 1.0 mg.

CHROMIUM CHLORIDE

Chromic Chloride

$CrCl_3 \cdot 6H_2O$; mol. wt. 266.48; anhydrous—59.44%; H_2O—40.56%; Cr—19.52%; Cl—39.92%.

Dark green granules or lumps; deliquescent. Very soluble in water or in alcohol. Frequently contains some basic chloride. *Keep in well closed containers.*

Standards

Assay...................18.5%–19.5% Cr	Aluminum (Al).............max 0.020%
Insoluble....................max 0.010%	Ammonia (NH_3).............max 0.030%
Sulfate (SO_4)...............max 0.020%	Heavy metals (as Pb)........max 0.000%
Alkalies, Earths, etc...........max 0.20%	Iron (Fe)...................max 0.010%

Assay: Weigh accurately about 1.5 g, dissolve it in water and dilute to exactly 100 ml. Transfer 25 ml to a 300 ml flask, heat to about 80° and cautiously add, in small portions, 2 g of sodium peroxide (NaOH and H_2O_2 can be used instead of the sodium peroxide) and dilute with 100 ml of H_2O. Boil gently until the volume is reduced to about 50 ml, or until the excess of peroxide is destroyed. Dilute to about 150 ml, add 7 ml of phosphoric acid and cool. Add 3 g of potassium iodide, allow to stand for 30 minutes, then titrate the liberated iodine with 0.1 N thiosulfate, adding starch toward the end. One ml of 0.1 N thiosulfate = 0.001734 g Cr, log 23905.

$$2CrCl_3 + 3Na_2O_2 + 4NaOH \rightarrow 2Na_2CrO_4 + 6NaCl + 2H_2O$$

$$Na_2CrO_4 + 3KI + acid \rightarrow \underset{\substack{\text{chrome salt} \\ \text{of the acid}}}{Cr^{+++}} + alkali\ salt\ of\ the\ acid + 3I + 4H_2O$$

Insoluble: Dissolve 10 g in 100 ml of water and warm on the steam bath for 30 minutes. Filter any undissolved matter, wash it with water until the washings are colorless, and dry at 105°. The insoluble residue does not exceed 1.0 mg.

Sulfate: Dissolve 3 g in 120 ml of water, heat the solution to boiling and add with stirring sufficient ammonium hydroxide to precipitate all the chromium. Boil to expel the excess of NH_3, filter and wash with hot H_2O to 150 ml. Evaporate 50 ml of the filtrate to about 15 ml and neutralize with dilute HCl. Filter, if necessary, and add to the filtrate 1 ml of 0.1 N HCl, dilute to 20 ml and add 2 ml of $BaCl_2$. Any turbidity produced is not greater than that in a control made with 0.2 mg of SO_4, 1 ml of 0.1 N HCl and 2 ml of $BaCl_2$ in the same volume as with the sample.

Alkalies, Earths, etc.: Evaporate 50 ml of the filtrate obtained in the test for *Sulfate* with 5 drops of H_2SO_4 and ignite. The residue is not over 2.0 mg.

Aluminum: Dissolve 2.5 g in 50 ml of H_2O and cautiously add to the solution, portionwise, 6 g of sodium peroxide. Heat to boiling, filter and wash with a small quantity of hot water. Acidify the filtrate with HCl, then add a slight excess of NH_4OH, boil to expel excess NH_3, filter any precipitate formed, wash with hot water until the washings are colorless and ignite. The residue of Al_2O_3 does not exceed 1.0 mg.

Ammonia: Dissolve 1 g in 60 ml of H_2O, add 20 ml of 10% NaOH, and distill about 40 ml into 5 ml of water containing 1 drop of dilute HCl. Dilute the distillate with water to 100 ml. Dilute 5 ml of the distillate to 50 ml and add 1 ml of 10% NaOH and 2 ml of Nessler solution. The color produced is not darker than that of a control made with 0.015 mg of NH_3, 1 ml of the NaOH and 2 ml of Nessler solution diluted to the same final volume as the sample.

Heavy metals: Dissolve 0.5 g in 30 ml of H_2O, add 3 ml of 1% aqueous mercuric chloride and saturate the solution with H_2S. Filter through a small paper, wash thoroughly with H_2S water and gently ignite the precipitate in porcelain to volatilize the mercury sulfide. Add to the residue 1 ml of HNO_3 and 1 ml of HCl and evaporate to dryness on the steam bath. Dissolve the residue in 20 ml of hot water, add 2 ml of 1 N acetic acid, cool, dilute to 40 ml and add 10 ml of H_2S. Any color produced is not darker than that of a control made with 0.025 mg of Pb, 2 ml of 1 N acetic acid and 10 ml of H_2S in the same volume as with the sample.

Iron: Dissolve 1 g in 15 ml of water, add 2 ml of HCl and boil for 2 minutes. Cool and dilute to 50 ml. To 10 ml of the solution, add 1 ml of HCl, about 30 mg of ammonium persulfate, and follow with 15 ml of butanolic potassium thiocyanate. Shake well for about 30 seconds and allow to separate. Any red color in the clear butanol (upper) layer is not darker than that in a blank to which 0.02 mg of Fe has been added.

CHROMIUM POTASSIUM SULFATE

Chrome Alum

$CrK(SO_4)_2 \cdot 12H_2O$; mol. wt. 499.43; anhydrous—56.71%; H_2O—43.29%; Cr—10.41%; K—7.83%; SO_4—38.47%.

Dark, violet-red crystals or granules; efflorescent in dry air. Soluble in 5 parts of water; insoluble in alcohol.

Standards

Insoluble....................max 0.010%	Ammonia (NH_3)............max 0.010%	
Chloride (Cl)...............max 0.002%	Heavy metals (as Pb)........max 0.005%	
Aluminium (Al)............max 0.200%	Iron (Fe)..................max 0.010%	
	Assay	

Insoluble: Dissolve 10 g in 100 ml of H_2O and warm on the steam bath for 30 minutes. Filter any undissolved matter, wash it with water until the washings are colorless and dry at 105°. The weight of the residue is not more than 1.0 mg.

Chloride: Dissolve 1 g in 25 ml of water, heat the solution to boiling and add with stirring 2 ml of NH_4OH. Boil to expel the excess of NH_3, filter and wash with hot water to 50 ml. To 25 ml, add 1 ml of HNO_3 and 1 ml of $AgNO_3$. Any resulting turbidity is not greater than that in a control made with 0.01 mg Cl, 1 ml HNO_3 and 1 ml of $AgNO_3$ in the same volume as with the sample.

Aluminium: Dissolve 4 g in 100 ml of H_2O and cautiously add, in small portions, 4 g of sodium peroxide. Heat to boiling, filter and wash with a small volume of hot water. Acidify the filtrate with HCl, then add a slight excess of ammonia and boil to expel excess of NH_3. Filter any precipitate formed, wash it with hot H_2O until the washings are colorless and ignite. The weight of the ignited residue is not more than 1.5 mg.

Ammonia: Dissolve 1 g in 60 ml of H_2O and add 20 ml of 10% NaOH. Distill over about 40 ml into 5 ml of water containing 1 drop of dilute HCl and dilute to 50 ml. Dilute 5 ml of the distillate to 50 ml, and add 1 ml of NaOH solution and 2 ml of Nessler solution. The color produced is not darker than that of a control made with 0.01 mg of NH_3, 2 ml of the NaOH solution and 2 ml of Nessler solution in the same final volume as with the sample.

Heavy metals: Dissolve 0.5 g in 30 ml of H_2O, add 5 ml of a 1% aqueous solution of mercuric chloride, and saturate with H_2S. Filter through a small paper, wash thoroughly with H_2S water, then gently ignite the precipitate in porcelain to volatilize the mercuric sulfide. Add to the residue 1 ml each of HCl and of HNO_3, and evaporate to dryness on the steam bath. Dissolve the residue in 20 ml of hot H_2O, add 2 ml of 1 N acetic acid, cool, dilute to 40 ml, and add 10 ml of H_2S. Any color produced is not darker than that of a control made with 0.025 mg of Pb, 2 ml of 1 N acetic acid and 10 ml H_2S in the same volume as with the sample.

Iron: Dissolve 1 g in 15 ml of H_2O, add 3 ml of HCl, and boil the solution for 2 minutes. Cool and dilute to 100 ml. To 10 ml add 1 ml of HCl, about 30 mg of ammonium persulfate, and follow with 15 ml of butanolic potassium thiocyanate. Shake well for about 30 seconds and allow to separate. Any resulting red color in the clear butanol (upper) layer is not darker than that in a blank to which 0.02 mg of Fe has been added.

Assay: Chromium potassium sulfate may be assayed as described for Chromium Chloride. One ml of 0.1 N sodium thiosulfate = 0.01665 g $CrK(SO_4)_3 \cdot 12H_2O$, log 22141.

CHROMIUM TRIOXIDE

"Chromic Acid"

CrO_3; mol. wt. 100.01; Cr—52.00%; active oxygen—24.00%.

Dark, brownish-red needles or granules; rapidly deliquescent. Melts at about 192°. Soluble in less than 1 part of water. Reduced by alcohol to the chromic state. When brought in contact with organic substances decomposition takes place, sometimes with dangerous violence. *Keep in glass-stoppered bottles.*

Standards

Assay.................min 98% CrO_3		Sulfate (SO_4)...............max 0.005%	
Insoluble.................max 0.005%		Alkali salts.................max 0.20%	
Chloride (Cl)..............max 0.003%		Aluminum; Barium;	
Nitrate (NO_3)..............max 0.005%		Iron etc..................max 0.030%	

Assay: Dissolve 5 g in H_2O, dilute to exactly 1000 ml and mix well. Transfer 25 ml to a glass-stoppered flask, add 5 ml of HCl and 3 g potassium iodide, and let stand in the dark for 15 minutes. Dilute with 100 ml of H_2O and titrate the liberated iodine with 0.1 N sodium thiosulfate, adding starch toward the end. Correct for blank. One ml of 0.1 N thiosulfate = 0.003333 g CrO_3, log 52284.

$$CrO_3 + 6HCl + 3KI \rightarrow 3I + CrCl_3 + 3KCl + 3H_2O$$

Insoluble: Dissolve 20 g in 200 ml of H_2O and heat on the steam bath 1 hour. Filter through a tared, filtering crucible, wash well and dry at 105°. The insoluble residue does not exceed 1.0 mg.

Chloride: Dissolve 2 g in 45 ml of water, add 15 ml of HNO_3 and divide into two equal portions. Heat both portions to 50°; to one portion add 1 ml of $AgNO_3$ (*A*), and to the other portion add 1 ml of water (*B*). At the end of 5 minutes *A* is not more turbid than *B*.

Nitrate: Dissolve 0.5 g in 15 ml of water and add 2 ml of HCl. Add to the solution, in small portions, sulfurous acid until the color of the solution is pure green. Discharge any excess of SO_2 by dropwise addition of 0.1 N $KMnO_4$ to the production of a reddish color, and discharge the reddish color by the addition of just sufficient diluted (1:5) SO_2 solution. Heat the solution to boiling and add it, in small portions, to 15 ml of 10% Na_2CO_3 solution and boil for 1–2 minutes. Cool, filter or centrifuge, and decant. Concentrate the filtrate by evaporation to about 8 ml, cool and dilute to 10.0 ml. Using 5.0 ml of this solution for sample solution and 3 ml of standard nitrate solution for the control, proceed as directed under Nitrate—Estimation of Small Amounts, page 575.

Sulfate: Dissolve 5.0 g in 120 ml of water and add 1.5 g of anhydrous Na_2CO_3. If the resulting solution is not clear, filter through a sintered glass crucible previously well washed with 10% HCl and then with water. To the clear solution add 15 ml of a solution, made by dissolving 1 g of $BaCl_2$ in 100 ml of water and adding 2 ml of HCl. Mix, and allow to stand overnight. The solution is clear and no precipitate is visible.

Alkali salts: Carefully ignite 0.5 g in porcelain, cool and triturate the residue with 10 ml of hot water. Filter through a small paper, wash with 10 ml of hot water, evaporate, and ignite. Warm the residue with 10 ml of water, filter, wash with 5 ml of hot water, evaporate and ignite. The weight of the residue does not exceed 1.0 mg.

Aluminum; Barium; Iron: Dissolve 5 g in 100 ml of water and filter through a filtering crucible. Add 1 ml of 30% H_2O_2 and 2 ml of 10% H_2SO_4 and digest on the steam bath for 1 hour. Now heat to boiling, add 7 ml of NH_4OH and boil for 5 minutes. If a precipitate is formed, filter, wash with small quantities of hot water until the washings are colorless; dry, ignite and weigh. The weight of the precipitate does not exceed 1.5 mg.

CHROMOTROPIC ACID

1,8-Dihydroxynaphthalene-3,6-Disulfonic Acid

$SO_3H \cdot 2H_2O$; mol. wt. 356.33.

It is usually available as its disodium salt, which is usually yellow to light brown in color and soluble in water. The acid form is white.

Chromotropic acid is used for the detection of formaldehyde and indirectly of methanol in ethanol, etc.; for colorimetric determination of chromium[1] and titanium[2], also for determination of nitrate in water.

Standards

Sensitiveness................to pass test   Solubility...................to pass test

Sensitiveness: Dilute 0.50 ml of 37% formaldehyde solution with water to 1 liter (A). Prepare a solution of 5 mg of chromotropic acid in 10 ml of a mixture of 9 ml of sulfuric acid and 4 ml of H_2O (B).   Add 5 ml of B to 0.2 ml of A and heat for 10 minutes at 60°.   A violet color is produced.

Solubility: One-tenth gram of the acid form of this reagent dissolves in 10 ml of alcohol and in 10 ml of water, yielding clear and complete solutions.

[1] Koenig, P., *Chem. Ztg.* **35**, 277 (1911); Garrott, F., *J. Ind. Eng. Chem.* **5**, 298 (1913).
[2] Hoffman, K. A., *Ber.* **45**, 2480 (1912); Tananoeff, N. A., and Patschenko, G. A., *Z. anorg. Chem.* **150**, 163 (1926).

CINCHONINE

$C_{19}H_{22}N_2O$; mol. wt. 294.38.

White crystals or a powder.   Very slightly soluble in water; soluble in 50 parts of alcohol, in 150 parts of chloroform; slightly soluble in ether.   Its solutions are dextrorotatory.   Cinchonine is used in connection with quantitative determination of tungsten (as WO_3); also for the colorimetric estimation of small amounts of bismuth and the detection of this element for which a sensitivity of 0.003 mg per ml of solution is attained.

Standards

Solubility in dilute H_2SO_4.....to pass test	Sulfate (SO_4)................max 0.02%
Ignition residue..............max 0.10%	Cinchonidine or Quinine.......to pass test
Chloride (Cl)................max 0.01%	

Solubility in dilute sulfuric acid: Dissolve 1 g in 25 ml of 10% H_2SO_4.   No insoluble residue remains.

Ignition residue: Ignite 1 g with 0.5 ml of H_2SO_4 to constant weight.   Not more than 1.0 mg of residue remains.

Chloride: Warm 0.5 g with 25 ml of water and 2 ml of nitric acid until dissolved. Cool and dilute to 50 ml.   To 20 ml add 0.02 mg of Cl, dilute to 30 ml and add 1 ml of silver nitrate (A).   To 30 ml (B) add 1 ml of silver nitrate.   B is no more turbid than A.

Sulfate: Heat 1.0 g with 25 ml of water and add, dropwise, 10% HCl until just dissolved.   Cool, dilute to 30 ml and add 3 ml of $BaCl_2$.   Any turbidity produced is not greater than that in a control made with 0.2 mg of SO_4, 1 ml of 1 N HCl and 3 ml of $BaCl_2$ in the same volume as with the sample.

Cinchonidine or Quinine: Heat 1.0 g with 30 ml of water and add, dropwise, 10% HCl until just dissolved.   Neutralize the solution, while boiling, to litmus with dilute NH_4OH, and add a solution of 1 g sodium tartrate in 10 ml of water.   No precipitate forms within 1 hour.

CITRIC ACID

$CO_2H \cdot CH_2 \cdot C(OH)CO_2H \cdot CH_2CO_2H \cdot H_2O$; mol. wt. 210.14; anhydrous acid— 91.42%; H_2O—8.58%.   This acid is also available in anhydrous form.

Colorless crystals, or white granules or a powder; efflorescent.   Soluble in 0.5 part of water; soluble in alcohol.   This reagent of commerce is substantially 99.9% pure, anhydrous basis.   *Keep in tightly closed containers.*

Standards

Insoluble.................max 0.005%	Sulfate (SO₄)...............max 0.003%
Ignition residue.............max 0.010%	Tartrate (H₂C₄H₄O₆).........max 0.020%
Chloride (Cl)...............max 0.001%	Iron.....................max 0.0005%
Oxalate (H₂C₂O₄).......max about 0.05%	Lead (Pb)....................0.0000%
Phosphate (PO₄)............max 0.001%	Other heavy metals (as Cu)..max 0.0005%

Insoluble: Dissolve 20 g in 100 ml of H_2O and heat on the steam bath for 1 hour. If an undissolved residue remains, filter, wash it with H_2O and dry at 105°. Its weight does not exceed 1.0 mg.

Ignition residue: Char 10 g in a tared crucible or dish. Cool, moisten the char with 2 ml of H_2SO_4 and ignite at first gently to expel the H_2SO_4, then strongly to constant weight. The residue, if any, does not exceed 1.0 mg.

Chloride: To a solution of 1 g in 15 ml of H_2O add 1 ml of HNO_3 and 1 ml of $AgNO_3$. No opalescence is produced.

Oxalate: Dissolve 5 g in 25 ml of H_2O and add 2 ml of 10% calcium acetate solution. No turbidity or precipitate is produced in 4 hours.

Phosphate: Dissolve 2 g in 5 ml of H_2O in a platinum crucible, add 0.5 g of magnesium nitrate, evaporate and ignite. Warm the residue with 2 ml of 25% H_2SO_4 and 5 ml of H_2O, then add 15 ml of H_2O and filter. Add to filtrate 1 ml each of phosphate reagents **A** and **B** and heat at 60° for 10 minutes. Any resulting blue color is not deeper than that of a control made with 0.02 mg of PO_4, 0.3 g of ignited magnesium nitrate, 2 ml of 25% H_2SO_4, and the same volumes of H_2O and phosphate reagents and in the same final volume as with the sample.

Sulfate: Dissolve 2.0 g in 10 ml of H_2O and add 0.5 ml of 1 N HCl. Heat the solution to about 75°, add 2 ml of $BaCl_2$ solution and allow to stand for 10 minutes. Any turbidity produced is not greater than that of a control made with 0.06 mg of SO_4 and 0.5 g of the citric acid, etc.

Tartrate: Carefully powder 1 g of the acid. Mix 0.5 g of the powder with 10 ml of H_2SO_4 in a test tube rinsed with H_2SO_4, cover and heat at 110° for 30 minutes. The color of the solution is clear yellow, not brown.

Iron: Dissolve 2 g in 30 ml of water and add 2 ml of HCl and about 50 mg of ammonium persulfate. Dilute to 50 ml and add 3 ml of ammonium thiocyanate. Any resulting red color is not darker than that of a blank to which 0.01 mg of Fe has been added.

Lead: Dissolve 25 g in 25 ml of H_2O in a separatory funnel, then add NH_4OH until the solution is slightly alkaline to phenolphthalein paper. Cool, add 3 ml of 15% potassium cyanide solution *under hood* and allow to stand 10 minutes. Make sure that the solution is alkaline to phenolphthalein paper; if not, add sufficient NH_4OH to make it so. Add 5 ml of a solution of dithizone in chloroform containing 2 mg of dithizone in a liter of chloroform, shake thoroughly and allow to separate. The chloroform layer does not acquire a pink or red color.

Other heavy metals: Dissolve 5 g in 30 ml of H_2O, add 3 drops of phenolphthalein and follow with 28% NH_3 until the solution is faintly pink. Add 1.0 ml of 10% HCl, dilute with water to 50 ml and mix well. To 10 ml of the solution add 0.015 mg of Cu and dilute with H_2O to 40 ml (A); then add 10 ml of H_2S to A and to the remaining 40 ml of the solution (B). B is not darker than A.

CLAYTON YELLOW, *see* THIAZOLE YELLOW

COBALT ACETATE

Cobaltous Acetate

$Co(CH_3CO_2)_2 \cdot 4H_2O$; mol. wt. 249.09; anhydrous—71.07%; H_2O—28.93%; Co—23.67%.

Red-violet crystals or granules; somewhat deliquescent. Freely soluble in water; soluble in alcohol.

Standards

Insoluble.....................max 0.010%	Copper (Cu)..................max 0.005%
Chloride (Cl)...............max 0.002%	Iron (Fe)......................max 0.002%
Nitrate (NO₃)................max 0.01%	Lead (Pb)....................max 0.003%
Sulfate (SO₄)................max 0.010%	Nickel (Ni)...................max 0.15%
Alkalies, Earths (as sulfates)...max 0.15%	Zinc (Zn).....................max 0.03%

Insoluble: Dissolve 10 g in 100 ml of H_2O and 1 ml of glacial acetic acid, and heat on steam bath for 1 hour. Filter any undissolved residue, wash it with 1% acetic acid and dry at 105°. Its weight does not exceed 1.0 mg (retain filtrate).

Chloride: To a solution of 1 g in 20 ml of water add 1 ml of HNO_3 and divide into two equal portions. To one portion add 1 ml of $AgNO_3$, bring to a boil, let stand for 10 minutes, cool, filter until clear and use for the control. To the other portion add 1 ml of $AgNO_3$. If a turbidity is produced it is not greater than that produced by adding 0.010 mg of Cl to the control and adjusting both to the same volume.

Nitrate: Dissolve 1.0 g of sample in 5 ml of water. Add the solution in small portions and with continuous stirring to 10 ml of 10% NaOH diluted with 5 ml of water. Cover the beaker and heat on the steam bath for 15 minutes. Cool, filter, neutralize the filtrate with 25% H_2SO_4 and dilute to 25 ml. Using 5.0 ml of this solution, and 2.0 ml of standard nitrate solution (0.02 mg NO_3) for the control, proceed as directed under Nitrate—Estimation of Small Amounts, page 575.

Sulfate: Add 1 ml of HCl to the filtrate from *Insoluble*, heat to boiling, add 10 ml of $BaCl_2$ and let stand overnight. If a precipitate is formed, filter, wash it well with water and ignite. The weight of the precipitate ($BaSO_4$) is not more than 0.0025 g.

Alkalies, Earths, etc.: Dissolve 2 g of the cobalt acetate and 2 g of ammonium chloride in 90 ml of H_2O, add 5 ml of NH_4OH and precipitate the cobalt with H_2S. Dilute to 100 ml and filter. To 50 ml of the filtrate add 0.5 ml of H_2SO_4, evaporate and ignite. Not more than 1.5 mg of residue remains.

Copper: To a solution of 2 g in 2 ml of HCl add water to make 50 ml, then add 2 ml of a 1% solution of mercuric chloride and saturate with H_2S. Filter through a small filter, wash with H_2S water until the washings are colorless, then ignite the filter and precipitate in porcelain. Dissolve the residue by warming with 0.5 ml of HNO_3 and a few drops of H_2O, dilute 10 ml, and filter if necessary. Dissolve in the solution 1 g of ammonium acetate, then add 0.3 ml of freshly prepared potassium ferrocyanide solution. Any red color produced is not darker than that of a control made with 0.1 mg of Cu, the same quantities of the reagents and in the same volume as with the sample.

Iron: Dissolve 1 g in 40 ml of H_2O and add 2 ml of HCl and 5 drops of HNO_3. Bring the solution to a boil and add sufficient NH_4OH to dissolve the precipitate first formed. Filter and wash with 2.5% NH_3 until the washings are colorless. Dissolve any precipitate on the filter with 5 ml of hot diluted $(1+1)$ HCl, and wash with 30 ml of hot water. Heat and repeat the precipitation with ammonium hydroxide. Filter and wash with 2.5% NH_3 until the washings are colorless. Dissolve the precipitate on the filter with 5 ml of hot 20% $(1+1)$ HCl and dilute with water to 40 ml. To 20 ml of the dilution add 2 ml of HCl and dilute to 50 ml. Add about 30 mg of ammonium persulfate and 3 ml of ammonium thiocyanate and mix. Any red color produced is not darker than that of a control made with 0.010 mg Fe, 2 ml of HCl, the same quantities of ammonium persulfate and thiocyanate and in the same final volume as with the sample.

Lead: To 2.0 g add 10 ml of water and 5 ml of HCl, and evaporate to dryness on the steam bath. Re-evaporate to dryness with 10 ml of H_2O. Dissolve the residue in a few ml of hot water, add 0.6 ml of glacial acetic acid, dilute to 20 ml, and filter if not clear. Divide the filtrate into two equal portions. To one portion add 0.2 ml of potassium chromate solution (10%) and mix. To the other portion add 0.2 ml of water. Both portions are equally clear in 5 minutes when viewed in the same light.

Nickel: Dissolve 0.50 g in 10 ml of water, add 10% sodium cyanide solution until the precipitate first formed redissolves. Add 0.5 ml of 30% H_2O_2 and evaporate to dryness on the steam bath. Dissolve the residue in 25 ml of water, filter if necessary, and wash slightly. Add to the filtrate 50 mg of *solid* dimethylglyoxime and 3 ml of formaldehyde solution (37%) and allow to stand for 1 hour. Filter any precipitated nickel dimethylglyoxime and wash with water. Dissolve the precipitate on the filter with about 5 ml of $1+1$ HCl, wash with water, and dilute filtrate and washings to 100 ml. Dilute 2.0 ml of the solution to about 30 ml, make just alkaline with 10% NH_3, add 5 ml of bromine water, 5 ml of 1% alcohol solution of dimethylglyoxime and 5 ml of 10% NaOH solution, dilute to 50 ml and mix. Any red color should not be darker than that produced by 0.015 mg of nickel (Ni) in 30 ml of water treated as the sample beginning with "make just alkaline. . . ."

Zinc: Dissolve 1.0 g in 15 ml of water. Add this solution in small portions and with continuous stirring to 25 ml of hot 10% NaOH and boil gently for 10 minutes. Filter and wash with 5 ml of hot water. Neutralize the filtrate with 10% HCl to a pH of about 3–4 using pH paper, and dilute to 50 ml. Transfer 10 ml of the solution to a small separatory funnel. For a control, place 0.2 ml (0.02 mg) of standard zinc solution in a similar separatory funnel and dilute with water to about 10 ml; then treat both as follows: Adjust the pH of the solutions to 4.5–5 by the addition of acetate buffer solution*, then add 10 ml of standard dithizone-carbon tetrachloride solution, shake well for 2 minutes, allow the layers to separate and draw off the carbon tetrachloride into a 50-ml tube. Repeat the extraction with 5-ml portions of the dithizone solution until the last portion remains unchanged in color after shaking for 2 minutes. Combine, separately, the extracts

* Mix 65 g of sodium acetate with 35 ml glacial acetic acid and dilute to 250 ml (pH—4.7).

from each solution and make them up to the same volume with carbon tetrachloride. Any pink color in the extract from the sample is not darker than that from the control.

Note: The actual amount of zinc may be approximated by diluting the dithizone extract of the sample or control, whichever has a darker pink color, with carbon tetrachloride until the red colors match. The quantiity of zinc is then calculated from the dilution.

COBALT CARBONATE

Cobaltous Carbonate

Approx. $2CoCO_3 \cdot 3Co(OH)_2 \cdot xH_2O$.

Pale red powder. Insoluble in water; soluble in diluted acids.

Standards

Assay.....................45%–50% Co	Alkalies, Earths (as sulfate)....max 0.30%
Hydrochloric acid—	Copper (Cu).................max 0.010%
insoluble.................max 0.010%	Iron (Fe)...................max 0.010%
Chloride (Cl)...............max 0.005%	Lead (Pb)..................max 0.003%
Nitrate (NO₃)...............max 0.03%	Nickel (Ni)..................max 0.30%
Sulfate (SO₄)...............max 0.020%	Zinc (Zn)....................max 0.50%

Assay: Weigh accurately about 0.4 g and transfer to a 250-ml glass-stoppered flask. Add 20 ml of H_2O and just sufficient HCl to dissolve, then add in small portions, while agitating, 25 ml of 10% NaOH and follow with 10 ml of dilute hydrogen peroxide (1 vol. 30% + 9 vols. H_2O). Dilute with 15 ml of H_2O and boil gently until the excess of hydrogen peroxide is completely destroyed and the volume is reduced to about 25 ml. Cool, add 3 g of potassium iodide and follow with 25 ml of 25% H_2SO_4. Stopper the flask and rotate until a clear solution results; then titrate the liberated iodine with 0.1 N sodium thiosulfate, using starch toward the end. One ml of 0.1 N thiosulfate = 0.005894 g Co, log 77041.

$$2Co + H_2O_2 \rightarrow Co_2O_3 + H_2O$$
$$Co_2O_3 + 2KI + 3H_2SO_4 \rightarrow 2CoSO_4 + 2I + K_2SO_4 + 3H_2O$$
and
$$2I + 2Na_2S_2O_3 \rightarrow Na_2S_4O_6 + 2NaI$$

Hydrochloric acid—insoluble: Mix 10 g with 50 ml of H_2O and add just sufficient HCl to dissolve. Dilute with water to 100 ml and heat on the steam bath for 1 hour. Filter any undissolved matter, wash it with hot H_2O and dry at 105°. Its weight does not exceed 1.0 mg (retain filtrate).

Chloride: Dissolve 0.4 g in 20 ml of water and 2 ml of HNO_3, filter if necessary, divide the filtrate into two equal portions and proceed as described under Cobalt Acetate. The result should be as there stated.

Nitrate: To 0.5 g add 5 ml of water and just enough glacial acetic acid to dissolve; proceed as under the test for *Nitrate* under Cobalt Acetate, beginning with "Add this solution. . . ." and using 3.0 ml of standard nitrate solution for the control.

Sulfate: Heat the filtrate from test for *Hydrochloric acid—insoluble* to boiling, add 10 ml of $BaCl_2$ and let stand overnight. If a precipitate is present, filter, wash it well with water, ignite and weigh. Its weight does not exceed 5.0 mg.

Alkalies, Earths, etc.: Dissolve 1 g in 100 ml of H_2O and 5 ml of HCl, add a slight excess of NH_4OH and precipitate the cobalt with H_2S. Dilute to 120 ml, mix and filter. To 60 ml of the filtrate add 0.5 ml of H_2SO_4, evaporate and ignite. Not more than 1.5 mg of residue remains.

Copper: Dissolve 1 g in 3 ml of HCl and H_2O to make 50 ml, and test as directed for Cobalt Acetate, beginning with "then add 2 ml of the 1% solution of mercuric chloride. . . ." It conforms to the requirement there stated.

Iron: Dissolve 1.0 g in a mixture of 30 ml of H_2O and 5 ml of HCl. Bring the solution to a boil and add sufficient NH_4OH to dissolve the precipitate first formed. Filter and wash with 2.5% NH_3 until the washings are colorless. Then proceed as described for Cobalt Acetate, beginning with "Dissolve any precipitate, . . ." and make up the iron solution to 200 ml instead of 40 ml. The result should be as there stated.

Lead: Heat 2.0 g with 10 ml of water and add HCl, a few drops at a time with stirring until dissolved. Evaporate the solution on the steam bath to dryness, add 10 ml of water and re-evaporate on the steam bath. Dissolve the resulting chloride in a few ml of hot water, add 0.6 ml of glacial acetic acid, dilute to 20 ml, filter if necessary and divide into 2 equal portions. To one portion add 0.2 ml of potassium chromate solution and mix. To the other portion add 0.2 ml of water. Both portions are equally clear in 5 minutes when viewed in the same light.

Nickel: Heat 0.5 g with 10 ml of water and add just sufficient HCl to dissolve. *Under a hood* add to the solution 10% sodium cyanide solution and proceed as directed under Cobalt Acetate, but using only 1.0 ml instead of 2 ml for the final test. The result should conform to the requirement there stated.

Zinc: Heat 0.5 g with 10 ml of water and add just sufficient HCl to dissolve. Then proceed as described under Cobalt Acetate, beginning with "Add this solution . . . ," but use only 6.0 ml of the solution instead of 10 ml. The result should be as there stated.

COBALT CHLORIDE

Cobaltous Chloride

$CoCl_2 \cdot 6H_2O$; mol. wt. 237.95; anhydrous—54.57%; H_2O—45.43%; Co—24.78%; Cl—29.80%.

Red crystals or granules; somewhat deliquescent. Soluble in 1 part of water; soluble in alcohol, ether or acetone.

Standards

Insoluble....................max 0.010%	Copper (Cu)................max 0.003%
Nitrate (NO_3)...............max 0.01%	Iron (Fe)...................max 0.003%
Sulfate (SO_4)...............max 0.010%	Nickel (Ni)................max 0.15%
Alkalies, Earths (as sulfate)....max 0.15%	Zinc (Zn)...................max 0.03%
Ammonia (NH_3)............max 0.01%	*Assay*......................min 99%

Insoluble: Dissolve 10 g in 100 ml of water and heat on the steam bath for 1 hour. If an undissolved residue remains, filter (retain filtrate) wash it well with water and dry at 105°. Its weight does not exceed 1.0 mg.

Nitrate: Dissolve 1.0 g in 10 ml of water. Add this solution in small portions and with constant stirring to 10 ml of 10% NaOH previously diluted with 5 ml of water. Cover the beaker and heat on the steam bath, stirring several times, for 15 minutes. Cool and filter. Neutralize the filtrate with 25% H_2SO_4 and dilute to 25 ml. Using 5 ml of this solution as *Sample Solution* and 2 ml of standard nitrate solution (0.02 mg NO_3) for control, proceed as directed under Nitrate—Estimation of Small Amounts, page 575.

Sulfate: Add 1 ml of HCl to the filtrate from *Insoluble*, heat to boiling, add 5 ml of $BaCl_2$, and allow to stand overnight. If a precipitate is present, filter, wash well with water and ignite. The weight of the ignited precipitate ($BaSO_4$) is not more than 2.5 mg.

Alkalies, Earths, etc.: Dissolve 2 g of the cobalt chloride and 1 g of ammonium chloride in 95 ml of water, add 5 ml of NH_4OH, precipitate the cobalt with H_2S and filter. To 50 ml of the filtrate add 0.5 ml of H_2SO_4, evaporate and ignite. Not more than 1.5 mg of residue remains.

Ammonia: Dissolve 1 g in 60 ml of H_2O in a suitable distilling outfit. Add 10 ml of 10% NaOH, previously diluted with 10 ml of H_2O, and distill over about 40 ml into 5 ml of H_2O containing 1 drop of 10% HCl. Dilute the distillate to 50 ml. Dilute 10 ml to 50 ml, and then add 1 ml of 10% NaOH and 2 ml of Nessler solution. Any resulting color is not darker than that of a control made with 0.02 mg of NH_3 and 3 ml of NaOH, and in the same volume as with the sample.

Copper: Dissolve 2 g in 1 ml of HCl and water to make 50 ml. Add 2 ml of a 1% solution of mercuric chloride and saturate with H_2S. Filter through a small filter, wash with H_2S water until the washings are colorless, then ignite the filter and precipitate in porcelain. Dissolve the residue by warming with 0.5 ml of HNO_3 and a few drops of H_2O, dilute to 10 ml, and filter if necessary. Dissolve in the solution 1 g of ammonium acetate; then add 0.3 ml of freshly prepared potassium ferrocyanide solution. Any red color produced is not darker than that of a control made with 0.06 mg of Cu, the same quantities of the reagents and in the same volume as with the sample.

Iron: Dissolve 1 g in 30 ml of H_2O and add 2 ml of HCl and a few drops of HNO_3. Bring to a boil and add sufficient NH_4OH to dissolve the precipitate first formed. Filter and wash with 2.5% NH_3 until the washings are colorless. Dissolve any precipitate on the filter with 3 ml of hot 20% HCl and wash with 20 ml of hot H_2O. Heat the solution and repeat the precipitation with ammonium hydroxide as before. Filter and wash with 2.5% NH_3 until the washings are colorless. Dissolve the precipitate on the filter with 5 ml of hot 20% HCl and dilute with water to 60 ml. To 20 ml of the dilution add 2 ml of HCl and dilute to 50 ml. Add about 30 mg of ammonium persulfate and 3 ml of ammonium thiocyanate and mix. Any resulting red color is not darker than that in a control made with 0.01 mg of Fe, 2 ml of HCl, the same quantities of ammonium persulfate and thiocyanate and in the same volume as with the sample.

Nickel: Dissolve 0.50 g in 10 ml of water and add 10% sodium cyanide solution until the precipitate first formed redissolves. Add 0.5 ml of 30% H_2O_2 and evaporate to dryness on the steam bath.   Dissolve the residue in 25 ml of water, filter if necessary, and wash slightly.   Add to the filtrate 50 mg of *solid* dimethylglyoxime and 3 ml of formaldehyde solution (37%) and allow to stand for 1 hour.   Filter any precipitated nickel dimethylglyoxime and wash with water.   Dissolve the precipitate on the filter with about 5 ml of 1 + 1 HCl, wash with water, and dilute filtrate and washings to 100 ml.   Dilute 2.0 ml of the solution to about 30 ml, make just alkaline with 10% NH_3, add 5 ml of bromine water, 5 ml of 1% alcohol solution of dimethylglyoxime and 5 ml of 10% NaOH solution, dilute to 50 ml and mix. Any red color should not be darker than that produced by 0.015 mg of nickel (Ni) in 30 ml of water treated as the sample beginning with "make just alkaline. . . .."

Zinc: Dissolve 1.0 g in 15 ml of water.   Add this solution in small portions and with continuous stirring to 25 ml of 10% NaOH and boil gently for 10 minutes. Filter and wash with 5 ml of hot water.   Neutralize the filtrate with 10% HCl to a *p*H of about 3–4 using *p*H paper, and dilute to 50 ml.   Transfer 10 ml of the solution to a small separatory funnel.   For a control place 0.2 ml (0.02 mg) of standard zinc solution in a similar separatory funnel and dilute with water to about 10 ml, then treat both as follows: Adjust the *p*H of the solutions to 4.5–5 by the addition of acetate buffer solution (see page 139), then add 10 ml of standard dithizone-carbon tetrachloride solution, shake well for 2 minutes, allow the layers to separate and draw off the carbon tetrachloride into a comparison tube.   Repeat the extraction with 5-ml portions of the dithizone solution until the last portion remains unchanged in color after shaking for 2 minutes.   Combine, separately, the extracts from each solution and make them up to the same volume with carbon tetrachloride.   Any pink color in the extract from the sample is not darker than that from the control.

Note: The actual amount of zinc may be approximated by diluting the dithizone extract of the sample or control, whichever has a darker pink color, with carbon tetrachloride until the colors match.   The quantity of zinc is then calculated from the dilution.

Assay: Cobalt chloride may be assayed as follows: Weigh accurately about 0.7 g, dissolve it in 20 ml of water in a 250-ml glass-stoppered flask.   Add in small portions, while agitating, 25 ml of 10% NaOH and follow with 10 ml of dilute hydrogen peroxide (1 vol. 30% + 9 vols. H_2O).   Dilute with 15 ml of H_2O and boil gently until the excess of hydrogen peroxide is completely destroyed and the volume is reduced to about 25 ml.   Cool, add 3 g of potassium iodide, and follow with 25 ml of 25% H_2SO_4.   Stopper the flask and rotate until a clear solution results, then titrate the liberated iodine with 0.1 N sodium thiosulfate, using starch toward the end.   One ml of 0.1 N sodium thiosulfate = 0.02380 g $CoCl \cdot 6H_2O$, log 37658.

COBALT NITRATE

Cobaltous Nitrate

$Co(NO_3)_2 \cdot 6H_2O$; mol. wt. 291.05; anhydrous—62.87%; H_2O—37.13%; Co—20.26%; NO_3—42.61%.

Red crystals or granules; somewhat deliquescent.   Soluble in 1 part of water; soluble in alcohol.

Standards

Insoluble.....................max 0.010%	Copper (Cu)................max 0.002%
Chloride (Cl)................max 0.002%	Iron (Fe)...................max 0.002%
Sulfate (SO$_4$)................max 0.010%	Lead (Pb)..................max 0.003%
Alkalies, Earths (as sulfate)....max 0.15%	Nickel (Ni)..................max 0.15%
Ammonia (NH$_3$)..............max 0.05%	Zinc (Zn)...................max 0.03%

Insoluble: Dissolve 10 g in 100 ml of water and heat on the steam bath for 1 hour. If an undissolved residue remains, filter, wash it well with water, and dry at 105°. Its weight does not exceed 1.0 mg.

Chloride: To a solution of 1 g in 20 ml of water add 1 ml of HNO$_3$ and divide into two equal portions. To one portion add 1 ml of AgNO$_3$, bring to a boil, let stand for 10 minutes, cool, filter until clear, and use for the control. To the other portion add 1 ml of AgNO$_3$. If a turbidity is produced it is not greater than is produced by adding 0.010 mg of Cl to the control and adjusting both to the same volume.

Sulfate: Dissolve 5 g in 20 ml of hot H$_2$O, add 15 ml of HCl, and evaporate to dryness. Re-evaporate to dryness on the steam bath with 5 ml of H$_2$O and 5 ml of HCl. Dissolve the residue in 1 ml of HCl and 100 ml H$_2$O, filter if necessary, heat to boiling, add 10 ml of BaCl$_2$, and allow to stand overnight. Filter, if a precipitate is present, wash it with water, and ignite. The weight of the precipitate (BaSO$_4$) is not more than 1.3 mg.

Alkalies, Earths, etc.: Dissolve 2 g of the cobalt nitrate and 1 g of ammonium chloride in 95 ml of water, add 5 ml of NH$_4$OH, precipitate the cobalt with H$_2$S, and filter. To 70 ml of the filtrate add 0.5 ml of H$_2$SO$_4$, evaporate and ignite. Not more than 1.5 mg of residue remains.

Ammonia: Dissolve 1 g in 60 ml of H$_2$O in a suitable distilling outfit. Add 10 ml of 10% NaOH, previously diluted with 10 ml of H$_2$O, and distill over about 40 ml into 5 ml of H$_2$O containing 1 drop of 10% HCl. Dilute the distillate to 100 ml. Dilute 4.0 ml to 50 ml, then add 1 ml of 10% NaOH and 2 ml of Nessler solution. Any resulting color is not darker than that of a control made with 0.02 mg of NH$_3$ and 3 ml of NaOH, and in the same volume as used with the sample.

Copper: Dissolve 2 g in 1 ml of HCl and sufficient water to make 50 ml, then add 2 ml of a 1% solution of mercuric chloride and saturate with H$_2$S. Filter through a small filter, wash with H$_2$S water until the washings are colorless, then ignite the filter and precipitate in porcelain. Dissolve the residue by warming with 0.5 ml of HNO$_3$ and a few drops of H$_2$O, dilute to 10 ml, and filter if necessary. Dissolve in the solution 1 g of ammonium acetate, then add 0.3 ml of freshly prepared potassium ferrocyanide solution. Any red color produced is not darker than that of a control made with 0.04 mg of Cu, the same quantities of the reagents and in the same volume as with the sample.

Iron: Dissolve 1 g in 30 ml of H$_2$O, add 2 ml of HCl and a few drops of HNO$_3$. Bring to a boil and add sufficient NH$_4$OH to dissolve the precipitate first formed. Filter and wash with 2.5% NH$_3$ until the washings are colorless. Dissolve any precipitate on the filter with 3 ml of hot diluted HCl (1 + 1) and wash with 20 ml of hot H$_2$O. Heat the solution and repeat the precipitation with ammonium hydroxide as before. Filter and wash with 2.5% NH$_3$ until the washings are colorless. Dissolve the precipitate on the filter with 5 ml of hot 20% HCl and dilute with water to 20 ml.   To 10 ml of the dilution add 2 ml of HCl, and dilute to 50 ml.   Add about 30 mg of ammonium persulfate and 3 ml of ammonium thiocyanate and mix. Any resulting red color is not darker than that in a control made with 0.010 mg of Fe, 2 ml of HCl, the same quantities of ammonium persulfate and thiocyanate and in the same volume as with the sample.

Lead: Dissolve 2.0 g in 20 ml of water, add 0.6 ml of glacial acetic acid, and filter if necessary.   Divide the solution (or filtrate) into 2 equal portions.   To one portion add 0.2 ml of potassium chromate solution and mix well.   To the other portion add 0.2 ml of water.   Both portions are equally clear in 5 minutes, when viewed in the same light.

Nickel, Zinc: Apply the tests described under Cobalt Chloride.   The results should be as there required.

COBALT SULFATE

Cobaltous Sulfate

$CoSO_4 \cdot 7H_2O$; mol. wt. 281.12; anhydrous—55.14%; H_2O—44.86%; Co—20.97%; SO_4—34.17%.

Red crystals or granules.   Soluble in 3 parts of water; slightly soluble in alcohol.

Standards

Insoluble .... max 0.010%	Copper (Cu) .... max 0.003%
Chloride (Cl) .... max 0.002%	Iron (Fe) .... max 0.003%
Nitrate (NO₃) .... max 0.01%	Nickel (Ni) .... max 0.20%
Alkalies, Earths, etc........... max 0.15%	Zinc (Zn) .... max 0.03%
Ammonia (NH₃) .... max 0.01%	

Insoluble; Nitrate; Alkalies, Earths, etc.; Ammonia; Copper; Iron; Zinc: Apply the test described under Cobalt Chloride.   The results conform to the requirement there stated.

Chloride: Dissolve 1 g in 20 ml of water and 1 ml of HNO_3, and divide into two equal portions.   To one portion add 1 ml of $AgNO_3$, bring to a boil, let stand for 10 minutes, cool, filter until clear, and use for the control.   To the other portion add 1 ml of $AgNO_3$.   If a turbidity is produced it is not greater than that produced by adding 0.010 mg of Cl to the control and adjusting both to the same volume.

Nickel: Proceed as directed under Cobalt Chloride, but dilute the nickel dimethylglyoxime solution to 130 ml.

COLLODION

Colorless or slightly yellowish, clear or slightly opalescent, viscous solution of pyroxylin in a mixture of alcohol and ether.   *Keep in tightly closed containers, in a cool place, remote from flame.*

Standards

Pyroxylin .... min 5%	Acids .... no reaction

Pyroxylin: Weigh accurately about 10 g in a tared flask and add to it, dropwise, with constant stirring, 10 ml of water. Then evaporate, dry to constant weight at 105° and weigh. The weight of the residue corresponds to not less than 5% of the weight of the sample taken.

Acids: Immerse a strip of moistened blue litmus paper in a portion of the sample. No immediate reddening is produced.

CONGO PAPER

Strips of 0.6 cm × 2.5 cm, or sheets of 20 cm × 25 cm. pH range: 3.0 blue; 5.0 red.

Sensitiveness: Place $\frac{1}{2}$ inch of strip, or a piece of sheet of the same size, in 100 ml of 0.0005 N HCl and stir continuously for 30 seconds. The color of the paper changes to bluish.

CONGO RED

; mol. wt. 696.67.

Brownish-red powder. Sparingly soluble in cold water or in alcohol; soluble in warm water, forming a blood-red solution. pH range: 3.0 blue; 5.0 red. It is usually used in a 0.1% aqueous solution.

Standards

Sensitiveness as acid-base indicator..................to pass test	Drying loss....................max 10%
	Assay, anhydrous basis..........min 93%

Sensitiveness: Dissolve 50 mg in a mixture of 1 ml of alcohol and 9 ml of water, and add 0.1 ml of this solution to 100 ml of CO_2-free water. The red color of the water changes to blue-violet on the addition of 0.05 ml of 0.1 N HCl and is restored by 0.05 ml of 0.1 N NaOH.

Drying loss: Weigh accurately about 0.5 g and dry at 110° to constant weight. The loss in weight corresponds to not more than 10%.

Assay: Weigh accurately about 0.25 g and dissolve it in 100 ml of water in a 300-ml Erlenmeyer flask. Add 10 g of potassium sodium tartrate, heat to boiling, and while maintaining a current of CO_2 through the flask titrate the hot solution with 0.1 N titanium trichloride until the solution in the flask is colorless or practically so. One ml of 0.1 N titanium trichloride = 0.008701 g of $C_{32}H_{22}N_6O_6S_2Na_2$, log 93957. Calculate to the anhydrous basis.

COPPER

Cu; at. wt. 63.54.

Reagent copper is in the form of bright sheets (foil), bright thin wire, or granules. It is soluble in dilute nitric acid, and in boiling sulfuric acid; slightly soluble in hydrochloric acid; also soluble in ammonium hydroxide. It is attacked by organic acids.

Standards

Insoluble in HNO_3............0.00%	Lead (Pb)...............max 0.005%
Antimony and Tin...........max 0.01%	Phosphorus (P).............max 0.001%
Arsenic (As).................max 5 ppm	Silver (Ag)...............max 0.0005%
Iron (Fe)..................max 0.005%	Not precipitated by H_2S......max 0.020%

Solution A: Dissolve 25 g in 175 ml of diluted HNO_3 (1 + 1) and dilute with water to 250 ml. No insoluble residue remains.

Antimony and Tin: Evaporate 75 ml of *Solution A* on the steam bath nearly to dryness, and then digest the residue with a mixture of 2 ml of HNO_3 and 50 ml of water for 15 minutes. No insoluble residue remains.

Arsenic: To 4 ml of *Solution A* add 3 ml of H_2SO_4 and evaporate to sulfuric fumes. Cautiously add 5 ml of H_2O and re-evaporate to sulfuric fumes. Cautiously dilute with 10 ml of H_2O and test by method on page 563, using 10 ml of the stannous chloride and 2.5 g of the zinc. The resulting stain is not greater than that produced by 0.002 mg of As.

Silver: To 25 ml of *Solution A* add 1 ml of 10% HCl. No turbidity is produced.

Iron: To the solution from the test for *Silver* add ammonium hydroxide until the precipitate first formed redissolves. Filter through a small filter paper and wash with 2.5% NH_3 until the washings are colorless. Dissolve any precipitate on the filter with 10 ml of warm 10% HCl and dilute to 120 ml. To 20 ml add 2 ml of HCl, dilute to 50 ml, and add 3 ml of ammonium thiocyanate. Any resulting red color is not darker than that of a control made with 0.02 mg of Fe, 2 ml of HCl and 3 ml of ammonium thiocyanate in the same volume as with the sample.

Lead: Dilute 5.0 ml of *Solution A* to 100 ml. Transfer 25 ml of this solution to a glass-stoppered cylinder. For a control place in a similar cylinder 5.0 ml of this solution and 0.010 mg of Pb, dilute to 25 ml and then treat each of the two solutions as follows: Add 2 ml of hydroxylamine hydrochloride solution and follow with 10% NH_3 dropwise and shaking after each addition until the precipitate formed no longer dissolves. Now, *under the hood*, add 5 ml of ammonium citrate solution and 15 ml of potassium cyanide solution. Cool in ice water, then add 20 ml of *dithizone standard solution in chloroform*, shake well for 2 minutes and allow the layers to separate. The pink color of the chloroform layer from the 25-ml solution of the sample is not darker than that from the control.

Phosphorus: To 20 ml of *Solution A* add 2 g of Na_2SO_4 and 2 ml of H_2SO_4, then evaporate to strong sulfuric fumes. Cautiously dilute to 200 ml and completely precipitate the copper with H_2S. Rapidly decant 150 ml of the clear supernatant liquid through a filter, evaporate to about 5 ml, then add 1 ml of

HNO_3 and evaporate on the steam bath. Dissolve the residue in 20 ml of water, add 1 ml each of 25% H_2SO_4 and of phosphate reagents **A** and **B** and heat at 60° for 10 minutes. Any blue color produced is not darker than that of a control made as follows:

Dissolve 2 g of Na_2SO_4 in 10 ml of H_2O, add 2 ml of H_2SO_4 and 0.06 mg of PO_4, then evaporate to strong fumes of SO_3. Cool, dilute with H_2O to 20 ml and, proceed as described in the preceding paragraph, beginning with "add 1 ml each...."

Metals not precipitated by H_2S: To 75 ml of *Solution A* add 10 ml of H_2SO_4 and evaporate until solution fumes strongly. Cautiously dissolve the residue in 300 ml of water in a flask, heat to 70° and precipitate the copper with H_2S. Stopper the flask, allow to stand overnight, and filter. Evaporate 200 ml of the filtrate and ignite. The weight of the residue does not exceed 1.0 mg.

CRESOL RED
o-Cresolsulfonphthalein

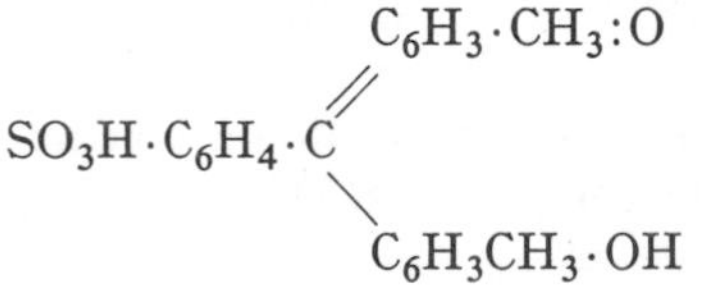

$$C_6H_3 \cdot CH_3 : O$$
$$SO_3H \cdot C_6H_4 \cdot C \qquad ; \text{mol. wt. } 382.42$$
$$C_6H_3CH_3 \cdot OH$$

Red-brown powder. Slightly soluble in water; soluble in alcohol and in dilute aqueous alkali hydroxides. pH range: 7.2 yellow; 8.8 purple.

Standards

Solubility....................to pass test	Ignition residue..............max 0.25%
Sensitiveness.................to pass test	

Solubility: Dissolve 0.1 g in 50 ml of alcohol and dilute with water to 100 ml. The solution is clear and complete.

Sensitiveness: To 100 ml of CO_2-free water add 0.2 ml of the solution obtained in the preceding test. A yellow color is produced which changes to purple by the addition of 0.2 ml of 0.01 N NaOH.

Ignition residue: Char 0.5 g, cool, add 0.5 ml of H_2SO_4, and ignite to constant weight. Not more than 1.0 mg of residue remains.

CRYSTAL VIOLET
Methylrosaniline Chloride; Methyl Violet; Gentian Violet

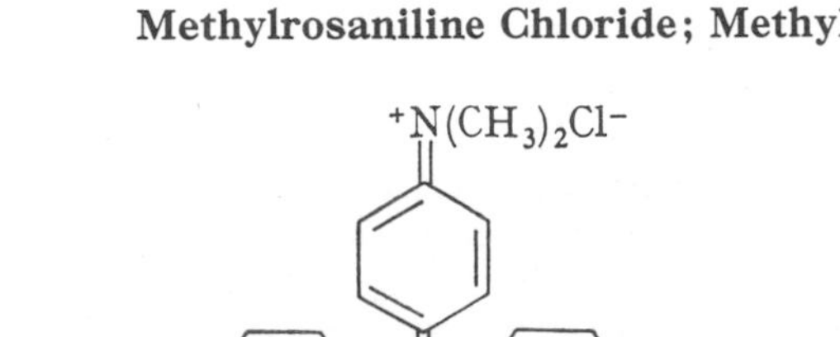

The following formula is for the hexamethylrosanilin compound. The article of commerce is usually a mixture of penta- and hexamethylrosanilin chlorides.

Greenish-bronze crystals or dark green, crystalline powder. It is moderately soluble in water (the reasonably exact solubility in water is not yet known), freely soluble in alcohol, soluble in chloroform, insoluble in ether. It usually contains about 5% of water, which may be determined by the iodine method. As indicator in nonaqueous titrations it is usually used as a 1% solution in glacial acetic acid. In aqueous solutions its pH is: yellow 0.1, blue 1.5.

Standards

Absorbancy.................to pass test
Sensitiveness as indicator......to pass test
Water........................max 6%

Alcohol—insoluble.............max 0.5%
Ignition residue..............max 1.0%

Absorbancy: Weigh 50 mg and dissolve it in 250 ml of water. Dilute 10 ml with water to 500 ml. Maximum absorption is at 588 to 592 mμ, and the absorption ratio of A at 575 mμ over A at 605 mμ is between 1.08 and 1.15.

Sensitiveness: (a) Dissolve 50 mg of crystal violet in 5 ml of glacial acetic acid. (b) Dilute 0.3 ml of 70% perchloric acid with dioxane to 25 ml. To 50 ml of glacial acetic acid add 2 drops of (a). The purplish blue color of the solution is changed to bluish-green by the addition of not more than 0.05 ml of (b).

Water: Dry about 1 g, accurately weighed, at 105° to constant weight. The loss in weight corresponds to not more than 6.0%. The water may also be determined by the iodine (Fischer) method.

Alcohol—insoluble: Reflux 1.00 g with 50 ml of alcohol for 15 minutes, filter through a tared filtering crucible, wash the residue on the filter with hot alcohol until the washings cease to be colored violet and dry at 105° for 2 hours. The weight of the residue does not exceed 5.0 mg.

Ignition residue: To 0.5 g add 1 ml of H_2SO_4 and ignite gently. Cool, add 1 ml of HNO_3 and a few drops of H_2SO_4, evaporate and ignite to constant weight. The weight of the residue does not exceed 5.0 mg.

CUPFERRON

Ammonium Nitrosophenylhydroxylamine

C_6H_5N
$\diagup$ NO
$\diagdown$ ONH$_4$
; mol. wt. 155.16.

White or buff-colored, crystalline flakes. Soluble in water or alcohol. Cupferron is used in aqueous solution for quantitative precipitation and separation of iron in strongly acid solutions from certain other metals, including aluminum.[1,2,3,4,5] It is also applicable for the estimation of titanium and zirconium and several other metals. *Keep in well closed containers with a piece of ammonium carbonate in it.*

Standards

Melting range.................148°–152°
Sensitiveness.................to pass test

Solubility....................to pass test
Ignition residue..............max 0.10%

Sensitiveness: (a) Dissolve 50 mg of cupferron in 5 ml of H_2O, add 1 drop of 10% NH_3, and filter if not clear.

(b) To 0.1 ml of ferric chloride solution add 2 ml of 1 N HCl and dilute to 20 ml.

Dilute 0.1 ml of (b) to 2 ml, add 1 drop of HCl and 0.2 ml of (a). A red-brown color (precipitate) is produced.

Solubility: A solution of 1 g in 20 ml of H_2O is not darker than pale yellow, and is clear or not more than slightly turbid.

Ignition residue: Char well 1.0 g, cool, add 1 ml of H_2SO_4, evaporate, and ignite to constant weight. Any remaining residue does not exceed 1.0 mg.

[1] Baudisch, O., *Chem. Ztg.* **33**, 1298 (1909).
[2] Thornton, W. M., *Am. J. Sci.* **37**, 173 (1914).
[3] Lundell, G. E. F., and Knowles, H. B., *J. Am. Chem. Soc.*, **12**, 344 (1920).
[4] Cunningham, T. R., *Ind. Eng. Chem.* **3**, 103 (1931).
[5] Gilchrist, R., and Wicherst, *J. Am. Chem. Soc.* **57**, 585 (1935).

CUPRIC ACETATE

$Cu(CH_3CO_2)_2 \cdot H_2O$; mol. wt. 199.65; anhydrous—90.98%; Cu—31.83%.

Dark bluish-green crystals, or a green powder; efflorescent in dry air. Slowly soluble in 15 parts of water; slightly soluble in alcohol.

Standards

Insoluble....................max 0.010%	Alkalies, Earths (as sulfate)....max 0.20%
Chloride (Cl)................max 0.002%	Iron (Fe)...................max 0.002%
Nitrate (NO_3)................max 0.01%	Lead (Pb)...................max 0.005%
Sulfate (SO_4)................max 0.010%	Other metals (as Ni)........max 0.010%

Insoluble: Dissolve 10 g in 150 ml of H_2O and 2 ml of glacial acetic acid, and heat on the steam bath for 1 hour. Filter any undissolved residue (retain filtrate), wash it with water and dry at 105°. Its weight does not exceed 1.0 mg.

Chloride: To a solution of 1 g of cupric acetate in 20 ml of water add 1 ml of HNO_3, and divide into two equal portions. To one portion add 1 ml of $AgNO_3$, bring to a boil, let stand for 10 minutes, cool, filter until clear and use for the control. To the other portion add 1 ml of $AgNO_3$. If a turbidity is produced it is not greater than is produced by adding 0.01 mg of Cl to the control and adjusting both to the same volume.

Nitrate: Dissolve 1.0 g in 10 ml of water. Add the solution in small portions and with constant stirring to 10 ml of 10% NaOH, previously diluted with 5 ml of water. Cover the beaker and heat it on the steam bath, stirring several times, for 15 minutes. Cool, filter, neutralize the filtrate with 25% H_2SO_4 and dilute to 25 ml. Using 5 ml of the solution as *Sample Solution*, and 2.0 ml of standard nitrate solution for the control, proceed as directed under Nitrate—Estimation of Small Amounts, page 575.

Sulfate: Add 5 ml of glacial acetic acid to the filtrate from the test for insoluble, heat to boiling, add 5 ml of $BaCl_2$ and let stand overnight. If a precipitate is present, filter, wash it with hot H_2O and ignite. Its weight does not exceed 2.5 mg.

Alkalies, Earths, etc.: Dissolve 2 g in 100 ml of water and 2 ml of H_2SO_4, heat the solution to 70° and precipitate the copper with H_2S. Allow the precipitate to settle and decant the clear supernatant liquid through a filter. Evaporate 50 ml of the filtrate, and ignite. Not more than 2.0 mg of residue remains (retain residue).

Iron: To the residue from *Alkalies, Earths, etc.*, add 2 ml of HCl, 2 ml of H_2O and 0.5 ml of HNO_3 and slowly evaporate to dryness on the steam bath. Take up in 1 ml of HCl and 10 ml of warm water, and dilute to 50 ml. To 25 ml of this solution add 2 ml of HCl and dilute to 50 ml. Add 30 mg of ammonium persulfate and 3 ml of ammonium thiocyanate solution, and mix. Any red color produced is not greater than in a control made with 0.01 mg Fe, the same quantities of the reagents and in the same final volume as with the sample.

Lead: Dissolve 1.0 g in 15 ml of water and add 5 drops of glacial acetic acid and 0.2 ml of potassium chromate solution. No turbidity is produced in 5 minutes.

Other metals: Add a slight excess of NH_4OH to 10 ml of the solution from the test for *Iron*, boil for 1 minute, filter, and wash with a little hot H_2O to 20 ml. Neutralize 10 ml with 10% HCl, dilute to 25 ml, and add 3 drops of NH_4OH and 1 ml of H_2S. Any color produced is not darker than that of a control made with 0.02 mg of nickel (Ni), 3 drops NH_4OH and 1 ml H_2S in the same volume as with the sample.

CUPRIC AMMONIUM CHLORIDE

$CuCl_2 \cdot 2NH_4Cl \cdot 2H_2O$; mol. wt. 277.48; anhydrous—87.02%; Cu—22.90%; NH_3—12.27%.

Blue crystals. Soluble in about 4 parts of water; soluble in ethanol.

Standards

Insoluble....................max 0.005%	Alkalies, Earths, etc...........max 0.15%
Free acid (as HCl)......max about 0.03%	Iron (Fe)...................max 0.005%
Nitrate (NO_3)...............max 0.003%	*Assay*........................min 98%
Sulfate (SO_4)................max 0.010%	

Insoluble: Dissolve 20 g in 100 ml of H_2O and heat on the steam bath for 1 hour. Filter any undissolved residue, wash it with H_2O and dry at 105°. Its weight does not exceed 1.0 mg (retain filtrate).

Free acid: To a solution of 4 g of the sample in 100 ml of water add 4 drops of methyl orange indicator, and divide into two equal portions. Upon adding 0.2 ml of 0.1 N NaOH to one portion, the purplish color, if any, disappears.

Nitrate: Dissolve 1.0 g in 10 ml of water, add the solution with stirring to 15 ml of 10% NaOH and boil gently while stirring until the NH_3 is expelled. Dilute with about 10 ml of water and filter. Neutralize the filtrate with 25% H_2SO_4 and dilute to 50 ml. Dilute 5 ml with 5 ml of water, add 0.2 ml of diphenylamine solution, then slowly run in 10 ml of H_2SO_4. After 5 minutes mix the liquids by swirling the beaker and allow to stand for 30 minutes. No distinct blue color is produced.

Sulfate: To the filtrate from the test for *Insoluble* add 1 ml of HCl, heat to boiling, add 5 ml of $BaCl_2$ and allow to stand overnight. Filter any precipitate, wash and ignite. The weight of the precipitate ($BaSO_4$) does not exceed 2.5 mg.

Alkalies, Earths, etc.: Dissolve 2 g in 100 ml of H_2O, add 1 ml of H_2SO_4, heat to 70° and precipitate the copper with H_2S. Allow the precipitate to settle and filter without washing. Evaporate 50 ml of the filtrate and ignite. Not more than 1.5 mg of residue remains (retain residue).

Iron: To the residue from *Alkalies, Earths, etc.*, add 2 ml of HCl, 2 ml of H_2O and 0.5 ml of HNO_3, then slowly evaporate to dryness on the steam bath. Take up 1 ml of HCl and 5 ml of warm H_2O, and dilute with H_2O to 50 ml. To 10 ml of this solution add 2 ml of HCl and dilute to 50 ml. Add about 30 mg of ammonium persulfate and 3 ml of ammonium thiocyanate solution, and mix. Any red color produced is not greater than that in a control made with 0.01 mg of Fe, the same quantities of the reagents and in the same final volume as with the sample.

Assay: Cupric ammonium chloride may be assayed as follows: Weigh accurately about 0.8 g and dissolve it in 100 ml of H_2O in a glass-stoppered flask. Add 2 ml of glacial acetic acid and 3 g of potassium iodide, and titrate the liberated iodine with 0.1 N sodium thiosulfate, adding starch solution toward the end. One ml of 0.1 N thiosulfate = 0.02775 g $CuCl_2 \cdot 2NH_4Cl \cdot 2H_2O$, log 44326. Correct for a blank.

CUPRIC BROMIDE

$CuBr_2$; mol. wt. 223.37; Cu—28.45%; Br—71.55%.

Almost black, deliquescent crystals or granules. Very soluble in water; soluble in ethanol or in acetone. *Keep in tightly closed bottles, protected from light.*

Standards

Assay..............98.5%–100.5% $CuBr_2$	Sulfate (SO_4)................max 0.015%
Insoluble....................max 0.010%	Alkalies, Earths, etc...........max 0.20%
Chloride (Cl).................max 0.20%	Iron (Fe)...................max 0.005%

Assay: Weigh accurately about 0.7 g and dissolve it in 75 ml of H_2O in a glass-stoppered flask. Add 2 ml of glacial acetic acid and 3 g of potassium iodide and titrate the liberated iodine with 0.1 N sodium thiosulfate, adding starch toward the end. One ml of 0.1 N thiosulfate = 0.02234 g $CuBr_2$, log 34908. Correct for a blank.

Insoluble: Dissolve 10 g in 100 ml of H_2O and 1 ml of HCl, and heat the solution on the steam bath for 10 minutes. Filter any undissolved residue, wash it with water and dry at 105°. The residue weighs not more than 1.0 mg (retain filtrate).

Chloride: Dissolve 0.25 g in 120 ml of water in a flask, add 3 g of ammonium persulfate and 10 ml of HNO_3. Heat for 3 hours on the steam bath with occasional stirring and until the solution is colorless. Cool and dilute to 250 ml, *Solution A*. To 50 ml of *Solution A* add 1 ml of $AgNO_3$, bring to a boil and filter until clear. Use the filtrate as a control. To another 50 ml of *Solution A* add 1 ml of $AgNO_3$. The resulting turbidity is not greater than that produced by adding 0.1 mg of Cl^- to the control.

Sulfate: Heat the filtrate from the test for *Insoluble* to boiling, add 5 ml of $BaCl_2$ and let stand overnight. Filter, if any precipitate is present, wash it with H_2O and ignite. The weight of the precipitate does not exceed 3.5 mg.

Alkalies, Earths, etc.: Dissolve 2 g in 100 ml of water, add 1 ml of H_2SO_4, heat the solution to 70° and precipitate the copper with H_2S. Allow the precipitate to settle and decant the clear supernatant liquid through a filter. Evaporate 50 ml of the filtrate and ignite. Not more than 2.0 mg of residue remains (retain residue).

Iron: To the residue from *Alkalies, Earths, etc.*, add 2 ml of HCl, 2 ml of H_2O and 0.5 ml of HNO_3 and slowly evaporate to dryness on the steam bath. Take up in 1 ml of HCl and 10 ml of warm H_2O, and dilute with H_2O to 50 ml. To 10 ml of this solution add 2 ml of HCl and dilute to 50 ml. Add about 30 mg of ammonium persulfate and 3 ml of ammonium thiocyanate solution, and mix. Any red color produced is not greater than that in a control made with 0.01 mg of Fe, the same quantities of the reagents and in the same final volume as with the sample.

CUPRIC CARBONATE

Approximately $CuCO_3 \cdot Cu(OH)_2 \cdot xH_2O$.

Fine, green powder. Insoluble in water or alcohol; soluble in dilute acids with effervescence; also soluble in ammonium hydroxide.

Standards

Assay....................52%–56% Cu	Sulfate (SO_4)...............max 0.010%
Sulfuric acid—insoluble......max 0.010%	Alkalies, Earths, etc..........max 0.40%
Chloride (Cl)................max 0.002%	Iron (Fe)...................max 0.005%
Nitrate (NO_3)...............max 0.02%	Lead (Pb).................max 0.005%

Assay: Weigh accurately about 0.4 g and transfer to a glass-stoppered flask. Add 20 ml of water and 5 ml of phosphoric acid and heat until the carbonate is dissolved. Cool, add 80 ml of water and 3 g potassium iodide, and titrate the liberated iodine with 0.1 N sodium thiosulfate, adding starch toward the end. One ml of 0.1 N sodium thiosulfate = 0.006357 g Cu, log 80325.

Sulfuric acid—insoluble: Heat 10 g with 100 ml of H_2O and 7 ml of H_2SO_4 until dissolved. Filter any undissolved residue, wash with water and dry at 105°. The insoluble residue does not exceed 1.0 mg.

Chloride: Dissolve 1 g in 20 ml of water and 1 ml of HNO_3 and divide into two equal portions. To one portion add 1 ml of $AgNO_3$, bring to a boil, let stand for 10 minutes, cool, filter until clear and use for the control. To the other portion add 1 ml of $AgNO_3$. If a turbidity is produced it is not greater than that produced by adding 0.010 mg of Cl to the control and adjusting both to the same volume.

Nitrate: To 0.5 g add 5 ml of water and just enough glacial acetic acid to dissolve. Dilute to 10 ml and proceed under the test for *Nitrate* under Cupric Acetate, beginning with "Add this solution . . ." and using 2.0 ml of standard nitrate solution for the control.

Sulfate: Dissolve 5 g in a mixture of 100 ml of H_2O and 10 ml of HCl and filter if necessary. Heat the filtrate to boiling, add 5 ml of $BaCl_2$ and allow to stand overnight. If a precipitate ($BaSO_4$) is present, filter, wash it with hot H_2O and ignite. Its weight does not exceed 2.5 mg.

Alkalies, Earths, etc.: Dissolve 1 g in 100 ml of water and 2 ml of H_2SO_4. Heat the solution to about 70° and precipitate the copper with H_2S. Allow the precipitate to settle and filter without washing.   Evaporate 50 ml of the filtrate and ignite.   The residue does not exceed 2.0 mg.

Iron: To the residue from *Alkalies, Earths, etc.*, add 2 ml of HCl, 2 ml of H_2O and 0.5 ml of HNO_3, then slowly evaporate to dryness on the steam bath.   Take up in 1 ml of HCl and 10 ml of warm H_2O, and dilute with H_2O to 50 ml.   To 10 ml of this solution add 2 ml of HCl and dilute to 50 ml.   Add about 30 mg of ammonium persulfate and 3 ml of ammonium thiocyanate solution, and mix.   Any red color produced is not greater than that in a control made with 0.01 mg of Fe, the same quantities of the reagents and in the same final volume as with the sample.

Lead: To 1.0 g add 15 ml of water, heat and add just sufficient glacial acetic acid to dissolve and a few drops more.   Filter, if necessary, and add 0.1 ml of potassium chromate solution and mix.   No turbidity is produced in 5 minutes.

CUPRIC CHLORIDE

Copper Dichloride

$CuCl_2 \cdot 2H_2O$; mol. wt. 170.50; anhydrous—78.87%; Cu—37.28%; Cl—41.59%.

Green crystals, deliquescent in moist air.   Soluble in 1 part of water; soluble in alcohol; slightly soluble in ether.

Standards

Insoluble....................max 0.010%	Arsenic (As).................max 2 ppm
Solubility in alcohol...........to pass test	Iron (Fe)...................max 0.003%
Nitrate (NO_3)................max 0.01%	Lead (Pb)..................max 0.002%
Sulfate (SO_4)................max 0.005%	Other metals (as Ni).........max 0.01%
Alkalies, Earths, etc...........max 0.10%	

Insoluble: Dissolve 10 g in a mixture of 100 ml of H_2O and 1 ml of HCl, and heat on the steam bath for 1 hour.   Filter any undissolved residue, wash it with water and dry at 105°.   Its weight does not exceed 1.0 mg (retain filtrate).

Solubility in alcohol: 1.0 g dissolves completely in 20 ml of warm alcohol and the solution remains clear on cooling.

Nitrate: Dissolve 1.0 g in 10 ml of water.   Add this solution in small portions and with constant stirring to 10 ml of 10% NaOH previously diluted with 5 ml of water.   Cover the beaker and heat on the steam bath, stirring several times, for 15 minutes.   Cool and filter.   Neutralize the filtrate with 25% H_2SO_4 and dilute to 25 ml.   Using 5 ml of this solution as *Sample Solution* and 2 ml of standard nitrate solution (0.02 mg NO_3) for control, proceed as directed under Nitrate— Estimation of Small Amounts, page 575.

Sulfate: Heat the filtrate from the test for *Insoluble* to boiling, add 5 ml of $BaCl_2$ and allow to stand overnight.   Filter, if a precipitate is present, wash it with H_2O and ignite.   Its weight it not more than 0.0012 g.

Alkalies, Earths, etc.: Dissolve 2 g in 100 ml of H_2O, add 1 ml of H_2SO_3, heat the solution to 70° and precipitate the copper with H_2S.   Allow the precipitate to settle and filter without washing.   Evaporate 50 ml of the filtrate and ignite.   Not more than 1.0 mg of residue remains (retain residue).

Arsenic: Determine in 1 g by the method on page 563 using 8 ml of stannous chloride and 2.5 g of zinc.   The stain is not more than from 0.002 mg of As.

Iron: To the residue from *Alkalies, Earths, etc.*, add 2 ml of HCl, 2 ml of H_2O and 0.5 ml of HNO_3, and slowly evaporate to dryness on the steam bath.   Take up in 1 ml of HCl and 10 ml of warm H_2O, and dilute with H_2O to 100 ml.   To 35 ml of this solution add 2 ml of HCl and dilute to 50 ml.   Add about 30 mg of ammonium persulfate and 3 ml of ammonium thiocyanate solution, and mix. Any red color produced is not greater than that of a control made with 0.01 mg of Fe, the same quantities of the reagents and in the same final volume as with the sample.

Lead: Dissolve 1.0 g in 25 ml of 1% HNO_3 in a glass-stoppered cylinder.   For a control place in a like cylinder 0.01 mg of Pb (1.0 ml standard lead solution) and 0.5 g of sample and dissolve in sufficient of the 1% HNO_3 to make 25 ml.   From here on treat each of the solutions as follows: Add 2 ml of hydroxylamine hydro-chloride solution, then add NH_4OH dropwise, shaking after each addition, until the precipitate formed no longer dissolves.   Now add *under the hood* 5 ml of ammonium citrate solution and 25 ml of potassium cyanide solution, cooling in cold water, then add 10 ml of dithizone standard solution.   Shake for 2 minutes and allow the layers to separate.   The pink color of the chloroform layer from the sample is not darker than that from the control.

Other metals: Add a slight excess of NH_4OH to 20 ml of the solution from the test for *Iron*, boil for 1 minute, filter, wash with hot H_2O to 20 ml.   Neutralize the filtrate with 10% HCl, dilute to 25 ml, and add 3 drops of NH_4OH and 1 ml of H_2S.   Any color produced is not darker than that of a control made with 0.02 mg of nickel (Ni), 3 drops NH_4OH and 1 ml H_2S in the same volume as with the sample.

CUPRIC NITRATE

$Cu(NO_3)_2 \cdot 3H_2O$; mol. wt. 241.60; anhydrous—77.63% Cu—26.31%; NO_3—51.32%.

Blue deliquescent crystals.   Soluble in 1 part of water or in alcohol.   *Keep in a cool place.*

Standards

Insoluble...................max 0.010%	Iron (Fe)...................max 0.005%
Chloride (Cl)...............max 0.002%	Lead (Pb)..................max 0.002%
Sulfate (SO_4)...............max 0.005%	Other metals (as Ni)..........max 0.01%
Alkalies, Earths, etc..........max 0.050%	*Assay*.......................min 99%

Insoluble: Dissolve 10 g in a mixture of 100 ml of H_2O and 0.5 ml of HNO_3 and heat on the steam bath for 1 hour.   Filter any undissolved residue, wash it with water and dry at 105°.   Its weight does not exceed 1.0 mg

Chloride: To a solution of 1 g of cupric nitrate in 20 ml of water add 1 ml of HNO_3 and divide into two equal portions.   To one portion add 1 ml of $AgNO_3$, bring to a boil, let stand for 10 minutes, cool, filter until clear and use for the control. To the other portion add 1 ml of $AgNO_3$.   If a turbidity is produced it is not greater than that produced by adding 0.01 mg of Cl to the control and adjusting both to the same volume.

Sulfate: Dissolve 8 g in 10 ml of hot H_2O, add 10 ml of HCl and evaporate to dryness on the steam bath.   Treat the residue with 5 ml of H_2O and 5 ml of HCl and re-evaporate to dryness.   Dissolve the residue in 100 ml of H_2O and 1 ml of HCl, and filter if necessary.   Heat the solution to boiling, add 5 ml of $BaCl_2$ and let stand overnight.   If a precipitate ($BaSO_4$) is present, filter, wash it with water and ignite.   Its weight is not more than 1.0 mg.

Alkalies, Earths, etc.: Dissolve 4 g in 200 ml of water, add 2 ml of H_2SO_4, heat to 70° and precipitate the copper with H_2S.   Allow the precipitate to settle and filter without washing.   Evaporate 100 ml of the filtrate and ignite.   The weight of the residue does not exceed 1.0 mg (retain residue).

Iron: To the residue from *Alkalies, Earths, etc.*, add 2 ml of HCl, 2 ml of H_2O and 0.5 ml of HNO_3 and evaporate to dryness on the steam bath.   Take up in 1 ml of HCl and 10 ml of warm H_2O, dilute with H_2O to 100 ml.   To 20 ml of the solution add 2 ml of HCl and dilute to 50 ml.   Add about 30 mg of ammonium persulfate and 3 ml of ammonium thiocyanate solution, and mix.   Any red color produced is not greater than that in a control made with 0.02 mg of Fe, the same quantities of the reagents and in the same final volume as with the sample.

Lead: Dissolve 1.0 g in 25 ml of 1% HNO_3 (1 vol. HNO_3 + 100 vol. H_2O) in a glass-stoppered cylinder.   For a control place in a like cylinder 0.01 mg of Pb (1.0 ml standard lead solution) and 0.5 g of sample and dissolve in sufficient of the 1% HNO_3 to make 25 ml.   From here on treat each of the solutions as follows: Add 2 ml of hydroxylamine hydrochloride solution, then add NH_4OH dropwise, shaking after each addition, until the precipitate formed no longer dissolves. Now add *under the hood* 5 ml of ammonium citrate solution and 25 ml of potassium cyanide solution, cooling in cold water, then add 10 ml of dithizone standard solution.   Shake for 2 minutes and allow the layers to separate.   The pink color of the chloroform layer from the sample is not darker than that from the control.

Other metals: Add a slight excess of NH_4OH to 10 ml of the solution from the test for *Iron*, boil for 1 minute, filter and wash with hot H_2O to 20 ml.   Neutralize the filtrate with 10% HCl, dilute to 25 ml, add 3 drops of NH_4OH and 1 ml of H_2S. The color produced is not darker than that of a control made with 0.02 mg of nickel, 3 drops of NH_4OH and 1 ml of H_2S in the same volume as with the sample.

Assay: Weigh accurately about 1.0 g and dissolve in a flask in 50 ml of water. Dissolve in the solution 2 g of sodium acetate and add 5.0 ml of acetic acid.   Now add a solution of 3 g KI in 25 ml of water and titrate the liberated iodine with 0.1 N sodium thiosulfate, adding starch solution, as indicator, toward the end.   One ml of 0.1 N thiosulfate = 0.02416 g $Cu(NO_3)_2 \cdot 3H_2O$, log 38310.

CUPRIC OXIDE, POWDER

Copper Oxide Black

CuO; mol. wt. 79.54; Cu—79.89%; O—20.11%.

Black, fine powder.   Insoluble in water; soluble in acids and in ammonium hydroxide.

Standards

Assay.....................min 98% CuO	Sulfur compound (as SO_4).....max 0.020%
Hydrochloric acid—insoluble..max 0.020%	Free alkali..................to pass test
Carbon compounds (as C)......max 0.01%	Alkalies, Earths, etc...........max 0.20%
Chloride (Cl)................max 0.005%	Ammonium hydroxide
Nitrogen compounds (as N)...max 0.002%	precipitate (Fe, etc.)........max 0.10%

Assay: Weigh accurately about 0.30 g and heat in a flask with 5 ml of phosphoric acid and 15 ml of water until dissolved. Cool, dilute with 80 ml of water, add 3 g of potassium iodide and titrate the liberated iodine with 0.1 N sodium thiosulfate, adding starch toward the end. One ml of 0.1 N thiosulfate = 0.007957 g CuO, log 99075. Correct for a blank.

Hydrochloric acid—insoluble: Warm 5 g with a mixture of 25 ml of hydrochloric acid and 15 ml of water on the steam bath until the oxide has dissolved. Add 100 ml of water, filter any undissolved residue, wash it with water and dry at 105°. Its weight is not more than 1.0 mg (retain filtrate).

Carbon compounds: Ignite 0.6 g in a stream of CO_2-free air or in oxygen, pass the gases into 20 ml of water containing 0.5 ml of ammonium hydroxide, then add 2 ml of $BaCl_2$. The resulting turbidity is not greater than that produced by 2 ml of $BaCl_2$ in a solution containing 0.5 mg of anhydrous sodium carbonate and 0.5 ml of ammonium hydroxide in 20 ml of water.

Chloride: Shake 1 g with 20 ml of water and 3 ml of nitric acid for 10 minutes. Filter, wash to 40 ml and divide the filtrate into two equal portions. To one portion add 1 ml of silver nitrate, warm for 10 minutes, filter until clear and use for the control. To the other portion add 1 ml of silver nitrate. Any resulting turbidity is not greater than that produced by adding 0.025 mg Cl to the control.

Nitrogen compounds: Place 1 g in a suitable distilling flask connected with a condenser and a receiver containing 5 ml of 0.1 N HCl. Add 20 ml of 10% NaOH and 1 g of fine aluminium wire in small pieces, and let stand for 2 hours. Then add 60 ml of water and slowly distill about 50 ml. Add to the distillate 1 ml of 10% NaOH and 2 ml of Nessler solution. The resulting color is not darker than that produced by treating 0.02 mg of nitrogen (0.08 mg NH_4Cl) in the same manner as the cupric oxide.

Sulfur compounds: To 5 g add a mixture of 15 ml of hydrochloric acid, 15 ml of H_2O and 5 ml of nitric acid, and evaporate to dryness on the steam bath. Dissolve the residue in 100 ml of water and 1 ml of hydrochloric acid, and filter. Heat the filtrate to boiling, add 5 ml of $BaCl_2$ and allow to stand overnight. If a precipitate is present, filter, wash it well with water and ignite. Its weight does not exceed 2.5 mg.

Free alkali: Boil gently 3 g with 30 ml of water, cool, dilute to 30 ml and allow to settle. Decant 20 ml and add 2 drops of phenolphthalein. No red color is produced.

Alkalies, Earths, etc.: Dissolve 2 g by heating with 10 ml of HCl and 5 ml of water, and dilute to 100 ml. Heat to 70° and precipitate the copper with H_2S. Allow the precipitate to settle and decant the clear supernatant liquid through a filter. To 50 ml of the filtrate add 0.5 ml of H_2SO_4, evaporate and ignite. The residue weighs not more than 2.0 mg.

Ammonium hydroxide precipitate: Dilute the filtrate from the test for *Hydrochloric acid—insoluble* to 200 ml, add ammonium hydroxide until the precipitate first formed is redissolved. Filter any undissolved precipitate, wash it with water containing 2.5% NH_3 until the washings are colorless, and ignite. The weight of the ignited precipitate is not more than 2.0 mg.

CUPRIC OXIDE, WIRE

Black wire, 1–3 cm long and approximately No. 15 B & S gauge. Consists principally of cupric oxide with variable proportions of cuprous oxide and metallic copper. Contains CuO and Cu_2O equivalent to about 75% as cupric oxide.

Standards

Assay..................about 75% CuO
Carbon compounds (as C).....max 0.002%
Chloride (Cl)...............max 0.005%

Nitrogen compounds (as N)...max 0.002%
Sulfur compounds (as SO_4)....max 0.010%

Assay: Weigh accurately about 1 g and heat it with a mixture of 15 ml of phosphoric acid and 50 ml of water until the residue is free from black particles. Cool and dilute with water to exactly 100 ml. Transfer 25 ml to a glass-stoppered flask, dilute with 50 ml of water, add 3 g of potassium iodide and titrate the liberated iodine with 0.1 N sodium thiosulfate, adding starch toward the end. One ml of 0.1 N thiosulfate = 0.007957 g CuO, log 90075. Correct for a blank.

Note: When cuprous oxide is treated with an oxyacid, the cupric salt of the acid is formed and one-half of the copper separates as the metal, thus:

$$Cu_2O + H_2SO_4 = CuSO_4 + Cu + H_2O$$

Carbon compounds: Ignite 6 g in a stream of CO_2-free air or in oxygen, pass the gases into 20 ml of water containing 0.5 ml of ammonium hydroxide, then add 2 ml of $BaCl_2$. The resulting turbidity is not greater than that produced by 2 ml of $BaCl_2$ in a mixture of 1 mg of anhydrous sodium carbonate, 20 ml of water and 0.5 ml of ammonium hydroxide.

Chloride: Shake 1 g of the powdered sample with 20 ml of water and 3 ml of nitric acid for 10 minutes, filter, wash to 40 ml and divide the filtrate into two equal portions. To one portion add 1 ml of silver nitrate, warm for 10 minutes, filter and use for the control. To the other portion add 1 ml of silver nitrate. Any resulting turbidity is not greater than that produced by adding 0.025 mg of Cl to the control.

Nitrogen compounds: Place 1 g of the powdered sample in a suitable distilling flask connected with a condenser and a receiver containing 5 ml of 0.1 N HCl. Add 20 ml of 10% NaOH and 1 g of fine aluminum wire in small pieces, and let stand for 2 hours. Then add 60 ml of water, distill about 50 ml, and add to the distillate 1 ml of 10% NaOH and 2 ml of Nessler solution. The resulting color is not darker than that produced by treating 0.02 mg of nitrogen (0.08 mg NH_4Cl) in the same manner as the sample.

Sulfur compounds: To 6 g add 15 ml of HCl and 5 ml of HNO_3 and evaporate on the steam bath to dryness. Dissolve the residue in 1 ml of HCl and 100 ml of water and filter if necessary. Heat the filtrate to boiling, add 5 ml of $BaCl_2$ and allow to stand overnight.   If any precipitate is present, filter, wash, ignite and weigh.   Its weight does not exceed 1.5 mg.

CUPRIC POTASSIUM CHLORIDE

$CuCl_2 \cdot 2KCl \cdot 2H_2O$; mol. wt. 319.6; anhydrous—88.73%; H_2O—11.27%; Cu—19.89%; K—24.46%; Cl—44.37%.

Blue crystals.   Soluble in 4 parts of water; slightly soluble in alcohol.

Standards

Insoluble....................max 0.005%	Ammonia (NH_3)..............max 0.05%
Free acid (as HCl)......max about 0.03%	Calcium and Magnesium.......max 0.10%
Nitrate (NO_3)...............max 0.003%	Iron (Fe)...................max 0.002%
Sulfate.....................max 0.010%	*Assay*........................min 98%

Insoluble: Determine as in Cupric Ammonium Chloride.   Not more than 1.0 mg of insoluble residue is obtained.

Free acid: Dissolve 4 g of sample in 100 ml of water, add 4 drops of methyl orange and divide into two equal parts.   Upon adding 0.1 ml of 0.1 N NaOH to one portion, the purplish color, if any, disappears.

Nitrate: Dissolve 1.0 g in 10 ml of water.   Add the solution in small portions and with constant stirring to 10 ml of 10% NaOH, previously diluted with 5 ml of water.   Cover the beaker and heat it on the steam bath, stirring several times, for 15 minutes.   Cool, filter, neutralize the filtrate with 25% H_2SO_4 and dilute to 50 ml.   Dilute 5 ml with 5 ml of water, add 0.2 ml of diphenylamine solution, then slowly run in 10 ml of H_2SO_4.   After 5 minutes mix the liquids by swirling the beaker and allow to stand for 30 minutes.   No distinct blue color is produced.

Sulfate: To the filtrate from the test for *Insoluble* add 1 ml of HCl, heat to boiling, add 5 ml of $BaCl_2$ and allow to stand overnight.   If a precipitate is present, filter, wash and ignite.   The weight of the ignited precipitate does not exceed 2.5 mg.

Ammonia: Dissolve 0.5 g in 10 ml of water in a small flask, add 5 ml of 10% NaOH, and heat gently.   The escaping vapor does not turn red litmus paper blue.

Calcium and Magnesium: Dissolve 4 g in 180 mg of H_2O, add 2 ml of HCl, heat to 70° and precipitate the copper with H_2S.   Cool, and dilute to 200 ml.   Allow to settle, filter, but do not wash.   Boil 100 ml of the filtrate for 2 minutes, refilter if necessary, add 5 ml of ammonium oxalate, 2 ml of ammonium phosphate, and 10 ml of NH_4OH; allow to stand overnight.   If a precipitate is then present, filter, wash with 2.5% NH_3, and ignite to constant weight.   The weight of the ignited precipitate does not exceed 2.0 mg.

Iron: Evaporate 25 ml of the filtrate from the cupric sulfide obtained in the preceding test to about 10 ml, filter and wash with a little water.   Add to the combined filtrate and washing 2 ml of HCl and dilute to 50 ml.   Add 50 mg of ammonium persulfate and 3 ml of ammonium thiocyanate solution, and mix.   Any red color produced is not greater than that in a blank to which 0.01 mg of Fe has been added.

Assay: Cupric potassium chloride may be assayed by the method described for Cupric Ammonium Chloride.   One ml of 0.1 N thiosulfate = 0.03196 g $CuCl_2 \cdot 2KCl \cdot 2H_2O$, log 50461.   Not less than 98% should be found.

CUPRIC SULFATE

$CuSO_4 \cdot 5H_2O$; mol. wt. 249.69; anhydrous—63.93% H_2O—36.07%; Cu—25.46%; SO_4—38.47%.

Large or small blue crystals; efflorescent in dry air.   Soluble in about 3 parts of water; slowly soluble in glycerol; almost insoluble in alcohol.   At 125° it loses 4 mols of water; the remainder at about 205°.   *Keep in well-closed containers.*

Standards

Insoluble.....................max 0.005%	Alkalies, Earths (as Sulfate)....max 0.10%
Chloride (Cl)................max 0.001%	Iron (Fe)....................max 0.003%
Nitrogen compounds (as N)...max 0.001%	Other metals (as Ni)........max 0.005%

Insoluble: Dissolve 20 g in 200 ml of water and 5 ml of H_2SO_4.   Filter through a tared filtering crucible, wash well with warm water, dry at 105° and weigh.   The weight of the insoluble residue does not exceed 1.0 mg.

Chloride: To a solution of 2 g of cupric sulfate in 20 ml of water add 1 ml of HNO_3 and divide into two equal portions.   To one portion add 1 ml of $AgNO_3$, bring to a boil, let stand for 10 minutes, cool, filter until clear and use for the control. To the other portion add 1 ml of $AgNO_3$.   If a turbidity is produced it is not greater than that produced by adding 0.01 mg of Cl to the control and adjusting both to the same volume.

Nitrogen compounds: Dissolve 2 g in 50 ml of H_2O, add 1 g of Devarda metal, or 0.5 g of fine aluminum wire, and 30 ml of 10% NaOH, and allow to stand protected from loss or access of NH_3 for 2 hours.   Then distill gently about 40 ml into 5 ml of H_2O containing 1 drop of diluted HCl.   Dilute the distillate to 50 ml, and add 1 ml of 10% NaOH and 2 ml of Nessler solution.   The color produced is not darker than that produced by treating 0.02 mg of nitrogen (0.08 mg NH_4Cl) in the same manner as the sample.

Alkalies, Earths, etc.: To a solution of 3 g of the cupric sulfate in 120 ml of water add 2 ml of HCl, warm to 70° and precipitate the copper with H_2S.   Dilute with water to 150 ml, allow to settle and filter without washing.   Evaporate 100 ml of the filtrate and ignite.   Not more than 2.0 mg of residue remains (retain).

Solution R: To the residue from the test for *Alkalies, Earths, etc.*, add 2 ml of HCl, 2 ml of water and 5 drops of HNO_3, and slowly evaporate on the steam bath to dryness.   Take up with 1 ml of HCl and 10 ml of water, filter, if necessary, and dilute to 50 ml.

Iron: To 10 ml of *Solution R* add 2 ml of HCl and dilute to 50 ml.   Add about 50 mg of ammonium persulfate and 3 ml of ammonium thiocyanate, and mix. Any red color produced is not darker than that in a blank to which 0.012 mg of Fe has been added.

Other metals: To 25 ml of *Solution R* add a slight excess of NH_4OH, boil for 1 minute, filter, wash with 15 ml of hot water.   Cool and dilute to 50 ml.   Neutralize 20 ml of the solution to litmus paper with 10% HCl.   Add 5 drops of 10% NH_3 and follow with 2 ml of H_2S.   The solution is not darker than that of a control made with 0.02 mg of Ni in 25 ml of H_2O, treated with 5 drops of 10% NH_3 and 2 ml of H_2S.

CUPRIC SULFATE, ANHYDROUS

$CuSO_4$; mol. wt. 159.61; Cu—39.81%; SO_4—60.19%.

Grayish-white powder; hygroscopic.   Soluble in about 5 parts of water; insoluble in alcohol.   *Keep in tightly closed containers.*

Standards

Assay.................min 98% $CuSO_4$	Alkalies, Earths (as Sulfate)....max 0.20%
Insoluble...................max 0.010%	Iron (Fe)...................max 0.005%
Chloride (Cl)...............max 0.002%	

Assay: Weigh accurately about 0.5 g and assay it as directed under Cupric Acetate.   One ml of 0.1 N sodium thiosulfate = 0.01596 g $CuSO_4$, log 20303.

Insoluble: Determine in 10 g of the sample as described for Cupric Sulfate. The insoluble residue weighs not more than 1.0 mg.

Chloride: Test as *Cupric Sulfate.*   Any resulting turbidity is not greater than that produced by adding 0.01 mg of Cl to the control.

Alkalies, Earths, etc.: Dissolve 2 g in 150 ml of water and 1 ml of H_2SO_4. Heat the solution to about 70° and precipitate the copper with H_2S.   Allow the precipitate to settle and filter without washing.   Evaporate 75 ml of the filtrate and ignite.   The residue does not exceed 2.0 mg.

Iron: Evaporate the residue obtained from *Alkalies, Earths, etc.* with 2 ml of HCl, 2 ml of H_2O and 0.5 ml of HNO_3 to dryness on the steam bath.   Take up the residue in 1 ml of HCl and 10 ml of warm H_2O, and dilute with water to 50 ml. To 20 ml of the dilution add 2 ml of HCl and dilute to 50 ml.   Add about 30 mg of ammonium persulfate and 3 ml of ammonium thiocyanate solution, and mix. Any red color produced is not darker than that of a blank to which 0.02 mg of Fe has been added.

CUPROUS CHLORIDE

Copper Monochloride

CuCl; mol. wt. 99.00; Cu—64.18%; Cl—35.82%.

Cuprous chloride is a nearly white, or grayish-white, crystalline powder.   On exposure to the air it quite rapidly becomes green, due to oxidation to cupric.   The presence of moisture accelerates the oxidation.   It is also discolored by light. Direct sunlight blackens it.

It is insoluble in water; soluble in an excess of hydrochloric acid and in ammonium hydroxide.   *Keep in tightly closed containers and protected from light.*

Cuprous chloride should not be used if it is pronouncedly green or brown.

Standards

Assay...................min 90% CuCl	Alkalies, Earths (as sulfate)....max 0.20%
Acid—insoluble..............max 0.02%	Arsenic (As)...............max 10 ppm
Sulfate (SO_4)...............max 0.10%	Iron (Fe)...................max 0.005%

Assay: Weigh accurately about 0.5 g and dissolve it in 30 ml of a cold solution, made by dissolving 10 g of ferric ammonium sulfate in 100 ml of $(1+1)$ HCl.   Add 5 ml of phosphoric acid and titrate with 0.1 N potassium permanganate.   Correct for a blank on the reagents.   One ml of 0.1 N permanganate $= 0.009903$ g CuCl, log 99577.

$$5CuCl + 8HCl + KMnO_4 \rightarrow 5CuCl_2 + MnCl_2 + KCl + 4H_2O$$

Acid—insoluble: Heat 5 g with 25 ml of water and 20 ml of HCl, and add HNO_3 in small portions until the sample is dissolved.   Dilute with 50 ml of H_2O, and if an undissolved residue remains, filter, wash with water (retain filtrate and washings) and dry at 105°.   The weight of the undissolved residue does not exceed 1.0 mg.

Solution S: Dilute the filtrate and washings from the preceding test to 200 ml.

Sulfate: Evaporate 50 ml of *Solution S* to dryness on the steam bath.   Take up the residue with 1 ml of HCl and dilute to 100 ml.   Heat the solution to boiling, add 5 ml of $BaCl_2$ and allow to stand overnight.   Filter any precipitate formed, wash it with hot water and ignite.   Its weight does not exceed 3.0 mg.

Alkalies, Earths, etc.: Dilute 80 ml of *Solution S* with 70 ml of water, heat to 70° and precipitate the copper with H_2S.   Allow the precipitate to settle and filter without washing.   To 75 ml of the filtrate add 5 drops of sulfuric acid, evaporate and ignite.   The residue does not exceed 2.0 mg.

Arsenic: Place 25 g of the cuprous chloride and 50 ml of HCl in a 250-ml distilling flask and distill about 25 ml into a 250 Erlenmeyer flask containing 30 ml of water and cooled in an ice bath.   Add to the distilling flask 20 ml more of HCl; continue the distillation until the volume in the distilling flask is about 15 ml. Add to the cooled distillate 2 drops of phenolphthalein and nearly neutralize with NaOH.   If the neutral point is passed, make slightly acid with HCl.   Dissolve in the distillate 2 g of sodium bicarbonate and titrate with 0.02 N iodine, using starch indicator.   Not more than 0.4 ml of the iodine is required, correcting for any iodine consumed by a blank made with the same volume of HCl and NaOH as used with sample acidified with HCl and 2 g sodium bicarbonate added.   Should copper chloride be carried over into the distillate, add 2 g of potassium sodium tartrate before neutralizing.

Iron: To the residue from the test for *Alkalies, Earths, etc.* add 2 ml of HCl, 2 ml of H_2O and 0.5 ml of HNO_3 and slowly evaporate on the steam bath to dryness.   Take up with 2 ml of HCl and 10 ml of water, filter, if necessary, and dilute to 50 ml.   To 20 ml of the solution add 2 ml of HCl and dilute to 50 ml.   Add 30 mg of ammonium persulfate and 3 ml of ammonium thiocyanate, and mix. Any resulting red color is not darker than that of a control made with 0.02 mg of Fe.

CYANOGEN BROMIDE

BrCN; mol. wt. 105.93.

Colorless crystals; volatilizes at ordinary temperatures.   The vapors are very irritant and *very poisonous*.   Melts at about 52°; boils at about 62°.   Freely soluble in water or alcohol.   *Keep tightly closed and in a cool place.*

Cyanogen bromide is used for the spectrophotometric determination of nicotinic acid and its derivatives in foods, medicinal preparations, etc.

Standards

Sensitiveness.................to pass test   Solubility....................to pass test

Sensitiveness: (*a*) Dissolve 0.5 g of sample in 25 ml of water.

(*b*) Dissolve 2.2 g of dibasic potassium phosphate and 2.7 g of ammonium chloride in 20 ml of water, add 0.5 ml of 10% NII_3 and dilute to 25 ml.

(*c*) Dilute 0.5 ml of pyridine with water to 500 ml.

Add 0.1 ml of (*c*) to 0.5 ml of water, then add 0.5 ml of (*b*) and follow with 0.1 ml of (*a*). A strong yellow color with a greenish tinge develops in 1–2 minutes.

Solubility: One gram dissolves completely in 20 ml of water or in 10 ml of alcohol, forming colorless solutions.

CYCLOHEXANE

Hexahydrobenzene; Hexamethylene

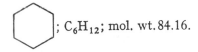 ; C_6H_{12}; mol. wt. 84.16.

Clear, colorless liquid; characteristic odor. Flammable. Sp. gr. about 0.77; melts at 6.5°; boils at 81°. Miscible with liquid alcohols, ethers, hydrocarbons and their chlorinated derivatives. It is a good solvent for various organic compounds.

In analytical chemistry it is principally used as a solvent and for molecular weight determinations.

Standards

Boiling range.................80°–81.5°	Water-soluble substances......to pass test
Freezing temperature........+5.5°–+6.5°	Acid (as acetic).............max 0.003%
Refractive index...........1.4262–1.4265	$KMnO_4$ reducing substances...to pass test
Evaporation residue.........max 0.010%	Substances affected by H_2SO_4..to pass test

Boiling range: Distill 50 ml. After the first 10 drops, all distills between 80° and 81.5°, correction being made for the difference from 760 mm in the barometric pressure, page 581.

Refractive index: Determine at 20°.

Evaporation residue: Evaporate 12.5 ml on the steam bath and dry at 105° for 1 hour. The weight of the residue does not exceed 1.0 mg.

Water-soluble substances: Place in a graduated cylinder 10 ml of H_2O and note the exact volume. Add exactly 10 ml of the sample, tightly stopper the cylinder, shake gently for a few minutes and allow to separate. No increase in the volume of the H_2O layer is noted.

Acid: To 50 ml of water add 0.2 ml of phenolphthalein and titrate with 0.02 *N* NaOH until the pink color persists after shaking for 10 seconds. Disregard the volume of the alkali consumed. Now add 10.0 ml of the sample and shake well.

If the pink color disappears, titrate with the 0.02 N NaOH until the pink color persists after shaking for a few seconds. Mot more than 0.3 ml of the 0.02 N NaOH is required.

Permanganate reducing substances: Mix 5 ml of sample with 25 ml of water, and add 5 ml of 25% H_2SO_4. Mix well and, while stirring, add 0.2 ml of 0.1 N KMnT_4. A pink color persists after 5 minutes.

Substances affected by H_2SO_4: In a graduated, glass-stoppered cylinder, mix gently for a few minutes equal volumes of the sample and of sulfuric acid, and allow to separate. Both layers remain colorless and neither volume is changed.

Note: The water content of cyclohexane may be determined by the iodine (Fischer) method.

CYCLOHEXANOL

Hexahydrophenol

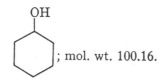 ; mol. wt. 100.16.

Colorless liquid at about 25°; crystalline below 22°. Camphor odor; hygroscopic. Sp. gr. 0.96. Soluble in about 30 parts of water; miscible with acetone, alcohol, chloroform, ether.

Standards

Freezing temperature.......+22° to +24°	Acid (as acetic).............max 0.005%
Boiling range.................160°–161°	Aldehyde....................to pass test
Solubility in water...........to pass test	Refractive index..........1.4650±0.002.
Evaporation residue.........max 0.05%	Water.......................max 0.2%

Freezing temperature: Determine as described on page 581.

Boiling range: Distill 50 ml. After the first 20 drops, all distills between 160° and 162°, correction being made for barometric pressure, page 581.

Solubility in water: Add 2.0 ml to 75 ml of water, shake well and allow to stand with frequent shaking. After a few hours the solution should be clear when shaken.

Evaporation residue: Evaporate 10 ml on the steam bath and dry at 120° for 2 hours. Not more than 5.0 mg of residue remains.

Acid: To 20 ml of alcohol add 2 drops of phenolphthalein and sufficient 0.02 N NaOH to produce a slight pink color which persists after shaking. Disregard the volume of the alkali consumed. Then add 10 ml of the sample and titrate with 0.02 N NaOH to the reproduction of the pink color. Not more than 0.4 ml of the NaOH is required for this titration.

Aldehyde: Dissolve 0.5 ml in 25 ml of water and add 2 ml of fuchsine-sulfurous acid. At the end of 10 minutes the mixture has no more color than a mixture of 25 ml of H_2O and 2 ml of the fuchsine-sulfurous acid.

Water: The water content of cyclohexanol may be determined by the iodine (Fischer) Method.

CYCLOHEXANONE

Ketohexamethylene

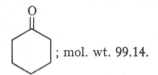 ; mol. wt. 99.14.

Clear, colorless, oily liquid; odor reminiscent of peppermint and acetone. Sp. gr. about 0.95 at 25°; melts at about −45°. Soluble in about 20 parts of water, more soluble in cold than in hot water; soluble in alcohol, ether, chloroform and other usual organic solvents. It dissolves a little less than 1/10 its volume of water.

Standards

Boiling range...............154°–157°	Acid (as acetic).............max 0.005%	
Solubility..................to pass test	Aldehyde...................to pass test	
Refractive index at 20°.....1.4508−±0.003	Water......................max 0.2%	
Evaporation residue.........max 0.05%		

Boiling range: Distill 50 ml. After the first 20 drops, all distills between 154° and 157°, correction being made for the difference from 760 mm in the barometric pressure, page 581.

Solubility in water: Add exactly 2 ml of sample to 60 ml of water at about 25°, and mix gently. A clear mixture results.

Refractive index: Determine at 20°.

Evaporation residue: Evaporate 5 ml on the steam bath and dry at 120° for 1 hour. The weight of the residue does not exceed 2.5 mg.

Acid (as acetic): Place 10 ml of alcohol in a glass-stoppered flask, add 0.2 ml of phenolphthalein and just sufficient 0.02 N NaOH to produce a pink color which persists after shaking for a few seconds. Disregard this volume of the alkali consumed. Add 10 ml of the cyclohexanol and shake for 15 seconds. If the pink color disappears titrate with the 0.02 N NaOH to the same intensity of red as with the alcohol alone. Not more than 0.35 ml of the NaOH is required.

Aldehyde: Dissolve 0.5 ml of sample in 20 ml of water and add 2 ml of fuchsine-sulfurous acid solution. At the end of 10 minutes the mixture has no more color than a blank.

Water: The water content of cyclohexanone may be determined by the iodine (Fischer) method.

L-CYSTINE

HOOC·CH(NH$_2$)CH$_2$—S—S—CH$_2$CH(NH$_2$)COOH; mol. wt. 240.30: N—11.66%; S—26.69%.

Colorless or white crystals; odorless or practically so. Almost insoluble in water or alcohol; soluble in diluted mineral acids and in alkaline solutions.

Standards

Nitrogen (N)................11.7 ± 0.25%	Chloride (Cl)................max 0.020%
Sulfur (S)................26.7% ± 0.3%	Phosphate (PO$_4$)............max 0.003%
Specific rotation in HCl at 25°..−210° ± 2°	Sulfate (SO$_4$)................max 0.010%
Solubility....................to pass test	Heavy metals (as Pb)........max 0.001%
Drying loss..................max 0.2%	Iron (Fe)..................max 0.002%
Ignition residue..............max 0.05%	

Nitrogen: Determine by the Kjeldahl method, using about 0.3 g of the dried sample, accurately weighed.

Sulfur: Determine by the bomb (Parr) method, using about 0.2 g of the dried sample, accurately weighed.

Specific rotation and Drying loss: Dry about 1 g, accurately weighed, for 3 hours over H_2SO_4 or P_2O_5; the loss in weight corresponds to not more than 0.2%. Dissolve 0.75 g of the dried sample in 1 N HCl to make exactly 25 ml. Observe the rotation of the solution on a 200-mm tube and calculate the specific rotation. When determined at 25° α_D is −210° ± 2°.

Note: The rotation of cystine in HCl solution is very sensitive to the temperature. Under the above described conditions, one degree difference in the temperature of the solution at the time of reading the rotation is responsible for the 2.5° of specific rotation—higher at temperature below 25°, and lower if above 25°.

Solubility: Solution of 0.5 g in 10 ml of 1 N HCl or in a mixture of 5 ml of 10% NH_3 and 5 ml of water are clear and colorless.

Chloride: Dissolve 0.10 g in a mixture of 5 ml of 10% HNO_3 and 15 ml of water and add 1 ml of $AgNO_3$. Any turbidity produced is not greater than in a control made with 0.02 mg of Cl.

Ignition residue, Phosphate, Sulfate, Heavy metals, Iron: Test as directed under Methionine. The results should be as there stated.

DECARDA METAL
Devarda's Alloy

Devarda metal is an alloy composed of: Cu—50%; Al—45%; Zn—5%. It is used in acid or alkaline solution, for reducing nitrates and/or nitrites to ammonia, the latter being then determined colorimetrically, or volumetrically by titration with standard acid.

Nitrogen: Place 7 g in a liter Kjeldahl flask, add, in small portions, 40 ml of HCl and agitate frequently until hydrogen ceases to be evolved. Cool, connect with a distillation trap and a condenser, add 100 ml of 30% NaOH, and distill 75 ml into 10 ml of 0.02 N HCl. Add to the distillate 2 drops methyl red and titrate the excess of the acid with 0.02 N NaOH. Not more than 0.7 ml of 0.02 N HCl is consumed in excess of that used when a 2-g sample is treated in the same manner, corresponding to not more than 0.004% N.

DEXTRIN

$(C_6H_{10}O_5)_n \cdot xH_2O$.

White, amorphous powder. Slowly and incompletely soluble in cold water; more readily soluble in hot water; insoluble in alcohol.

Standards

Insoluble......................trace	Chloride (Cl)...............max 0.002%
Ignition residue.............max 0.5%	Sulfate (SO$_4$)...............max 0.020%
Reducing sugars (as dextrose)...max 5.0%	Oxalate...............max about 0.05%
Alcohol-soluble substances......max 1.0%	Heavy metals (as Pb).......max 0.002%
Drying loss (water)..........max 10.0%	Iron (Fe)..................max 0.001%

Insoluble: Boil 2 g with 60 ml of H_2O. The solution is colorless or nearly so, and not more than a trace of insoluble remains.

Ignition residue: Char 1 g, cool, add 0.5 ml of H_2SO_4 and ignite to constant weight. Not more than 5.0 mg of residue remains (retain).

Reducing sugars: Shake 2 g with 100 ml of H_2O for 10 minutes and filter until clear. To 50 ml of the filtrate add 50 ml of Fehling solution and boil for 3 minutes. Filter through a Gooch crucible, wash with water, then with alcohol and finally with ether, and dry at 105°. The weight of the precipitate (Cu_2O) is not more than 0.115 g.

Alcohol-soluble substances: Boil 1 g with 20 ml of alcohol for 5 minutes under a reflux condenser and filter while hot. Evaporate 10 ml of the filtrate on the steam bath and dry at 105°. Not more than 5.0 mg of residue remains.

Drying loss: Dry 1 g to constant weight at 105°. The loss does not exceed 10.0%.

Chloride: Dissolve 3 g in 75 ml of boiling water, cool, dilute to 75 ml and filter if necessary. To 25 ml of the filtrate add 2 ml of HNO_3 and 1 ml of silver nitrate and let stand for 5 minutes. Any turbidity produced is not greater than that of a blank to which 0.02 mg of Cl has been added.

Sulfate: To another 25-ml portion of the filtrate from the test for *Chloride* add 1 ml of 1 N HCl, 2 ml of $BaCl_2$ and let stand for 10 minutes. Any turbidity produced is not greater than that in a blank to which 0.2 mg of SO_4 has been added.

Oxalate: Shake 1 g with 20 ml of cold water for 5 minutes, filter and add to filtrate 2 ml of 10% calcium acetate. No turbidity is produced in 5 minutes.

Solution R: To the residue from the test for *Ignition residue* add 2 ml of HCl, 2 ml of H_2O and 0.5 ml of HNO_3, and slowly evaporate to dryness on the steam bath. Take up in 2 ml of 0.1 N HCl and 10 ml of hot water, cool and dilute to 40 ml.

Heavy metals: Dilute 20 ml of *Solution R* to 40 ml and add 10 ml of H_2S. Any color produced is not darker than that of control made with 0.02 mg of Pb, 1 ml of 0.1 N HCl and 10 ml of H_2S in the same volume as with the sample.

Iron: To 20 ml of *Solution R* add 2 ml of HCl and dilute to 50 ml. Add about 30 mg of ammonium persulfate and 3 ml of ammonium thiocyanate, and mix. Any red color produced is not darker than that of a blank to which 0.01 mg of Fe has been added.

DEXTROSE ANHYDROUS

Glucose

$HO \cdot CH_2(CHOH)_4CHO$; mol. wt. 180.16.

White, crystalline powder. Very soluble in water; slightly soluble in alcohol; insoluble in ether. Its solutions are dextrorotatory.

Standards

Drying loss (water)............max 0.3%	Lactose....................to pass test
Specific rotation........+52.5° to +53.0°	Chloride (Cl)...............max 0.004%
Insoluble...................max 0.005%	Nitrogen compounds (as N)...max 0.005%
Ignition residue.............max 0.02%	Sulfate (SO_4)...............max 0.005%
Acid (as acetic).............max 0.015%	Heavy metals (as Cu).......max 0.0005%
Dextrin; Starch; SO_2.........to pass test	Iron (Fe)...................max 0.001%

Drying loss: Dry about 6 g, accurately weighed, at 105° for 4 hours.   The loss in weight corresponds to not more than 0.3%.

Specific rotation: Weigh accurately 5 g of the dried sample, dissolve it in 40 ml of H_2O, add 0.2 ml of ammonium hydroxide and dilute with H_2O to exactly 50 ml. Observe the rotation of the solution in a 200-mm tube at 25°, using sodium light. The observed rotation in degrees multiplied by 5 = $[\alpha]$**II.**

Insoluble: Dissolve 20 g in 100 ml of water.   A clear and colorless or nearly colorless solution results, and there is no appreciable change after heating the solution for 1 hour on the steam bath.   Filter, wash with water and dry at 105°. The weight of the insoluble residue does not exceed 1.0 mg.

Ignition residue: Gently ignite 5 g until charred.   Cool, moisten the char with 1 ml of H_2SO_4, then re-ignite slowly to constant weight.   The weight of the residue does not exceed 1.0 mg.

Acid: To 100 ml of CO_2-free water, add 2 drops of phenolphthalein, then add, dropwise, 0.02 N NaOH until a pink color is produced.   Dissolve 10 g of the sample in this solution and titrate with 0.02 N NaOH until the pink color is reproduced. Not more than 1.25 ml of the NaOH is required.

Dextrin; Starch; Sulfite: Dissolve 5 g in 50 ml of H_2O, boil the solution for 1 minute, cool and add 1 drop of 0.1 N iodine; no red or blue color is produced. Now add a few drops of starch; a blue color is produced.

Lactose: Reflux 1 g, finely powdered, with 30 ml of alcohol.   No insoluble residue remains.

Chloride: Dissolve 0.5 g in 20 ml of H_2O, add 2 drops of HNO_3 and 1 ml of $AgNO_3$.   If a turbidity is produced it is not greater than that in a blank to which 0.02 mg of Cl has been added.

Nitrogen: Place 1.0 g in a 500-ml Kjeldahl flask, add 0.05 g of salicylic acid and 10 ml of H_2SO_4 and let stand for 30 minutes.   Add 0.2 g of sodium thiosulfate and 5 g of potassium sulfate and heat over a small flame until colorless or nearly so. Cool, cautiously dilute with 50 ml of water, add 60 ml of 30% NaOH, connect with a suitable trap condenser and distill, collecting about 40 ml of the distillate in 5 ml of water containing a drop of dilute HCl.   Dilute the distillate to 50 ml.   To 25 ml add 30 ml of H_2O, 1 ml of 10% NaOH and 2 ml Nessler solution.   The color is not darker than that produced when 0.025 mg of nitrogen (0.1 mg NH_4Cl) is treated as the sample.

Sulfate: Dissolve 2 g in 20 ml of H_2O, add 1 ml of 0.1 N HCl and 2 ml of $BaCl_2$, and allow to stand for 15 minutes.   If a turbidity is produced, it is not greater than that in a blank to which 0.1 mg of SO_4 has been added.

Heavy metals: Dissolve 5 g in water to make 50 ml.   To 10 ml of the solution add 0.015 mg of Cu, dilute to 40 ml and add 1 ml of 1 N acetic acid (A).   To the remaining 40 ml add 1 ml of 1 N acetic acid (B). Then to each add 10 ml of H_2S, mix and observe in 3–5 minutes. B is not darker than A.

Iron: Dissolve 1 g in water, add 2 ml of HCl and dilute to 50 ml. Add about 50 mg of ammonium persulfate and 3 ml of 30% ammonium thiocyanate, and mix. Any resulting red color is not darker than that of a blank to which 0.01 mg of Fe has been added.

DIACETAL MONOXIME

$CH_3C:NOHCOCH_3$; mol. wt. 101.10.

White to pale yellow, crystalline powder. Freely soluble in water or in ethanol.

Standards

Melting range....................74°–76°	Solubility in H_2O or alcohol....to pass test
Sensitiveness.................to pass test	Ignition residue..............max 0.10%

Sensitiveness: To 3 ml of water containing 0.05 mg of urea, add 5 ml of HCl and 0.5 ml of a 3% aqueous solution of the sample and heat in a bath of boiling water for 10 minutes. The solution should have a pronounced yellow color in comparison with a control run in exactly the same manner without urea.

Solubility in water or alcohol: A solution of 0.5 g in 10 ml of water or in 10 ml of alcohol is complete and clear.

Ignition residue: To 1 g add 0.5 ml of H_2SO_4 and ignite gently at first, then strongly to constant weight. The weight of residue does not exceed 1.0 mg.

DIANTHRIMIDE; ANTHRIMIDE

$C_{28}H_{15}NO_4$; mol. wt. 429.41.

Dark red, insoluble in water, alcohol or other low boiling organic solvents; sparingly soluble in nitrobenzene, chlorobenzene or quinolene; soluble in sulfuric acid.

This dye in sulfuric acid solution reacts with boron (boric acid) to a blue colored complex having a maximum absorption at 620 mμ.[1,2]

Standards

Sensitiveness.................to pass test	Ignition residue..............max 0.2%

Sensitiveness: (a) Dissolve 20 mg of the dianthrimide in 20 ml of H_2SO_4. Dilute 2.0 ml of this solution with H_2SO_4 to 20 ml. (b) To 1.0 ml of standard boric acid solution in a 150-ml beaker add 5 ml of H_2SO_4 and heat to sulfuric fumes.

Allow to cool for 2–3 minutes, then add 10 ml of (*a*), mix and heat 90° for 1 hour. The greenish-yellow color of the reagent solution is changed to blue, having a maximum absorption at 620 mμ.

Ignition residue: Char 0.5 g, allow to cool, add 0.5 ml of H_2SO_4 and ignite to constant weight. Any residue remaining does not exceed 1.0 mg.

1 Elis, G. H., Zook, E. G., and Baudish, O., *Anal. Chem.* **21**, 1345 (1949).
2 Brewster, Dwaine A., *ibid.* **23**, 1809 (1951).

2,6-DIBROMOQUINONE-CHLORIMIDE

Br—⟨ ⟩—Br; mol. wt. 299.37.

Yellow, crystalline powder. Insoluble in water; soluble in alcohol, also in dilute alkali hydroxides. Should not be used if it is brown.

Standards

Melting range....................82°–84°	Solubility in alcohol...........to pass test
Sensitiveness to phenol........to pass test	Ignition residue..............max 0.10%

Sensitiveness: To 10 ml of a solution containing 0.01 mg of phenol add 0.5 ml of borax buffer (see Note) and 0.1 ml of a solution of 10 mg of the sample in 20 ml of ethanol, and let stand 10 minutes. A distinct blue color should develop.

Note: The borax buffer is made by dissolving 2.84 g of crystallized borax in 90 ml of warm water, adding 8.2 ml of 1 *N* NaOH and diluting with H_2O to 100 ml.

Solubility in alcohol: A solution of 0.1 g in 10 ml of alcohol is complete or practically so, or not more than faintly turbid.

Ignition residue: To 1 g add 0.5 ml of H_2SO_4 and ignite gently at first, then strongly to constant weight. The weight of the residue does not exceed 1.0 mg.

DICHLOROFLUORESCEIN

=O; mol. wt. 401.19.

Orange crystalline powder. Insoluble in water; soluble in alcohol and in dilute aqueous alkali solutions.

It is used as an adsorption indicator for the titration of halogens with silver nitrate solution. The indicator solution is prepared by dissolving 100 mg in 60 ml of alcohol, then adding 2.5 ml of 0.1 N NaOH and diluting to 100 ml.

Standards

Sensitiveness.................to pass test   Ignition residue...............max 0.2%

Sensitiveness: Weigh accurately about 0.1 g of potassium iodide, previously dried at 105° for 1 hour, and dissolve it in 50 ml of water. Add 1 ml of the solution of the sample prepared as above described and 1 ml of glacial acetic acid, and titrate with 0.1 N silver nitrate until the color of the precipitate changes from yellowish orange to pink. The volume of 0.1 N silver nitrate consumed is within ± 0.05 ml of the theoretically calculated volume of the silver nitrate.

Ignition residue: Moisten 0.5 g with 0.5 ml of H_2SO_4 and ignite to constant weight. Not more than 1.0 mg of residue remains.

2,6-DICHLOROPHENOL-INDOPHENOL SODIUM
Sodium 2,6-Dichlorobenzenone-indophenol

NaO—⟨ ⟩—N=⟨ ⟩:O; mol. wt. 290.09.

Dark green powder. May contain about 2 mols of water. Freely soluble in water, also soluble in alcohol. The aqueous solution is deep blue, becoming red on the addition of acid. It is used for the estimation of ascorbic acid (vitamin C), the ascorbic acid reducing the dye to a hydroxy compound which is colorless.

Standards

Assay, anhydrous basis.........min 90%   Interfering dyes..............to pass test
Drying loss....................max 12%

Assay: Weigh accurately about 0.3 g of sample previously dried to constant weight at 120° and dissolve it in 100 ml of water. Add to the solution 3 g of potassium iodide dissolved in 10 ml of H_2O, then add 25 ml of 10% H_2SO_4. Allow to stand in the dark for 20 minutes, and titrate the liberated iodine with 0.1 N thiosulfate, adding starch solution toward the end. One ml of 0.1 N thiosulfate corresponds to 0.01450 g of $C_{12}H_6Cl_2NO_2Na$ (the anhydrous compound), log 16137.

Drying loss: Weigh accurately about 1 g and dry it at 120° to constant weight. The loss in weight corresponds to not more than 12%.

Interfering dyes: Dissolve 25 mg of sample and 20 mg of sodium bicarbonate in water to make 100 ml, and filter through a small dry filter, rejecting the first 10 ml of the filtrate (A). Dissolve 25 mg of ascorbic acid in 25 ml of a solution composed of 3 g metaphosphoric acid, 4 ml of glacial acetic acid and sufficient water to make 50 ml (B). To 15 ml of A add 2.5 ml of B. The resulting mixture is colorless.

2,6-DICHLOROQUINONE-CHLOROIMIDE

"Chlorimide"

$O:C_6H_2Cl_2ClN$; mol. wt. 211.45.

Pale yellow, crystalline powder. Insoluble in water; soluble in alcohol, and in dilute alkali hydroxide solutions. It is a sensitive reagent for phenols.

Standards

Melting range....................65°–67°	Solubility in alcohol...........to pass test
Sensitiveness.................to pass test	Ignition residue..............max 0.10%

Sensitiveness: Carry out this test as for 2,6-dibromoquinone-chloroimide: The result should be as there stated.

Solubility in alcohol: A solution of 0.1 g in 10 ml of alcohol is complete and clear.

Ignition residue: Ignite 1 g ml of H_2SO_4. Not more than 1.0 mg of residue remains.

DIETHANOLAMINE

2,2-Dihydroxydiethylamine

$NH(CH_2CH_2OH)_2$; mol. wt. 105.14; N—13.52%.

Diethanolamine melts at about 28°, but when once melted it does not readily solidify even at considerably lower temperatures.

Diethanolamine is a colorless, viscid liquid with an amine-like odor. Sp. gr. about 1.096; boils at 268°. Miscible with water or alcohol; insoluble in chloroform, benzene, ether.

Diethanolamine is a strong base absorbing CO_2 from air. *Keep in tightly closed containers.*

Standards

Assay.................99.0% to 100.5%	Other amines................to pass test
Boiling range..................265°–270°	Ignition residue............max 0.030%

Assay: Weigh accurately about 2 g, dilute with 30 ml of H_2O and titrate with 0.5 N HCl, using methyl orange as indicator. One ml of 0.5 N HCl = 0.05257 g of $HN(CH_2CH_2OH)_2$, log 72074.

Boiling range: Distill 50 ml. After the first 10 drops, not less than 48 ml distills between 265° and 270°, making the necessary correction for difference in barometric pressure from 760 mm (page 581).

Other amines: Weigh accurately about 1 g, transfer this with the aid of a small volume of H_2O to a tared beaker or evaporating dish, add a slight excess of 0.5 N or 1 N HCl over the volume indicated by the assay. Evaporate to dryness on the steam bath, dry at 105° for 3 hours and weigh. The weight of the diethanol-amine hydrochloride so obtained multiplied by 0.7424 represents diethanolamine, and it corresponds to not less than 99% and to not more than 100.5% of the percentage found by the assay.

Ignition residue: Weigh about 3 g, add 0.5 ml of H_2SO_4, evaporate and ignite to constant weight. The weight of the residue corresponds to not more than 0.03%.

DIGITONIN

$C_{56}H_{92}O_{29}$; mol. wt. 1229.3.

White, crystalline powder. Almost insoluble in water; soluble in warm alcohol or in acetic acid; slightly soluble in chloroform or ether.

Standards

Specific rotation.............about $-48°$	Ignition residue..............max 0.20%
Solubility in alcohol...........to pass test	Drying loss..................max 6.0%

Specific rotation: Weigh accurately a quantity of the sample equivalent to 1 g of the dried sample, and dissolve it in sufficient 75% acetic acid to make 10 ml. Determine the angle of rotation of the solution at 25° and calculate the specific rotation by the formula on page 582.

Solubility in alcohol: A solution of 0.5 g in 20 ml of warm alcohol is complete and colorless.

Ignition residue: Char 0.5 g, cool, add 0.5 ml of H_2SO_4 and ignite to constant weight. Not more than 1.0 mg of residue remains.

Drying loss: Dry about 0.5 g, accurately weighed, to constant weight at 105°. The loss corresponds to not more than 6%.

DIIODOFLUORESCEIN

$C_{20}H_{10}I_2O_5$; mol. wt. 584.12.

Orange-red powder. Slightly soluble in water; soluble in alcohol and in solutions of alkali hydroxide.

It is used as an adsorption indicator for the titration of iodide with silver nitrate in the presence of chloride. Its solution is prepared by dissolving 0.5 g in a mixture of 70 ml of alcohol and 30 ml of water.

Standards

Sensitiveness.................to pass test	Ignition residue..............max 0.20%

Sensitiveness: Weigh accurately about 0.1 g of reagent potassium iodide, previously dried at 105° for 1 hour, and dissolve it in 50 ml of H_2O. Add 1 ml of the solution of the sample prepared as described above and 1 ml of glacial acetic acid, and titrate with 0.1 N $AgNO_3$ until the color of the precipitate of silver iodide changes from a brownish-red to a bluish-red. The volume of the 0.1 N $AgNO_3$ consumed is within ± 0.05 ml of the theoretically calculated volume of the silver nitrate.

Ignition residue: Moisten 0.5 g with 0.5 ml of sulfuric acid and ignite to constant weight. Not more than 1.0 mg of residue remains.

p-DIMETHYLAMINOAZOBENZENE

Butter Yellow; Methyl Yellow

; mol. wt. 225.28.

Yellow, crystalline powder or plates. Insoluble in water; soluble in alcohol. pH range: 2.9 red; 4.0 yellow. It is usually used in 0.5% alcohol solution.

Standards

Melting range..................114°–117°	Solubility in alcohol...........to pass test
Sensitiveness................to pass test	Ignition residue.............max 0.20%

Sensitiveness: Dissolve 0.1 g in 20 ml of ethanol, add 1 drop of the solution and 2 g of ammonium chloride to 25 ml CO_2-free water. The lemon-yellow color is changed to orange by 0.05 ml of 0.1 N HCl, and restored by 0.05 ml of 0.1 N NaOH.

Solubility in alcohol: A solution of 0.1 g of sample in 20 ml of ethanol is complete and clear.

Ignition residue: Ignite 0.5 g with 0.5 ml of H_2SO_4 to constant weight. Not more than 1.0 mg of residue remains.

p-DIMETHYLAMINOBENZALDEHYDE

Ehrlich's Reagent

; mol. wt. 149.19.

White or yellowish crystals. Slightly soluble in water; soluble in alcohol or ether; also soluble in dilute hydrochloric acid.

Standards

Melting range....................73°–75°	Solubility in HCl.............to pass test
Solubility in alcohol...........to pass test	Ignition residue.............max 0.20%

Solubility in alcohol: One g dissolves completely in 25 ml of alcohol.

Solubility in hydrochloric acid: Dissolve 1 g in 20 ml of 10% HCl. The solution is clear and colorless, or only slightly yellow.

Ignition residue: Char 0.5 g, cool, add 0.5 ml of sulfuric acid and ignite gently to constant weight. Not more than 1.0 mg of residue remains.

p-DIMETHYLAMINOBENZALRHODANINE

p-Dimethylaminobenzylidenerhodanine

; mol. wt. 264.36.

Brilliant red, crystalline powder. Insoluble in water; sparingly soluble in alcohol or acetone. Used as 0.03% solution in acetone for detection of silver,[1] copper,[2] gold,[3] platinum,[3] palladium[3] and mercury.[2]

Standards

Sensitiveness................to pass test	Ignition residue.............max 0.20%
Solubility in acetone..........to pass test	

Sensitiveness: (a) Dissolve 10 mg of the reagent in 10 ml of alcohol. (b) Add 0.5 ml of 0.1 N AgNO$_3$ to 100 ml of water and mix well. To 5 ml of this solution add 5 ml of water, mix and add 1 g of ammonium acetate and 1 ml of (a). A distinct reddish color is produced.

Ignition residue: Char 0.5 g, cool, then add 0.5 ml of sulfuric acid and ignite gently to constant weight. Not more than 1.0 mg of residue remains.

Solubility in acetone: Boil, under a reflux condenser, 0.2 g of the sample with 30 ml acetone. The resulting solution is clear or nearly so.

[1] Feigl, F., Z. anal. Chem. **74**, 380 (1928).
[2] Kalthoff, I. M., J. Am. Chem. Soc. **52**, 2222 (1930).
[3] Feigl, Krumholtz, and Rajmann, Mikrochemie, **9**, 165 (1931).

DIMETHYLANILINE

C$_6$H$_5$N(CH$_3$)$_2$; mol. wt. 121.18.

Clear liquid; colorless when freshly distilled, but acquires a reddish to reddish-brown color. Sp. gr. 0.960. Freezes at about 2°. Insoluble in water; soluble in alcohol, chloroform and ether; also soluble in dilute mineral acids.

Standards

Boiling range..................191°–194°	Hydrocarbons................to pass test
Freezing temperature........not below 1°	Aniline or Monomethylaniline..to pass test

Boiling range: Distill 50 ml.   After the first 10 drops not less than 48 ml distills between 191° and 194°, correcting for barometric pressure (page 581).

Freezing temperature: Determine as described on page 581.

Hydrocarbons: Dissolve 5 ml of the sample in a mixture of 10 ml of hydrochloric acid and 15 ml of water.   A clear solution results and it remains clear on cooling to about 10°.

Aniline or Monoethylaniline: Mix in a glass-stoppered flask 5 ml of the sample with 5 ml of a 10% solution of acetic anhydride in benzene, and allow to stand for 30 minutes.   Then add 30 ml of 0.5 N NaOH, shake well and titrate the excess of the NaOH with 0.5 N acid, using phenolphthalein as indicator.   Carry out a blank test in the same manner, omitting the dimethylaniline.   Not more than 0.3 ml of the NaOH is consumed by the sample.

DIMETHYLFORMAMIDE

D.M.F.

$H \cdot CO \cdot N(CH_3)_2$; mol. wt. 73.09.

Colorless liquid, characteristic odor.   Miscible with water, alcohol, chloroform, ether; only slightly soluble in benzene.   It is a neutral substance (pH in 0.5 M solution = 6.7); and is a good solvent for many organic compounds and for alkali salts of weak organic acids, phenolates, etc.

Because of solvent properties and "neutrality," dimethylformamide is useful for titrations in nonaqueous solvents.

Standards

Specific gravity (25°/25°)....0.945 to 0.947	Miscibility with H_2O, $CHCl_3$...to pass test
Boiling range..................152°–156°	Neutrality....................to pass test
Evaporation residue..........max 0.02%	Water........................max 0.5%

Specific gravity: Determine with a pycnometer at 25°/25°.

Boiling range: Distill 50 ml.   After 10 drops has come over, all distills between 152° and 156°, after correcting for the barometric pressure.

Evaporation residue: Evaporate 10 ml on the steam bath and dry the residue at 120° for 1 hour.   Any residue remaining weighs not more than 2.0 mg.

Miscibility: Dilutions of dimethylformamide with 3 times its volume of water or of chloroform are clear.

Neutrality: A dilution of 5 ml of dimethylformamide with 20 ml of water does not change the color of blue and red litmus paper within 5 minutes, and on the subsequent addition of 2 drops of phenolphthalein solution and 0.05 ml of 0.1 N NaOH, a slight pink color is produced.

Water: Water in dimethylformamide may be determined by the iodine (Fischer) method.

DIMETHYLGLYOXIME
Diacetyldioxime

$$CH_3—C{=}N—OH$$
$$CH_3—C{=}N—OH$$
; mol. wt. 116.12.

White, needle-shaped crystals, or a crystalline powder. Almost insoluble in water; soluble in alcohol. This reagent will detect 0.004 mg of nickel in 1 ml of solution.

Standards

Melting range.................238°–242°   Solubility in alcohol...........to pass test
Assay.....................min 98.5%   Ignition residue.............max 0.05%

Assay: Dry about 0.25 g of sample at 105° for 1 hour. Weigh 0.20 g of the dried sample and dissolve it in 20 ml of warm alcohol. Add to this solution a hot solution of 0.45 g of nickel ammonium sulfate in 100 ml of water; then add a solution of 1 g of sodium acetate in 10 ml of H_2O and let stand for 2 hours. Filter on a tared filtering crucible, previously dried at 120° for 1 hour, wash with 30–40 ml of water containing 2 drops of 10% NH_3 and dry to constant weight at 120°. The weight of the nickel dimethylglyoxime compound so obtained × 0.8038 = weight of dimethylglyoxime, log 90515.

Solubility in alcohol: One gram dissolves in 50 ml of hot alcohol, leaving not more than a trace of insoluble residue.

Ignition residue: Ignite gently 2 g, cool, moisten the char with 0.5 ml of sulfuric acid and ignite to constant weight. Not more than 1.0 mg of residue remains.

DIMETHYL SULFATE

$(CH_3)_2SO_4$; mol. wt. 126.13.

Clear, colorless, or pale brownish liquid of ethereal odor. Very slightly soluble in water and gradually hydrolyzed by it. Miscible with alcohol, acetone or ether. Boils with decomposition at about 188°. Sp. gr. 1.33. *Caution: Dimethyl sulfate is poisonous.*

Standards

Solubility in acetone   Ignition residue.............max 0.20%
  or ether..................to pass test   Free acid (as H_2SO_4)...........max 0.5%

Solubility in acetone or ether: To separate 2-ml portions of the sample, add 10 ml of acetone and 10 ml of ether; both solutions are clear.

Ignition residue: Evaporate 4 ml and ignite. Not more than 1.0 mg of residue remains.

Free acid: Mix 2.0 ml with 20 ml of neutral alcohol, add 2 drops of phenolphthalein and titrate with 0.1 N NaOH. Not more than 5.0 ml of the alkali is required to produce a pink color.

Note: The water content of dimethyl sulfate may be determined by the iodine (Fischer) method.

DIMETHYLSULFOXIDE

D.M.S.O.

$(CH_3)_2SO$; mol. wt. 78.13; S—41.03%.

Colorless; liquid at room temperature.   Freezes at 18.5° and easily supercools. Sp. gr. 25°/25° about 1.1.   Faint odor, hygroscopic.   Miscible with water with generation of heat; also miscible with alcohol, acetone, benzene, chloroform and ether.

Standards

Freezing temperature........ $+18.5° \pm 0.5°$	Acid (as acetic).............max 0.006%
Boiling range.................187°–190°	Reaction with H_2SO_4.........to pass test
Miscibility (with water, etc.)....to pass test	*Assay*.....................99.5–100.2%
Evaporation residue.........max 0.010%	

Freezing temperature: Determine as described on page 581.

Boiling range: Distill 100 ml.   Not more than 1 ml distills below 187°, then all distills to 190°, corrected for variation in barometric pressure from 760 mm.

Miscibility with water, acetone, chloroform: To separate 5-ml portions of the sample add 5 ml of water, acetone, chloroform benzene and mix.   The resulting mixtures are clear.

Evaporation residue: Place 20 ml of sample in a tared beaker or dish, evaporate on the hot plate to about 1–2 ml, then dry at 150° to constant weight.   Not more than 2.0 mg of residue remains.

Acid: To 25 ml of water add 0.1 ml of phenolphthalein; then add dropwise 0.02 N NaOH until a pink color is produced which persists after shaking for 10–15 seconds.   Disregard the volume of the alkali thus consumed.   Now add to the pink liquid 5.0 ml of the dimethylsulfoxide and shake.   If the pink color fades, add 0.02 N NaOH, a drop at a time, shaking after each addition.   Not more than 0.25 ml of the alkali is required to restore the pink color.

Reaction with H_2SO_4: Cautiously (much heat generated) add 5 ml of H_2SO_4 to 5 ml of the sample.   The mixture has not more than a very slight brownish color when compared with an equal volume of the sample.

Assay: Tare a glass-stoppered weighing bottle containing about 10 ml of water, add 1 ml of sample, stopper immediately, allow to cool and reweigh.   Transfer the solution completely into a 100-ml volumetric flask, add water to volume and mix well.   Transfer 10.0 ml of this solution into a beaker and add 25 ml of 10% H_2SO_4 and 15 ml of water.   Slowly run into the beaker with continuous stirring 0.1 N $KMnO_4$ until the liquid over the precipitate MnO_2 retains purple color after stirring for 15 seconds.   Note the volume.   Now add while gently stirring 25.0 ml of 0.1 N ferrous ammonium sulfate, and as soon as the MnO_2 is completely dissolved, back titrate the excess of the ferrous solution with the 0.1 N $KMnO_4$ to a pale purplish color.   From the total volume of the $KMnO_4$ solution subtract the volume of the ferrous solution added. The difference represents the volume of 0.1 N $KMnO_4$ consumed by the sample. One ml of 0.1 N $KMnO_4 = 0.00390.7$ g of dimethylsulfoxide.

$$H_3C-\overset{\overset{\displaystyle O}{\|}}{S}-CH_3 + \text{Oxygen} \rightarrow H_3C-\overset{\overset{\displaystyle O}{\|}}{\underset{\underset{\displaystyle O}{\|}}{S}}-CH_3$$

dimethylsulfone

3,5-DINITROBENZOYL CHLORIDE

COCl; mol. wt. 230.57.

Pale yellow, crystalline powder. Soluble in alcohol, freely soluble in 1 N sodium hydroxide solution.

Standards

Melting range.................67°–69°   Ignition residue.............max 0.10%
Solubility in NaOH...........to pass test

Solubility in sodium hydroxide: A solution of 0.5 g in 25 ml of 1 N NaOH is clear or not more than slightly turbid.

Ignition residue: Char well 1.0 g, cool, add 0.5 ml of H_2SO_4, evaporate and ignite to constant weight. Any remaining residue does not exceed 1.0 mg.

2,4-DINITROCHLOROBENZENE

—NO₂; mol. wt. 202.56.

Yellowish crystals, slightly soluble in water; 1 g dissolves in approximately 12 ml of alcohol or 10 ml of carbon tetrachloride; very soluble in benzene, chloroform, ether.

This reagent is chiefly used for the detection and quantitative colorimetric determination of pyridine compounds.

Standards

Melting range . . . . 52°–54°	Solubility in benzene or carbon
Sensitiveness . . . . to pass test	tetrachloride . . . . to pass test
	Ignition residue . . . . max 0.10%

Sensitiveness: Dissolve 10 mg of sample in 1 ml of pyridine. Place 0.1 ml of the solution in a small test tube and heat in steam or in boiling water for 2–3 minutes. Cool and add 1 ml of 3% alcoholic KOH. A wine-red color is produced.

Solubility in benzene or carbon tetrachloride: 0.25-g portions of the reagent dissolve completely in 5 ml of benzene or 5 ml of carbon tetrachloride, forming clear solutions.

Ignition residue: Char well 1.0 g, cool, add 0.5 ml of H_2SO_4, evaporate and ignite to constant weight. Any remaining residue does not exceed 1.0 mg.

2,4-DINITROPHENOL; 2,5-DINITROPHENOL

O_2N—⟨benzene ring⟩—OH; mol. wt. 184.11. with NO_2

Yellow or brownish-yellow crystals or flakes, or a yellow powder. Insoluble in water; soluble in alcohol, benzene, and chlorofom; also soluble in solution of sodium or potassium hydroxide. It is used as a saturated, aqueous solution or as a 0.1% solution in dilute alcohol.

Standards

Melting range . . . . 111°–113°	Ignition residue . . . . max 0.10%
Solubility in alcohol . . . . to pass test	pH range (2,4-) 2.6–4.4
Solubility in NaOH . . . . to pass test	pH range (2,5-) 4–5.8

Solubility in alcohol: Dissolve 2 g in 50 ml of warm alcohol. A clear and complete solution results.

Solubility in sodium hydroxide: One gram of the sample dissolves completely in 50 ml of warm, 5% NaOH solution, giving a clear solution.

Ignition residue: Char 1.0 g, allow to cool, add 0.5 ml H_2SO_4 and ignite strongly to constant weight. Any residue does not exceed 1.0 mg.

pH range: Consult pages 584–586 for the buffers.

2,4-Dinitrophenol: To 50 ml each of buffer solutions of pH-2.6 (*a*) and pH-4.4 (*b*) add 0.2 ml of the solution from the test for *Solubility in alcohol*; (*a*) remains colorless or practically so; (*b*) becomes yellow.

2,5-Dinitrophenol: To 50 ml each of buffer solutions pH-4 and pH-5.8, add 0.2 ml of the solution from the test for *Solubility in alcohol*; (*a*) remains colorless or practically so; (*b*) becomes yellow.

2,4-DINITROPHENYLHYDRAZINE

O_2N-⟨benzene ring⟩$-HN \cdot NH_2$; mol. wt. 198.14.

NO_2

Red, crystalline powder. Slightly soluble in water or in alcohol; soluble in moderately dilute inorganic acids. Melts at about 200°. *Keep protected from light.*

Standards

Melting range.................197°–200°   Ignition residue.............max 0.10%
Solubility in H_2SO_4..........to pass test

Solubility in sulfuric acid: Dissolve 0.5 g in a mixture of 25 ml of H_2SO_4 and 25 ml of H_2O. The solution is clear or not more than slightly turbid.

Ignition residue: Cautiously ignite 1 g to constant weight. Not more than 1.0 mg of residue remains.

DIOXANE

Diethylene Dioxide

H_2C—O—CH_2
 | | ; mol. wt. 88.10.
H_2C—O—CH_2

Colorless liquid, ethereal odor. Sp. gr. about 1.031 at 25°. Miscible with water and the usual organic solvents.

Dioxane is a very useful solvent for chemical reactions, combining the properties of water and alcohol. Dioxane is an ether (alkyl oxide) and, like other alkyl ethers, it forms peroxide in presence of air. The use of peroxidized dioxane may lead to grossly erroneous results. Peroxide containing dioxane liberates iodine from potassium iodide, and should be redistilled after being shaken well with 2% of its weight of powdered iron or charcoal and filtering after 1 hour and carefully distilling. The first 5% of the distillate is to be discarded and about 5% left in the distillation flask. The redistilled dioxane should be distributed in small bottles filled to the neck, and protected from light.

Standards

Boiling range.................101°–103°   Evaporation residue.........max 0.010%
Freezing temperature........+9.5° to 11°   Peroxide (as H_2O_2)..........max 0.015%
Miscibility..................to pass test   Water......................max 0.25%
Acid (as acetic)..............max 0.010%

Boiling range: Distill 50 ml. After the first 10 drops not less than 48 ml distills between 101° and 103°, correction being made for barometric pressure.

Freezing temperature: Determine as described on page 581.

Miscibility: Separate mixtures of 5 ml of sample with 10 ml of water and carbon disulfide are clear after standing for 10 minutes.

Acid: Mix 10 ml with 15 ml of water, add 2 drops of phenolphthalein and titrate with 0.1 N NaOH.   Not more than 0.15 ml of the NaOH is required to produce pink color.

Evaporation residue: Evaporate 10 ml on a steam bath and heat at 105° for 1 hour.   The weight of the residue does not exceed 1.0 mg.

Peroxide: Transfer 10 ml to 50 ml glass-stoppered flask, add 10 ml of water, 0.5 ml of glacial acetic acid, 5 ml of chloroform and 1 ml of 10% KI solution.   Mix, let stand for 2 minutes and titrate the liberated iodine with 0.1 N sodium thiosulfate until the liquid remains colorless for 2 minutes.   One ml of 0.1 N thiosulfate = 1.7 mg H_2O_2.   Not more than 0.9 ml of the thiosulfate is required.   Correct for a blank.

Water: The water content of dioxane may be determined by the iodine (Fischer) method.

DIPHENYLAMINE

; mol. wt. 169.22.

White, or nearly white crystals with slight aromatic odor.   Discolors in light. Slightly soluble in water; soluble in alcohol, ether, also in strong acids.   *Keep protected from light.*

Standards

Melting range............52.5°–53.5°	Sensitiveness............to pass test
Nitrate (NO_2)...........no reaction	Ignition residue............max 0.05%

Nitrate: Add (*caution*) 8 ml of H_2SO_4 to 2 ml of H_2O, cool the mixture to 50°, and add 1 drop of HCl and 3 mg of the diphenylamine.   No blue color is produced in 3 minutes.

Sensitiveness: Add 1.0 ml of standard nitrate solution (0.01 mg NO_3) to the solution from the test for *Nitrate*.   A distinct blue color is produced in 3 minutes (the extreme sensitiveness of this reagent for NO_3 is claimed to be 1 part in 2,000,000).

Ignition residue: To 2 g of sample add 1 ml of H_2SO_4 and slowly ignite to constant weight.   Not more than 1.0 mg of residue remains.

DIPHENYLBENZIDINE

C_6H_5HN— —NHC_6H_5; mol. wt. 336.42.

White, or nearly white, leaflets or crystalline powder.   Darkens in air and light. Insoluble in water; slightly soluble in ethanol; freely soluble in hot ethyl acetate or toluene.   *Keep protected from light.*

Diphenylbenzidine is used for detection of nitrate.   It is similar to diphenyl-amine, but is three to five times as sensitive as the latter.   It has the advantage over diphenylamine in that it better utilizes the oxidizing action of the nitrate.

Standards

Melting range..................240°–243°	Sensitiveness.................to pass test
Nitrate.....................to pass test	Ignition residue..............max 0.10%

Melting range: Determine by the capillary tube method, introducing the sample in the bath preheated at 220°.

Nitrate: To 10 ml of H_2SO_4, add (*cautiously*) 0.2 ml of a solution of 25 mg of sample in 1 ml of HCl.   No blue color is produced.

Sensitiveness: Dilute 0.2 ml of standard nitrate solution to 10 ml.   Add 0.1 ml of this solution (= 0.0002 mg NO_3) to the solution from the test for *Nitrate*. A blue color is produced in 3 minutes (this reagent is claimed to be sensitive to 1 part of NO_3 in 10,000,000 parts of solution.

Ignition residue: Ignite 0.5 g with 0.5 ml of H_2SO_4.   Not more than 0.5 mg of residue remains.

s-DIPHENYLCARBAZIDE

$C_6H_5 \cdot NH \cdot NH \cdot CO \cdot NH \cdot NH \cdot C_6H_5$; mol. wt. 242.27; N—23.13%.

White, crystalline powder; gradually becomes pink in the air.   Very slightly soluble in water; soluble in hot alcohol, in acetone or in acetic acid.   Its solution in glacial acetic acid is used for the colorimetric determination of chromium;[1] also used for the detection of cadmium,[2] magnesium[2] and mercury.[2,3]   This reagent will detect 0.005 mg of chromium or 1 ml of solution (1:200,000).

Standards

Melting range..................167°–169°	Ignition residue..............max 0.10%
Sensitiveness.................to pass test	Solubility in alcohol...........to pass test

Sensitiveness: (*a*) Dissolve 10 mg of the diphenylcarbazide in 2 ml of glacial acetic acid, and dilute with water to 20 ml.

(*b*) Dissolve 15 mg of potassium dichromate in water to make 500 ml.

To 0.2 ml of (*b*) add 1 drop of 10% HCl, dilute with water to 1 ml and add 0.1 ml of (*a*).   A distinct violet-red color is produced.

Ignition residue: Char 1.0 g, cool, then moisten the char with 0.5 ml of sulfuric acid and ignite to constant weight.   Not more than 1.0 mg of residue remains.

Solubility in alcohol: A solution of 0.2 g in 40 ml of warm alcohol is clear or practically so.

[1] Stover, N. M., *J. Am. Chem. Soc.* **50**, 2363 (1928).
[2] Feigl, F., *Z. anal. Chem.* **72**, 113 (1927).
[3] Scott, A. W., *J. Am. Chem. Soc.*, **51**, 3551 (1929).

DIPHENYLCARBAZONE

$C_6H_5 \cdot NH \cdot NH \cdot CO \cdot N:N \cdot C_6H_5$; mol. wt. 240.26.

Orange, crystalline powder.   Insoluble in water; soluble in alcohol, benzene or chloroform.

In a saturated alcohol solution, it is used for the detection and estimation of mercury.   It is capable of detecting 0.002 mg of Hg in 1 ml of solution (1:500,000).

Standards

Melting range..................154°–157°	Solubility in chloroform.......to pass test
Sensitiveness................to pass test	Ignition residue.............max 0.10%

Sensitiveness: Dissolve 135 mg of mercuric chloride in 500 ml of water.   To 20 ml of this solution add 0.1 ml of a solution of 0.1 g of the sample in 5 ml of alcohol. A violet color is produced.

Solubility in chloroform: A solution of 0.2 g of sample in 20 ml of chloroform is complete or practically so.

Ignition residue: Char 1.0 g, cool, then moisten the cooled char with 0.5 ml of H_2SO_4 and ignite to constant weight.   Not more than 1.0 mg of residue remains.

α,α′-DIPYRIDYL

2,2′-Dipyridyl

; mol. wt. 156.18.

White or pink, crystalline powder.   Soluble in water or alcohol.   It is used for the determination of iron and also for detection of ferrous iron, for which it has a sensitiveness of 0.001 mg in 5 ml of solution.

Standards

Melting range....................70°–72°	Solubility....................to pass test
Sensitiveness................to pass test	Ignition residue.............max 0.20%

Sensitiveness: (a) Dissolve 50 mg of the sample in water to make 50 ml.

(b) Dissolve 0.35 g of ferrous ammonium sulfate in 50 ml of water containing 1 ml of sulfuric acid, add 0.5 g of hydrazine sulfate and dilute to 500 ml.   Dilute 10 ml of this solution with H_2O to make 500 ml (1 ml = 0.002 mg Fe^2).

(c) Dissolve 8.3 g of sodium acetate and 12 ml of glacial acetic acid in sufficient water to make 100 ml.

To 10 ml of water, add 1 ml of solution (b), 1 ml of (c) and 1 ml of (a) and mix well.   An immediate pink color should be produced.

Solubility: Dissolve 0.1 g of sample in 10 ml of H_2O.   A clear solution results.

Ignition residue: To 0.5 g add 0.5 ml of H_2SO_4 and ignite to constant weight. Not more than 1.0 mg of residue remains.

DISODIUM ETHYLENEDIAMINE TETRAACETATE

EDTA; Disodium Versenate; Disodium Sequestrinate

$C_{10}H_{14}N_2O_8Na_2 \cdot 2H_2O$; mol. wt. 372.26; H_2O—9.67%.

White, crystalline powder.   Slowly soluble in about 7.5 parts of water at 25°; very slightly soluble in alcohol.   Its pH in a 2% solution is about 4.7.

For the use of this reagent in analytical chemistry and other properties, see under Ethylenediamine Tetraacetic Acid.

Standards

Drying loss.................max 10.0%   Solubility....................to pass test
Chelating capacity............to pass test

Drying loss: Weigh accurately about 1 g and dry it at 130° to constant weight. The loss in weight corresponds to not more than 10.0% and not less than 8.0%.

Chelating capacity: (a) Weigh accurately 0.33 g of the dried sample from the preceding test and dissolve it in sufficient water to make 100 ml (0.01 M).

(b) Dissolve 0.100 g of calcium carbonate, previously dried at 200° for 2 hours, in 10 ml of water and about 1 ml of 10% HCl, neutralize the solution, using litmus paper, with diluted ammonium hydroxide, and dilute to 100 ml (0.01 M).

(c) Dissolve 0.250 g of uneffloresced cupric sulfate in water to make 100 ml (0.01 M).

To exactly 5 ml of (a) add 2–3 drops of 10% NH_3 and 2 ml of 5% ammonium oxalate solution and mix well.   Then add, while agitating, exactly 5 ml of (b). The mixture is clear, or if a turbidity persists after shaking for 1 minute it clears upon the addition of 0.2 ml of (a) and shaking for about 1 minute.

To exactly 5 ml of (a) add 0.5 ml of 1% NH_3 and 0.5 ml of 10% potassium ferrocyanide solution, and mix.   Then add, while agitating, 4.8 ml of (c).   The resulting mixture is pale blue without any red tint.

Solubility: Dissolve 1 g in 20 ml of warm water.   No insoluble residue remains, and the solution is colorless.

DITHIZONE

Diphenylthiocarbazone

$C_6H_5 \cdot NH \cdot NH \cdot CS \cdot N:N \cdot C_6H_5$; mol. wt. 256.32.

Fine, nearly black powder.   Insoluble in water; soluble in alcohol, chloroform or carbon tetrachloride, yielding intensely green solutions.   These solutions are not stable due to oxidation by air, but may be preserved by a layer of sulfur dioxide solution.   A solution in chloroform or carbon tetrachloride is used for colorimetric determination of lead, copper, zinc, and several other metals.

Standards

Sensitiveness.................to pass test	Ignition residue..............max 0.3%
Solubility in chloroform.......to pass test	Heavy metals (as Pb)........max 0.002%

Sensitiveness: Prepare a chloroform solution of the dithizone in the proportion of 10 mg per liter.   To 5 ml of the solution add 0.001 mg of Pb (0.1 ml of standard lead solution), then add 5 ml of ammonium citrate solution and shake well.   The color of the chloroform layer is distinctly pink in comparison with a blank made with 5 ml of the same dithizone solution treated in the same manner but without the addition of lead.

Solubility in chloroform: One-tenth gram dissolves completely or nearly so in 20 ml of chloroform.

Ignition residue: Char 0.5 g, cool, add 1 ml of nitric acid and 1 ml of sulfuric acid, evaporate and ignite to constant weight.   The residue weighs not more than 1.5 mg (retain residue).

Heavy metals: Evaporate the residue obtained from the test for *Ignition residue* with 2 ml of HCl to dryness on the steam bath, then digest with 10 ml of 10% ammonium acetate in the covered crucible on the steam bath for 30 minutes. Filter, wash with water to 25 ml and mix well.   Transfer 10 ml of the solution to a small separator, make the solution slightly alkaline to phenol red with ammonia and add 5 ml of ammonia-cyanide solution.   Then add 10 ml of a solution of the dithizone in chloroform (10 mg per liter), shake for 1 minute and allow to separate. The color of the chloroform layer is not more red than that of a control made with a solution of 0.004 mg Pb in 10 ml of water, contained in a small separatory funnel and treated as described above beginning with "add 5 ml of ammonia-cyanide mixture. . . ."

EOSIN

Eosin yellowish; Eosin ys; Tetrabromofluorescein Soluble

Br; $C_{20}H_6O_5Br_4Na_2$; mol. wt. 691.91; Br—46.21%.

Brown-red crystals or crystalline powder.   Freely soluble in water; soluble in alcohol.   Its 1:500 water solution is reddish-yellow with a greenish fluorescence.

Eosin is used as an adsorption indicator for the titration of bromide and chloride with silver nitrate.   The latter halide is best titrated in 60–70% methanol solutions.

Standards

Sensitiveness................to pass test

Drying loss....................max 10%

Chloride (Cl)................max 0.02%

Ignition residue (as sulfate,

  anhydrous basis)............20%–23%

Sensitiveness: Dissolve 50 mg of the indicator in 10 ml of water.   Measure exactly 10 ml of 0.1 N HCl into a flask, add 5 ml of glacial acetic acid and 50 ml of methanol.   Add 2–3 drops of the indicator solution and titrate with 0.1 N silver nitrate until the color of the mixture suddenly changes from yellowish-red to intense red.   The volume of the silver nitrate required is not over 0.05 ml in excess of the theoretical volume.

Drying loss: Dry about 500 mg at 105°.   The loss in weight corresponds to not more than 10%.

Chloride: Dissolve 100 mg in 10 ml of water, add 1 ml of HNO_2.   Filter and add to the filtrate 1 ml of $AgNO_3$ solution   Any resulting turbidity corresponds to not more than 0.02 mg of Cl.

Ignition residue: Transfer the dried sample from the test for *Drying loss* to a tared crucible, add 0.5 ml of H_2SO_4 and ignite gently.   Cool, add 1 ml of HNO_3 and a few drops of H_2SO_4, and ignite to constant weight (theory 20.5%).

ERIOCHROME BLACK T

Eriochromeschwartz T

; $C_{20}H_{12}N_3O_7SNa$; mol. wt. 461.38.

Brownish-black powder.   Soluble in water and alcohol.   It is used as an indicator in the EDTA method for the determination of total hardness (Ca and Mg) of waters, and for determination of calcium, magnesium or mercury by the above method.   *See* under Ethylenediamine Tetraacetic Acid.

Sensitiveness: Dissolve 50 mg of the sample in 100 ml of water.   Add 0.5 ml of this solution to 50 ml of water; the latter is colored red or bluish red. Add 2 drops of 10% NH_3; the color changes to blue.   Now add 1 ml of a solution of 200 mg of magnesium sulfate in 100 ml of water; the red color is restored.

ERIOCHROME CYANINE

=O ; $C_{23}H_{15}O_9Na_3S$; mol. wt. 496.4.

Dark red-brown.   Freely soluble in water; insoluble in alcohol.

With slightly acid (pH 5.6), dilute solutions of aluminum, this dye forms an intensely colored lake—red, red-violet or violet—depending on the concentration, and this reaction is utilized for the determination of very small amounts of Al in steel, zinc, etc.[1,2,3,4,5]

Standards

Solubility....................to pass test	Drying loss....................max 2.0%
Sensitiveness................to pass test	Yield of Na_2SO_4............42.0%–44.0%

Solubility: Dissolve 200 mg of sample in 100 ml of water and let stand for 30 minutes.   The resulting solution is clear and free from any undissolved matter.

Sensitiveness: (*a*) Dilute 1.0 ml of standard aluminum solution to 100.0 ml, (*b*) Dissolve 20 mg of the eriochrome cyanine in 20 ml of water.   (*c*) Dissolve 4 g of sodium acetate trihydrate in water to 20 ml.

To 10 ml of (*a*) add 2.0 ml of (*b*) and place the mixture in a bath of 35°–40° for 5 minutes.   Cool to room temperature, than add 1.0 ml of (*c*).   After a few minutes the mixture assumes a strong red to red-violet color.

Drying loss: Dry about 1 g, accurately weighed, in a vacuum over an efficient desiccator to constant weight.   The loss in weight, if any, amounts to not more than 2.0%.

Yield of Na_2SO_4: Weigh accurately about 0.5 g of the dried sample from the preceding test and heat in a tared crucible until well charred.   Cool, slowly add 1 ml of H_2SO_4, then 2 ml of HNO_3 and cautiously evaporate on a hot plate until sulfuric fumes cease to be evolved.   Now ignite strongly (600°–700°) to constant weight. The weight of the resulting Na_2SO_4 corresponds to not less than 42.0% and to not more than 44.0% of the weight of the dried sample taken (theory 42.9%).

[1] Eegriwe, E., *Z. anal. Chem.* **76**, 238 (1929).
[2] Alten, F., Weilland, W., *et al., ibid.* **96**, 91 (1935).
[3] Richter, F., *ibid.* **126**, 43 (1938).
[4] Thrun, W. E., *Anal. Chem.* **18**, 1117 (1946).
[5] Ikenberry, L. C., Thomas, A. *ibid.* **23**, 1808 (1951).

ESCHKA'S MIXTURE

White powder or small, soft granules, composed of 65% of magnesium oxide and 35% of sodium carbonate. Partly soluble in water; entirely soluble in acids with effervescence. Used for the determination of sulfur in coal and similar materials.

Standards

Hydrochloric acid—insoluble...max 0.02%   Sulfur compounds (as SO_4)....max 0.003%

Hydrochloric acid—insoluble: Mix 5 g with 75 ml of water and gradually add 20 ml of hydrochloric acid. Heat on the steam bath for 1 hour, filter any undissolved residue, wash it with hot water and dry at 105°. The weight of the insoluble residue does not exceed 1.0 mg.

Sulfur compounds: Mix 12 g with 120 ml of water, add 2 ml of bromine water and stir well. Add hydrochloric acid in small portions until the oxide just dissolves, then add 1 ml excess of the acid. Heat the solution to boiling and filter. Add to the filtrate 5 ml barium chloride and let stand overnight. If a precipitate appears, filter, wash and ignite. The weight of the ignited precipitate does not exceed 1.0 mg.

ETHANOLAMINE

2-Aminoethanol; 2-Hydroxyethylamine; Monoethanolamine

$H_2NCH_2CH_2OH$; mol. wt. 61.08; N—22.93%.

Colorless, somewhat viscid liquid with a slight amine-like odor. Sp. gr. 1.015. Solidifies at about 10°. It is miscible with water and alcohol; moderately soluble in chloroform or carbon tetrachloride. Ethanolamine is a strong base and absorbs CO_2 from the air. *Keep in tightly closed containers.*

Standards

Assay....................99.0%–100.3%   Other amines...............to pass test
Boiling range.................169°–172°   Evaporation residue..........max 0.2%

Assay: Weigh accurately about 1 g, dilute with 30 ml of H_2O and titrate with 0.5 N HCl, using methyl orange as indicator. One ml of 0.5 N HCl corresponds to 0.003054 g of C_2H_7NO, log 48458.

Boiling range: Distill 50 ml. After the first 10 drops, not less than 48 ml distills between 169° and 172°, making correction for difference in barometric pressure from 760 mm (page 581).

Other amines: Weigh accurately about 1 g, transfer it to a tared beaker or evaporating dish with the aid of a small volume of water, and add a slight excess of 0.5 N or 1 N HCl over the volume indicated by the assay. Evaporate to dryness on the steam bath, dry at 105° for 3 hours and weigh. The weight of the ethanolamine hydrochloride so obtained, multiplied by 0.625, represents ethanolamine, and it corresponds to not less than 99.0% and to not more than 100.3% of that found by the assay.

Evaporation residue: Evaporate 2 ml, accurately measured, on the steam bath and dry at 150° for 2 hours.   Not more than 4.0 mg of residue remains.

ETHER

Diethyl Ether; Ethyl Ether

$CH_3CH_2 \cdot O\text{---}CH_2CH_3$; mol. wt. 74.12.

This grade of ether contains about 2% of alcohol and about 0.3% water.

By the action of air, ether is gradually oxidized to some extent with the formation of ethyl peroxide, followed by aldehyde and acetic acid.   Exposure to light greatly accelerates the oxidation.   When ether containing ethyl peroxide is gently evaporated, the peroxide is left as a residue, and if heated at about 100° or higher it violently explodes.

Keep tightly closed, protected from light, in a cool place and remote from fire.

Caution: Ether giving a reaction for peroxide (see test for *Peroxide* under Ether, Absolute) should not be used if the ether solution is to be evaporated to dryness, because the peroxide may cause an explosion, or the evaporation residue may be affected by the peroxide.

Standards

Specific gravity (25°/25°)......0.712–0.714	Aldehydes and Ketones.......to pass test
Evaporation residue........max 0.0010%	(limit about 0.001% as acetaldehyde)
Acid (as acetic)............max 0.0010%	Substances darkened
Peroxides (as H_2O_2)..........to pass test	by H_2SO_4.................to pass test
(limit about 0.001%)	Foreign odor.................to pass test

Apply the tests described for Ether, Absolute, omitting the tests for *Water* and *Alcohol*.   The results conform to the requirements there stated.

ETHER, ABSOLUTE

Diethyl Ether; Ethyl Ether

Clear, colorless, highly volatile liquid.   Ether is highly flammable.   Sp. gr. 0.7096.   Boils at 35°.   It dissolves in about 15 volumes of water at 25°.   Miscible with alcohol, benzene, chloroform and many other organic liquids.

Standards

Specific gravity (25°/25°)....max 0.7100%	Substances darkened
Evaporation residue........max 0.0010%	by H_2SO_4.................to pass test
Acid (as acetic)............max 0.0010%	Foreign odors.................to pass test
Peroxide (as H_2O_2)..........to pass test	Alcohol.................max about 0.1%
(limit about 0.001%)	Water......................max 0.02%
Aldehydes and Ketones.......to pass test	
(limit about 0.001% as acetaldehyde)	

Evaporation residue: Allow 140 ml to evaporate and dry at 105° for 1 hour. Not more than 1.0 mg of residue remains.

Acid: Place 10 ml of 70% ethanol in a 100-ml glass-stoppered flask, add 0.2 ml of bromocresol purple solution and just sufficient 0.01 N NaOH to produce a blue color which persists after shaking for 1 minute. Now add 25 ml of the ether and shake vigorously to mix. If the blue color disappears, add the 0.01 N NaOH, shaking after the addition of each 0.1 ml, until the same blue color is restored. Not more than 0.3 ml of the NaOH is required. One ml of 0.01 N NaOH = 0.6 mg CH_3COOH.

Peroxide: Place 10 ml in a small, glass-stoppered cylinder, previously rinsed with another portion of the sample, add 1 ml of fresh 10% potassium iodide, shake and let stand for 1 minute. No yellow color is observed in either layer.

Note: Fresh ether should meet this test, but after storage for some time peroxides may be formed, and the ether will not conform to this test.

Aldehydes and Ketones: To 20 ml of the ether contained in a glass-stoppered cylinder add 7 ml of a mixture of 1 ml of Nessler solution and 17 ml of a saturated aqueous solution of sodium chloride. Stopper, shake vigorously for 10 seconds and allow to stand for 1 minute. The aqueous layer shows no turbidity.

Substances darkened by sulfuric acid: Cool 10 ml of H_2SO_4 to 10° and add to it dropwise, with stirring, 10 ml of the sample. The resulting mixture is not more than faintly colored.

Foreign odor: Allow 10 ml to evaporate spontaneously in a dry dish to about 1 ml. No foreign odor is perceptible. Transfer the residue to a clean, odorless filter paper. No foreign odor is perceptible when the last traces of ether evaporate from the paper.

Water; Alcohol: Place 20 ml of the ether in a dry, glass-stoppered cylinder, add 2–3 freshly cut pieces of sodium about the size of a pea, and let stand for 2 hours. Only a slight evolution of gas occurs, and the sodium is not covered with a white coating, but retains its metallic appearance.

Alcohol and **water** in ether may be determined quantitatively, with a reasonable degree of accuracy, by the following procedures:

Alcohol: Prepare a standard alcohol solution by dissolving 0.50 ml (400 mg) of absolute alcohol in 1 liter of water. Transfer 0.5 ml, 1 ml, 1.5 ml and 2.0 ml portions (or other suitable quantities of the standard alcohol solution) into separate comparison tubes. Add sufficient water to each to make 5 ml.

Shake 50 ml of the ether (35 g) in a separatory funnel—first with two 15-ml portions of H_2O, then with four 5-ml portions at about 25°, shaking each time for 2 minutes. Slowly pour the combined water extracts in a thin stream from one flask to another several times to eliminate as much as possible of the ether held in the water, finally adding water to make 50 ml. Pipette 2 ml of the water solution into a suitable comparison tube and add with a pipette 3 ml of water.

To the tube containing the water extract of the ether and to each of the standard alcohol solution add exactly 10 ml of the nitro-chronic acid solution (see Note), mix, and allow to stand at about 25° for 1 hour. At the end of this period, match the green or a blue color of the tube containing the water extract of the ether against those of the alcohol standard solution and the quantity of C_2H_5OH deduced therefrom.

Note: The nitro-chronic acid solution is made by mixing 1 volume of 5% potassium chromate solution with 120 volumes of water and 70 volumes of colorless nitric acid. This solution should not be used if it is more than about 1 month old.

Water: The actual amount of water in ether may be determined by the iodine (Fischer) method, using 10 to 15 ml of the absolute ether and 25 ml of anhydrous methanol as solvent. The absolute ether now available, when the container is freshly opened, contains less than 0.02% of H_2O—usually 0.01%.

ETHYL ACETATE

$CH_3CO_2C_2H_5$; mol. wt. 88.10.

Colorless, clear liquid; characteristic, fragrant odor. Soluble in 12 parts of water at 25°; miscible with alcohol. Sp. gr. about 0.90. *Keep in well-stoppered bottles away from fire and light.*

Standards

Assay..........min 99.5% $CH_3CO_2C_2H_5$	Evaporation residue.........max 0.005%
Boiling range....................76°–77°	Water......................max 0.20%
Free acid (as acetic)..........max 0.005%	

Assay: Weigh accurately a 100-ml glass-stoppered flask containing 15 ml of alcohol, add quickly 5 ml of the ethyl acetate, immediately stopper and reweigh. Dilute with diluted alcohol (1 + 1) to volume and mix well. To 25 ml of the dilution add 40 ml of 0.5 N NaOH, and heat on the steam bath under a reflux condenser for 1 hour. Cool and titrate excess alkali with 0.5 N HCl, using phenolphthalein as indicator. Run a blank determination with the same volume of the 0.5 N NaOH and in the same manner. One ml of 0.5 N NaOH = 0.04405 g $CH_3CO_2C_2H_5$, log 64375.

Boiling range: Distill 50 ml. After the first 10 drops all distills between 76°–77°, correction being made for the barometric pressure, page 581.

Free Acid: To 10 ml of alcohol add 2 drops of phenolphthalein, neutralize with 0.02 N NaOH and add 0.4 ml excess, then add 10 ml of the sample. The pink color persists for 15 seconds.

Evaporation residue: Evaporate 22 ml of dryness on the steam bath and dry at 105° for 1 hour. Not more than 1.0 mg of residue remains.

Water: The water content of ethyl acetate may be determined by the iodine (Fischer) method, and it should not exceed 0.2%.

ETHYL BROMIDE

C_2H_5Br; mol. wt. 108–98; Br—73.35%.

Clear, colorless liquid; pleasant, ethereal odor. *Flammable.* Slightly soluble in water; miscible with alcohol or ether. Boils at 38.4°. Sp. gr. about 1.45. *Keep in tightly closed bottles, in a cool place, protected from light.*

Standards

Boiling range....................38°–40°	Acid.......................to pass test
Specific gravity............1.450–1.4525	Evaporation residue........max 0.002%

Boiling range: Distill 50 ml, receiving the distillate in a cylinder well closed with a stopper carrying a capillary tube and surrounded with ice. After the first 10 drops, all distills between 38° and 40°, correction being made for barometric pressure, page 581.

Specific gravity: Determine with a pycnometer at 25°/25°.

Acid: Shake 10 ml with 10 ml of water for 1 minute in a separatory funnel. The aqueous layer, immediately separated from the ethyl bromide, does not affect blue litmus paper.

Evaporation residue: Evaporate 18 ml on the steam bath and dry at 105° for 30 minutes. Not more than 0.5 mg of residue remains.

ETHYL CYANOACETATE

$NC \cdot CH_2 \cdot COOC_2H_5$; mol. wt. 113.1; CN—23.0%.

Colorless to pale yellow liquid. Slightly soluble in water; miscible with alcohol or ether. Under atmospheric pressure it boils between 205° and 209°, with decomposition. At 10 mm pressure it boils at about 92°.

Standards

Specific gravity..............1.057–1.062	Free acid (as acetic).........max 0.15%
Sensitiveness.................to pass test	*Assay*....................96%–100.5%

Specific gravity: Determine with a pycnometer at 25°/25°.

Sensitiveness: Dissolve 5 mg of quinhydrone in a mixture of 50 ml H_2O and 50 ml ethanol. To 1 ml of this solution add one drop of 28% NH_3 and 0.5 ml of a solution of 10 mg of the ethyl cyanoacetate in 100 ml of alcohol. A distinct blue color is produced. In place of quinhydrone 1 ml of a 1:1000 solution of benzoquinone or methylnaphthaquinone (menadione) in alcohol may be used, in which case a strong purplish-blue color is produced.

Free acid: Add 2 drops of phenolphthalein to 25 ml of alcohol and add dropwise 0.1 N NaOH until a pink color is produced. Add to this solution 2.0 ml of the sample, mix and titrate with 0.1 N NaOH to the restoration of the pink color. No more than 0.5 ml of the NaOH is required.

Assay: Tare a weighing bottle with 10 ml of water, then add 2.0 ml of sample and reweigh. Completely transfer the contents of the bottle, with the aid of 50 ml of water, into the flask of an ammonia distillation apparatus containing in the receiver 30.0 ml of 1 N H_2SO_4. Add to the flask 50 ml of 10% NaOH and heat the flask at first gently for 30–40 minutes so that little, if any, liquid distills; then raise the temperature and distill, adding water if necessary, until 75 ml has distilled over. Titrate the excess of acid in the receiver with 1 N NaOH, and methyl red as indicator. One ml of 1 N H_2SO_4 = 0.1131 g $C_5H_7NO_2$. Not less than 8.5 ml and not more than 8.9 ml of the 1 N H_2SO_4 should be consumed per 1 g of sample.

ETHYLENEDIAMINE
1,2-Diaminomethane

$H_2N—CH_2=CH_2—NH_2$; mol. wt. 60.10; N—46.62%.

Clear, colorless, somewhat viscous liquid; ammonia-like odor.   Miscible with water, alcohol or methanol; practically insoluble in ether or chloroform.

Ethylenediamine is a strong base and absorbs water, forming a monohydrate. The specific gravity of the anhydrous is about 0.895 at 25°/25°, melts at +8.5° and boils at 116°–117°.   It readily forms compounds with metallic salts.

Ethylenediamine is available in concentrations of 70% and upwards, and the concentration is stated on the label.

Standards

Assay.......not less than stated on label
Ammonia and other amines....to pass test

Evaporation residue.........max 0.030%
Heavy metals (as Pb).......max 0.0005%

Assay: Accurately weigh a glass-stoppered flask with 10 ml of water, add about 1 ml of sample and reweigh.   Dilute with water to 30 ml and titrate with 1 N HCl, using 3 drops of bromophenol blue as indicator.   One ml of 1 N HCl = 0.03005 g of $C_2H_8N_2$, log 47784.

Ammonia and other amines: Weigh accurately about 1 ml of sample and transfer it, with the aid of alcohol, to a small tared dish, or beaker.   Add, with stirring, 20 ml of 10% HCl, rinse the rod with some alcohol, evaporate to dryness on a steam bath, then dry at 105° for 2 hours.   The weight of the ethylenediamine dihydrochloride so obtained, multiplied by 0.4517, represents the weight of ethylenediamine, and corresponds to within 1% above or below that found in the assay.

Evaporation residue: Evaporate 5.5 ml in glass or porcelain on the steam bath, and dry the residue at 105° for 1 hour.   The weight of the residue does not exceed 1.5 mg (retain).

Heavy metals: Add to the Evaporation residue 1 ml of HNO_3 and 3 ml of H_2O, and evaporate to dryness on the steam bath.   Take up the residue with 1 ml of 1 N acetic acid and 5 ml of hot H_2O, dilute to 40 ml and add 10 ml of H_2S.   Any color produced is not darker than that of a control made with 0.025 mg of Pb and 1 ml of 1 N acetic acid in the same final volume as with the sample.

ETHYLENEDIAMINE TETRAACETIC ACID
EDTA; Ethylenedinitrilo-Tetraacetic Acid; Versene; Sequestrin; Complexon

; mol. wt. 292.24

White powder.   Insoluble in cold water, alcohol or in the usual organic solvents. It dissolves in about 160 parts of boiling water and it readily dissolves in solutions of alkali hydroxides, ammonia and their carbonates.

This acid is stable in either acid or alkaline solutions and at elevated temperatures, and is hardly affected by chemical compounds, but is slowly attacked by strong oxidizing agents.

The table below, by courtesy of Bersworth Chemical Company, shows the order of chelation of some of the common metals at various pH's in the presence of phosphate and carbonate buffers.   The metal to the left is more strongly complexed than the metal to the right.   A metallic ion which is capable of forming a stronger chelate compound with EDTA will displace a less strongly chelated metal from the chelate compound.

pH	4.00	Cr	Cu	Ni	Pb	Co			
pH	6.50	Ni	Cu	Co	Zn & Cd	Ca			
pH	8.65	Ni	Co	Cu	Zn & Cd	Ca	Mg	Sr	Ba
pH	11.00	Co	Ni	Cu	Zn & Cd	Ca	Mg	Sr	Ba

Standards

Chelating capacity............to pass test		Heavy metals (as Pb)........max 0.001%
Solubility in Na_2CO_3 solution . . to pass test		Iron (Fe).................max 0.002%
Ignition residue.............max 0.10%		

Chelating capacity: (a) Dissolve 0.292 g of the EDTA in 2 ml of 1 N NaOH and 10 ml of water and dilute to 100 ml (0.01 molar).

(b) Dissolve 0.100 g of calcium carbonate, previously dried for 2 hours at 200°, in 10 ml of water and about 1 ml of 10% HCl.   Neutralize the solution, using litmus paper, with dilute ammonium hydroxide and dilute to 100 ml (0.01 M).

(c) Dissolve 0.250 g of uneffloresced cupric sulfate in water to make 100 ml (0.01 M).

To exactly 5 ml of (a) add 2–3 drops of 10% NH_3 and 2 ml of 5% ammonium oxalate and mix well.   Then add, while agitating, exactly 5 ml of (b).   The mixture is clear or, if a turbidity persists after shaking for 1 minute, it clears upon the addition of 0.2 ml of (a) and shaking for about 1 minute.

To exactly 5 ml of (a) add 0.5 ml of 1% NH_3 and 0.5 ml of 10% potassium ferrocyanide solution, and mix.   Then add, while agitating, 4.8 ml of (c).   The resulting solution is pale blue without any red tint.

Solubility in Na_2CO_3: To 1 g of sample add 20 ml of water; then add in small portions 0.5 g of anhydrous sodium carbonate.   No insoluble residue remains, and the solution, after CO_2-bubbles have disappeared, is clear and colorless.

Ignition residue: Char 2 g thoroughly, cool, add 1 ml of H_2SO_4 and ignite to constant weight.   The weight of the residue does not exceed 2.0 mg.

Solution R: To the residue from the preceding test, add 2 ml of HCl, 2 ml of H_2O and 0.5 ml of HNO_4, and slowly evaporate to dryness on the steam bath. Add to the residue 0.5 ml of 1 N HCl and 15 ml of hot water and digest for 5 minutes. Cool and dilute to 20 ml.

Heavy metals: Dilute 10 ml of *Solution R* to 20 ml and add 10 ml of H_2S.   Any color produced is not darker than that of a control made with 0.01 mg of Pb, 0.3 ml of 1 N HCl and 10 ml of H_2S in the same final volume as with the sample.

Iron: To the remaining 10 ml of *Solution R* add 2 ml of HCl and dilute to 50 ml. Add about 30 mg of ammonium persulfate and 3 ml of ammonium thiocyanate solution. Any resulting red color is not darker than that of a blank to which 0.02 mg of Fe has been added.

ETHYLENE GLYCOL

Glycol

$HO \cdot CH_2 : CH_2 \cdot OH$; mol. wt. 62.07.

Colorless, somewhat syrupy, odorless liquid. Miscible with water and alcohol; soluble in about 200 parts of ether.

Standards

Specific gravity 1.1140–1.1144	Chloride (Cl) . . . . max 0.010%
Boiling range . . . . 196°–199°	Sulfate (SO$_4$) . . . . max 0.002%
Miscibility with H$_2$O . . . . to pass test	Heavy metals (as Pb) . . . . max 0.0005%
Acid (as acetic) . . . . max 0.005%	Water . . . . max 0.30%

Specific gravity: Determine with a pycnometer at 25°/25°.

Boiling range: Distill 50 ml. Not less than 48 ml distill between 196° and 199°, correction being made for the difference in the barometric pressure from 760 mm (page 581).

Miscibility with water: Mix 10 ml of the ethylene glycol with 30 ml of water. A clear solution results, and it remains clear for 30 minutes.

Acid: Add 1 ml of phenolphthalein solution to 50 ml of H$_2$O, then add 0.1 N NaOH dropwise until the pink color persists after shaking for a few seconds. Now add 10 ml of the sample and shake. If the pink color has disappeared, it is restored by the addition of not more than 0.1 ml of 0.1 N NaOH.

Chloride: Dilute 2.0 ml of sample with water to 100 ml. To 10 ml of the dilution add 1 ml of 10% HNO$_3$ and 1 ml of AgNO$_3$. Any turbidity produced is not greater than that in a blank to which 0.02 mg of Cl has been added.

Sulfate: Dilute 5 ml of sample to 20 ml and add 1 ml of 0.1 N HCl and 2 ml of BaCl$_2$. Any turbidity produced is not greater than that in a blank to which 0.1 mg of SO$_4$ has been added.

Heavy metals: Dilute 5.0 ml to 50 ml. To 10 ml add 0.015 mg of Pb, dilute to 40 ml and add 2 ml of 1 N acetic acid (A). To the remaining 40 ml add 2 ml of 1 N acetic acid (B). Then to each add 10 ml of H$_2$S. B is not darker than A.

Water: Water content of ethylene glycol may be determined by the iodine (Fischer) method.

ETHYL IODIDE

C_2H_5I; mol. wt. 155.98; iodine—81.37%.

Clear liquid, ethereal odor. When freshly distilled it is colorless, but exposure to air and light causes liberation of iodine, coloring the liquid yellow or reddish. The color may be removed by shaking with a globule of mercury or with silver leaf.

Soluble in about 250 parts of water; miscible with alcohol, ether or petroleum ether. Sp. gr. 1.93. *Keep in almost completely filled, tightly closed containers, protected from light.*

Standards

Assay.................min 98.5% C_2H_5I	Acid........................to pass test	
Boiling range..................71°–72.5°	Water.......................to pass test	
Evaporation residue..........max 0.01%	(limit about 0.2%)	

Assay: Weigh accurately a 100-ml volumetric flask containing 10 ml of alcohol, add quickly 1 ml of the sample, immediately stopper and reweigh. Dilute to exactly 100 ml with alcohol and mix well. Transfer 20.0 ml to a glass-stoppered flask, add 50 ml of 0.1 N $AgNO_3$ and follow with 2 ml of nitric acid. Stopper immediately, shake frequently during 2 hours and let stand in the dark overnight. Shake again frequently during 2 hours, then add 50 ml of H_2O and 3 ml of ferric ammonium sulfate and titrate the excess of $AgNO_3$ with 0.1 N thiocyanate. One ml of 0.1 N silver nitrate = 0.01560 g C_2H_5I, log 19312.

Boiling range: Distill 50 ml, receiving the distillate in a well-cooled, stoppered cylinder closed with a stopper carrying a capillary tube. After the first 10 drops not less than 48 ml distills between 71° and 72.5°, correction being made for barometric pressure, page 581.

Evaporation residue: Evaporate 5 ml of dryness on the steam bath and dry at 105° for 1 hour. Not more than 1.0 mg of residue remains.

Acid: Shake 5 ml with 5 ml of H_2O for 30 seconds and immediately separate the liquids. The aqueous layer is neutral to litmus paper, and not more than an opalescence is produced on the addition of 1 ml of silver nitrate and 2 drops of HNO_3.

Water: Mix 2 ml with 10 ml of petroleum ether. The mixture is clear.

Note: The *Water* may be quantitatively determined by the iodine (Fischer) method.

N-ETHYLPIPERIDINE

C_2H_5

; $C_7H_{15}N$, mol. wt. 113.2.

Clear, colorless, or practically colorless liquid; characteristic, ammonia-like odor; hygroscopic. It is a strong base and absorbs CO_2 from the air. Boils at 130°. Soluble in 25 parts of water; soluble in petroleum ether; miscible with alcohol, amyl acetate, chloroform, ether, carbon disulfide. Used for the determination of benzyl penicillin (penicillin G). *Keep tightly closed.*

Standards

Assay.....................99%–100.3%	Boiling range..................129°–132°	
Specific gravity..............0.833–0.835	Water and certain bases.......to pass test	

Assay: Accurately weigh a glass-stoppered flask with 10 ml of water, add about 0.5 ml of the sample and reweigh. Add 50 ml of 0.1 N HCl, then titrate excess acid with 0.1 N NaOH, using methyl red indicator. One ml of 0.1 N acid = 0.01132 g of $C_7H_{15}N$, log 05385.

Specific gravity: Determine with a pycnometer at 25°/25°.

Boiling range: Distill 50 ml. Not more than 1% distills below 126°, and not less than 95% between 129° and 132°.

Water and certain bases: Mix 0.5 ml of sample with 5 ml of petroleum ether; the mixture is clear. Add 1 ml of carbon disulfide; the solution remains clear.

FERRIC AMMONIUM SULFATE

Ferric Alum

$FeNH_4(SO_4)_2 \cdot 12H_2O$; mol. wt. 482.20; anhydrous—55.17%; H_2O—44.83%; Fe—11.58%; NH_3—3.53%; SO_4—39.85%.

Pale, violet, translucent crystals. Soluble in 3 parts of water; insoluble in alcohol. Keep protected from light.

Standards

Insoluble....................max 0.10%	Ferrous Iron (Fe)............max 0.001%
Chloride (Cl)................max 0.001%	Copper (Cu).................max 0.003%
Nitrate (NO₃)...............max 0.010%	Manganese (Mn).............max 0.005%
Alkalies, Earths (as sulfate)....max 0.05%	Zinc (Zn)...................max 0.003%

Insoluble: Dissolve 10 g in a mixture of 100 ml of water and 1 ml of HCl and heat on the steam bath for 1 hour. Filter any insoluble residue, wash it with water and dry at 105°. Its weight does not exceed 1.0 mg.

Chloride: Dissolve 2 g in 15 ml of water, add 2 ml of HNO_3, dilute to 20 ml and divide into two equal portions. To one portion add 1 ml of $AgNO_3$, heat at about 70° for 10 minutes, filter until clear (A). To the other portion add 1 ml of $AgNO_3$ (B). Any resulting turbidity in B is not greater than that produced by adding 0.01 mg of Cl to A.

Nitrate: Dissolve 1.0 g in 10 ml of water. Add the solution in small portions and with constant stirring to 10 ml of 10% NaOH, previously diluted with 5 ml of water. Cover the beaker and heat it on the steam bath, stirring several times, for 10 minutes. Filter, neutralize the filtrate with 25% H_2SO_4 and dilute to 25 ml. Using 5 ml of the solution diluted with 5 ml of water and 2.0 ml of standard nitrate solution for the control, proceed as directed under Nitrate—Estimation of Small Amounts, page 575.

Solution S: Dissolve 5 g in 70 ml of H_2O, heat to boiling and pour the solution into a mixture of 40 ml of H_2O and 7 ml of ammonium hydroxide. Filter while hot and wash with hot H_2O to 150 ml.

Alkalies, Earths, etc.: Evaporate in a tared dish 60 ml of *Solution S* to a small volume, add 0.5 ml of H_2SO_4, and evaporate to dryness. Ignite gently to expel ammonium salts, then at cherry red heat for 15 minutes. The weight of the ignited residue is not more than 1.0 mg.

Ferrous Iron: To a solution of 1 g in 20 ml of oxygen-free H_2O and 1 ml of HCl, add 1 drop of fresh 5% potassium ferricyanide. No blue or green color appears within 1 minute.

Manganese: Dissolve 0.5 g in 35 ml of water. Add 5 ml of H_2SO_4, 5 ml of phosphoric acid, and 5 ml of HNO_3 and boil for 5 minutes. Cool, add 0.25 g of potassium periodate and again boil for 5 minutes. Any pink color produced is not deeper than that of a control made by treating a solution of 0.025 mg of Mn in 35 ml of H_2O in the same manner as above described beginning with "add 5 ml of H_2SO_4. . . ."

Copper, Zinc: Using 10 ml of a solution of 1.0 g of sample in 30 ml of water, make the tests described under Copper and Zinc—Estimation of Small Amounts in Iron Salts, page 565. The pink color of the dithizone solution from the sample is not deeper than the color of the controls made with 0.01 mg of Cu or 0.01 mg of Zn.

FERRIC CHLORIDE

$FeCl_3 \cdot 6H_2O$; mol. wt. 270.32; anhydrous—60.0%; H_2O—39.98%; Fe—20.66%; Cl—39.35%.

Brownish-yellow, crystalline masses; deliquescent. It is reduced to ferrous in sunlight. Soluble in 0.5 part of water, soluble in alcohol or ether. *Keep in well-closed containers, in a cool place, protected from light.*

Standards

Insoluble....................max 0.010%	Arsenic (As)..................max 5 ppm	
Free acid (as HCl)...........max 0.10%	Ferrous iron (Fe″)......max about 0.002%	
Oxychloride..................to pass test	Copper (Cu).................max 0.003%	
Nitrate (NO_3)..........max about 0.01%	Lead (Pb)...................max 0.002%	
Phosphate (PO_4)............max 0.010%	Manganese (Mn).............max 0.005%	
Sulfate (SO_4)..............max 0.010%	Zinc (Zn)...................max 0.003%	
Alkalies, Earths (as sulfate)....max 0.10%	*Assay*.......................min 99.0%	

Insoluble: Dissolve 10 g in 50 ml of water and 1 ml of hydrochloric acid and heat on the steam bath for 1 hour. If an insoluble residue remains, filter, wash it with warm H_2O containing about 0.5% HCl, and dry at 105°. Its weight does not exceed 1.0 mg.

Free acid: Dissolve 6 g of potassium fluoride in 25 ml of water and add 4 drops of phenolphthalein. If a pink color is produced, discharge it by the addition of just sufficient 0.1 N HCl. If no pink color is produced, add just sufficient 0.1 N NaOH to produce a pink color.

Weigh 3.0 g of the ferric chloride and dissolve it in 20 ml of water. Slowly add to this solution the neutralized potassium fluoride solution, then add sufficient water to make the mixture measure 50 ml, mix well and allow to stand for 3 hours. Filter through a dry filter, rejecting the first filterful, and then titrate 25 ml of the clear filtrate with 0.1 N NaOH to a pale pink color. Not more than 0.40 ml of the NaOH is required.

Oxychloride: Five grams dissolve in a mixture of 35 ml of alcohol and 15 ml of ether, yielding a clear or practically clear solution.

Nitrate: Dissolve 1.0 g in 5 ml of water. Add the solution, in small portions and with continuous stirring, to 10 ml of 10% NaOH previously diluted with 5 ml of water. Cover the beaker and heat it on the steam bath for 15 minutes. Filter, neutralize the filtrate with 25% H_2SO_4 and dilute to 25 ml. Using 5 ml of this solution for sample solution and 2.0 ml of standard nitrate solution (0.02 mg NO_3) for the control, proceed as directed under Nitrate—Estimation of Small Amounts, page 575.

Phosphate: Dissolve 5 g in 30 ml H_2O, add 15 ml of HNO_3 and evaporate on the steam bath to a syrupy liquid. Add 30 ml of water, 15 ml of HNO_3 and 10 ml of ammonium hydroxide, then add 40 ml of ammonium molybdate-nitric-acid solution. Shake at about 40° for 5 minutes and allow to stand for 1 hour. If a yellow precipitate is formed, filter and wash with a 5% solution of potassium nitrate until the filtrate is neutral to litmus paper. Transfer the filter with the precipitate into a flask, add 10 ml of H_2O and 5 ml of 0.1 N NaOH, and agitate until the yellow precipitate has dissolved. Add 5 drops of phenolphthalein and titrate the excess of NaOH with 0.1 N HCl. One ml of 0.1 N NaOH = 0.41 mg PO_4. Not more than 1.2 ml of the NaOH is consumed.

Solution S: Dissolve 10 g of the ferric chloride in 100 ml of water, heat the solution to boiling, and slowly pour it, while stirring, into a mixture of 170 ml of water and 20 ml of ammonium hydroxide. Filter hot and wash with hot water to 300 ml.

Sulfate: Evaporate 60 ml of *Solution S* with 0.5 g of anhydrous sodium carbonate to dryness and ignite gently to expel the ammonium salts. Add to the cooled residue 2 ml of HCl and evaporate to dryness on the steam bath. Take up the residue with 10 ml of H_2O, filter, if necessary, and add 1 ml of 0.1 N HCl and 2 ml of $BaCl_2$. Any resulting turbidity is not greater than that of a control made as follows: Evaporate 10 ml of ammonium hydroxide to expel ammonia. Add 0.2 mg of SO_4, 0.5 g of anhydrous sodium carbonate and 2 ml of HCl and evaporate to dryness on the steam bath. Take up the residue with 10 ml of H_2O, and add 1 ml of 0.1 N HCl and 2 ml $BaCl_2$.

Alkalies, Earths, etc.: Evaporate 30 ml of *Solution S* with 0.5 ml of H_2SO_4 and ignite slowly. Not more than 1.0 mg of residue remains.

Arsenic: Dissolve 1 g in 0.5 ml of hydrochloric acid, add 5 ml of freshly prepared stannous chloride solution. Heat the mixture at 70°–80° for 5 minutes and allow to stand for 25 minutes. The color is not noticeably darker than that of a solution prepared with 0.005 mg As, of the same quantities of sample, hydrochloric acid and stannous chloride solution immediately before making the comparison.

Ferrous iron: Dissolve 0.5 g in 20 ml of H_2O, add 1 ml of HCl and one drop of fresh 5% potassium ferricyanide. No blue color is produced in one minute.

Lead: Dissolve 1 g of sample in water, add 3 ml of HNO_3, dilute to 100 ml, mix and transfer 10.0 of the solution to a separatory funnel. For the control place in a similar funnel 0.002 mg of Pb, 0.3 ml of HNO_3 and 9 ml of water, and then treat each as follows: Add 10 ml of ammonium citrate solution, 3 ml of potassium cyanide solution and 3 ml of hydroxylamine hydrochloride solution. Add 2 drops of phenol red, and make the solutions alkaline (red color) with NH_4OH. Immediately extract the solutions with 5-ml portions of dithizone in chloroform extraction solution, draining off each extract into a second separatory funnel. Repeat the extraction with 5-ml portions of the extraction solution if necessary, until the last dithizone extract is unchanged in color. Shake the combined dithizone extracts with 20 ml of 1% HNO_3, allow to separate well, draw off and discard the chloroform layer. Now add to the aqueous layer 10 ml of standard dithizone solution, 5 ml of ammonia-cyanide solution, and shake for 1 minute. The red color of the chloroform layer of the sample is no darker than that of the control.

Manganese: Dissolve 2 g in a few ml of H_2O, add 3 ml of H_2SO_4 and heat to strong sulfuric fumes. Cool, and cautiously add water to make 100 ml. Dilute 10 ml of the solution to 25 ml, add 5 ml each of H_2SO_4, phosphoric acid and HNO_3, and boil for 5 minutes. Cool, add 0.25 g of potassium periodate and again boil for 5 minutes. Any pink color produced is not deeper than that of a control made by treating a solution of 0.01 mg of Mn in 25 ml of H_2O in the same manner as above described beginning with "add 5 ml of H_2SO_4. . . ."

Copper, Zinc: Using 10 ml of a solution of 1.0 g of sample in 30 ml of water, make the tests as described under Copper and Zinc—Estimation of Small Amounts in Iron Salts, page 565. The pink color of the dithizone solution from the sample is not deeper than the color of the controls made with 0.01 mg of Cu and/or 0.01 mg of Zn.

Assay: Ferric chloride may be assayed by the following procedure: Weigh accurately about 1 g and dissolve it in 50 ml of water in a 300-ml glass-stoppered flask. Add 3 ml of hydrochloric acid and 3 g potassium iodide and let stand for 30 minutes in the dark. Dilute with 100 ml of water and titrate with 0.1 N sodium thiosulfate, adding starch toward the end. Correct for a blank. One ml of 0.1 N thiosulfate = 0.02703 g $FeCl_3 \cdot 6H_2O$, log 43185.

FERRIC CHLORIDE, LOW IN PHOSPHORUS

Standards

Insoluble	max 0.010%	Arsenic (As)	max 1 ppm
Free acid (as HCl)	max 0.010%	Ferrous iron (Fe″)	max 0.002%
Oxychloride	to pass test	Copper (Cu)	max 0.003%
Nitrate (NO_3)	max about 0.01%	Manganese (Mn)	max 0.010%
Phosphate (PO_4)	max about 0.0005%	Zinc (Zn)	max 0.003%
Sulfate (SO_4)	max 0.010%	Lead (Pb)	max 0.003%
Alkalies, Earths, etc.	max 0.10%		

Phosphate: Dissolve 10 g in 20 ml of H_2O and evaporate twice on the steam bath to a syrupy liquid with 20-ml portions of nitric acid. Add to the residue 50 ml of H_2O, 15 ml of HNO_3, 13 ml of ammonium hydroxide, and follow with 50 ml of ammonium molybdate-nitric acid solution. Shake at 40° for 5 minutes and allow to stand for 1 hour. No yellow precipitate forms.

Apply all the other tests as described for the preceding grade. The results conform to the requirements stated there.

FERRIC NITRATE

$Fe(NO_3)_3 \cdot 9H_2O$; mol. wt. 404.02; anhydrous—59.87%; H_2O—40.13%; Fe—13.82%; NO_3—46.05%.

Clear, pale violet or grayish crystals; deliquescent. Very soluble in water; soluble in ethanol. *Keep protected from light.*

Standards

Insoluble................max 0.010%	Copper (Cu)...............max 0.003%
Chloride (Cl)..............max 0.0005%	Lead (Pb)................max 0.002%
Phosphate (PO_4)...........max 0.005%	Manganese (Mn)...........max 0.005%
Sulfate (SO_4)..............max 0.010%	Zinc (Zn)................max 0.003%
Alkalies, Earths, etc..........max 0.10%	

Insoluble: Dissolve 10 g in a mixture of 100 ml of H_2O and 1 ml of HNO_3, and heat on the steam bath for 1 hour. Filter any insoluble residue, wash it well with water and dry at 105°. Its weight is not more than 1.0 mg.

Chloride: Dissolve 4 g in 25 ml of H_2O and 2 ml of HNO_3, and divide into two equal portions. To one portion add 1 ml of $AgNO_3$, let stand for 10 minutes, filter until clear and use for the control. To the other portion add 1 ml of $AgNO_3$. Any resulting turbidity is not greater than that produced when 0.01 mg of Cl is added to the control.

Phosphate: To a solution of 5 g in 20 ml of H_2O add 15 ml of HNO_3, follow with 10 ml of ammonium hydroxide and then add 40 ml of ammonium molybdate-nitric acid solution. Shake at 40° for 5 minutes and allow to stand for 1 hour. If a yellow precipitate is present, filter and wash with a 5% solution of potassium nitrate until the filtrate is neutral to litmus. Transfer the filter with the precipitate into a flask, add 5 ml of H_2O and 10 ml of 0.02 N NaOH and agitate until the yellow precipitate has dissolved. Add 3 drops of phenolphthalein and titrate the excess of NaOH with 0.02 N HCl. One ml of 0.02 N NaOH = 0.08 mg PO_4. Not more than 3.0 ml of the NaOH is consumed.

Solution S: Dissolve 5 g in 50 ml of H_2O and pour the solution into a mixture of 10 ml of ammonium hydroxide and 100 ml of H_2O. Filter and wash with hot H_2O to 150 ml.

Sulfate: Evaporate 30 ml of *Solution S* to about 10 ml, filter if necessary, and add 1 ml of 0.1 N HCl and 2 ml of $BaCl_2$. Any turbidity produced is not greater than that in a control made as follows; Boil 3 ml of ammonium hydroxide with 15 ml of H_2O until the NH_3 is expelled, add 0.1 mg of SO, dilute to 10 ml, then add 1 ml of 0.1 N HCl and 2 ml of $BaCl_2$.

Alkalies, Earths, etc.: Evaporate 30 ml of *Solution S* with 0.5 ml of H_2SO_4 and ignite. The residue does not exceed 1.0 mg.

Copper, Zinc: Using 10 ml of solution of 1.0 g of sample in 30 ml of water, make the tests as described under Copper and Zinc—Estimation of Small Amounts in Iron Salts, page 565. The pink color of the dithizone solution from the sample is not deeper than the color of the controls made with 0.01 mg of Cu and/or 0.01 mg of Zn.

Lead, Manganese: Test as described under Ferric Chloride, but use 0.002 mg Pb, and 0.006 mg of Mn for the respective controls.

FERRIC SULFATE

$Fe_2(SO_4)_3$ with about $6H_2O$; mol. wt. of the anhydrous—399.9.

Grayish-white to slightly yellow powder. It is hygroscopic. Slowly soluble in water; sparingly in alcohol. *Keep well closed and protected from light.*

Standards

Assay.................21.0%–23.0% Fe	Nitrate (NO_3)..........max about 0.02%
Insoluble...................max 0.010%	Alkalies, Earths (as sulfate)....max 0.20%
Chloride (Cl).................max 0.004%	Copper (Cu)................max 0.005%
Ferrous iron (Fe″)............max 0.05%	Zinc (Zn)..................max 0.005%

Assay: Weigh accurately about 0.7 g, transfer it completely to a glass-stoppered flask and dissolve in a mixture of 50 ml of H_2O and 3 ml of HCl. Add 3 g of potassium iodide and allow to stand for 30 minutes in the dark. Dilute with 100 ml cold water and titrate with 0.1 N sodium thiosulfate, adding starch toward the end. Correct for a blank. One ml of 0.1 N thiosulfate = 0.005585 g of Fe, log 74695.

Insoluble: Add 10 g to a mixture of 100 ml of H_2O and 1 ml of H_2SO_4, and heat on the steam bath for 1 hour. If an insoluble residue remains, filter (*retain filtrate*), wash well with H_2O, dry at 105° and weigh. The weight of the residue does not exceed 1.0 mg.

Chloride: Dissolve 1 g in 20 ml H_2O, add 2 ml of nitric acid and divide into 2 equal portions. To one portion add 1 ml of $AgNO_3$, let stand for 10 minutes, filter until clear, then add 0.02 mg of Cl (*A*). To the other portion add 1 ml of $AgNO_3$ (*B*) and adjust both to the same volume. Any resulting turbidity in *B* is not greater than that in *A*.

Ferrous iron: Dissolve 2 g in a mixture of 50 ml of oxygen-free H_2O and 5 ml of H_2SO_4 and titrate with 0.1 N permanganate. Not more than 0.20 ml is required to produce a reddish color.

Solution S: Heat the filtrate obtained in the test for *Insoluble* to boiling and slowly pour it, while stirring, into a mixture of 160 ml of water and 30 ml of ammonium hydroxide. Filter while hot and wash with water to 300 ml.

Nitrate: Dissolve 0.50 g in 5 ml of water. Add the solution in small portions and with continuous stirring to 5 ml of 10% NaOH previously diluted with 10 ml of water. Cover the beaker and heat it on the steam bath for 10 minutes. Filter, neutralize the filtrate with 25% H_2SO_4 and dilute to 25 ml. Using 5.0 ml of the solution, dilute to 10 ml, and use 2.0 ml of standard nitrate solution (0.02 mg NO_3) for the control; proceed as directed under Nitrate—Estimation of Small Amounts, page 575.

Alkalies, Earths, etc.: Evaporate 30 ml of *Solution S* to dryness and slowly ignite. Not more than 2.0 mg of residue remains.

Copper, Zinc: Using 6.0 ml of a solution of 1.0 g of sample in 30 ml of water, make the tests as described under Copper and Zinc—Estimation of Small Amounts in Iron Salts, page 565. The pink color of the dithizone solutions from the sample is not deeper than the color of the controls made with 0.01 mg of Cu and/or 0.01 mg of Zn.

FERROUS AMMONIUM SULFATE

$Fe(NH_4)_2(SO_4)_2 \cdot 6H_2O$; mol. wt. 392.16; anhydrous—72.44%; H_2O—27.56%; Fe—14.24%; NH_3—8.69%; SO_4—48.99%.

Pale bluish-green crystals or granules. Slowly oxidizes in the air. Soluble in about 6 parts of water; insoluble in alcohol. *Keep in well-closed containers, protected from light.*

Standards

Assay.....................99.5%–100.5% $Fe(NH_4)_2(SO_4)_3 \cdot 6H_2O$	Ferric iron (Fe″).............max 0.010%
	Alkalies, Earths (as sulfate)....max 0.05%
Insoluble....................max 0.010%	Copper (Cu).................max 0.003%
Chloride (Cl)................max 0.001%	Manganese (Mn).............max 0.005%
Phosphate (PO₄)............max 0.002%	Zinc (Zn)...................max 0.003%

Assay: Weigh accurately about 1.5 g, dissolve in a mixture of 100 ml of freshly boiled and cooled water and 3 ml of H_2SO_4, and titrate with 0.1 N potassium permanganate. One ml of 0.1 N permanganate = 0.03921 g $Fe(NH_4)_2(SO_4)_2$. $6H_2O$, log 59340.

$$10Fe(NH_4)_2(SO_4)_2 + 2KMnO_4 + 8H_2SO_4 \rightarrow$$
$$5Fe_2(SO_4)_3 + 10(NH_4)_2SO_4 + 2MnSO_4 + K_2SO_4 + 8H_2O$$

Insoluble: Dissolve 10 g in a mixture of 100 ml H_2O and 1 ml of H_2SO_4, filter any insoluble residue, wash it with water and dry at 105°. Its weight does not exceed 1.0 mg.

Chloride: To a solution of 1 g in 20 ml of H_2O add slowly 2 ml of HNO_3. After the evolution of the nitrogen oxides has ceased, filter if necessary, and divide into two equal portions. To one portion add 0.5 ml of $AgNO_3$. The two portions are equally clear after 1 minute.

Phosphate: Dissolve 10 g in 75 ml of H_2O, add 15 ml of HNO_3 and boil gently until nitrous fumes are no longer evolved. Cool, and nearly neutralize the solution with NH_4OH. Add 15 ml of HNO_3 and 10 ml of NH_4OH, then add 40 ml of ammonium molybdate-nitric acid solution. Shake at about 40° for 5 minutes and allow to stand for 1 hour. If yellow precipitate is present, filter, and wash it with 5% potassium nitrate solution until the filtrate is neutral to litmus paper. Transfer the filter with the precipitate into a flask, add 5 ml of H_2O and 10 ml of 0.02 N NaOH, and agitate until the yellow precipitate has dissolved. Add 3 drops of phenolphthalein and titrate the excess of NaOH with 0.02 N HCl. One ml of 0.02 N NaOH = 0.08 mg of PO_4. Not more than 2.5 ml of the NaOH is consumed.

Ferric iron: Dissolve 1 g in a mixture of 35 ml of oxygen-free water and 1 ml of H_2SO_4, and dilute with H_2O to 50 ml. To 10 ml add 0.02 mg of ferric Fe and 0.5 ml H_2SO_4, and dilute to 50 ml with oxygen-free water (*A*). To 30 ml of the solution add 0.5 ml of H_2SO_4 and dilute with oxygen-free H_2O to 50 ml (*B*). Then add to each 3 ml of ammonium thiocyanate. *B* has no more red color than *A*. This test must be performed rapidly to minimize oxidation by air.

Solution S: Dissolve 5 g in 70 ml of H_2O, add 7 ml of HNO_3 and boil to expel the gases. Pour the hot solution, with stirring, into a mixture of 50 ml of H_2O and 20 ml of NH_4OH, filter and wash with hot H_2O to 150 ml.

Alkalies, Earths, etc.: Evaporate 60 ml of *Solution S* and ignite. No more than 1.0 mg of residue remains.

Manganese: Dissolve 1.0 g in 10 ml of H_2O and 2 ml of H_2SO_4, and dilute to 100 ml. To 40 ml of the solution add 10 ml of HNO_3, 5 ml of H_2SO_4 and 5 ml of phosphoric acid, and boil for 5 minutes. Cool, add 0.25 g of potassium periodate and again boil for 5 minutes. Any pink color produced is not deeper than that of a control made by treating a solution of 0.02 mg of Mn in 40 ml of water, in the same manner as above described beginning with "add 10 ml of HNO_3 . . ."

Copper, Zinc: Dissolve 1.0 g of sample in 20 ml of water, heat the solution to boiling and, in small portions, add with stirring 2 to 3 ml of HNO_3. Continue boiling gently until nitrous fumes are no longer evolved. Cool, and dilute to 30 ml. Using 6.0 ml of the solution, make the test as described under Copper and Zinc—Estimation of Small Amounts in Iron Salts, page 565. The pink color of the dithizone solution is not deeper than the color of the controls made with 0.01 mg of Cu and/or 0.01 mg of Zn.

FERROUS CHLORIDE

$FeCl_2 \cdot 4H_2O$; mol. wt. 198.82; anhydrous—63.76%; H_2O—36.24%; Fe—28.08%; Cl—35.68%.

Pale green crystals; deliquescent. Oxidizes in the air to a basic ferric chloride. Soluble in 1 part of water containing some HCl; soluble in alcohol. *Keep in well-closed containers, protected from light.*

Standards

Assay............min 98% $FeCl_2 \cdot 4H_2O$	Arsenic (As)................max 5 ppm
Insoluble...................max 0.010%	Copper (Cu)................max 0.005%
Sulfate (SO_4)...............max 0.010%	Manganese (Mn).............max 0.01%
Alkalies, Earths (as sulfate)....max 0.10%	Zinc (Zn)..................max 0.005%

Assay: As for Ferrous Ammonium Sulfate, using 0.7 g of sample. One ml of 0.1 N $KMnO_4$ = 0.01988 g $FeCl_2 \cdot 4H_2O$, log 29842.

Insoluble: Dissolve 10 g in a mixture of 100 ml of H_2O and 2 ml of hydrochloric acid and heat on steam bath for 30 minutes. Filter any insoluble residue, wash it with H_2O containing 0.5% HCl and dry at 105°. The insoluble does not exceed 1.0 mg.

Solution S: Dissolve 5 g in 100 ml of H_2O, add 7 ml of HNO_3, boil to expel the oxides of nitrogen, and pour the hot solution, with stirring, into a mixture of 30 ml of H_2O and 20 ml of NH_4OH. Filter and wash with hot H_2O to 150 ml.

Sulfate: Evaporate 60 ml of *Solution S* with 0.5 g of anhydrous sodium carbonate to dryness and ignite gently to expel the ammonium salts. Add to the cooled residue 2 ml of HCl and evaporate to dryness on the steam bath. Take up the residue with 10 ml of H_2O, filter, if necessary, and add 1 ml of 0.1 N HCl and 2 ml of $BaCl_2$. Any resulting turbidity is not greater than that of a control made as follows: Evaporate 6 ml of NH_4OH to expel ammonia. Add 0.2 mg of SO_4, 0.5 g of anhydrous sodium carbonate and 2 ml of HCl and evaporate to dryness on the steam bath. Take up with 10 ml of H_2O and add 1 ml of 0.1 N HCl and 2 ml of $BaCl_2$.

Alkalies, Earths, etc.: Evaporate 60 ml of *Solution S* with 0.5 ml of H_2SO_4 and ignite. Not more than 2.0 mg remains.

Arsenic: Dissolve 1 g in 5 ml of 10% HCl, add 10 ml of stannous chloride solution, and allow to stand for 1 hour. Any color is not noticeably darker than that of a solution of 0.005 mg of As with the same quantities of 10% HCl and the stannous chloride solution, prepared as the sample solution.

Copper, Zinc: Dissolve 1.0 g of sample in 20 ml of water, heat the solution to boiling, and in small portions add with stirring 2 to 3 ml of HNO_3. Continue boiling gently until nitrous fumes are no longer evolved. Cool, and dilute to 30 ml. Using 6.0 ml of the solution make the test as described under Copper and Zinc— Estimation of Small Amounts in Iron Salts, page 565. The pink color of the dithizone solutions is not deeper than the color of the controls made with 0.01 mg of Cu and/or 0.01 mg of Zn.

Manganese: Dissolve 1.0 g in 5 ml of water, add 3 ml of H_2SO_4 and heat to strong sulfuric fumes. Cool, and *cautiously* add water to 100 ml. Dilute 20.0 ml of the solution to 35 ml, add 5 ml each of H_2SO_4, H_3PO_4 and HNO_3, and boil for 5 minutes. Cool, add 0.25 g of potassium periodate and again boil for 5 minutes. Any pink color produced is not darker than that of a control made by treating a solution of 0.02 mg of Mn in 35 ml of water in the same manner as above described, beginning with "add 5 ml each. . . ."

FERROUS SULFATE

$FeSO_4 \cdot 7H_2O$; mol. wt. 278.03; anhydrous—54.64%; H_2O—45.36%; Fe—20.09%; SO_4—34.55%.

Pale bluish-green crystals; efflorescent: oxidizes in the air. Soluble in 2 parts of water; insoluble in ethanol. *Keep in well-closed containers, protected from light.*

Standards

Assay . . . . 99.0–101.0% $FeSO_4 \cdot 7H_2O$	Arsenic (As) . . . . max 10 ppm	
Insoluble . . . . max 0.01%	Ferric Iron (Fe) . . . . max 0.050%	
Chloride (Cl) . . . . max 0.001%	Copper (Cu) . . . . max 0.005%	
Phosphate (PO_4) . . . . max 0.002%	Manganese (Mn) . . . . max 0.030%	
Alkalies, Earths (as sulfate) . . . . max 0.05%	Zinc (Zn) . . . . max 0.005%	

Assay: Weigh accurately about 1.0 g, dissolve in a mixture of 100 ml of freshly boiled and cooled water and 3 ml of H_2SO_4, and titrate with 0.1 N potassium permanganate. One ml of 0.1 N permanganate = 0.02780 g $FeSO_4 \cdot 7H_2O$, log 44404.

Insoluble: Dissolve 10 g in a mixture of 100 ml water and 2 ml of H_2SO_4. If an insoluble residue remains, filter, wash with water and dry at 105°. Its weight does not exceed 1.0 mg.

Chloride: To a solution of 2 g in 25 ml of water add, slowly, 4 ml of HNO_3, and after the evolution of the nitrogen oxides has ceased, filter, if necessary, and divide into two equal portions. To one portion add 0.5 ml of $AgNO_5$; to the other portion add an equal volume of water. The two portions are equally clear after 1 minute.

Phosphate: Dissolve 10 g in 75 ml of H_2O, add 15 ml of HNO_3 and boil gently until nitrous fumes are no longer evolved. Cool, nearly neutralize the solution with NH_4OH, add 15 ml of HNO_3 and 10 ml of NH_4OH, then add 40 ml of ammonium molybdate-nitric acid solution. Shake at about 40° for 5 minutes and allow to stand for 1 hour. If yellow precipitate is present, filter, and wash it with 5% potassium nitrate solution until the filtrate is neutral to litmus paper. Transfer the filter with the precipitate into a flask, add 5 ml of H_2O and 10 ml of 0.02 N NaOH and agitate until the yellow precipitate has dissolved. Add 3 drops of phenolphthalein, and titrate the excess of NaOH. One ml of 0.02 N NaOH = 0.08 mg of PO_4. Not more than 2.5 ml of the NaOH is consumed.

Alkalies, Earths, etc.: Dissolve 5 g in 70 ml of H_2O, add 7 ml of HNO_3 and boil to expel nitrous fumes. Pour the hot solution, while stirring, into a mixture of 50 ml of H_2O and 20 ml of NH_4OH, filter, and wash with hot water to 150 ml. Evaporate 60 ml of the filtrate and ignite. Not more than 1.0 mg of residue remains.

Arsenic: Dissolve 1 g in 5 ml of 10% HCl, add 10 ml of stannous chloride solution. Allow to stand for 1 hour. Any color is not noticeably darker than that of a solution of the same volumes of 10% HCl, 0.01 mg of As and stannous chloride solution, prepared as the sample solution.

Ferric iron: Dissolve 1 g of ammonium sulfate in 80 ml of oxygen-free water containing 2 ml of H_2SO_4, then dissolve in this solution 1 g of the sample, and dilute to 100 ml. To 5 ml of this solution add 0.05 mg of Fe, 0.5 ml of H_2SO_4 and dilute with oxygen-free water to 50 ml (A). To 15 ml of the solution add 0.5 ml of H_2SO_4 and dilute with oxygen-free water to 50 ml (B). Then to each add 3 ml of ammonium thiocyanate. B has no darker red color than A.

Manganese: Dissolve 1 g in 10 ml of H_2O and 2 ml of H_2SO_4, and dilute to 100 ml. Dilute 5 ml of the solution to 35 ml, add 10 ml of HNO_3, 5 ml of H_2SO_4 and 5 ml of phosphoric acid, then boil for 5 minutes. Cool, add 0.25 g of potassium periodate and again boil for 5 minutes. Any pink color produced is not darker than that of a control made by treating a solution of 0.03 mg of Mn in 35 ml of H_2O in the same manner as above described, beginning with "add 10 ml of HNO_3. . . ."

Copper, Zinc: Dissolve 1.0 g of sample in 20 ml of water, heat the solution to boiling and, in small portions, add with stirring 2–3 ml of HNO_3. Continue boiling gently until nitrous fumes are no longer evolved. Cool, and dilute to 30 ml. Using 6.0 ml of the solution, make the test as described under Copper and Zinc—Estimation of Small Amounts in Iron Salts, page 565. The pink color of the dithizone solutions is not deeper than the color of the controls made with 0.01 mg and/or 0.01 mg of Zn.

FERROUS SULFIDE

FeS; mol. wt. 87.92.

Dark brown lumps, granules or cylindrical sticks. Insoluble in water; soluble in acids, liberating hydrogen sulfide.

Assay: Powder the sample and weigh accurately 0.2 g. Transfer it to a distilling flask containing 2 g of sodium bicarbonate and connect with a dropping funnel and condenser, the end of which dips into a solution of 1 g of cadmium acetate in 50 ml of H_2O, and to which 20 ml of NH_4OH has been added. Add through the dropping funnel 20 ml of HCl, previously diluted with 30 ml of H_2O, and distill until about 35 ml has distilled over. Filter the yellow precipitate of cadmium sulfide and wash it with H_2O until the washings are no longer alkaline. Place the filter and precipitate in a glass-stoppered flask, and add 50 ml of 0.1 N iodine. Then add 10 ml of HCl, stopper and shake occasionally during 30 minutes. Add 50 ml of H_2O and titrate the excess of iodine with 0.1 N sodium thiosulfate, adding starch toward the end. One ml of 0.1 N iodine = 0.004395 g FeS, log 64296.

FLUORESCEIN SODIUM

Soluble Fluorescein; Uranine

$C_{20}H_{10}O_5Na_2$; mol. wt. 376.27; fluorescein—88.26%.

Orange-red, hygroscopic powder. Freely soluble in water; sparingly in alcohol. In aqueous solution it exhibits a strong green fluorescence, even when highly diluted.

In addition to its use for the detection of underground water, etc., it is a useful reagent for the detection of small quantities of bromine, applicable in the presence of large amounts of chloride.[1,2,3] It is capable of detecting 0.010 mg of free bromine in 1 ml of solution.

Standards

Sensitiveness.................to pass test	Water.......................max 7.0%
Acriflavine...................to pass test	*Assay*

Sensitiveness: (a) Dissolve 20 mg in 100 ml of water.

(b) Dissolve 100 mg of potassium bromide in 100 ml water (1 ml = 0.67 mg Br).

(c) *Buffer solution:* Dissolve 1.4 g of sodium acetate crystals in 5 ml of water, add 1 ml of 1 N acetic acid and dilute with water to 10 ml.

(d) Dissolve 0.5 g of sodium thiosulfate in 100 ml of approximately 1 N NaOH.

To 5 ml of water add 0.2 ml each of (a) and (b), then add 1 ml of (c) and follow with 0.5 ml of sodium hypochlorite solution (4% to 5% active chlorine) (see Note), then add 1 ml of (d). A distinct pink color is produced.

Add 0.05 ml of (a) to 100 ml of CO_2-free water and follow with 0.05 ml of 0.1 N NaOH. A bright yellow-green fluorescence is produced.

Note: If sodium hypochlorite solution is not available, 0.3 ml of a 2% solution of chloramine-T may be used, and after the addition of the chloramine-T solution the mixture should be shaken for 2–3 minutes or until the solution is decolorized.

Acriflavine: Dissolve 10 mg in 5 ml of water and add a few drops of a 10% aqueous solution of sodium salicylate. No precipitate is produced.

Water: Dried to constant weight at 120°, the loss corresponds to not more than 7%.

Assay: Dry about 1 g of sample at 120° to constant weight; then weigh accurately about 0.5 g of the dried sample and dissolve it in 20 ml of water in a separator. Add 5 ml of 10% HCl and extract the precipitated fluorescein with five 20-ml portions of a mixture of equal volume of neutral isobutanol and chloroform. Wash the combined extract with 10 ml of water, re-extract the water washing with 5 ml of isobutanol-chloroform mixture and add it to the main extract. Evaporate the isobutanol-chloroform solution to dryness on the steam bath with the aid of a current of air, dissolve the residue in 10 ml of alcohol, re-evaporate to dryness and dry at 110° for 1 hour.   The weight of the fluorescein so obtained multiplied by $1.132 = C_{20}H_{10}O_5Na_2$.

1 Baines, H., *J. Soc. Chem. Ind.* **47**, T-11 (1928).
2 Tenny, H. M., and Long, H. J. *J. Chem. Educ.* **13**, 82 (1936).
3 Hardwick, P. J. *Analys*, **67**, 223 (1942).

FORMALDEHYDE

Formalin; Formaldehyde Solution

HCHO; mol. wt. 30.03.

Colorless, clear liquid; pungent odor.   Miscible with water or alcohol.   Sp. gr. about 1.08.   Contains 10% to 15% methanol to prevent polymerization.   On long standing, especially in the cold, it becomes cloudy from the separation of para-formaldehyde.   *Keep in well-stoppered bottles, protected from light, in a moderately warm place.*

Standards

Assay.................min 36% HCHO		Sulfate (SO₄)...............max 0.002%	
Ignition residue.............max 0.005%		Heavy metals (as Pb).......max 0.0005%	
Acid (as formic acid).........max 0.030%		Iron (Fe).................max 0.0005%	
Chloride (Cl)...............max 0.0005%			

Assay: Weigh accurately a glass-stoppered flask containing 10 ml of H_2O, add 3 ml of the formaldehyde and reweigh.   Add this solution completely to 50 ml of 1 N NaOH and follow slowly with 50 ml of 3% hydrogen peroxide neutralized to bromothymol blue.   Cover with a small funnel and heat on the steam bath for 15 minutes, shaking occasionally.   Cool, rinse the funnel into the flask, then add 0.2 ml of bromothymol blue and titrate the excess of NaOH with 1 N H_2SO_4 to a bluish-green end point.   Run simultaneously a blank test with the same quantities of the reagents and in the same manner, and deduct the volume of NaOH consumed by it from that used up by the sample.   One ml of 1 N NaOH = 0.03003 g HCHO, log 47756.

Ignition residue: Evaporate 20 ml on the steam bath, add 1 ml of H_2SO_4 and ignite at first gently, then more strongly to constant weight.   Any residue remaining does not exceed 1.0 mg.

Acid: Dilute 10 ml with 10 ml of H_2O and titrate with 0.1 N NaOH, using bromothymol blue as indicator.   Not more than 0.75 ml of the NaOH is required to produce a pink color.   One ml of 0.1 N NaOH = 0.004603 g of formic acid.

Chloride: Dilute 2 ml with 10 ml of water and add 1 ml of HNO_3 and 1 ml of $AgNO_3$ solution.   Any resulting turbidity is not greater than that produced by treating 0.01 mg of Cl as the sample.

Sulfate: Dilute 5 ml with water to 15 ml.   Add 2 ml of 1 N HCl and 2 ml of $BaCl_2$ solution.   Any turbidity resulting after 10 minutes is not greater than that produced by treating 0.1 mg of SO_4 as the sample.

Solution R: To the *Ignition residue* add 2 ml of HCl, 2 ml of H_2O and 1 ml of HNO_3, and evaporate to dryness on the steam bath.   Take up the residue with 1 ml of 1 N HCl and 10 ml of hot water and dilute to 100 ml.

Heavy metals: Dilute 20-ml of *Solution R* to 40 ml and add 10 ml of H_2S. Any color produced is not darker than that of a control made with 0.02 mg Pb, 0.5 ml of 1 N HCl and 10 ml of H_2S in the same volume as used with the sample.

Iron: To 10 ml of *Solution R* add 2 ml of HCl and dilute to 40 ml.   Add about 30 mg of ammonium persulfate and 3 ml of ammonium thiocyanate.   Any resulting red color is not darker than that of a control made with 0.01 mg of Fe, 2 ml of HCl and the same quantities of the other reagents and in the same volume as with the sample.

FORMAMIDE

$H \cdot CO \cdot NH_2$; mol. wt. 45.04; N—31.10%; formic acid = 102.2%.

Clear, colorless, oily liquid with slight ammonia-like odor.   Miscible with water or alcohol but very slightly soluble in benzene, chloroform or ether.   It is hygroscopic and in presence of moisture it hydrolyzes into NH_3 and formic acid.   At ordinary atmospheric pressure it boils with decomposition at about 190°, but at 20 mm pressure it distills at about 110° without decomposition.   Solidifies at about +2.5°.   *Keep tightly closed.*

Standards

Specific gravity 25°/25°........1.132–1.134	Ammonia, Amines, etc.........to pass test
Freezing temperature......not below +2°	Evaporation residue...........max 0.1%
Miscibility with H_2O..........to pass test	Water.......................max 0.3%

Specific gravity: Determine with a pycnometer at 25°/25°.

Freezing temperature: Determine as described on page 581.

Miscibility: Dilutions of formamide with 3 times its volume of water and of alcohol are clear.

Ammonia, Amines, etc.: Weigh accurately about 0.7 ml of formamide, and transfer it completely with about 40 ml of water to a 200-ml refluxing flask.   Add 20 ml of 10% HCl and reflux for 2 hours.   Completely transfer the liquid, with the aid of 15–20 ml of water, to a tared beaker and evaporate to dryness on the steam bath.   Dissolve the residue in 25 ml of water, re-evaporate to dryness on the steam bath, and dry at 105° to constant weight.   The weight of the ammonium chloride so obtained multiplied by 0.842 represents formamide and corresponds to not less than 99.3% and to not more than 100.2% of the weight of the sample taken.

Evaporation residue: Evaporate 4.5 ml of sample to dryness on the steam bath, then dry at 120° for 3 hours.   The weight of the residue does not exceed 2.5 mg.

Water: The water content of formamide may be determined by the iodine (Fischer) method.

FORMIC ACID

HCO_2H; mol. wt. 46.03.

Colorless, clear liquid; pungent odor; *dangerously caustic.*   Miscible with water, alcohol, ether, glycerol.   Sp. gr. 1.2.

Standards

Assay................min 88% HCO_2H	Sulfate (SO_4)...............max 0.002%
Evaporation residue.........max 0.002%	Sulfite (SO_2).................to pass test
Miscibility with H_2O..........to pass test	Heavy metals (as Pb).......max 0.0005%
Acetic acid..............max about 0.3%	Iron (Fe).................max 0.0005%
Chloride (Cl)................max 0.001%	

Assay: Weigh accurately a flask containing 10 ml of water, quickly add 1 ml of the acid and reweigh.   Dilute with 50 ml of water and titrate with 1 N NaOH, using phenolphthalein indicator.   One ml of 1 N NaOH = 0.04603 g HCO_2H, log 66304.

Evaporation residue: Evaporate 42 ml (50 g) to dryness on the steam bath and dry at 105° for 1 hour.   Not more than 1.0 mg of residue remains (*retain*).

Miscibility with water: Mix 5 ml of the acid with 15 ml of water.   No turbidity ensues in 1 hour.

Acetic acid: Dilute 1 ml with water to make 100 ml.   To 20 ml of the dilution add 2 g of yellow mercuric oxide, cover, heat on the steam bath for 20 minutes and filter.   The filtrate does not redden blue litmus paper in 30 seconds.

Chloride: Dilute 2 ml with 18 ml of water, and add 2 ml of nitric acid and 1 ml of silver nitrate.   Any turbidity produced is not greater than that in a blank to which 0.025 mg of Cl has been added.

Sulfate: To 4 ml add about 10 mg of sodium carbonate and evaporate to dryness on the steam bath.   Take up with 5 ml of H_2O, filter, if necessary, and dilute to 10 ml.   Add 1 ml of 0.1 N HCl and 2 ml of $BaCl_2$.   Any turbidity produced is not greater than that in a blank to which 0.1 mg of SO_4 has been added.

Sulfite: Dilute 10 ml with 10 ml of H_2O and add 0.05 ml of 0.1 N iodine.   A distinct yellow color is produced which persists after mixing.

Solution R: Take up the *Evaporation residue* with 2 ml of 1 N HCl and 20 ml of hot water and dilute to 100 ml.

Heavy metals: Dilute 20 ml of *Solution R* to 40 ml and add 10 ml of H_2S. Any color produced is not darker than that of a control made with 0.025 mg of Pb, 0.2 ml of 1 N HCl and 10 ml of H_2S in the same final volume as with the sample.

Iron: To 8 ml of *Solution R* add 2 ml of HCl and dilute to 50 ml.   Add about 50 mg of ammonium persulfate and 3 ml of ammonium thiocyanate, and mix. Any resulting red color is not darker than that of a blank to which 0.01 mg of Fe has been added.

FUCHSINE

Magenta

A mixture of the hydrochlorides of rosaniline and pararosaniline.   Greenish-bronze crystals or fragments.   Soluble in water, in alcohol or in amyl alcohol.

Standards

Suitability for reagent.........to pass test	Solubility...................to pass test
Ignition residue..............max 0.20%	Drying loss..................max 5.0%

Suitability for fuchsine-sulfurous acid solution: Dissolve 0.2 g in 120 ml of hot water.   Cool, add a solution of 2 g of sodium sulfite in 20 ml of water, then add 2 ml of HCl, dilute with water to 200 ml and allow to stand for 1 hour.   The solution may be only slightly yellow or brownish, but should not have any pink or violet color.

Ignition residue: Char well 0.5 g.   Allow to cool, add 0.5 ml of H_2SO_4 and ignite at first gently to expel the acid, then strongly (600°–800°) to constant weight. Any residue does not exceed 1.0 mg.

Solubility: One-tenth gram dissolves in 20 ml of water, forming a clear or practically clear solution.

Drying loss: Dry 1 g at 105° for 4 hours.   The loss in weight does not exceed 5.0%.

FURFURAL

—CHO; mol. wt. 96.08.

Clear liquid; colorless when freshly distilled, but rapidly turns yellow to brown. It has a characteristic odor.   Volatile in steam.   Soluble in 15 parts of water. Miscible with alcohol or ether.   Sp. gr. 1.16.

Standards

Boiling range..................159°–162°	Miscibility with benzene.......to pass test
Solubility in water............to pass test	

Boiling range: Distill 50 ml.   After the first 10 drops, less than 48 ml distill between 159° and 162°, correction being made for barometric pressure, page 581.

Solubility in water: A solution of 5 ml in 100 ml of water is clear.

Miscibility with benzene: On mixing 5 ml of the sample with 20 ml of benzene a clear solution results.

α-FURILDIOXIME

; $C_{10}H_8N_2O_4$; mol. wt. 220.18.

White to slightly yellow, needle crystals.   Almost insoluble in water; freely soluble in alcohol or ether; slightly soluble in benzene or in petroleum ether.

As a reagent in alcohol solution it is extremely sensitive to nickel—10 to 15 times more so than dimethylglyoxime, and will detect 0.2 microgram of the metal in

1 ml of solution (1 in 5,000,000). The nickel complex with furildioxime—$C_{20}H_{14}N_4O_6Ni$—contains 11.0% Ni.

Standards

Melting range.................166°–169°	Sensitiveness................to pass test
Solubility in alcohol..........to pass test	Ignition residue..............max 0.2%

Solubility in alcohol: 0.25 g dissolves in 25 ml of alcohol forming a clear solution. Let the solution stand undisturbed for 1 hour; no insoluble matter separates.

Sensitiveness: Dilute 1.0 ml of standard nickel solution to 200 ml. Add 1.0 ml of this dilution (0.005 mg Ni) to 10 ml of water, make alkaline with 2 drops of NH_4OH, then add 0.5 ml of the solution of the sample prepared in the test for *Solubility in alcohol*. A distinct red turbidity is produced.

Ignition residue: To 0.5 g add 0.5 ml of H_2SO_4 and heat moderately to evaporate the H_2SO_4, then ignite strongly to constant weight. Any residue does not exceed 1.0 mg.

GALACTOSE

$$OH \cdot H_2C \cdot C \overset{H}{\underset{|}{\text{—}}} C \overset{OH}{\underset{H}{\text{—}}} C \overset{OH}{\underset{H}{\text{—}}} C \overset{H}{\underset{OH}{\text{—}}} C \cdot OH; \text{ mol. wt. } 180.16.$$

White crystals, granules or powder. Soluble in 2 parts of water; slightly soluble in alcohol.

Standards

Specific rotation..........+79.0° to 80.0°	Chloride (Cl)................max 0.003%
Insoluble....................max 0.010%	Sulfate (SO_4)................max 0.005%
Ignition residue..............max 0.10%	Heavy metals (as Cu)........max 0.001%

Specific rotation: Prepare an aqueous solution containing the equivalent of 5 g of the sample, previously dried to constant weight over H_2SO_4, in 50 ml, and allow to stand overnight. Then determine the rotation of this solution at 25° using a 200-mm tube. The observed rotation in degrees multiplied by 5 = $[\alpha]_D^{25}$.

Insoluble: Dissolve 10 g in 100 ml of H_2O and heat on the steam bath for 30 minutes. If an insoluble residue remains, filter, wash it with H_2O and dry at 105°. The weight of the insoluble residue is not more than 1.0 mg.

Ignition residue: Char well 2.0 g, cool, add 0.5 ml of H_2SO_4, evaporate the acid and ignite to constant weight. Any remaining residue does not exceed 1.0 mg.

Chloride: Dissolve 0.5 g in 20 ml of H_2O, add 1 ml of HNO_3 and 1 ml of $AgNO_3$. If a turbidity is produced, it is not greater than that in a blank to which 0.015 mg of Cl has been added.

Sulfate: Dissolve 2 g in 15 ml of H_2O, add 1 ml of 0.1 N HCl and 2 ml of $BaCl_2$. Any turbidity produced is not greater than that in a blank to which 0.1 mg of SO_4 has been added.

Heavy metals: Dissolve 2 g in 40 ml of H_2O and add 0.5 ml of 1 N HCl and 10 ml of H_2S. Any darkening produced is not more than that in a blank to which 0.02 mg of Cu has been added.

GALLIC ACID

; mol. wt. 188.13.

White or pale fawn-colored crystals or a powder. Soluble in 85 parts of water, 6 parts of alcohol, 2 parts of boiling water; slightly soluble in ether.

Standards

Solubility	to pass test	Sulfate (SO_4)	max 0.010%
Ignition residue	max 0.05%	Drying loss	7% to 10%

Solubility: Two grams dissolve completely in 40 ml of hot water.

Ignition residue: Char well 2.0 g, cool, add 0.5 ml of H_2SO_4, evaporate the acid and ignite to constant weight. Any remaining residue does not exceed 1.0 mg.

Sulfate: Dissolve 2 g in 40 ml of hot water, cool on ice with stirring and filter. To 20 ml of the filtrate add 1 ml of 0.1 N HCl and 2 ml $BaCl_2$, and allow to stand for 15 minutes. Any turbidity produced is not greater than that in a blank to which 0.1 mg of SO_4 has been added.

Drying loss: Dry 1 g to constant weight at 105°C. The loss in weight corresponds to from 7% to 10.0%.

GLASS WOOL

Fine glass filaments

Standards

Acid-soluble substances	max 0.5%	Heavy metals (Cu, Pb, etc.)....to pass test

Acid-soluble substances: Boil 1 g for 30 minutes with 50 ml of 10% HCl and filter. Evaporate the filtrate and dry at 105°. The residue does not exceed 5 mg.

Heavy metals: Boil 2 g for 5 minutes with 50 ml of 10% HNO_3, filter and wash with H_2O to 50 ml. Evaporate 25 ml of the filtrate to dryness on the steam bath, moisten the residue with 2 drops of HCl and take up in 20 ml of hot H_2O. Cool and add 10 ml of H_2S. No darkening is produced.

L-GLUTAMIC ACID

HO·OC·CH(NH$_2$)CH$_2$·CH$_2$·CO·OH; mol. wt. 147.13; N—9.52%.

Colorless or white crystals.   Soluble in about 12 parts water, in 1500 of alcohol, in 40 of dioxans.   Insoluble in acetone, chloroform, ether or in cold glacial acetic acid.   With HCl it forms a crystalline hydrochloride.   The pH of its monosodium salt is 7.

Standards

Nitrogen (N) content.........9.5%±0.2%	Phosphate (PO$_4$)............max 0.002%
Specific rotation in HCl.....+31.5°±0.70	Sulfate (SO$_4$)...............max 0.010%
Solubility....................to pass test	Ammonia (NH$_3$).............max 0.010%
Drying loss..................max 0.20%	Heavy metals (as Pb)........max 0.002%
Ignition residue.............max 0.050%	Iron (Fe)...................max 0.003%
Chloride (Cl)...............max 0.020%	

Nitrogen: Determine by the Kjeldahl method, using about 0.4 g of the dried sample accurately weighed.

Specific rotation; Drying loss: Weigh a suitable quantity (1.5–2 g) and dry at 105° for 2 hours.   Any loss in weight corresponds to not more than 0.2%.   Dissolve 1 g of the dried sample, accurately weighed, in 20% HCl to make 25.0 ml and observe the rotation of the solution in a 200-mm tube at 25° ± 2° and calculate the specific rotation (page 582).

Solubility: A solution of 1.0 g in 20 ml of H$_2$O is clear, complete and colorless.

Chloride: Dissolve 0.5 g in 50 ml of water.   To 10 ml of the solution add 1 ml of HNO$_3$ and 1 ml of AgNO$_3$ solution.   Any resulting turbidity is not greater than that of a control made with 0.02 mg of Cl.

Sulfate: To a solution of 1.0 g in 8 ml of warm water and 2 ml of 1 N HCl add 2 ml of BaCl$_2$.   Any turbidity ensuing in 15 minutes is not greater than that in a control made with 0.1 mg of SO$_4$ and 1.0 ml of 1 N HCl.

Ignition residue, Phosphate, Ammonia, Heavy metals, Iron: Test for these as described under Leucine.   The results should be as there stated.

GLYCEROL

Glycerin

CH$_2$OH·CHOH·CH$_2$OH; mol. wt. 92.10.

Clear, colorless, viscous liquid; almost odorless.   Boils at 290° with decomposition, but is distillable in vacuum.   Miscible with water or alcohol; insoluble in ether, chloroform, carbon disulfide or benzene.

Standards

Assay..............min 95% C$_3$H$_5$(OH)	Ammonia (NH$_3$)............max 0.0005%
Color........................to pass test	Arsenic (As).................max 1 ppm
Ignition residue.............max 0.005%	Heavy metals (as Pb).......max 0.0002%
Reaction.......................neutral	Fatty acid esters (as
Chloride (Cl)...............max 0.0005%	glyceryl butyrate).........max 0.05%
Chlorinated compounds	Silver reducing substances..........none
(as Cl)...................max 0.001%	Substances darkened by
Sulfate (SO$_4$)................max 0.001%	H$_2$SO$_4$....................to pass test

Assay: Determine the specific gravity at 25°/25° with a pycnometer.   It should be not less than 1.249.

Color: The color of glycerol when viewed downwards against a white surface in a 50-ml Nessler tube should not be darker than the color of a standard made by diluting 0.3 ml of ferric chloride color solution to 50 ml in a Nessler tube of the same diameter as that containing the glycerol.

Note: The ferric chloride color solution is made by dissolving 45.2 g of reagent ferric chloride in sufficient of a mixture of 975 volumes of H_4O and 25 volumes of HCl to make 1 liter.

Ignition residue: Heat 20 g in an open, shallow dish in a place free from drafts, then ignite the vapors and allow to burn without further application of heat.   Not more than a thin film of carbonaceous matter remains.   Finally ignite at low red heat.   The residue does not exceed 1.0 mg.

Reaction; Chloride: Dilute 4 ml with 25 ml H_2O; the dilution is neutral to litmus paper.   Now add 1 ml of HNO_3 and 1 ml of $AgNO_3$.   If a turbidity is produced, it is not greater than that in a blank with 0.025 mg of Cl added.

Chlorinated compounds: Dilute 10 ml of the glycerol to 25 ml.   Transfer 10 ml of the dilution to a small, round-bottom flask connected with a reflux condenser, add 20 ml of 10% NaOH and reflux gently for 1 hour.   Cool, cautiously add 5 ml of HNO_3 and dilute to 50 ml.   To 20 ml of the dilution add 1 ml of $AgNO_3$. Any turbidity produced is not greater than that in a control made with 4 ml of the glycerol dilution, 0.02 mg of Cl, 8 ml of the 10% NaOH and 2 ml of HNO_3, and in the same volume as with the sample.

Sulfate: Dilute 4 ml with 20 ml of H_2O, add 1 ml of 0.1 N HCl and 2 ml of $BaCl_2$.   No turbidity is produced in 20 minutes.

Ammonia: Dilute 4 ml with 40 ml of H_2O, and add 5 ml of 10% NaOH and 1 ml of Nessler solution.   The color produced in 1 minute is not darker than that of a blank to which 0.03 mg of NH_3 has been added.

Arsenic: Heat 2.5 ml with 15 ml of H_2SO_4 in a Kjeldahl flask and add, in small portions, 5 ml of perchloric acid.   Continue heating over a small flame until the liquid is colorless and determine the arsenic by the method on page 563.   The stain is not greater than that obtained by treating 0.003 mg of As with the same quantities of reagents and in the same manner as the sample.

Heavy metals: Dilute 8 ml with H_2O to 40 ml.   To 10 ml of the dilution add 0.015 mg of Pb and 1 ml of 1 N acetic and dilute to 40 ml (A).   To the remaining 30 ml add 1 ml of 1 N acetic acid and dilute to 40 ml (B).   Then to each add 10 ml of H_2S. B is not darker than A.

Fatty acid esters: Dilute 40 ml with 100 ml of freshly boiled H_2O in a flask, add 10 ml of 0.1 N NaOH and boil for 10 minutes.   Cool, add 3 drops phenolphthalein and titrate the excess of NaOH with 0.1 N HCl.   Run a blank with the same volumes of H_2O and 0.1 N NaOH and in the same manner as with the sample. The difference between the volumes of the acid is not greater than 3 ml.

Silver reducing substances: Mix 5 ml with 5 ml of 10% NH_3, heat to 60°, add 0.5 ml of $AgNO_3$ and let stand for 5 minutes in the dark.   No darkening is produced.

Substances darkened by sulfuric acid: Shake 5 ml with 5 ml of H_2SO_4 for 1 minute in a glass-stoppered cylinder of about 1 cm internal diameter, previously rinsed with H_2SO_4, and allow to stand for 10 minutes. The resulting color is not darker than pale yellow.

Water: The water content of glycerol may be determined by the iodine (Fischer) method.

GOLD CHLORIDE

Auric Chloride; Chloroauric Acid; Yellow Gold Chloride

$AuCl_3 \cdot HCl \cdot 4H_2O$; mol. wt. 411.90; Au—47.85%; Cl—34.42%; H_2O—17.49%.

Bright, golden-yellow crystals; rapidly deliquescent. It is affected by exposure to sunlight. Very soluble in water; soluble in ethanol and ether. *Keep in well-closed, glass-stoppered bottles or in sealed tubes, in a cool place.*

Standards

Assay....................min 48% Au	Nitrate (NO_3)...............max 0.02%
Solubility in ether............to pass test	Alkalies and other metals......max 0.20%

Assay: Weigh accurately about 0.5 g and dissolve it in 5 ml of H_2O in a tall beaker. Add a solution of 2 g of oxalic acid in 20 ml of hot H_2O (10 ml of sulfurous acid can be used instead of the oxalic acid) and cover the beaker immediately. After the reaction has ceased, rinse the cover and the sides of the beaker with H_2O and evaporate on the steam bath to 10 ml. Filter the precipitated gold, wash it with hot H_2O and ignite. Its weight corresponds to not less than 48% of the gold chloride taken.

$$2AuCl_3 + 3(COOH)_2 \rightarrow 2Au + 6HCl + 6CO_2$$

Solubility in ether: One-half gram dissolves completely and clearly in 15 ml of ether (retain).

Nitrate: Dissolve 0.1 g in 5 ml of H_2O, add 0.5 g of sodium carbonate, evaporate to dryness and ignite *gently.* Cool, take up the residue with 10 ml of H_2O and filter. To 5 ml of the filtrate add 25% H_2SO_4 dropwise until effervescence ceases, then add 0.1 ml of indigo carmine and 8 ml of H_2SO_4. The blue color persists for 30 seconds.

Alkalies and other metals: Evaporate the solution from *Solubility in ether* in a crucible to dryness on the steam bath. Add to the residue 5 ml of H_2O and follow carefully with a solution of 1 g of ammonium oxalate in 15 ml of warm H_2O. After the reaction has ceased, evaporate and ignite gently. Heat the residue with 5 ml of dilute HNO_3 (1 + 2) on the steam bath for 15 minutes, add 10 ml of hot H_2O and filter. Evaporate the filtrate and ignite gently. Not more than 1.0 mg of residue remains.

GOLD CHLORIDE "BROWN"

This form of gold chloride differs from the preceding in that it contains 1 ml less of H_2O, and hence it should assay not less than 49% Au. It conforms to the tests for *Solubility in Ether* and *Alkalies and other metals* given for the preceding (yellow).

HEXAMETHYLENETETRAMINE, *see* METHENAMINE

n-HEPTANE

C_7H_{16}; mol. wt. 100.20.

Clear, colorless liquid, free from fluorescence. Flammable. Sp. gr. about 0.70 (25°/25°). Insoluble in water; miscible with absolute alcohol, benzene, chloroform, ether.

Standards

Color........................to pass test	Acid (as acetic)...............to pass test
Boiling range...................95°–99°	max about 0.002%
Refractive index.............1.385 ± 0.001	Sulfuric acid test.............to pass test
Evaporation residue.........max 0.001%	Sulfur compounds
	(sulfidic as S).............max 0.002%

Color: The color of *n*-heptane is not darker than that of a solution of 2.0 mg of potassium dichromate in 1 liter of water.

Boiling range: Distill 100 ml. Not more than 1.0 ml distills below 94.5°, then all distills to not above 99° (dry point), correction being made for variation in barometric pressure from 760 mm.

Refractive index: Determine at 20°.

Evaporation residue: Evaporate 145 ml in a tared dish on the steam bath to dryness and dry at 105° for 1 hour. The weight of the residue, if any, does not exceed 1.0 mg.

Acid: Thoroughly shake 20 ml of sample with 10 ml of H_2O for 2 minutes and allow to separate. The aqueous layer does not turn blue litmus paper red in 15 seconds.

Sulfuric acid test: In a graduated, glass-stoppered cylinder gently mix for 3 minutes equal volumes of sample and of H_2SO_4. Neither layer is more colored than the original substance, and neither volume is changed.

Sulfur compounds: To 10 ml of the sample add 15 ml of absolute ethanol or methanol and 4 ml potassium plumbite solution, and gently boil the mixture under a reflux condenser for 20 minutes, agitating the contents of the flask several times during the refluxing, then set aside for 5 minutes. The aqueous (lower) layer is colorless.

The sulfur may be quantitatively determined by the method on page 579.

n-HEXANE

$CH_3(CH_2)_4CH_3$; mol. wt. 86.17.

Clear, colorless liquid, free from fluorescence. Volatile and highly flammable. Sp. gr. 0.670 (25°/25°). Insoluble in water; miscible with absolute alcohol, benzene, chloroform, and ether. Boils at 69°.

Standards

Color.......................to pass test	Acid.......................to pass test
Boiling range....................67°–71°	Sulfuric acid test.............to pass test
Refractive index.............1.374–1.377	Sulfur compounds............to pass test
Evaporation residue.........max 0.001%	

Color: The color of *n*-hexane is not darker than that of a solution of 2 mg of potassium dichromate in 1 liter of water.

Boiling range: Distill 100 ml from a small distilling flask connected with a relatively short but effective cooling condenser and a well-cooled receiver. Not more than 20 drops distill below 67° and not less than 96 ml distill between 67° and 71°.

Refractive index: Determine at 20°.

Evaporation residue: Evaporate 150 ml on the steam bath in a tared dish and dry at 105° for 30 minutes. The weight of the residue does not exceed 1.0 mg.

Acid: Thoroughly shake 10 ml with 5 ml of water for 2 minutes and allow to separate. The aqueous layer does not turn blue litmus paper red in 15 seconds.

Sulfuric acid test: In a graduated glass-stoppered cylinder gently mix equal volumes of the sample and of H_2SO_4 for 5 minutes. Neither layer is more colored than the original substances and neither volume is changed.

Sulfur compounds: To 10 ml of the sample add 15 ml of absolute ethanol or methanol and 4 ml potassium plumbite solution, and gently boil the mixture under a reflux condenser for 15 minutes, agitating the contents of the flask several times during the refluxing, then set aside for 5 minutes. The aqueous (lower) layer is colorless.

The sulfur may be quantitatively determined by the method on page 579.

L-HISTIDINE MONOHYDROCHLORIDE

    CH
   / \
  N   NH.HCl
  | /
  HC=CCH₂CH(NH₂)COOH·H₂O

$HC=CCH_2CH(NH_2)COOH \cdot H_2O$; mol. wt. 209.64; N—20.52%; HCl—17.4%; H_2O—8.6%.

Colorless or white crystals or white crystalline powder. Soluble in about 15 parts of water; sparingly soluble in alcohol.

Standards

Nitrogen, anhydrous basis....21.7%±0.25	Ignition residue.............max 0.05%
HCl content, anhydrous	Phosphate (PO₄)............max 0.002%
basis....................19.0%±0.25%	Sulfate (SO₄)...............max 0.010%
Specific rotation in 1 N HCl...+10.5±0.5°	Ammonium Salts (as NH₃)....max 0.010%
Solubility....................to pass test	Heavy metals (as Pb)........max 0.001%
Drying loss.................max 9.0%	Iron (Fe)..................max 0.002%

Nitrogen: Determine by the Kjeldahl method, using about 0.2 g of the dried sample, accurately weighed.

HCl Content: Using an accurately weighed quantity of about 0.5 g, determine the HCl by either of the methods for Assays of Chlorides and Thiocyanates, page 565, and calculate to the anhydrous basis.   One ml of 0.1 N AgNO$_3$ = 0.003646 g HCl, log 56182.

Specific rotation; Drying loss: Dry about 1 g of the sample, accurately weighed, at 130° for 3 hours: the loss in weight corresponds to not more than 9.0%. Dissolve 0.75 g of the dried sample in 1 N HCl to make exactly 25 ml.   Measure the rotation of the solution in a 200 mm tube at 25° ± 2° and calculate the specific rotation.

Solubility: A solution of 1.0 g in 20 ml of water is clear and colorless.

Ignition residue; Phosphate; Sulfate; Ammonium Salts; Heavy Metals; Iron: Test for these as described under Arginine Monohydrochloride, but using 20 ml of the solution (instead of 10 ml) in the test for Ammonium Salts.   The results should be as there stated.

HYDRAZINE SULFATE

(NH$_2$)$_2$H$_2$SO$_4$; mol. wt. 130.13; N—21.53%.

Colorless crystals, or a white crystalline powder.   Soluble in 40 parts of water; insoluble in alcohol.

Standards

Assay............min 99% (NH$_2$)$_2$H$_2$SO$_4$	Chloride (Cl)................max 0.003%
Solubility...................to pass test	Heavy metals (as Pb)........max 0.002%
Ignition residue............max 0.050%	Iron (Fe)...................max 0.001%

Assay: Weigh accurately 0.10 g and dissolve in 20 ml of H$_2$O.   Dissolve in the solution 1 g of sodium bicarbonate, add slowly 50 ml of 0.1 N iodine, then titrate the excess of iodine with 0.1 N sodium thiosulfate, using starch solution toward the end as indicator.   One ml of 0.1 N iodine = 0.003253 g (NH$_2$)$_2$·H$_2$SO$_4$, log 51228.

$$(NH_2)_2H_2SO_4 + 4I + 6NaHCO_3 \rightarrow 2N + 4NaI + Na_2SO_4 + 6CO_2 + 6H_2O$$

Solubility: One gram dissolves completely in 50 ml of warm water, and the solution is colorless.

Ignition residue: Char 2.0 g, cool, add 0.5 ml of H$_2$SO$_4$, ignite at first gently, then strongly to constant weight.   The residue, if any, does not exceed 1.0 mg (*retain*).

Chloride: Dissolve 0.7 g in 30 ml of warm water, then add 0.5 ml of nitric acid and 1 ml of silver nitrate.   Any turbidity is not greater than that in a blank with 0.02 mg Cl added.

Heavy metals: Dissolve 1 g in 40 ml of warm water, then add 1 ml of 1 N acetic acid and 10 ml of H$_2$S.   Any darkening produced is not more intense than that of a blank to which 0.02 mg of Pb has been added.

Iron: To the *Ignition residue* add 2 ml of HCl, 2 ml of H$_2$O and 0.5 ml of HNO$_3$, and slowly evaporate to dryness on the steam bath.   Take up the residue with 2 ml of HCl and dilute to 50 ml.   Add about 30 mg of ammonium thiocyanate.

Any red color produced is not darker than that of a control made with 0.02 mg of Fe, 2 ml of HCl and the same quantities of the reagents and in the same volume as with the sample.

HYDRIODIC ACID, 55%—Without Preservative

HI; mol. wt. 127.93; I—99.21%.

Nearly colorless when freshly made, but rapidly becomes yellow to brown due to liberation of iodine by air. Boils at about 127°. Miscible with water. Sp. gr. 1.7.

The acid is chiefly used for the determination of methoxyl groups. Its suitability for this purpose may be ascertained by running a blank with the same volume of hydriodic acid and in the same manner as the determination of methoxyl group according to the Zeisal method as detailed in the U.S.P. XV, the British Pharmacopœia 1958, etc. No precipitant or turbidity is produced in the silver nitrate solution which does not dissolve on heating with a few ml of diluted nitric acid.

This hydriodic acid dissolves, especially when hot, many "acid insoluble" inorganic substances, such as the alkaline earth sulfates, mercuric iodides, etc. *Keep in tightly closed, glass-stoppered bottles, protected from light.*

Standards

Assay....................54%–57% HI	Sulfate (SO_4)...............max 0.005%
Free iodine...................max 0.75%	Arsenic (As).................max 2 ppm
Ignition residue.............max 0.010%	Heavy metals (as Pb)........max 0.001%
Chloride and Bromide (as Cl)...max 0.05%	Iron (Fe)...................max 0.001%
Phosphorus (P)............max 0.0003%	

Assay; Free iodine: Weigh a glass-stoppered flask with 15 ml of H_2O, add 3 ml of the acid and reweigh. Dilute with 40 ml of H_2O and titrate with 0.1 N sodium thiosulfate to the disappearance of the yellow color. Not more than 0.60 ml of the thiosulfate should be required per g of the acid. Now add to the solution 3 drops of phenolphthalein and titrate with 1 N NaOH to a pink color. One ml of 1 N NaOH = 0.1279 g HI, log 10687.

Ignition residue: Evaporate 6 ml (10 g) to dryness and ignite gently. The residue weighs not more than 1.0 mg (retain residue).

Chloride and Bromide: Dilute 0.6 ml (1 g) of the acid to 50 ml. To 1.0 ml add 0.04 mg of Cl and dilute to 20 ml (*A*). Dilute 5 ml of the original dilution to 20 ml (*B*). Add to each 1 ml of ammonium hydroxide, then add slowly and with stirring 5 ml of 5% $AgNO_3$ solution. Heat to boiling and boil for 3 minutes while stirring well. Cool, filter, neutralize the filtrates with HNO_3 and add an excess of 1 ml of the acid. Any turbidity in *B* is not greater than in *A*.

Solution S: Evaporate 6.0 ml (10 g) of the acid with 2 ml of HNO_3 to dryness on the steam bath. Re-evaporate with several portions of water until all the iodine has been volatilized. Warm the residue with 2 ml of 1 N HCl and take up with 40 ml of hot water. Cool, dilute to 50 ml and mix well.

Phosphorus: To 10 ml of *Solution S* add 10 ml of H_2O and 2 ml of 25% H_2SO_4, 1 ml each of phosphate reagents **A** and **B** and heat at 60° for 10 minutes. Any blue color produced is not darker than that of a blank to which 0.02 mg of PO_4 has been added.

Sulfate: To 10 ml of *Solution S* add 1 ml of 0.1 N HCl and 2 ml of $BaCl_2$.   Any turbidity produced is not greater than that in a blank to which 0.1 mg of SO_4 has been added.

Arsenic: Dilute 0.6 ml (1 g) to 10 ml.   Add 2 ml of HNO_3 and evaporate on the steam bath to expel all the iodine, adding more water if necessary and re-evaporating.   Determine the arsenic in the residue by the method on page 563. Any stain produced is not greater than that produced by 0.002 mg of As.

Heavy metals: Dilute 10 ml of *Solution S* to 40 ml and add 10 ml of H_2S.   Any color produced is not darker than that of a control made with 0.02 mg of Pb, 0.5 ml of 1 N HCl, the same volume of H_2S and in the same final volumes as with the sample.

Iron: To 5 ml of *Solution S* add 2 ml of HCl and dilute to 50 ml, then add about 30 mg of ammonium persulfate and 3 ml of ammonium thiocyanate, and mix. Any resulting red color is not darker than that of a control made with 0.01 mg of Fe, 2 ml of HCl and the same quantities of the reagents and in the same final volume as with the sample.

HYDRIODIC ACID, 47%—With Preservative (H_3PO_2)

Colorless or slightly yellow.   Sp. gr. about 1.5.

This acid contains about 1.5% of hypophosphorous acid as preservative.   For use for methoxyl determination, the acid is usually redistilled to free it from the H_3PO_2.   To avoid danger of explosion (due to the reduction of the H_3PO_2 to phosphine and the possibility of its spontaneous ignition) *the acid should be redistilled only in an inert atmosphere*, preferably nitrogen.

Standards

Assay.....................min 47% HI	Heavy metals (as Pb)........max 0.001%
Chloride, Bromide (as Cl)......max 0.05%	Iron (Fe)...................max 0.001%
Sulfate (SO_4)...............max 0.005%	Preservative (H_3PO_2)..........max 1.5%
Arsenic (As)................max 3 ppm	

Assay: Weigh a 250-ml glass-stoppered flask with 25 ml of water.   Add 0.6–0.7 ml of the acid and reweigh.   Add 50.0 ml of 0.1 N $AgNO_3$, shake well; then add 5 ml of HNO_3 and heat on the steam bath until the precipitate is bright yellow. Cool, and titrate the excess of $AgNO_3$ with 0.1 N thiocyanate, using 1 ml of ferric ammonium sulfate as indicated.   One ml of 0.1 N $AgNO_3$ = 0.01279 g HI, log 10687.

Chloride, Bromide: Dilute 1.3 ml (2 g) of the acid to 100 ml.   To 1.0 ml of the dilution add 0.04 mg of Cl and dilute to 20 ml (A).   Dilute 5 ml of the original dilution to 20 ml (B).   Add to each 1 ml of ammonium hydroxide, then add slowly and with stirring 8 ml of 5% $AgNO_3$ solution.   Heat to boiling and boil gently for 3 minutes.   Cool, filter, neutralize the filtrate with HNO_3, and add an excess of 1 ml of HNO_3.   Any turbidity in B is not greater than in A.

Solution S: To 6.7 ml (10 g) add 3 ml of HNO_3 and evaporate to dryness on the steam bath. Re-evaporate, if necessary, with several portions of water until all iodine has volatilized. Warm the residue with 2 ml of 1 N HCl; take up with 40 ml of hot water, cool, and dilute with water to 50 ml.

Sulfate: To 10 ml of *Solution S* add 1 ml of 0.1 N HCl and 2 ml of $BaCl_2$. Any turbidity produced is not greater than that in a control made with 0.1 mg of SO_4.

Arsenic: Dilute 0.7 ml to 10 ml. Add 2 ml of HNO_3 and evaporate on the steam bath to expel the iodine. Determine the arsenic in the residue by the method described on page 563. Any stain produced is not greater than that produced by 0.003 mg of As.

Heavy metals: To 5 ml of *Solution S* add 0.02 mg of Pb and 1 ml of 1 N acetic acid and dilute to 40 ml (A). To 15 ml of *Solution A* add 1 ml of 1 N acetic acid and dilute to 40 ml (B); then to each add 10 ml of H_2S. B is not darker than A.

Iron: To 5 ml of *Solution S* add 2 ml of HCl and dilute to 50 ml. Add about 30 mg of ammonium persulfate and 3 ml of ammonium thiocyanate and mix. Any resulting red color is not darker than that of a control made with 0.01 mg of Fe and the same quantities of the reagents and in the same volume as with the sample.

Preservative: Weigh about 2 ml of the acid in a glass-stoppered weighing bottle and transfer to a beaker with about 20 ml of water. Add, in small portions 1.5 ml of 30% H_2O_2. Allow to stand for 15 minutes, and then evaporate on the steam bath until the solution is colorless. To the residue add 15 ml of water and 2 ml of HNO_3, then add ammonia until the solution is neutral or nearly neutral to litmus paper. Add 2 ml of 10% HNO_3, heat to about 50°, and add 40 ml of ammonium molybdate-nitric acid solution. Maintain the temperature at 40° to 50° for 30 minutes, stirring occasionally. Wash the yellow precipitate once or twice by decantation with 40 ml of water each time. Transfer the precipitate to a filter and wash 2 to 3 times with cold water, then with a 5% solution of potassium nitrate until the last washing is not acid to litmus paper. Transfer the filter with the precipitate to the precipitating vessel, add 40 ml of 0.5 N NaOH, stir until the precipitate has dissolved and titrate the excess of NaOH with 0.5 N H_2SO_4, using phenolphthalein as indicator. One ml of 0.5 N NaOH = 1.435 mg of H_3PO_2.

HYDROBROMIC ACID, 48%

HBr; mol. wt. 80.92.

Clear, colorless, or faintly yellow liquid. On prolonged exposure to air it develops a yellow color. Miscible with water or ethanol. Sp. gr of the 48% acid is about 1.5. *Keep protected from light.*

Standards

Color......................to pass test	Sulfate (SO_4)................max 0.002%	
Assay........................47%–49%	Sulfite (SO_2)................max 0.002%	
Organic substances...........to pass test	Arsenic (As)................max 0.5 ppm	
Evaporation residue.........max 0.003%	Heavy metals (as Pb).......max 0.0005%	
Chloride (Cl).................max 0.05%	Iron (Fe)..................max 0.0002%	
Phosphate (PO_4)............max 0.001%		

Color: The color of hydrobromic acid, when viewed horizontally in a test tube of approximately 2.5 cm diameter, should not be darker than a solution of 20 mg of potassium chromate per liter, and this color should be discharged by the addition of 10 mg of anhydrous sodium sulfite to 10 ml of the acid.

Assay: Weigh a glass-stoppered flask with 15 ml of H_2O, add about 4 ml of the sample and reweigh. Dilute with 30 ml of H_2O, add 2 drops of methyl orange and titrate with 1 N NaOH to a yellow color. One ml of 1 N NaOH = 0.08092 g HBr, log 90806.

Organic substances: Dilute 10 ml with 10 ml of water in a glass-stoppered cylinder, shake well and note odor. No foreign odor is noticeable.

Evaporation residue: Evaporate 20 ml on the steam bath and dry at 105° for 3 hours. The residue weighs not more than 1.0 mg (retain residue).

Chloride: Place 0.7 ml (1 g) in a 150-ml conical flask, add 50 ml of diluted nitric acid (1–3) and digest on the steam bath until the solution is colorless. Wash down the sides of the flask with 10 ml of water and digest for 15 minutes longer. Cool, transfer to a 100-ml volumetric flask, dilute to volume and mix. Dilute 5 ml of this solution to 25 ml (A). For a control, dilute a volume of standard chloride solution equivalent to 0.025 mg of Cl to 25 ml (B). Then to each add 1 ml of HNO_3 and 1 ml of $AgNO_3$. Any turbidity in A is not greater than that in B.

Phosphate: Evaporate 1.3 ml (2 g) of the acid with 5 ml of HNO_3 to dryness on the steam bath. Warm the residue with 2 ml of 25% H_2SO_4, add 20 ml of H_2O, 1 ml each of phosphate reagents **A** and **B** and heat at 60° for 10 minutes. Any blue color produced is not deeper than that produced by 0.02 mg of PO_4 treated in the same manner.

Sulfate: To 3.5 ml (5 g) add 20 mg of sodium carbonate and evaporate to dryness on the steam bath. Take up the residue with 10 ml of H_2O and 1 ml of 0.1 N HCl and add 2 ml of $BaCl_2$. Any turbidity produced is not greater than that in a blank to which 0.10 mg of SO_4 has been added.

Sulfite: Dilute 10 ml with 150 ml of oxygen-free water and add 0.1 ml of 0.1 N iodine and 2 ml of starch solution. A bluish color is produced.

Arsenic: Determine in 4 ml by the method on page 563. The stain is not more than that from 0.003 mg of As.

Solution R: To the *Evaporation residue* add 2 ml of 1 N HCl and 10 ml of hot water, digest for 2 minutes and dilute to 150 ml.

Heavy metals: Dilute 20 ml of *Solution R* to 40 ml and add 10 ml of H_2S. Any color produced is not darker than that in control made with 0.02 mg of Pb, 0.2 ml of 1 N HCl and 10 ml of H_2S in the same volume as with the sample.

Iron: To 25 ml of *Solution R* add 2 ml of HCl and dilute to 50 ml. Add 50 mg of ammonium persulfate and 3 ml of ammonium thiocyanate. Any red color produced is not darker than that of a blank to which 0.01 mg of Fe has been added.

HYDROCHLORIC ACID

HCl; mol. wt. 36.47.

Colorless, clear, fuming liquid, pungent odor. Sp. gr. 1.18–1.19 at 15°. Miscible with water or alcohol. *Keep in glass-stoppered bottles, in a cool place.*

Standards

Assay.................36%–38% HCl	Sulfite (as SO_2)............max 0.0002%
Evaporation residue.........max 0.001%	Arsenic (As)..............max 0.02 ppm
Ignition residue............max 0.0005%	Heavy metals (as Pb).......max 0.0001%
Free chlorine........max about 0.0001%	Iron (Fe).................max 0.0001%
Sulfate (SO_4)..............max 0.0001%	

Assay: Weigh a glass-stoppered flask with 25 ml of H_2O; then add quickly 3 ml of the sample and reweigh. Dilute with water to 50 ml, add 2 drops of methyl orange and titrate with 1 N NaOH to a yellow color. One ml of 1 N NaOH = 0.03646 g HCl, log 56182.

Evaporation residue: Evaporate 85 ml (100 g) of the acid to dryness in a platinum dish on the steam bath, and dry at 105° for 1 hour. The weight of the residue does not exceed 1.0 mg (retain).

Ignition residue: To the residue from the preceding test add 2 drops of H_2SO_4 and ignite at a cherry redness for 5 minutes. Not more than 0.5 mg of residue remains.

Free chlorine: Dilute 25 ml with 25 ml of freshly boiled H_2O, cool and add 2 drops of 2% potassium iodide (free from iodate) and 1 ml of carbon disulfide. No pink color is produced in the carbon disulfide in 30 seconds.

Sulfate: To 43 ml of the acid add 20 mg sodium carbonate and evaporate to dryness. Take up the residue with 5 ml of H_2O and 0.5 ml of 1 N HCl. Filter, wash with H_2O to 10 ml, add to the filtrate 1 ml of $BaCl_2$ and allow to stand for 10 minutes. Any turbidity produced is not greater than that in a blank to which 0.05 mg of SO_4 has been added.

Sulfite: To 100 ml of oxygen-free water add 1 ml of KI solution, 10 drops of starch solution and 0.05 ml of 0.1 N iodine; then add 40 ml of the sample previously diluted with 50 ml of water. The blue remains after mixing.

Arsenic: To 85 ml of the acid add 5 ml of HNO_3 and 3 ml of H_2SO_4, and evaporate in glass or porcelain to sulfuric fumes. Cool, cautiously add 10 ml of water, and re-evaporate to strong fumes. Cool, cautiously add 10 ml of water, and then test by the method described on page 563. Any stain produced is not greater than that from 0.002 mg of As.

Heavy metals: Slowly evaporate 17 ml (20 g) of the hydrochloric acid in glass or in porcelain to dryness on the steam bath. Take up the residue with 1 ml of 1 N acetic acid and 20 ml of hot H_2O, dilute to 40 ml and add 10 ml of H_2S. Any color produced is not darker than that of a control made with 0.02 mg of Pb, 1 ml of 1 N acetic acid and 10 ml of H_2S in the same final volume as with the sample.

Iron: Evaporate 8.5 ml (10 g) of the acid in porcelain or glass almost to dryness. Take up the residue with 2 ml of the acid and dilute to 50 ml. Add about 30 mg of ammonium persulfate and 3 ml of ammonium thiocyanate, and mix. Any red color produced is not darker than that of a control made with 0.01 mg of Fe, 2 ml of the sample and the same quantities of ammonium persulfate and thiocyanate as with the sample.

HYDROFLUORIC ACID

HF; mol. wt. 20.01.

Colorless or nearly colorless, fuming liquid.   It readily attacks and dissolves glass and other siliceous materials.   Sp. gr. about 1.15.   Miscible with water or alcohol.   *Keep in well-closed containers of paraffin, ceresin or other noncorrodible material.*

Standards

Assay.....................min 48% HF	Phosphate (PO$_4$)...........max 0.0002%
Fluosilicic acid...............max 0.10%	Sulfate (SO$_4$)................max 0.001%
Evaporation residue.........max 0.002%	Sulfite (SO$_2$)...............max 0.002%
Ignition residue..............max 0.001%	Heavy metals (as Pb).......max 0.0002%
Chloride (Cl)................max 0.001%	Iron (Fe).................max 0.0001%

Assay; Fluosilicic acid: Weigh a platinum weighing bottle with 5 to 7 ml of water; then add, quickly, about 2 ml of the acid and reweigh.   Place 10 ml of a saturated aqueous solution of potassium nitrate in a platinum dish, add a little less than the volume of 1 N NaOH (see Note) necessary to neutralize the quantity of the sample weighed, and add 3 drops of phenolphthalein indicator.   Cool the solution to 0° and slowly add to it the weighed sample of the acid, rinsing out the weighing bottle with a small quantity of cold water.   Finally titrate with the 1 N NaOH, while maintaining the temperature of the solution at near 15°–20°, until the pink color persists for 15 seconds.   Let A represent the ml of 1 N NaOH used.   Heat to boiling and titrate to a permanent pink color.   Let B represent the ml of additional NaOH used, and W the weight of the sample.

$$\% \text{ HF} = \frac{2.001(A - 0.5B)}{W}; \qquad \% \text{ H}_2\text{SiF}_6 = \frac{3.602B}{W}$$

$$\log 2.001 = 30125; \log 3.602 = 55654$$

Note: Either reasonably freshly prepared 1 N NaOH should be used or the alkali should have been kept in a plastic container; otherwise high results may be obtained for the H$_2$SiF$_6$ due to SiO$_2$ dissolved from the glass.

Evaporation residue: Evaporate 45 ml of the acid in a platinum dish to dryness on the steam bath *under the hood*, and dry at 105° for 1 hour.   The weight of the residue does not exceed 1.0 mg (retain).

Ignition residue: To the residue from the preceding test add 3 drops of H$_2$SO$_4$ and ignite at cherry redness for 5 minutes.   Not more than 0.5 mg of residue remains.

Chloride: Mix in a beaker 35 ml of H$_2$O, 2 ml of HNO$_3$ and 1 ml of AgNO$_3$, and add 2 ml of the sample.   Any turbidity produced in 1 minute is not more than that in a blank to which 0.02 mg of Cl is added.

Phosphate: To 9 ml in a platinum dish add 10 mg of sodium carbonate and evaporate to dryness on the steam bath.   Take up the residue with 2 ml of 25% H$_2$SO$_4$ and 20 ml of hot water, add to the solution 1 ml each of phosphate reagents **A** and **B** and heat at 60° for 10 minutes.   Any blue color produced is not darker than that in a blank to which 0.02 mg of PO$_4$ has been added.

Sulfate: Evaporate 9 ml with 10 mg of sodium carbonate to dryness in a platinum dish on the steam bath *under the hood*. Warm the residue with 0.5 ml of 1 N HCl and 5 ml of H_2O, filter, wash with H_2O to 10 ml and add to filtrate 1 ml of $BaCl_2$. Any turbidity produced is not more than that in a blank to which 0.1 mg of SO_4 has been added.

Sulfite: Mix 10 ml with 40 ml of oxygen-free H_2O and add 0.05 ml of 0.1 N iodine. The solution acquires a distinct yellowish color.

Heavy metals: Mix in a beaker 30 ml of H_2O with 10 ml of H_2S, add 5 ml of the sample, quickly neutralize to litmus paper with NH_4OH (about 6 ml) and add 1 ml of 1 N HCl. No brown color is produced.

Iron: Quickly measure 9 ml of the acid, transfer it at once to a platinum crucible containing about 10 mg of sodium carbonate and evaporate to dryness on the steam bath. Take up the residue with 2 ml of HCl and 10 ml of hot H_2O and transfer to a small separate funnel. Cool, add 15 ml of butanolic potassium thiocyanate, shake well and allow to separate. Any red color in the butanol layer is not darker than that in a blank to which 0.01 mg of Fe has been added.

HYDROFLUOSILICIC ACID

Fluosilic Acid; Hydrosilicofluoric Acid; Silicofluoric Acid

H_2SiF_6; mol. wt. 144.08; Si—19.47%; F—79.12%.

A solution of about 30% of hydrogen silicofluoride in water.

Colorless, clear liquid. Miscible with water. Sp. gr. about 1.3. On boiling it decomposes into silicon tetrafluoride and hydrogen fluoride, both of which volatilize. *Keep in ceresin bottles.*

Standards

Assay.....................30%–32%	Sulfate (SO_4)...............max 0.005%
Ignition residue..............max 0.10%	Heavy metals (as Pb)........max 0.002%
Chloride (Cl)................max 0.005%	Iron (Fe)...................max 0.001%

Assay: Weigh accurately about 3 g and dilute with 100 ml of cold water. Add 3 drops of phenolphthalein and titrate with 1 N NaOH to a pink color (*a*). Then heat to boiling and titrate to a permanent pink color (*b*). One ml of 1 N NaOH = 0.02401 g ($\frac{1}{6}$ mol) H_2SiF_6, log 38039.

$$(a)\ \ H_2SiF_6 + 2NaOH \rightarrow Na_2SiF_6 + 2H_2O$$
$$(b)\ \ Na_2SiF_6 + 4NaOH \rightarrow 6NaF + Si(OH)_4$$

The difference between twice the volume of the NaOH required for (*a*) and that required for (*b*) is not greater than ± 0.5 ml for each 25 ml consumed by (*a*).

Ignition residue: Evaporate 2.5 ml with about 2 ml of hydrofluoric acid and 3 drops of H_2SO_4 in a platinum dish and ignite. The weight of the residue does not exceed 3.0 mg.

Chloride: Dilute 1.5 ml with water to 100 ml. To 20 ml add 1 ml of nitric acid and 1 ml of silver nitrate. Any turbidity produced in 1 minute is not more than that in a blank to which 0.02 mg of Cl has been added.

Sulfate: Evaporate 3.5 ml in platinum with about 2 ml of hydrofluoric acid on the steam bath.   Take up the residue with 2 ml of 1 N hydrochloric acid, dilute to 20 ml and filter.   To 10 ml of the filtrate add 2 ml of $BaCl_2$.   Any turbidity produced is not greater than that in a blank with 0.1 mg of SO_4 added.

Heavy metals: Dilute 1 ml with 35 ml of water, neutralize with dilute ammonium hydroxide, add 1 ml of 1 N HCl and 10 ml of H_2S.   Any resulting brown color is not deeper than that of a control made with 0.025 mg of Pb, 1 ml of 1 N HCl and 10 ml of H_2S in the same volume as with the sample.

Iron: To the *Ignition residue* add 2 ml of HCl and 1 ml of H_2O and evaporate to dryness on the steam bath.   Take up the residue with 1 ml of HCl and 10 ml of hot H_2O, and dilute to 30 ml.   Transfer 20 ml to a small separatory funnel.   Add 2 ml of HCl and 15 ml of butanolic potassium thiocyanate, shake well, and allow to separate.   Any red color in the butanol layer is not darker than that in a control made with 0.02 mg of Fe.

HYDROGEN PEROXIDE, 30%

H_2O_2; mol. wt. 34.02; active O—47.03%.

Clear, colorless liquid, miscible with water.   Sp. gr. about 1.1.   Slowly loses H_2O_2 by decomposition into oxygen and water.

It should be kept in partly filled containers, preferably with a small vent in the stopper, and in a cool place.

Handle with caution as it attacks the skin!

Standards

Assay....................min 29% H_2O_2	Phosphate (PO_4)...........max 0.0003%
Evaporation residue.........max 0.005%	Sulfate (SO_4)...............max 0.0005%
Acid (as H_2SO_4).............max 0.003%	Heavy metals (as Pb).......max 0.0001%
Chloride (Cl)................max 0.001%	Iron (Fe)................max 0.00005%
Nitrogen compounds (as N)...max 0.005%	

Assay: Weigh accurately about 2 ml, taking precautions to prevent evaporation, and dilute to exactly 200 ml.   To 20 ml of the dilution add 20 ml of 10% H_2SO_4 and titrate with 0.1 N potassium permanganate to a permanent pink color. One ml of 0.1 N permanganate = 0.001701 g H_2O_2, log 23070.

$$5H_2O_2 + 2KMnO_4 + 3H_2SO_4 \rightarrow K_2SO_4 + 2MnSO_4 + 8H_2O + 5O_2$$

Evaporation residue: Evaporate 18 ml to dryness on the steam bath and dry at 105° to constant weight.   Not more than 1.0 mg of residue remains.

Acid: Dilute 9 ml with 90 ml of CO_2-free water, add 3 drops of methyl red and titrate with 0.02 N NaOH.   Not more than 0.3 ml of the NaOH is required to produce a yellow color, making correction for alkali consumed by a blank.

Chloride: Dilute 1 ml with 10 ml of H_2O, then add 1 ml of HNO_3 and 1 ml of $AgNO_3$.   Any resulting turbidity is not greater than that in a blank to which 0.01 mg of Cl has been added.

Nitrogen compounds: To 3.8 ml of the hydrogen peroxide add 0.1 ml of 1 N H_2SO_4 and evaporate on the steam bath to about 2 ml in a Kjeldahl flask. Add 6 ml of H_2SO_4 and 0.1 g of salicylic acid.   Allow to stand for 30 minutes.   Then add 0.05 g of sodium thiosulfate and 3 g of potassium sulfate and digest over a small flame for 2 hours or until colorless.   Cool, dilute with 40 ml of water, again cool, add 40 ml of 30% NaOH and distill 40 ml into 5 ml of water containing 2 drops of 1 N HCl.   Add to the distillate 2 ml of 10% NaOH and 2 ml of Nessler solution. The color produced is not darker than that produced by treating 0.013 mg of nitrogen (0.05 mg NH_4Cl) in the same manner as the sample.

Phosphate: Evaporate 6.5 ml to dryness on the steam bath and take up the residue with 2 ml of 25% H_2SO_4 and 20 ml of hot water.   Add to the solution 1 ml each of phosphate reagents **A** and **B** and heat at 60° for 10 minutes.   Any resulting blue color is not darker than that of a blank to which 0.02 mg of PO_4 has been added.

Sulfate: Evaporate 18 ml to dryness on the steam bath.   Take up the residue with 0.5 ml of 1 N HCl and 10 ml of hot water, and after cooling add 2 ml of $BaCl_2$. Any resulting turbidity is not greater than that in a blank to which 0.1 mg of SO_4 has been added.

Solution S: Evaporate 45 ml (50 g) to dryness on the steam bath.   Add 1 ml of HCl and 2 ml of H_2O and re-evaporate to dryness.   Take up the residue in 10 ml of hot water and dilute to 50 ml.

Heavy metals: To 20 ml of *Solution S*, add 1 ml of 1 N acetic acid and 10 ml of H_2S.   Any color produced is not darker than that in a blank to which 0.02 mg of Pb has been added.

Iron: To 20 ml of *Solution S* add 2 ml of HCl, dilute to 50 ml and add 3 ml of ammonium thiocyanate.   Any red color produced is not darker than that in a blank to which 0.01 mg of Fe has been added.

HYDROQUINONE

p-Dihydroxybenzene; Quinol

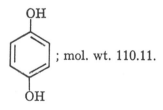 ; mol. wt. 110.11.

Colorless or white crystals.   Discolors in air and light.   Soluble in 15 parts of water; freely soluble in alcohol and in ether.   *Keep in well-closed containers, protected from light.*

Standards

Melting range	171°–173°	Resorcinol	no reaction
Solubility	to pass test	Sulfate (SO_4)	max 0.010%
Ignition residue	max 0.05%	Heavy metals (as Pb)	max 0.001%
Catechol	no reaction		

Solubility: A solution of 2 g in 50 ml of H_2O is clear and colorless, or nearly so.

Ignition residue: Char 2 g, cool, add 1 ml of H_2SO_4 and ignite to constant weight.   The residue does not exceed 1.0 mg.

Catechol: Dissolve 1 g in 20 ml of H_2O and add 2 ml of lead acetate.   No precipitate is produced.

Resorcinol: Dissolve 0.2 g in 10 ml of H_2O and add a clear solution of 1 g of basic lead acetate in 5 ml of H_2O.   The solution remains clear.

Sulfate: Dissolve 1 g in 20 ml of H_2O, add 1 ml of 0.1 N HCl and 2 ml of $BaCl_2$. Any turbidity produced is not greater than that in a blank to which 0.1 mg of SO_4 has been added.

Heavy metals: Dissolve 1 g in 20 ml of water and add 10 ml of H_2S.   The solution is no darker than a solution of 1 g of the sample in 30 ml of water.

HYDROXYLAMINE HYDROCHLORIDE

$NH_2OH \cdot HCl$; mol. wt. 69.50; N—20.17%; Cl—51.02%.

Colorless, hygroscopic crystals.   Soluble in 2 parts of water or in 15 parts of alcohol; soluble in glycerol.   Slowly decomposes when moist.   *Keep in well-closed containers.*

Standards

Assay............min 96% $NH_2OH \cdot HCl$	Sulfate (SO_4)...............max 0.005%
Free acid (as HCl).............max 0.6%	Ammonium salts.........max about 0.1%
Solubility in alcohol...........to pass test	Heavy metals (as Pb)........max 0.001%
Ignition residue..............max 0.05%	Iron (Fe)..................max 0.001%

Assay: Dry about 0.2 g over H_2SO_4 or other efficient desiccant for a few hours or overnight.   Weigh accurately about 0.12 g of the dried sample and dissolve it in a conical flask in 25 ml of oxygen-free water.   Add to the solution a solution of 5 g of ferric ammonium sulfate in a mixture of 15 ml of 10% H_2SO_4 and 20 ml of water and boil gently for 5 minutes.   Cool rapidly to room temperature, dilute with 150 ml of oxygen-free water, and at once titrate with 0.1 N $KMnO_4$.   One ml of the $KMnO_4$ = 0.003475 g of $NH_2OH \cdot HCl$, log 50495.

$$2H_2N \cdot OH \cdot HCl + 4FeNH_4(SO_4)_2 \rightarrow$$
$$4FeSO_4 + 4(NH_4)HSO_4 + 2HCl + H_2O + N_2O$$

Free acid: Dissolve 5 g in 25 ml of H_2O, add a few drops of bromophenol blue indicator solution and titrate with 1 N NaOH to the production of a green to blue color.   Not more than 0.8 ml of the NaOH is required.

Solubility in alcohol: One gram dissolves completely in 25 ml of alcohol, producing a clear and colorless solution (retain).

Ignition residue: Char well 2.0 g, cool, add 0.5 ml of H_2SO and ignite gently at first, then strongly to constant weight.   The weight of the residue does not exceed 1.0 mg.

Sulfate: Dissolve 1.0 g in 10 ml of water and add 2 ml of $BaCl_2$.   Any turbidity produced in 10 minutes is not greater than that in a control with 0.05 mg of SO_4 and 1 ml of 0.01 N HCl.

Ammonium salts: To the solution from *Solubility in alcohol* add 1 ml of 10% platinic chloride and shake well.   No precipitate is produced in 10 minutes.

Heavy metals: Dissolve 4 g in water to make 40 ml.   To 10 ml of the solution add 0.02 mg of Pb and dilute to 40 ml (*A*).   Dilute the remaining 20 ml to 40 ml (*B*). Then add to each 10 ml of H_2S.   *B* is not darker than *A*.

Iron: To the *Ignition residue* add 2 ml of HCl and 2 ml of H_2O, and slowly evaporate on the steam bath to dryness.   Take up the residue with a few drops of HCl and dilute to 20 ml.   To 10 ml add 2 ml of HCl, dilute to 50 ml and add 30 mg of ammonium persulfate and 3 ml of ammonium thiocyanate.   Any resulting red color is not darker than that in a blank to which 0.01 mg of Fe has been added.

8-HYDROXYQUINOLINE

8-Quinolinol; Oxine

; mol. wt. 145.15.

White, or nearly white crystals, or crystalline powder.   Insoluble in water; soluble in alcohol or in dilute acids.

This reagent is used for the precipitation and separation of many metals, notably aluminium, bismuth and magnesium.

Standards

Melting range.....................73°–75°	Ignition residue............max 0.050%
Assay...................99.0%–100.5%	Sulfate (SO_4)................max 0.01%
Solubility in acetic acid.......to pass test	Heavy meatals (as Pb).......max 0.002%

Assay: Dry about 0.3 g for 18 hours over H_2SO_4; then weigh accurately 0.15 g and dissolve it in 10 ml of HCl and 150 ml of water, in a 500-ml volumetric or iodine flask.   Add 50 ml of 0.1 *N* bromine, immediately stopper the flask and allow to stand for 10 minutes.   Cool in ice water, add 70 ml of water and 10 ml of 10% potassium iodide solution and titrate the liberated iodine, representing the excess of the bromine, with 0.1 *N* thiosulfate.   One ml of 0.1 *N* bromine = 0.003627 g of $HO \cdot C_9H_6N$, log 55955.

$$HO \cdot C_9H_6N + 4Br \rightarrow HO \cdot C_9H_4Br_2N + 2HBr$$

Solubility in acetic acid: To 1 g add a mixture of 20 ml of water and 5 ml of glacial acetic acid, cover, and heat on the steam bath for 1 hour.   No insoluble residue remains.

Ignition residue: Char well 2.0 g, cool, add 0.5 ml of H_2SO_4, evaporate the acid and ignite to constant weight.   Any remaining residue does not exceed 1.0 mg.

Sulfate: To 1 g add 15 ml of hot water and sufficient 10% HCl (about 2 ml) to dissolve.   Filter, if necessary, and add 2 ml of $BaCl_2$ and heat to boiling.   Any resulting turbidity in 10 minutes is not greater than that in a control prepared with 0.1 mg of SO_4.

Heavy metals: To the *Ignition residue* add 2 ml of HCl and 1 ml of HNO_3, and slowly evaporate on the steam bath to dryness. Add to the residue 5 drops of HCl and 10 ml of hot water, digest for 5 minutes, filter, if necessary, and dilute to 20 ml. Dilute 10 ml of the solution to 40 ml and add 10 ml of H_2S. Any resulting dark color is not greater than that in a control made with 0.02 mg of Pb, 2 drops of HCl in a volume of 40 ml and treated with 10 ml of H_2S.

HYPOPHOSPHOROUS ACID, 50%

H_3PO_2; mol. wt. 66.00.

Colorless liquid. Sp. gr. 1.27. Miscible with water, alcohol, and ether. It is a powerful reducing agent.

Standards

Assay..........not less than 49% H_3PO_2	Sulfate (SO_4)................max 0.03%
Sodium carbonate precipitate..max 0.15%	Barium (Ba)...............max 0.005%
Chloride (Cl)................max 0.005%	Heavy metals (as Pb)........max 0.001%
Phosphate (PO_4).............max 0.01%	Iron (Fe)..................max 0.010%

Assay: Weigh accurately 3 ml and dilute with 50 ml of water. Add 1–2 drops of methyl red and titrate with 1 N NaOH. One ml of 1 N NaOH = 0.06600 g H_3PO_2, log 81954.

Sodium carbonate precipitate: Dilute 4.0 ml (5 g) with 50 ml of water. Slowly add to the dilution a solution of 2.5 g anhydrous sodium carbonate in 25 ml of H_2O, then boil gently for a few minutes and allow to cool. If a precipitate is present, filter, wash it with small volumes of water and dry at about 150°. Its weight does not exceed 7.5 mg (retain the precipitate).

Chloride: Dilute 4.0 ml (5 g) with 20 ml of water, add 5 ml of $AgNO_3$ solution, then add 10 ml of HNO_3. After the reaction has subsided, heat gently to expel nitrogen oxide and allow to stand in subdued light for 2 hours. If a precipitate is present, filter, wash it with small volumes of water and dry at 120° to constant weight which should not exceed 4.0 mg.

Phosphate: Dilute 1.5 ml (2 g) with 40 ml of water and add to the solution 3 ml of magnesia mixture. Neutralize to litmus paper with 10% NH_3, add 10 ml excess of the ammonia, mix well and allow to stand for at least 2 hours, preferably overnight. If any precipitate is present filter it on a small filter and wash with several 3-ml portions of 2.5% NH_3. Dissolve the washed precipitate by pouring over it two 5-ml portions of warm 25% H_2SO_4, and wash with 10 ml of hot water. Dilute the total filtrate to 100 ml. To 10 ml add 2 ml of 25% H_2SO_4 and 20 ml of H_2O, then add 1 ml each of phosphate reagents **A** and **B**, mix and heat at 60° for 10 minutes. Any resulting blue color is not darker than that of a control made with 0.02 mg of PO_4, 2 ml of 25% H_2SO_4, the same volumes of the phosphate reagents and in the same final volume as with the sample.

Sulfate: Dilute 0.8 ml to 100 ml. To 10 ml of the dilution add 10 ml of H_2O, 1 ml of 1 N HCl and 2 ml of $BaCl_2$ solution, shake well and allow to stand for 15 minutes.   Any resulting turbidity is not greater than that in a control made with 0.3 mg of SO_4.

Barium: Dilute 0.8 ml to 20 ml.   Add 1 ml of 1 N HCl and 2 ml of 5% K_2SO_4 solution and shake well.   No turbidity is apparent afer 15 minutes.

Heavy metals: Dilute 3.2 ml (4 g) with 20 ml of H_2O, and make slightly alkaline to litmus paper with NH_3.   Add 2 ml of 1 N HCl and dilute to 40.0 ml.   To 10 ml add 0.02 mg of Pb and dilute to 40 ml (A).   To the remaining 30 ml add water to make 40 ml (B).   Then to each add 10 ml of H_2S. B is not darker than A.

Iron: Dilute 0.8 ml to 100 ml.   To 20 ml of this dilution add 0.5 g of hydroxylamine hydrochloride, and when it has dissolved add 10 ml of o-phenanthroline solution.   After 1 hour the color is not darker than that produced by treating 0.02 mg of Fe in 20 ml of water exactly as the sample beginning with "add 0.5 g. . . ."

ICELAND SPAR

$CaCO_3$; mol. wt. 100.09; Ca—40.05%; CaO—56.05%; CO_2—43.96%.

Iceland spar is native, crystalline calcium carbonate.   It occurs in the form of large, colorless or practically colorless, transparent crystals.   It is used as a primary standard for calcium or CO_2.   For use it should be powdered and dried at 150°.

Standards

Hydrochloric acid—insoluble. . max 0.010%	Heavy metals (as Pb) . . . . max 0.002%
Ammonium hydroxide	Iron (Fe) . . . . max 0.007%
precipitate. . . . . max 0.025%	Not precipitated as oxalate . . . . max 0.10%
Sulfate (SO_4) . . . . max 0.005%	

Hydrochloric acid—insoluble: To 10 g of the powdered sample add 50 ml of H_2O, then add, in small portions, 25 ml of HCl.   After all the acid has been added and effervescence has ceased, evaporate on a steam bath to dryness and heat at 120° for 2 hours.   Add 10 ml of HCl and re-evaporate to dryness.   Dissolve in 100 ml of hot water, and if any undissolved matter remains filter it (retain filtrate), wash well with hot water and dry at 105°.   The weight of the insoluble should not exceed 1.0 mg.

Ammonium hydroxide precipitate: To the filtrate obtained in the test for *Hydrochloric acid—insoluble* add ammonia to a slight but distinct alkaline reaction and heat to boiling.   If a precipitate is formed filter (retain filtrate), wash well with hot water and ignite.   The weight of the ignited residue is not more than 2.5 mg.

Solution S: Cover 5 g with 50 ml of H_2O, add in small portions 15 ml HCl.   Evaporate to dryness on the steam bath.   Take up the residue with H_2O to make 100 ml and filter.

Sulfate: Evaporate 40 ml of *Solution S* to 10 ml.   Cool, add 1 ml of 0.1 N HCl and 2 ml of $BaCl_2$.   Any turbidity ensuing in 15 minutes is not greater than that of a control made with 0.1 mg SO_4 in 10 ml of water treated with the same volumes of 0.1 N HCl and $BaCl_2$ as the sample solution.

Heavy metals: To 10 ml of *Solution S* add 0.02 mg Pb, 1 ml of 1 N acetic acid and dilute to 40 ml (A).   To 30 ml of *Solution S* add 1 ml of 1 N acetic acid and dilute to 40 ml (B).   Then to each add 10 ml of H_2S. B is not darker than A.

Iron: To 2.0 ml of *Solution S* add 2 ml of HCl, dilute to 50 ml and add 30 mg of ammonium persulfate and 3 ml of ammonium thiocyanate. Any resulting red color is not darker than that of a blank to which 0.014 mg of Fe has been added.

Not precipitated as oxalate: Dilute the filtrate from the test for *Ammonium hydroxide precipitate* with H_2O to 250 ml. To 50 ml add 5 ml of HCl, heat to boiling and add 100 ml of ammonium oxalate solution. Slowly neutralize with NH_4OH while the solution is cooling. Dilute to 200 ml with H_2O and allow to stand for 4 hours or overnight. Filter and to 100 ml of the filtrate add 0.5 ml of sulfuric acid, evaporate and ignite. Not more than 1.0 mg of residue remains. Correct for the weight of residue obtained by mixing the same volume of oxalic solution and NH_4OH as used in the test, evaporating and igniting.

INDIGO CARMINE

Sodium Indigotindisulfonate

$[NaSO_3 \cdot C_6H_3(NH)(CO):C]_2$; mol. wt. 466.37; indigotin—56.2%.

Purplish-blue powder, or blue granules having a copper luster. Soluble in about 100 parts of water; almost insoluble in alcohol. In aqueous solution it deteriorates through bacterial action.

Standards

Assay.........min 95% $C_{16}H_8N_2O_8Na_2S_2$	Insoluble....................max 0.5%
(anhydrous basis)	Drying loss.................max 10%

Assay: Weigh accurately about 0.25 g and dissolve it in 30 ml of water. Add 1 ml of H_2SO_4, dilute in a porcelain dish with 600 ml H_2O and titrate with 0.1 N potassium permanganate. The end point of the titration is the change of color from green to light yellow. One ml of 0.1 N permanganate = 0.01165 g $C_6H_8O_2N_2(SO_3Na)_2$, log 06633.

$$10C_{16}H_8N_2O_2(SO_3Na)_2 + 8KMnO_4 + 22H_2SO_4 \rightarrow$$
$$10C_{16}H_8N_2O_4(SO_3H)_2 + 4K_2SO_4 + 10Na_2SO_4 + 8MnSO_4 + 12H_2O$$

Insoluble: Dissolve 1 g in 150 ml of H_2O, filter on a tared asbestos Gooch or a tared filtering glass crucible, wash with H_2O until the washings are colorless and dry at 105°. The weight of the insoluble residue does not exceed 5.0 mg.

Drying loss: Dry about 1 g, accurately weighed, at 105° to constant weight. The loss corresponds to not more than 10%.

IODIC ACID

HIO_3; mol. wt. 175.93; I—72.14%; available O—22.73%.

Colorless crystals, or a white powder. Soluble in 1 part of water; slightly soluble in alcohol; insoluble in ether. *Keep protected from light.*

Standards

Assay.................min 99.8% HIO_3	Sulfate (SO_4)...............max 0.005%
Insoluble...................max 0.01%	Heavy metals (as Pb)........max 0.001%
Ignition residue..............max 0.03%	Iron (Fe)..................max 0.001%
Nitrogen compounds (as N)...max 0.003%	

Assay: Dry about 0.6 g over H_2SO_4 for 3 hours, then weigh accurately 0.5 g, dissolve in H_2O and dilute to exactly 100 ml. Transfer 20 ml to a glass-stoppered flask, add 30 ml of H_2O, 2 g of potassium iodide and 5 ml of 25% H_2SO_4. Allow to stand for 10 minutes in the dark, add 100 ml of cold water, then titrate the liberated iodine with 0.1 N sodium thiosulfate. Correct for a blank. One ml of 0.1 N thiosulfate = 0.002932 g HIO_3, log 46716.

$$2HIO_3 + 10KI + 5H_2SO_4 \rightarrow 12I + 5K_2SO_4 + 6H_2O$$

Insoluble: Heat 10 g with 100 ml H_2O for 30 minutes. If an undissolved residue remains, filter, wash it with water and dry at 105°. Its weight does not exceed 1.0 mg.

Ignition residue: Ignite 5 g to constant weight. Not more than 1.5 mg of residue remains (retain the residue).

Nitrogen compounds: Dissolve 1.0 g in 50 ml of H_2O, add 1 g of powdered Devarda metal (or 0.5 g of aluminium wire in small pieces) and 10 ml of 10% NaOH. Allow to stand for 2 hours, protected from loss or access of NH_3, then slowly distill 40 ml into 5 ml of H_2O containing 0.1 ml of 1 N HCl, and dilute to 50 ml. To 20 ml of the distillate add 30 ml of water, 1 ml of 10% NaOH and 2 ml of Nessler solution. The color is not darker than that produced by treating 0.03 mg of nitrogen (0.12 mg NH_4Cl) in the same manner as the sample.

Sulfate: Evaporate 2 g of iodic acid and 20 mg of sodium carbonate with 5 ml of HCl to dryness on the steam bath, then re-evaporate twice with 5 ml of HCl. Treat the residue with 5 ml of hot H_2O, filter, wash to 10 ml with H_2O and add to the filtrate 1 ml of 0.1 N HCl and 2 ml of $BaCl_2$. Any turbidity produced is not greater than that produced in a control made as follows: Evaporate 10 ml of the HCl with 20 mg of sodium carbonate to dryness on the steam bath. Dissolve the residue and 0.1 mg of SO_4 in 10 ml of H_2O, and add 1 ml of 0.1 N HCl and 1 ml of $BaCl_2$.

Solution R: To the *Ignition residue* add 2 ml of HCl and 2 ml of water, and slowly evaporate to dryness on the steam bath. Take up the residue with 1 ml of 1 N HCl and 10 ml of hot water and dilute to 40 ml.

Heavy metals: Dilute 20 ml of *Solution R* to 40 ml and add 10 ml of H_2S. Any darkening produced is not greater than that produced by adding 10 ml of H_2S to 40 ml of H_2O containing 0.02 mg of Pb and 0.5 ml of 1 N HCl.

Iron: To 10 ml of *Solution R* add 2 ml of HCl and dilute to 50 ml. Add about 30 mg of ammonium persulfate and 3 ml of ammonium thiocyanate, and mix. Any resulting red color is not darker than that of a blank to which 0.01 mg of Fe has been added.

IODINE

I; at. wt. 126.91.

Bluish-black, heavy plates or scales, with a metallic luster. Slightly soluble in water; soluble in alcohol, carbon disulfide, chloroform and ether. *Keep in tightly closed, glass-stoppered bottles.*

This reagent, in the form of plates, is substantially 100% pure.

Standards

Nonvolatile.................max 0.010%   Chlorine and Bromine (as Cl)..max 0.003%

Nonvolatile: Cautiously heat 10 g in a tared, porcelain dish on the steam bath until the iodine has completely volatilized and the weight is constant. Any residue remaining does not exceed 1.0 mg.

Chlorine and Bromine: Triturate 1 g with 30 ml of H_2O, let stand covered for 30 minutes, with frequent stirring, and filter. To 20 ml of the filtrate add dilute sulfurous acid until the color is just discharged, then add 0.5 ml of 10% NH_3 and 1 ml of $AgNO_3$ and filter. To the clear filtrate add 2 ml of HNO_3. The turbidity does not exceed that produced in a blank to which 0.02 mg of Cl has been added.

IODINE PENTOXIDE

Iodic Acid Anhydride

I_2O_5; mol. wt. 333.84; I—76.04%; available O—23.96%.

White, crystalline powder. Soluble in water, forming iodic acid; insoluble in absolute alcohol, chloroform or ether. At about 300° it decomposes into iodine and oxygen. *Keep in well-closed containers, protected from light.*

Standards

Assay....................min 99% I_2O_5	Sulfate (SO_4)...............max 0.010%
Insoluble..................max 0.010%	Heavy metals (as Pb)........max 0.001%
Ignition residue.............max 0.050%	Iron (Fe)..................max 0.001%
Nitrogen compounds (as N)...max 0.005%	

Assay: Dry to constant weight at 200°, then weigh accurately 0.5 g and dissolve in sufficient water to make exactly 100 ml. Transfer 20 ml to a glass-stoppered flask, dilute with 30 ml of H_2O and add 2 g of potassium iodide and 5 ml of 25% H_2SO_4. Allow to stand for 10 minutes, add 100 ml of cold water, then titrate the liberated iodine with 0.1 N sodium thiosulfate. Correct for a blank. One ml of 0.1 N thiosulfate = 0.002782 g I_2O_5, log 44436.

Insoluble: Heat 5 g with 70 ml of H_2O on the steam bath for 30 minutes. Should an insoluble residue remain, filter, wash it with water and dry at 105°. Its weight does not exceed 0.5 mg.

Ignition residue: Ignite 4 g to constant weight. Not more than 2.0 mg of residue remains (retain the residue).

Nitrogen compounds: Dissolve 0.5 g in 50 ml of H_2O, add 1 g of powdered Devarda metal (or 0.5 g fine aluminum wire in small pieces) and 10 ml of 10% NaOH. Allow to stand for 2 hours protected from loss or access of NH_3, then slowly distill 40 ml into 5 ml of H_2O containing 0.1 ml of 1 N HCl and dilute to 50 ml. To 20 ml add 1 ml of 10% NaOH and 2 ml of Nessler solution. The color is not darker than that produced by treating 0.05 mg of nitrogen (0.2 mg NH_4Cl) in the same manner as the sample.

Sulfate: Evaporate 1 g of the sample and 20 mg of sodium carbonate with 5 ml of HCl to dryness on the steam bath, and then re-evaporate twice with 5 ml of HCl. Treat the residue with 5 ml of hot H_2O, filter, wash with water to 10 ml and add to the filtrate 1 ml of 0.1 N HCl and 2 ml of $BaCl_2$. Any resulting turbidity is not greater than that of a control made as follows: Evaporate 15 ml of HCl and 25 mg of sodium carbonate to dryness on the steam bath. Dissolve the residue and 0.1 mg of SO_4 in 10 ml of H_2O and add 1 ml of 0.1 N HCl and 2 ml of $BaCl_2$.

Solution R: To the *Ignition residue* add 2 ml of HCl, 2 ml of H_2O and slowly evaporate to dryness on the steam bath. Take up the residue with 1 ml of 1 N HCl and 10 ml of hot water and dilute to 40 ml.

Heavy metals: Dilute 20 ml of *Solution R* to 40 ml and add 10 ml of H_2S. Any color produced is not darker than that produced by adding 10 ml of H_2S to 40 ml of water containing 0.02 mg of Pb and 0.5 ml of 1 N HCl.

Iron: To 10 ml of *Solution R* add 2 ml of HCl and dilute to 50 ml. Add about 30 mg of ammonium persulfate and 3 ml of ammonium thiocyanate, and mix. Any resulting red color is not darker than that in a blank to which 0.01 mg of Fe has been added.

IODOXYQUINSULFONIC ACID

Ferron; 7-Iodo-8-hydroxyquinoline-5-sulfonic acid; Loretin

; mol. wt. 351.13.

Yellow powder; melts at about 260°–270° with decomposition. Moderately soluble in water or alcohol.

It is a specific reagent for *ferric* iron, and the only interference arises from the presence of considerable quantities of colored ions.[1,2,3,4] The pH of the solution to be tested should be between 2 and 3.5.

Standards

Sensitiveness	to pass test	Ignition residue	max 0.20%
Solubility	to pass test		

Sensitiveness: Dissolve 10 mg of sample in 10 ml of water. To 1 ml of a solution containing 0.005 mg of Fe''' add 2 drops of 1 N HCl, then add 1 drop of

3% H_2O_2 and 0.1 ml of the solution of the sample.   A green or bluish-green color is produced.

Solubility: One-tenth gram of the reagent dissolves completely in 20 ml of water.

Ignition residue: To 0.5 g add 0.5 ml of H_2SO_4 and slowly ignite to constant weight.   Not more than 1.0 mg of residue remains.

[1] Yoe, J. H., *J. Am. Chem. Soc.* **54**, 4139 (1932).
[2] Clark, N. A., and Sieling, D. H., *Ind. Eng. Chem., Anal. Ed.* **8**, 256 (1936).
[3] Thiel, A., and Van Hendel, E., *Ber.* **17**, 2491 (1937).
[4] Fahey, J. J., *Ind. Eng. Chem., Anal. Ed.* **10**, 362 (1939).

IRON REDUCED
Iron "by Hydrogen"
Fe; at. wt. 55.85.

Gray, fine powder.   Insoluble in water; soluble in dilute acids.   It oxidizes on exposure to air and moisture.   *Keep in well-closed containers.*

Standards

Assay..............min 93% metallic Fe	Sulfide (S)...................to pass test
Sulfuric acid—insoluble.......max 0.20%	(max 0.02%)
Water soluble................max 0.03%	Arsenic (As).................max 5 ppm
Nitrogen (N)................max 0.003%	Foreign metals (Cu, Zn).......to pass test
	(max 0.005%)

Assay: Weigh accurately 1.0 g and transfer to a 200-ml volumetric flask.   Add 10 g of powdered mercuric chloride and 50 ml of water and boil for 5 minutes with frequent agitation.   Cool, dilute to the 200-ml mark with freshly boiled and cooled H_2O, mix and filter.   Immediately add 15 ml of 10% H_2SO_4 to 50 ml of the filtrate and titrate the ferrous chloride formed with 0.1 N potassium permanganate.   One ml of 0.1 N permanganate = 0.005584 g Fe, log 74695.

$$Fe + 2HgCl_2 \rightarrow FeCl_2 + 2HgCl$$

Sulfuric acid—insoluble: To 2 g add 50 ml of 10% H_2SO_4 and warm on the steam bath until the evolution of hydrogen ceases.   Filter any undissolved residue, wash it with approximately 2% H_2SO_4, then with water and dry at 105°.   Its weight does not exceed 2.0 mg.

Water soluble: Shake 5 g with 50 ml of H_2O for 10 minutes and filter.   Evaporate 30 ml of the filtrate on the steam bath and dry at 105°.   The residue does not exceed 1.0 mg.

Nitrogen: Add in small portions 1.5 g of the sample to a mixture of 2 ml of H_2SO_4 and 30 ml of H_2O contained in a distilling flask.   Cool, add 20 ml of H_2O and 15 ml of 30% NaOH, and slowly distill about 40 ml into 5 ml of H_2O containing 0.1 ml of 1 N HCl.   Add to the distillate 1 ml of 10% NaOH and 2 ml of Nessler solution.   Any color produced is not darker than that produced by treating 0.12 mg of NH_4Cl (0.03 mg N) and 0.5 g of the sample in the same manner.

Sulfide: Add 20 ml of 10% H_2SO_4 to 1 g of the sample contained in a 150-ml flask.   The hydrogen evolved is nearly odorless and does not darken moist lead acetate paper within 2 minutes.

Arsenic: Place in a flask 1.0 g of sample and 1 g of potassium chlorate.   Add 15 ml of 20% HCl, and when the reaction has subsided, warm the solution to expel free chlorine.   Cool, dilute to 10 ml and filter if necessary.   Add to the filtrate 10 ml of stannous chloride solution.   The mixture remains colorless for 1 hour.

Foreign metals: Dissolve 1.0 g in 20 ml of a mixture of equal volumes of HCl and H_2O, add to the solution 3 ml of HNO_3 and boil for 1 minute.   Dilute with 50 ml of water, add, while continuously stirring, a moderate excess of NH_4OH, and filter.   The filtrate is colorless (Cu), and no darkening or precipitation is produced on the addition of a few drops of sodium sulfide solution.

IRON WIRE

Fe; at. wt. 55.85.

Bright, fine wire.   *Keep in well-closed containers.*

Standards

Assay.....................min 99.8% Fe   Sulfuric acid—insoluble......max 0.050%

Assay: Weigh accurately 0.20 g to 0.22 g of the wire and put it in a 250-ml, glass-stoppered Erlenmeyer flask.   Insert a small funnel in the flask, and add through the funnel, in small portions at a time, 25 ml of 10% H_2SO_4.   Allow to stand until the reaction ceases, warming toward the end if necessary.   When all the metal has dissolved rinse the inside and outside of the funnel into the flask and also wash down the inside of the flask.   Now add 0.1 N $KMnO_4$ until the solution, after shaking, is slightly pink, and then discharge the pink color by the addition of just enough diluted hydrogen peroxide (1 ml of 30% + 100 ml H_2O) or diluted sulfurous acid.   Add 3 ml of HCl, mix, then add 3 g of potassium iodide and allow to stand in the dark for 30 minutes.   Add 50 ml of cold H_2O and titrate the liberated iodine with 0.1 N thiosulfate, adding starch toward the end.   Correct for a blank using 30 ml of 10% H_2SO_4, 5 ml HCl, 3 g of potassium iodide and the same volume of water as with the sample.   One ml of 0.1 N thiosulfate = 0.005584 g Fe, log 74695.

Sulfuric acid—insoluble: To 5 g add a mixture of 8 ml of H_2SO_4 and 50 ml of H_2O, and heat on steam bath until no more hydrogen is evolved.   Filter any undissolved residue, wash it first with approximately 2% H_2SO_4, then with water alone and dry at 105°.   Its weight does not exceed 2.5 mg.

ISATIN

; mol. wt. 147.13.

Small, yellowish-red crystals.   Slightly soluble in cold water; freely soluble in hot water, in alcohol or in ether; also soluble in dilute solutions of aqueous alkali hydroxides with a violet color, which on standing or heating becomes yellow.

Standards

Melting range.................198°–201°   Solubility in alcohol...........to pass test
Ignition residue..............max 0.2%

Ignition residue: To 0.5 g add 0.5 ml of H_2SO_4 and ignite to constant weight. The residue does not exceed 1.0 mg.

Solubility in alcohol: A solution of 0.5 g in 10 ml of alcohol is complete or nearly so.

ISOAMYL ACETATE

iso-Amyl Acetate; "Amyl Acetate"

$CH_3CO_2C_5H_{11}$; mol. wt. 130.18.

Clear, colorless liquid, characteristic odor. Boils at 142°. Sp. gr. 0.868 at 25°/25°. Almost insoluble in water; miscible with ethyl and amyl alcohols, benzene and carbon disulfide.

Standards

Assay.............97%–100.5% $C_7H_{14}O_2$	Solubility in dilute alcohol.....to pass test
Boiling range..................137°–142°	Free acid (as acetic)..........max 0.005%
Evaporation residue.........max 0.020%	Water.......................to pass test

Assay: Weigh accurately about 1 ml and dissolve it in 25 ml of neutral alcohol. Add 25 ml of 0.5 N alcoholic KOH and boil gently under a reflux condenser for 2 hours. Cool, add 3 drops of phenolphthalein and titrate the excess of KOH with 0.5 N HCl. One ml of 0.5 N KOH = 0.06505 g $CH_3CO_2C_5H_{11}$, log 81325.

Boiling range: Distill 50 ml. After the first 10 drops not less than 48 ml distills between 137° and 142°, correction being made for the difference of the barometric pressure from 760 mm.

Evaporation residue: Evaporate 12 ml to dryness on the steam bath and dry at 105° for 2 hours. Not more than 2.0 mg of residue remains.

Solubility in dilute alcohol: A 1.0-ml portion of the sample dissolves in a mixture of 10 ml alcohol and 10 ml of water to a clear solution.

Free acid: To 20 ml of alcohol add 0.2 ml of phenolphthalein, then 0.1 N NaOH, dropwise, until the pink color persists after shaking. Disregard the alkali so consumed. Now add 5.0 ml of the sample and titrate with 0.1 N NaOH to the restoration of the pink color. Not more than 0.4 ml of the NaOH is required.

Water: A 5-ml portion of the isoamyl acetate gives a clear solution with 5 ml carbon disulfide.

Note: The water content of this reagent may be quantitatively determined by the iodine (Fischer) method.

ISOAMYL ALCOHOL

"Amyl Alcohol"

$(CH_3)_2CHCH_2CH_2OH$; mol. wt. 88.15.

Colorless, clear liquid; characteristic odor. Slightly soluble in water; miscible with alcohol, benzene, ether. Sp. gr. about 0.81; boils at 131° C.

Boiling range.................129°–132°

Evaporation residue.........max 0.003%

Acids and Esters (as amyl
acetate)..................max 0.06%

Aldehyde..................to pass test

Pyridine.............max about 0.003%

Substances darkened by
H_2SO_4....................to pass test

Water.......................max 0.5%

Boiling range: Distill 50 ml. After the first 10 drops, not less than 48 ml distills between 129° and 132°, correction being made for the barometric pressure (page 581).

Evaporation residue: Evaporate 40 ml on the steam bath and dry at 105° for 2 hours. The residue is not more than 1.0 mg.

Acids and Esters: Mix 20 ml with 20 ml of neutral alcohol, add 5 ml of 0.1 N NaOH and reflux for 10 minutes. Cool, add 0.2 ml of phenolphthalein and titrate the excess of alkali with 0.1 N HCl. The volume of the NaOH consumed is not more than 0.75 ml greater than the volume consumed in a complete blank.

Aldehyde: Shake 5 ml with 5 ml of 30% potassium hydroxide in a glass-stoppered cylinder for 5 minutes and allow to separate. No color appears in either layer.

Pyridine: Mix 2 ml with 5 ml of H_2O and acidify to litmus with dilute H_2SO_4. Evaporate on the steam bath until no odor remains, then make alkaline with sodium hydroxide. No distinct odor of pyridine is noticeable.

Substances darkened by H_2SO_4: Cool 10 ml to 10°, add 10 ml of sulfuric acid, also cooled to 10°, and shake for 2 minutes. The color is not darker than that of a mixture of 5 ml of 1% cobalt chloride solution. 0.4 ml of a 1% potassium dichromate solution and 15 ml of H_2O.

Water: Water in isoamyl alcohol may be determined by the iodine (Fischer) method.

ISOBUTYL ALCOHOL

Isobutanol; Isopropyl Carbinol

$(CH_3)_2CHCH_2OH$; mol. wt. 74.12.

Clear, colorless liquid, characteristic odor. Soluble in 10 parts of water; miscible with alcohol, ether or benzene. Sp. gr. 0.806 at 15°/15°.

Boiling range.................107°–109°

Evaporation residue.........max 0.005%

Solubility in H_2O............to pass test

Acid (as butyric)...........max 0.014%

Alkalinity...................to pass test

Aldehyde....................to pass test

Fluorescence.................to pass test

Water.......................max 0.5%

Boiling range: Distill 50 ml. After the first 10 drops not less than 48 ml distills between 107° and 109°, correction being made for barometric pressure (page 581).

Evaporation residue: Evaporate 25 ml to dryness on the steam bath and dry for 1 hour at 105°. Not more than 1.0 mg of residue remains.

Solubility in water: 5 ml of the sample gives a clear solution with 50 ml of water.

Acid: To 60 ml of H_2O add 0.2 ml of phenolphthalein, then add 0.02 N NaOH until a pink color is produced. Disregard this volume of the NaOH consumed. Then add 5 ml of the sample, mix and titrate with 0.02 N NaOH until the pink color is reproduced. Not more than 0.3 ml of the NaOH is required for this titration.

Alkalinity: A solution of the sample in 15 parts of water does not affect moistened red litmus paper.

Fluorescence: The fluorescence of isobutyl alcohol measured in a suitable fluorophotometer is not greater than that of a solution of quinine base or of quinine sulfate in 0.1 N H_2SO_4 containing the equivalent of 0.020 mg of anhydrous quinine base per ml.

Aldehyde: Dilute 0.5 ml of the sample with 20 ml of water, add 2 ml of fuchsine-sulfurous acid solution and mix well. At the end of 10 minutes the mixture has substantially no more color than a mixture of 20 ml of water and 2 ml of the fuchsine-sulfurous acid solution.

Water: A mixture of 5 ml of the sample and 50 ml of benzene is clear.

Note: The actual water content of isobutyl alcohol may be determined by the iodine (Fischer) method.

L-ISOLEUCINE

α-Amino-β-Methylvaleric Acid

$CH_3CH_2CH(CH_3)CH(NH_2)COOH$; mol. wt. 131.17; N—10.68%.

Crystalline leaflets, or white, crystalline powder. Sublimes at about 170°. Soluble in 25 parts of water; slightly soluble in hot alcohol; soluble in diluted mineral acids and in alkaline solution.

Standards

Nitrogen (N)...............10.7% ± 0.2%	Ammonium salts (as NH_3)....max 0.010%
Specific rotation	Heavy metals (as Pb).......max 0.001%
in 20% HCl...............+40.5° ± 0.6°	Iron (Fe)...................max 0.002%
Solubility....................to pass test	Methionine.................to pass test
Drying loss...................max 0.2%	(max about 0.05%)
Ignition residue.............max 0.50%	Tryptophan.................to pass test
Chloride (Cl)...............max 0.005%	(max about 0.03%)
Phosphate (PO_4)...........max 0.002%	Tyrosine....................to pass test
Sulfate (SO_4)...............max 0.010%	(max about 0.03%)

Specific rotation and Drying loss: Dry about 1 g of accurately weighed sample for 3 hours over H_2SO_4 or P_2O_5. The loss in weight corresponds to not more than 0.2%. Weigh accurately about 0.75 g of the dried sample and dissolve it in 20% HCl to make 25.0 ml. Observe the rotation of the solution at 25° ± 2° in a 200-mm tube, and calculate the specific rotation.

Nitrogen; Solubility; Ignition residue; Chloride; Phosphate; Sulfate; Ammonium salts; Heavy metals; Iron; Methionine; Tryptophan; Tyrosine. Test for these as described under L-*leucine*. The results should be as there stated.

ISO-OCTANE

2,2,4-Trimethylpentane

$(CH_3)_3CCH_2CH(CH_3)_2$; mol. wt. 114.22.

Clear, colorless, practically odorless liquid. Sp. gr. 0.690 at 25°/25°. Insoluble in water. Miscible with absolute alcohol, but not with the 95%; also miscible with chloroform and ether.

Standards

Boiling range..............96°–100°	Unsaturated compounds.......to pass test
Solubility in 90% alcohol.......max 15%	Acid (as acetic)................max 0.002%

Boiling range: Distill at least 50 ml. All distills between 96° and 100°, and not less than 80% distills between 98° and 100°.

Solubility in 90% alcohol: To exactly 10 ml contained in a tightly stoppered, graduated cylinder, add 10 ml of 90% (vol./vol.) alcohol, mix gently for a few minutes and allow to separate. The alcohol layer is not increased by more than 1.5 ml.

Unsaturated compounds: Place 10 ml of H_2SO_4 in a graduated, glass-stoppered cylinder and note the exact volume. Add 10.0 ml of the sample, shake gently for 3 minutes and allow to separate. The upper layer (iso-octane) is colorless. The acid acquires not more than a slight yellowish color, and its volume is not increased.

Acid: Place 30 ml of water in a separatory funnel, add 30 ml (20 g) of sample, shake gently but well for 2–3 minutes and allow to separate. Draw off the aqueous (lower) layer, add to it 2 drops (0.1 ml) of phenolphthalein and titrate with 0.02 N NaOH to the production of a pink color which persists after shaking for 5 seconds. Not more than 0.5 ml of the NaOH is required.

ISOPROPYL ALCOHOL

Isopropanol; 2-Propanol

$(CH_3)_2CHOH$; mol. wt. 60.09.

Colorless liquid, with a slight alcoholic odor. Miscible with water, alcohol or ether. Boils at 83°. Sp. gr. 0.79. *Keep well-closed in containers.*

Standards

Boiling range...................82°–83°	Evaporation residue.........max 0.003%
Specific gravity (25°/25°)....0.7830–0.7850	Acid (as propionic acid)......max 0.003%
Miscibility with H_2O.........to pass test	Alkalinity (as NH_3)..........max 0.001%
Aldehyde...................to pass test	Water......................max 0.5%

Boiling range: Distill 50 ml. After the first 10 drops all distills between 82° and 83°, correction being made for the difference in the barometric pressure from 760 mm (page 581).

Specific gravity: Determine with a pycnometer at 25°/25°.

Miscibility with H_2O: Mix 10 ml of the alcohol with 30 ml of H_2O. A clear solution results and it remains clear after 30 minutes.

Aldehyde: Dilute 1 ml of sample with 20 ml of water, add 2 ml of fuchsine-sulfurous acid solution and mix. At the end of 10 minutes the mixture has substantially no more color than a mixture of 20 ml of H_2O and 2 ml of the fuchsine-sulfurous acid.

Evaporation residue: Evaporate 42 ml (33 g) on the steam bath and dry at 105° for 30 minutes. Not more than 1.0 mg of residue remains.

Acid: To 20 ml of water add 0.2 ml of phenolphthalein, then add 0.02 N NaOH until a slight pink color persists after shaking. Disregard the volume of the NaOH consumed. Now add 20 ml of the sample, mix and titrate with 0.02 N NaOH until the pink color is reproduced. Not more than 0.30 ml of the NaOH is required.

Alkalinity: Dilute 10 ml with 20 ml of water and add 1 drop of methyl red. If the solution is yellow it requires not more than 0.25 ml of 0.02 N H_2SO_4 to change it to pink.

Water: The water content of isopropyl alcohol may be determined by the iodine (Fischer) method.

ISOPROPYL ETHER

$(CH_3)_2CH—O—CH(CH_3)_2$; mol. wt. 102.17.

Colorless liquid; odor like ethyl ether. Flammable, sp. gr. 0.720, boils at 69° Slightly soluble in water; miscible with alcohol, chloroform, ether, benzene, and many other organic liquids.

Like other alkyl ethers, ispropyl ether on prolonged contact with air forms a peroxide; light greatly accelerates the oxidation. Caution must be exercised in evaporating or distilling isopropyl ether containing peroxide, as the residue of the latter may explode on heating.

Keep in small, nearly full bottles protected from light.

Standards

Specific gravity (25°/25°)......0.719–0.721	Aldehyde...................to pass test
Boiling range...................68°–69°	Peroxide (as peroxide oxygen).max 0.005%
Evaporation residue........max 0.005%	Water......................max 0.25%
Acid (as propionic)..........max 0.003%	

Specific gravity: Determine with a pycnometer at 25°/25°.

Boiling range: Distill 50 ml from a small distilling flask. After the first 20 drops not less than 47 ml distills between 68° and 69°, the observed temperature being corrected for variation in the barometric pressure from 760 mm by the formula given on page 581.

Note: If peroxide is present, the ether should *not be distilled to dryness;* otherwise the peroxide may decompose with violence.

Evaporation residue: Allow 30 ml to evaporate and dry at 105° for 1 hour. Not more than 1.0 mg of residue remains.

Acid: Place 10 ml of alcohol and 2 ml of water in a small, glass-stoppered flask, add 0.5 ml of phenolphthalein and just sufficient 0.02 N NaOH to produce a pink color after shaking for 30 seconds. Now add 15 ml of the isopropyl ether and titrate with 0.02 N NaOH to the same end point. Not more than 0.4 ml of the NaOH is required for the titration.

Aldehyde: Shake well 1 ml of sample with 20 ml of water, allow the layers to separate and discard the ether layer. Add 2 ml of fuchsine-sulfurous acid solution to the aqueous layer and mix. After 5 minutes, this mixture has substantially no more color than a mixture of 20 ml of water and 2 ml of fuchsine-sulfurous acid.

Peroxide: Transfer 15 ml of the ether to a 100-ml glass-stoppered flask, add 10 ml of water, 0.5 ml of glacial acetic acid, 5 ml of chloroform and 1 ml of 10% KI solution. Shake, let stand for 5 minutes, and titrate any liberated iodine with 0.1 N sodium thiosulfate until the liquid remains colorless for 1 minute. Not more than 0.6 ml of the thiosulfate is required. Correct for a blank. One ml of 0.1 N sodium thiosulfate = 0.8 mg of peroxide oxygen.

Water: Determine by the iodine (Fischer) method, using 10 ml of the sample and 25 ml of dry methanol as solvent.

LACMOID

Resorcinol Blue

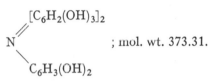

$\big[C_6H_2(OH)_3\big]_2$

N

$C_6H_3(OH)_2$

; mol. wt. 373.31.

Lustrous, dark-violet scales or granules. Slightly soluble in water; soluble in alcohol or acetone. pH range: 4.4 red; 6.2 blue. It is usually used in a 0.5% solution in 50% alcohol. Like methyl orange it is not suitable for organic acid or weak bases.

Sensitiveness: Add 0.1 ml of a 0.5% alcohol solution to 100 ml of CO_2-free water, then add 0.05 ml of 0.1 N HCl; the blue color is changed to red. The subsequent addition of 0.05 ml of 0.1 N NaOH restores the blue color.

Lacmoid indicator is usually used in the form of paper. It is prepared by impregnating unglazed paper with a 0.5% solution in 50% alcohol, and drying.

LACTIC ACID

$CH_3CHOHCO_2H$; mol. wt. 90.08.

Lactic acid ordinarily contains 10% to 15% of lactic anhydride, formed during the concentration of the acid. The assay method given below includes the anhydride.

Colorless or slightly yellow, clear liquid; faint odor. Miscible with water, alcohol, ether; insoluble in chloroform or petroleum ether. Sp. gr. about 1.2. *Keep protected from light.*

Standards

Assay.................85%–90% $C_3H_6O_3$		Aldehyde....................to pass test	
Ignition residue.............max 0.020%		Heavy metals (as Pb).......max 0.0005%	
Miscibility with H_2O or ether.....complete		Iron (Fe)...................max 0.001%	
Chloride (Cl)...............max 0.002%		Substances darkened by H_2SO_4	
Sulfate (SO_4)...............max 0.005%		(sugars, etc.)...............to pass test	

Assay: Weigh accurately about 3 ml, add 50 ml of 1 N NaOH and boil for 20 minutes, replacing water lost during boiling. Add 3 drops of phenolphthalein and titrate the excess of NaOH with 1 N H_2SO_4. One ml of 1 N NaOH = 0.09008 g $HC_3H_5O_3$, log 95463.

Ignition residue: Ignite 4 ml (5 g) to constant weight. Not more than 1.0 mg of residue remains (retain residue).

Miscibility with water or ether: Separate 5-ml portions give a clear solution with 5 ml of water, and with 10 ml of ether.

Chloride: Dilute 0.8 ml with 20 ml of H_2O, add 1 ml of HNO_3 and 1 ml of $AgNO_3$. Any turbidity produced is not greater than that in a blank to which 0.02 mg of Cl has been added.

Sulfate: Dilute 1.7 ml (2 g) with 10 ml of H_2O, then add 0.5 ml of 0.1 N HCl and 2 ml of $BaCl_2$. Any resulting turbidity is not greater than that in a blank with 0.10 mg of SO_4 added.

Aldehyde: Mix 1 ml with 5 ml of H_2O, neutralize with ammonium hydroxide and add 2 ml of Tollens reagent (page 560). No darkening is produced in 5 minutes.

Heavy metals: Dilute 3.5 ml (4 g) of the acid to 40 ml and add 10 ml of H_2S. Any darkening produced is not deeper than that in a control made with 0.02 mg Pb and 2 ml of 1 N acetic acid in the same final volume as with the sample.

Iron: To the *Ignition residue* add 2 ml of HCl and 2 ml of H_2O and slowly evaporate on the steam bath. Take up the residue with a few drops of HCl and water to make 50 ml. To 10 ml of the solution add about 30 mg of ammonium persulfate, dilute to 50 ml and add 3 ml of ammonium thiocyanate solution. Any red color produced is not darker than that of a blank to which 0.01 mg of Fe has been added.

Substances darkened by H_2SO_4: Overlay 5 ml of the sample on 5 ml of H_2SO_4, both being previously cooled to 15°. Not more than a slight color appears at the interface of the two layers in 10 minutes.

Note: The water content of lactic acid may be determined by the iodine (Fischer) method.

LACTOSE

Milk Sugar

$C_{12}H_{22}O_{11} \cdot H_2O$; mol. wt. 360.30.

White, odorless powder. Soluble in 5 parts of cold water, 3 parts of boiling water; almost insoluble in alcohol; insoluble in chloroform or ether.

Standards

Specific rotation	+52.2° to +52.5°	Fatty substances	max 0.010%
Insoluble	max 0.005%	Chloride (Cl)	max 0.002%
Ignition residue	max 0.050%	Nitrogen (N)	max 0.005%
Acid (as acetic)	max 0.012%	Sulfate (SO₄)	max 0.005%
Dextrose	max 0.05%	Heavy metals (as Cu)	max 0.0005%
Sucrose	max 0.05%	Iron (Fe)	max 0.001%

Specific rotation: Dry about 6 g at 80° for 3 hours. Weigh accurately 5.0 g of the dried sample, dissolve it in 40 ml of H_2O, add 0.2 ml of NH_4OH and dilute with H_2O to exactly 50 ml; then observe the rotation of the solution in a 200-mm tube at 25°, using sodium light. From the observed angular rotation, calculate the specific rotation.

Insoluble: Dissolve 20 g in 150 ml of H_2O and heat on the steam bath for 1 hour. Filter any undissolved residue, wash it with water and dry at 105°. Its weight does not exceed 1.0 mg.

Ignition residue: Gently ignite 2 g until charred. Cool, moisten the char with 1 ml of H_2SO_4, then heat to evaporate the acid and ignite slowly to constant weight. The weight of the residue does not exceed 1.0 mg.

Acid: To 100 ml of CO_2-free water add 0.2 ml of phenolphthalein and, dropwise, 0.1 N NaOH until a pink color is produced, then dissolve 10 g of the lactose in the solution. If the pink color disappears, not more than 0.2 ml of 0.1 N NaOH is required to reproduce it.

Dextrose: Add 10 g of the finely powdered sample to 50 ml of 70% alcohol (by volume), shake frequently during 30 minutes, then filter through a small dry filter. Evaporate 10 ml of the filtrate on the steam bath and dissolve the residue in 5 ml of water. Transfer the solution to a thin-walled test tube, filter, if necessary, and add 5 ml of Barfoed's reagent. Immerse the test tube in boiling water or live steam for 3 minutes and let stand at room temperature for 25 minutes. No red precipitate of cuprous oxide is formed.

Sucrose: Evaporate 25 ml of the alcoholic filtrate from the preceding test to dryness on the steam bath. Dissolve the residue in 9 ml of water and add 1 ml of 25% HCl (22 + 10) and 0.1 g resorcinol. Transfer the solution to a thin-walled test tube and immerse it in boiling water or live steam for 8 minutes. The liquid remains colorless or becomes only slightly yellow.

Fatty substances: Shake 10 g with 50 ml of petroleum ether in a glass-stoppered cylinder and let stand for 4 hours, shaking frequently. Decant through a filter moistened with petroleum ether and further extract with two 25-ml portions of petroleum ether and filter. Allow the combined filtrates to evaporate spontaneously, then dry at 105° for 30 minutes. Not more than 1.0 mg of residue remains.

Chloride: Dissolve 1 g in 20 ml of H_2O and add 5 drops of HNO_3 and 1 ml of $AgNO_3$. Any resulting turbidity is not greater than that in a blank to which 0.02 mg of Cl has been added.

Nitrogen: Place 0.5 g in a 500-ml Kjeldahl flask, add about 25 mg of salicylic acid and 10 ml of H_2SO_4 and let stand for 30 minutes. Add 0.2 g of sodium thiosulfate and 7 g of potassium sulfate, and heat over a small flame until the liquid is colorless or nearly so.   Cool, add 60 ml of H_2O and 60 ml of 30% NaOH and distill about 50 ml into 5 ml of water containing 0.1 ml of 1 N HCl.   Add to the distillate 1 ml of 10% NaOH and 2 ml of Nessler solution.   The color is not darker than that produced by treating 0.025 mg of nitrogen (0.1 mg NH_4Cl) in the same manner as the lactose.

Sulfate: Dissolve 2 g in 15 ml of warm H_2O, add 1 ml of 0.1 HCl and 2 ml of $BaCl_2$ and allow to stand for 15 minutes.   Any resulting turbidity is not greater than that in a blank with 0.1 mg of SO_4 added.

Heavy metals: Dissolve 5 g in water to make 50 ml.   To 10 ml of the solution add 0.015 mg of Cu, dilute to 40 ml and add 1 ml of 1 N acetic acid (A).   To the remaining 40 ml add 1 ml of 1 N acetic acid (B).   Then to each add 10 ml of H_2S, mix and observe in 3–5 minutes. B is not darker than A.

Iron: Dissolve 1 g in water, add 2 ml of HCl and dilute to 50 ml.   Add about 50 mg of ammonium persulfate and 3 ml of ammonium thiocyanate solution, and mix.   Any resulting red color is not darker than that of a blank to which 0.01 mg of Fe has been added.

LEAD

Pb; at. wt. 207.21.

Bluish-gray, soft, granules, shot or sheets.   Soluble in dilute nitric acid; also slowly dissolved by solutions of the fixed alkali hydroxides.

Standards

Antimony and Tin (Sb, Sn)...max 0.005%		Iron (Fe)....................max 0.001%	
Arsenic (As)..................max 2 ppm		Nickel (Ni)..................max 0.001%	
Bismuth (Bi)...............max 0.001%		Silver (Ag)................max 0.0002%	
Copper (Cu)...............max 0.0005%		Total foreign metals..........max 0.05%	

Antimony and Tin: Dissolve 10 g in a mixture of 40 ml of H_2O and 15 ml of HNO_3 by warming on the steam bath.   Evaporate the solution to dryness on the steam bath and take up the residue with 100 ml of hot H_2O.   The solution is clear (antimony) and no insoluble matter (tin) remains.

Silver: Add 4 ml of H_2SO_4 to the above solution, let stand for 15 minutes, filter and wash with 10 ml of H_2O.   Evaporate the filtrate to copious acid fumes, cool, and *cautiously* dilute with water to 40 ml.   Allow to stand for 1 hour and filter.   To the filtrate add 3 drops of HCl.   No opalescence is produced.

Total foreign metals: To the solution from the preceding test add 40 ml of alcohol and allow to stand for 2 hours.   Filter without washing, evaporate the filtrate and ignite.   The residue does not exceed 5.0 mg.

Solution S: Dissolve 20 g of the lead in a mixture of 100 ml of water and 20 ml of HNO_3, warming on the steam bath if necessary.   Cool, slowly add with stirring 10 ml of H_2SO_4 previously mixed with 20 ml of water, and allow to stand until the precipitate has settled.   Filter on a sintered glass crucible and wash with about 25 ml of cold water.   Evaporate the filtrate and washings to sulfuric fumes. Cool, *continuously* add about 20 ml of water, cool again, filter, wash with 5 ml of cold water and dilute the filtrate with H_2O to 200 ml.

Arsenic: To 10 ml of *Solution S* add 2 ml of H_2SO_4 and evaporate to copious sulfuric fumes. Cool, add 10 ml of water, and determine the arsenic by the method on page 563. The stain, if any, is not greater than that produced by 0.002 mg of As.

Bismuth: Neutralize 40 ml of *Solution S* with ammonia, add 3 ml of 10% HNO_3, dilute to 50 ml, add 5 ml of a 5% solution of thiourea and mix. The solution is no more yellow than a control made with 0.02 mg of bismuth, 1 ml of 10% HNO_3 and 5 ml of the thiourea solution and in the same volume as the sample.

Copper: To 40 ml of *Solution S* contained in a separatory funnel add 5 ml of deleaded ammonium citrate solution; then add 3 drops of thymol blue indicator and 10% NH_3 until the indicator changes to bluish. Add 2 ml of a 0.1% solution of sodium diethyldithiocarbamate and 10 ml of carbon tetrachloride and shake for 1–2 minutes. The carbon tetrachloride separated from the aqueous layer is not darker than a control made with 0.02 mg of copper in an equal volume of solution treated in the same manner as the sample.

Iron: Dilute 10 ml of *Solution S* with 40 ml of H_2O, add 2 ml of HCl, 50 mg of ammonium persulfate and 3 ml of ammonium thiocyanate solution. Any resulting red color is not darker than that of control made with 0.01 mg of Fe, treated with the same quantities of the reagents and in the same final volume as the sample.

Nickel: Neutralize 20.0 ml of *Solution S* with NH_4OH and add 1 ml of HNO_3, 5 ml of a 10% solution of citric acid and 2 ml of bromine water. Stir and add diluted NH_4OH (1 + 1) until the bromine color is discharged. Now add 2 ml more of the NH_4OH, cool if necessary, and add 2 ml of an alcohol solution (1 + 100) of dimethylglyoxime. Dilute to 30 ml and let stand for 15 minutes. Any red color is not darker than that produced by treating 0.02 mg of nickel (Ni) in the same manner and in the same final volume as in the test with the sample.

LEAD ACETATE

$Pb(CH_3CO_2)_2 \cdot 3H_2O$; mol. wt. 379.34; anhydrous—85.75%; H_2O—14.25% Pb—54.62%; PbO—58.85%.

Colorless crystals or white granules; efflorescent. Soluble in 2 parts of water, 0.5 part of boiling water or 40 parts of alcohol; soluble in glycerol. It takes up CO_2 from the air, changing to an insoluble basic carbonate. *Keep in well-closed containers.*

Standards

Insoluble....................max 0.010%	Copper (Cu)................max 0.002%
Chloride (Cl)...............max 0.0005%	Iron (Fe)...................max 0.001%
Nitrate (NO₃)..............max 0.003%.	Zinc.......................max 0.01%
Alkalies, Earths (as sulfate)...max 0.050%	*Assay*

Insoluble: Dissolve 10 g in 100 ml of CO_2-free water containing 1 ml of glacial acetic acid. If an undissolved residue remains, filter, wash it with water slightly acidulated with acetic acid and dry at 105°. Its weight does not exceed 1.0 mg.

Chloride: To a solution of 2 g in 10 ml of H_2O add 1 ml of HNO_3 and 1 ml of $AgNO_3$. Any turbidity produced is not greater than that in a blank to which 0.01 mg of Cl has been added.

Nitrate: Dissolve 0.50 g in 20 ml of water and add 5 ml of 25% H_2SO_4. Shake well and allow to stand for 20 minutes, shaking several times during this period. Filter, or centrifuge and decant. To 10 ml of the filtrate add 20 mg of NaCl, 0.2 ml of diphenylamine solution, mix, then run in slowly 10 ml of H_2SO_4. Mix gently and allow to stand for 1 hour. No blue color results.

Alkalies, Earths, etc.: Dissolve 4 g in a mixture of 100 ml of water and 2 ml of glacial acetic acid, precipitate the lead with H_2S and filter. To 50 ml of the filtrate add 5 drops of H_2SO_4, evaporate and ignite. The residue does not exceed 1.0 mg (retain).

Copper: Dissolve 1 g in 15 ml of H_2O, add 5 ml of ammonium acetate solution, 2 ml of glacial acetic acid, 0.3 ml of pyridine and 1 ml of ammonium thiocyanate; then add 5 ml of chloroform and shake well. Any blue or green color in the chloroform is not deeper than that produced by treating 0.02 mg of Cu in the same manner as the sample.

Iron: Evaporate the residue from *Alkalies, Earths, etc.*, with 2 ml of HCl and 5 drops of HNO_3 to dryness on the steam bath. Take up the residue with 10 ml of water and 4 ml of HCl, and dilute to 100 ml. To 50 ml add about 30 mg of ammonium persulfate and 3 ml of ammonium thiocyanate, and mix. Any resulting red color is not darker than that of a control made with 0.01 mg of Fe, 2 ml of HCl and the same quantities of the reagents in the same final volume as with the sample.

Zinc: Dissolve 2 g in 25 ml of water, add while stirring 1 ml of H_2SO_4, and allow to settle for a few minutes. Filter and wash with 5 ml of water. Add to the filtrate 5 into drops of nitric acid, heat to boiling and add it while stirring to 20 ml 10% NH_3. Filter while hot and wash with a few ml of water. Neutralize the of filtrate with diluted $(1+1)$ HCl and add an excess of 1 ml of the acid. Cool and add 2 ml of freshly prepared 5% potassium ferrocyanide solution. No turbidity is produced in 15 minutes.

Assay: Weigh accurately about 1.5 g and dissolve it in 5 ml of glacial acetic acid and sufficient H_2O to make exactly 100 ml. Transfer exactly 20 ml to a 200-ml volumetric flask, dilute with 50 ml of water, heat to boiling and add 50 ml of 0.1 N potassium dichromate. Boil for 2 to 3 minutes, cool, dilute with H_2O to the 200-ml mark, mix well and allow the precipitate to subside. Withdraw exactly 100 ml of the clear liquid, transfer to a glass-stoppered flask, add 10 ml of 10% H_2SO_4 and 1 g of potassium iodide, let stand for 10 minutes, then titrate the liberated iodine, representing the excess of potassium dichromate, with 0.1 N thiosulphate, adding starch solution toward the end. One ml of 0.1 N dichromate = 0.01264 g $Pb(CH_3CO_2)_2 \cdot 3H_2O$, log 10175.

LEAD CARBONATE

$(PbCO_3)_2Pb(OH)_2$; mol. wt. 775.67; Pb—80.14%; PbO—86.33%.

White, heavy powder. Insoluble in water; soluble in dilute acids with effervescence.

Standards

Acetic acid—insoluble........max 0.020%		Copper (Cu)................max 0.003%	
Chloride (Cl)...............max 0.002%		Iron (Fe)..................max 0.005%	
Nitrate (NO₃)..............max 0.003%		Zinc (Zn)..................max 0.01%	
Alkalies, Earths (as sulfate)....max 0.20%		*Assay*....................min 79% Pb	

Acetic acid—insoluble: Heat 5 g with 50 ml of H_2O and 7 ml of glacial acetic acid until dissolved. Filter any undissolved matter, wash it with 2% acetic acid and dry at 105°. Its weight does not exceed 1.0 mg.

Chloride: Dissolve 1 g in 30 ml of H_2O and 2 ml of HNO_3, and add 1 ml of $AgNO_3$. Any resulting turbidity is not greater than that in a blank to which 0.02 mg of Cl has been added.

Nitrate: Suspend 0.50 g of sample in 5 ml of water and add glacial acetic acid, 2–3 drops at a time, shaking after each addition, until dissolved. Dilute to 20 ml and add 5 ml of 25% H_2SO_4. Shake well and allow to stand for 15 minutes, shaking several times during this period. Filter or, preferably, centrifuge and decant. To 10 ml of the filtrate add 20 mg of NaCl, 0.2 ml of diphenylamine solution, mix, then run in slowly without agitation 10 ml of H_2SO_4. After 5 minutes mix gently by swirling and allow to stand for 1 hour. No blue color results.

Alkalies, Earths, etc.: Dissolve 2 g in 20 ml of H_2O and 3 ml of HNO_3, dilute to 100 ml and precipitate the lead with H_2S. Filter, and to 50 ml of filtrate add 5 drops of H_2SO_4, evaporate and ignite. The residue does not exceed 2.0 mg (retain residue).

Copper: Dissolve 1 g by heating with 2 ml of glacial acetic acid and 5 ml of H_2O, then dilute to 15 ml. Add 5 ml of ammonium acetate solution, 0.3 ml of pyridine and 1 ml of ammonium thiocyanate, then add 5 ml chloroform and shake well. Any blue or green color produced in the chloroform is not deeper than that produced by treating 0.03 mg of Cu in the same manner as the sample.

Iron: Evaporate the residue from *Alkalies, Earths, etc.*, with 2 ml of HCl and 5 drops of HNO_3 to dryness on the steam bath. Take up the residue with 2 ml of HCl and dilute to 50 ml. To 10 ml add 2 ml of HCl and dilute to 50 ml. Add about 30 mg of ammonium persulfate and 3 ml of ammonium thiocyanate, and mix. Any red color produced is not darker than that of a blank to which 0.02 mg of Fe has been added.

Zinc: Dissolve 2 g in a mixture of 5 ml of glacial acetic acid and 20 ml of water. While stirring, add 2 ml of H_2SO_4 and allow to settle. Filter and wash with 5 ml of water. Add to the filtrate 5 drops of HNO_3, heat to boiling and pour, while stirring into 10 ml of 10% NH_3. Filter while hot and wash with a few ml of hot water. Neutralize the filtrate with HCl and add an excess of 1 ml of the acid. Cool and add 2 ml of freshly prepared 5% potassium ferrocyanide solution. No turbidity is produced in 15 minutes.

Assay: Lead carbonate may be assayed by the following method, and when so assayed it should show not less than 79% Pb. Weigh accurately about 0.30 g and dissolve it by warming with 10 ml of H_2O and 1 ml of glacial acid. Transfer the solution to a 200-ml volumetric flask and dilute with H_2O to about 75 ml. Heat to boiling, add 50 ml of 0.1 N potassium dichromate and boil for 2 to 3 minutes. Cool, dilute with water to the mark, mix well and allow to subside. Withdraw exactly 100 ml of the clear liquid and transfer into a glass-stoppered flask. Add 10 ml of 10% H_2SO_4 and 1 g of potassium iodide, let stand for 10 minutes, then titrate the liberated iodine, representing the excess of dichromate, with 0.1 N sodium thiosulfate, adding starch solution toward the end. One ml of 0.1 N dichromate = 0.006907 g Pb, log 83929.

LEAD CHLORIDE

$PbCl_2$; mol. wt. 278.12; Pb—74.49%; Cl—25.51%.

White, crystalline powder. Soluble in 100 parts of cold water or 35 parts of boiling water; insoluble in alcohol.

Standards

Insoluble in hot H_2O...........max trace	Alkalies, Earths, etc...........max 0.05%
Nitrate (NO_3)...............max 0.003%	Iron (Fe)..................max 0.001%

Insoluble: Dissolve 2 g in 100 ml of boiling H_2O. Not more than a trace of insoluble matter remains.

Nitrate: Dissolve 0.5 g in 20 ml of hot water, add a hot solution of 0.5 g of K_2SO_4 in 5 ml of water and stir well. Allow to cool to room temperature, filter or decant. To 10 ml of the filtrate add 0.2 ml of diphenylamine solution and 10 ml of H_2SO_4. No blue color is produced in 20 minutes.

Alkalies, Earths, etc.: Dissolve 3 g in 150 ml of hot H_2O, add 5 drops of HCl and precipitate the lead with H_2S. Dilute to 150 ml and filter. To 100 ml of the filtrate add 5 drops H_2SO_4, evaporate and ignite. The residue does not exceed 1.0 mg (retain).

Iron: Evaporate the residue from *Alkalies, Earths, etc.*, with 2 ml of HCl and 5 drops of HNO_3 to dryness on the steam bath. Take up the residue with 10 ml of water and 4 ml of HCl, and dilute to 20 ml. Dilute 10 ml of the solution to 50 ml. Add about 30 mg of ammonium persulfate and 3 ml of ammonium thiocyanate, and mix. Any red color produced is not darker than that of a blank to which 0.01 mg of Fe has been added.

LEAD CHROMATE

$PbCrO_4$; mol. wt. 323.22; Pb—64.10%; CrO_3—30.94%; Cr—16.09%.

Yellow to brownish-yellow powder. Insoluble in water; soluble·in hydrochloric or nitric acid and in solutions of alkali hydroxides.

Standards

Assay.................min 98% $PbCrO_4$	Carbon compounds (as C).....max 0.003%
Soluble substances............max 0.15%	Nitrate (NO_3)................max 0.01%

Assay: Weigh 0.4 g of the powdered sample, transfer to a 250-ml glass-stoppered flask and dissolve it by warming with 40 ml of 10% NaOH. Add 2 g of potassium iodide, 100 ml of H_2O and 15 ml of HCl, and let stand protected from light for

5 minutes.   Titrate the liberated iodine with 0.1 N sodium thiosulfate, adding starch solution toward the end.   One ml of 0.1 N thiosulfate $= 0.01077$ g $PbCrO_4$, log 03222.

$$PbCrO_4 + 3KI + 8HCl \rightarrow PbCl_2 + CrCl_3 + 3KCl + 3I + 4H_2O$$
and
$$2I + 2Na_2S_2O_3 \rightarrow Na_2S_4O_6 + 2NaI$$

Soluble substances: Boil 0.5 g of the powdered sample for 5 minutes with 100 ml of H_2O and 5 ml of glacial acetic acid, while stirring well.   Cool and filter. Evaporate 25 ml of the filtrate to dryness on the steam bath, dry the residue at 105° and weigh.   Heat 50 ml of the filtrate with 2g of the powdered sample for 5 minutes at 90°, cool, dilute to 50 ml and filter.   Evaporate 25 ml of this filtrate, dry at 105° and weigh the residue.   The difference between the two residues does not exceed 1.5 mg.

Carbon compounds: Ignite 4.0 g in a current of CO_2-free air or oxygen and pass the evolved gases into 20 ml of 2.5% NH_3.   For a control, add 1.1 ml of standard sodium carbonate solution ($= 0.12$ mg C) to 20 ml of the 2.5% NH_3.   Add 3 ml of barium chloride solution to each, mix and compare promptly.   The turbidity in the sample solution is not greater than that in the control.

Nitrate: To 10 ml of the filtrate obtained in the test for *Soluble substances* after heating with 2 g of the lead chromate, add 0.5 ml of 10% H_2SO_4 and follow with 0.2 ml of sulfurous acid and stir.   Allow to stand for 2 minutes, then add dropwise 0.1 N $KMnO_4$ until a permanent reddish color is produced.   Discharge the reddish color with a drop of diluted ($1+5$) sulfurous acid.   Now add 3 ml of 5% Na_2CO_3 solution and boil for a minute.   Filter or centrifuge and dilute the filtrate to 30 ml. To 15 ml of the filtrate contained in a small dish or small beaker, add 10 mg of Na_2CO_3.   For a control place in a similar vessel 5 ml of the filtrate, 2.0 ml of standard nitrate solution (0.02 mg NO_3) and add 10 mg of Na_2CO_3.   From here on treat both alike as follows: Evaporate on the steam bath to dryness, wash down the inside of the vessel with a few ml of water and re-evaporate on the steam bath to dryness.   Add 2 ml of warm phenoldisulfonic acid, mix well with the dry residue and heat on the steam bath for 15 minutes.   Cool, add 25 ml of water, make alkaline with NH_4OH, and dilute to 50 ml.   Any yellow color in the test sample is not darker than that of the control.

LEAD DIOXIDE

Brown Lead Oxide

PbO_2; mol. wt. 239.21; Pb—86.62%; active O—6.69%.

Dark brown powder.   Insoluble in water; soluble in hot, diluted hydrochloric acid or in nitric acid in the presence of reducing agents or hydrogen peroxide.

Standards

Assay.....................min 95% PbO_2	Nitrate (NO_3)...............max 0.005%	
Nitric acid H_2O_2 insoluble.....max 0.20%	Sulfate (SO_4)................max 0.050%	
Water-soluble substances......max 0.15%	Manganese (Mn)...........max 0.0002%	
Carbon compounds (as C).....max 0.003%	Other heavy metals...........to pass test	
Chloride (Cl)................max 0.002%	Not precipitated by H_2S.......max 0.50%	

Assay: Dry over H_2SO_4 for 4 hours, weigh accurately about 0.5 g, transfer to a flask. Add 15 ml of diluted HNO_3 $(1+2)$ and exactly 20 ml of diluted hydrogen peroxide (made by diluting 1 volume of 30% hydrogen peroxide with 30 volumes of H_2O). Stir until solution is complete, adding, if necessary, 100 ml of warm H_2O to hasten solution. Titrate the excess of hydrogen peroxide with 0.1 N potassium permanganate. Titrate also exactly 20 ml of the diluted hydrogen peroxide to which has been added 15 ml of the diluted HNO_3 and the same volume of H_2O as with sample. The difference represents the permanganate equivalent of sample. One ml of 0.1 N permanganate = 0.01196 g PbO_2, log 07773.

$$PbO_2 + 2HNO_3 + H_2O_2 \rightarrow Pb(NO_3)_2 + 2H_2O + O_2$$
$$5H_2O_2 + 6HNO_3 + 2KMnO_4 \rightarrow 2Mn(NO_3)_2 + 2KNO_3 + 8H_2O + 5O_2$$

Nitric acid—insoluble: To 1 g add 25 ml of H_2O, 3 ml of HNO_3 and, in small portions, 3 ml of 30% hydrogen peroxide or more if necessary. Stir and warm until no more dissolves. If an undissolved residue remains, filter, wash and ignite gently. Its weight does not exceed 2.0 mg.

Water-soluble substances: Boil 3 g with 75 ml of H_2O for 5 minutes, cool, dilute to 75 ml and filter. Evaporate 50 ml of the filtrate and ignite gently. No more than 3.0 mg of residue remains.

Carbon compounds: Ignite 4.00 g in a combustion tube in a current of CO_2-free air or oxygen and pass the evalued gases into 20 ml of 2.5% NH_3. For a control add 1.1 ml of standard sodium carbonate solution (0.12 mg C), to 20 ml of the 2.5% NH_3. Add 3 ml of barium chloride solution to each, mix and compare promptly. The turbidity in the sample solution is not greater than that in the control.

Chloride: To 1 g add 20 ml of H_2O, 2 ml of HNO_3 and 2 ml of 30% hydrogen peroxide. When dissolved, filter and add to the filtrate 1 ml of $AgNO_3$. Any resulting turbidity is not greater than that in a blank to which 0.02 mg of Cl has been added.

Nitrate: Dissolve 0.5 g of sample in a mixture of 15 ml of water, 1.5 ml of glacial acetic acid and 0.7 ml of 30% H_2O_2. Add while stirring 1.5 ml of 25% H_2SO_4, allow the precipitate to settle, filter and wash with water to 25 ml. Transfer 15 ml of the filtrate into a small dish and add 10% NaOH to slight alkalinity to litmus paper. For a control place 7.5 ml of the filtrate in a similar dish, add 3.0 ml of standard nitrate solution (0.03 mg NO_3) and the same volume of 10% NaOH as was used with the test sample. From here on treat both alike as follows: Evaporate on the steam bath to dryness. Wash down the inside of the dish with a few ml of water and re-evaporate to dryness on the steam bath. Add 2 ml of warm phenoldisulfonic acid, mix well with the dry residue, and heat on the steam bath for 15 minutes. Cool, add 25 ml of water, make alkaline with 10% NH_3 and dilute to 50 ml. Any yellow color in the test sample is not darker than that of the control.

Note: The approximate actual amount of NO_3 present may be found by measuring the color intensities of sample and control with a spectrophotometer and calculating the NO_3 in mg by the formula:

$$\frac{As}{Ac} \times \frac{0.03 \times 100}{wt}$$

$A$$s$ and $A$$c$ representing respectively the intensities of sample (s) and control solutions (c), and wt the weight of the sample in mg.

Sulfate: To 1 g add 10 ml of H_2O, 1 ml of glacial acetic acid, 1 ml of 30% hydrogen peroxide and 1 g of ammonium acetate, and gently boil until dissolved. Cool, dilute to 100 ml and mix well. To 20 ml add 2 ml of 10% barium acetate solution. Any turbidity produced in 15 minutes is not greater than that in a blank to which 0.1 mg of SO_4 has been added.

Manganese: Decompose 5 g with 15 ml of HCl, then add 10 ml of H_2SO_4 and evaporate to copious acid fumes. Cool, *cautiously* add 20 ml of H_2O and 0.5 g of the sample and heat on the steam bath for 5 minutes. Dilute to 50 ml and filter through asbestos or a glass filtering crucible. The color of the filtrate is not deeper than that of a control made by treating 0.01 mg Mn in the same manner, beginning with "then add 10 ml of H_2SO_4. . . ."

Other heavy metals: Dissolve 0.5 g in a mixture of 2 ml of HNO_3, 10 ml of H_2O and 5 ml of 3% hydrogen peroxide. Add to the solution 3 ml of H_2SO_4 and evaporate to sulfuric fumes. Cool, dilute to 100 ml and allow to settle. Filter (do not wash) and pass H_2S through the filtrate. No red color is produced, and any darkening is not greater than that produced by H_2S in the same volume of water containing 0.1 mg of Pb.

Not precipitated by H_2S: Evaporate the filtrate from the test for *Nitric acid—insoluble* to dryness on the steam bath. Moisten the residue with 5 drops of HCl, take it up in 100 ml of hot H_2O, and precipitate the lead with H_2S. Filter without washing, evaporate 50 ml of the filtrate, and ignite. The residue is not more than 2.5 mg.

LEAD MONOXIDE

Litharge; Yellow Lead Oxide

PbO; mol. wt. 223.21; Pb—92.83%.

Yellow or orange-yellow powder. Almost insoluble in water; soluble in nitric or acetic acid, also in warm solutions of fixed alkali hydroxides.

Standards

Assay.....................min 98% PbO	Bismuth (Bi)................max 0.003%
Acetic acid—insoluble.........max 0.20%	Copper (Cu).................max 0.005%
Ignition loss.................max 0.50%	Iron (Fe)....................max 0.002%
Chloride (Cl)................max 0.005%	Silver (Ag)...................to pass test
Nitrate (NO_3)...............max 0.003%	(limit about 0.0003%)
Alkalies, Earths, etc...........max 0.20%	

Assay: Apply the method of assay described for Lead Carbonate, previously drying the lead monoxide at 150°. One ml of 0.1 N potassium dichromate = 0.007441 g PbO, log 87157.

Acetic-acid—insoluble: Heat 4 g with 40 ml of H_2O and 10 ml of glacial acetic acid until no more dissolves. Filter any undissolved residue, wash it with 2% acetic acid, and dry at 105°. Its weight does not exceed 8.0 mg.

Ignition loss: Heat 3 g in a covered crucible to incipient fusion. The loss in weight is not more than 15.0 mg.

Chloride: Dissolve 0.5 g in a mixture of 25 ml of H_2O and 2 ml of HNO_3 and add 1 ml of $AgNO_3$. Any resulting turbidity is not greater than that in a blank to which 0.025 mg of Cl has been added.

Nitrate: Suspend 0.50 g of sample in 5 ml of water and add glacial acetic acid, 2–3 drops at a time, shaking after each addition, until the sample is dissolved. Dilute to 20 ml and add 5 ml of 25% H_2SO_4. Shake well and allow to stand for 15 minutes, shaking several times during this period. Filter or, preferably, centrifuge and decant. To 10 ml of the filtrate add 20 mg of NaCl, 0.2 ml of diphenylamine solution, mix, then run in slowly without agitation 10 ml of H_2SO_4. After 5 minutes mix gently by swirling and allow to stand for 30 minutes. No blue color results.

Alkalies, Earths, etc.: Dissolve 2 g by heating with 2 ml of HNO_3 and 30 ml of H_2O, dilute to 100 ml and precipitate the lead with H_2S. Filter, and to 50 ml of the filtrate add 5 drops of H_2SO_4, evaporate and ignite. Not more than 2.0 mg of residue remains (retain residue).

Bismuth: Dissolve 2 g in a mixture of 2 ml of HNO_3 and 15 ml of water, add 3 ml of H_2SO_4 and evaporate to copious sulfuric fumes. Cool, *cautiously* add 20 ml of water, again allow to cool, add sufficient water to make the volume 40 ml, and filter. Neutralize 20 ml of the filtrate with NH_3, add 3 ml of 10% HNO_3, and dilute to 30 ml. Add 10 ml of a freshly prepared 5% solution of thiourea and mix. The solution has no darker yellow color than a control made with 0.03 mg of Bi contained in 20 ml of water and treated as the solution of the sample beginning with "add 3 ml of 10% HNO_3 . . . ."

Copper: Dissolve 1 g by heating with 2.5 ml of glacial acetic acid and 15 ml of H_2O. Add to the solution 5 ml of ammonium acetate solution, 0.3 ml of pyridine and 2 ml of ammonium thiocyanate, then add 5 ml of chloroform and shake vigorously. Any blue or green color produced in the chloroform is not deeper than that produced by treating 0.03 mg of Cu in the same manner as the sample.

Iron: To the residue from *Alkalies, Earths, etc.*, add 2 ml of HCl, 2 ml of H_2O and 0.5 ml of HNO_3, and evaporate to dryness on the steam bath. Take up the residue with 2 ml of HCl and dilute to 50 ml. Add about 30 mg of ammonium persulfate and 3 ml of ammonium thiocyanate, and mix. Any red color produced is not darker than that of a blank to which 0.02 mg of Fe has been added.

Silver: Dissolve 5 g by heating with 50 ml of H_2O and 5 ml of HNO_3, then add 3 ml of H_2SO_4, previously diluted with 10 ml of H_2O. Allow to stand for 15 minutes, filter and evaporate the filtrate to strong fumes of SO_3. Cool, add cautiously 20 ml of H_2O and allow to stand for 1 hour. Filter and add 2 drops of HCl to the filtrate. No opalescence is produced.

LEAD NITRATE

$Pb(NO_3)_2$; mol. wt. 331.23; Pb—62.56%; NO_3—37.44%.

Colorless or white crystals. Soluble in 2 parts of water; almost insoluble in alcohol or in concentrated nitric acid.

Standards

Insoluble	max 0.005%	Copper (Cu)	max 0.002%
Chloride (Cl)	max 0.001%	Iron (Fe)	max 0.001%
Alkalies, Earths, etc.	max 0.10%	Silver (Ag)	to pass test
Bismuth (Bi)	max 0.0003%		(limit about 0.0003%)

Insoluble: Dissolve 20 g in 200 ml of H_2O and 2 ml of HNO_3 and heat on steam bath for 1 hour. Filter any undissolved matter, wash it with water and dry at 105°. Its weight does not exceed 1.0 mg.

Chloride: To a solution of 2 g in 20 ml of H_2O add 1 ml of HNO_3 and 1 ml of $AgNO_3$. Any resulting turbidity is not greater than that in a blank to which 0.02 mg of Cl has been added.

Alkalies, Earths, etc.: Dissolve 2 g in 100 ml of H_2O, precipitate the lead with H_2S and filter. To 50 ml of the filtrate add 5 drops of H_2SO_4, evaporate and ignite. Not more than 1.0 mg of residue remains (retain residue).

Bismuth: Dissolve 6.0 g in 20 ml of water, add 5 ml of H_2SO_4 and evaporate to the appearance of dense sulfuric fumes. Cool, *cautiously* add 25 ml of water and allow to stand for 15 minutes. Filter and wash with 5 ml of 10% H_2SO_4. Neutralize the filtrate with NH_3, add 2 ml of 10% HNO_3 and dilute to 40 ml. Now add 10 ml of a freshly prepared 5% solution of thiourea and mix. The solution has no darker yellow color than that obtained by treating a solution 0.02 mg of Bi in 40 ml of water as described above beginning with "add 2 ml of HNO_3. ..."

Copper: Dissolve 2 g in 25 ml of H_2O, add 10 ml of ammonium acetate solution, 2 ml of glacial acetic acid, 0.3 ml of pyridine and 2 ml of ammonium thiocyanate, then add 10 ml of chloroform and shake vigorously. Any blue or green color in the chloroform is not deeper than that produced by treating 0.04 mg of Cu in the same manner as the sample.

Iron: To the residue from *Alkalies, Earths, etc.*, add 2 ml of HCl and 2 ml of H_2O, and slowly evaporate to dryness on the steam bath. Take up the residue with 2 ml of HCl and dilute to 50 ml. Add about 30 mg of ammonium persulfate and 3 ml of ammonium thiocyanate, and mix. Any red color produced is not darker than that of a blank to which 0.01 mg of Fe has been added.

Silver: Dissolve 5 g in 50 ml of water, add 3 ml of H_2SO_4 previously diluted with 10 ml of H_2O and allow to stand for 15 minutes. Filter and evaporate the filtrate to copious acid fumes. Cool, cautiously add 20 ml of H_2O and allow to stand for 1 hour. Filter and add to the filtrate 2 drops of HCl. No opalescence is produced.

LEAD OXIDE, RED

Red Lead, Minium

Pb_3O_4; mol. wt. 685.63; PbO—65.10%; PbO_2—34.90%; available O—2.33%; total Pb—90.68%.

Heavy, orange-red powder. Insoluble in water; soluble in nitric or acetic acid in the presence of reducing substances or of hydrogen peroxide.

Standards

Assay................min 95% Pb_3O_4	Carbon compounds (as C).....max 0.005%
Nitric acid—insoluble..........max 0.1%	Manganese (Mn)............max 0.0005%
Water-soluble substances.......max 0.2%	Not precipitated by H_2S.......max 0.40%

Assay: Weigh accurately about 1 g, add 30 ml of diluted HNO_3 (1+1), then add exactly 20 ml of diluted hydrogen peroxide (made by diluting 1 volume of 30% hydrogen peroxide with 30 volumes of H_2O). Stir until no more dissolves, add 25 ml of water and titrate the excess of hydrogen peroxide with 0.1 N potassium permanganate. Titrate also with 0.1 N potassium permanganate exactly 20 ml of the same diluted hydrogen peroxide to which has been added 30 ml of the diluted HNO_3 and the same volume of water as with the sample. The difference represents the permanganate equivalent of the sample. One ml of 0.1 N permanganate = 0.03428 g Pb_3O_4, log 53504.

Nitric acid—insoluble: To 2 g add 40 ml of H_2O, 3 ml of HNO_3, then add, with stirring, sufficient hydrogen peroxide to dissolve. Filter, wash with water and dry at 105°. The insoluble does not exceed 2.0 mg.

Water-soluble substances: Boil 2 g with 50 ml of H_2O for 5 minutes, cool, dilute to 50 ml and filter. Evaporate 25 ml of the filtrate and ignite gently. Not more than 2.0 mg of residue remains.

Carbon compounds: Test as described for Lead Dioxide, but use only 2.5 g of sample. The result should be as there required.

Manganese: Decompose 5 g with 15 ml HCl, then add 10 ml of H_2SO_4 and evaporate to copious acid fumes. Cool, add *cautiously* 20 ml of H_2O and 0.5 g of lead dioxide and heat on the steam bath for 5 minutes. Dilute to 50 ml and filter through asbestos. The color of the filtrate is not deeper than that of a control made by treating 0.025 mg of Mn in the same manner, beginning with "then add 10 ml of H_2SO_4. . . ."

Not precipitated by H_2S: To 1 g add 20 ml of water and 2 ml of HNO_3, then add with stirring sufficient hydrogen peroxide to dissolve and dilute to 100 ml. Precipitate the lead with H_2S and filter. To 50 ml of the filtrate add 2 drops of H_2SO_4, evaporate and ignite. Not more than 2.0 mg of residue remains.

LEAD SUBACETATE

Basic Lead Acetate for Sugar Analysis

$Pb(CH_3CO_2)_2 \cdot Pb(OH)_2$; mol. wt. 566.5; Pb—73.1%; total PbO—78.8%; basic Pb—35.6%; basic PbO—39.4%.

White or nearly white, heavy powder. Soluble in water; almost insoluble in alcohol. Gradually absorbs carbon dioxide, becoming incompletely soluble in water. *Keep in tightly closed containers.*

Standards

Assay for basic Pb.............min 33%	Nitrate (NO_3)..............max 0.002%
Drying loss...................max 1.5%	Copper (Cu)................max 0.003%
Water–insoluble...............max 1.0%	Iron (Fe)...................max 0.002%
Acetic acid—insoluble........max 0.03%	Not precipitated by H_2S.......max 0.30%

Assay for basic lead: Weigh 1.0 g and dissolve it in exactly 50 ml of 0.1 N acetic acid.   Add 20 ml of 2% sodium oxalate solution, dilute to 100 ml, mix and filter, rejecting the first 25 ml.   To 25 ml of the filtrate add 2 drops of phenolphthalein and titrate the excess of acetic acid with 0.1 N NaOH.   One ml of 0.1 N acetic acid = 0.01116 g Pb, log 04766.

Drying loss: Weigh accurately about 1 g and dry at 105° for 2 hours.   The loss in weight corresponds to not more than 1.5%.

Water—insoluble: Shake 2 g in a small, stoppered flask with 50 ml of CO_2-free water for 10 minutes, filter at once, wash with CO_2-free water and dry at 105°. The insoluble residue weighs not more than 2.0 mg.

Acetic acid—insoluble: Dissolve 5 g in a mixture of 100 ml of H_2O and 5 ml of glacial acetic acid, warming if necessary.   Filter any undissolved residue, wash it with 5% acetic acid and dry at 105°.   Its weight does not exceed 1.5 mg.

Solution S: Dissolve 5 g in 42 ml of H_2O and 3 ml of glacial acetic acid, add 5 ml of 25% H_2SO_4, let stand for 10 minutes and filter.

Nitrate: To 5.0 ml of *Solution S* add 5 ml of water, 20 mg of NaCl and 0.2 ml of diphenylamine solution.   Mix, then slowly add 10 ml of H_2SO without agitation. After 5–10 minutes mix the liquids by swirling the beaker and allow to stand for 30 minutes.   No blue color results.

Copper: To 10 ml of *Solution S* add 10 ml of 10% ammonium acetate solution, 0.3 ml of pyridine, 2 ml of ammonium thiocyanate and 5 ml of chloroform, and shake vigorously.   Any resulting blue or green color in the chloroform is not deeper than that produced by treating 0.03 mg Cu in the same manner as the sample.

Iron: Dissolve 1 g in 5 ml of H_2O, add 2 ml of H_2SO_4 and heat to evolution of acid fumes.   Cool, dilute *cautiously* with H_2O to 40 ml and filter.   To 20 ml add 2 ml of HCl and dilute to 50 ml.   Add about 30 mg of ammonium persulfate and 3 ml of ammonium thiocyanate, and mix.   Any red color produced is not darker than that of a blank to which 0.01 mg of Fe has been added.

Not precipitated by H_2S: Dilute 10 ml of *Solution S* to 100 ml, precipitate all the lead with H_2S and filter.   Evaporate 50 ml of the filtrate and ignite.   The residue does not exceed 1.5 mg.

LEAD TETRAACETATE

$Pb(CH_3COO)_4$; mol. wt. 443.39; active oxygen—3.6%.

Colorless or nearly colorless small crystals.   The product in commerce, however, is usually more or less brown, due to the presence of PbO_2, and contains some free acetic acid.   Insoluble in and decomposed by water into PbO_2 and acetic acid; moderately soluble in glacial acetic acid, benzene, chloroform and nitrobenzene. With mineral acids it reacts like PbO_2.   *Avoid contact with the skin.   Keep tightly closed, protected from moisture, and in a cool place.*

Standards

Assay............min 90% $Pb(C_2H_3O_2)_4$ Not precipitated by H_2SO_4....max 0.20%
Insoluble in $HNO_3 + H_2O_2$....max 0.05%

Assay: Weigh accurately in a glass-stoppered weighing bottle about 1.5 g, and transfer it quickly into a 100-ml volumetric flask. Add 2 g of potassium acetate and 80 ml of 90% acetic acid (90 ml glacial acid + 10 ml H_2O); shake for a few minutes and let stand for 30 minutes with frequent shaking. Add 90% acetic acid to mark, mix well, and filter through a dry filter into a dry flask, rejecting the first 5 ml of the filtrate. Pipette 25 ml of the subsequent filtrate into a 2000-ml glass-stoppered flask and add a solution of 3 g of KI in 25 ml of water. Allow to stand for 15 minutes, then titrate the liberated iodine with 0.1 N thiosulfate, adding starch solution toward the end. One ml of 0.1 N thiosulfate = 0.02217 g $Pb(C_2H_3O_2)_4$, log 37967. Correct for a blank.

Insoluble in HNO_3 + H_2O_2: To 2.0 g add 25 ml of water and 3 ml of HNO_3; then add, in small portions, while warming and stirring, 3 ml of 30% H_2O_2, or more if necessary, until no more dissolves. If an insoluble residue remains, filter (reserve filtrate for next test), wash with water, dry at 105°, and weigh. The weight does not exceed 1.0 mg.

Not precipitated by H_2SO_4: To the filtrate from the preceding test add 3 ml of H_2SO_4 and evaporate to copious sulfuric fumes. Cool, *cautiously* dilute with 25 ml of water, and allow to stand for 1 hour. Filter, but do not wash, and evaporate one-half of the filtrate to dryness, and ignite. The weight of the residue does not exceed 2.0 mg.

L-LEUCINE

α-Aminocaproic Acid

$CH_3 \cdot CH(CH_3) \cdot CH_2 \cdot CH(NH_2) \cdot COOH$; mol. wt. 131.17; N—10.67%.

Small, white, lustrous plates, or white crystalline powder; odorless. Sublimes at about 150°. Soluble in about 40 parts of water, sparingly soluble in alcohol; soluble in diluted HCl, alkali hydroxides, and carbonates; moderately soluble in acetic acid.

Standards

Nitrogen (N).............10.7% ± 0.2%	Ammonium salts (as NH_3)....max 0.010%
Specific rotation in 20% HCl +	Heavy metals (as Pb).......max 0.001%
15.6° ± 0.5°	Iron (Fe)..................max 0.002%
Solubility...................to pass test	Methionine.................to pass test
Drying loss..................max 0.3%	(max about 0.05%)
Ignition residue.............max 0.05%	Tryptophan.................to pass test
Chloride (Cl)...............max 0.005%	(max about 0.03%)
Phosphate (PO_4)...........max 0.002%	Tyrosine....................to pass test
Sulfate (SO_4)..............max 0.010%	(max about 0.03%)

Nitrogen: Determine by the Kjeldahl method, using about 0.3 g of the dried sample, accurately weighed.

Specific rotation and Drying loss: Dry about 1 g, accurately weighed at 105°, for 2 hours: the loss in weight corresponds to not more than 0.3%. Dissolve

0.75 g of the dried sample in 20% HCl to make exactly 25 ml, observe the rotation of the solution in a 200-mm tube at 25° ± 2°, and calculate the specific rotation.

Solubility: Separate solutions of 0.5 g in 20 ml of warm water and 0.5 g in 10 ml of 10% HCl are clear and colorless.

Ignition residue: Moisten 2.0 g with 1 ml of H_2SO_4 and ignite to constant weight. The weight of the residue does not exceed 1.0 mg (retain residue).

Chloride: To a solution of 0.40 g of sample in 20 ml of water add 1 ml of HNO_3 and 1 ml of 0.1 N AgNO$_3$. Any resulting turbidity is not greater than that in a blank to which 0.02 mg of Cl has been added.

Phosphate: To a 0.5-g sample in a platinum crucible add 0.5 g of magnesium nitrate and 5 ml of water. Evaporate to dryness and ignite at a low temperature until the residue is nearly white. Add 10 ml of water and 3 ml of 25% H_2SO_4, and heat for 5 minutes. Then add 10 ml of hot water, filter, and wash to 20 ml. Add to the filtrate 1 ml each of phosphate reagent **A** and **B** and heat at 60° for 10 minutes. Any resulting blue color is not darker than that of a blank to which 0.01 mg PO_4 has been added.

Sulfate: Dissolve 1.0 g in 20 ml of warm water and 2 ml of 1 N HCl; add 2 ml of BaCl$_2$. If a turbidity is produced, it is not greater than that in a blank to which 0.1 mg of SO_4 has been added.

Ammonium salts: Dissolve 0.50 g in 60 ml of water in a small distilling flask, add 1 g of magnesium oxide, and distill about 40 ml into 5 ml of water containing 1 drop of 10% HCl. Dilute the distillate to 100 ml. To 40 ml of the dilution add 2 ml of 10% NaOH and 2 ml of Nessler solution. Any color produced is not darker than that of a control made with 0.05 mg of NH_3 (0.15 mg NH_4Cl) and treated as the sample.

Heavy metals: To the *Ignition residue* add 2 ml of HCl and 0.5 ml of HNO_3 and evaporate to dryness on the steam bath. Add to the residue 1 ml of 1 N HCl and 20 ml of hot water, digest for 5 minutes, cool, and dilute to 40 ml. To 20 ml of the dilution add 5 ml of H_2S. Any color produced is not darker than that in a control made with 0.01 mg of Pb, 0.2 ml of 1 N HCl, and 5 ml of H_2S in the same final volume as with the sample.

Iron: Dilute 10 ml of the solution prepared in the preceding test to 50 ml, add 2 ml of HCl and about 50 mg of ammonium persulfate, then add 3 ml of ammonium thiocyanate solution, and mix. If a red color is produced, it is not darker than that of a blank to which 0.01 mg of Fe has been added.

Methionine: Dissolve 0.10 g in 0.3 ml of H_2SO_4 saturated with anhydrous cupric sulfate. No yellow color is produced in 2 minutes.

Tryptophane: To 0.10 g of sample add 2 ml of water, 0.5 ml of 0.5% of vanillin in 50% acetic acid, 3 drops of a 10% solution of mercuric sulfate in 10% H_2SO_4, then add 15 ml of HCl and heat in water bath at 60° for 30 minutes. No pink or violet color appears.

Tyrosine: Dissolve 0.10 g in 3 ml of 10% H_2SO_4, and add 3 ml of a 10% solution of mercuric sulfate in 10% H_2SO_4; then add 0.5 ml of 5% sodium nitrite solution and allow to stand for 15 minutes. No red or pink color appears during this interval.

LEVULOSE

Fructose

H H H OH
HC—C—C—C—C(OH)·HC·OH; mol. wt. 180.16.
|OH OH H | H
|_____O_____|

White granules or a powder.   Very soluble in water; soluble in 10 parts of 75%
alcohol.

Standards

Specific rotation............ −88° to −90°	Sulfate (SO_4)................max 0.005%
Insoluble...................max 0.010%	Heavy metals (as Cu)........max 0.001%
Ignition residue.............max 0.050%	Iron (Fe)...................max 0.001%
Chloride (Cl)................max 0.001%	

Specific rotation: Prepare an aqueous solution containing the equivalent of
5 g of the sample, previously dried to constant weight over H_2SO_4, in 50 ml and
determine the rotation of the solution at 25°, using a 200-mm tube.   From the
observed angular rotation calculate the specific rotation, page 582.

Insoluble: Dissolve 10 g in 100 ml of H_2O and heat on the steam bath for 30
minutes.   If an insoluble residue remains, filter, wash it with H_2O and dry at 105°.
The weight of the insoluble residue does not exceed 1.0 mg.

Ignition residue: Char 2.0 g.   Cool, add 0.5 ml of H_2SO_4 and ignite gently at
first, then strongly (600°–800°) to constant weight.   Any residue present is not
more than 1.0 mg.

Chloride: Dissolve 1 g in 10 ml of H_2O, add 0.5 ml of HNO_3 and 1 ml of $AgNO_3$.
If a turbidity is produced it is not greater than that in a blank to which 0.01 mg of
Cl has been added.

Sulfate: Dissolve 2 g in 15 ml of H_2O, add 1 ml of 1 N HCl and 2 ml of $BaCl_2$
and allow to stand for 15 minutes.   Any turbidity produced is not greater than that
in a blank to which 0.10 mg of SO_4 has been added.

Heavy metals: Dissolve 2 g in 40 ml of H_2O, add 1 ml of 1 N acetic acid and
10 ml of H_2S.   Any darkening produced is not more than that in a blank to which
0.02 mg of Cu has been added.

Iron: Dissolve 1 g in 40 ml of H_2O.   Add 2 ml of HCl and dilute to 50 ml.   Add
about 50 mg of ammonium persulfate and 3 ml of ammonium thiocyanate, and mix
well.   Any red color produced is not darker than that in a blank to which 0.01 mg of
Fe has been added.

LITHIUM CARBONATE

Li_2CO_3; mol. wt. 73.89; Li—18.78%; CO_3—81.22%; CO_2—59.58%.

White powder.   Soluble in 80 parts of water, less soluble in hot water.

Standards

Acetic acid—insoluble........max 0.010%	Heavy metals (Pb)..........max 0.002%
Chloride (Cl)...............max 0.003%	Iron (Fe)..................max 0.002%
Nitrate (NO₃)..............max 0.001%	Magnesium (Mg)............max 0.010%
Phosphate (PO₄)...........max 0.001%	Potassium and Sodium
Sulfate (SO₄)...............max 0.10%	(K + Na).................max 0.1%
Ammonia (NH₃)............max 0.001%	*Assay*.......................min 99%
Calcium (Ca)..............max 0.020%	

Acetic acid—insoluble: To 10 g add 75 ml of water, then add in small portions 20 ml of glacial acetic acid and boil gently for 10 minutes. If an insoluble residue remains, filter, wash it with water (retain filtrate) and dry at 105°. The weight of the insoluble matter is not more than 1.0 mg.

Solution A: Dilute the filtrate from the preceding test with water to 150 ml.

Chloride: Dilute 5 ml of *Solution A* to 10 ml, and add 1 ml each of HNO_3 and $AgNO_3$. Any ensuing turbidity is not greater than that in a control made with 0.01 mg of Cl, 0.7 ml of the acetic acid and the same quantities of the reagents and in the same final volume as with the sample.

Nitrate: To 0.5 g add 5 ml of water, then add in small portions sufficient 25% H_2SO_4 to dissolve and dilute to 10 ml. Add 20 mg of NaCl and 0.2 ml diphenyl-amine solution and follow with 10 ml of H_2SO_4. No blue color appears on standing for 30 minutes.

Phosphate: To 15 ml of *Solution A* add 2 ml of 25% H_2SO_4 and 1 ml each of phosphate reagents **A** and **B** and heat at 60° for 10 minutes. Any blue color produced is not darker than that of a control made with 0.01 mg of PO_4 and the same quantities of the reagents and in the same final volume as used with the sample.

Sulfate: Dilute 7.5 ml of *Solution A* to 25 ml. To 10 ml of this solution add 1 ml of 1 N HCl and 2 ml of $BaCl_2$. Any turbidity produced in 10 minutes is not greater than that of a control made with 0.2 mg of SO_4 and the same quantities of the reagents in the same final volume as with the sample.

Calcium: Heat 75 ml of *Solution A* to boiling, add 5 ml of ammonium oxalate, make slightly alkaline with NH_3 and allow to stand for 4 hours. If a precipitate is present, filter on a filtering crucible, and wash with small volumes of cold water until washings give no turbidity with calcium acetate solution. Place the crucible in a beaker, add 50 ml of water and 3 ml of H_2SO_4, heat to 80° stirring the crucible during the heating, then titrate with 0.1 N $KMnO_4$ to a pale pink color persisting for 30 seconds. Not more than 0.5 ml of the $KMnO_4$ is consumed.

Note: The calcium may be determined by Flame Photometry (consult page 566).

Heavy metals: To 2.5 g add 15 ml of water and sufficient HCl to decompose the carbonate (about 7 ml). Evaporate to dryness on the steam bath and dissolve the residue in 50 ml of water. To 10 ml of the solution add 0.02 mg of Pb, 1 ml of 1 N acetic acid and dilute to 40 ml (*A*). To 30 ml of the solution add 1 ml of 1 N acetic acid and dilute to 40 ml (*B*). Then to each add 10 ml of H_2S. *B* is not darker than *A*.

Iron: Dissolve 1 g in 20 ml of H_2O and 5 ml of HCl. Boil the solution for 1 minute, cool and dilute to 50 ml. Add about 50 mg of ammonium persulfate and 3 ml of ammonium thiocyanate and mix. Any red color produced is not darker than that of a blank to which 0.02 mg of Fe has been added.

Magnesium: To 1.0 g add 15 ml of water and just sufficient HCl to dissolve. Heat to expel CO_2 and dilute to 20 ml. To 5 ml of the solution add 0.05 mg of magnesium (Mg) and dilute to 20 ml (A). Dilute the remaining 15 ml to 20 ml. To each add in succession 0.2 ml of thiazole yellow (titan yellow) solution and 2 ml of 10% NaOH (B). Any pink color in B is not deeper than that in A.

Potassium and Sodium: Dissolve 0.50 g in a few ml of water and a slight excess of HCl. Filter if necessary into a small flask and evaporate on a plate until all the water has evaporated and vapors of the alcohol are freely evolved. Add 1 drop of HCl and continue boiling 1–2 minutes longer. Remove from the hot plate, and if on cooling nearly to room temperature (about 30°) a turbidity or crystalline precipitate is present, filter on a small, tared, sintered glass crucible, wash with 1–2 ml of warm isoamyl alcohol, then with a few drops of absolute ether and dry at 105 for 30 minutes. The weight of the alkali chlorides does not exceed 1.2 mg.

Note: The individual amounts of potassium and sodium may be most expeditiously determined by Flame Photometry.

Assay: Weigh accurately about 1.3 g, add 50 ml of water, then add *cautiously* 50 ml of 1 N HCl. Boil gently to expel carbon dioxide, then cool and titrate the excess of acid with 1 N NaOH, using methyl red indicator. One ml of 1 N acid = 0.03694 g Li_2CO_3, log 56750.

LITHIUM CHLORIDE

LiCl; mol. wt. 42.40; Li—16.37%; Cl—83.63%.

White, deliquescent crystals or granules. Soluble in about 1 part of water; soluble in ethanol, ether, acetone and amyl alcohol. *Keep in tightly closed containers.*

Standards

Assay dried basis..........min 98% LiCl	Barium (Ba)................max 0.005%
Insoluble...................max 0.010%	Calcium (Ca)...............max 0.020%
Neutrality...................to pass test	Heavy metals (as Pb)........max 0.001%
Nitrate (NO_3)...............max 0.001%	Iron (Fe)...................max 0.002%
Phosphate (PO_4)...........max 0.001%	Magnesium (Mg).............max 0.010%
Sulfate (SO_4)...............max 0.020%	Potassium and Sodium K + Na..max 0.1%
Ammonium compounds	
(as NH_3).................max 0.003%	

Assay: Weigh accurately about 1.3 g previously dried at 120°, and dissolve it in water to make exactly 50 ml. Using 5.0 ml of the solution, determine the LiCl by either of the methods for Assay of Chlorides and Thiocyanates, page 565. One ml of 0.1 N $AgNO_3$ = 0.004240 g LiCl, log 62737.

Insoluble: Dissolve 10 g in 100 ml of water and heat on the steam bath for 30 minutes. Filter any undissolved matter, wash it with water and dry at 105°. The insoluble residue does not exceed 1.0 mg.

Neutrality: Dissolve 2 g in 20 ml of water, and add 1 drop of methyl red. If a red color is produced, it requires not more than 0.3 ml of 0.02 N alkali to change to yellow. If a yellow color is produced, not more than 0.3 ml of 0.02 N acid is required to change it to pink.

Nitrate: Dissolve 0.5 g in water, add 0.2 ml of diphenylamine solution and dilute to 10 ml. Cool the solution in ice water for 2–3 minutes, then withdraw it from the cooling bath and holding the beaker at an angle of about 45°, slowly run in along the sides of the beaker 10 ml of H_2SO_4 without agitation. Allow to stand for 10 minutes, then mix gently by swirling the contents and allow to stand for 1 hour. No blue color appears.

Phosphate: Dissolve 2 g in 20 ml of H_2O, add 2 ml of 25% H_2SO_4 and 1 ml each of phosphate reagents Λ and **B**, and place in water at 60° for 10 minutes. Any resulting blue color is not darker than that of a control made with 0.02 mg of PO_4, 2 ml of 25% H_2SO_4 and 1 ml each of the phosphate reagents in the same volume as used with the sample.

Sulfate: To a solution of 1 g in 15 ml of H_2O, add 1 ml of 0.1 N HCl and 2 ml of $BaCl_2$. Any turbidity produced is not greater than that in a blank with 0.2 mg of SO_4 added.

Ammonium compounds: To a solution of 0.7 g in 50 ml of H_2O, add 1 ml of 10% NaOH and 2 ml of Nessler solution. The resulting color is not darker than that of a blank to which 0.02 mg of NH_3 has been added.

Barium: Dissolve 2 g in 20 ml of H_2O, filter, if necessary, and divide the filtrate into 2 equal portions. To one portion add 1 ml of 10% H_2SO_4; to the other portion add 1 ml of H_2O. At the end of 2 hours the two portions are equally clear.

Calcium: Dissolve 5 g in 50 ml of H_2O, add 1 ml of HCl and heat to boiling. Add to the hot solution 5 ml of ammonium oxalate, make alkaline with ammonia, and allow to stand for 4 hours. Filter on a filtering crucible and wash with H_2O until the washings give no turbidity with calcium acetate solution. Place the crucible in a beaker, cover it with H_2O, add 3 ml of H_2SO_4, heat to 80°, and titrate with 0.1 N potassium permanganate to a pale pink color persisting for 30 seconds. Not more than 0.5 ml of the permanganate is consumed.

Heavy metals: Dissolve 4 g in water to make 40 ml. To 10 ml add 0.02 mg of Pb and 1 ml of 1 N acetic acid and dilute to 40 ml (A). To the remaining 30 ml add 1 ml of 1 N acetic acid and dilute to 40 ml (B). Then to each add 10 ml of H_2S; B is not darker than A.

Iron: Dissolve 1 g in 10 ml of water, add 2 ml of HCl and dilute to 50 ml. Add about 50 mg of ammonium persulfate and 3 ml of ammonium thiocyanate solution, and mix. Any red color produced is not darker than that of a blank to which 0.02 mg of Fe has been added.

Magnesium: Dissolve 1 g in 45 ml of water. Add 0.5 ml of Thiazole Yellow solution and follow with 5 ml of 10% NaOH. Any pink color produced is not deeper than that of a control made with 0.1 mg of magnesium (Mg), and the same quantities of the reagents in the same volume as the sample.

Potassium and Sodium: Dissolve 0.50 g in 1 ml of water in a small flask. Add 1 drop of HCl and 15 ml of isoamyl alcohol and heat on the hot plate until the water has evaporated and vapors of the alcohol are freely evolved, then boil for 1–2 minutes longer. Remove from the hot plate and allow to cool to about 30°. If a turbidity or crystalline matter is present, filter on a tared, small, sintered glass crucible, wash with 1–2 ml of warm isoamyl alcohol, then with a few drops of absolute ether and dry at 110° for 30 minutes. The weight of the NaCl and KCl does not exceed 1.2 mg.

Note: The individual amounts of potassium and of sodium may be most expeditiously determined by Flame Photometry.

LITHIUM NITRATE

$LiNO_3$; mol. wt. 68.95; Li—10.07%; NO_3—89.93%.

Colorless crystals or white granules; deliquescent.   Soluble in 2 parts of water; soluble in alcohol.   *Keep in tightly closed containers.*

Standards

Insoluble	max 0.010%	Barium (Ba)	max 0.005%
Drying loss (water)	max 4.0%	Calcium (Ca)	max 0.020%
Neutrality	to pass test	Heavy metals (as Pb)	max 0.001%
Chloride (Cl)	max 0.002%	Iron (Fe)	max 0.002%
Phosphate (PO_4)	max 0.001%	Magnesium (Mg)	max 0.010%
Sulfate (SO_4)	max 0.030%	Potassium and Sodium,	
Ammonium compounds		K + Na	max 0.1%
(as NH_3)	max 0.003%		

Drying loss: Dry about 1 g, accurately weighed, to constant weight at 120°. The loss in weight is not over 4%.

Neutrality: Dissolve 2 g in 20 ml of water, and add 1 drop of methyl red.   If a red color is produced, not more than 0.2 ml of 0.02 N alkali is required to change it to yellow.   If a yellow color is produced, not more than 0.2 ml of 0.02 N acid is required to change it to pink.

Chloride: To a solution of 1 g in 20 ml of H_2O add 1 ml of HNO_3 and 1 ml of $AgNO_3$.   Any resulting turbidity is not greater than that in a blank to which 0.02 mg of Cl has been added.

Phosphate: Dissolve 2 g in 5 ml of H_2O, add 6.5 ml of 25% H_2SO_4 and heat to incipient SO_3 fumes.   Cool, *cautiously* add 20 ml of H_2O and 1 ml each of phosphate reagents **A** and **B**, and heat at 60° for 10 minutes.   Any resulting blue color is not darker than that of a control made with 0.02 mg of PO_4, 2 ml of 25% H_2SO_4 and 1 ml each of the phosphate reagents in the same volume as with the sample.

Sulfate: Dissolve 1 g in 5 ml of water, add 5 ml of hydrochloric acid and evaporate to dryness on the steam bath.   Dissolve the residue in 20 ml of water.   To 10 ml of the solution add 1 ml of 0.1 N HCl and 2 ml of $BaCl_2$.   Any resulting turbidity is not greater than that in a control made with 0.2 mg of SO_4, 1 ml of 0.1 N HCl and 1 ml of $BaCl_2$ in the same volume as the sample.

Calcium: Determine as described for Lithium Chloride.   Not more than 0.5 ml of the permanganate is consumed.

Heavy metals: Dissolve 4 g in 40 ml water.   To 10 ml add 0.02 mg of Pb, 1 ml of 1 N acetic acid and dilute to 40 ml (A).   To the remaining 30 ml add 1 ml of 1 N acetic acid and dilute to 40 ml (B).   Then to each add 10 ml of H_2S; B is not darker than A.

Insoluble; Ammonium compounds; Barium; Iron; Magnesium: Apply the tests described for Lithium Chloride.   The results conform to those there stated.

Potassium and Sodium: Evaporate 0.5 g of the sample in a small flask with two 5-ml portions of HCl to dryness on the water bath.   Dissolve the residue in 1 ml of water, add 1 drop of HCl, add 10 ml of isomyl alcohol, and proceed as described under Lithium Chloride beginning with "and heat on a hot plate. ..." The result should be as there stated.

Note: The determination of the alkali metals (K, Na) is preferably made by Flame Photometry.   Consult page 566, etc.

LITHIUM SULFATE

$LiSO_4 \cdot H_2O$; mol. wt. 127.96; anhydrous—85.92%; H_2O—14.08%; Li—10.85%; SO_4—75.07%.

Colorless crystals or white granules.   Soluble in 3 parts of water; almost insoluble in alcohol.

Standards

Insoluble	max 0.010%	Calcium (Ca)	max 0.020%
Neutrality	to pass test	Heavy metals (as Pb)	max 0.001%
Chloride (Cl)	max 0.003%	Iron (Fe)	max 0.002%
Phosphate (PO₄)	max 0.001%	Magnesium (Mg)	max 0.010%
Nitrate (NO₃)	max 0.001%	Potassium and Sodium,	
Ammonium compounds		K + Na	max 0.1%
(as NH₃)	max 0.003%		

Neutrality: Dissolve 2 g in 20 ml of water, and add 1 drop of methyl red.   If a red color is produced, it requires not more than 0.2 ml of 0.02 N alkali to change to yellow.   If a yellow color is produced, not more than 0.2 ml of 0.02 N acid is required to change it to pink.

Chloride: Dissolve 0.7 g in 20 ml of H_2O, add 1 ml of HNO_3 and 1 ml of $AgNO_3$. Any resulting turbidity is not greater than that in a blank to which 0.02 mg of Cl has been added.

Insoluble; Phosphate; Nitrate; Ammonium compounds; Calcium; Heavy metals; Iron; Magnesium: Apply the tests given for Lithium Chloride. The results comply with the requirements there stated.

Potassium and Sodium: Dissolve 1.0 g in 50 ml of H_2O and add a solution of 3.5 g of lead acetate in 40 ml of H_2O.   Dilute to 100 ml, mix well, let settle and filter. Precipitate the lead from 50 ml of the filtrate with H_2S, filter and wash the lead sulfide with 10 ml of H_2O.   Add to the filtrate 5 ml of HCl and evaporate to dryness on the steam bath in a small flask, then proceed as described under Lithium Chloride. The results should be as there required.

Note: The above procedure for the determination of potassium and sodium is very cumbersome.   Flame photometry (consult page 566, etc.) offers a more advantageous method for this purpose and should be used if the necessary equipment, etc., are available.

LITMUS PAPER

Strips of 0.6 × 5 cm, or sheets 20 × 25 cm.   *Keep in well-closed containers.* The pH range of litmus is: 4.5 red; 8.3 blue.

LITMUS PAPER, BLUE

Standards

Sensitiveness (to 0.0005 N acid).....................to pass test

Rosin acids.................to pass test

Ignition residue.............to pass test

Sensitiveness: A strip of the paper stirred continuously in 100 ml of 0.0005 N HCl changes to red in 45 seconds.

Rosin acids: Immerse a strip of the paper in a solution of 0.1 g $AgNO_3$ in 50 ml of water.   The color of the paper does not change in 30 seconds.

Ignition residue: Ignite 10 strips or a piece of sheet 5 × 7 cm.   The residue does not exceed 4.0 mg.

LITMUS PAPER, RED

Standards

Sensitive (to 0.0005 N alkali).....................to pass test

Ignition residue.............to pass test

Sensitiveness: A strip of the paper stirred continuously in 100 ml of 0.0005 N alkali changes to blue in 30 seconds.

Ignition residue: Ignite 10 strips or a piece of sheet 5 × 7 cm.   The residue does not exceed 4.0 mg.

L-LYSINE MONOHYDROCHLORIDE

1,5-Diamino-*n*-Caproic Acid Hydrochloride

$HCl \cdot H_2N \cdot CH_2(CH_2)_3CH(NH_2)COOH$;   mol. wt. 182.66;   N—15.34%;   HCl—19.97%.

Colorless or white crystals or white crystalline powder.   Soluble in about 3 parts of water, sparingly soluble in alcohol.   Melts at about 264°.

Standards

Nitrogen (N)............15.3% ± 0.25%
HCl content.............20.0% ± 0.3%
Specific rotation in
   1 N HCl...............+20.5° ± 0.5%
Solubility....................to pass test
Drying loss...................max 0.3%

Ignition residue.............max 0.05%
Phosphate (PO_4)...........max 0.002%
Sulfate (SO_4)...............max 0.010%
Ammonium salts (as NH_3)....max 0.010%
Heavy metals (as Pb)........max 0.001%
Iron (Fe)...................max 0.002%

Nitrogen: Determine by the Kjeldahl method, using about 0.2 g of the dried sample.

HCl content: Using an accurately weighed quantity of about 0.5 g of the dried (at 105°) sample, determine the HCl by either of the methods for Assay for Chlorides and Thiocyanates, page 565. One ml of 0.1 N $AgNO_3$ = 0.003646 g HCl, log 56182.

Specific rotation; Drying loss: Dry about 1 g, accurately weighed, at 105° for 2 hours. The loss in weight corresponds to not more than 0.3%. Dissolve 0.75 g of the dried sample in 1 N HCl to make exactly 25 ml, and determine the rotation of the solution in a 200-mm tube at 25° ± 2°; then calculate the specific rotation.

Solubility: A solution of 1.0 g in 20 ml of water is complete, clear, and colorless.

Ignition residue: Char well 2.0 g, cool, add 0.5 ml of H_2SO_4 and ignite gently at first, then strongly to constant weight. The weight of the residue does not exceed 1.0 mg.

Ammonium salts (as NH_3): Perform this test as described under Arginine Hydrochloride, but use 20 ml of the solution (instead of 10 ml). The result conforms with the requirement there stated.

Phosphate, Sulfate, Heavy metals, Iron: Test as described under Arginine Monohydrochloride. The results should be as there stated.

MAGNESIUM

Mg; at wt. 24.32.

Magnesium is silver white and is available in the form of ribbon, turnings, wire and powder. Sp. gr. 1.738; melts at 651°; boils at 1100°. Readily reacts with acids with the evolution of hydrogen.

Standards

Solubility in HCl.............to pass test	Heavy metals (as Pb)........max 0.005%
Metals precipitated by NH_4OH—	Iron (Fe)..................max 0.030%
Al etc. (as oxides).........max 0.30%	Zinc (Zn)..................max 0.005%

Solubility in HCl: Place 2.5 g of the metal in a 300-ml Erlenmeyer flask, add 50 ml of water, then add through a funnel in the neck of the flask 2–3 ml portions of HCl at a time, allowing the reaction to subside before adding the next portion of the acid (about 20 ml of the acid will be required). No insoluble residue remains (retain the solution).

Solution S: Dilute the solution from the preceding test to 100 ml.

Metals precipitated by NH_4OH: Dilute 40 ml of *Solution S* to 75 ml and dissolve 3 g of ammonium chloride in the solution. Neutralize with NH_4OH, and add 5 drops of bromine water. Heat to boiling, add 2 ml of NH_4OH, boil for 1 minute and filter. Set aside the filtrate without the washing for the test for zinc. Wash the precipitate well with hot water, dry and ignite. The weight of the ignited precipitate does not exceed 3.0 mg.

Heavy metals: To 20 ml of *Solution S* add 10% NH_3 until a slight precipitate is produced which does not dissolve on stirring. Add just sufficient warm, diluted HCl to dissolve the precipitate and 5 drops more, then dilute to 50 ml. To 10 ml add 0.015 mg of Pb and dilute to 40 ml (A). Then add to A and to the remaining 40 ml of the solution (B) 10 ml of H_2S. B is not darker than A.

Iron: To 2.0 ml of *Solution S* add 2 ml of HCl and 50 mg of ammonium persulfate, shake, dilute to 50 ml and add 3 ml of ammonium thiocyanate. The resulting red color is not darker than that of a blank to which 0.015 mg of Fe has been added.

Zinc: To the filtrate from the test for *Metals precipitated by NH₄OH*, add HCl to make it slightly acid and dilute to 100 ml. To 20 ml add 0.5 g of ammonium tartrate and 2 ml of NH_4OH and shake with 10 ml of dithizone-chloroform solution. If the chloroform solution is free of pink color, zinc (and copper) is absent and the test is discontinued. If a pink color is present, draw off the chloroform solution into a small separatory funnel and shake it out with two 15-ml portions of approximately 0.01 N HCl. Discard the chloroform solution. To the HCl extract in the separatory funnel add approximately 0.5 M (7%) sodium acetate until the pH is 4.5 to 5.0; then shake the solution with 10 ml of dithizone-carbon tetrachloride solution. If this solution acquires a pink color, it is not darker than that produced by treating a solution of 0.01 mg of Zn with the same volume of the sodium acetate solution and dithizone-carbon tetrachloride as the sample.

MAGNESIUM ACETATE

$Mg(CH_3CO_2)_2 \cdot 4H_2O$; mol. wt. 214.47; anhydrous—66.39%; Mg—11.34%.

Small colorless or white crystals; deliquescent. Freely soluble in water or alcohol. *Keep in well-closed containers.*

Standards

Insoluble.................max 0.005%	Calcium (Ca).................max 0.02%
Chloride (Cl)...............max 0.002%	Heavy metals (as Pb)........max 0.001%
Nitrogen compounds (as N)...max 0.001%	Iron (Fe).................max 0.0005%
Sulfate (SO₄)...............max 0.005%	Manganese (Mn).............max 0.001%
Barium (Ba)................max 0.003%	Sodium (Na)......to pass test max 0.02%

Insoluble: Dissolve 10 g in 100 ml of water and 1 ml of glacial acetic acid and heat for 30 minutes. Filter any undissolved matter, wash, and dry at 105°. The weight of the insoluble residue is not more than 1.0 mg.

Chloride: Dissolve 1 g in 20 ml of water, add 1 ml of nitric acid and 1 ml of silver nitrate. Any turbidity produced is not more than that in a blank with 0.02 mg of Cl added.

Nitrogen compounds: Dissolve 1 g in 40 ml of H_2O in a distilling flask. Add 20 ml of 10% NaOH and 0.5 g of powdered Devarda metal, and let stand for 2 hours protected from loss or access of NH_3. Then distill about 40 ml into 5 ml of water containing 1 drop of diluted HCl and add to the distillate 1 ml of 10% NaOH and 2 ml of Nessler solution. The color is not darker than that produced by treating 0.01 mg of nitrogen (0.04 mg NH_4Cl) in the same manner as the sample.

Sulfate: Dissolve 2 g in 10 ml of water, add 2 ml of 1 N HCl and 2 ml of $BaCl_2$, and shake well. Any turbidity observed in 10 minutes is not greater than that of a control made with 0.1 mg of SO_4.

Barium: Dissolve 1 g in 10 ml of H_2O and add 2 ml of 1 N H_2SO_4. Any turbidity produced in 30 minutes is not more than that in a similar solution of the sample to which no H_2SO_4 has been added.

Calcium: Dissolve 1 g in 50 ml of 95% alcohol, add 25 ml of 25% H_2SO_4 and let stand overnight. No precipitate or turbidity is produced. If crystals are formed, they should dissolve upon slightly warming the solution.

Heavy metals: Dissolve 4 g in 20 ml of water, add 5 ml of 10% HCl and dilute to 40 ml. To 10 ml of the solution add 0.02 mg of Pb and dilute to 40 ml (A). Dilute the remaining 30 ml to 40 ml (B). Then to each add 10 ml of H_2S. B is not darker than A.

Iron: Dissolve 2 g in 10 ml of water. Add 3 ml of HCl, 30 mg of ammonium persulfate and dilute to 50 ml. Now add 3 ml of ammonium thiocyanate solution and mix. Any red color produced is not darker than that of a blank to which 0.01 mg of Fe has been added.

Manganese: Dissolve 4 g in 30 ml of water, add 10 ml of HNO_3, 5 ml of H_3PO_4 and 5 ml of H_2SO_4 and boil for 2 minutes. Cool a little, add 0.25 g of potassium periodate and boil gently for 5 minutes. Any resulting pink color is not darker than that produced by treating 0.01 mg of Mn (0.2 ml of standard manganese solution) exactly as the sample.

Sodium: Dissolve 1.0 g of sample in 1 ml of water and filter if not clear. Add to the clear solution 15 ml of uranyl magnesium acetate solution (page 558) and 5 ml of alcohol, and stir well. The solution is clear in 20 minutes.

Note: The sodium and calcium may also be determined by Flame Photometry.

MAGNESIUM CARBONATE

Approx. $(MgCO_3)_4 \cdot Mg(OH)_2 \cdot 5H_2O$; mol. wt. 485.8; Mg—25.0%; MgO—41.5%.

White powder, or light, friable masses. Insoluble in water; soluble in dilute acids with effervescence.

Standards

Acid—insoluble, Alumina, etc..max 0.020%	Barium (Ba)...............max 0.003%
Chloride (Cl)...............max 0.005%	Calcium (Ca)................max 0.10%
Nitrate (NO₃)..............max 0.003%	Heavy metals (as Pb)........max 0.002%
Phosphate (PO₄)............max 0.001%	Iron (Fe)...................max 0.005%
Sulfur compounds (as SO₄)....max 0.020%	Water-soluble substances......max 0.40%
Alkali carbonate (Na₂CO₃)....max 0.040%	Assay (MgO)...................min 40%

Acid–insoluble, Alumina, etc.: Mix 10 g with 20 ml of water, add slowly, with stirring, 10 ml of H_2SO_4 and heat in a platinum dish to strong sulfuric fumes. Cool, *cautiously* take up the residue with 120 ml of water, neutralize to methyl red with ammonium hydroxide and add 1 ml excess of the ammonium hydroxide. Boil the solution and filter while hot through a small filter paper. Discard the filtrate. Pour over the precipitate on the paper a few ml of hot 1:1 HCl, and wash with a little hot water. Make the filtrate just alkaline with ammonium hydroxide, boil to remove free NH_3, and filter through the same filter paper. Wash the filter thoroughly with hot water, then ignite it in a tared platinum crucible and weigh. The weight does not exceed 2.0 mg.

Chloride: Dissolve 2 g in 20 ml of H_2O and 2 ml of HNO_3 and dilute to 50 ml. To 20 ml add 1 ml of $AgNO_3$. Any turbidity produced is not greater than that in a blank to which 0.02 mg of Cl has been added.

Nitrate: Suspend 0.20 g in 5 ml of water, add 25% H_2SO_4 until dissolved and dilute to 10 ml. Add 20 mg of NaCl and 0.2 ml of diphenylamine solution, mix and then add 10 ml of H_2SO_4. No blue color is produced in 1 hour.

Phosphate: Dissolve 2 g in 20 ml of H_2O and 2.0 ml of H_2SO_4; boil for 1 minute. Cool, dilute with H_2O to 20 ml and filter. Add to the filtrate 1 ml each of phosphate reagents **A** and **B** and heat at 60° for 10 minutes. If a blue color is produced it is not darker than a control made with 0.02 mg of PO_4, 0.3 ml of H_2SO_4 and 1 ml each of the phosphate reagents in the same volume as used with the sample.

Sulfur compounds: Mix 1 g with 10 ml of H_2O and 5 drops of bromine water, heat for a few minutes, then add, in small portions, 3 ml HCl and evaporate to dryness on the steam bath. Dissolve the residue in 20 ml of H_2O and 1 ml of 0.1 N HCl, filter and add to the filtrate 2 ml of $BaCl_2$. Any resulting turbidity after 15 minutes is not greater than that in a control made with 0.2 mg of SO_4, 1 ml of 0.1 N HCl and 2 ml of $BaCl_2$ in the same volume as with the sample.

Alkali carbonate; Water-soluble substances: Boil 3 g with 45 ml of H_2O for 5 minutes, restore original volume with hot H_2O, and filter while hot. Titrate 15 ml of the filtrate with 0.1 N acid, using methyl red indicator. Not more than 0.7 ml of the acid is required. Evaporate another 15 ml of the filtrate and ignite. The residue is not more than 4.0 mg.

Barium: Dissolve 2.0 g in 15 ml of water with a moderate excess of HCl (about 5 ml) and boil the solution for 1 minute. Now make it slightly alkaline with ammonia, add 2 g of NH_4Cl, bring to a boil and filter. Dilute the filtrate to 20 ml, add 1.0 ml of potassium chromate solution and sufficient ammonia to produce a clear yellow color. No turbidity is produced in 5 minutes.

Calcium: Mix 2 g with 5 ml of H_2O, add HCl dropwise until just dissolved, then dilute to 10 ml and filter. Add to the filtrate 30 ml of 25% H_2SO_4 and 75 ml of alcohol and let stand overnight. Filter (if crystals are formed, warm until they dissolve), wash with a mixture of 2 volumes alcohol and 1 volume of 25% H_2SO_4, dry and ignite. The weight of the ignited precipitate ($CaSO_4$) does not exceed 7.0 mg.

Note: The calcium may be determined directly by Flame Photometry (page 566)

Heavy metals: Heat 2 g with 15 ml of water, add HCl until just dissolved, and evaporate to dryness on the steam bath. Redissolve the crystals formed in 10 ml of H_2O, and re-evaporate. Dissolve the residue in water to make 40 ml. To 10 ml of the solution add 0.02 mg of Pb and 1 ml of 1 N acetic acid, and dilute to 40 ml (A). To the remaining 30 ml of the solution add 1 ml of 1 N acetic acid and dilute to 40 ml (B). Then to each add 10 ml of H_2S. B is not darker than A.

Iron: Dissolve 0.5 g in 10 ml of water and 2 ml of HCl and boil for 1 minute. Cool, and dilute to 50 ml. To 20 ml of the solution add 2 ml of HCl and dilute to 50 ml. Add about 30 mg of ammonium persulfate and 3 ml of ammonium thiocyanate, and mix. Any red color produced is not darker than that of a blank to which 0.01 mg of Fe has been added.

Assay: The MgO (or Mg) content of magnesium carbonate may be determined by the following method. Weigh accurately 2.0 g, add 30 ml of water and just sufficient HCl to dissolve. Dilute with water to exactly 200 ml and mix well. Determine the magnesium in 25 ml of the solution by the method described for Magnesium Oxide, beginning with "Dissolve in it 2 g of ammonium chloride. . . ."

MAGNESIUM CHLORIDE

$MgCl_2 \cdot 6H_2O$; mol. wt. 203.33; anhydrous—46.84%; H_2O—53.16%; Mg—11.96%; Cl—34.88%.

Colorless, deliquescent crystals. Soluble in 0.6 part of water or 2 parts of alcohol. Keep in well-closed containers.

Standards

Insoluble....................max 0.005%	Ammonia (NH_3)............max 0.002%
Alcohol—insoluble............to pass test	Arsenic (As)................max 1 ppm
Neutrality...................to pass test	Barium (Ba)...............max 0.003%
Nitrate (NO_3)...............max 0.001%	Calcium (Ca).........max about 0.010%
Phosphate (PO_4)...........max 0.0005%	Heavy metals (as Pb).......max 0.0005%
Sulfate (SO_4)...............max 0.002%	Iron (Fe).................max 0.0005%
Alkali metals (Na + K).......max 0.05%	Manganese (Mn)...........max 0.0005%

Insoluble: Dissolve 20 g in 100 ml of water and heat on the steam bath for 1 hour. If an undissolved residue is present, filter, wash with water and dry at 105°. Its weight does not exceed 1.0 mg.

Alcohol—insoluble: Two grams dissolve completely in 10 ml of alcohol.

Neutrality: Dissolve 5.0 g in 50 ml of CO_2-free water, and add 2 drops of bromothymol blue solution. If a yellow color is produced it changes to blue by the addition of 0.2 ml of 0.02 N NaOH. The pH of a 2 M solution of $MgCl_2$ is 5.6–6.2 (theory 6.0).

Nitrate: Dissolve 0.5 g in water, add 0.2 ml diphenylamine solution and dilute to 10 ml. Cool the solution in water for 2–3 minutes; then holding the beaker at an angle of about 45°, slowly run in along the sides of the beaker 10 ml of H_2SO_4 without agitation. Allow to stand for 15 minutes; then mix gently by swirling the contents of the beaker and allow to stand for 1 hour. No blue color appears.

Phosphate: Dissolve 4 g in 20 ml of H_2O, add 2 ml of 25% H_2SO_4 and 1 ml each of phosphate reagents **A** and **B**; then heat at 60° for 10 minutes. Any blue color produced is not deeper than that of a blank with 0.02 mg of PO_4 added.

Sulfate: To 2 g dissolved in 10 ml of H_2O, add 1 ml of 0.1 N HCl and 2 ml of $BaCl_2$. No turbidity is produced in 1 hour.

Alkali metals: Dissolve 2.0 g in 50 ml of water and add 50 ml of alcohol. Add in small portions and with stirring sufficient of alcoholic ammonium carbonate solution (see Note at end of this paragraph) to precipitate all the magnesium. Stir vigorously for a few minutes and allow to stand for 1 hour. Dilute with water to 150 ml, mix and filter through a fritted glass crucible, or dry paper filter. Evaporate 75 ml of the filtrate in a tared dish to a few ml, add 3 drops of H_2SO_4, evaporate, heat gently to expel excess H_2SO_4 and ammonium salts, then ignite strongly to constant weight. After correcting for the weight of ignited residue from half the volume of the alcoholic ammonium carbonate solution as used in the test, the weight of the residue does not exceed 1.7 mg.

Note: The alcoholic ammonium carbonate solution is prepared as follows: Mix in a flask 80 ml of water, 90 ml of alcohol and 18 ml of 28% NH_3. Add 20 g of *coarsely* powdered ammonium carbonate, stopper and let stand with frequent shaking for several hours (or overnight). For use decant the clear liquid from any excess of ammonium carbonate.

Note: The estimation of the sodium (and of potassium if present) may be most satisfactorily accomplished by Flame Photometry (consult page 566).

Ammonia: Dissolve 1 g in 90 ml of H_2O, add 10 ml of 10% NaOH and allow to settle. Decant 50 ml and add 2 ml of Nessler solution. The color is not darker than that in a control made with 0.01 mg NH_3, 5 ml of the NaOH and 2 ml of Nessler solution in the same volume as with the sample.

Arsenic: Determine in 2 g by the method on page 563. The stain is not greater than that from 0.002 mg of As.

Barium: Dissolve 2.0 g in 15 mi of water, add 2 drops of glacial acetic acid and filter if not clear. Add to the solution 2 g of NH_4Cl, 1 ml of 10% potassium chromate solution, and sufficient 10% NH_3 to make the color clear yellow, and mix well. Treat 15 ml of the water as used for solution of sample, including filtration if solution was filtered, exactly as the solution of the reagent. After 10 minutes both are equally clear when viewed in the same light.

Calcium: Dissolve 2.5 g in 50 ml of 95% alcohol, add 25 ml of 25% H_2SO_4, and let stand overnight. No precipitate or turbidity is produced. If crystals are formed, they should dissolve upon slightly warming the solution.

Note: The calcium may be quantitatively determined by Flame Photometry.

Heavy metals: Dissolve 5 g of sample in sufficient H_2O to make 50 ml. To 10 ml add 0.015 mg of Pb, dilute to 50 ml and add 1 ml of 1 N acetic acid (A). To the remaining 40 ml add 1 ml of 1 N acetic acid (B). Then to each add 10 ml of H_2S. B is not darker than A.

Iron: Dissolve 2 g in 10 ml of water, add 2 ml of HCl and dilute to 50 ml. Add about 30 mg of ammonium persulfate and 3 ml of ammonium thiocyanate solution, and mix. Any red color produced is not darker than that of a blank to which 0.01 mg of Fe has been added.

Manganese: Dissolve 4 g in 30 ml of water, add 10 ml of HNO_3 and 5 ml of H_2SO_4, and evaporate to the appearance of dense sulfuric fumes. Cool, *cautiously* add 35 ml of water, 10 ml of HNO_3 and 5 ml of phosphoric acid, and boil gently for 5 minutes. Cool a little, add 0.25 g of potassium periodate and boil gently for 5 minutes. Any resulting pink color is not darker than that produced by treating 0.02 mg of Mn (0.2 ml of standard manganese solution) exactly like sample.

MAGNESIUM NITRATE

$Mg(NO_3)_2 \cdot 6H_2O$; mol. wt. 256.43; anhydrous—57.85%; H_2O—42.15%; Mg—9.48%; NO_3—48.37%.

Colorless crystals; deliquescent. Soluble in 1 part of water; soluble in alcohol. *Keep in well-closed containers.*

Standards

Insoluble....................max 0.005%	Ammonia (NH_3).............max 0.005%
Neutrality...................to pass test	Barium (Ba)................max 0.003%
Chloride (Cl)...............max 0.002%	Calcium (Ca)................max 0.01%
Phosphate (PO_4)...........max 0.0005%	Heavy metals..............max 0.0005%
Sulfate (SO_4)...............max 0.005%	Iron (Fe)..................max 0.0005%
Alkali metals (Na + K).......max 0.05%	Manganese (Mn)...........max 0.0005%

Chloride: Dissolve 1 g in 50 ml of water and add 1 ml of nitric acid and 1 ml of silver nitrate. Any turbidity resulting in the test is not greater than that in a blank with 0.02 mg of Cl added.

Phosphate: To 4 g add 10 ml of 25% H_2SO_4 and heat to incipient sulfuric fumes. Cool, dilute to 20 ml and add 1 ml each of phosphate reagents **A** and **B**, and heat at 60° for 10 minutes. Any blue color produced is not darker than that in a control made with 0.02 mg of PO_4, 2 ml of 25% H_2SO_4 and the same quantities of the other reagents and in the same volume as with the sample.

Sulfate: Evaporate 2 g with 5 ml of HCl to dryness on the steam bath. Dissolve the residue in 20 ml of H_2O and add 1 ml of 0.1 N HCl and 2 ml of $BaCl_2$. If a turbidity is produced, it is not greater than that in a control made with 0.2 mg of SO_4, 1 ml of 0.1 N HCl and 2 ml of $BaCl_2$ in the same volume as the sample.

Alkali metals: Dissolve 2.0 g in 50 ml of water, add 50 ml of alcohol and proceed as described under Magnesium Chloride, beginning with "Add in small portions. . . ." The results should be as there stated.

Ammonia: Dissolve 1 g in 90 ml of H_2O, add 10 ml of 10% NaOH and allow to settle. Decant 40 ml, dilute to 50 ml and add 2 ml of Nessler solution. The color is not darker than that in a control made with 0.02 mg NH_3, 4 ml of the NaOH and 2 ml of Nessler solution in the same volume as with the sample.

Barium: Dissolve 2.0 g in 15 ml of water, add 2 drops of glacial acetic acid and filter if not clear. Add to the solution 2 g of NH_4Cl, 1 ml of 10% potassium chromate solution, and sufficient 10% NH_3 to make the color clear yellow, and mix well. Treat 15 ml of the water as used for solution of sample, including filtration if solution was filtered, exactly as the solution of the reagent. After 10 minutes both are equally clear when viewed in the same light.

Manganese: Dissolve 4 g in 40 ml of water, add 10 ml of HNO_3, 5 ml of phosphoric acid and 5 ml of H_2SO_4, and boil gently for 2 minutes. Cool slightly, add 0.25 g of potassium periodate and boil for 5 minutes. Any resulting pink color is not darker than that produced by treating 0.02 mg of Mn (0.2 ml of standard manganese solution) exactly like the sample.

Insoluble; Neutrality; Calcium; Heavy Metals; Iron: Apply the tests described under Magnesium Chloride. The results conform to the requirements there given.

MAGNESIUM OXIDE

MgO; mol. wt. 40.32; Mg—60.32%.

Fine white powder. Absorbs moisture and carbon dioxide from the air. Almost insoluble in water; soluble in dilute acids. *Keep in well-closed containers.*

Standards

Hydrochloric acid—insoluble.. max 0.020%	Alkali carbonate (Na_2CO_3)...... max 0.5%
Ammonium hydroxide precipitate	Water-soluble substances....... max 0.5%
(Al_2O_3, etc.)............. max 0.020%	Barium (Ba)............... max 0.005%
Ignition loss.................. max 3.0%	Calcium (Ca)........... max about 0.05%
Chloride (Cl)............... max 0.010%	Heavy metals (as Pb)........ max 0.003%
Nitrate (NO_3)............... max 0.003%	Iron (Fe)................... max 0.010%
Phosphate (PO_4)........... max 0.002%	Manganese (Mn)............. max 0.001%
Sulfur compounds (as SO_4).... max 0.005%	*Assay* (of ignited)............. min 98.5%

Hydrochloric acid—insoluble: Dissolve 5 g in 100 ml of H_2O and 25 ml of HCl. Boil the solution for 5 minutes, filter any undissolved matter, retain filtrate, wash it, and dry at 105°. The insoluble matter does not exceed 1.0 mg.

Ammonium hydroxide precipitate: To the filtrate from *Hydrochloric acid— insoluble* add 2 drops of methyl red indicator solution, then add NH_4OH until the color just turns yellow and follow with an excess of 1 ml. Boil the solution for 5 minutes, allow to cool, and filter. Dissolve the precipitate on the filter with 10 ml of hot 1:1 HCl and wash with H_2O to 25 ml. Add to filtrate 1 drop methyl red and follow with NH_4OH until the color of the solution just changes to yellow; then add 0.5 ml excess. Boil for 5 minutes, filter through the same filter, wash with hot water, and ignite. The weight of the ignited precipitate is not more than 2.0 mg.

Ignition loss: Weigh accurately about 0.5 g and ignite it in a covered platinum crucible at a bright red heat or in a muffle furnace for 30 minutes. The loss in weight corresponds to not more than 3.0 %.

Chloride: Dissolve 0.2 g in 15 ml of water and 2 ml of nitric acid, filter, dilute to 20 ml and add 1 ml of silver nitrate. The resulting turbidity is not greater than that in the blank to which 0.02 mg of Cl has been added.

Nitrate: Suspend 0.20 g in 5 ml of water, add 25% H_2SO_4 until dissolved and dilute to 10 ml. Add 20 mg of NaCl and 0.2 ml of diphenylamine solution, mix and then add 10 ml of H_2SO_4. No blue color is produced in 1 hour.

Phosphate: Mix 1 g with 10 ml of H_2O, add cautiously 3 ml of H_2SO_4 and boil for 1 minute. Cool, *cautiously* add 15 ml H_2O and filter. Add to the filtrate 1 ml each of phosphate reagents **A** and **B** and heat at 60° for 10 minutes. Any blue color produced is not deeper than that in a control made with 0.02 mg of PO_4, 0.3 ml of H_2SO_4 and the same quantities of the phosphate reagents and in the same volume as with the sample.

Sulfur compounds: Mix 4.0 g with 20 ml of H_2O, add 10 mg of sodium carbonate and 5 drops of bromine water, and heat for a few minutes. Add 20 ml of HCl and evaporate to dryness on the steam bath. Dissolve the residue in 20 ml of H_2O, add 1 ml of 0.1 N HCl, filter and add to the filtrate 2 ml $BaCl_2$. The resulting turbidity, after 15 minutes, is not greater than that of a control made as follows: Evaporate 10 mg of sodium carbonate, 20 ml of HCl, 0.2 mg of SO_4 and 5 drops bromine water to dryness on the steam bath. Take up the residue with 1 ml of 0.1 N HCl and 20 ml of water, then add 2 ml of $BaCl_2$.

Alkali carbonate; Water-soluble substances: Boil 3 g with 45 ml of H_2O for 5 minutes, dilute to the original volume with hot H_2O and filter while hot. Titrate 15 ml of the cooled filtrate with 0.1 N acid, using methyl red indicator.

Not more than 1.0 ml of the acid is required to produce a pink color.   Evaporate another 15 ml of the filtrate and ignite gently.   The residue is not more than 5.0 mg.

Note: Some of the alkalinity and of the residue in this test is derived from dissolved MgO.   The actual sodium (Na) content may be determined by Flame Photometry.

Barium: Dissolve 1.0 g in 15 ml of water with a slight excess of HCl (about 5 ml) and boil the solution for 1 minute.   Now make it slightly alkaline with ammonia, bring to a boil and filter.   Dilute the filtrate to 20 ml, add 2 g of NH_4Cl, 1.0 ml of potassium chromate solution and sufficient ammonia to produce a clear yellow color.   No turbidity is produced in 5 minutes.

Calcium: Mix 1 g with 4 ml of H_2O, add HCl dropwise until dissolved, dilute to 10 ml and filter.   To 5 ml of the filtrate add 50 ml of alcohol (95%) and 20 ml of 25% H_2SO_4 and allow to stand overnight.   No precipitate or turbidity is produced which does not clear up on warming the solution slightly.

Note: The calcium may be advantageously determined by Flame Photometry.

Heavy metals: Mix 2 g with 10 ml of H_2O and add just sufficient HCl to dissolve.   Evaporate to dryness on the steam bath, dissolve the magnesium chloride formed in 20 ml of H_2O and re evaporate.   Dissolve the residue in water to make 40 ml.   To 10 ml add 0.03 mg of Pb and 1 ml of 1 N acetic acid, and dilute to 40 ml (A).   To the remaining 30 ml add 1 ml of 1 N acetic acid, and dilute to 40 ml (B). Then to each add 10 ml of H_2S. B is not darker than A.

Iron: Dissolve 0.5 g in 10 ml of water and 3 ml of HCl, boil for 1 minute and dilute to 50 ml.   To 10 ml add 2 ml of HCl, dilute to 50 ml, add about 30 mg of ammonium persulfate and 3 ml of ammonium thiocyanate, and mix.   Any red color produced is not darker than that of a blank to which 0.01 mg of Fe has been added.

Manganese: Dissolve 2.0 g in 40 ml of water and 5 ml of H_2SO_4.   Add 10 ml of HNO_3 and 5 ml of phosphoric acid and boil gently for 2 minutes.   Cool slightly, add 0.25 g of potassium periodate and boil gently for 5 minutes.   Any resulting pink color is not darker than that produced by treating 0.02 mg of Mn (0.2 ml of standard manganese solution) exactly like the sample.

Assay: Weigh accurately in a closed weighing bottle about 0.4 g of the ignited sample, or use the ignited residue from the test for *Ignition loss*.   Add 15–20 ml of water, then add cautiously just sufficient HCl to dissolve, dilute to exactly 200 ml and mix well.   Dilute 50 ml of the solution with 25 ml water.   Dissolve in it 2 g of ammonium chloride and add sufficient ammonium hydroxide to make the solution distinctly alkaline to litmus paper.   Heat to 60°–70° and add to the hot solution, while stirring, 8-hydroxyquinoline solution until the supernatant liquid becomes yellow.   Now add 4 ml of ammonium hydroxide or more, if necessary, to make the solution strongly alkaline, stir for 10 minutes, and allow to stand until the precipitate has settled well.   Filter on a tared filtering crucible which has been previously dried at 105°, and wash the precipitate well with hot 1% aqueous NH_3. Finally dry the precipitate of magnesium oxyquinoline $Mg(C_9H_6NO)_2 \cdot H_2O$ for 2 hours at 105°.   The weight of the magnesium oxyquinoline multiplied by 0.122 = MgO, or by 0.07352 = Mg.

MAGNESIUM PERCHLORATE, ANHYDROUS

$Mg(ClO_4)_2$; mol. wt. 223.23.

White powder, granular or flaky. It is quite stable to heat up to 250°. At higher temperatures it decomposes. It dissolves in water with the evolution of much heat.

Anhydrous magnesium perchlorate is a most efficient drying agent for gases. The product of commerce may contain an amount of water equivalent to a dihydrate, but according to G. Frederick Smith et al.,[1] even the trihydrate is very effective for drying gases.

Standards

Water......................max 5.0%	Nitrate (NO_3)...............max 0.005%
Free acid (as $HClO_4$)..........max 0.05%	Sulfate (SO_4).................max 0.20%
Alkalinity (as MgO)...........max 0.02%	Calcium (Ca).................max 0.15%
Chloride (Cl)................max 0.02%	

Water: Weigh accurately about 1 g and dry to constant weight at 180°–200°. The loss in weight corresponds to not more than 5.0%.

Free acid; Alkalinity: Dissolve 2 g in 25 ml of water and add a drop of methyl orange. If a red color is produced, it requires not more than 0.1 ml of 0.1 N NaOH to change it to yellow. If a yellow color is produced, it requires not more than 0.1 ml of 0.1 N HCl to change the color to pink.

Chloride: Dissolve 1 g in 25 ml of water, add 0.5 ml of nitric acid and 1 ml of silver nitrate. Any resulting turbidity is not greater than that produced in a blank to which 0.02 mg of Cl has been added.

Nitrate: Dissolve 50 mg in 10 ml of water and add to the solution 10 mg of NaCl and 0.10 ml of diphenylamine solution. Mix, cool in ice water for 1 minute, remove from the cooling bath and gradually add 10 ml of H_2SO_4. No blue color is produced after 30 minutes.

Sulfate: Dissolve 1 g in 100 ml of water. Dilute 10 ml of the solution with water to 20 ml and add 1 ml of 1 N HCl and 2 ml of barium chloride. The resulting turbidity is not greater than that of a control made with 0.10 mg of SO_4, the same quantities of the reagents used with the sample and in the same volume of solution.

Calcium: Dissolve 1 g in 25 ml of water containing 3 ml of sulfuric acid, add 50 ml of alcohol and allow to stand overnight. If a precipitate is present, warm the solution gently and filter through a Gooch crucible with an asbestos mat which has been previously washed with dilute sulfuric acid and ignited. Wash the precipitate well with a mixture of two volumes of alcohol and one volume of 25% H_2SO_4 and ignite. The weight of the ignited precipitate of calcium sulfate does not exceed 0.005 g.

[1] Willard, H. H., and Smith, G. Frederick, *J. Am. Chem. Soc.* **44**, 2255 (1922).

MAGNESIUM SULFATE

$MgSO_4 \cdot 7H_2O$; mol. wt. 246.49; anhydrous—48.84%; H_2O—51.16%; Mg—9.87%; SO_4—38.97%; MgO—16.36%.

Colorless crystals; efflorescent. Soluble in 2 parts of water; almost insoluble in ethanol; slowly soluble in glycerol.

Standards

Insoluble...................	max 0.005%	Arsenic (As)................ max 1 ppm
Neutrality.................	to pass test	Calcium (Ca)........... max about 0.02%
Chloride (Cl)...............	max 0.0005%	Heavy metals (as Pb)....... max 0.0005%
Nitrate (NO_3).............	max 0.001%	Iron (Fe).................. max 0.0005%
Phosphate (PO_4)..........	max 0.0005%	Manganese (Mn)........... max 0.0005%
Alkali metals (K, Na)........	max 0.05%	Sodium (Na).......... max about 0.02%
Ammonia (NH_3)............	max 0.002%	

Insoluble: Dissolve 20 g in 200 ml of water and heat on the steam bath for 1 hour.   If an insoluble residue is present, filter, wash it with water and dry at 105°. The weight of the insoluble residue does not exceed 1.0 mg.

Neutrality: Dissolve 5 g in 50 ml of CO_2-free water and add 2 drops of bromo-thymol blue.   If a yellow color is produced, it is changed to blue by 0.25 ml of 0.02 N NaOH.   If a blue color is produced, it changes to yellow on the addition of 0.20 ml of 0.02 N HCl.

Chloride: To a solution of 2 g of the sample in 20 ml of water add 1 ml of nitric acid and 1 ml of silver nitrate.   Any resulting turbidity is not greater than that in a blank to which 0.01 mg of Cl has been added.

Nitrate: Dissolve 0.5 g in 10 ml of water.   Add to the solution 20 mg of NaCl, 0.2 ml diphenylamine solution and follow slowly with 10 ml of H_2SO_4.   No blue color appears after 30 minutes.

Phosphate: Dissolve 2 g in 20 ml of water, add 2 ml of 25% H_2SO_4, 1 ml each of phosphate reagents **A** and **B** and heat at 60° for 10 minutes.   If a blue color is produced, it is not darker than the blank with 0.01 mg of PO_4 added.

Alkali metals (as Na): Dissolve 2.0 g in 50 ml of water, add 50 ml of alcohol, then add in small portions and while stirring sufficient alcoholic ammonium car-bonate solution (see Note at end of this paragraph) to precipitate all the magnesium. Stir vigorously for a few minutes and allow to stand for 1 hour.   Dilute with water to 150 ml, mix and filter through a fritted glass crucible or dry paper filter.   Evapo-rate 75 ml of the filtrate in a tared dish to a few ml.   Add 5 drops of H_2SO_4, evaporate, heat gently to expel any excess of H_2SO_4 and of ammonium salts, then ignite strongly to constant weight.   After correcting for the weight of ignited residue from half the volume of the alcoholic ammonium carbonate as used in the test, the weight of the residue does not exceed 2.0 mg.

Note: The alcoholic ammonium carbonate solution is prepared as follows: Mix in a flask 80 ml of water, 90 ml of alcohol and 18 ml of 28% NH_3.   Add 20 g of coarsely powdered ammonium carbonate, stopper and let stand with frequent shaking for several hours (or overnight).   For use decant the clear liquid from any excess of ammonium carbonate.

Ammonia: Dissolve 2 g in 90 ml of water, add 10 ml of 10% NaOH and allow to settle.   Decant 50 ml and add 2 ml of Nessler solution.   The color is not darker than that of a control made with 0.02 mg NH_3 (0.06 mg NH_4Cl), 5 ml of the NaOH and 2 ml of Nessler solution in the same volume as used with the sample.

Arsenic: Test 2 g by the method on page 563.   The stain is not greater than that from 0.002 mg of As.

Calcium: Dissolve 1.5 g in 25 ml of 25% H_2SO_4, add 50 ml of alcohol and let stand overnight.   No precipitate or turbidity is formed.   If crystals separate, they should dissolve on warming the solution.

Note: The calcium and strontium may be determined directly by Flame Photometry.

Heavy metals: Dissolve 5 g in water to make 50 ml.   To 10 ml add 0.015 mg of Pb, dilute to 40 ml and add 1 ml of 1 N acetic acid (A).   To the remaining 40 ml add 1 ml of 1 N acetic acid (B).   Then to each add 10 ml of H_2S; B is not darker than A.

Iron: Dissolve 2 g in 20 ml of water, add 2 ml of HCl and dilute to 50 ml.   Add about 50 mg of ammonium persulfate and 3 ml of ammonium thiocyanate, and mix.   Any resulting red color is not darker that that of a blank to which 0.01 mg of Fe has been added.

Manganese: Dissolve 2 g in 40 ml of H_2O, add 5 ml of HNO_3, 5 ml of phosphoric acid and 5 ml of H_2SO_4, and boil gently for 2 minutes.   Cool, add 0.25 g of potassium periodate and boil for 5 minutes.   Any pink color produced is not darker than that in a blank to which 0.01 mg of Mn has been added.

Sodium: A 10% solution gives no pronounced yellow color when tested on a platinum wire in a flame.   The Na may be quantitatively determined by Flame Photometry.

MAGNESON

p-Nitrobenzene-azo-resorcinol

$O_2N-\!\langle\ \rangle\!-N\!=\!N-\!\langle\ \rangle\!-OH$; mol. wt. 259.22.

Brownish-red powder.   Insoluble in water; soluble in dilute aqueous sodium hydroxide solutions.   It is used for the detection of magnesium,[1,2,3] with which it forms, in alkaline solutions, a bright blue lake.   Most metals, other than alkali and alkaline earths, interfere.   Large quantities of ammonium salts impair its sensitiveness.   It is claimed to have a sensitiveness of 0.01 mg in 10 ml of solution.

Standards

Melting range.................196°–198°	Ignition residue................max 0.2%
Sensitiveness................to pass test	

Sensitiveness: (*a*) Dissolve 5 mg of sample in a mixture of 40 ml of 10% NaOH and 10 ml of water.

(*b*) Dissolve 20 mg of crystals of magnesium chloride or sulfate in 200 ml of water (1 ml = 0.01 mg of Mg).   Dilute 1 ml of (*b*) to 5 ml and add 1 ml of (*a*).   A distinct blue color is produced.

Ignition residue: Char 0.5 g, cool, add 0.5 ml of H_2SO_4 and ignite to constant weight. Not more than 1.0 mg of residue remains.

1 Suitsu and Okuma, *J. Soc. Chem. Ind. Japan* **29**, 122 (1926).
2 Ruigh, W. L., *J. Am. Chem. Soc.* **51**, 1456 (1929).
3 Engel, E. W., *ibid.* **52**, 1812 (1930).

MANGANESE CARBONATE

Manganous Carbonate

$MnCO_3$ with some H_2O.

White powder when freshly made, but oxidizes in the air, acquiring a light brown color. Insoluble in water; soluble in dilute acids.

Standards

Assay....................44%–48% Mn	Alkalies, Earths (as sulfate)....max 0.30%
Nitric acid—insoluble........max 0.05%	Heavy metals (as Pb)........max 0.002%
Alkali carbonate (as Na_2CO_3)..max 0.01%	Iron (Fe)...................max 0.003%
Chloride (Cl)...............max 0.02%	Nickel (Ni).................max 0.05%
Sulfate (SO_4)...............max 0.01%	Zinc (Zn)...................max 0.02%

Assay: Weigh accurately about 0.5 g and dissolve in 50 ml of water and 3 ml of HNO_3. Filter and wash well with water. To the combined filtrate and washings add 10 ml of NH_4OH and 5 ml of 30% hydrogen peroxide, previously diluted with 30 ml water, and boil until precipitation is complete. Filter, wash with hot H_2O, and ignite at a red heat. The weight of the Mn_3O_4 multiplied by 0.7203 = Mn, log 85751.

Nitric acid—insoluble: Dissolve 5 g in a mixture of 80 ml of H_2O and 20 ml of HNO_3. Filter, wash the insoluble residue with hot H_2O, and ignite. Its weight does not exceed 2.5 mg.

Alkali carbonate: Boil 2 g with 30 ml of H_2O, filter, wash with 20 ml of hot water, cool, and add to the filtrate 2 drops of phenolphthalein. If a pink color is produced, it requires not more than 0.2 ml of 0.02 N HCl to discharge it.

Chloride: Dissolve 1 g in a mixture of 3 ml of HNO_3 and 20 ml H_2O, adding sufficient 30% hydrogen peroxide to dissolve any oxidized manganese. Dilute to 200 ml. To 20 ml add 1 ml of $AgNO_3$. Any resulting turbidity is not greater than that in a blank to which 0.02 mg of Cl has been added.

Solution S: To 5 g add 20 ml of H_2O, 2 ml of 30% hydrogen peroxide and sufficient HCl to dissolve. Evaporate to dryness on the steam bath, dissolve the residue in 50 ml of H_2O, filter if necessary and dilute to 100 ml.

Sulfate: To 20 ml of *Solution S*, add 1 ml of 0.1 HCl and 2 ml of $BaCl_2$. Any turbidity produced is not greater than that in a control made with 0.10 mg of SO_4, 1 ml of 0.1 N HCl, and 2 ml of $BaCl_2$ in the same volume as used with the sample.

Alkalies, Earths, etc.: Dilute 20 ml of *Solution S* to 85 ml and add 15 ml of NH_4OH. Precipitate the manganese with H_2S and filter. To 50 ml of the filtrate add 5 drops of H_2SO_4, evaporate and ignite. Not more than 1.5 mg of residue remains.

Heavy metals: To 5 ml of *Solution S* add 0.01 mg Pb and 1 ml of 1 N acetic acid and dilute to 40 ml (A). To 15 ml of *Solution S* add 1 ml of 1 N acetic acid and dilute to 40 ml (B). Then to each add 10 ml of H_2S. B is not darker than A.

Iron: To 7.0 ml of *Solution S* add 2 ml of HCl and dilute to 50 ml. Add about 50 mg of ammonium persulfate and 3 ml of ammonium thiocyanate solution, mix. Any red color produced is not darker than that of a control made with 0.01 mg of Fe, 2 ml of HCl, the same quantities of ammonium persulfate and thiocyanate and in the same final volume as with the sample.

Nickel: Dilute 2.0 ml of *Solution S* to 30 ml, add 2 g of sodium acetate and 10 ml of H_2S, and after 1 minute add 5 ml of glacial acetic acid. Any color produced is not darker than that in a blank to which 0.05 mg of Ni has been added.

Zinc: To 30 ml of *Solution S* add 1 ml of H_2SO_4 and mix (A). To 10 ml of *Solution S* add 0.20 mg of Zn (2 ml standard zinc solution), dilute to 30 ml and add 1 ml of H_2SO_4 (B). Then to each add 1 ml of freshly prepared potassium ferrocyanide solution, stir well and allow to stand for 10 minutes. A is no more turbid than B.

MANGANESE CHLORIDE

Manganese Chloride

$MnCl_2 \cdot 4H_2O$; mol. wt. 197.91; anhydrous—63.59%; Mn—27.76%; Cl—35.83%.

Pink, slightly deliquescent crystals. Soluble in 1 part H_2O; soluble in alcohol.

Standards

Insoluble.....................max 0.010%	Iron (Fe)...................max 0.001%
Sulfate (SO_4)................max 0.010%	Nickel (Ni)..................max 0.02%
Alkalies, Earths (as sulfate)....max 0.30%	Zinc (Zn)....................max 0.01%
Heavy metals...............max 0.001%	

Insoluble: Dissolve 10 g in 100 ml of water and heat on the steam bath for 30 minutes. Filter any undissolved matter, wash it and dry at 105°. The weight of the insoluble residue is not more than 1.0 mg.

Sulfate: Dissolve 1 g in 10 ml of water, add 1 ml of 0.1 N HCl and 2 ml of $BaCl_2$. Any resulting turbidity is not greater than in a blank to which 0.1 mg of SO_4 has been added.

Alkalies, Earths, etc.: To a solution of 2 g in 90 ml of water add 10 ml of ammonium hydroxide and precipitate the manganese with H_2S. Filter, evaporate 50 ml of the filtrate with 0.5 ml of H_2SO_4 and ignite. Not more than 3.0 mg of residue remains.

Heavy metals: Dissolve 4 g in water to make 40 ml. To 10 ml of the solution add 1 ml of 1 N acetic acid and 0.02 mg of Pb, and dilute to 40 ml (A). To the remaining 30 ml of the solution add 1 ml of 1 N acetic acid and dilute to 40 ml (B). Then to each add 10 ml of H_2S. B is not darker than A.

Iron: Dissolve 1 g in 10 ml of water, add 2 ml of HCl and dilute to 50 ml. Add about 30 mg of ammonium persulfate and 3 ml of ammonium thiocyanate; mix.

Any red color produced is not darker than that of a blank to which 0.01 mg of Fe has been added.

Nickel: Dissolve 0.5 g in 100 ml of H_2O. To 20 ml of the solution add 2 g of sodium acetate and 10 ml of H_2S, and after 1 minute add 5 ml of glacial acetic acid. Any color produced is not darker than that in a blank to which 0.02 mg of Ni has been added.

Zinc: Dissolve 3.0 g of sample and 2 g of NH_4Cl in water to 30 ml. To 10 ml of the solution add 0.1 mg of Zn, dilute to 20 ml and add 1 ml of H_2SO_4 (*A*). To the remaining 20 ml add 1 ml of H_2SO_4 (*B*). Cool the solutions, add to each 1 ml of freshly prepared potassium ferrocyanide solution, shake well and allow to stand for 10 minutes. *B* is no more turbid than *A*.

MANGANESE DIOXIDE, PRECIPITATED

MnO_2; mol. wt. 86.94; Mn—63.19%; available O—18.41%.

Black, fine, heavy powder. Insoluble in water; soluble in warm hydrochloric acid with evolution of chlorine. In the presence of hydrogen peroxide it dissolves in other acids.

Standards

Assay....................min 98.5%		Nitrate (NO_3)...............max 0.05%	
Acid—insoluble..............max 0.05%		Sulfate (SO_4)................max 0.05%	
Chloride (Cl)................max 0.02%		Alkalies, Earths, etc...........max 0.30%	

Assay: Weigh accurately 0.1 to 0.12 g and transfer into a 300-ml flask with the aid of 20 ml of water. Add 3 ml of sulfuric acid, previously mixed with 10 ml of water, then add exactly 20 ml of diluted hydrogen peroxide (1 volume of the 30% + 40 volumes water). Allow to stand in the dark with occasional agitation until no more black particles are visible, then titrate the excess of hydrogen peroxide with 0.1 *N* potassium permanganate. In another flask put in 20 ml water, add 3 ml of sulfuric acid, previously mixed with 10 ml of water, then add exactly 10 ml of the same hydrogen peroxide dilution, let stand for the same length of time as the test with the sample, and titrate with 0.1 *N* permanganate. The difference between twice the volume of permanganate consumed in the latter titration and that with the sample represents the permanganate consumed by the sample. One ml of 0.1 *N* permanganate = 0.004347 g MnO_2, log 63819.

Acid—insoluble: To 4 g add 50 ml of H_2O, 10 ml of HCl and sufficient 30% hydrogen peroxide to dissolve. Filter (save filtrate), wash the insoluble residue with hot H_2O and ignite. Its weight does not exceed 2.0 mg.

Chloride: Mix 0.5 g with 20 ml of H_2O, add 3 ml HNO_3 and sufficient 30% hydrogen peroxide to dissolve. Filter and dilute to 100 ml. To 20 ml of the solution add 1 ml of $AgNO_3$. Any resulting turbidity is not greater than that of a blank to which 0.02 mg of Cl has been added.

Nitrate: Shake 0.2 g of the manganese dioxide with an ice cooled mixture of 10 ml of H_2SO_4 and 15 ml of H_2O for 5 minutes and allow to settle. If the supernatant liquid is not clear, filter it on a sintered glass crucible. To 5.0 ml of the clear solution add 2 ml of brucine sulfate solution and dilute to 10 ml. For a control add

2 ml of standard nitrate solution to 2 ml of brucine sulfate solution and dilute to 10 ml. Then to each add slowly 20 ml of H_2SO_4 and immediately place in ice water.   The yellow color of the sample solution is not darker than that of the control.   For a quantitative evaluation of the nitrate, prepare a blank with 2 ml of brucine sulfate and proceed as directed under Nitrate—Estimation of Small Amounts.

Sulfate: Treat 1 g with 20 ml of H_2O, 2 ml of HCl and sufficient 30% hydrogen peroxide to dissolve, and evaporate to dryness on the steam bath.   Dissolve the residue in 50 ml of H_2O and filter.   To 20 ml of the filtrate add 1 ml of 0.1 N HCl and 2 ml of $BaCl_2$.   Any turbidity produced is not greater than that in the control made with 0.2 mg SO_4, 1 ml of 0.1 N HCl and 2 ml of $BaCl_2$ in the same volume as used with the sample.

Alkalies, Earths, etc.: Dilute the filtrate from *Acid—insoluble* to 175 ml, add 25 ml of NH_4OH, precipitate the manganese with H_2S and filter.   To 50 ml of the filtrate add 0.5 ml of H_2SO_4, evaporate and ignite.   Not more than 3.0 mg of residue remains.

MANGANESE SULFATE, MONOHYDRATE

Manganous Sulfate

$MnSO_4 \cdot H_2O$; mol. wt. 169.01; anhydrous—89.34%; H_2O—10.66%; Mn—32.50%; SO_4—56.84%.

Pale pink crystals.   Soluble in about 1 part H_2O; insoluble in alcohol.

Standards

Ignition loss (water)...........10%–12%	Nickel (Ni).................max 0.02%
Insoluble...................max 0.010%	Zinc (Zn)...................max 0.01%
Chloride (Cl)...............max 0.005%	Permanganate-reducing substances
Alkalies, Earths, etc..........max 0.30%	(0.1 N per g)............max 0.015 ml
Heavy metals...............max 0.002%	*Assay*
Iron (Fe)..................max 0.002%	

Ignition loss (water): Weigh accurately about 2 g and ignite at 400°–500° to constant weight.   The loss in weight is not less than 10.0% and not more than 12.0%.

Note: The water content of manganese sulfate can be determined by the iodine (Fischer) method.

Insoluble: Dissolve 10 g in 100 ml of water and heat on the steam bath for 30 minutes.   Filter any undissolved matter, wash it and dry at 105°.   The weight of the insoluble residue is not more than 1.0 g.

Chloride: Dissolve 1 g in 100 ml of water.   To 20 ml of the solution add 1 ml of nitric acid and 1 ml of silver nitrate.   Any resulting turbidity is not greater than that in a blank to which 0.01 mg of Cl has been added.

Alkalies, Earths, etc.: To a solution of 2 g in 90 ml of water add 10 ml of ammonium hydroxide and precipitate the manganese with H_2S.   Filter, evaporate 50 ml of the filtrate, and ignite.   Not more than 3.0 mg of residue remains.

Heavy metals: Dissolve 2 g in water to make 40 ml.   To 10 ml add 0.02 mg of Pb and 1 ml of 1 N acetic acid and dilute to 40 ml (A).   To the remaining 30 ml

add 1 ml of 1 N acetic acid and dilute to 40 ml (B). Then to each add 10 ml of
H_2S. B is not darker than A.

Iron: Dissolve 1 g in 20 ml of H_2O. To 10 ml of the solution add 2 ml of HCl
and dilute to 50 ml. Add about 50 mg of ammonium persulfate and 3 ml of ammonium thiocyanate, and mix. Any red color produced is not darker than that of
a blank to which 0.01 mg of Fe has been added.

Nickel: Dissolve 0.5 g in 100 ml of water. To 20 ml of the solution add 2 g of
sodium acetate and 10 ml of H_2S; after 1 minute add 5 ml of glacial acetic acid.
Any darkening is not greater than that in a blank to which 0.02 mg of Ni has been
added.

Zinc: Dissolve 3 g in 30 ml of water. To 10 ml of the solution add 0.20 mg of Zn
and 1 ml of H_2SO_4 and dilute to 25 ml (A). To the remaining 20 ml add 1 ml of
H_2SO_4 and dilute to 25 ml (B). Then to each add 2 ml of freshly prepared potassium
ferrocyanide solution, stir well and allow to stand for 10 minutes. B is no more
turbid than A.

Permanganate-reducing substances: Mix 200 ml of water with 3 ml of
sulfuric acid and 3 ml of phosphoric acid, and add 0.1 N potassium permanganate
until a slight pink color is produced. Disregard the volume of permanganate used.
Then dissolve in the mixture 10 g of the sample and add 0.15 ml of 0.1 N potassium
permanganate. The pink color persists for 1 minute.

Assay: Manganese sulfate may be assayed as follows and should indicate not
less than 98.5% $MnSO_4$ in the anhydrous product: Weigh accurately about 0.5 g
of the ignited sample from test for *Ignition loss* and dissolve in 100 ml of water.
Add 10 ml of NH_4OH and 5 ml of 30% hydrogen peroxide, previously diluted with
30 ml of water, and boil until precipitation is complete. Filter, wash, and ignite at
a red heat. The weight of the Mn_3O_4 multiplied by 1.980 = $MnSO_4$, log 29667.

MANNITOL

Mannite

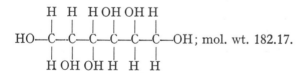

HO—C—C—C—C—C—C—OH; mol. wt. 182.17.

Fine, white, needle crystals, a powder, or irregular pieces. Soluble in 6 parts of
water; slightly soluble in cold alcohol; soluble in boiling alcohol. Melts at 167°.

Standards

Specific rotation........+23.0° to +24.0°	Acid (as acetic)..............max 0.006%
Melting range.................166°–168°	Reducing sugars..............to pass test
Insoluble...................max 0.010%	Heavy metals (as Cu)........max 0.001%
Ignition residue.............max 0.05%	

Specific rotation: Dissolve 5 g of the sample dried to constant weight over
H_2SO_4 and 6.4 g of sodium borate in water to make 100 ml, and let stand for 1 hour.

Then determine the rotation of the solution at 20°, using a 200-mm tube. The observed rotation in degrees multiplied by $10 = [\alpha]_D^{25}$.

Insoluble: Dissolve 10 g in 100 ml of hot H_2O, filter any undissolved matter, wash and dry at 105°. The weight of the insoluble residue does not exceed 1.0 mg.

Ignition residue: Char 2 g well, cool, add 0.5 ml of H_2SO_4 and ignite at first gently, then strongly to constant weight. The weight of the residue does not exceed 1.0 mg.

Acid: To 60 ml of H_2O add 0.2 ml of phenolphthalein and follow with sufficient 0.02 N NaOH until the pink color persists for 15 seconds. Dissolve in this solution 5 g of the sample and titrate with the NaOH to the reproduction of the pink color. Not more than 0.25 ml is required.

Reducing sugars: Dissolve 5 g in 30 ml of hot H_2O, add 3 ml of HCl and heat to boiling. Cool, and make slightly alkaline with NaOH. Add 10 ml of Fehling solution, boil for 2 to 3 minutes, and allow to stand 30 minutes. No red color or precipitation of cuprous oxide is produced.

Heavy metals: Dissolve 4 g in water to make 40 ml. To 10 ml of the solution add 1 ml of 1 N acetic acid and 0.02 mg of Cu, and dilute to 40 ml (A). To the remaining 30 ml add 1 ml of 1 N acetic acid and dilute to 40 ml (B). Then to each add 10 ml of H_2S, mix and observe in 3–5 minutes. B is not darker than A.

MERCURIC ACETATE

$Hg(C_2H_3O_2)_2$; mol. wt. 318.70; Hg—62.95%; acetic acid $= 37.68\%$.

White crystals or crystalline powder; slight odor of acetic acid. Soluble in 5 parts of water; soluble in alcohol. *Keep protected from light.*

Standards

Solubility....................to pass test	Sulfate (SO_4)................max 0.005%
Ignition residue.............max 0.020%	Foreign heavy metals (as Pb)..max 0.002%
Chloride (Cl)................max 0.005%	Mercurous mercury (as Hg)....max 0.50%
Nitrate (NO_3)...............max 0.003%	*Assay*.........................min 99%

Solubility: A 3-g portion of the sample dissolves completely in 60 ml of water acidified with 1 ml of glacial acetic acid.

Ignition residue: Moisten 5 g with 1 ml of H_2SO_4 and gently ignite to constant weight. The residue is not more than 1.0 mg (retain residue).

Solution S: Dissolve 2 g of sample in 30 ml of water and 2 ml of 36% acetic acid, add 5 g of granulated zinc (20–40 mesh), and allow to stand at about 50° for 2 hours with frequent agitation. Filter and wash with water to 50 ml.

Prepare a blank with the same quantities of acetic acid and zinc, and in the same manner and the same volume as with the sample.

Chloride: To 10 ml of the blank add 0.02 mg of Cl and 1 ml of HNO_3 and dilute to 20 ml. To 10 ml of *Solution S* add 1 ml of HNO_3 and dilute to 20 ml; then to each add 1 ml of $AgNO_3$ solution. Any turbidity in the solution made with the sample is not greater than that in the blank.

Nitrate: Dissolve 1.0 g in 10 ml of water with 3 drops of glacial acetic acid. Add to the solution 3 g of granulated zinc metal (20–40 mesh), 1 g at a time, swirling the zinc for 1 minute after each addition. Let stand for 30 minutes, swirling the zinc a few times, then dilute to 50 ml. To 10 ml add 30 mg of NaCl and 0.2 ml of diphenylamine solution, and slowly run in 10 ml of H_2SO_4. Mix gently and allow to stand for 1 hour. No blue color results.

Sulfate: To 25 ml of the blank prepared above add 0.05 mg of SO_4 and evaporate to 10 ml. Evaporate 25 ml of *Solution S* to 10 ml. Then add to each 1 ml of 0.1 N HCl and 2 ml of $BaCl_2$. Any turbidity in the solution made with the sample is not greater than that in the blank.

Solution R: Evaporate the *Ignition residue* with 2 ml of HCl to dryness on the steam bath. Add 1 ml of 1 N HCl and 20 ml of hot water, digest for 5 minutes, and dilute to 50 ml.

Foreign heavy metals: Dilute 10 ml of *Solution R* with H_2O to 40 ml and add 10 ml of H_2S. Any color produced is not darker than that of a control made with 0.02 mg of Pb, 0.2 ml of 1 N HCl and the same quantities of the other reagents and in the same volume as used with the sample.

Mercurous mercury: Dissolve 4 g in 50 ml of H_2O and 0.5 ml of glacial acetic acid in a glass-stoppered flask, and add a solution of 10 g of potassium iodide in 30 ml of H_2O. Then add 5 ml of 0.1 N iodine and follow with 2 ml of 1 N HCl. Allow to stand for 1 hour in the dark with frequent agitation, then titrate the excess iodine with 0.1 N thiosulfate, using starch indicator. Not more than 1 ml of the iodine is consumed. Correct for a blank.

Assay: Mercuric acetate may be assayed as follows: Weigh accurately about 0.7 g and dissolve in 5 ml of nitric acid and 100 ml of water. Add 2 ml of ferric ammonium sulfate, cool to about 20°, and titrate with 0.1 N thiocyanate. One ml of 0.1 N thiocyanate = 0.01593 g $Hg(C_2H_3O_2)_2$, log 20222.

MERCURIC BROMIDE

$HgBr_2$; mol. wt. 360.44; Hg—55.66%; Br—44.35%.

White crystals or a crystalline powder. Soluble in 200 parts of water or 25 parts of boiling water; soluble in methanol or in boiling alcohol. *Keep protected from light.*

Standards

Methanol—insoluble..........max 0.05%		Chloride (Cl)................max 0.20%
Ignition residue.............max 0.020%		

Methanol—insoluble: Dissolve 2 g in 30 ml of warm methanol, filter any undissolved residue, wash it with methanol until washings are unaffected by H_2S and dry at 105°. The insoluble residue weighs not more than 1.0 mg.

Ignition residue: Moisten 5 g with 1 ml of sulfuric acid and ignite gently to constant weight. Not more than 1.0 mg remains.

Chloride: Dissolve 0.50 g in 25 ml of hot water and add, while stirring, 6 ml of 5% NaOH solution. Now add 5 ml of 30% H_2O_2 and heat on steam bath for 30 minutes. Cool, filter, wash well with water, and make up the filtrate to 50 ml. Transfer 10 ml of the filtrate to a 100-ml Erlenmeyer flask, add 5 ml of HNO_3 and 4 ml of 30% H_2O_2, and gently boil down to about 10 ml. Wash down the sides of the flask with a little water, add 1 ml of the H_2O_2, and heat on the steam bath for 20 minutes. The solution should now be colorless; if not, add a little more H_2O_2 and heat until colorless. Cool, and dilute to 100 ml. To 20 ml add 1 ml of HNO_3 and 1 ml of $AgNO_3$. Any turbidity produced is not greater than that of a control made by treating 1.0 mg of chloride (Cl^-) in 25 ml of water in the same manner as the sample, beginning with "add 6 ml of 5% NaOH . . . ."

MERCURIC CHLORIDE

Mercury Bichloride

$HgCl_2$; mol. wt. 271.52; Hg—73.88%; Cl—26.12%.

Colorless crystals or a white powder. Soluble in 16 parts of water or in 3 parts of alcohol; soluble in ether.

This reagent is substantially 100% pure.

Standards

Solubility in water............to pass test	Foreign heavy metals (as Pb)..max 0.001%
Solubility in ether............to pass test	Iron (Fe)...................max 0.001%
Ignition residue.............max 0.020%	

Solubility in water: A solution of 2 g in 50 ml of H_2O is complete and clear.

Solubility in ether: Two grams of the sample dissolve completely in 60 ml of ether.

Ignition residue: Moisten 5 g with 1 ml of sulfuric acid and ignite gently to constant weight. The residue weighs not more than 1.0 mg (retain residue).

Foreign heavy metals: Evaporate the *Ignition residue* with 2 ml of HCl and 0.5 ml HNO_3 to dryness on the steam bath. Take up the residue with 1 ml of 1 N HCl and 25 ml of hot water, cool and dilute to 50 ml. Dilute 20 ml of the solution to 40 ml and add 10 ml of H_2S. Any darkening produced is not deeper than that of a control made with 0.02 mg of Pb, 0.2 ml of 1 N HCl and 10 ml H_2O in the same volume as with the sample.

Iron: To 10 ml of the solution obtained in the preceding test add 2 ml of HCl and dilute to 50 ml. Add 30 mg of ammonium persulfate and 3 ml of ammonium thiocyanate, and mix. Any resulting red color is not darker than that of a blank to which 0.01 mg of Fe has been added.

MERCURIC CYANIDE

Hg(CN)$_2$; mol. wt. 252.65; Hg—79.41%; CN—20.59%.

White crystals or powder.   Soluble in 15 parts of water; soluble in alcohol, in ammonium hydroxide and in alkali cyanide solution.   *Keep protected from light.*

Standards

Assay....................99.0%–100.5%	Oxycyanide.................to pass test	
Insoluble....................max 0.020%	Sulfate (SO$_4$)................max 0.010%	
Ignition residue.............max 0.030%	Foreign heavy metals (as Pb)..max 0.002%	
Chloride (Cl).................max 0.10%	Iron (Fe)...................max 0.001%	

Assay: Dissolve 0.3 g of sample, previously dried over sulfuric acid for 3 hours, in 50 ml of H$_2$O, and add 15 ml of potassium iodide solution.   Add 2 drops of methyl orange and titrate the potassium cyanide formed in the reaction with 0.1 N HCl to a pinkish color.   One ml of 0.1 N HCl = 0.01263 g of Hg(CN$_2$), log 10140.

Insoluble: Dissolve 5 g in 100 ml of hot H$_2$O and heat on the steam bath for 30 minutes.   Filter any undissolved residue, wash and dry at 105°.   The insoluble residue does not exceed 1.0 mg.

Ignition residue: Moisten 3 g with 1 ml of H$_2$SO$_4$ and ignite gently under a hood with a good draft to constant weight.   Not more than 1.0 mg of residue remains (retain residue).

Chloride: Dissolve 0.5 g of the sample in 10 ml of water.   Add 7 ml of 10% NaOH and 15 ml of formaldehyde solution and boil gently for 10 minutes.   Cool, filter and wash with a few ml of water.   Neutralize the filtrate with nitric acid, add 2 ml excess of the acid, and dilute to 100 ml.   Dilute 5 ml with water to 20 ml and add 1 ml of silver nitrate.   Any resulting turbidity is not greater than that produced in a control made with 0.025 mg of Cl, 0.5 ml of the NaOH and 1 ml of HNO$_3$ in the same final volume as with the sample.

Oxycyanide: Dissolve 1 g in a solution of 2 g of sodium chloride in 20 ml of water and add 2 drops of phenolphthalein.   No pink color is produced.

Sulfate: Dissolve 2 g in 25 ml of hot water, filter if necessary, add 1 ml of 0.1 N HCl and 2 ml of BaCl$_2$, and allow to stand for 15 minutes.   Any turbidity produced is not greater than that in a blank to which 0.2 mg SO$_4$ has been added.

Foreign heavy metals: Evaporate the *Ignition residue* with 2 ml of HCl and 0.5 ml HNO$_3$ to dryness on the steam bath.   Take up the residue with 1 ml of 1 N HCl and 25 ml of hot water, cool and dilute to 30 ml.   Dilute 10 ml of the solution to 40 ml and add 10 ml of H$_2$S.   Any darkening produced is not deeper than that of a control made with 0.02 mg of Pb, 0.2 ml of 1 N HCl and 10 ml H$_2$S in the same volume as with the sample.

Iron: To 10 ml of the solution obtained in the preceding test add 2 ml of HCl and dilute to 50 ml.   Add about 30 mg of ammonium persulfate and 3 ml of ammonium thiocyanate, and mix.   Any resulting red color is not darker than that in a blank to which 0.01 mg of Fe has been added.

MERCURIC IODIDE, RED

HgI_2; mol. wt. 454.45; Hg—44.14%; I—55.86%.

Scarlet red powder.   Insoluble in water; soluble in solutions of alkali iodides or in about 100 parts of alcohol or ether.   *Keep protected from light.*

Standards

Assay.................min 99.0% HgI_2
Solution in potassium iodide...to pass test
Ignition residue.............max 0.030%

Foreign heavy metals (as Pb)..max 0.001%
Mercurous mercury (as Hg)....max 0.10%
Soluble mercury salts (as Hg)...max 0.05%

Assay: Dry about 1 g for 4 hours over sulfuric acid, then weigh accurately about 0.5 g, transfer it into a glass-stoppered flask, and add a cooled mixture of 30 ml of HCl and 20 ml of H_2O.   Rotate the flask until dissolved, then add 5 ml of chloroform and titrate with 0.05 M potassium iodate until the iodine color disappears from the aqueous layer.   Stopper, shake for 30 seconds, and continue the titration, shaking vigorously after each addition of the iodate, until the iodine in the chloroform is discharged.   One ml of 0.05 M potassium iodate = 0.02272 g HgI_2, log 35601.

Solution in potassium iodide: Ten g of the sample dissolve completely, or practically so, in a solution of 10 g of potassium iodide in 100 ml of water (retain solution).

Ignition residue: To 3.0 g of sample add 1 ml of H_2SO_4 and heat at first gently to volatilize the acid, then ignite moderately strongly to constant weight.   Not more than 1.0 mg of residue remains.

Foreign heavy metals: To the *Ignition residue* add 2 ml of HCl and slowly evaporate to dryness on the steam bath.   Add to the residue 0.5 ml of 1 N HCl and 20 ml of hot water, digest for 5 minutes, and dilute to 30 ml.   To 20 ml add 10 ml of H_2S.   Any color produced is not darker than that of a blank to which 0.02 mg of Pb has been added.

Mercurous mercury: To the solution from *Solution in potassium iodide* contained in a glass-stoppered flask, add 5 ml of 0.1 N iodine and 3 ml of 1 N HCl. Allow to stand 1 hour in the dark with frequent agitation, then titrate the excess of iodine with 0.1 N thiosulfate, using starch indicator.   Not more than 0.5 ml of the 0.1 N iodine is consumed.   Correct for a blank.

Soluble mercury salts: Shake 1 g with 20 ml of H_2O for 2 minutes and filter. Dilute 10 ml of the filtrate to 40 ml and add 10 ml of H_2S.   The color produced is not darker than that of a blank to which 0.34 mg of $HgCl_2$ (0.25 mg Hg) has been added.

MERCURIC NITRATE

$Hg(NO_3)_2 \cdot H_2O$; mol. wt. 342.64; anhydrous—94.74%; Hg—58.55%; NO_3—36.10%.

White, deliquescent powder, having an odor of nitric acid.   Soluble in a small amount of water, but much water precipitates a basic salt; soluble in dilute acids. *Keep in tightly closed bottles, protected from light.*

Standards

Solubility..................to pass test	Foreign heavy metals (as Pb)..max 0.002%
Ignition residue.............max 0.020%	Iron (Fe)...................max 0.001%
Chloride (Cl)...............max 0.003%	Mercurous mercury (as Hg)....max 0.10%
Sulfate (SO₄)...............max 0.010%	Assay........................min 99%

Solubility: Dissolve 2 g in 20 ml of 10% HNO_3.   The solution is colorless and no insoluble residue remains.

Ignition residue: Ignite 5 g with 1 ml of H_2SO_4.   Not more than 1.0 mg of residue remains (retain residue).

Solution S: Dissolve 2 g in a mixture of 20 ml of H_2O and 2 ml of glacial acetic acid, add 5 g of granulated zinc (20–40 mesh) and allow to stand for 2 hours with frequent agitation.   Filter, and wash with water to 50 ml.

Prepare a blank with the same quantities of acetic acid and zinc, and in the same manner and in the same volume as with the sample.

Chloride: To 15 ml of the blank add 0.02 mg of Cl, 1 ml of HNO_3 and dilute to 20 ml.   To 15 ml of *Solution S* add 1 ml of HNO_3 and dilute to 20 ml.   Then to each add 1 ml $AgNO_3$ solution.   Any turbidity in the test with *Solution S* is not greater than that in the blank.

Sulfate: To 25 ml of the blank prepared above add 0.1 mg of SO_4 and 1 ml of 0.1 N HCl and evaporate to 10 ml.   To 25 ml or *Solution S* add 1 ml of H_2O and 1 ml of 0.1 N HCl and evaporate to 10 ml.   Then to each add 2 ml of $BaCl_2$.   Any turbidity in the test with *Solution S* is not greater than that in the blank.

Solution R: Evaporate the *Ignition residue* with 2 ml of HCl to dryness on the steam bath.   Add 1 ml of 1 N HCl and 20 ml of hot water, digest for 5 minutes and dilute to 50 ml.

Foreign heavy metals: Dilute 10 ml of *Solution R* with H_2O to 40 ml and add 10 ml of H_2S.   Any color produced is not darker than that of a control made with 0.02 mg of Pb, 0.2 ml of 1 N HCl and the same quantities of the other reagents and in the same volume as with the sample.

Iron: To 10 ml of *Solution R* add 2 ml of HCl and dilute to 50 ml.   Add about 30 mg of ammonium persulfate and 3 ml of ammonium thiocyanate, and mix.   Any resulting red color is not darker than that in a blank to which 0.01 mg of Fe has been added.

Mercurous mercury: Dissolve 5 g in a cold mixture of 50 ml of H_2O and 0.5 ml of HNO_3, add a solution of 3 g of sodium chloride in 15 ml of H_2O and allow to stand overnight.   If a precipitate is present, filter through a small filter paper and wash it with 50 ml cold H_2O.   Place the filter with the precipitate in a small glass-stoppered flask, add 10 ml of H_2O and 5 ml of 0.1 N iodine, and let stand for 1 hour in the dark with frequent agitation.   Then titrate the excess iodine with 0.1 N thiosulfate, using starch indicator.   Not more than 0.3 ml of the iodine is consumed.   Correct for a blank.

Assay: Mercuric nitrate may be assayed as follows: Weigh accurately about 0.5 g and dissolve in 5 ml of HNO_3 and 100 ml of H_2O.   Add 2 ml of ferric nitrate solution and titrate with 0.1 N thiocyanate.   One ml of 0.1 N thiocyanate = 0.01713 g $Hg(NO_3)_2 \cdot H_2O$, log 23376.

MERCURIC OXIDE, RED

HgO; mol. wt. 216.61; Hg—92.61%; O—7.39%.

Orange-red, crystalline. Almost insoluble in water; soluble in dilute nitric or hydrochloric acid. It is reduced by light to mercurous oxide and mercury. *Keep protected from light.*

Standards

Assay..................min 99.5% HgO	Nitrogen compounds (as N)...max 0.005%
Hydrochloric acid—insoluble..max 0.030%	Sulfate (SO$_4$)................max 0.015%
Ignition residue.............max 0.030%	Foreign heavy metals (as Pb)..max 0.002%
Chloride (Cl)................max 0.003%	Iron (Fe)...................max 0.003%

Assay; Hydrochloric acid—insoluble; Nitrogen compounds: Apply the tests described for Mercuric Oxide, Yellow. The results conform to the requirements there stated.

Ignition residue: Ignite 3 g with 1 ml of H$_2$SO$_4$. Not more than 1.0 mg of residue remains (retain residue).

Solution S: Dissolve 1 g by gently warming with a mixture of 5 ml of glacial acetic acid and 20 ml of H$_2$O. Dilute to 30 ml, add 5 g of granulated zinc (20–40 mesh), and allow to stand for 2 hours with frequent agitation. Filter, and wash with H$_2$O to 50 ml.

Prepare a control as follows: To 10 ml of H$_2$O add 0.03 mg of Cl and 0.3 mg of SO$_4$, then add 5 ml of glacial acetic acid and proceed as above described beginning with "Dilute to 30 ml . . . ."

Chloride: To 20 ml each of *Solution S* and the control add 1 ml of HNO$_3$ and 1 ml of AgNO$_3$. Any turbidity produced in *Solution S* is not greater than that in the control.

Sulfate: Evaporate 25 ml each of *Solution S* and the control to 10 ml. Add to each 2 ml of BaCl$_2$ and allow to stand for 15 minutes. Any resulting turbidity in *Solution S* is not greater than that in the control.

Solution R: To the *Ignition residue* add 2 ml of HCl and evaporate to dryness on the steam bath. Add to the residue 1 ml of 1 *N* HCl and 20 ml of hot water, digest for 5 minutes and dilute to 30 ml.

Foreign heavy metals: Dilute 10 ml of *Solution R* to 40 ml and add 10 ml of H$_2$S. Any darkening produced is not deeper than that of a control made with 0.02 mg of Pb, 0.3 ml of 1 *N* HCl and 10 ml of H$_2$S in the same volume as with the sample.

Iron: To 10 ml of *Solution R* add 2 ml of HCl and dilute to 50 ml. Add 30 mg of ammonium persulfate and 3 ml of ammonium thiocyanate, and mix. Any resulting red color is not darker than that of a blank to which 0.03 mg of Fe has been added.

MERCURIC OXIDE, YELLOW

HgO; mol. wt. 216.61; Hg—92.61%; O—7.39%.

Yellow to orange-yellow powder. Almost insoluble in water; soluble in dilute acids; darkened by light. *Keep protected from light.*

Standards

Assay................min 99.5% HgO	Sulfate (SO$_4$)...............max 0.010%
Hydrochloric acid—insoluble..max 0.030%	Nitrogen compounds (as N)...max 0.005%
Ignition residue............max 0.050%	Foreign heavy metals (as Pb)..max 0.002%
Chloride (Cl)...............max 0.030%	Iron (Fe)..................max 0.003%

Assay: Dry to constant weight at 110°, then weigh accurately 0.5 g of the dried sample, dissolve it in a mixture of 10 ml of H_2O and 5 ml of HNO_3, and dilute with cold water to 150 ml. Add 2 ml of ferric nitrate solution and titrate with 0.1 N thiocyanate. One ml of 0.1 N thiocyanate = 0.01083 g HgO, log 03463.

Hydrochloric acid—insoluble: Heat 5 g with a mixture of 10 ml of HCl and 50 ml of water on the steam bath for 30 minutes. Filter through a tared filtering crucible, wash with water until free from chloride, and dry at 105°. The insoluble residue is not more than 1.5 mg.

Ignition residue: Ignite 3 g with 1 ml of H_2SO_4. Not more than 1.5 mg of residue remains (retain residue).

Solution S: Dissolve 2 g by gently warming with a mixture of 5 ml of glacial acetic acid and 20 ml of H_2O. Dilute to 30 ml, add 5 g of granulated zinc (20–40 mesh) and allow to stand for 2 hours with frequent agitation. Filter and wash with H_2O to 50 ml.

Prepare a control as follows: To 20 ml of H_2O add 0.6 mg of Cl and 0.2 mg of SO$_4$; then add 5 ml of glacial acetic acid and proceed as above described beginning with "Dilute to 30 ml . . . ."

Chloride: Dilute 5 ml each of *Solution S* and of the control to 25 ml and add to each 1 ml of HNO_3 and 1 ml of $AgNO_3$. Any turbidity produced in *Solution S* is not greater than that in the control.

Sulfate: Evaporate 25 ml of *Solution S* and the control to 10 ml. Add to each 2 ml of $BaCl_2$ and allow to stand for 15 minutes. Any resulting turbidity in *Solution S* is not greater than that in the control.

Nitrogen compounds: Place 0.5 g in a Kjeldahl flask, add 40 ml of H_2O, 15 ml of 10% NaOH, 1 g of potassium iodide, and 0.5 g of fine aluminium wire in small pieces and let stand for 1 hour. Then slowly distill 40 ml into 5 ml 0.1 N HCl, and add to the distillate 1 ml of 10% NaOH and 2 ml of Nessler solution. The resulting color is not darker than that produced by treating 0.025 mg nitrogen (0.1 mg NH_4Cl) in the same manner as the sample.

Solution R: Evaporate the *Ignition residue* with 2 ml of HCl and 0.5 ml HNO_3 to dryness on the steam bath. Take up with 1 ml of 1 N HCl and 20 ml of hot water, cool and dilute to 30 ml.

Foreign heavy metals: Dilute 10 ml of the *Solution R* to 40 ml and add 10 ml of H_2S. Any darkening produced is not deeper than that of a control made with 0.02 mg of Pb, 0.3 ml of 1 N HCl and 10 ml of H_2S in the same volume as with the sample.

Iron: To 5 ml of *Solution R* add 2 ml of HCl and dilute to 50 ml. Add about 30 mg of ammonium persulfate and 3 ml of ammonium thiocyanate, and mix. Any resulting red color is not darker than that of a blank to which 0.015 mg of Fe has been added.

MERCURIC SULFATE

"Mercury Bisulfate"

$HgSO_4$; mol. wt. 296.68; Hg—67.62%; SO_4—32.38%.

White granules or crystalline powder. Decomposed by water; soluble in dilute acids. *Keep protected from light.*

Standards

Assay.................min 99% $HgSO_4$	Nitrate (NO_3)...............max 0.005%
Solubility in H_2SO_4...........to pass test	Foreign heavy metals (as Pb)..max 0.002%
Ignition residue.............max 0.050%	Iron (Fe)...................max 0.002%
Chloride (Cl)................max 0.002%	Mercurous mercury (as Hg)....max 0.20%

Assay: Weigh accurately about 0.5 g and dissolve in 5 ml of HNO_3 and 100 ml of H_2O. Add 2 ml of ferric nitrate and titrate with 0.1 N thiocyanate. One ml of 0.1 N thiocyanate = 0.01484 g $HgSO_4$, log 17143.

Solubility in sulfuric acid: Two grams dissolve completely in 60 ml of 10% H_2SO_4.

Ignition residue: Ignite 5 g. Not more than 2.5 mg of residue remains (retain residue).

Chloride: Dissolve 1 g by gently warming with a mixture of 3 ml of glacial acetic acid and 10 ml of H_2O. Dilute to 25 ml, add 5 g of granulated zinc (20–40 mesh), allow to stand for 2 hours with frequent agitation and filter. Prepare a control as follows: To 10 ml of H_2O add 0.02 mg of Cl and 3 ml of glacial acetic acid and proceed as described above beginning with "Dilute to 25 ml. . . ." Then to 10 ml each of *Solution S* and of the control add 1 ml of HNO_3 and 1 ml of $AgNO_3$. Any turbidity produced in *Solution S* is not greater than that in the control.

Nitrate: Dissolve 1.0 g in 10 ml of water and 0.5 ml glacial acetic acid. Add 2 g of granulated zinc (20–40 mesh) and allow to stand with frequent agitation for 30 minutes. Decant the liquid from the zinc-mercury (or filter) and dilute it to 50 ml. Dilute 3.0 ml of this solution to 10 ml, add 20 mg of NaCl and 0.2 ml of diphenylamine solution, then run in 10 ml of H_2SO_4 and mix gently. No blue color is produced in 30 minutes.

Solution R: To the *Ignition residue* add 2 ml of HCl and evaporate to dryness on the steam bath. Add to the residue 1 ml of 1 N HCl and 20 ml of hot water, digest for 5 minutes and dilute to 50 ml.

Foreign heavy metals: Dilute 10 ml of *Solution R* to 40 ml and add 10 ml of H_2S. Any darkening produced is not deeper than that of a control made with 0.02 mg of Pb, 0.3 ml of 1 N HCl and 10 ml of H_2S in the same volume as with the sample.

Iron: To 5 ml of *Solution R* add 2 ml of HCl and dilute to 50 ml. Add about 30 mg of ammonium persulfate and 3 ml of ammonium thiocyanate, and mix. Any resulting red color is not darker than that in a blank to which 0.01 mg of Fe has been added.

Mercurous mercury: Put 5 g of the powdered sample in a glass-stoppered flask, add a solution of 10 g of potassium iodide in 100 ml of H_2O, 5 ml of 1 N iodine and 3 ml of 1 N HCl, and let stand for 1 hour in the dark with frequent agitation. Then titrate the excess iodine with 0.1 N thiosulfate, using starch indicator. Not more than 0.5 ml of the iodine is consumed. Correct for a blank.

MERCUROUS CHLORIDE

Calomel

HgCl; mol. wt. 236.07; Hg—84.98%; Cl—15.02%.

White powder. It is darkened on exposure to light and heat, and blackened by alkali hydroxides. Insoluble in water or alcohol. *Keep protected from light.*

Standards

Ignition residue............max 0.020%	Foreign heavy metals (as Pb)..max 0.002%
Mercuric chloride............max 0.01%	Iron (Fe)................max 0.001%
Sulfate (SO₄)...............max 0.010%	

Ignition residue: Ignite 5 g with 1 ml of sulfuric acid. Not more than 1.0 mg of residue remains.

Mercuric chloride: Shake 1 g with 10 ml of alcohol for 5 minutes and filter. To 5 ml of the filtrate add 2 drops of HCl and 5 ml of H_2S. Any darkening is not greater than that of a blank with 0.05 mg of $HgCl_2$ added.

Sulfate: Digest 2 g with 20 ml of 10% HCl for 15 minutes and filter. To 10 ml of the filtrate add 10 mg of sodium carbonate and evaporate to dryness on the steam bath. Take up the residue with 1 ml of 0.1 N HCl and 10 ml of hot water, filter if necessary, and add to the filtrate 2 ml of $BaCl_2$. Any turbidity produced in not greater than that in a blank to which 0.1 mg of SO_4 has been added.

Solution R: To the *Ignition residue* add 2 ml of HCl and slowly evaporate to dryness on the steam bath. Add to the residue 1 ml of 1 N HCl and 20 ml of hot water, digest for 5 minutes, and dilute to 50 ml.

Foreign heavy metals: Dilute 10 ml of *Solution R* to 40 ml and add 10 ml of H_2S. Any color produced is not darker than that in a blank of which 0.02 mg of Pb has been added.

Iron: To 10 ml of *Solution R* add 2 ml of HCl and dilute to 50 ml. Add 30 mg of ammonium persulfate and 3 ml of ammonium thiocyanate, and mix. Any resulting red color is not darker than that in a blank to which 0.01 mg of Fe has been added.

MERCUROUS NITRATE

$HgNO_3 \cdot H_2O$; mol. wt. 280.63; anhydrous—93.58%; H_2O—6.42%; Hg—71.48%; NO_3—22.10%.

Colorless, translucent crystals usually with a slight odor of HNO_3. Soluble in 13 parts of H_2O containing 1% HNO_3. With water alone an insoluble basic salt is formed. Its water content may be determined by the iodine (Fischer) method.

Standards

Insoluble and chloride.........to pass test	Iron (Fe)....................max 0.001%
Ignition residue.............max 0.020%	Mercuric salt (as Hg)...........max 0.5%
Sulfate (SO_4)................max 0.010%	*Assay*........................min 98%
Foreign heavy metals (as Pb)..max 0.002%	

Insoluble and chloride: A solution of 2 g in a mixture of 10 ml of 10% HNO_3 and 10 ml of H_2O is colorless and no insoluble residue remains.

Ignition residue: Ignite 5 g with 0.5 ml of H_2SO_4. Not more than 1.0 mg of residue remains (retain residue).

Sulfate: Dissolve 1 g in a mixture of 10 ml of H_2O and 2 ml of glacial acetic acid, add 3 g of granulated zinc (20–40 mesh), and allow to stand for 2 hours with frequent agitation. Filter and wash with water to 20 ml. Prepare a control by treating 0.1 mg of SO_4 with the same quantities of the reagents and making it up to the same volume as the sample. Then to each add 2 ml of $BaCl_2$. Any turbidity produced in 15 minutes in the solution of the sample is not greater than that in the control.

Solution R: Slowly evaporate the *Ignition residue* with 2 ml of HCl to dryness on the steam bath. Add 1 ml of 1 N HCl and 20 ml of hot water, digest for 5 minutes and dilute to 50 ml.

Foreign heavy metals: Dilute 10 ml of *Solution R* with H_2O to 40 ml and add 10 ml of H_2S. Any color produced is not darker than that of a control made with 0.02 mg of Pb, 0.2 ml of 1 N HCl and the same quantities of the other reagents and in the same volume as with the sample.

Iron: To 10 ml of *Solution R* add 2 ml of HCl and dilute to 50 ml. Add about 30 mg of ammonium persulfate and 3 ml of ammonium thiocyanate and mix. Any resulting red color is not darker than that of a blank to which 0.01 mg of Fe has been added.

Mercuric salt: Dissolve 1 g in a mixture of 10 ml of H_2O and 2 ml of glacial acetic acid and dilute to 40 ml. Add 4 ml of 10% HCl, allow to stand for 15 minutes, filter, wash, and dilute the filtrate to 200 ml. To 50 ml add 10 ml of H_2S. Any darkening produced does not exceed that produced by 10 ml of H_2S in 50 ml of water containing 1.7 mg of mercuric chloride.

Assay: Weigh accurately about 0.8 g and place it in a glass-stoppered flask, add 5 ml of 36% acetic acid and 1 g of sodium acetate previously dissolved in 5 ml of water. Then add 50 ml of 0.1 N iodine and follow with 2 g of potassium iodide. Stopper, allow to stand with frequent agitation until solution is complete, then titrate the excess of iodine with 0.1 N sodium thiosulfate. One ml of 0.1 N thiosulfate = 0.02806 g $HgNO_3 \cdot H_2O$, log 14706.

MERCURY

Hg; at. wt. 200.61.

Heavy, silvery-white liquid having a bright, mirror-like surface. It pours freely and completely from a clean, dry, glass container. Sp. gr. about 13.5; boils at 357.5°. Soluble in nitric acid; insoluble in hydrochloric or cold sulfuric acid.

Standards

Appearance.................to pass test   Solubility in nitric acid........to pass test
Foreign metals..............max 0.001%

Appearance: The mercury should have a bright surface, free from film or scum. It pours freely from a clean, dry, glass container without leaving any mercury adhering to the glass.

Foreign metals: Evaporate 100 g *under the hood* in a tared porcelain crucible. After the mercury has all or nearly all evaporated, ignite gently. If any residue remains, it does not exceed 1.0 mg.

Solubility in HNO_3: Dissolve 25 g in 50 ml of diluted HNO_3 $(1+1)$. The solution is clear with no insoluble matter remaining.

METACRESOL PURPLE

m-Cresolsulfonephthalein

$\overline{C_6H_4SO_2OC}(C_6H_3\text{—}2\text{—}CH_3\text{—}4OH)_2$; mol. wt. 283.42.

Reddish brown; moderately soluble in water, soluble in alcohol. *p*H Range: Acid—1.2 red, 2.8 yellow; alkaline—7.4 yellow, 9.0 purple.

Standards

Solubility...................to pass test   *p*H range:
Sensitiveness................to pass test   Acid: 1.2 red; 2.8 yellow
Ignition residue.............max 0.20%   Alkaline: 7.4 yellow; 9.0 purple

Solubility: Dissolve 0.1 g in 50 ml of alcohol and dilute with water to 100 ml. The solution is clear and complete.

Sensitiveness: To 100 ml of CO_2-free water, add 0.3 ml of the solution from the test for *Solubility*: The water is reddish, and on the subsequent addition of 0.5 ml of 0.01 *N* NaOH the color changes to yellow.

Ignition residue: Char 0.5 g, cool, add 0.5 ml H_2SO_4, evaporate the acid and ignite to constant weight. Not more than 1.0 mg of residue remains.

***p*H-Acid range:** To 25 ml each of *p*H buffer solutions (page 584), *p*H—1.2(*a*) and 2.8(*b*) add 0.3 ml of the solution from the test for *Solubility*: (*a*) is red; (*b*) is yellow.

***p*H-Alkaline range:** To 25 ml each of *p*H buffer solutions, *p*H—7.4(*a*) and 9.4(*b*) add 0.3 ml of the solution from the test for *Solubility*: (*a*) is yellow; (*b*) is purple.

METAPHOSPHORIC ACID

White, glassy pellets or cylindrical sticks. Contains sodium phosphate to render it firm. It is deliquescent and very slowly soluble in water. Keep in well-stoppered bottles. Mol. wt. of HPO_3 is 79.98.

Standards

Assay.................min 35% HPO₃	Iron (Fe)...................max 0.005%
Chloride (Cl)...............max 0.001%	Dichlorophenolindophenol-reducing
Nitrate (NO₃)..............max 0.001%	substances.................to pass test
Sulfate (SO₄)..............max 0.002%	Permanganate-reducing
Arsenic (As)................max 1 ppm	substances (as H₃PO₃).....max 0.020%
Heavy metals (as Pb)........max 0.002%	

Assay.................min 35% HPO_3

Chloride (Cl)...............max 0.001%

Nitrate (NO_3)..............max 0.001%

Sulfate (SO_4)..............max 0.002%

Arsenic (As)................max 1 ppm

Heavy metals (as Pb)........max 0.002%

Iron (Fe)...................max 0.005%

Dichlorophenolindophenol-reducing substances.................to pass test

Permanganate-reducing substances (as H_3PO_3).....max 0.020%

Assay: Weigh accurately 3 to 4 g in a glass-stoppered flask and dissolve in 75 ml of water. Add 3 drops of bromocresol green indicator solution and titrate with 1 N NaOH to the appearance of a blue color (not green). One ml of 1 N NaOH = 0.07998 g of HPO_3, log 90301.

Chloride: Dissolve 1 g in 15 ml of H_2O, add 1 ml HNO_3 and 1 ml $AgNO_3$. Any turbidity produced is not greater than that in a blank to which 0.01 mg of Cl has been added.

Nitrate: Dissolve 1.0 g in 20 ml of water. To 10 ml of the solution add 50 mg of NaCl and 0.2 ml of diphenylamine solution and mix. Then slowly add 10 ml of H_2SO_4, mix gently and allow to stand for 1 hour. No blue color is produced.

Sulfate: Dissolve 20 g in 100 ml of H_2O, add 4 ml of HCl, bring to a boil, add 5 ml of $BaCl_2$, and allow to stand overnight. Filter, wash, and ignite. The weight of the $BaSO_4$ is not more than 1.0 mg.

Arsenic: Test 2 g by method on page 563. The stain produced is not greater than that from 0.002 mg of As.

Heavy metals: Dissolve 2 g in 20 ml of water, add 2 drops of phenolphthalein, then add 10% NH_3 until a slight pink color is produced. Now adjust the pH to 3–4 with 1 N H_2SO_4 by spotting on universal indicator paper and dilute to 40 ml. To 10 ml of the solution add 0.02 mg of Pb and dilute to 40 ml (A). Dilute the remaining 30 ml of the solution to 40 ml (B). Then to each add 10 ml of H_2S. B is not darker than A.

Iron: Dissolve 1 g of the acid in 20 ml of H_2O, add 5 ml of HCl and boil, preferably under a reflux condenser, for 20 minutes. Cool and dilute to 25 ml. Dilute 5 ml of the solution to 15 ml, add 50 mg of ammonium persulfate and 15 ml of butanolic potassium thiocyanate, shake well, and allow to separate. Any red color in the clear butanol (upper) layer is not darker than that of a blank to which 0.01 mg of Fe has been added.

Dichlorophenolindophenol-reducing substances: Dissolve 1 g of the acid in a mixture of 25 ml of water and 2 ml of glacial acetic acid. Add to this solution 0.2 ml of a solution of 10 mg of dichlorophenolindophenol sodium in 20 ml of water, The color should not disappear within 5 minutes.

Permanganate-reducing substances: Dissolve 5 g in 30 ml of hot water and add 5 ml of 25% H_2SO_4. Heat the solution to boiling and run in from a burette, dropwise, 0.1 N potassium permanganate, mixing well after each addition until the pink color persists for 3 minutes. Not more than 0.25 ml of the permanganate is required. Run a blank and correct if necessary.

METHANOL

Methyl Alcohol

CH$_3$OH; mol. wt. 32.04.

Colorless liquid. Sp. gr. 0.790 (25°/25°). Boils at 66°. Miscible with water, ethanol, ether, etc. *Keep in well-closed bottles, in a cool place, protected from direct sunlight.*

Standards

Assay.....min 99.5% CH$_3$OH by volume
Boiling range.................64.0°–65.0°
Evaporation residue.........max 0.001%
Miscibility with water.........to pass test
Acetone; aldehydes (as acetone)....0.001%
Acid (as formic).............max 0.002%
Alkalinity (as NH$_3$).........max 0.0003%

Ethanol.....................to pass test
Substances darkened
 by H$_2$SO$_4$..................to pass test
Permanganate-reducing
 substances................to pass test
Water.......................max 0.2%

Assay: The specific gravity at 25°/25° is not higher than 0.290.

Boiling range: Distill 50 ml. After the first 10 drops all distills between 64° and 65°, correction being made for the difference in the barometric pressure during the distillation from 760 mm (page 581).

Evaporation residue: Evaporate 120 ml on the steam bath and dry for 30 minutes at 105°. Not more than 1.0 mg of residue remains.

Miscibility with water: A mixture of 15 ml of methanol with 45 ml of water is as clear after 1 hour as an equal volume of water.

Acetone; Aldehydes: Mix 2.5 ml with 4 ml of water and add 5 ml of Nessler solution. Any resulting turbidity is not greater than that produced in a control made with 0.02 mg of acetone, sufficient water to make 5 ml, and 5 ml of Nessler solution added.

Acid: To 25 ml of carbon dioxide-free water add 1.0 ml of 0.02 N NaOH and 25 ml (20 g) of the sample, and gently boil until the methanol is expelled. Add 0.2 ml of phenolphthalein and titrate the hot solution with 0.02 N H$_2$SO$_4$. Run a control by adding 1.0 ml of 0.02 N NaOH to 25 ml of the same water, heat to about 90°, add 0.2 ml of phenolphthalein and titrate, while hot, with 0.02 N H$_2$SO$_4$ to the disappearance of the pink color. The difference between the volume of alkali consumed in the control and that consumed in the sample of methanol is not greater than 0.5 ml.

Alkalinity: Dilute 25 ml with 25 ml of water and add 1 drop of methyl red. Not more than 0.20 ml of 0.02 N H$_2$SO$_4$ is required to change the yellow color to pink.

Ethanol: Dilute 12.5 ml with 50 ml of water, add 10 ml of 1 N NaOH and mix; than add 30 ml of 0.1 N iodine, shake and let stand for one-half hour at 40°. No more yellow color or precipitate is observable than in a similar mixture without iodine.

Substances darkened by sulfuric acid: Cool 10 ml of sulfuric acid to 10°, then add dropwise, with constant agitation, 10 ml of the sample. Not more than a slight brown color is produced.

Permanganate-reducing substances: Cool 20 ml to 15°, add 0.1 ml of 0.1 N potassium permanganate and let stand for 5 minutes at 15°. The pink color does not entirely disappear.

Water: The water content of methanol can be determined by the iodine (Fischer) method.

METHENAMINE

Hexamethylenetetramine; Hexamine

; mol. wt. 140.19; N—39.97%.

Colorless or white crystals. Soluble in 1.5 parts of water; soluble in alcohol and ether. It is useful as a precipitant for several metals, in place of ammonia.

Standards

Ignition residue..............max 0.03%	Sulfate (SO$_4$)................max 0.005%
Ammonia (NH$_3$).............max 0.001%	Heavy metals (as Pb)........max 0.001%
Chloride (Cl)................max 0.005%	*Assay*......................min 98.5%

Ignition residue: To 3 g add 1 ml of H_2SO_4 and ignite gently to constant weight. Not more than 1.0 mg of residue remains.

Ammonia: Dissolve 0.5 g in 20 ml of H_2O, and add 1 ml of Nessler solution. The color is not darker than that of a blank.

Chloride: Dissolve 0.4 g in 20 ml of H_2O, add 2 ml of HNO_3 and 1 ml of $AgNO_3$. Any resulting turbidity is not greater than that in a blank to which 0.02 mg of Cl has been added.

Sulfate: Dissolve 2 g in 10 ml of H_2O, add 2 ml of 1 N HCl and 2 ml of $BaCl_2$. If a turbidity is produced it is not greater than that in a blank to which 0.1 mg of SO_4 has been added.

Heavy metals: Dissolve 4 g in water to make 40 ml. To 10 ml of the solution add 2 ml of 1 N HCl, 0.02 mg of Pb, and dilute to 40 ml (A). To the remaining 30 ml add 5 ml of 1 N HCl and dilute to 40 ml (B). Then to each add 10 ml of H_2S. B is not darker than A.

Assay: Weigh accurately about 1 g of sample, add 50 ml of 1 N H_2SO_4 and evaporate on the steam bath, or boil gently, adding 50-ml portions of water and evaporating until the odor of formaldehyde is no longer perceptible. Cool, add 25 ml of water, and titrate the excess of the H_2SO_4 with 1 N NaOH, using methyl red indicator. One ml of 1 N N_2SO_4 = 0.03503 g of $(CH_2)_6N_4$, log 54444.

$$(CH_2)_6N_4 + 6H_2O + 2H_2SO_4 \rightarrow 2(NH_4)_2SO_4 + 6HCHO$$

L-METHIONINE

$CH_3 \cdot CH_2 \cdot CH_2 \cdot CH(NH_2)COOH$; mol. wt. 149.21; N—9.39%; S—21.49%.

Colorless or white lustrous plates, or white crystalline powder.   It has a slight, characteristic odor.   Soluble in water, slightly soluble in alcohol; soluble in alkali solutions and in diluted mineral acids.

Standards

Nitrogen (N)..............9.4% ± 0.2%	Chloride (Cl)...............max 0.005%
Sulfur (S)................21.5% ± 0.3%	Phosphate (PO_4)...........max 0.002%
Specific rotation in H_2O.....−7.5° ± 0.5°	Sulfate (SO_4)...............max 0.010%
Solubility....................to pass test	Ammonium salts (as NH_3)....max 0.010%
Drying loss...................max 0.2%	Heavy metals (as Pb).......max 0.001%
Ignition residue..............max 0.05%	Iron (Fe)...................max 0.002%
Some other sulfur compounds..to pass test	

Nitrogen: Determine by the Kjeldahl method, using about 0.25 g of the dried sample.

Sulfur: Determine by the Parr bomb method, using 0.2 g to 0.22 g of the dried sample accurately weighed.

Specific rotation and Drying loss: Dry about 1 g of accurately weighed sample for 3 hours over H_2SO_4 or P_2O_5.   The loss in weight corresponds to not more than 0.2%.   Weigh accurately about 0.75 g of the dried sample and dissolve it in water to exactly 25.0 ml.   Observe the rotation of the solution at 25° ± 2° in a 200-mm tube and calculate the specific rotation.

Solubility: Solutions of 0.5-g portions in 20 ml of water or in a mixture of 5 ml of 1 N NaOH and 5 ml of water are clear and colorless or practically so.

Ignition residue: Moisten 2.0 g with 1 ml of H_2SO_4 and ignite to constant weight.   The weight of the residue does not exceed 1.0 mg (retain residue).

Some other sulfur compounds: Dissolve 0.5 g in 5 ml of 10% NaOH, add a few drops of lead acetate solution, and boil for 1 minute.   No distinct dark color is produced.

Chloride: To a solution of 0.20 g of sample in 10 ml of water add 5 ml of 10% HNO_3 and 1 ml of $AgNO_3$.   Any resulting turbidity is not greater than that in a blank to which 0.01 mg of Cl has been added.

Phosphate: Place 0.5 g of sample in a platinum crucible, add an equal quantity of magnesium nitrate and 5 ml of water.   Evaporate to dryness and ignite at a low temperature until the residue is nearly white.   Add to the residue 5 ml of water and 3 ml of 25% H_2SO_4, heat for 5 minutes; then add 10 ml of hot water, filter, and wash to 20 ml.   To the filtrate add 1 ml each of phosphate reagents **A** and **B** and heat at 60° for 10 minutes.   Any resulting blue color is not darker than that of a blank to which 0.01 mg of PO_4 has been added.

Sulfate: Dissolve 1.0 g in 15 ml of warm water and 1 ml of 1 N HCl and add 2 ml of $BaCl_2$.   If a turbidity is produced it is not greater than that in a blank to which 0.1 mg of SO_4 has been added.

Ammonium salts: Dissolve 0.50 g in 60 ml of water in a small distilling flask, add 1 g of magnesium oxide and distill about 40 ml into 5 ml of water containing 1 drop of 10% HCl. Dilute the distillate to 100 ml. To 40 ml of the dilution add 2 ml of 10% NaOH and 2 ml of Nessler solution. Any color produced is not darker than that of a blank to which 0.05 mg of NH_3 (0.16 mg NH_4Cl) has been added and treated in the same manner as the sample.

Heavy metals: To the *Ignition residue* add 2 ml of HCl and 0.5 ml of HNO_3 and evaporate to dryness on the steam bath. Add to the residue 1 ml of 1 N HCl and 20 ml of hot water, digest for 5 minutes, cool, and dilute to 40 ml. To 20 ml of the dilution add 5 ml of H_2S. Any color produced is not darker than that of a control made with 0.01 mg of Pb, 0.2 ml of 1 N HCl, and 5 ml of H_2S in the same final volume as with the sample.

Iron: Dilute 10 ml of the solution prepared in the preceding test to 50 ml, add 2 ml of HCl and about 50 mg of ammonium persulfate, then add 3 ml of ammonium thiocyanate solution and mix. If a red color is produced it is not darker than that of a blank to which 0.01 mg of Fe has been added.

p-METHYLAMINOPHENOL SULFATE

"Metol"; "Photol"

$\left(\begin{array}{c} OH \\ \end{array} -NHCH_3\right)_2 \cdot H_2SO_4$; mol. wt. 344.38.

White, or nearly white, small crystals, or a crystalline powder. Discolors by exposure to air. Soluble in 20 parts of cold water or 6 parts of boiling water. *Keep in well-closed containers.*

Standards

Ignition residue..............max 0.10%	*o*-Aminophenol...............to pass test
Solubility in HCl.............to pass test	Chloride (Cl)................max 0.002%

Ignition residue: To 1 g add 0.5 ml of H_2SO_4 and ignite gently at first, then strongly to constant weight. The weight of the residue does not exceed 1.0 mg.

Solubility in HCl: Add 0.1 g to 2 ml of HCl; it dissolves quickly and completely.

***o*-Aminophenol:** To the solution from the preceding test add 1 drop of ferric chloride. No reddish-brown color is produced.

Chloride: Dissolve 1 g in 20 ml of water, add 1 ml of 10% HNO_3 and 1 ml of silver nitrate. Not more than a faint opalescence is produced.

METHYL CHLOROFORM

1,1,1-Trichloroethane

CH_3CCl_3; mol. wt. 133.42; Cl—79.72%.

Colorless liquid, odor resembling chloroform. Nonflammable. Sp. gr. about 1.32. Boils at about 75°. Insoluble in water; miscible with organic solvents.

Specific gravity (25°/25°)......1.315–1.325		Chloride (Cl$^-$).............max 0.0002%	
Boiling range...................73°–76°		Evaporation residue........max 0.002%	
Aldehyde...................to pass test		Substances darkened	
Acid......................no reaction		by H_2SO_4................to pass test	

Specific gravity: Determine at 25° with reference to water at 25°.

Boiling range: Distill 50 ml. After the first 10 drops all distills between 73° and 76°, correction being made for the difference of the atmospheric pressure from 760 mm, page 581.

Aldehyde: Shake 3 ml with 10 ml of ammonia-free water for 5 minutes in a separatory funnel and discard the lower layer. To 5 ml of the aqueous layer add 40 ml of ammonia-free water and 5 ml of Nessler solution. No turbidity is apparent within 1 minute.

Acid; Chloride: Shake 15 ml with 25 ml of water for 5 minutes in a separatory funnel and discard the lower layer. A 10-ml portion of the aqueous layer does not redden blue litmus paper. To another 10-ml portion add 5 drops of $AgNO_3$ solution. No turbidity is produced in 1 minute.

Evaporation residue: Evaporate 40 ml on the steam bath and dry at 105° for 30 minutes. The residue does not exceed 1.0 mg.

Substances darkened by H_2SO_4: In a glass-stoppered cylinder, previously rinsed with H_2SO_4, shake 15 ml of the methyl chloroform with 5 ml of sulfuric acid for 5 minutes, and allow to separate. The methyl chloroform (upper) layer is colorless, and the acid layer is colorless or practically so.

METHYL CELLOSOLVE

2-Methoxyethanol; Karl Fischer Reagent Diluent

$HOCH_2CH_2OCH_3$; mol. wt. 74.10.

Colorless, *Poisonous!* Miscible with water, alcohol, ether, dimethylformamide. Used in analytical chemistry as a diluent for the Karl Fischer Reagent.

Standards

Sp. gr. (25°/25°).............0.964–0.968		Acid (as acetic)...............max 0.02%	
Boiling range.................123°–125°		Reaction with H_2SO_4........to pass test	
Miscibility with H_2O, ether....to pass test		Iodine consuming substances...to pass test	
Evaporation residue.........max 0.01%			

Specific gravity: Determine at 25°/25°.

Boiling range: Distill 50 ml. After 10 drops has distilled over, it all distills between 123.0° and 125°, correction being made for barometric pressure from 760 mm.

Miscibility with water, ether: Mix 10-ml portions of the sample, separately, with 25 ml of water and with 25 ml of ether. Clear solutions result and remain clear after 30 minutes.

Evaporation residue: Evaporate 11 ml (10 g) on the steam bath to dryness and dry at 120° for 1 hour. Any resulting residue weighs not more than 1.0 mg.

Acid: To 15 ml of alcohol add 0.1 ml of phenolphthalein; then add dropwise 0.02 N NaOH, shaking after each drop is added, until a pink color is produced. Now add 15 ml of sample and shake for 5 seconds. If the pink color fades it should not require the addition of more than 0.25 ml of the alkali to restore it.

Reaction with H_2SO_4: Slowly mix 10 ml of the Methyl Cellosolve with 5 ml of H_2SO_4 and allow to stand for 5 minutes. No darkening is produced.

Iodine Consuming Substances: Add 0.1 ml of 0.1 N iodine to 25 ml of sample, mix well and allow to stand for 10 minutes. The color imparted by the iodine is not discharged.

METHYLENE BLUE

Methylthionine Chloride

$$(CH_3)N \qquad N(CH_3)_2;\ 3H_2O;\ \text{mol. wt. } 373.90;\ \text{anhydrous;}$$

$$N-13.14\%;\ S-10.03\%;\ Cl-11.09\%.$$

Lustrous, dark green crystals or crystalline powder. Soluble in water and in alcohol. Usually contains 12%–15% water.

Standards

Drying loss.................max 15.0%	Copper (Cu)................max 0.105%	
Ignition residue..............max 0.5%	Zinc (Zn)...................max 0.02%	
Arsenic (As)................max 5 ppm	*Assay*	

Drying loss: Weigh accurately about 1 g and dry it for 18 hours at 110°. The loss in weight corresponds to not more than 15%.

Ignition residue: Slowly char 1 g in a porcelain crucible, cool, add to the char 1 ml each of HNO_3 and H_2SO_4, evaporate over a small flame, then ignite strongly to constant weight. Not more than 5.0 mg of residue remains.

Arsenic: Mix 0.4 g with 1 g each of powdered potassium nitrate and anhydrous sodium carbonate and ignite gently until the organic matter is destroyed. Dissolve the residue in 30 ml of 10% H_2SO_4, evaporate to sulfuric fumes, then test for arsenic by the method on page 568. The stain is not greater than that obtained by evaporating 0.002 mg of As, 1 g each of potassium nitrate and sodium carbonate with 30 ml of 10% H_2SO_4 to sulfuric fumes, then testing for arsenic by the same method.

Solution S: Add to the *Ignition residue* 3 ml of HNO_3 and 10 ml of water and gently boil for 2 minutes. Cool, add a moderate excess of NH_4OH and boil for 1 minute. Filter, wash with 20 ml of 2.5% NH_3 and dilute the filtrate to 100 ml.

Copper: Transfer 10 ml of *Solution S* to a small separatory funnel, add 1 g of citric or tartaric acid and 2 ml of 28% NH_3, and dilute to about 25 ml. Prepare a control by placing in a similar funnel 10 ml of water, adding to it 0.015 mg of Cu and 0.02 mg of Zn, 1 g of either of the organic acids mentioned above and diluting to about 25 ml. Extract each solution with 15 ml of dithizone chloroform (10 mg per liter), then with three 10-ml portions, shaking 2–3 minutes with each extraction, and allowing the layers to separate well before drawing off the dithizone chloroform layer. Transfer the combined dithizone chloroform extract to a separatory funnel and extract the solution twice, or three times, if necessary, with 10 ml of approximately 0.05 N HCl (1 vol. HCl + 200 vol. H_2O) to remove the zinc. Reserve this acid extract for the zinc determination. The pink color of the sample is not darker than that of the control.

Zinc: Adjust the combined HCl extract obtained in the test for copper to pH 4.5 to 5.5 with approximately 0.5 N (7%) sodium acetate solution, add 1 ml of 0.1 N thiosulfate and shake out twice with 10-ml portions of dithizone-carbon tetrachloride standard solution. The pink color of the combined dithizone-carbon tetrachloride extracts of the sample is not darker than that of the control.

Note: The approximate actual amounts of copper or zinc present may be ascertained by diluting solution from the sample or the control, whichever is darker, with chloroform for copper or with carbon tetrachloride for zinc until the colors match, noting the exact volume of the diluent required. The quantity of the metals is then calculated from the dilution.

Assay: Dissolve 0.1 to 0.12 g of the sample, accurately weighed, in 70 ml of warm water. Allow to cool, then add 30 ml of a saturated aqueous solution of potassium perchlorate (or a solution of 0.5 g of sodium perchlorate in 19 ml of water) and stir the mixture several times during a period of 10 minutes. Filter through asbestos in a Gooch crucible that has been dried at 105° and weighed. Completely transfer any precipitate in the beaker with the aid of 50 ml of methylene perchlorate (made by adding 1% solution of methylene blue to a 0.1% solution of potassium perchlorate) into the crucible and wash with an additional 50 ml of the methylene perchlorate solution. Finally dry the crucible and precipitate for 1 hour at 105° and weigh. The weight of the precipitate multiplied by 0.8333 corresponds to not less than 98.5% calculated on the anhydrous basis.

METHYLENE CHLORIDE

Dichloromethane

CH_2Cl_2; mol. wt. 84.94; Cl—83.49%.

Colorless liquid; odor resembling chloroform: nonflammable. Slowly soluble in about 50 parts of cold water; miscible with most organic liquids.

Standards

Specific gravity (25°/25°) 1.320–1.325	Chloride ion.................max 0.001%
Boiling range....................40°–41°	Water.......................max 0.02%
Evaporation residue.........max 0.020%	Suitability for use in infrared and ultra-
Acid (as HCl)...............max 0.002%	violet absorbancy..to meet requirements

Specific gravity: Determine with a pycnometer at 25°/25°.

Boiling range: Distill 100 ml, adding 200–300 mg of sand to the liquid in the flask before commencing distillation to prevent spurting.   The receiver should be well closed with a stopper carrying a capillary tube and be immersed to a suitable level in a cooling medium.   The bulb of the distilling flask is heated by the vapor of a water bath at about 60°, the level of the liquid in the flask being kept above the level of the water in the bath during distillation.   After the first ml has been distilled into the receiver not less than 95 ml distills between 40° and 41°, correction being made for the barometric pressure from 760 mm, page 581.

Evaporation residue: Slowly evaporate 40 ml (50 g) on the steam bath and dry at 105° for 1 hour.   Any residue remaining does not exceed 1.0 mg.

Acid: To 25 ml of alcohol add 0.1 ml of phenolphthalein, then add dropwise 0.02 N NaOH, shaking after each addition, until the pink color persists for 10 seconds.   Now add 20 ml (25 g) of sample and mix well.   If the pink color disappears, add dropwise 0.02 N NaOH until the pink color is just restored and persists after shaking for 10 seconds.   Not more than 0.35 ml of the NaOH is required.

Chloride ion: Shake 1.5 ml (2 g) of sample with 10 ml of water for 2 minutes, allow to separate, draw off the methylene chloride layer and discard it.   Add to the aqueous layer 0.5 ml of 10% HNO_3 and 1 ml of $AgNO_3$.   Any turbidity is not greater than that in a blank to which 0.02 mg of Cl ion has been added.

Water: Determine by the Iodine (Fischer) method, using 20 ml (25 g) of the sample.

Suitability for use in measuring absorbancy in ultraviolet: Determine the absorbancy of the sample with a suitable spectrophotometer in 1-cm quartz cell against distilled water set at zero.   The absorbancies at the given wavelengths should not exceed those indicated:

Wavelength (mμ)	Absorbancy Reading	Wavelength (mμ)	Absorbancy Reading
500	0.005	270	0.050
400	0.010	254	0.100
300	0.030	235	1.0

Suitability for infrared use: The methylene chloride should show not less than 50% transmittancy in a 0.02-mm cell in the following wavelength range, in microns, with a ±0.2 micron tolerance:

2.5–3.5; 3.5–6.3; 7.2–7.4; 8.7–10.8; 11.5–12.0

METHYL ETHYL KETONE

2-Butanone

$CH_3CO \cdot CH_2CH_3$; mol. wt. 72.11.

Colorless flammable liquid; acetone-like odor.   Solubility in about 5 parts of water at 25°; less soluble at higher temperatures.   Miscible with alcohol, benzene, chloroform, ether.

Specific gravity (25°/25°)......0.800–0.804   Acid (as acetic)..............max 0.003%
Boiling range...................79°–80°   Water......................max 0.20%
Evaporation residue........max 0.003%

Specific gravity: Determine with a pycnometer at 25°/25°.

Boiling range: Distill 50 ml. After the first 10 drops not less than 48 ml distills between 79° and 80°, correction being made for barometric pressure.

Evaporation residue: Evaporate 63 ml (50 g) on the steam bath and dry at 105 for 1 hour. The weight of the residue, if any, does not exceed 1.0 mg.

Acid: To 20 ml of alcohol add 0.2 ml of phenolphthalein and then add 0.02 N NaOH, dropwise, until a pink color is produced after shaking for 10 seconds. Now add 25 ml (20 g) of the sample and mix. If the pink color disappears, titrate with 0.02 N NaOH until the pink color is restored and persists after shaking for 10 seconds. Not more than 0.5 ml of the 0.02 N NaOH is required.

Water: Determine by the iodine (Fischer) method, using 10 ml of sample and 25 ml of pyridine as solvent.

METHYL IODIDE

CH_3I; mol. wt. 141.95; I—89.41%.

Colorless liquid. Turns brown on exposure to light due to liberation of iodine. Slightly soluble in water; miscible with alcohol, ether or petroleum ether.

Standards

Boiling range................41.5°–43.0°   Acid........................to pass test
Specific gravity..............2.270–2.285   Water..................max about 0.1%
Evaporation residue.........max 0.01%   Assay......................min 98.5%

Boiling range: Distill 50 ml, receiving the distillate in a cylinder closed with a stopper carrying a capillary tube and immersed in cold water. After the first 20 drops not less than 48 ml distills between 41.5° and 43°, correction being made for the difference in barometric pressure from 760 mm, page 581.

Specific gravity: Determine with a pycnometer at 25°/25°. It should be between 2.270 and 2.285.

Evaporation residue: Evaporate 8.0 ml (20 g) to dryness on the steam bath and dry at 105° for 1 hour. The weight of the residue does not exceed 2.0 mg.

Acid: Shake 3 ml with 5 ml of water for 30 seconds and immediately separate the liquids. The aqueous layer is neutral to litmus, and not more than an opalescence is produced on the addition of 1 ml of silver nitrate and 1 ml of HNO_3.

Water: Mix 1 ml with 10 ml of petroleum ether. The mixture is clear.

Note: Water in methyl iodide may be quantitatively determined by the iodine (Fischer) method.

Assay: Methyl iodide may be assayed as follows: Weigh accurately a 100-ml volumetric flask containing 10 ml of ethanol, add 1 ml of the sample and reweigh. Dilute to exactly 100 ml with ethanol and mix well. Transfer 20 ml to a glass-stoppered flask, add 50 ml of 0.1 N AgNO$_3$ and follow with 2 ml of nitric acid.

Stopper immediately, shake frequently during 2 hours and let stand in the dark overnight.   Shake again frequently during 2 hours, then add 50 ml of H_2O and 3 ml of ferric ammonium sulfate and titrate the excess of $AgNO_3$ with 0.1 N thiocyanate. One ml of 0.1 N silver nitrate = 0.01419 g CH_3I, log 15198.

Note: Methyl iodide may also be assayed by titration in diluted (50–70%) alcohol solution with 0.1 N NaOH and phenolphthalein as indicator.   The solution must be vigorously shaken after each addition of the NaOH; or a measured excess of the alkali added, allowed to stand for 1–2 hours, then the excess alkali titrated with 0.1 N HCl.

METHYL ISOBUTYL KETONE

Isopropyl Acetone

$CH_3COCH_2CH(CH_3)_2$: mol. wt. 100.16.

Colorless liquid, slight camphoric odor.   Sp. gr. 250.80.   Boils at 117°.   Soluble in 50 parts water, miscible with alcohol, benzene, ether, chloroform.

Standards

Specific gravity (25°/25°)......0.798–0.802	Miscibility with benzene, ether . to pass test
Boiling range.................116°–118°	Evaporation residue.........max 0.005%
Refractive index at 20°........1.393–1.398	Acid (as acetic)..............max 0.002%

Specific gravity: Determine at 25°/25°.

Boiling range: Distill 50 ml.   After 1 ml has been distilled into the receiver all distills between 116° and 118°, correction being made for the barometric pressure from 760 mm, page 581.

Refractive index: Determine at 20°.   It should be 1.393 to 1.398.

Miscibility with benzene, ether: Mix, separately, 5-ml portions of the sample with 10 ml of benzene and with 10 ml of ether.   The mixtures are clear and remain so after standing for 30 minutes.

Evaporation residue: Evaporate 25 ml (20 g) to dryness on the steam bath and dry at 105° for 1 hour.   Not more than 1.0 mg of residue remains.

Acid: To 15 ml of alcohol add 0.1 ml of phenolphthalein, then add dropwise 0.02 N NaOH until a pale pink color is produced after shaking.   Now add 20 ml (16 g) of the sample and shake for 5 seconds.   If the pink color fades it should take not more than 0.25 ml of the alkali to restore it.

METHYL ORANGE

Helianthine B; Tropaeolin D

NaO_3S—⟨benzene ring⟩—$N{=}N$—⟨benzene ring⟩—$N(CH_3)_2$; mol. wt. 327.34.

Orange-yellow powder or crystalline scales.   Slightly soluble in cold water; readily soluble in hot; almost insoluble in alcohol. pH range: 3.2 pink; 4.4 yellow. It is usually used in a 0.1% aqueous solution.

Standards

Solubility..................to pass test   Sensitiveness................to pass test

Solubility: Dissolve 0.1 g in 100 ml of warm H_2O; the solution is orange-red and clear or practically so.

Sensitiveness: To 100 ml of CO_2-free water add 0.1 ml of the solution from the test for *Solubility*. The color of the water is reddish-yellow. On the addition of 0.3 ml of 0.01 N NaOH the color changes to yellow. Then, on the addition of 0.5 ml of 0.01 N H_2SO_4 the solution becomes red.

METHYL RED

p-Dimethylaminoazobenzene-*o*-Carboxylic Acid

$-N(CH_3)_2$; mol. wt. 269.29.

Glistening, violet crystals. Almost insoluble in water; soluble in alcohol or in acetic acid. *p*H range: 4.2 pink; 6.2 yellow. It is usually used in a 0.1% alcoholic solution. Methyl red is also available at the sodium salt.

Standards

Solubility..................to pass test   Sensitiveness................to pass test

Solubility: Dissolve 0.1 g in 100 ml of warm alcohol; the solution is orange-red and clear. For the sodium salt use water instead of alcohol.

Sensitiveness: To 100 ml of CO_2-free water add 0.1 ml of the solution from the test for *Solubility*. The water is pink or orange. On adding 0.3 ml of 0.01 N NaOH the color is yellow. Now add 0.5 ml of 0.01 N H_2SO_4. The solution becomes strongly red.

METHYLROSANILINE CHLORIDE, *see* CRYSTAL VIOLET

MOLYBDENUM TRIOXIDE

Molybdic Anhydride

MoO_3; mol. wt. 143.95; Mo—66.65%.

White, or slightly yellow, or slightly bluish powder. Insoluble in water; soluble in solutions of alkali or ammonium hydroxides.

Standards

Assay................min 99.5% MoO_3	Phosphate (PO_4)..........max 0.0005%
Ammonium hydroxide—	Sulfate (SO_4)...............max 0.020%
insoluble................max 0.010%	Ammonia (NH_4).............max 0.005%
Chloride (Cl)................max 0.002%	Heavy metals (as Pb)........max 0.003%
Nitrate (NO_3)...............max 0.003%	

Assay: Determine the MoO_3 by the assay method described for Molybdic Acid, 85%.

Ammonium hydroxide—insoluble: Dissolve 10 g in a mixture of 20 ml of ammonium hydroxide and 50 ml of water, heating on steam bath for 1 to 2 hours to aid solution, and adding more ammonium hydroxide, if necessary. Filter any undissolved residue through a tared filtering crucible, wash, and dry at 105°. Not more than 1.0 mg of insoluble residue is obtained. (Reserve the filtrate separately from the washings for the phosphate test.)

Chloride: Digest 1.0 g with a mixture of 15 ml of water and 5 ml of nitric acid for 15 minutes, filter, and wash to 20 ml. To 5 ml of the filtrate add 0.01 mg of Cl and dilute to 20 ml (A). Dilute the remaining 15 ml of the filtrate to 20 ml (B). Then to each add 1 ml of $AgNO_3$. Any turbidity in B is not greater than that in A.

Nitrate: Triturate 1.0 g with 10 ml of water for 2 minutes, dilute to 20 ml, mix and allow to settle or centrifuge. Decant 10 ml, add to it 10 mg of NaCl and 0.10 ml of freshly prepared indigo carmine solution, then add 10 ml of H_2SO_4. The blue color does not entirely disappear in 5 minutes.

Phosphate: Pour the filtrate from *Ammonium hydroxide—insoluble* into a mixture of 75 ml of water and 50 ml of nitric acid, shake for 5 minutes at 40°, and then let stand for 1 hour. Any yellow precipitate formed is not more than that in a control made by treating a mixture of 2 g of the sample, 0.04 mg of PO_4, 10 ml of ammonium hydroxide and 50 ml of water in the same manner as the filtrate.

Sulfate: Boil 1 g with a mixture of 5 ml of nitric acid and 15 ml of water for 5 minutes. Cool, dilute to 40 ml, mix and filter. Evaporate 20 ml of the filtrate to dryness on the steam bath. Take up the residue with 1 drop of HCl and 5 ml of warm water, filter, wash to 10 ml, and add to filtrate 2 ml of $BaCl_2$. Any turbidity produced is not more than that in a control made with 0.1 mg of SO_4, the same quantities of HCl and $BaCl_2$, and in the same final volume as in the test with the sample.

Ammonia: Dissolve 0.5 g in 10 ml of 10% NaOH and dilute to 50 ml. Dilute 20 ml of the solution to 50 ml and add 2 ml of Nessler solution. The color is not darker than that of a control made with 0.01 mg of NH_3, 4 ml of the NaOH and 2 ml of Nessler solution in the same total volumes as with the sample.

Heavy metals: Dissolve 1 g in 15 ml of 10% NaOH, add 2 ml of ammonium hydroxide, and dilute to 40 ml. To 10 ml of the solution add 0.015 mg of Pb and dilute to 40 ml (A). Dilute the remaining 30 ml of the solution to 40 ml (B). Then to each add 10 ml of H_2S. B is not darker than A.

MOLYBDIC ACID, 85%

Not true molybdic acid, but largely an ammonium molybdate.

White or slightly yellowish powder. Insoluble or partly soluble in water; soluble in solutions of alkali or ammonium hydroxides.

Standards

Assay....................min 85% MoO_3	Phosphate (PO_4)...........max 0.0005%
Ammonium hydroxide—	Sulfate (SO_4)................max 0.20%
insoluble................max 0.010%	Heavy metals (as Pb)........max 0.003%
Chloride (Cl)...............max 0.003%	

Assay: Weigh accurately about 1.0 g of sample and dissolve it, heating on the steam bath if necessary, in 20 ml of water and 2 ml of NH_4OH. Transfer the solution to a 200-ml volumetric flask, dilute to the mark, and mix well. Transfer 50 ml of the solution to 400-ml beaker, add 2 ml of glacial acetic acid and dilute to 200 ml. Bring to a boil. Add, while stirring, a clear solution of 1.5 g of lead acetate in 20 ml of water and heat on a hot plate until the precipitate becomes granular. Decant through a Gooch crucible which has been ignited and weighed, then wash several times by decantation with 30-ml portions of hot water. Filter, wash with a solution containing 20 g of ammonium acetate and 1 ml of HNO_3 in 100 ml, dry, and ignite to constant weight. The weight of the lead molybdate so obtained multiplied by $0.3922 = MoO_3$, log 59351.

Ammonium hydroxide—insoluble: Heat on the steam bath in a covered beaker 10 g with a mixture of 75 ml of water and 10 ml of ammonium hydroxide for 2 hours. If an undissolved residue remains, filter, wash it with water, and dry at 105°. The weight of the residue does not exceed 1.0 mg. (Reserve the filtrate separately from the washings for the phosphate test.)

Chloride: Digest 1.0 g with a mixture of 15 ml of water and 5 ml of nitric acid for 15 minutes, filter, and wash to 20 ml. To 5 ml of the filtrate add 0.015 mg of Cl and dilute to 20 ml (A). Dilute the remaining 15 ml of the filtrate to 20 ml (B). Then to each add 1 ml of $AgNO_3$. Any turbidity in B is not greater than that in A.

Phosphate: Pour the filtrate from *Ammonium hydroxide—insoluble* into 75 ml of water, add 50 ml of nitric acid, shake for 5 minutes at 40° and then let stand for 1 hour. Any yellow precipitate formed is not more than that in a control made by treating a mixture of 2 g of the sample, 0.04 mg of PO_4, 10 ml of ammonium hydroxide and 75 ml of water in the same manner beginning with the addition of 75 ml of water.

Sulfate: Boil 1 g with a mixture of 5 ml of nitric acid and 15 ml of water for 5 minutes. Cool, dilute to 100 ml, mix, and filter. Evaporate 5 ml of the filtrate to dryness on the steam bath. Take up the residue with 1 drop of HCl and 10 ml of warm water, filter, and add to filtrate 2 ml of $BaCl_2$. Any turbidity produced is not more than that in a control made with 0.1 mg of SO_4, the same quantities of HCl and $BaCl_2$, and in the same final volume as with the sample.

Heavy metals: Dissolve 1 g in 15 ml of 10% NaOH, add 2 ml of ammonium hydroxide, and dilute to 40 ml. To 10 ml of the solution add 0.015 mg of Pb, and dilute to 40 ml (A). Dilute the remaining 30 ml of the solution to 40 ml (B). Then to each add 10 ml of H_2S. B is not darker than A.

MONOCHLOROACETIC ACID

CH_2ClCO_2H; mol. wt. 94.50; Cl—37.53%.

Colorless crystals; odorless in the cold; deliquescent. Very soluble in water, alcohol or ether. *Keep in well-closed containers in a cool place.*

Standards

Melting range................61.0°–62.5°	Substances darkened by
Assay.............min 99% CH_2ClCO_2H	H_2SO_4....................to pass test
Ignition residue..............max 0.05%	Heavy metals (as Pb)........max 0.002%
Chloride ions (Cl)............max 0.003%	Iron (Fe)..................max 0.002%
Sulfate (SO_4)................max 0.01%	

Assay: Weigh accurately about 3.0 g, dissolve in 50 ml of H_2O, and titrate with 1 N NaOH, using phenolphthalein indicator.   One ml of 1 N NaOH = 0.09450 g $ClCH_2CO_2H$, log 97543.

Ignition residue: Moisten 2 g with 0.5 ml of H_2SO_4 and ignite to constant weight.   Not more than 1.0 mg of residue remains.

Chloride ions: To a solution of 1 g in 20 ml of H_2O add 1 ml of HNO_3 and 1 ml of $AgNO_3$.   Any turbidity produced is not greater than that in a blank to which 0.03 mg of Cl has been added.

Sulfate: Dissolve 1 g in 10 ml of H_2O, add 1 ml of 0.1 N HCl and 2 ml of $BaCl_2$. If a turbidity is produced it is not greater than that in a blank with 0.1 mg of SO_4 added.

Substances darkened by H_2SO_4: Heat 1 g with 10 ml of H_2SO_4 at 50° for 5 minutes.   The liquid is not more than faintly brown.

Heavy metals: To the *Ignition residue* add 2 ml of HCl and 2 ml of water, and slowly evaporate to dryness on the steam bath.   Take up the residue with 1 ml of 1 N acetic acid and 20 ml of hot water.   Cool, dilute to 80 ml.   To 40 ml add 10 ml of H_2S.   Any color produced is not darker than that of a blank to which 0.02 mg of Pb has been added.

Iron: Dissolve 1 g in water to make 20 ml.   To 10 ml of the solution add 2 ml of HCl and dilute to 50 ml.   Add about 30 mg of ammonium persulfate and 3 ml of ammonium thiocyanate, and mix.   Any resulting red color is not darker than that of a blank to which 0.01 mg of Fe has been added.

MUREXIDE

Ammonium Purpurate

$$
\begin{array}{llll}
HN-CO & OC & NH & \\
| \quad | & | & | & \\
OC \quad C---N=C & CO; & C_8H_8N_6O_6; & \text{mol. wt. 284.2.} \\
| \quad \| & | & | & \\
HN \quad CONH_4 & OC-NH &
\end{array}
$$

Dark purple-red; crystalline.   Soluble in water, insoluble in alcohol or ether. Its aqueous solution (1:2000) is intensely purple, becoming blue when made strongly alkaline with NaOH.   In acid solutions the indicator is colorless.   In aqueous solution it rapidly deteriorates.

Murexide is used as an indicator for the volumetric determination of calcium, especially in the presence of substantial amounts of magnesium, with ethylene-diamine tetraacetic acid in the presence of NaOH.

Standards

Sensitiveness................to pass test   Drying loss..................max 2.0%
Ignition residue..............max 0.20%

Sensitiveness: Dissolve 10 mg of the murexide in 10 ml of water immediately before use.   Add 1.0 ml of this solution to 100 ml of water, then add 10 ml of 1 N NaOH and divide into 2 equal portions.   To one portion add from a graduated pipette standard calcium solution (0.1 mg Ca per ml) until the blue component of the color is discharged, readily discernible by comparison with the other portion. About 0.5 ml of the standard calcium solution is required.

Note: A quantitative, gravimetric method for the evaluation of murexide based on precipitation of the dye as the calcium salt was advanced by James H. Moser and Max B. Williams, *Anal. Chem.* **26**, 1167 (1954).

Ignition residue: Ignite 0.5 g until well charred. Allow to cool, add 0.5 ml of H_2SO_4 and reignite to constant weight. The weight of the residue, if any, does not exceed 1.0 mg.

Drying loss: When dried at 105°, murexide loses not more than 2% of its weight.

α-NAPHTHOL

Alphanaphthol

; mol. wt. 144.16.

Colorless or pinkish crystals, or a crystalline powder; characteristic odor. Discolors in air and light. Insoluble in water; soluble in alcohol, ether or benzene. *Keep in well-closed containers, protected from light.*

Standards

Melting range.....................95°–97°	Acid.......................no reaction
Solubility in alcohol..........to pass test	Naphthalene.................to pass test
Ignition residue.............max 0.05%	

Solubility in alcohol: The solution of 1 g in 10 ml of alcohol is clear and nearly colorless.

Ignition residue: Moisten 2 g with 1 ml of H_2SO_4 and ignite to constant weight. The weight of the residue does not exceed 1.0 mg.

Acid: Shake 1 g with 50 ml of H_2O occasionally during 15 minutes and filter. The filtrate is neutral to litmus paper.

Naphthalene: Dissolve 1 g in 3 ml of alcohol and add 50 ml of 10% ammonia. The solution is not more than slightly opalescent and colorless or nearly so.

β-NAPHTHOL

Betanaphthol

—OH; mol. wt. 144.16.

White leaflets or a crystalline powder; faint characteristic odor.   Discolors on exposure to light.   Very slightly soluble in cold water; more soluble in boiling water; soluble in alcohol, ether, chloroform or solutions of alkali hydroxides. *Keep protected from light.*

Standards

Melting range..................121°–123°	Acid.......................no reaction
Solubility in alcohol..........to pass test	α-Naphthol.................to pass test
Ignition residue.............max 0.05%	Naphthalene................to pass test

Solubility in alcohol: The solution of 1 g in 10 ml of alcohol is complete and colorless.

Ignition residue: Moisten 2 g with 1 ml of H_2SO_4 and ignite to constant weight. The residue does not exceed 1.0 mg.

Acid: Shake 1 g with 50 ml of H_2O occasionally during 15 minutes and filter. The filtrate is neutral to litmus.

α-Naphthol: Boil 0.1 g with 10 ml of H_2O until dissolved, then cool and filter. Add to filtrate 0.3 ml of 1 N NaOH and 0.3 ml of 0.1 N iodine.   No violet color is produced.

Naphthalene: Shake 0.5 g with 30 ml of 10% ammonia.   The sample dissolves completely and the solution is not darker than pale yellow.

β-NAPHTHOQUINONE-4-SODIUM SULFONATE

; mol. wt. 260.20.

Yellow to orange-yellow crystals.   Soluble in about 10 parts of water; insoluble in alcohol.

Standards

Sensitiveness................to pass test	Sulfated ignition residue.....26.5%–28.0%
Solubility...................to pass test	(theory 27.3%)
Drying loss..................max 4.0%	

Sensitiveness: (*a*) Dissolve 10 mg of the sample in 10 ml of 50% alcohol. (*b*) Dissolve 0.1 ml of aniline in 100 ml of water.

Place one drop of (*b*) in a small porcelain crucible or dish, add one drop of (*a*) and one drop of 1 N NaOH.   A brick-red color is produced which changes to bright orange-red upon acidifying with 3 drops of 1 N acetic acid.

Solubility: A solution of 1 g in 20 ml of H_2O is clear or practically so.

Drying loss: Dry in a vacuum at about 60°.   The loss in weight corresponds to not more than 4%.

Sulfated ignition residue: Weigh accurately about 1 g of the dried sample, add 1 ml of H_2SO_4 and heat until the H_2SO_4 is vaporized.   Cool, add 2 ml of HNO_3 and 0.5 ml of H_2SO_4, evaporate, then ignite to constant weight.   The weight of the residue corresponds to 26.5%–28.0% of the weight of the dried sample taken.

α-NAPHTHYLAMINE HYDROCHLORIDE

Alpha-naphthylamine Hydrochloride

$C_{10}H_7NH_2 \cdot HCl$; mol. wt. 179.65.

White, crystalline powder; becomes bluish on exposure to light and air.   Soluble in water, in alcohol, or in ether.   It is chiefly used for the detection and determination of nitrite in water, bacterial cultures, etc.   A discolored solution may be decolorized by shaking with a little zinc dust.   *Keep in tightly closed containers, protected from light.*

Standards

Assay.....................99%–100.5%   Ignition residue..............max 0.1%
Solubility....................to pass test

Assay: Dissolve 2 g in a mixture of 150 ml of water and 15 ml of hydrochloric acid.   Run into the solution slowly, and with continuous stirring, 0.5 *M* sodium nitrite until 2 drops of the solution placed on starch-iodide paper produce a bluish color.   One ml of 0.5 *M* $NaNO_2$ = 0.08977 g $C_{10}H_7NH_2 \cdot HCl$, log 95313.

$$C_{10}H_7NH_2 \cdot HCl + NaNO_2 + HCl \rightarrow C_{10}H_7N_2Cl + 2H_2O + NaCl$$
naphthalene
diazonium chloride

Solubility: Dissolve 1 g in 40 ml of warm water.   The solution is colorless or nearly so and not more than opalescent.

Ignition residue: Moisten 1 g with 1 ml of H_2SO_4 and ignite to constant weight. The residue weighs not more than 1.0 mg.

N-NAPHTHYL-ETHYLENEDIAMINE HYDROCHLORIDE

N-(1-Naphthyl)-ethylenediamine Dihydrochloride

White or slightly pinkish, crystalline powder; soluble in about 30 parts of water, sparingly in alcohol.

Standards

Sensitiveness.................to pass test   Ignition residue..............max 0.20%
Solubility....................to pass test

Sensitiveness: (*a*) Dissolve 10 mg of *N*-(1-naphthyl)-ethylenediamine dihydrochloride in 100 ml of water; then dilute 2 ml with water to 100 ml.

(*b*) Dissolve 50 mg of reagent sulfanilic acid in 4 ml of glacial acetic acid and dilute with water to 100 ml.

(*c*) Dissolve 350 mg of sodium nitrite in 10 ml of water.

To 10 ml of (*b*) add 0.2 ml of (*c*), allow to stand for 5 minutes, then add 1 ml of (*a*). A distinct pink color develops within 1 minute.

Solubility: A solution of 0.1 g in 5 ml of water is complete and clear or practically so.

Ignition residue: To 0.5 g add 0.5 ml of H_2SO_4 and ignite gently at first, then strongly to constant weight. The residue does not exceed 1.0 mg.

NICKEL ACETATE

$Ni(CH_3CO_2)_2 \cdot 4H_2O$; mol. wt. 248.84; annydrous—71.06%; H_2O—28.94%; Ni—23.60%.

Green, crystalline mass or powder; slight odor of acetic acid. Soluble in 6 parts of water. *Keep well closed.*

Standards

Insoluble	max 0.010%	Copper (Cu)	max 0.010%
Chloride (Cl)	max 0.002%	Iron (Fe)	max 0.002%
Nitrate (NO₃)	max 0.02%	Lead (Pb)	max 0.003%
Sulfate (SO₄)	max 0.010%	Zinc (Zn)	max 0.03%
Alkalies, Earths, etc.	max 0.20%	*Assay*	
Cobalt (Co)	max 0.10%		

Insoluble: Dissolve 10 g in 100 ml of water and 1 ml of glacial acetic acid and heat on steam bath for 1 hour. Filter any undissolved residue (retain filtrate), wash it, and dry at 105°. Not more than 1.0 mg of insoluble residue is obtained.

Chloride: Dissolve 1 g in 20 ml of water, add 2 ml of HNO_3 and divide into two equal portions. To one portion add 1 ml of $AgNO_3$, bring to a boil, let stand for 10 minutes, cool, filter until clear, and use for the control. To the other portion add 1 ml of $AgNO_3$. If a turbidity is produced, it is not greater than that produced by adding 0.01 mg of Cl to the control and adjusting both to the same volume.

Nitrate: Dissolve 0.50 g in 5 ml of water. Add the solution, in small portions and with continuous stirring, to 5 ml of 10% NaOH previously diluted with 10 ml of water. Cover the beaker and heat it on the steam bath for 15 minutes. Cool, filter, neutralize the filtrate with 25% H_2SO_4 and dilute to 25 ml. Using 5 ml of this solution for sample solution and 2.0 ml of standard nitrate solution (0.02 mg NO₃) for the control, proceed as directed under Nitrate—Estimation of Small Amounts, page 575.

Sulfate: Add 1 ml of hydrochloric acid to the filtrate from *Insoluble*, heat to boiling, add 5 ml of $BaCl_2$, and allow to stand overnight. If a precipitate is present, filter, wash, ignite, and weigh. Its weight is not more than 2.5 mg.

Alkalies, Earths, etc.: Dissolve 2 g in 95 ml of H_2O, add 5 ml of NH_4OH, precipitate the nickel with H_2S and filter. Boil 50 ml of the filtrate until evaporated to about 10 ml, refilter if necessary, add a few drops of sulfuric acid, evaporate and ignite. The residue does not exceed 2.0 mg.

Cobalt: Dissolve 2 g in 30 ml of H_2O, add 1 ml of 10% KOH, then add 2 ml of glacial acetic acid and heat to boiling. Add a solution of 5 g of potassium nitrite in 10 ml of water, stir, digest on the steam bath for 30 minutes, then allow to stand at room temperature overnight. Filter through a filtering crucible and wash with small quantities of cold 5% ammonium nitrate solution containing 1% acetic acid, until free from nitrite. Place the crucible in the same beaker in which the precipitation has been made, add 10 ml of 0.1 N potassium permanganate, follow with 25 ml 10% H_2SO_4 and sufficient water to cover the crucible. Heat to about 50° until the yellow precipitate has dissolved, cool, add 1 g of potassium iodide, and titrate the liberated iodine, representing the excess of permanganate, with 0.1 N sodium thiosulfate. Determine the value of the permanganate in terms of 0.1 N thiosulfate by running a blank with the same volumes of permanganate, sulfuric acid, and potassium iodide in the same manner as with the sample. Not more than 4.1 ml of 0.1 N $KMnO_4$ is consumed.

For a method of determining microquantities of cobalt in nickel (and salts), see **Note** under Nickel Ammonium Sulfate.

Copper: Dissolve 1.0 g in 2 ml of HCl, add sufficient water to make 50 ml. Add 2 ml of a 1% solution of mercuric chloride and saturate with H_2S. Filter through a small filter, wash with H_2S water until the washings are colorless, then ignite the filter and precipitate in porcelain. Dissolve the residue by warming with 0.5 ml of HNO_3 and a few drops of H_2O, dilute to 10 ml, and filter if necessary. Dissolve in the solution 1 g of ammonium acetate; then add 0.3 ml of freshly prepared potassium ferrocyanide solution. Any red color produced is not darker than that of a control made with 0.1 mg of Cu, the same quantities of HNO_3, ammonium acetate and potassium ferrocyanide, and in the same volume as with the sample.

Iron: Dissolve 1 g in 20 ml of H_2O and add 2 ml of HCl and 5 drops of HNO_3. Bring the solution to a boil and add sufficient NH_4OH to dissolve the precipitate first formed. Filter and wash with 2.5% NH_3 until the washings are colorless. Dissolve any precipitate on filter with 5 ml of hot 20% HCl and dilute to 40 ml. To 20 ml of the dilution add 1 ml of HCl and dilute to 50 ml. Add 30 mg of ammonium persulfate and 3 ml of ammonium thiocyanate, and mix. Any resulting red color is not darker than that of a control made with 0.010 mg of Fe, 2 ml of HCl, and the same quantities of the ammonium persulfate and thiocyanate and in same final volume as with the sample.

Lead: Dissolve 1 g in 10 ml of water, add 5 drops of glacial acetic acid, and 0.2 ml of potassium chromate. No turbidity is produced in 5 minutes.

Zinc: Dissolve 2.5 g in 20 ml of water. Heat the solution and slowly add it with stirring to 20 ml of 10% NaOH solution. Boil for 2 minutes, cool, filter and wash to 50 ml. Neutralize 30 ml of the filtrate with HCl, add 1 ml excess of the acid and dilute to 40 ml (A). To 10 ml of the filtrate add 0.3 mg of Zn, neutralize with HCl, add 1 ml excess of the acid and dilute to 40 ml (B). Then add to each 2 ml of freshly prepared potassium ferrocyanide solution, stir well and allow to stand for 10 minutes. Any turbidity in A does not exceed that of B.

Assay: Nickel acetate may be assayed by the method described for Nickel Sulfate. The weight of the nickel dimethylglyoxime multiplied by 0.8615 = $Ni(CH_3CO_2)_2 \cdot 4H_2O$, log 93526, and not less than 98% should be found.

NICKEL AMMONIUM SULFATE

$NiSO_4 \cdot (NH_4)_2SO_4 \cdot 6H_2O$; mol. wt. 395.00; anhydrous—72.63%; H_2O—27.37%; Ni—14.86%; NH_3—8.62%; SO_4—48.64%.

Bluish-green crystals. Soluble in about 10 parts of water; insoluble in alcohol.

Standards

Insoluble....................max 0.010%	Copper (Cu)................max 0.003%
Chloride (Cl)................max 0.001%	Iron (Fe)...................max 0.002%
Alkalies, Earths (as sulfate)....max 0.10%	Zinc (Zn)....................max 0.03%
Cobalt (Co).................max 0.05%	

Insoluble: Dissolve 10 g in 150 ml of water and heat on the steam bath for 1 hour. Filter any undissolved residue, wash, and dry at 105°. The insoluble residue does not exceed 1.0 mg.

Chloride: Dissolve 2 g in 20 ml of water, add 2 ml of HNO_3, and divide into two equal portions. To one portion add 1 ml of $AgNO_3$, bring to a boil, let stand for 10 minutes, cool, filter until clear, and use for the control. To the other portion add 1 ml of $AgNO_3$. If a turbidity is produced, it is not greater than that produced by adding 0.01 mg of Cl to the control and adjusting both to the same volume.

Alkalies, Earths, etc.: Dissolve 2 g in 95 ml of H_2O, add 5 ml of NH_4OH, precipitate the nickel with H_2S, and filter. Boil 50 ml of the filtrate until evaporated to about 10 ml; refilter if necessary, add a few drops of sulfuric acid, evaporate, and ignite. The residue does not exceed 1.0 mg.

Cobalt: Dissolve 2 g in 40 ml of H_2O, add 30 ml of 5% KOH, boil until NH_3 is removed, and evaporate or dilute to 30 ml. Add just sufficient glacial acetic acid to dissolve the precipitate and 2 ml excess. Add a solution of 5 g of potassium nitrite in 10 ml of water, stir well, digest on the steam bath for 30 minutes, and allow to stand overnight. Filter through a filtering crucible and wash until free from nitrite with small quantities of cold 5% ammonium nitrate solution containing 1% acetic acid. Place the crucible in the same beaker in which the precipitation has been made, add 10 ml of 0.1 N potassium permanganate, follow with 25 ml 10% H_2SO_4 and sufficient water to cover the crucible. Heat to about 50° until the yellow precipitate has dissolved, then cool, add 1 g of potassium iodide, and titrate the liberated iodine representing the excess of permanganate with 0.1 N sodium thiosulfate. Determine the value of the permanganate in terms of 0.1 N thiosulfate by running a blank with the same volumes of permanganate, sulfuric acid and potassium iodide in the same manner as with the sample. Not more than 2.05 ml of 0.1 N $KMnO_4$ is consumed.

Note: To determine microquantities of cobalt in nickel (or its salts), E. L. Luke [*Anal. Chem.* **32**, 836 (1960)], has developed a photometric method. Separate the cobalt from the nickel by converting the cobalt with H_2O_2 in the presence of NH_3 into the stable cobaltic amine, and precipitating the nickel with perchloric acid as the hexamino-perchlorate. Concentrate the filtrate containing the cobalt by evaporation, etc., then treat it with a solution of nitroso R salt. Determine the the absorption of standard cobalt solutions photometrically at 515 mμ, then measure the color of the test sample at the same wavelength.

Copper: Dissolve 2 g in 2 ml of HCl and sufficient water to make 50 ml, then add 2 ml of a 1% solution of mercuric chloride and saturate with H_2S. Filter through a small filter, wash with H_2S water, and ignite the filter and precipitate in porcelain. Dissolve the residue by warming with 0.5 ml of HNO_3 and a few drops of H_2O, dilute to 10 ml, and filter if necessary. Dissolve in the solution 1 g of ammonium acetate, then add 5 drops of freshly prepared potassium ferrocyanide solution. Any red color produced is not darker than that of a control made with 0.06 mg of Cu, the same quantities of HNO_3, ammonium acetate and potassium ferrocyanide and in the same volume as with the sample.

Iron: Dissolve 1 g in 20 ml of H_2O and add 2 ml of HCl and 5 drops of HNO_3. Bring the solution to a boil and add sufficient NH_4OH to dissolve the precipitate first formed. Filter and wash with 2.5% NH_3 until the washings are colorless. Dissolve any precipitate on the filter with 5 ml of hot 20% HCl, and dilute to 40 ml. To 40 ml of the dilution add 1 ml of HCl and dilute to 50 ml. Add 30 mg of ammonium persulfate and 3 ml of ammonium thiocyanate, and mix. Any resulting red color is not darker than that of a control made with 0.01 mg of Fe, 2 ml of HCl, and the same quantities of the ammonium persulfate and thiocyanate and in the same final volume as with the sample.

Zinc: Dissolve 2.0 g in 10 ml of water and 2 drops of 10% H_2SO_4. Heat the solution and slowly add it with stirring to 20 ml of 10% NaOH. Boil gently for 2 minutes, cool, filter and dilute filtrate to 40 ml. Neutralize 30 ml of the filtrate with HCl, add 1 ml excess of the acid and dilute to 40 ml (A). To the remaining 10 ml of the filtrate add 0.3 mg Zn, neutralize with HCl, add 1 ml excess of the acid and dilute to 40 ml (B). Then add to each 2 ml of freshly prepared potassium ferrocyanide solution, stir well and allow to stand for 10 minutes. Any turbidity in A does not exceed that in B.

NICKEL CARBONATE

Approximately $NiCO_3 \cdot 2Ni(OH)_2 \cdot 4H_2O$.

A light green powder. Insoluble in water; soluble in acids.

Standards

Assay.....................min 45% Ni	Alkalies, Earths, etc...........max 0.30%
Hydrochloric acid—insoluble..max 0.010%	Cobalt (Co)................max 0.10%
Chloride (Cl)...............max 0.005%	Copper (Cu)...............max 0.010%
Nitrate (NO_3)...............max 0.030%	Iron (Fe)..................max 0.005%
Sulfate (SO_4)...............max 0.010%	Lead (Pb)..................max 0.005%
Alkali carbonate (Na_2CO_3).........0.10%	Zinc (Zn)...................max 0.06%

Assay: Weigh accurately about 1 g and cautiously dissolve it in 15 ml of 10% HCl, warming if necessary. Filter and wash with hot water until washings are colorless. Dilute the combined filtrate and washings to exactly 200 ml and mix well.   Transfer 50 ml of the solution to a 500–600 ml beaker and dilute with H_2O to 200 ml.   Add 1.5 g of sodium citrate, and proceed as described in the *Assay* under Nickel Sulfate beginning with "heat to boiling . . . ."   The weight of the nickel dimethyglyoxime multiplied by 0.2031 = Ni.

Hydrochloric acid—insoluble: Mix 10 g with 80 ml of H_2O, add 25 ml of HCl, and heat on the steam bath for 1 hour.   Filter any undissolved matter (retain filtrate), wash, and dry at 105°.   Not more than 1.0 mg of insoluble residue is obtained.

Chloride: Dissolve 0.4 g in a mixture of 20 ml of H_2O and 2 ml of HNO_3, filter, and divide into 2 equal portions.   To one portion add 1 ml of $AgNO_3$, bring to a boil, let stand for 10 minutes, cool, filter until clear, and use for the control.   To the other portion add 1 ml of $AgNO_3$.   If a turbidity is produced it is not greater than that produced by adding 0.01 mg of Cl to the control and adjusting both to the same volume.

Nitrate: Dissolve 0.50 g in 5 ml of water and just sufficient HCl to dissolve. Add the solution, in small portions and with continuous stirring, to 10 ml of 20% NaOH previously diluted with 10 ml of water.   Cover the beaker and heat it on the steam bath for 15 minutes.   Cool, filter, neutralize the filtrate with 25% H_2SO_4 and dilute to 25 ml.   Using 5 ml of this solution for sample solution and 3.0 ml of standard nitrate solution (0.03 mg NO_3) for the control, proceed as directed under Nitrate—Estimation of Small Amounts, page 575.

Sulfate: Heat the filtrate from *Hydrochloric acid—insoluble* to boiling, add 5 ml of $BaCl_2$, and allow to stand overnight.   Filter any precipitate formed, wash it, and ignite.   The weight of the precipitate of $BaSO_4$ is not more than 2.5 mg.

Alkali carbonate: Boil 2 g with 50 ml of water for 10 minutes, cool, dilute with water to 40 ml, mix well, and filter.   To 20 ml of the filtrate add a drop of methyl orange.   The yellow color of the solution is changed to pink by not more than 0.2 ml of 0.1 N HCl.

Alkalies, Earths, etc.: Heat 2 g with 20 ml of water and add *cautiously* 5 ml of HCl.   Add sufficient NH_4OH to dissolve the precipitate first formed.   Dilute to 100 ml, precipitate the nickel with H_2S, and filter.   Boil 50 ml of the filtrate until evaporated to about 10 ml, refilter if necessary, add 2 drops of H_2SO_4, evaporate, and ignite.   The residue does not exceed 3.0 mg.

Cobalt: Dissolve 2 g by heating to boiling with a mixture of 25 ml of H_2O and 6 ml of glacial acetic acid.   Add to the hot solution a solution of 5 g potassium nitrite in 10 ml of H_2O, stir thoroughly, digest on the steam bath for 30 minutes, then allow to stand at room temperature overnight.   Filter through a filtering crucible and wash with a cold 5% ammonium nitrate solution until free of nitrite; then proceed as described for the determination of *Cobalt* under Nickel Acetate beginning with "Place the crucible in the same beaker . . . ."   Not more than 4.1 ml of the permanganate is consumed.

Solution S: Heat 2 g with 20 ml of water, add HCl until just dissolved, and dilute with water to 20 ml.

Copper: To 5.0 ml of *Solution S*, add 2 ml of HCl and sufficient H_2O to make 50 ml; then proceed as described under Nickel Acetate beginning with "then add 2 ml of a 1% solution of mercuric chloride . . . ."   The results conform to the requirements there stated.

Iron: To 10 ml of *Solution S*, add 1.5 ml of HCl and 5 drops of HNO_3, bring the solution to a boil, and add sufficient NH_4OH to dissolve the precipitate first formed. Filter and wash with 2.5% NH_3 until the washings are colorless. Dissolve any precipitate on the filter with 5 ml of hot 20% HCl and dilute with water to 50 ml. To 20 ml of the dilution add 2 ml of HCl and dilute to 50 ml. Add 30 mg of ammonium persulfate and 3 ml of ammonium thiocyanate, and mix. Any resulting red color is not darker than that of a control made with 0.02 mg of Fe, 2 ml of HCl, and the same quantities of ammonium persulfate and thiocyanate and in the same final volume as with the sample.

Lead: To 1.0 g add 5 ml of water and 5 ml of HCl and evaporate to dryness on the steam bath. Re-evaporate with 10 ml of water. Dissolve the residue in 20 ml of water, add 0.5 ml of glacial acetic acid, filter if not clear and divide into two equal portions. To one portion add 0.2 ml of 10% potassium chromate and mix well. To the other portion add 0.2 ml of water. Both portions are equally clear in 10 minutes when viewed in the same light.

Zinc: Dissolve 2.5 g in 15 ml of water and just sufficient H_2SO_4 to dissolve. Heat the solution and slowly add it with stirring to 25 ml of 10% NaOH. Boil for 2 minutes, cool, filter and wash with water to make filtrate 50 ml. Neutralize 30 ml of the filtrate with HCl, add an excess of 1 ml of the acid dilute to 40 ml (*A*). To 10 ml of the filtrate add 0.6 mg of Zn, neutralize, etc., as with the 30 ml (*B*). Then add to each 2 ml of freshly prepared potassium ferrocyanide solution, stir well and allow to stand for 10 minutes. Any turbidity in *A* does not exceed that of *B*.

NICKEL CHLORIDE

$NiCl_2 \cdot 6H_2O$; mol. wt. 237.70; anhydrous—54.52%; H_2O—45.48%; Ni—24.69%; Cl—29.84%.

Green crystals or crystalline granules. Soluble in one part of water; soluble in alcohol.

Standards

Insoluble	max 0.010%	Cobalt (Co)	max 0.10%
Nitrate (NO_3)	max 0.02%	Copper (Cu)	max 0.005%
Sulfate (SO_4)	max 0.010%	Iron (Fe)	max 0.001%
Alkalies, Earths, etc.	max 0.10%	Zinc (Zn)	max 0.03%

Insoluble: Dissolve 10 g in 100 ml of H_2O and 1 ml of HCl and heat on the steam bath for 1 hour. Filter any undissolved residue (retain filtrate), wash, and dry at 105°. The weight of the insoluble residue does not exceed 1.0 mg.

Nitrate: Dissolve 0.5 g in 10 ml of water. Add this solution in small portions and with constant stirring to 10 ml of 10% NaOH previously diluted with 5 ml of water. Cover the beaker and heat on the steam bath, stirring several times, for 15 minutes. Cool and filter. Neutralize the filtrate with 25% H_2SO_4 and dilute to 25 ml. Using 5 ml of this solution as *Sample Solution* and 2 ml of standard nitrate solution (0.02 mg NO_3) for Control, proceed as directed under Nitrate— Estimation of Small Amounts, page 575.

Sulfate: Heat the filtrate from the test for *Insoluble* to boiling, add 5 ml $BaCl_2$, and allow to stand overnight.   If a precipitate is present filter, wash, ignite, and weigh.   Its weight does not exceed 2.5 mg.

Cobalt: Determine as in Nickel Sulfate.   Not more than 4.1 ml of the permanganate is consumed.

For a method to estimate microquantities of cobalt in nickel (and salts) see **Note** under Nickel Ammonium Sulfate.

Alkalies, Earths, etc.; Copper; Iron; Zinc: Apply the tests described for Nickel Sulfate.   The results conform to the requirements there stated.

NICKEL NITRATE

$Ni(NO_3)_2 \cdot 6H_2O$; mol. wt. 290.80; anhydrous—62.83%; H_2O—37.17%; Ni—20.18%; NO_3—42.65%.

Green, deliquescent crystals.   Soluble in 1 part of water; soluble in alcohol.

Standards

Insoluble....................max 0.010%	Copper (Cu)................max 0.005%
Chloride (Cl)................max 0.002%	Iron (Fe)....................max 0.002%
Sulfate (SO₄)................max 0.010%	Lead (Pb)..................max 0.003%
Alkalies, Earths, etc...........max 0.10%	Zinc (Zn)....................max 0.03%
Cobalt (Co)..................max 0.05%	

Insoluble: Dissolve 10 g in 100 ml of H_2O and 1 ml of HNO_3 and heat on the steam bath for 1 hour.   Filter any undissolved residue, wash, and dry at 105°. Not more than 1.0 mg of insoluble residue is found.

Chloride: Dissolve 2 g in 20 ml of water, add 2 ml of HNO_3 and divide into two equal portions.   To one portion add 1 ml of $AgNO_3$, bring to a boil, let stand for 10 minutes, cool, filter until clear, and use for the control.   To the other portion add 1 ml of $AgNO_3$.   If a turbidity is produced it is not greater than that produced by adding 0.02 mg of Cl to the control and adjusting both to the same volume.

Sulfate: Dissolve 5 g in 10 ml of H_2O, add 10 ml of HCl and evaporate to dryness on the steam bath.   Take up the residue with 100 ml of H_2O, add 1 ml of HCl, heat to boiling, add 5 ml of $BaCl_2$ and let stand overnight.   If a precipitate is formed, filter, wash, ignite, and weigh.   Its weight does not exceed 1.2 mg.

Alkalies, Earths, etc.: Cobalt; Coppper; Zinc: Apply the tests as for Nickel Sulfate.   The results should be as there stated.

Iron: Dissolve 1 g in 20 ml of H_2O, and add 2 ml of HCl and 5 drops of HNO_3. Bring the solution to a boil and add sufficient NH_4OH to dissolve the precipitate first formed.   Filter, and wash with 2.5% NH_3 until the washings are colorless. Dissolve any precipitate on the filter with 5 ml of hot 10% HCl and dilute to 40 ml. To 20 ml of the dilution add 2 ml of HCl and dilute to 50 ml.   Add 30 mg of ammonium persulfate and 3 ml of ammonium thiocyanate, and mix.   Any resulting red color is not darker than that of a control made with 0.01 mg of Fe, 2 ml of HCl, and the same quantities of the ammonium persulfate and thiocyanate and in same final volume as with the sample.

Lead: Dissolve 2.0 g in water, add 0.5 ml of glacial acetic acid and dilute to 20 ml. Filter if not clear and divide the filtrate into 2 equal portions.   To one portion add

0.2 ml of potassium chromate solution and mix well. To the other portion add 0.2 ml of water. Both portions are equally clear in 10 minutes when viewed in the same light.

NICKEL SULFATE

$NiSO_4 \cdot 6H_2O$; mol. wt. 262.85; anhydrous—58.88%; H_2O—41.12%; Ni—22.33%; SO_4—36.55%.

Emerald-green crystals. Soluble in 3 parts of water; almost insoluble in alcohol.

Standards

Insoluble	max 0.010%	Copper (Cu)	max 0.005%
Chloride (Cl)	max 0.001%	Iron (Fe)	max 0.001%
Nitrate (NO₃)	max 0.005%	Zinc (Zn)	max 0.03%
Alkalies, Earths, etc.	max 0.10%	*Assay*	
Cobalt (Co)	max 0.05%		

Insoluble: Dissolve 10 g in 100 ml of H_2O and 1 ml of H_2SO_4 and heat on steam bath for 1 hour. Filter any undissolved residue, wash, and dry at 105°. Not more than 1.0 mg of insoluble residue is found.

Chloride: Dissolve 2 g in 20 ml of water and 1 ml of HNO_3 and divide into two equal portions. To one portion add 1 ml of $AgNO_3$, bring to a boil, let stand for 10 minutes, cool, filter until clear, and use for the control. To the other portion add 1 ml of $AgNO_3$. If a turbidity is produced, it is not greater than that produced by adding 0.01 mg of Cl to the control and adjusting both to the same volume.

Nitrate: Dissolve 1.0 g in 10 m of water. Add the solution in small portions and with constant stirring to 10 ml of 10% NaOH, previously diluted with 5 ml of water. Cover the beaker and heat it on the steam bath, stirring several times, for 15 minutes. Cool, filter, neutralize the filtrate with 25% H_2SO_4 and dilute to 25 ml. Using 5 ml of the solution diluted with 5 ml of water and 1.0 ml of standard nitrate solution for the control, proceed as directed under Nitrate—Estimation of Small Amounts, page 575.

Alkalies, Earths, etc.: Dissolve 2 g in 95 ml of H_2O, add 5 ml of NH_4OH, precipitate the nickel with H_2S, and filter. Boil 50 ml of the filtrate until evaporated to about 10 ml, refilter if necessary, evaporate, and ignite. The residue does not exceed 1.0 mg.

Cobalt: Dissolve 2 g in 40 ml of H_2O, add 1 ml of 10% KOH, then add 2 ml glacial acetic acid and heat to boiling. Add a solution of 5 g of potassium nitrite in 10 ml of water, stir, digest on the steam bath for 30 minutes, then allow to stand at room temperature overnight. Filter through a Gooch crucible or sintered glass funnel and wash with small quantities of cold 5% ammonium nitrate solution containing 1% acetic acid, until free from nitrite. Place the crucible in the same beaker in which the precipitation has been made, add 10 ml of 0.1 N potassium permanganate, follow with 25 ml 10% H_2SO_4 and sufficient water to cover the crucible. Heat to about 50° until the yellow precipitate has dissolved, then cool, add 1 g of potassium iodide and titrate the liberated iodine representing the excess of permanganate with 0.1 N sodium thiosulfate. Determine the value of the permanganate in terms of 0.1 N thiosulfate by running a blank with the same volumes of permanganate, sulfuric acid and potassium iodide in the same manner as with the sample.   Not more than 2.05 ml of 0.1 N KMnO$_4$ is consumed.

For a method of determining microquantities of cobalt in nickel (and salts) see **Note** under Nickel Ammonium Sulfate.

Copper: Dissolve 2 g in 2 ml of HCl and sufficient water to make 50 ml, then add 2 ml of a 1% solution of mercuric chloride and saturate with H$_2$S.   Filter through a small filter, wash with H$_2$S water, and ignite the filter and precipitate in porcelain.   Dissolve the residue by warming with 0.5 ml of HNO$_3$ and a few drops of H$_2$O, dilute to 10 ml, and filter if necessary.   Dissolve in the solution 1 g of ammonium acetate, then add 5 drops of freshly prepared potassium ferrocyanide solution.   Any red color produced is not darker than that of a control made with 0.1 mg of Cu, the same quantities of HNO$_3$, ammonium acetate and potassium ferrocyanide and in the same volume as with the sample.

Iron: Dissolve 2 g in 20 ml of H$_2$O and add 2 ml of HCl and 5 drops of HNO$_3$. Bring the solution to a boil and add sufficient NH$_4$OH to dissolve the precipitate first formed.   Filter and wash with 2.5% NH$_3$ until the washings are colorless. Dissolve any precipitate on the filter with 5 ml of hot 10% HCl and dilute with H$_2$O to 40 ml.   To 20 ml add 2 ml of HCl and dilute to 50 ml.   Add about 30 mg ammonium persulfate and 3 ml of ammonium thiocyanate, and mix.   Any resulting red color is not darker than that of a control made with 0.01 mg of Fe, 2 ml of HCl, and the same quantities of ammonium persulfate and thiocyanate and in the same final volume as with the sample.

Zinc: Dissolve 2.0 g in 10 ml of H$_2$O and 2 drops of 10% H$_2$SO$_4$.   Heat the solution and slowly add it with stirring to 10 ml of 10% NaOH.   Boil for 2 minutes, cool, filter and dilute filtrate to 40 ml.   Neutralize 30 ml of the filtrate with H$_2$SO$_4$, add 1 ml excess of the acid and dilute to 40 ml (A).   To the remaining 10 ml of the filtrate add 0.3 mg Zn (3.0 ml standard zinc solution), neutralize with H$_2$SO$_4$, add 1 ml excess of the acid and dilute to 40 ml (B).   Then add to each 2 ml of freshly prepared potassium ferrocyanide solution, stir well and allow to stand for 10 minutes. Any turbidity in A does not exceed that in B.

Assay: Nickel sulfate may be assayed as follows: Weigh accurately 1.5 to 2 g, dissolve in water and dilute to exactly 200 ml.   Transfer 50 ml to a 500–600 ml beaker and dilute with H$_2$O to 200 ml.   Add 1 g of sodium citrate, heat to boiling, then add to the boiling solution, with stirring, a solution of 0.6 g of dimethylglyoxime in 100 ml of warm alcohol, follow with 5 ml of NH$_4$OH and let stand overnight. Filter on a Gooch crucible, wash with hot water, then with 50% alcohol and dry at 110° to constant weight.   The weight of the nickel dimethylglyoxime multiplied by 0.9100 = NiSO$_4 \cdot$6H$_2$O, log 95904.

NICOTINAMIDE

Niacinamide

—CONH$_2$; mol. wt. 122.13; total N—22.94%; Amide N—12.29%.

White, crystalline.   Soluble in about 1 part of water, 1.5 alcohol; insoluble in ether.

Standards

Melting range.................128.5°–130°	Ignition residue.............max 0.03%
Assay (from NH₂).............min 99%	Drying loss.................max 0.20%
*p*H (0.5 *M*)....................6.6 ± 0.2	Heavy metals (as Pb).......max 0.001%
Solubility....................to pass test	

Assay: Weigh accurately about 0.3 of the dried sample and dissolve it in 30 ml of glacial acetic acid in a 250-ml glass-stoppered flask, warming, if necessary, to effect solution.   Add 75 ml of benzene and 2 drops of methylrosaniline chloride solution (crystal violet, methyl violet) in glacial acetic acid (1 in 100), and titrate with 0.1 *N* perchloric acid to a violet color.   Correct for a blank.   1 ml of 0.1 *N* $HClO_4$ = 0.01221 g of nicotinamide, log 08672.

pH: Determine in a 0.5 molar solution (6%).   It should be 6.6 ± 0.2.

Solubility: A solution of 3 g in 25 ml of water is complete, clear and colorless.

Ignition residue: To 3.5 g add 1 ml of H_2SO_4 and ignite at first gently, then strongly to constant weight.   The residue, if any, does not exceed 1.0 mg.

Drying loss: When dried over H_2SO_4 or other efficient desiccant in a vacuum to constant weight, the loss in weight, if any, does not exceed 0.2%.

Heavy metals: Dissolve 4 g in 30 ml of water, add 5 ml of 10% HCl and dilute to 40 ml.   To 10 ml of the dilution add 0.02 mg of Pb and dilute to 40 ml (*A*).   Dilute the remaining 30 ml to 40 ml (*B*).   Then to each add 10 ml of H_2S.   *B* is no darker than *A*.

NICOTINIC ACID

Niacin, Pyridine-3-carboxylic Acid

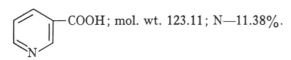

—COOH; mol. wt. 123.11; N—11.38%.

Colorless or white crystals or crystalline powder.   Soluble in about 60 parts of water, in about 40 parts of alcohol, and in solution of alkali hydroxides and carbonates.   Insoluble in chloroform or ether.   Maximum absorption in H_2O is at 263 mm.

Standards

Melting range.................235°–237°	Chloride (Cl)....................0.002%
Assay....................99.7%–100.2%	Nitrate (NO₃)...............max 0.005%
Solution in Na₂CO₃...........to pass test	Sulfur compounds (as SO₄).....max 0.01%
Solution in H₂SO₄............to pass test	Heavy metals (as Pb)...........0.001%
Ignition residue.............max 0.03%	Iron (Fe)..................max 0.002%

Melting range: Determine in a bath preheated to 220°.

Assay: Dry about 0.5 g at 105° for 2 hours.   Dissolve about 0.4 g of the dried sample, accurately weighed, in 40 ml of water, warming if necessary; add 0.1 ml of phenolphthalein, and titrate with 0.1 N NaOH.   One ml of 0.1 N NaOH = 0.01231 g of C_5H_4NCOOH, log 09026.

Solution in sodium carbonate: A solution of 1.0 g in 10 ml of 10% Na_2CO_3 is clear and colorless.

Solution in sulfuric acid: A solution of 1.0 g in 10 ml of H_2SO_4 is colorless.

Ignition residue: Ignite 3.0 g until well charred; cool, add 1 ml of H_2SO_4 and ignite to constant weight.   The residue does not exceed 1.0 mg (retain residue).

Chloride: To a solution of 1 g in 30 ml of warm water, add 2 ml of HNO_3 and 2 ml of $AgNO_3$.   Any turbidity produced is not greater than that in a blank to which 0.02 mg of Cl has been added.

Nitrate: Dissolve 50 mg of sample in 5 ml of water.   Add to the solution 10 mg of NaCl, 0.1 ml of diphenylamine and 5 ml of H_2SO_4.   No blue color is produced in 30 minutes.

Sulfur compounds (as SO_4): To 2.0 g contained in a platinum dish or crucible add 10 ml of H_2O, then slowly add 1.0 g of anhydrous Na_2CO_3.   Evaporate and ignite until thoroughly charred.   Add 20 ml of H_2O and 2 ml of 30% H_2O_2 and boil for a few minutes.   Filter, and wash with some hot water.   Add to filtrate 3 ml of HCl and evaporate to dryness on the steam bath.   Dissolve the residue in 15 ml of water, add 1 ml of 0.1 N HCl and 2 ml of $BaCl_2$.   Any turbidity produced is not greater than that in a control made by adding 0.2 mg of SO_4 to 1.0 g Na_2CO_3 and evaporate on the steam bath with 3 ml of HCl.

Heavy metals: Warm 2 g of nicotinic acid with 40 ml of H_2O and 1 ml of 1 N acetic acid until dissolved, then add 10 ml of H_2S.   Any darkening produced is not deeper than that in a blank to which 0.02 mg of Pb has been added.

Iron: To the *Ignition residue* add 1 ml each of H_2O and HCl, and evaporate to dryness on the steam bath.   Dissolve the residue in 5 ml of HCl, add 50 mg of ammonium persulfate and dilute to 30 ml.   Dilute 10 ml to 50 ml, and add 3 ml of ammonium thiocyanate.   Any red color produced is not darker than that in a blank to which 0.02 mg of Fe has been added.

NINHYDRIN

Triketohydrindene Hydrate

$=(OH)_2$; mol. wt. 178.14.

White to brownish-white crystals or crystalline powder.   Soluble in water or alcohol; slightly soluble in ether or chloroform.   When heated above 100° it becomes red and melts between 240°–245° with decomposition.

It is used as a sensitive reagent for proteins, amino acids and peptones.

Standards

Sensitiveness.................to pass test   Ignition residue..............max 0.20%
Solubility....................to pass test

Sensitiveness: (a) Dissolve 5 mg of Ninhydrin in 1 ml of H_2O.
(b) Dissolve 5 mg of aminoacetic acid in 10 ml of H_2O.
To 1 ml of (b) add a solution of 50 mg of sodium acetate in 2 ml of H_2O, then add 0.2 ml of (a) and gently boil the mixture for 1 to 2 minutes. A violet color is produced which becomes intense after a few minutes.

Solubility: A solution of 0.1 g in 10 ml of H_2O is clear and complete.

Ignition residue: Char 0.5 g well, cool, add 0.5 ml of H_2SO_4 and ignite at first gently, then strongly to constant weight. The weight of the residue does not exceed 1.0 mg.

NITRAMINE

; mol. wt. 287.15.

Tetralite; Tetryl; 2,4,6-Trinitrophenylmethylnitroamine

Yellow powder. Slightly soluble in water; soluble in alcohol and in solutions of alkali hydroxides. pH range: 11 colorless; 13.0 brown. It is usually used for pH determinations of the above range in a 0.05% alcoholic solution.

Standards

Melting range.................130°–132°	Solubility in alcohol..........to pass test
Sensitiveness................to pass test	Ignition residue..............max 0.20%

Sensitiveness: Dissolve 10 mg of nitramine in 15 ml of ethanol and add 5 ml of water. Add 0.5 ml of this solution to 50 ml of CO_2-free water. It requires the addition of not more than 0.1 ml of 0.1 N NaOH to produce a brown color and the color is discharged by 0.1 ml of 0.1 N HCl.

Solubility in alcohol: One-tenth gram yields a clear and complete solution with 10 ml of ethanol.

Ignition residue: Moisten 0.5 g with 0.5 ml of sulfuric acid and ignite gently to constant weight. The weight of the residue does not exceed 1.0 mg.

NITRIC ACID

Sp. Gr. 1.40

HNO_3; mol. wt. 63.02; N—22.23%; N_2O_5—85.69%.

Colorless or faintly yellow, clear liquid. Discolors on exposure to light due to the formation of N_2O_4. *Keep in amber-colored, glass-stoppered bottles.*

Standards

Assay...............69%–71% HNO₃	Sulfate (SO₄)...............max 0.0001%
Evaporation residue........max 0.0010%	Arsenic (As)...............max 0.01 ppm
Ignition residue...........max 0.0005%	Heavy metals (as Pb).......max 0.0001%
Chloride (Cl).............max 0.00005%	Iron (Fe).................max 0.0001%

Assay: Weigh a glass-stoppered flask with 15 ml of H_2O, then add about 2 ml of the acid and reweigh. Dilute with 40 ml of water and titrate with 1 N NaOH, using methyl orange indicator. One ml of 1 N NaOH = 0.06302 g HNO_3, log 79948.

Evaporation residue: Evaporate 70 ml (100 g) of the acid in a platinum dish on the steam bath to dryness, and dry at 105° for 2 hours. The weight of the residue does not exceed 1.0 mg (retain).

Ignition residue: To the residue from the preceding test add 5 drops of H_2SO_4 and ignite at cherry redness for 5 minutes. Not more than 0.5 mg of residue remains.

Chloride: Dilute 15 ml (20 g) with 15 ml of H_2O and add 1 ml of silver nitrate. Any resulting turbidity is not greater than that of a control made with 0.01 mg of Cl, 1 ml of the HNO_3 and 1 ml of silver nitrate in the same volume as with the sample.

Sulfate: To 70 ml (100 g) of the acid add 10 mg of sodium carbonate and evaporate to dryness. Take up the residue with 5 ml of H_2O and 0.5 ml of 1 N HCl, filter, wash with water to 10 ml, and add 2 ml of $BaCl_2$. Any resulting turbidity is not greater than that in a blank to which 0.1 mg of SO_4 has been added.

Arsenic: Mix 140 ml (200 g) ml with 5 ml of H_2SO_4 and evaporate *under hood* to copious fumes. Cool, dilute *cautiously* with H_2O, and re-evaporate a second or third time to fumes, if necessary, to remove nitrate. Cool and test by the method on page 563. The stain is not greater than that from a blank to which 0.002 mg of As has been added.

Heavy metals: Evaporate 15 ml to dryness on steam bath. Take up the residue with 20 ml of hot water and digest for 5 minutes. Add 1 ml of 1 N acetic acid, dilute to 40 ml and add 10 ml of H_2S. Any color produced is not darker than that in a blank to which 0.02 mg of Pb has been added.

Iron: Evaporate 7 ml (10 g) in glass or porcelain to dryness on the steam bath. Take up the residue with 2 ml of HCl and dilute to 50 ml. Add about 30 mg of ammonium persulfate and 3 ml of ammonium thiocyanate, and mix. Any resulting red color is not darker than that of a blank to which 0.01 mg of Fe has been added.

NITRIC ACID, 90% (FUMING)

Sp. Gr. 1.5

Colorless to slightly yellow or slightly brownish, clear liquid. Sp. gr. about 1.5 at 15°. It is a very powerful oxidant and should be handled with extreme care to prevent its coming in contact with the skin or with any oxidizable matter. *Keep it in a cool place.*

Standards

Assay.................min 90% HNO$_3$	Chloride (Cl)..............max 0.00005%
Evaporation residue.........max 0.003%	Sulfate (SO$_4$)...............max 0.0005%
Ignition residue.............max 0.002%	Arsenic (As)...............max 0.02 ppm
Free nitrogen oxides	Heavy metals (as Pb).......max 0.0005%
(as N$_2$O$_3$)..................max 0.1%	Iron (Fe).................max 0.0002%

Assay: Assay this acid by titration with 1 N alkali, using methyl orange as indicator, and taking the necessary precautions in the weighing out of the sample for the assay. One ml of 1 N NaOH = 0.06302 g HNO$_3$, log 79948.

Evaporation residue: Evaporate 33 ml (50 g) of the acid in a platinum dish on the steam bath to dryness and dry at 105° for 2 hours. The weight of the residue does not exceed 1.5 mg.

Ignition residue: To the residue from the preceding test add 5 drops of H$_2$SO$_4$ and ignite at cherry redness for 5 minutes. Not more than 1.0 mg of residue remains.

Free nitrogen oxides: Add 3.5 ml (5 g) of the acid to a cooled mixture of 2 ml of H$_2$SO$_4$ and 75 ml of water, and slowly titrate with 0.1 N potassium permanganate until the pink color persists for 3 minutes. Not more than 0.3 ml of the permanganate is required. One ml of 0.1 N potassium permanganate corresponds to 0.0019 g of N$_2$O$_3$.

Chloride: Dilute 13 ml (20 g) with 20 ml of H$_2$O and add 1 ml of silver nitrate. Any turbidity produced is not greater than that in a control made with 0.01 mg of Cl, 1 ml of the HNO$_3$ and 1 ml of AgNO$_3$ in the same volume as with the sample.

Sulfate: To 13 ml (20 g) of the acid add 10 mg of sodium carbonate and evaporate to dryness. Take up the residue with 5 ml of H$_2$O and 0.5 ml of 1 N HCl, filter, wash with H$_2$O to 10 ml, and add to the filtrate 1 ml of BaCl$_2$. If a turbidity is produced it is not greater than that in a blank to which 0.1 mg of SO$_4$ has been added.

Arsenic: Mix 6.5 ml (10 g) with 3 ml of H$_2$SO$_4$ and proceed as described for Nitric Acid. The stain produced is not greater than from a blank with 0.002 mg of As added.

Heavy metals: Evaporate 3.5 ml (5 g) to dryness on the steam bath. Take up the residue with 20 ml of hot water and digest for 5 minutes. Add 1 ml of 1 N acetic acid, dilute to 40 ml, and add 10 ml of H$_2$S. Any color produced is not darker than that of a blank to which 0.025 mg of Pb has been added.

Iron: Evaporate 3.5 ml to dryness on the steam bath. Take up the residue with 2 ml of HCl and dilute to 50 ml. Add 30 mg of ammonium persulfate and 3 ml of ammonium thiocyanate, and mix. Any red color produced is not darker than that of a blank to which 0.01 mg of Fe has been added.

p-NITROANILINE

O$_2$N·C$_6$H$_4$·NH$_2$; mol. wt. 138.12.

Bright yellow powder; odorless or faint odor. Insoluble in water; soluble in about 25 parts of alcohol or 30 parts of ether.

Standards

Melting range.................146°–148°	Ignition residue.............max 0.10%
Solubility in alcohol or ether...to pass test	

Solubility in alcohol or ether: A solution of 1 g in 30 ml of alcohol or in 40 ml of ether shows not more than a trace of insoluble matter.

Ignition residue: Char 1 g well, cool, add 0.5 ml of H_2SO_4 and ignite at first gently, then strongly to constant weight. The weight of the residue does not exceed 1.0 mg.

o-NITROBENZALDEHYDE

NO_2; mol. wt. 151.12.

Pale yellow or light, greenish-yellow needles, benzaldehyde-like odor. Almost insoluble in water; soluble in alcohol, benzene and ether.

Standards

Melting range....................42°–44°	Ignition residue.............max 0.10%
Solubility in alcohol...........to pass test	

Solubility in alcohol: One gram dissolves completely in 20 ml of alcohol, giving a clear, pale yellow or greenish-yellow solution.

Ignition residue: Gently ignite 1 g with 0.5 ml of H_2SO_4 to constant weight. Not more than 1.0 mg of residue remains.

NITROBENZENE

$C_6H_5 \cdot NO_2$; mol. wt. 123.11.

Pale yellow liquid; characteristic odor. Almost insoluble in water; miscible with alcohol, benzene and ether. Sp. gr. 1.2.

Standards

Boiling range..................210°–212°	Acid (as HNO_3).............max 0.003%
Freezing point............not below +5°	Water......................max 0.05%

Boiling range: Distill 50 ml. Not less than 48 ml distills between 210° and 212°, correction being made for the barometric pressure (page 581).

Freezing point: Determine by method on page 581. It should not be below +5° and not above 6.5°.

Acid: Shake 16 ml (20 g) with 50 ml of water for 1 minute and allow the liquids to separate. Withdraw the lower layer of the nitrobenzene, and add to the aqueous layer 2 drops of bromophenol blue. The yellow color of the liquid is changed to bluish violet by not more than 0.5 ml of 0.02 N NaOH.

Water: The water content of nitrobenzene may be determined by the iodine (Fischer) method.

p-NITROBENZOYL CHLORIDE

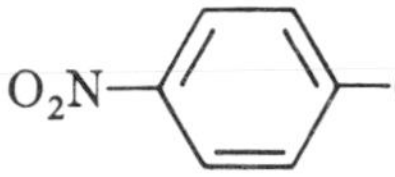

O_2N—⟨benzene ring⟩—$COCl$; mol. wt. 185.57.

Bright yellow crystals, pungent odor. Decomposed by water or alcohol; soluble in ether. *Keep in tightly closed containers.*

Standards

Melting range.....................73°–75°	Solubility in alcohol or ether...to pass test
Assay.........98.5%–100.3% $C_7H_4ClNO_3$	Ignition residue.............max 0.05%

Assay: Weigh accurately about 3 g, dissolve in exactly 50 ml of 1 N NaOH and allow to stand for 20 minutes. Then titrate the excess of NaOH with 1 N H_2SO_4, using phenolphthalein indicator. 1 ml of 1 N NaOH = 0.09275 g $NO_2 \cdot C_6H_4 \cdot COCl$, log 96731.

Solubility in alcohol or ether: One gram dissolves clearly and completely in 20 ml of alcohol, or in 20 ml of ether.

Ignition residue: To 2 g add 1 ml of sulfuric acid and ignite to constant weight. Not more than 1.0 mg of residue remains.

NITRON

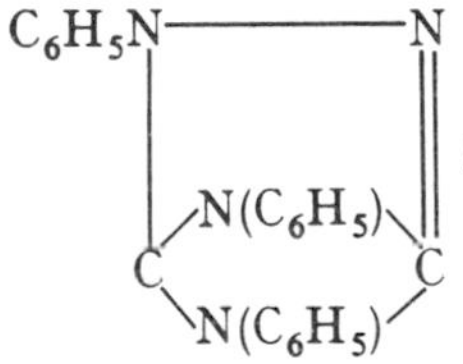

C_6H_5N————N
$N(C_6H_5)$
C————C
$N(C_6H_5)$
; mol. wt. 312.36.

Lustrous yellow leaflets or yellow powder. Insoluble in water; soluble in alcohol, benzene, chloroform, ethyl acetate, and dilute acids; with difficulty soluble in ether. Decomposes in alcoholic solutions. It is used in dilute acetic acid solution for the precipitation of nitrate. *Keep protected from light.*

Standards

Sensitiveness.................to pass test	Ignition residue.............max 0.20%
Solubility in 1 N acetic acid...to pass test	

Sensitiveness: To 10 ml of a solution containing 0.5 mg of KNO_3 (0.3 mg NO_3) add 2 drops of 10% H_2SO_4, and follow with 1 ml of the solution from the following test. A distinct crystalline precipitate forms in 30 minutes.

Solubility in 1 N acetic acid: One g dissolves readily and completely in 10 ml of 1 N acetic acid.

Ignition residue: Char 0.5 g of coal, add 0.5 ml of H_2SO_4 and ignite to constant weight. Not more than 1.0 mg of residue remains.

NITROSO-BETANAPHTHOL

α-Nitroso-β-naphthol; 1-Nitroso-2-naphthol

; mol. wt. 173.16.

Brown or yellowish-brown.   Insoluble in water; soluble in alcohol, benzene, ether, carbon tetrachloride, caustic alkali and acetic acid.

The reaction of this reagent with cobalt is sensitive to 0.001 mg Co in 1 ml of solution.

Standards

Melting range.............not below 109°	Ignition residue..............max 0.20%
Solubility in acetic acid.......to pass test	Sensitiveness................to pass test
Insoluble in CCl_4.............max 0.25%	Assay........................min 95%

Melting range: Dry about 200 mg at 90° to constant weight, then determine the melting temperature of the dried by the capillary tube method, preheating the "bath" to 100°.

Solubility in acetic acid: Dissolve 1 g in 50 ml of hot 50% acetic acid; the solution is clear or nearly so.

Insoluble in CCl_4: To 3.0 g in a conical flask add 100 ml of CCl_4, cover the flask with an inverted beaker and heat at about 50° until no more appears to dissolve, replacing any of the CCl_4 lost during the heating.   If any insoluble matter is present, filter on a tared filtering crucible, wash with 300 ml of warm CCl_4, dry at 105° for 2 hours and weigh.   The weight of the residue does not exceed 7.5 mg.

Ignition residue: Char well 1.0 g.   Cool, add 0.5 ml of H_2SO_4 and ignite gently at first, then strongly to constant weight.   The residue, if any, does not exceed 2.0 mg.

Sensitiveness: (a) Dissolve 20 mg of sample in 20 ml of a mixture of equal volume of glacial acetic acid and of water. (b) Dissolve 20 mg of cobalt chloride in 50 ml of water (1 ml = 0.1 mg Co).

Dilute 1 ml of (b) to 10 ml.   Dissolve 0.5 g of sodium acetate in the solution. Add 2 drops of glacial acetic acid and follow with 1 ml of solution (a) and shake. A distinct red turbidity is produced in 2 minutes.

Assay: Dry about 1 g in a vacuum over an efficient desiccant to constant weight. Transfer an accurately weighed quantity of about 0.25 of the dried sample into a glass-stoppered flask and add 10 ml of 10% NaOH to dissolve.   Add to the well-cooled solution 25% H_2SO_4 in small portions until a slight precipitate is formed which does not redissolve on shaking and the solution is slightly acid.   Now add 3 g of KI, and after it has dissolved, add 20 ml of 25% H_2SO_4.   Immediately stopper the flask and let it stand in the dark for 2 hours.   Then titrate the liberated iodine with 0.1 N thiosulfate, adding starch near the end.   Correct for a blank.   One ml of 0.1 N thiosulfate = 0.008758 g of $C_{10}H_7NO_2$.

NITROSO-R SALT

1-Nitroso-2-hydroxynaphthalene-3,6-sodiumsulfonate

$C_{10}H_5NO_8S_2Na_2$; mol. wt. 377.27.

Yellow crystals or crystalline powder. Soluble in about 40 parts of water; practically insoluble in alcohol. Its principal application is for the detection and colorimetric determination of small quantities of cobalt.

This reagent for cobalt will detect 2 micrograms of Co in 1 ml of solution.

Standards

Sensitiveness.................to pass test	Drying loss...................max 1.0%
Solubility....................to pass test	Assay.........................min 97%

Sensitiveness: (a) Dissolve 10 mg of sample in 10 ml of H_2O. (b) Dissolve 20 mg of cobalt chloride in 50 ml of H_2O (1 ml = 0.1 mg Co).

Dilute 1 ml of solution (b) with water to 10 ml. Dissolve 0.5 g sodium acetate in the dilution, add 1 ml of 1 N acetic acid, and follow with 1 ml of solution (a). A red color is produced which persists when the solution is boiled with 1 ml of HCl for 1 minute.

Solubility: Dissolve 1.0 g in 20 ml of water. A clear and complete or practically complete solution is obtained.

Drying loss: Dry 1 g of the reagent at 105° for 2 hours. The loss in weight corresponds to not more than 1.0%.

Assay: Dry about 1 g at 105° for 2 hours. Weigh accurately 0.5 g of the dried reagent and dissolve it in a glass-stoppered flask in 25 ml of water. Add 3 g of KI and after it has dissolved add 5 ml of H_2SO_4 previously mixed with 10 ml of water. Immediately stopper the flask and allow to stand for 2 hours in the dark. Dilute with 25 ml of water and titrate the liberated iodine with 0.1 N thiosulfate, adding starch indicator near the end. Correct for a blank. One ml of 0.1 N thiosulfate = 0.01886 g of $C_{10}H_5NO_8Na_2S_2$.

$$C_{10}H_5NO\cdot etc. + 2H \rightarrow C_{10}H_5NH_2\cdot etc. + H_2O$$

OSMIUM TETROXIDE

Osmic Acid; "Perosmic Anhydride"

OsO_4; mol. wt. 254.20; Os—74.82%.

Colorless or white crystals, or slightly yellow. Melts at about 42° but begins to soften several degrees lower. Boils at 130° but begins to sublime and distill well below this temperature. Very pungent, chlorine-like odor, perceptible even in a concentration of only 0.02 mg per liter of air. Soluble in about 200 parts of water;

very soluble in carbon tetrachloride (1 in 0.5); soluble in alcohol, in ether and in solutions of alkali hydroxides.

Its use, both industrially and as a reagent, rests upon its powerful activity as a catalyzer of oxidation-reduction reactions.

Caution: *Vapors of osmium tetroxide are highly irritating to the eye, respiratory tract and the skin.*

Standards

Insoluble in CCl₄............max 0.10%	Foreign heavy metals (as Pb)..max 0.003%
Nonvolatile................max 0.10%	Assay........................min 98%

Insoluble in CCl_4: Dissolve 0.50 g in 5 ml of carbon tetrachloride, warming gently if necessary. The solution is, at most, only slightly yellow, and if any insoluble matter remains filter on a tared, previously dried at 105°, small sintered glass crucible, wash with small volumes of CCl_4 and dry at 105°. Its weight does not exceed 0.5 mg.

Nonvolatile: Evaporate the filtrate from the preceding test on the steam bath and dry the residue, if any, at 105° for 1 hour. Its weight does not exceed 0.5 mg.

Foreign heavy metals: Evaporate the residue from the test for *Nonvolatile* with 1 ml of HCl to dryness on the steam bath. Add to the residue 1 ml of 1 N acetic acid and warm water to 15 ml, then add 5 ml of H_2S. Any resulting color is not darker than that of a blank to which 0.015 mg of Pb has been added.

Assay: Compliance with the preceding tests provides a product of reasonably high purity—98% or better. If an actual quantitative determination is desired, the Klobbie[1] titrimetric method, based on the reaction, $OsO_4 + 4KI + 2H_2SO_4 \rightarrow 2I_2 + OsO_2 + 2K_2SO_4 + 2H_2O$, may be used.

An accurately weighed (best by difference) quantity of about 100 mg of OsO_4 is dissolved in 5–7 ml of 1 N NaOH in a glass-stoppered flask, 3 g of KI is dissolved in it, and 40 ml of 25% H_2SO_4 slowly added, then stoppered and allowed to stand in the dark for 20 minutes. The liberated iodine is now titrated with 0.05 N thiosulfate, using starch solution as an external indicator (the reduced osmium solution is green and the end point may be difficult to determine with indicator internally). One ml of 0.05 N thiosulfate = 0.003178 g OsO_4, log 50229.

Note: Osmium tetroxide reacts with urea, in presence of acid, to form a stable rose-red color having a moderately sharp minimum transmittancy of 480 mμ, and Ayres *et al.*[2,3] have utilized this reaction to elaborate a spectrophotometric-colorimetric method for the quantitative determination of less than 1 mg amounts of OsO_4.

[1] Klobbie, E. A., *Chem. Zentr.* **11**, 65 (1898).
[2] Ayres *et al.*, *Anal. Chem.* **20**, 317 (1950).
[3] Allon, W. J., and Beamish, F. E., *Anal. Chem.* **24**, 1608 (1952).

OXALIC ACID

$HO \cdot OC—CO \cdot OH \cdot 2H_2O$; mol. wt. 126.07.

Colorless crystals; efflorescent in warm, dry air. Soluble in 7 parts of water, in 3 parts of alcohol, in about 70 parts of ether; insoluble in chloroform. *Keep in well-closed containers.*

Standards

Assay....99.8%–100.2% (CO·OH)$_2$·2H$_2$O Sulfate (SO$_4$)...............max 0.003%
Insoluble..................max 0.010% Heavy metals (as Pb).......max 0.0005%
Ignition residue............max 0.010% Iron (Fe).................max 0.0002%
Chloride (Cl)..............max 0.001% Substances darkened by
Nitrogen compounds (as N)...max 0.001%   H$_2$SO$_4$....................to pass test

Assay: Weigh accurately about 0.25 g, dissolve it in 30 ml of water, and add 3 ml of H$_2$SO$_4$ previously diluted with 5 ml of water. Run in slowly 30 ml of 0.1 N potassium permanganate, heat to about 70°, and complete the titration with the potassium permanganate. One ml of 0.1 N potassium permanganate = 0.006304 g (CO·OH)$_2$·2H$_2$O, log 79962.

$$5(CO·OH)_2 + 2KMnO_4 + 3H_2SO_4 \rightarrow 10CO_2 + 8H_2O + 2MnSO_4 + K_2SO_4$$

Insoluble: Dissolve 10 g in 200 ml of H$_2$O and heat on the steam bath 1 hour. If an insoluble residue is present, filter, wash it with water and dry at 105°. Its weight does not exceed 1.0 mg.

Ignition residue: Slowly ignite 10 g to volatilize, then cool, add 5 drops of H$_2$SO$_4$ and ignite to constant weight. Not more than 1.0 mg of residue remains (retain residue).

Chloride: Dissolve 1 g in 20 ml of H$_2$O, add 2 ml of HNO$_3$ and 1 ml of AgNO$_3$. Any turbidity produced is not greater than that in the blank to which 0.01 mg of Cl has been added.

Nitrogen compounds: Dissolve 1 g in 50 ml of H$_2$O in a distilling flask and, while cooling in ice, add 15 ml of 10% NaOH. Add 0.5 g of fine aluminium wire in small pieces, allow to stand for 2 hours protected from loss or access of ammonia, then distill slowly about 40 ml into 5 ml of H$_2$O containing 1 drop of dilute HCl. Add to the distillate 1 ml of 10% NaOH and 2 ml of Nessler solution. The color produced is not darker than that produced by treating 0.01 mg of nitrogen in the same manner as the sample.

Sulfate: Place in a beaker 3.0 g of sample and 20 mg of Na$_2$CO$_3$, and add 5 ml of 30% H$_2$O$_2$ and 1 ml of HNO$_3$. Cover the beaker and digest on the steam bath until reaction ceases (15–20 minutes). Remove the cover and evaporate to dryness. Add to the residue 5 ml of water and 1 ml of HCl and re-evaporate to dryness. Dissolve the residue in 8 ml of water and 2 ml of 0.1 N HCl, filter if necessary, and add to the filtrate 2 ml of BaCl$_2$. Any turbidity resulting in 15 minutes is not greater than that produced by treating 0.1 mg SO$_4$ exactly as the sample.

Solution R: Evaporate the *Ignition residue* with 2 ml of HCl and 1 ml of H$_2$O to dryness on the steam bath. Warm the residue with 2 ml of 0.1 N HCl and dilute with H$_2$O to 50 ml.

Heavy metals: Dilute 20 ml of *Solution R* to 40 ml and add 10 ml of H$_2$S. Any resulting color is not darker than that of a control made with 0.02 mg of Pb, 1 ml of 0.1 N HCl and 10 ml of H$_2$S in the same final volume as in the test with the sample.

Iron: To 25 ml of *Solution R* add 2 ml of HCl and dilute to 50 ml. Add 50 mg of ammonium persulfate and 3 ml of ammonium thiocyanate, and mix. Any red color produced is not darker than that of a blank to which 0.01 mg of Fe has been added.

Substances darkened by H_2SO_4: Heat 1 g with 10 ml of H_2SO_4 in a previously ignited test tube to sulfuric fumes.   At most, only a faint color is produced.

PALLADIUM CHLORIDE

Palladous Chloride

$PdCl_2$; mol. wt. 177.33, Pd—60.0%; Cl—40.0%.

Dark brown, hygroscopic, crystalline powder.   With water it forms a basic insoluble salt; easily soluble in dilute hydrochloric acid.

Assay: Dry at 105°, then weigh accurately about 0.25 g of the dried sample, dissolve in 10 ml of warm 10% HCl, and dilute with water to 100 ml.   Add 100 ml of 1% alcoholic dimethylglyoxime and heat on the steam bath for 1 hour.   Filter while warm, wash the precipitated palladium dimethylglyoxime with hot water dry, ignite, and weigh the palladium.   It amounts to about 59% of the weight of the sample taken.

PEPTONE

Meat Peptone

Reddish-yellow to brown powder, with a characteristic, but not putrescent odor.   Soluble in water; insoluble in alcohol or ether.

Standards

Nitrogen (dry basis)........14.2%–15.5%	Coagulable proteins...........to pass test
Ignition residue (as sulfate).....max 5.0%	Proteoses...................to pass test
Drying loss..................max 7.0%	Ammonium salts.............to pass test

Nitrogen: Dry to constant weight at 105° and determine the nitrogen in 0.3 g of the dried sample by the Kjeldahl method described on page 576.   One ml of 0.1 N HCl = 0.001401 g N, log 14644.

Ignition residue: Slowly ignite 1 g in porcelain until it is thoroughly charred. Cool, add 1 ml of sulfuric acid, and ignite to constant weight.   Not more than 50 mg of residue remains.

Drying loss: Weigh accurately about 1 g and dry to constant weight at 105°. The loss corresponds to not more than 7%.

Coagulable proteins: Dissolve 1 g in 20 ml of water, filter, and heat the filtrate to boiling.   No precipitate forms.

Proteoses: Dissolve 1 g in 10 ml of water, filter, and to 5 ml of the filtrate add a filtered solution of 10 g of zinc sulfate in 10 ml of water.   Not more than a slight flocculent precipitate is formed.

Ammonium salts: Heat 1 g with 10 ml of 10% Na_2CO_3 solution to boiling. The odor of NH_3 is not evolved.

PERCHLORIC ACID, 70%

$HClO_4$; mol. wt. 100.47.

Colorless, clear liquid.   Sp. gr. about 1.6.   Miscible with water.

Standards

Assay................70%–72% $HClO_4$	Sulfate (SO_4)...............max 0.001%
Nonvolatile.................max 0.003%	Heavy metals (as Pb).......max 0.0003%
Chloride (Cl)................max 0.001%	Iron (Fe)..................max 0.0002%
Nitrogen compounds (as N)...max 0.001%	

Assay: Weigh about 3 ml, dilute with 50 ml of water, and titrate with 1 N NaOH, using phenolphthalein indicator.   One ml of 1 N NaOH = 0.1005 g $HClO_4$, log 00217.

Nonvolatile: Measure 20 ml (32 g) of the acid into a previously ignited and tared platinum dish, evaporate and ignite to constant weight.   Any residue remaining does not exceed 1.0 mg.

Chloride: Dilute 0.6 ml with 20 ml of water, add 1 ml of nitric acid and 1 ml of silver nitrate.   Any turbidity produced is not greater than that in a blank to which 0.01 mg of Cl has been added.

Nitrogen compounds: Dilute 1.3 ml (2 g) with 40 ml H_2O in a Kjeldahl distilling flask.   Add 15 ml of 10% NaOH and 1 g of powdered Devarda metal. Allow to stand for 1 hour, then distill 35 ml into 5 ml of water containing 1 drop of dilute HCl.   Add to the distillate 2 ml of 10% NaOH, dilute to 50 ml, and add 2 ml of Nessler solution.   The color is not darker than that produced by treating 0.02 mg N (0.08 mg NH_4Cl) in the same manner as the acid.

Sulfate: Dilute 25 ml (40 g) with 150 ml of water, neutralize with ammonium hydroxide using litmus paper as indicator, and add 1 ml of HCl.   Heat the solution to boiling, add 5 ml of $BaCl_2$, and let stand overnight.   If a precipitate is present, filter, wash it with hot water, and ignite.   The weight of the precipitate ($BaSO_4$) is not more than 1.2 mg.

Heavy metals: To a solution of 20 mg of sodium carbonate in 2 ml of water, add 4 ml (6 g) of the sample and evaporate to dryness over a low flame.   Add 10 ml of warm water and 1 ml of 1 N acetic acid, dilute to 40 ml and add 10 ml of H_2S.   Any dark color produced is not greater than that of a control made with 0.02 mg of Pb and treated as the sample.

Iron: To 3.0 ml add 20 mg of sodium carbonate dissolved in a few ml of water and evaporate to dryness over a small flame.   Add to the residue 2 ml of HCl and a few ml of hot water, and dilute to 50 ml.   Add 30 mg of ammonium persulfate and 3 ml of ammonium thiocyanate.   Any red color is not greater than that of control made with 0.01 mg of Fe and the same quantities of the reagents and in the same final volume as with the sample.

PETROLEUM ETHER

Petroleum Benzin, Ligroin

Clear, colorless liquid, free from fluorescence.   It has a characteristic odor and is *highly flammable*.   Sp. gr. 0.625 to 0.650 at 25°.   Insoluble in water; miscible with absolute alcohol, benzene, chloroform, carbon disulfide, ether, and oils (except caster oil). *Keep in tightly closed containers, in a cool place, remote from fire.*

The boiling range of petroleum ether suitable for analytical work lies between 30° and 80°.   Three grades of this solvent are generally available, differing only in the spread of their distillation temperatures: (*a*) boiling range 30° to 75°; (*b*) boiling range 30° to 60°; (*c*) boiling range 40° to 60°.

Standards

Color.......................to pass test	Acid.......................to pass test
Odor and Spot Test..........to pass test	Fatty and heavy oils
Evaporation residue........max 0.0010%	(spot test)................to pass test

Boiling range: For the determination of the boiling range, distill 100 ml of the sample from a small distilling flask connected with a short but well-cooled condenser.   The lower boiling point is that recorded by the thermometer when 2 drops have come off the tip of the condenser tube; none should remain in the flask when the temperature just reaches the higher boiling point claimed.

Color: The color of petroleum ether should not be darker than the color of a solution of 2.5 mg of potassium dichromate in 1 liter of water.

Odor and Spot Test: Note the odor of the sample, then pour gradually 10 ml on a clean filter paper.   After 30 minutes the paper has no foreign or disagreeable odor and no greasy stain remains.

Evaporation residue: Evaporate completely 150 ml on the steam bath and dry for 15 minutes at 105°.   Not more than 1.0 mg of residue remains.

Acid: Thoroughly shake 10 ml with 5 ml of H_2O for 2 minutes and allow to separate.   The aqueous layer does not turn blue litmus paper red in 15 seconds.

o-PHENANTHROLINE

"Ferroin"; 1,10-Phenanthroline

$\cdot H_2O$; mol. wt. 198.23.

White or faintly yellow crystals.   Slightly soluble in water; freely soluble in alcohol or benzene; also soluble in dilute alcohol.

Standards

Melting range, anhydrous.......117°–119°	Solubility in 50% alcohol......to pass test
Sensitiveness................to pass test	Ignition residue.............max 0.20%

Sensitiveness: (*a*) Dissolve 25 mg of the reagent in 1 ml of alcohol and dilute with water to 25 ml.

(*b*) Dissolve 0.40 g of ferrous ammonium sulfate in 100 ml of oxygen-free water containing 2 ml of H_2SO_4.

Mix 25 ml of oxygen-free water with 2 ml of H_2SO_4, cool, add 0.5 ml of (*b*), and follow with 1 ml of (*a*). A red color is produced which changes to blue upon the addition of 0.1 ml of 0.1 N potassium dichromate.

Solubility in 50% alcohol: Dissolve 0.1 g in 10 ml of 50% (by volume) of alcohol. The solution is complete and clear.

Ignition residue: Char 0.5 g of sample, cool, add 0.5 ml of H_2SO_4, and ignite to constant weight. The residue weighs not more than 1.0 mg.

PHENOL

Carbolic Acid

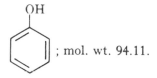 ; mol. wt. 94.11.

Colorless crystals or a crystalline mass; characteristic odor. Usually acquires a pink or brownish color on exposure to air and light. Soluble in 15 parts of water; liquefied by about 8 parts of water. Freely soluble in alcohol, chloroform, ether, glycerol. *Keep in tightly closed containers, protected from light.*

Standards

Freezing temperature....... not below 39°	Solubility................... to pass test
Evaporation residue.......... max 0.02%	*Assay* min 99%

Freezing temperature: Determine as described on page 581.

Evaporation residue: Evaporation 10 g on the steam bath and dry at 105° for 1 hour: not more than 2.0 mg of residue remains.

Solubility: Dissolve 2 g in 40 ml of water. The solution is clear and colorless.

Water: The water content of phenol may be determined by the iodine (Fischer) method. It usually is about 0.5%. The freezing point of 39° limits the H_2O to about 0.5%.

Assay: Phenol may be assayed by the following procedure.

Weigh accurately about 1.5 g and dissolve in sufficient water to make exactly 1000 ml. Transfer 25 ml into a 500-ml glass-stoppered volumetric flask, add 30 ml of 0.1 N bromine and 5 ml of HCl, and immediately stopper the flask. Shake frequently during one-half hour and allow to stand for 15 minutes. Then quickly add 10 ml of 10% potassium iodide, being careful that no bromine escapes, and stopper immediately. Shake, add 1 ml of chloroform, and titrate the liberated iodine (which represents the excess of bromine) with 0.1 N thiosulfate, using starch indicator. One ml of 0.1 N bromine = 0.001568 g C_6H_5OH, log 19535.

$$C_6H_5OH + 6Br \rightarrow C_6H_2Br_3OH + 3HBr$$
$$\text{tribromophenol}$$

PHENOLPHTHALEIN

; mol. wt. 318.31.

White powder.   Insoluble in water; soluble in 10 parts of alcohol; slightly soluble in ether; soluble in dilute alkali, forming deep red solutions. pH range: 8.2 colorless; 10 red.   It is usually used in a 1% alcoholic solution.

Standards

Melting range.................258°–262°	Solubility in NaOH solution....to pass test	
Sensitiveness................to pass test	Ignition residue.............max 0.050%	
Solubility in alcohol..........to pass test		

Sensitiveness: Dissolve 100 mg in 10 ml of neutral alcohol.   Add 0.1 ml of this solution to 200 ml CO_2-free water, then add 0.05 ml of 0.1 N NaOH; a strong pink color is produced.

Solubility in alcohol: One gram dissolves clearly and completely in 15 ml alcohol.

Solubility in NaOH solution: One gram dissolves completely in a mixture of 90 ml of water and 10 ml of 1 N NaOH.

Ignition residue: Char 2.0 g.   Cool, add 0.5 ml of H_2SO_4 and ignite gently at first, then strongly (600°–800°) to constant weight.   Any residue present is not more than 1.0 mg.

PHENOL RED

Phenolsulfonphthalein

; mol. wt. 354.37.

Red, crystalline powder.   Soluble in about 1500 parts of water; soluble in dilute alkali hydroxide solutions; also soluble in 350 parts of alcohol. pH range: 6.8 yellow; 8.4 red.   Used as a 0.02%–0.5% solution.

Standards

Sensitiveness................to pass test	Ignition residue..............max 0.1%	
Solubility in NaOH solution...to pass test		

Sensitiveness: Dissolve 100 mg in a mixture of 50 ml of alcohol and 50 ml of H_2O. Add 0.2 ml of the solution to 100 ml CO_2-free water. A yellow color is produced, which is changed to red by 0.2 ml of 0.02 N NaOH.

Solubility in NaOH solution: One-half gram dissolves completely in a mixture of 45 ml of H_2O and 5 ml of 1 N NaOH.

Ignition residue: Char well 1.0 g. Allow to cool, add 0.5 ml of H_2SO_4, and ignite gently at first, then strongly to constant weight. Any residue present does not exceed 1.0 mg.

L-PHENYLALANINE

α-Amino-β-phenylpropionic Acid

$C_6H_5CH_2CH(NH_2)COOH$; mol. wt. 165.19; N—8.48%.

Colorless or white plate-like crystals; or white, crystalline powder. Soluble in about 35 parts of water at 25°. Slightly soluble in alcohol; soluble in diluted mineral acids and in alkali hydroxide solutions.

Standards

Nitrogen (N)................8.5 ± 0.25%	Phosphate (PO_4)...........max 0.003%
Specific rotation.............35.0 ± 0.5°	Sulfate (SO_4)...............max 0.010%
Solubility...................to pass test	Ammonium salts (as NH_3)....max 0.010%
Drying loss........ ...max 0.2%	Heavy metals (as Pb)........max 0.001%
Ignition residue.............max 0.05%	Iron (Fe)...................max 0.002%
Chloride (Cl)...............max 0.005%	

Nitrogen: Determine by the Kjeldahl method, using about 0.3 g of sample.

Specific rotation; Drying loss: Dry about 1 g, accurately weighed, at 105° for 2 hours. The loss in weight corresponds to not more than 0.2%. Dissolve about 0.5 g of the dried sample, accurately weighed, in water to make exactly 25 ml. Determine the rotation of the solution at 25° in a 200-mm tube and calculate the specific rotation.

Solubility: Separate solutions of 0.5 g in 25 ml of warm water and in 10 ml of 10% HCl are clear and colorless.

Ignition residue: Moisten 2.0 g with 1 ml of H_2SO_4 and ignite at first gently, then strongly to constant weight. The weight of the residue does not exceed 1.0 mg (retain residue).

Phosphate: Place 0.5 g of sample in a platinum crucible; add an equal quantity of magnesium nitrate and 5 ml of H_2O. Evaporate to dryness and ignite at a low temperature until the residue is nearly white. Add to the residue 5 ml of water and 3 ml of 25% H_2SO_4, heat for 5 minutes, then add 10 ml of hot water, filter, and wash to 20 ml. Add to the filtrate 1 ml each of phosphate reagents **A** and **B** and heat at 60° for 10 minutes. Any resulting blue color is not darker than that of a blank to which 0.01 mg of PO_4 has been added.

Chloride; Sulfate; Ammonium salts; Heavy metals; Iron: Apply the tests described under L-Leucine. The results should be as there stated.

PHENYLARSONIC ACID

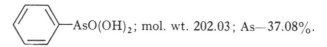—$AsO(OH)_2$; mol. wt. 202.03; As—37.08%.

White to creamy white, crystalline powder.   Soluble in about 40 parts of H_2O and in about 70 parts of alcohol.   Freely soluble in solutions of alkali hydroxides or carbonates.

Standards

Melting range.................156°–158°	Solubility....................to pass test
Sensitiveness................to pass test	Ignition residue.............max 0.50%

Sensitiveness: (*a*) Dissolve 0.24 g of thorium nitrate in sufficient water to make 100 ml (1 ml = 1 mg thorium).

(*b*) Dissolve 10 mg of sample in 10 ml of H_2O, and filter if not clear.

Dilute 0.5 ml of (*a*) with water to 10 ml, add 0.5 ml of (*b*), and mix well.   A distinct opacity should be produced in 1 minute.

Solubility: Warm 1 g of sample with 50 ml of water.   The resulting solution is clear.

Ignition residue: Ignite 0.5 g at a cherry red heat.   Not more than 2.5 mg of residue remains.

m-PHENYLENEDIAMINE HYDROCHLORIDE

Metadiaminobenzene Hydrochloride

$C_6H_4(NH_2)_2 \cdot 2HCl$; mol. wt. 181.07.

White or slightly reddish, crystalline powder.   Freely soluble in water; soluble in alcohol.   On exposure to light it acquires a reddish or brownish color.   A discolored solution may be decolorized before use by shaking with a little decolorizing carbon.   *Keep in well-closed containers, protected from light.*

Standards

Sensitiveness................to pass test	Ignition residue.............max 0.10%
Solubility....................to pass test	

Sensitiveness: (*a*) Dissolve 10 mg of the sample in 10 ml of water.

(*b*) Dissolve 15 mg of sodium nitrite in water to make 100 ml.

To 50 ml of water add 0.5 ml of (*b*) and mix; then add 0.5 ml of (*a*) and 3 ml of HCl, and mix.   A pronounced yellow color develops in 10 minutes (due to formation of Bismarck brown).

Solubility: A solution of 1 g in 25 ml of water is clear and complete or practically so.

Ignition residue: Char 1 g, cool, add 0.5 ml of H_2SO_4, and ignite to constant weight. The weight of the residue does not exceed 1.0 mg.

PHENYLHYDRAZINE

$C_6H_5NH \cdot NH_2$; mol. wt. 108.14.

Clear, colorless, or slightly yellow liquid; faint aromatic odor. It acquires a red color on exposure to air. Slightly soluble in water; soluble in alcohol and in ether. Boils at 241°. Sp. gr. 1.1. *Keep in tightly stoppered bottles, protected from light.*

Standards

Assay........99%–100.5% $C_6H_5NH \cdot NH_2$ Solubility in 1 N acetic acid....to pass test
Freezing temperature.......not below 17°   Ignition residue..............max 0.10%

Assay: Weigh accurately about 1.0 g and dissolve it with the aid of 1 ml of hydrochloric acid in water to make 100 ml. Transfer 20.0 ml of the solution to a glass-stoppered flask, add 30 ml of hydrochloric acid, cool, if necessary, and titrate with 0.05 M potassium iodate until the dark brown solution becomes light in color. Then add 5 ml of chloroform and continue the titration with vigorous shaking until the chloroform is colorless. One ml of 0.05 M potassium iodate = 0.005408 g $C_6H_5NH \cdot NH_2$, log 73304.

$$C_6H_5NH \cdot NH_2 + KIO_3 + 3HCl \rightarrow C_6H_5Cl + N_2 + ICl + 3H_2O + KCl$$

Freezing temperature: Determine as described on page 581.

Solubility in 1 N acetic acid: Shake 1 ml with 20 ml of 1 N acetic acid. The resulting solution is clear or not more than slightly turbid.

Ignition residue: Gently ignite 1 ml with 0.5 ml of sulfuric acid to constant weight. Not more than 1.0 mg of residue remains.

PHENYLHYDRAZINE HYDROCHLORIDE

$C_6H_5NH \cdot HCl$; mol. wt. 144.61.

White or slightly yellow crystals or powder. Soluble in water or alcohol. *Keep in tightly stoppered bottles, protected from light.*

Standards

Assay.....98%–100% $C_6H_5NH \cdot NH_2 \cdot HCl$ Ignition residue..............max 0.10%
Solubility...................to pass test

Assay: As for Phenylhydrazine. One ml of 0.05 M potassium iodate = 0.00723 g $C_6H_5NH \cdot NH_2 \cdot HCl$, log 85914.

Solubility: A solution of 1 g in 20 ml of water is clear and complete or practically so.

Ignition residue: Char well 1 g, cool, add 0.5 ml of H_2SO_4 and ignite gently at first, then strongly to constant weight. Not more than 1.0 mg of residue remains.

PHENYLSEMICARBAZIDE

Cryogenine

$$C_6H_5—NH—\overset{H}{N}—CONH_2; \text{ mol. wt. } 151.17.$$

White, odorless, crystalline powder; discolored by exposure to light. Soluble in about 100 parts of water; soluble in alcohol, chloroform, and ether. *Keep protected from light.*

Standards

Melting range..................171°–173°	Ignition residue.............max 0.10%
Solubility in chloroform.......to pass test	

Solubility in chloroform: Dissolve 0.5 g in 20 ml of chloroform. The solution is complete and clear or nearly so.

Ignition residue: Ignite 1 g with 0.5 ml of H_2SO_4 to constant weight. The residue is not more than 1.0 mg.

PHLOROGLUCINOL

Phloroglucin; 1,3,5-Trihydroxybenzene

; mol. wt. 162.14.

White or slightly yellow crystals, or crystalline powder. Discolors in light. Soluble in 100 parts of water or in 10 parts of alcohol: soluble in ether. *Keep protected from light.*

Standards

Melting range..................216°–219°	Ignition residue.............max 0.10%
Solubility in alcohol..........to pass test	Diresorcinol.................no reaction

Melting range: Powder about 0.1 g, dry at 105° for 1 hour, then determine the melting range, preheating the bath to 200° and heating rapidly after introducing the tube with the substance into the bath.

Solubility in alcohol: One gram dissolves completely in 20 ml of alcohol.

Ignition residue: Moisten 1 g with 0.5 ml of H_2SO_4 and ignite to constant weight. Not more than 1.0 mg of residue remains.

Diresorcinol: To 0.1 g add 10 ml of acetic anhydride, heat to boiling, cool, and superimpose on 10 ml of H_2SO_4. No violet color is produced at the interface of the liquids.

PHOSPHOMOLYBDIC ACID

$H_3PO_4 \cdot 10MoO_3$ + about $24H_2O$ (21%). In anhydrous: P_2O_5—4.7%; MoO_3—93%.

Bright yellow crystals soluble in water, alcohol, ether.

Standards

Solubility in H_2O, alcohol.....to pass test	Calcium (Ca)................max 0.01%
Chloride (Cl)................max 0.005%	Ammonia insoluble..........to pass test
Nitrate (NO_3)...............max 0.003%	Heavy metals................to pass test
Sulfate (SO_4)................max 0.02%	Drying loss (H_2O)..............max 22%
Ammonia (NH_3).............max 0.02%	Assays for P_2O_5, MoO_3

Solubility in H_2O, Alcohol: One g dissolves completely in 10 ml of warm water, and in 15 ml of alcohol.

Chloride: To a solution of 0.2 g in 40 ml of H_2O add 1 ml of HNO_3, filter and divide into 2 equal portions. To one portion add 1 drop of 0.1 N HCl and 1 ml of $AgNO_3$, let stand 10 minutes, filter until clear, and add 0.02 mg of Cl (A). To the other portion (B) add 1 ml of $AgNO_3$, and dilute to the same volume as A. The turbidity in B is not greater than that in A.

Nitrate: Dissolve 0.2 g in 10 ml of H_2O, add about 10 mg of NaCl, 0.1 ml of indigo carmine and 10 ml of H_2SO_4. The blue color persists after 5 minutes.

Sulfate: Dissolve 0.5 g in 10 ml of H_2O, add 2 ml of 1 N HCl, filter, if necessary, and add 1 ml of $BaCl_2$. Any turbidity produced is not greater than that in a blank to which 0.1 mg of SO_4 has been added.

Ammonia: To a solution of 0.5 g in 5 ml of H_2O add 10 ml of 10% NaOH and heat on the steam bath. The vapors do not affect red litmus paper.

Calcium: Dissolve 1 g in 10 ml of hot H_2O, make alkaline with NH_4OH, then add 2 ml of ammonium oxalate. No turbidity is produced in 15 seconds.

Ammonia insoluble; Heavy metals: Dissolve 1.0 g in 10 ml of warm water and add 5 ml of 10% NH_3. A complete solution results. Add to the solution 2 drops of sodium sulfide solution. At most only a slight green color is produced, but no precipitate is formed.

Drying loss: Heat about 1.5 g, accurately weighed, at 120° to constant weight. The loss in weight amounts to not more than 22%.

Assay for P_2O_5: Accurately weigh about 1 g of the dehydrated reagent obtained in the test for *Drying loss* and dissolve it in 50 ml of water and just sufficient 10% NH_3 to complete solution. Filter, if not clear, and wash with a little water. Add to the filtrate 1–2 drops of phenolphthalein, and then add just sufficient 10% HCl to discharge the red color. Now add 5–7 ml of magnesia mixture, mix and run in dropwise, with continuous stirring, 10% NH_3 until a permanent red color is produced. Add 10 ml of NH_4OH, stir well and allow to stand for at least 2 hours or overnight. Filter on a previously ignited and tared Gooch or sintered glass crucible, and wash with 2.5% NH_3 containing 5% ammonium nitrate until free from chloride (retain the filtrate and washings for the determination of MoO_3). Dry at about 100°, then gradually ignite, preferably in an electric furnace at about 500°

until ammonia fumes are no longer evolved, and then raise the temperature to 800°–900°, maintaining this temperature for 10–15 minutes. Cool and weigh. The $Mg_2P_2O_7$ thus obtained × 0.6379, log 9.848, represents P_2O_5, and amounts to from 4.5% to 4.9%.

Assay for MoO_3: Pass H_2S into the filtrate (and washings) from the assay for P_2O_5 until it assumes a red color, make acid with 25% H_2SO_4 and heat on the steam bath until the precipitate of the molybdenum sulfide has settled. Cool, filter, wash with 2% H_2SO_4, then with alcohol until the H_2SO_4 is completely removed, and dry at about 100°. Cover the crucible loosely and heat carefully over a small flame until gases are no longer evolved; then remove the cover and gradually raise the temperature until fumes of SO_2 cease to be evolved. Cool, add 1–2 g of ammonium nitrate and reignite to constant weight. The MoO_3 thus found amounts to from 90% to 95%, and the ratio of $\dfrac{\%MoO_3}{\%P_2O_5}$ is between 19 and 22.

PHOSPHORIC ACID, 85%

H_3PO_4; mol. wt. 98.00; P—31.61%; P_2O_5—72.43%.

Colorless, or nearly so, odorless, syrupy liquid. Sp. gr. 1.70. Miscible with water or alcohol. *Keep protected from freezing.*

Standards

Assay..................min 85% H_3PO_4	Arsenic (As).................max 1 ppm
Volatile acids (as acetic).....max 0.0010%	Heavy metals (as Pb)........max 0.001%
Chloride (Cl)...............max 0.0003%	Iron (Fe)...................max 0.003%
Nitrate (NO_3)..............max 0.0003%	Permanganate-reducing
Sulfate (SO_4)...............max 0.003%	substances (as H_3PO_3)......max 0.05%
Alkali and other phosphates....max 0.20%	

Assay: Weigh 1 ml and dilute with 100 ml of H_2O. Add 0.5 ml of 0.1% thymolphthalein solution and titrate with 1 N NaOH to a blue color (not green). One ml of 1 N NaOH = 0.04900 g H_3PO_4, log 69037.

Volatile acids: Dilute 30 ml with 75 ml of CO_2-free water and distill off 50 ml. The distillate, upon the addition of 3 drops of phenolphthalein and 0.1 ml of 0.1 N NaOH, acquires a pink color.

Chloride: Dilute 3.0 ml (5 g) with H_2O to 20 ml, and add 1 ml of HNO_3 and 1 ml of $AgNO_3$. Any turbidity produced is not greater than that in a blank to which 0.015 mg of Cl has been added.

Nitrate: Dilute 2.5 ml of *Solution S* to 10 ml, add 50 mg of NaCl and 0.2 ml of diphenylamine solution, mix and slowly run in 10 ml of H_2SO_4. Mix gently and allow to stand for 1 hour. No blue color results.

Sulfate: Dilute 12 ml (20 g) with 180 ml of H_2O, heat to boiling, add 10 ml of $BaCl_2$, and allow to stand overnight. Filter; if a precipitate is present, wash with H_2O and ignite. The weight of the precipitate ($BaSO_4$) does not exceed 1.5 mg.

Alkali and other phosphates: Mix 2.0 ml with 100 ml of H_2O, add a solution of 12 g of lead acetate in 50 ml of H_2O, make up to 200 ml with water, and filter. Precipitate the excess of lead from 100 ml of the filtrate with H_2S, filter, and wash with 20 ml of H_2O.   Evaporate the filtrate with 2 drops of H_2SO_4 and ignite.   The residue is not more than 3.5 mg after correcting for blank from 5 g of the lead acetate.

Solution S: Dilute 6 ml (10 g) of the acid with water to 50 ml.

Arsenic: Determine in 10 ml of *Solution S* by method on page 563.   The stain is not greater than that from 0.002 mg of As.

Heavy metals: To 5 ml of *Solution S* add 0.02 mg Pb, 5 ml of 10% HCl, dissolve in it 3 g of sodium acetate and dilute to 40 ml (*A*).   Dissolve 3 g of the sodium acetate in 15 ml of *Solution S* and dilute to 40 ml (*B*).   Then to each add 10 ml of H_2S.   *B* is not darker than *A*.

Iron: Dilute 2.5 ml of *Solution S* to 10 ml, add 2 ml of HCl and boil gently for 2 minutes.   Cool, add about 30 mg of ammonium persulfate and 15 ml of butanolic potassium thiocyanate, shake well for 30 seconds, and allow to separate.   Any red color in the clear butanol (upper) layer is not darker than that of a blank to which 0.015 mg of Fe has been added.

Permanganate-reducing substances: Dilute 10 ml with 10 ml of H_2O, add 0.20 ml of 0.1 N potassium permanganate, heat to boiling, and leave on steam bath for 10 minutes.   The pink color does not entirely disappear.

PHOSPHOROUS ACID

H_3PO_3; mol. wt. 82.0; P—37.78%.

Colorless or white, hygroscopic crystals or crystalline masses.   Melts at about 73°.   Very soluble in water; also soluble in alcohol.   *Keep tightly closed.*

Standards

Assay.................min 99% H_3PO_3	Phosphate (PO_4)............max 0.03%
Solubility...................to pass test	Sulfate (SO_4)...............max 0.005%
Chloride (Cl)...............max 0.001%	Heavy metals (as Pb)........max 0.001%

Assay: Dissolve 1 g in 50 ml of H_2O and titrate with 1 N NaOH, using thymolphthalein as indicator.   One ml of 1 N NaOH = 0.0410 g H_3PO_4, log 61278.

Solubility: A solution of 2 g in 25 ml of H_2O is clear and colorless.

Chloride: To a solution of 1 g in 20 ml of H_2O add 2 ml of HNO_3 and 1 ml of $AgNO_3$.   No opalescence is produced in 5 minutes.

Phosphate: Dissolve 1 g in 20 ml of H_2O, add 5 ml of 10% NH_3 and 5 ml of magnesia mixture.   No turbidity is produced in 10 minutes.

Sulfate: Dissolve 1 g in 20 ml of H_2O and add 2 ml of $BaCl_2$.   No turbidity is produced in 5 minutes.

Heavy metals: Dissolve 4 g in water to make 40 ml.   To 10 ml of the solution add 0.02 mg of Pb, 2 ml of 10% HCl, dissolve in it 2 g of sodium acetate, and dilute to 40 ml (*A*).   Dissolve 2 g of the sodium acetate in the remaining 30 ml of the solution of the acid and dilute to 40 ml (*B*).   Then to each add 10 ml of H_2S.   *B* is not darker than *A*.

PHOSPHORUS OXYCHLORIDE

$POCl_3$; mol. wt. 153.35; P—20.20%; Cl—69.36%.

Clear, colorless, fuming liquid; pungent odor. Solidifies at about $-10°$. Decomposed by water or alcohol with evolution of heat. Sp. gr. 1.7. *Keep in tightly closed, glass-stoppered bottles.*

Standards

Boiling range	105°–109°	Sulfate (SO_4)	max 0.02%
Solubility	to pass test	Heavy metals (as Pb)	max 0.002%
Ignition residue	max 0.25%	Iron (Fe)	max 0.001%

Caution! *Care must be used when mixing phosphorus oxychloride with water because of the heat produced.*

Boiling range: Not less than 90% distills between 105° and 109°.

Solubility: A solution of 2 ml in 20 ml of water is colorless and clear, or nearly so.

Ignition residue: Evaporate 2 ml (3.4 g) to dryness *under hood* and ignite to constant weight. Not more than 7.0 mg of residue remains.

Sulfate: Dissolve 2 ml in 75 ml of water, and make the solution just alkaline to congo red with NH_4OH. Add 2 ml of HCl, heat to boiling and add 5 ml of $BaCl_2$. No turbidity is produced in 5 minutes.

Solution S: Dilute 3.0 ml (5 g) with about 40 ml of water, boil the solution for 2 minutes, cool and dilute to 50 ml.

Heavy metals: To 5 ml of *Solution S* add 0.02 mg of Pb, 7 ml of 10% HCl and 4 g of sodium acetate, and dilute to 40 ml (*A*). To 15 ml of *Solution S* add 4 g of sodium acetate and dilute to 40 ml (*B*). Then to each add 10 ml of H_2S. *B* is not darker than *A*.

Iron: To 10 ml of *Solution S* add 1 ml of HCl and 50 mg of ammonium persulfate, and dilute to about 15 ml. Completely transfer the solution to a separatory funnel, add 15 ml of butanolic potassium thiocyanate, and shake for 30 seconds. Any red color in the clear butanol layer (upper) is not darker than that of a control made with 15 ml of a solution containing 0.01 mg of Fe, 1 ml of HCl, and 50 mg of ammonium persulfate, and treated as described above, beginning with "add 15 ml of butanolic potassium thiocyanate . . . ."

PHOSPHORUS PENTACHLORIDE

PCl_5; mol. wt. 208.27; P—14.88%; Cl—85.12%.

Pale yellow, fuming crystals; deliquescent. Decomposed by water or alcohol, with evolution of heat. *Keep in tightly closed, glass-stoppered bottles.*

Standards

Solubility	to pass test	Heavy metals (as Pb)	max 0.002%
Ignition residue	max 0.050%	Iron (Fe)	max 0.002%
Sulfate (SO_4)	max 0.01%		

Caution! *Care must be used in adding phosphorus pentachloride to water because of the heat produced.*

Solubility: Dissolve 2 g in 20 ml of H_2O and heat to boiling. The solution is colorless and clear, or nearly so.

Ignition residue: Ignite 3 g in porcelain *under the hood*. Not more than 1.5 mg of residue remains.

Sulfate: Dissolve 3 g in 75 ml of H_2O and make the solution just alkaline to congo paper with NH_4OH. Add 2 ml of HCl, heat to boiling and add 5 ml of $BaCl_2$. No turbidity is produced in 5 minutes.

Solution S: Dissolve 5 g in 40 ml of water, boil the solution for 2 minutes, cool and dilute to 50 ml.

Heavy metals: To 5 ml of *Solution S* add 0.02 mg of Pb, 7 ml of 10% HCl and 4 g of sodium acetate, and dilute to 40 ml (*A*). To 15 ml of *Solution S* add 4 g of sodium acetate and dilute to 40 ml (*B*). Then to each add 10 ml of H_2S. *B* is not darker than *A*.

Iron: To 5 ml of *Solution S* add 1 ml of HCl and 50 mg of ammonium persulfate, and dilute to about 15 ml. Completely transfer the solution to a separatory funnel, add 15 ml of butanolic potassium thiocyanate, and shake for 30 seconds. Any red color in the clear butanol (upper) layer is not darker than that of a control made with 15 ml of a solution containing 0.010 mg of Fe, 1 ml of HCl, and 50 mg of ammonium persulfate, and treated as described above, beginning with "add 15 ml of butanolic potassium thiocyanate . . . ."

PHOSPHORUS PENTOXIDE

Phosphoric Anhydride

P_2O_5; mol. wt. 141.96; P—43.64%.

White, amorphous, bulky powder; rapidly deliquescent. Soluble in water with evolution of heat, forming phosphoric acid; also soluble in alcohol. *Keep in tightly closed containers.*

Standards

Assay...................min 98% P_2O_5	Sulfate (SO_4)................max 0.20%
Insoluble..................max 0.020%	Ammonia (NH_3).............max 0.01%
Organic matter..............to pass test	Arsenic (As)................max 5 ppm
Phosphorus trioxide..........max 0.02%	Heavy metals (as Pb)........max 0.005%

Caution! *When making a solution, the phosphorus pentoxide must be added to the water in small portions to prevent excessive sputtering.*

Assay: Weigh accurately in a glass-stoppered weighing bottle about 2 g and transfer it with the aid of *cold* water to a 300-ml flask. Dilute with H_2O to about 150 ml and boil down to about 75 ml. Cool, add 0.5 ml of 0.1% thymolphthalein solution, and titrate with 1 *N* NaOH to a blue color. One ml of 1 *N* NaOH = 0.03549 g P_2O_5, log 55011.

Insoluble: Add 5 g, in small quantities, to 40 ml of H_2O; heat, if necessary, to effect complete solution, and filter through a small filtering crucible. Set the filtrate aside for *Solution S*.   Wash the residue well with water and dry at 105°.   Its weight does not exceed 1.0 mg.

Organic matter: Heat about 1 g in a test tube.   Not more than a slight darkening occurs.

Phosphorus trioxide: Dissolve 3 g in 50 ml of H_2O, add 0.2 ml of 0.1 N potassium permanganate and heat for 10 minutes on the steam bath.   The pink color does not entirely disappear.

Solution S: Dilute the filtrate from the *Insoluble* with H_2O to 100 ml and mix well.

Sulfate: To 20 ml of *Solution S* add 1 ml of 1 N HCl and 2 ml of $BaCl_2$.   Any turbidity produced in 15 minutes is not greater than that in a blank to which 0.2 mg of SO_4 has been added.

Ammonia: Dilute 2 ml of *Solution S* to 40 ml, add 10 ml of 10% NaOH and 2 ml of Nessler solution.   The color produced is not darker than that produced by 0.01 mg of NH_3 (0.03 mg NH_4Cl) treated with the same quantities of the reagents and in the same volume as the sample.

Arsenic: Test an aliquot of 2.0 ml of *Solution S* corresponding to 0.2 g of sample by the method on page 563.   The stain produced is not greater than that from 0.002 mg of As.

Heavy metals: To 5 ml of *Solution S* add 0.025 mg of Pb, 3 ml of 10% HCl and 2 g of sodium acetate, and dilute to 40 ml (*A*).   To 15 ml of *Solution S* add 2 g of sodium acetate and dilute to 40 ml (*B*).   Then to each add 10 ml of H_2S.   *B* is not darker than *A*.

PHOSPHORUS, RED

Amorphous Phosphorus

P; at. wt. 30.98.

Dark red powder.   Insoluble in water or dilute acids; soluble in absolute alcohol.

Standards

Yellow phosphorus (P) . . . . max 0.015%   Soluble substances . . . . max 0.60%

Yellow phosphorus: Prepare cupric sulfate test paper by immersing 0.5 × 10 cm strips of filter paper in 10% cupric sulfate solution and drying in air.

Prepare a control as follows: Dissolve about 0.1 g of yellow phosphorus weighed to within ±2 mg in 100 ml of carbon disulfide.   Dilute a volume of the solution equivalent to 3 mg of the phosphorus with sufficient carbon disulfide to make 10 ml.

Shake 20 g of the sample with 75 ml of carbon disulfide in a glass-stoppered cylinder and let stand in the dark overnight.   Filter and wash to 100 ml with carbon disulfide, collecting the filtrate in a graduated cylinder.   Immerse the cylinder in hot water and evaporate to 10 ml.   Immerse a strip of the cupric sulfate paper in the solution.   The stain produced is not darker than a strip immersed in the control.

Soluble substances: Heat 2 g with 30 ml of 36% acetic acid on the steam bath for 15 minutes.   Cool, dilute with H_2O to 40 ml, and filter.   Evaporate 20 ml of the filtrate on the steam bath and dry at 105° for 2 hours.   The weight of the residue does not exceed 6.0 mg.

PHOSPHORUS TRICHLORIDE

PCl_3; mol. wt. 137.35; P—22.54%; Cl—77.46%.

Colorless, clear, fuming liquid of a pungent odor.   Sp. gr. 1.6.   Decomposed by water or alcohol.   *Keep in tightly closed, glass-stoppered bottles.*

Standards

Boiling range.................75°–77°	Sulfate (SO_4)................max 0.02%	
Solubility in water...........to pass test	Heavy metals (as Pb)........max 0.002%	
Solubility in benzene..........to pass test	Iron (Fe)..................max 0.003%	

Caution! *Care must be used when mixing phosphorus trichloride with water because of the heat developed.*

Boiling range: Not less than 95% distills between 75° and 77°.

Solubility in water: A solution of 2 ml in 20 ml of H_2O is clear and colorless, or practically so.

Solubility in benzene: Five ml dissolve in 10 ml of benzene, yielding a clear or practically clear solution.

Sulfate: Dissolve 2 ml (3 g) in 75 ml of water and make the solution just alkaline (red) to congo red with NH_4OH.   Add 2 ml of HCl, heat to boiling, and add 5 ml of $BaCl_2$.   No turbidity is produced in 5 minutes.

Solution S: Dilute 3.0 ml (5 g) with about 30 ml of water, add 2 ml of HNO_3, boil the solution gently for 15 minutes, cool, and dilute to 50 ml.

Heavy metals: To 5 ml of *Solution S* add 0.02 mg of Pb, 7 ml of 10% HCl, and 4 g of sodium acetate, and dilute to 40 ml (*A*).   To 15 ml of *Solution S* add 4 g of sodium acetate and dilute to 40 ml (*B*).   Then to each add 10 ml of H_2S.   *B* is not darker than *A*.

Iron: To 5 ml of *Solution S* add 1 ml of HCl and about 50 mg of ammonium persulfate, and dilute to about 15 ml.   Completely transfer the solution to a separatory funnel, add 15 ml of butanolic potassium thiocyanate, and shake for 30 seconds.   Any red color in the clear butanol layer (upper) is not darker than that of a control made with 15 ml of a solution containing 0.015 mg of Fe, 1 ml of HCl, and 50 mg of ammonium persulfate, and treat as described above, beginning with "add 15 ml of butanolic potassium thiocyanate . . . ."

PHOSPHOTUNGSTIC ACID

$H_3PO_4 \cdot 12WO_3$ + about 10% H_2O.   In anhydrous: P_2O_5—2.06%; WO_3—96.6%.

White or yellowish-green crystals; slightly efflorescent.   Very soluble in water. *Keep in well-closed containers.*

Standards

Solubility in H_2O, alcohol . . . . . to pass test

Chloride (Cl) . . . . max 0.005%

Nitrate (NO_3) . . . . max 0.003%

Sulfate (SO_4) . . . . max 0.02%

Ammonia (NH_3) . . . . max 0.02%

Heavy metals; Iron . . . . to pass test

(max about 0.002%)

Drying loss (H_2O) . . . . max 10%

Assay

Solubility in water, alcohol: One gram dissolves completely in 10 ml of water and in 10 ml of alcohol, and the solutions are colorless.

Chloride: Dissolve 1.0 g in 100 ml of H_2O. To 20 ml of the filtered solution add 1 ml of HNO_3 and 1 ml of $AgNO_3$. Any turbidity produced is not greater than that in a blank to which 0.010 mg of Cl has been added.

Nitrate: Dissolve 0.2 g in 10 ml of H_2O, add about 10 mg of NaCl and 0.1 ml of indigo carmine, and follow with 10 ml of H_2SO_4. The blue (or green) color persists for 5 minutes.

Sulfate: Dissolve 0.5 g in 10 ml H_2O, add 1 ml of 1 N HCl and 1 ml $BaCl_2$. Any turbidity produced is not greater than that in a blank to which 0.1 mg SO_4 has been added.

Ammonia: To a solution of 0.5 g in 10 ml of H_2O add 10 ml of 10% NaOH and heat on steam bath. The vapors do not affect red litmus paper.

Heavy metals; Iron: Dissolve 1 g in 40 ml of H_2O, add 2 ml of ammonium hydroxide and 5 ml of H_2S. No brown or green color is produced in 1 minute.

Drying Loss (Water): Weigh accurately about 1 g into a tared small porcelain dish and dry it at about 200° to constant weight. The loss in weight does not exceed 10%.

Assay for WO_3: Weigh accurately about 1 g of the dehydrated reagent from the test for *Drying loss* and dissolve it in 75 ml of water and several ml of 10% NH_3. Filter, if not clear, and wash with a little water. Add to the filtrate 15 ml of HCl and 3 ml of HNO_3, boil for 5 minutes and evaporate to 10 ml. Dilute to 100 ml and add 10 ml of a 2.5% solution of cinchonine in 10% HCl (benzidine HCl may be used instead of cinchonine), and heat on a hot plate for 30 minutes, stirring a few times. Allow the precipitate to settle and decant through a filter paper containing some paper pulp or through a previously ignited tared Gooch. Then filter the precipitate, wash it with a dilute cinchonine HCl solution (1 in 100). Retain filtrate and washings for the assay for P_2O_5. Dry and ignite in platinum at a relatively low temperature. Cool, add about 1 g of NH_4NO_3 if paper filter was used, and reignite. Cool and weigh the WO_3 which amounts to not less than 95% and not more than 98%.

Assay for P_2O_5: Evaporate the filtrate and washings from the *Assay for WO_3* to 50 ml, cool, make ammoniacal with NH_3 and extract any cinchonine by shaking with 20 ml of chloroform. Discard the chloroform extract. Add to the aqueous layer 1–2 drops of phenolphthalein and discharge the red color with just sufficient HCl. Now add 5 ml of magnesia mixture, mix and run in dropwise with constant stirring 10% NH_3 until a permanent red color is produced, then add 10 ml of NH_4OH. Stir well and allow to stand at least 2 hours or overnight. Filter on a previously ignited and tared Gooch or sintered glass crucible and wash with 2.5% NH_3 containing 5 g ammonium nitrate in 100 ml until free from chloride. Dry and then gradually ignite, preferably in an electric furnace (at about 500°) until ammonia fumes are no longer evolved, then raise the temperature to 800°–900° and maintain this temperature for 10–15 minutes.   Cool and weigh.   The $Mg_2P_2O_7$ thus obtained × 0.6379, log 9.8048, represents P_2O_5, and it amounts to from 1.9% to 2.2%.   The ratio of $\%WO_3/\%P_2O_5$ is between 44 and 51.

PHTHALIC ANHYDRIDE

Phthalic Acid Anhydride

; mol. wt. 148.11.

White, lustrous needles.   Slightly soluble in cold water; more soluble in hot water, forming phthalic acid; soluble in alcohol or ether.

Standards

Melting range.................129°–131°	Sulfur compounds (as SO_4).....max 0.01%
Ignition residue..............max 0.01%	Heavy metals (as Pb)........max 0.001%
Chloride (Cl)................max 0.001%	Assay....................99.5%–100.2%

Ignition residue: Place 10 g in a tared porcelain dish and heat slowly until most has volatilized.   Allow to cool, add a few drops of H_2SO_4, heat to evaporate excess H_2SO_4 and then ignite strongly to constant weight.   Any residue remaining is not over 1.0 mg.

Chloride: Mix 1 g of sodium carbonate in a platinum crucible, gradually add 10 ml of H_2O, evaporate to dryness, and ignite thoroughly.   Cool, dissolve the residue in 10 ml of hot H_2O, acidify with HNO_3 and add 1 ml excess.   Filter, wash with 10 ml of water, and add to the filtrate 1 ml of $AgNO_3$.   Any resulting turbidity is not greater than that in a blank to which 0.01 mg of Cl has been added.

Sulfur compounds: Mix 2 g with 1 g of sodium carbonate in a platinum crucible, gradually add 20 ml of H_2O, evaporate to dryness, and ignite until nearly white, protecting from access of sulfur.   Cool, dissolve the residue in 20 ml of H_2O, add 2 ml of 30% hydrogen peroxide, and boil for 5 minutes.   Add 3 ml of HCl and evaporate to dryness on the steam bath.   Dissolve the residue in 10 ml of H_2O, filter, wash with 10 ml of H_2O, and add to the filtrate 1 ml of 1 N HCl and 2 ml of $BaCl_2$.   Should a turbidity be produced it is not greater than that produced in a control made as follows: Evaporate 1 g of sodium carbonate, 2 ml of 30% hydrogen peroxide, and 3 ml of HCl to dryness on the steam bath.   Dissolve the residue and 0.2 mg of SO_4 in sufficient H_2O to make 20 ml and treat the solution with 1 ml of 1 N HCl and 2 ml of $BaCl_2$.

Heavy metals: Dissolve 0.5 g in 15 ml of H_2O and 2 ml of NH_4OH, and add 5 ml of H_2S.   Nl darkening occurs.

Assay: Phthalic anhydride may be assayed as follows: Weigh accurately about 2.5 g, dissolve in 50 ml of 1 N NaOH, and titrate the excess of NaOH with 1 N

H_2SO_4, using phenolphthalein indicator. One ml of 1 N NaOH = 0.07402 g $C_6H_4(CO)_2O$, log 86935.

PICRIC ACID

2,4,6-Trinitrophenol

; mol. wt. 229.11.

Pale yellow crystals; odorless; explosive when dry. Soluble in 100 parts of cold water; more soluble in hot water; soluble in 15 parts of alcohol or 20 parts of benzene.

For safety in transportation it is mixed with 10%–15% water.

Keep in well-closed containers, in a cool place, remote from fire.

Standards

Melting range....................121°–123°	Sulfate (SO_4).................max 0.04%
Water—insoluble............max 0.020%	Water.......................to pass test
Oxalic acid...................to pass test	*Assay*
Benzene—insoluble...........max 0.05%	

Water—insoluble: Dissolve 5 g in 200 ml of hot water and 0.5 ml of sulfuric acid and heat on steam bath for 1 hour. Filter any undissolved residue, wash it with hot water, and dry at 105°. No resinous matter is apparent and the insoluble residue does not exceed 1.0 mg.

Oxalic acid: Dissolve 1.0 g in 100 ml of warm water and filter if not clear. Add to the solution 5 ml of 10% calcium acetate solution, mix and let stand. No precipitate or turbidity is observable at the end of 1 hour.

Benzene—insoluble: Dry about 2.5 g over sulfuric acid, then dissolve 2 g of the dried sample in 50 ml of warm benzene. If an insoluble residue is present, filter while warm, wash with warm benzene and dry at 105°. The insoluble residue is not more than 1.0 mg.

Sulfate: Evaporate 2 g with 10 ml of nitric acid on the steam bath, add to the residue 1 ml of HCl, dissolve in 100 ml of boiling water; cool and filter. Heat the filtrate to boiling, add 5 ml of $BaCl_2$, and let stand overnight. If a precipitate is formed, filter, wash with H_2O, and ignite. Its weight does not exceed 2.0 g.

Water: The water content of picric acid may be determined by the iodine (Fischer) method.

Assay: Weigh accurately about 0.5 g of the sample, previously dried over H_2SO_4 and dissolve it in 50 ml of warm water. Let cool, add 2 drops of phenolphthalein and titrate with 0.1 N NaOH to pink color. One ml of 0.1 N NaOH = 0.02291 g $HO \cdot C_6H_2(NO_2)_3$, log 36003.

PICROLONIC ACID

1-*p*-Nitrophenyl-3-methyl-4-nitropyrazolone

; mol. wt. 264.20.

Yellow to pale brownish-yellow, crystalline powder. Slightly soluble in water, soluble in alcohol, chloroform, ether, and solutions of alkali hydroxides.

Picrolonic acid is used as a precipitant for alkaloids, some amino acids, for the detection and estimation of calcium[1,2] and of thorium.[3]

This reagent will detect 0.1 mg of calcium in 1 ml of solution.

Standards

Melting range.................115°–117°   Ignition residue.............max 0.10%
Sensitiveness................to pass test

Sensitiveness: (*a*) Dissolve 25 mg of sample in 10 ml of warm H_2O containing 0.1 ml of glacial acetic acid and filter the solution if necessary.

(*b*) Dissolve 100 mg of calcium chloride ($CaCl_2 \cdot 2H_2O$) in 250 ml of H_2O.

Heat 1 ml of (*b*) in a test tube to about 60° and add to it 1 ml of (*a*). A bulky precipitate forms in 5 minutes or less.

Ignition residue: Ignite 1.0 g until charred. Allow to cool, add 0.5 ml of H_2SO_4, heat to expel the acid, then ignite strongly to constant weight. Any residue remaining does not exceed 1.0 mg.

[1] Dworzak, R., and Reich-Rohrwig, *Z. anorg. Chem.* **86**, 98 (1931).
[2] Hecht, F., and Ehrman, W., *ibid.* **100**, 87 (1935).
[3] Alten, F., and Knippenberg, E., *Biochem. Z.* **265**, 85 (1933).

PLATINIC CHLORIDE

Chloroplatinic Acid

$H_2PtCl_6 \cdot 6H_2O$; mol. wt. 517.94; anhydrous—79.14%; H_2O—20.86%; Pt—37.68%; Cl—41.07%.

Brownish-yellow, crystalline masses; rapidly deliquescent. Very soluble in water or alcohol. *Keep in tightly closed bottles.*

Standards

Assay....................min 37.5% Pt   Metals soluble in HNO_3 and
Solubility in alcohol..........to pass test   alkali salts................max 0.1%
Nitrate (NO_3)...............max 0.03%

Assay: Weigh accurately about 1 g and dissolve in 20 ml H_2O.　(If insoluble matter is present, filter, wash thoroughly, and evaporate filtrate and washings to about 20 ml.)　Add 10 ml of a saturated solution of ammonium chloride (3 in 10), cover, and allow to stand overnight.　Filter, wash the precipitate with 20 ml of saturated ammonium chloride solution, dry, ignite carefully, and weigh.　The residue is the platinum content of sample taken.

Solubility in alcohol: Dissolve 1.0 g in 10 ml of alcohol.　The solution should be complete and clear or practically so.

Nitrate: Dissolve 0.1 g in 10 ml of water and 1–2 drops of acetic acid.　Add 1 g of granular zinc (20–40 mesh) and let stand for 30–60 minutes until the solution is decolorized.　Decant 5 ml of the liquid and dilute it to 10 ml.　Add 15 mg of NaCl and 0.1 ml of indigo carmine solution, mix, and then add 10 ml of H_2SO_4.　The blue color should still be present after 5 minutes.

Metals soluble in HNO_3 and alkali salts: Transfer the solution from the test for *Solubility in alcohol* to a porcelain crucible or small dish.　Add 5 ml of water and 2 ml of formic acid, evaporate to dryness on the steam bath, then ignite at a moderate temperature (500°–600°) for 10–15 minutes.　After allowing to cool, add 15 ml of 30% HNO_3 and digest in the covered dish on the steam bath for 15 minutes.　Filter, wash with a few ml of water, evaporate and dry at 120°.　The weight of the residue, if any, does not exceed 1.0 mg.

POTASSIUM

K; at. wt. 39.10.

Soft lumps or balls.　The freshly cut surface is silvery white, rapidly changing to dull gray.　Rapidly decomposes water or alcohols with the evolution of hydrogen which ignites.　Melts at 62.5°.　Sp. gr. 0.875.　*Keep in tightly closed containers, suitably protected from air and moisture.*

Standards

Chloride (Cl) . . . . max 0.010%	Heavy metals (as Pb) . . . . max 0.002%
Nitrogen (as NH_3) . . . . max 0.010%	Iron (Fe) . . . . max 0.001%
Sulfate (SO_4) . . . . max 0.010%	Sodium (Na) . . . . max about 0.1%

Solution S: Free the metal from mechanical impurities by shaving off a thin layer, then cut 5 g into small pieces under petrolatum and add them one at a time, to 80 ml of H_2O cooled in an ice bath.　When all of the metal has gone in solution, dilute with water to 100 ml and, by means of a separatory funnel, separate from any of the petrolatum.

Chloride: Acidify 5 ml of *Solution S* with HNO_3, dilute to 25 ml, and add 1 ml of silver nitrate.　Any turbidity produced is not greater than that in a blank to which 0.025 mg of Cl has been added.

Nitrogen: To 5 ml of *Solution S* add 1 ml of 10% NaOH, dilute to 50 ml and add 2 ml of Nessler solution.　The color produced is not darker than that produced in a blank to which 0.025 mg of NH_3 (0.075 mg NH_4Cl) has been added.

Sulfate: Neutralize 20 ml of *Solution S* with HCl and evaporate to dryness on the steam bath.　Dissolve the residue in 10 ml of H_2O, add 1 ml of 0.1 N HCl and

2 ml of $BaCl_2$.   Any resulting turbidity is not greater than that of a control made with 0.1 mg of SO_4, 1 ml of 0.1 N HCl, and 2 ml of $BaCl_2$ in the same volume as with the sample.

Heavy metals: Neutralize 40 ml of *Solution S* with HCl and evaporate to dryness on the steam bath.   Dissolve the residue in water to make 40 ml.   To 10 ml of the solution add 0.02 mg of Pb, 1 ml of 1 N acetic acid, and dilute to 40 ml (A).   To the remaining 30 ml add 1 ml of 1 N acetic acid and dilute to 40 ml (B).   Then to each add 10 ml of H_2S. B is not darker than A.

Iron: Neutralize 20 ml of *Solution S* with HCl, then add an excess of 2 ml of the acid and dilute to 50 ml.   Add 50 mg of ammonium persulfate and 3 ml of ammonium thiocyanate, and mix.   Any resulting red color is not darker than that of a blank to which 0.01 mg of Fe has been added.

Sodium: A small portion of *Solution S* diluted with twice its volume of water and neutralized with HCl, when tested on a platinum wire, imparts no pronounced yellow color to a colorless flame.

POTASSIUM ACETATE

$KC_2H_3O_2$; mol. wt. 98.15; K—39.85%; acetic acid = 61.18%.

Colorless crystals; rapidly deliquescent.   Soluble in 0.5 part of water or in 3 parts of alcohol.   *Keep in tightly closed containers.*

Standards

Insoluble	max 0.005%	Calcium, Magnesium, and	
Free acid (as acetic)	max 0.10%	NH$_4$OH precipitate	max 0.010%
Free alkali	to pass test	Heavy metals (as Pb)	max 0.0005%
Chloride (Cl)	max 0.002%	Iron (Fe)	max 0.0005%
Phosphate (PO$_4$)	max 0.001%	Sodium (Na)	max about 0.02%
Sulfate (SO$_4$)	max 0.002%	Permanganate-reducing	
Arsenic (As)	max 1 ppm	substances	to pass test
		Assay	min 99.0%

Insoluble: Dissolve 20 g in 150 ml of H_2O and heat on steam bath for 30 minutes.   Filter any undissolved residue, wash with water, and dry at 105°.   The insoluble residue does not exceed 1.0 mg.

Free acid; Free alkali: Dissolve 5 g in 60 ml of CO_2-free water and add 0.2 ml of phenolphthalein.   If a pink color is produced, it is discharged by the addition of not more than 0.10 ml of 0.1 N HCl.   If no pink color is produced, it requires not more than 0.85 ml of 0.1 N NaOH to produce a pink color.

Chloride: Dissolve 1 g in 20 ml of water, add 1 ml of nitric acid and 1 ml of silver nitrate.   The turbidity produced is not greater than that in a blank with 0.02 mg of Cl added.

Phosphate: Dissolve 2.0 g in 10 ml of water, add 0.5 ml of HNO_3 and 1 ml of H_2SO_4, and evaporate on the steam bath.   Re-evaporate with 10 ml of water.   Dissolve the residue in 20 ml of water, add 1 ml each of phosphate reagents **A** and **B** and heat at 60° for 10 minutes.   Any blue color produced is not darker than that of a control made with 0.02 mg of PO_4.

Sulfate: Dissolve 5 g in 15 ml of water, add 5 ml of 1 N HCl and 2 ml of $BaCl_2$. Any turbidity resulting in 15 minutes is not greater than that in a blank to which 0.1 mg of SO_4 has been added.

Arsenic: Test 2 g by the method on page 563. The stain is not greater than that from 0.002 mg of As.

Calcium, Magnesium, and NH_4OH precipitate: Dissolve 10 g in 50 ml of water, add 5 ml of ammonium oxalate, 2 ml of ammonium phosphate, and 15 ml of ammonium hydroxide and allow to stand overnight. If a precipitate is present, filter, wash it with 2.5% NH_3, and ignite. The weight of the ignited precipitate does not exceed 0.0010 g.

Heavy metals: Dissolve 5 g in 10 ml of water, add 5 ml of 10% HCl, and dilute to 25 ml. To 5 ml of the solution add 0.015 mg of Pb, and dilute to 40 ml (A). To the remaining 20 ml add water to make 40 ml (B). Then to each add 10 ml of H_2S. B is not darker than A.

Iron: Dissolve 2 g in 20 ml of H_2O, add 3 ml of HCl, and dilute to 50 ml. Add about 30 mg of ammonium persulfate and 3 ml of ammonium thiocyanate, and mix. Any red color produced is not darker than that of a blank to which 0.01 mg of Fe has been added.

Sodium: Ignite 1 g until thoroughly charred. Dissolve the residue in 10 ml of hot water, neutralize with HCl, and filter. The filtrate, tested on a platinum wire, imparts no distinct yellow color to a colorless flame.

Note: The sodium may be quantitatively determined by Flame Photometry (page 566).

Permanganate-reducing substances: Dissolve 5 g in 40 ml of water, add 10 ml of 10% H_2SO_4 and 0.2 ml of 0.1 N potassium permanganate. The pink color is not entirely discharged in 1 hour.

Assay: Potassium acetate may be assayed, after drying to constant weight at 150°, by the general methods for Alkali Salts of Organic Acids, page 564. One ml of 0.1 N acid = 0.009814 g of $KC_2H_3O_2$. When so assayed, not less than 99.5% and not more than 100.3% should be indicated.

POTASSIUM BICARBONATE

$KHCO_3$; mol. wt. 100.11; K—39.06%; CO_2—43.95%; K_2O—47.05%.

Colorless, transparent crystals. Soluble in 5 parts of water; insoluble in alcohol. When its aqueous solution is boiled, carbon dioxide escapes and potassium carbonate is formed.

Standards

Assay............99.7%–100.3% $KHCO_3$	Sulfur compounds (as SO_4)....max 0.003%
Normal carbonate............to pass test	Calcium, Magnesium, and
Insoluble..................max 0.010%	NH_4OH precipitate.......max 0.010%
Chloride (Cl)...............max 0.002%	Heavy metals (as Pb).......max 0.0005%
Nitrogen compounds (as N)..max 0.0005%	Iron (Fe).................max 0.0005%
Phosphate (PO_4)...........max 0.0005%	Sodium (Na)..........max about 0.02%

Assay; Normal carbonate: Dry about 3 g over H_2SO_4 for 3 hours, then weigh accurately, dissolve in 50 ml of water, add 2 drops of methyl orange, and titrate with 1 N HCl to a brownish yellow color. One ml of 1 N acid = 0.1001 g of $KHCO_3$, log 00043.

Insoluble: Dissolve 10 g in 100 ml of H_2O and heat on the steam bath for 30 minutes. Filter any insoluble residue, wash, and dry at 105°. Its weight does not exceed 1.0 mg.

Chloride: To a solution of 1 g in 20 ml of H_2O add a slight excess of HNO_3 and 1 ml of $AgNO_3$. Any resulting turbidity is not greater than that in a blank to which 0.02 mg of Cl has been added.

Nitrogen compounds: Dissolve 4 g in 50 ml of H_2O, add 20 ml of 10% NaOH and 1 g of powdered Devarda metal or 0.5 g of fine aluminum wire in small pieces and allow to stand for 2 hours, protected from loss or access of NH_3. Decant 35 ml and add to it 2 ml of Nessler solution. The resulting color is not darker than that produced by treating 0.02 mg of nitrogen (0.08 mg NH_4Cl) in the same manner.

Phosphate: Dissolve 4 g in a mixture of 15 ml of H_2O and 10 ml of 25% H_2SO_4, add 1 ml each of phosphate reagents **A** and **B**, and heat at 60° for 10 minutes. Any blue color produced is not darker than that of a control made with 0.02 mg of PO_4, 2 ml of 25% H_2SO_4, 1 ml each of the phosphate reagents, and in the same volume as with the sample.

Sulfur compounds: Dissolve 3.0 g of sample and 10 mg of sodium carbonate in 15 ml of warm water, add 5 drops of bromine water, boil for 2 minutes, then add 5 ml of HCl and evaporate to dryness on the steam bath. Prepare a control by evaporating 10 mg of sodium carbonate, 5 drops of bromine water, 5 ml of HCl, and 0.1 mg of SO_4 to dryness on the steam bath. Dissolve the residue from each in 1 ml of 0.1 N HCl and sufficient water to make 15 ml and add to each 2 ml of $BaCl_2$. Any turbidity appearing in 15 minutes in the solution of the sample is not greater than that in the control.

Calcium, Magnesium, and NH_4OH precipitate: Dissolve 10 g in 100 ml of hot water, neutralize with HCl and add 0.3 ml excess of the acid. Filter, if necessary, add to the filtrate 5 ml of ammonium oxalate, 2 ml of ammonium phosphate, and 20 ml of NH_4OH; allow to stand overnight. Filter any precipitate present, wash it with 2.5% NH_3, and ignite. The weight of the ignited precipitate is not more than 1.0 mg.

Heavy metals: Dissolve 5 g in 10 ml of warm water and *cautiously* add, in small portions, 6 ml of HCl. Evaporate on the steam bath to dryness, take up with 25 ml of H_2O, add a drop of phenolphthalein, and neutralize with 0.1 N NaOH. Add 2 ml of 1 N acetic acid, and dilute to 50 ml. To 10 ml add 0.015 mg of Pb and dilute to 40 ml (A). Add to A and to the remaining 40 ml (B) 10 ml of H_2S. A is not darker than B.

Iron: Dissolve 2 g in 20 ml of H_2O, add 4 ml of HCl, bring to a boil, cool, and dilute to 50 ml. Add about 30 mg of ammonium persulfate and 3 ml of ammonium thiocyanate, and mix. Any red color produced is not darker than that of a blank to which 0.01 mg of Fe has been added.

Sodium: A 10% solution, tested on a platinum wire, imparts no pronounced yellow color to a colorless flame.

Note: A quantitative estimation of sodium content may be readily achieved by Flame Photometry.

POTASSIUM BIPHTHALATE

Potassium Acid Phthalate

$KHC_8H_4O_4$; mol. wt. 204.22; K—19.15%; phthalic acid = 81.34%.

Colorless, fine crystals or a white crystalline powder.   Soluble in 10 parts of cold water or in 3 parts of hot water.

Standards

Assay.........99.9%–100.2% $KHC_8H_4O_4$	Sulfur compounds (as SO_4)....max 0.003%
Insoluble...................max 0.005%	Heavy metals (as Pb).......max 0.0005%
Chlorine compounds (as Cl)...max 0.003%	Iron (Fe)...................max 0.001%
Nitrogen compounds (as N)...max 0.002%	Sodium (Na)...........max about 0.02%

Assay: Dry for 1 hour at 120°, then weigh accurately about 0.8 g and transfer to a 300-ml flask free from CO_2.   Add 50 ml of CO_2-free water, stopper and shake until dissolved; then add 3 drops of phenolphthalein and titrate with carbonate-free 0.1 N NaOH.   Determine the volume of 0.1 N NaOH required to produce the end point in the same volume of H_2O and with the same quantity of phenolphthalein as used with the sample, and deduct from the NaOH used for the sample.   One ml of 0.1 N NaOH = 0.02042 g $KHC_8H_4O_4$, log 31006.

Insoluble: Dissolve 20 g in 200 ml of hot H_2O; the solution is colorless.   Heat the solution on the steam bath for 1 hour.   Should an insoluble residue remain, filter through a tared filtering crucible, wash it well, and dry at 104°.   Its weight does not exceed 1.0 mg.

Chlorine compounds: Mix 1 g with 0.5 g of sodium carbonate, moisten with water, evaporate, and ignite gently until thoroughly charred.   Treat the residue with 20 ml of H_2O and add dropwise 2 ml of HNO_3.   Filter, wash with 10 ml of hot H_2O, and add to the cooled filtrate 1 ml of $AgNO_3$.   Any resulting turbidity is not greater than that in a blank to which 0.03 mg of Cl has been added.

Nitrogen compounds: Dissolve 1 g in 40 ml of H_2O, add 20 ml of 10% NaOH and 0.5 g of powdered Devarda metal or 0.5 g of fine Al wire and allow to stand for 3 hours protected from loss or access of NH_3.   Then distill about 40 ml into 5 ml of H_2O containing 1 drop of diluted HCl.   Dilute to 50 ml and add 1 ml of 10% NaOH and 2 ml of Nessler solution.   The color produced is not darker than that produced by treating 0.02 mg of nitrogen (0.08 mg NH_4Cl) in the same manner as the sample.

Sulfur compounds: Mix 3.0 g with 0.1 g of sodium carbonate, moisten with water, evaporate and ignite, protected from access of sulfur, preferably in an electric muffle furnace, until nearly free of carbon.   Treat the residue with 20 ml of H_2O and 2 ml of 30% hydrogen peroxide, and heat on the steam bath for 15 minutes; then add 5 ml of HCl and evaporate to dryness on the steam bath.   Dissolve the residue in 10 ml of H_2O, filter and wash to 15 ml.   Add to the filtrate 1 ml of 0.1 N HCl and 2 ml of $BaCl_2$.   Any turbidity produced after 15 minutes is not greater than that of a control made as follows: Evaporate 0.1 g of sodium carbonate, 2 ml of 30% hydrogen peroxide, and 5 ml of HCl to dryness on the steam bath. Dissolve the residue and 0.10 mg of SO_4 in H_2O to make 15 ml, and treat with 1 ml of 0.1 N HCl and 2 ml of $NaCl_2$.

Heavy metals: Dissolve 5 g in warm water to make 50 ml. To 10 ml of the solution add 0.015 mg of Pb and dilute to 40 ml (A). Add to this solution and to the remaining 40 ml (B) 10 ml of H_2S. B is not darker than A.

Iron: Dissolve 1 g in 20 ml of water, add 2 ml of HCl and bring to a boil. Cool, filter, wash with about 10 ml of H_2O, and dilute the filtrate to 50 ml. Add about 30 mg of ammonium persulfate and 3 ml of ammonium thiocyanate, and mix. Any resulting red color is not darker than that of a blank to which 0.01 mg of Fe has been added.

Sodium: Ignite 1 g, take up the residue in 10 ml of H_2O and 1 ml of HCl and filter. The filtrate, tested on a platinum wire, imparts no distinct yellow color to a colorless flame.

Note: The sodium may be quantitatively determined by Flame Photometry.

POTASSIUM BISULFATE

$KHSO_4$; mol. wt. 136.17; K—28.71%; SO_4—70.55%; free H_2SO_4—36.01%.

Colorless crystals or white fragments; hygroscopic. Soluble in about 3 parts of water. *Keep in well-closed containers.*

Standards

Assay (% acidity)......35%–37% H_2SO_4	Arsenic (As)................max 2 ppm
Insoluble and NH_4OH	Calcium and Magnesium......max 0.010%
precipitate...............max 0.010%	Heavy metals (as Pb)........max 0.001%
Chloride (Cl)...............max 0.002%	Iron (Fe)...................max 0.002%
Nitrate (NO_3)..............max 0.002%	Sodium (Na)..........max about 0.02%
Phosphate (PO_4)...........max 0.001%	

Assay: Weigh accurately about 4 g, dissolve in 50 ml of H_2O, and titrate with 1 N NaOH, using methyl orange indicator. One ml of 1 N NaOH = 0.04904 g H_2SO_4, log 69055, or 0.1369 g $KHSO_4$, log 13418.

Insoluble and NH_4OH precipitate: Dissolve 10 g in 100 ml of H_2O and make alkaline to methyl red with NH_4OH. Boil the solution for 1 minute and, if a precipitate is present, filter hot (retain filtrate), wash it with hot H_2O and dry at 105°. Its weight is not more than 1.0 mg.

Chloride: To a solution of 1 g in 20 ml of H_2O add 1 ml of HNO_3 and 1 ml of $AgNO_3$. Any resulting turbidity is not greater than that in a blank to which 0.02 mg of Cl has been added.

Nitrate: Dissolve 0.5 g in 10 ml of water, add 20 mg of NaCl and 0.2 ml of diphenylamine solution and slowly run in 10 ml of H_2SO_4. Mix gently and allow to stand for 1 hour. No blue color results.

Phosphate: Dissolve 2 g in 20 ml of H_2O, add 1 ml each of phosphate reagents **A** and **B** and heat at 60° for 10 minutes. Any blue color produced is not darker than that of a control made by treating 0.02 mg of PO_4 with 2 ml of 25% H_2SO_4 and 1 ml each of the phosphate reagents in the same volume and in the same manner as with the sample.

Arsenic: Determine in 1 g of sample by method on page 563. The stain is not greater than that from 0.002 mg of As.

Calcium and Magnesium: To the filtrate (without the washings) from *Insoluble* add 5 ml of ammonium oxalate, 3 ml of ammonium phosphate, and 25 ml of NH_4OH; let stand overnight. If a precipitate is formed, filter, wash with 2.5% NH_3, and ignite. The weight of the ignited precipitate is not more than 1.0 mg.

Heavy metals: Dissolve 4 g in 25 ml of water, neutralize the solution to phenolphthalein with NH_4OH, and dilute to 40 ml. To 10 ml add 0.02 mg of Pb and 2 ml of 1 N acetic acid, and dilute to 40 ml (A). To the remaining 30 ml add 2 ml of 1 N acetic acid, and dilute to 40 ml (B). Then to each add 10 ml of H_2S. B is not darker than A.

Iron: Dissolve 2 g in 25 ml of H_2O, add 2 ml of HCl, and boil gently for 5 minutes. Cool and dilute to 40 ml. Dilute 10 ml of the solution to 50 ml and add about 30 mg of ammonium persulfate and 3 ml of ammonium thiocyanate. Any red color produced is not darker than that in a control made with 0.01 mg of Fe, 2 ml of HCl, the same quantities of the ammonium persulfate and thiocyanate and in the same final volume as with the sample.

Sodium: A 10% solution, tested on a platinum wire, imparts no pronounced yellow color to a colorless flame.

POTASSIUM BITARTRATE

Potassium Hydrogen Tartrate; Potassium Acid Tartrate

$KHC_4H_4O_6$; mol. wt. 188.18; K—20.78%; tartaric acid—79.74%.

Colorless crystals or a white, crystalline powder. Soluble in 170 parts of water at 25°, 20 parts of boiling water, practically insoluble in alcohol. Its saturated or nearly saturated aqueous solution has a pH of 3.57 $\pm$ 0.02 at about 25°.

Standards

Assay..........99.7%–100.2% $KHC_4N_4O_6$	Ammonia (NH_3).............max 0.005%
Insoluble in NH_4OH.........max 0.010%	Calcium (Ca)................max 0.005%
Alcohol—insoluble...........max 0.10%	Heavy metals (as Pb)........max 0.001%
Chloride (Cl)...............max 0.002%	Iron (Fe)...................max 0.001%
Phosphate (PO_4)...........max 0.001%	Sodium (Na)...........max about 0.02%
Sulfate (SO_4)...............max 0.010%	

Assay: Dry 1 g, well crushed if in crystal form, for 2 hours at 105°; then weigh accurately about 0.7 g, dissolve it in 50 ml of hot water, and titrate with 0.1 N NaOH, using phenolphthalein indicator. One ml of 0.1 N NaOH = 0.01881 g $KHC_4H_4O_6$, log 27439.

Insoluble in ammonium hydroxide: Dissolve 10 g in a mixture of 100 ml of water and 30 ml of NH_4OH. Filter any insoluble residue, wash it with hot H_2O, and dry at 105°. Its weight does not exceed 1.0 mg.

Alcohol—soluble: To 2 g of the well-powdered sample, add 20 ml of alcohol, shake for 5 minutes, allow to stand for 30 minutes, shake, and filter through a dry filter paper. Evaporate 10 ml of the filtrate on the steam bath, dry at 105° for 30 minutes, and weigh. The weight of the residue does not exceed 1.0 mg.

Chloride: Dissolve 1 g in a mixture of 20 ml of H_2O and 3 ml of HNO_3 and add 1 ml of $AgNO_3$. Any turbidity produced is not greater than that in a blank to which 0.02 mg of Cl has been added.

Phosphate: Ignite 2 g in platinum, preferably in an electric muffle furnace. Break up the thoroughly charred mass well, add 25 ml of water and 2 ml of 30% H_2O_2, and boil for a few minutes. Neutralize with 25% H_2SO_4, add 2 ml excess of the acid, filter, and evaporate filtrate to incipient sulfuric fumes. Dilute to 20 ml, add 1 ml each of phosphate reagents **A** and **B**, and heat at 60° for 10 minutes. If a blue color is produced it is not darker than that in a control made with 0.02 mg of PO_4.

Sulfate: Ignite 2 g, protected from sulfur, preferably in an electric muffle furnace, until nearly free from carbon. Boil the residue with 20 ml of water and 2 ml of 30% H_2O_2 for 5 minutes; then add 10 mg of sodium carbonate and 5 ml of HCl and evaporate on the steam bath to dryness. Prepare a control by evaporating 10 mg of sodium carbonate, 2 ml of the H_2O_2, 0.1 mg SO_4, and 5 ml of HCl to dryness on the steam bath. Dissolve the residue from each in 10 ml of water and filter. Then to each add 1 ml of 0.1 N HCl and 2 ml of $BaCl_2$. Any turbidity appearing in 15 minutes in the solution of the sample is not greater than that in the control.

Ammonia: Dissolve 1 g in 200 ml of warm H_2O; cool. Transfer 80 ml of the solution to a distilling flask connected with a condenser and a receiver container containing 5 ml of H_2O and 1 ml of 0.1 N HCl; add 10 ml of 10% NaOH and distill over about 40 ml. Dilute the distillate to 50 ml, add 2 ml of 10% NaOH, and 2 ml of Nessler solution. Any color produced is not darker than that of a control made with 0.02 mg of NH_3, 4 ml of the NaOH, and 2 ml of Nessler solution in the same volume as with the sample.

Calcium: Ignite 2.0 g in a spacious platinum crucible or dish until nearly free of carbon. Add 10 ml of water and 5 ml of HCl and evaporate to dryness on the steam bath. Dissolve the resulting chloride in 7 to 8 ml of hot water, filter, and wash to 10 ml. Warm to about 50°, add 1 drop of acetic acid and 1 ml of ammonium oxalate solution, and allow to stand for 20 minutes. Any resulting turbidity is not greater than that produced by 0.1 mg of calcium (Ca) contained in a solution of 1 g of sodium chloride and treated as the sample solution beginning with "Warm to about 50° . . . ."

Heavy metals: To 4 g add 25 ml of warm H_2O and just sufficient NH_4OH to dissolve. Add to the solution 2 drops phenolphthalein and follow with just sufficient 36% acetic acid to discharge the pink color and 5 drops excess. Cool, and dilute to 40 ml. To 10 ml add 0.02 mg of Pb and dilute to 40 ml (A). Dilute the remaining 30 ml to 40 ml (B). Then to each add 10 cc of H_2S. B is not darker than A.

Iron: To 2 g add 25 ml of H_2O, 3 ml of HCl, 3 drops of HNO_3, and boil for 1 minute. Cool, dilute to 50 ml, and add 3 ml of ammonium thiocyanate. Any red color produced is not darker than that of a blank with 0.02 mg of Fe added.

Sodium₁: Ignite 1 g in platinum. Treat the residue with 20 ml of water, add 1 ml of HCl, and filter. The filtrate, tested on a platinum wire, imparts no pronounced yellow color to a colorless flame.

Note: The sodium may be quantitatively estimated by Flame Photometry.

POTASSIUM BROMATE

$KBrO_3$; mol. wt. 167.02; K—23.41%; active O—28.74%; Br—47.85%.

Colorless or white crystals, or granules. Soluble in about 15 parts of water. *Keep protected from organic matter.*

Caution: *When triturated with organic substances, sulfides, or other readily oxidizable substances, it may react with explosive violence.*

Standards

Assay............99.8%–100.2% $KBrO_3$	Sulfate (SO_4)...............max 0.005%
Insoluble...................max 0.005%	Heavy metals (as Pb).......max 0.0005%
Neutrality...................to pass test	Iron (Fe)...................max 0.001%
Bromide (as Br)..............max 0.05%	Sodium (Na)...........max about 0.02%
Nitrogen compounds (as N)...max 0.001%	

Assay: Powder about 0.5 g and dry for 3 hours over H_2SO_4. Weigh accurately about 0.1 g of the dried sample (or use a portion of a stock solution corresponding to this quantity) and dissolve in 50 ml of H_2O in a glass-stoppered flask. Add 3 g of potassium iodide and 3 ml of HCl previously diluted with 10 ml of water, allow to stand for 5 minutes, then add 50 ml of cold water, and titrate the liberated iodine with 0.1 N thiosulfate, adding starch solution toward the end. Correct for a blank. One ml 0.1 N thiosulfate = 0.002784 g $KBrO_3$, log 44467.

$$KBrO_3 + 6KI + 6HCl \rightarrow 6I + KBr + 6KCl + 2H_2O$$

Insoluble: Dissolve 20 g in 200 ml of hot H_2O and heat on the steam bath for 1 hour. Should an insoluble residue remain, filter, wash it with hot H_2O, and dry at 105°. Its weight does not exceed 1.0 mg.

Neutrality: Dissolve 5 g in 60 ml of warm H_2O and add 3 drops of phenolphthalein; no pink color is produced. Now add 0.02 N NaOH to the production of a pink color; not more than 0.2 ml of the NaOH is required.

Bromide: Dissolve 4 g in 80 ml of H_2O. To 40 ml add 0.25 ml of 1 N H_2SO_4. At the end of 2 minutes the liquid is not darker than the remaining 40 ml.

Nitrogen compounds: Dissolve 1 g in 40 ml of H_2O, add 1 g of powdered Devarda metal and 10 ml of 10% NaOH. Allow to stand 2 hours protected from loss or access of NH_3, then distill 40 ml into 5 ml of water containing 1 drop of dilute HCl. Add to the distillate 1 ml of 10% NaOH, dilute to 50 ml, and add 2 ml of Nessler solution. The resulting color is not darker than that produced by treating 0.010 mg of nitrogen (0.04 mg NH_4Cl) in the same manner as the sample.

Sulfate: To 2 g add 20 mg of sodium carbonate, 10 ml of water, and 10 ml of HCl, and evaporate to dryness on the steam bath. Take up the residue with 10 ml of water; add to the solution 1 ml of 0.1 N HCl and 2 ml of $BaCl_2$. Any turbidity produced in 15 minutes is not greater than that in a control prepared as follows: To 10 ml of water add 20 mg of sodium carbonate, 0.1 mg of SO_4, and 10 ml of HCl, and evaporate to dryness on the steam bath. Dissolve the residue in 10 ml of water, and add 1 ml of 0.1 N HCl and 2 ml of $BaCl_2$.

Heavy metals: To 2.5 g of the sample add 10 ml of hot water and 10 ml of HCl (A). To 0.5 g of sample add 15 ml of HCl and 0.01 mg of Pb (B). Evaporate both to dryness on the steam bath. Add to (A) 5 ml of HCl and re-evaporate to dryness. Dissolve the residues in 20 ml of water each, add a drop of phenolphthalein and neutralize with 1 N NaOH. Add to each 1 ml of 1 N acetic acid, dilute to 25 ml, and add 5 ml of H_2S. A is not darker than B.

Iron: To 1 g of sample add 5 ml of HCl and 5 ml of water and evaporate to dryness on the steam bath. Add 5 ml of HCl and again evaporate to dryness. Prepare a control by adding to 0.01 mg of Fe, 10 ml of HCl, and evaporating on the steam bath to dryness. Take up each in 2 ml of HCl and water to make 50 ml. Add to each about 30 mg of ammonium persulfate and 3 ml of ammonium thiocyanate. Any red color in the sample solution is not darker than that in the control.

Sodium: A 10% solution in hot water, tested on a platinum wire, imparts no distinct yellow color to a colorless flame.

POTASSIUM BROMIDE

KBr; mol. wt. 119.02; K = 32.85%; Br = 67.15%.

Colorless or white crystals or granules. Soluble in 2 parts of water; or in 200 parts of alcohol.

Standards

Insoluble	max 0.005%		Barium (Ba)	max 0.002%
Alkalinity (as K_2CO_3)	max 0.007%		Calcium, Magnesium, and	
Bromate (BrO_3)	max 0.001%		NH₄OH precipitate	max 0.005%
Chloride (Cl)	max 0.20%		Heavy metals (as Pb)	max 0.0005%
Iodide (I)	max 0.005%		Iron (Fe)	max 0.0005%
Nitrogen compounds (as N)	max 0.001%		Sodium (Na)	max about 0.02%
Sulfate (SO_4)	max 0.005%			

Insoluble: Dissolve 20 g in 150 ml of H_2O and heat on steam bath for 30 minutes. Filter any insoluble residue (retain filtrate), wash it with H_2O, and dry at 105°. Its weight is not more than 1.0 mg.

Alkalinity: A solution of 5 g in 50 ml of H_2O requires not more than 0.25 ml of 0.02 N HCl to neutralize it to methyl orange.

Bromate: Dissolve 1 g in 10 ml of oxygen-free H_2O, add 2 drops of 10% potassium iodide, 1 ml starch, and 5 drops of 1 N H_2SO_4, and allow to stand at 25° for 10 minutes. No blue or violet color appears.

Chloride: Dissolve 0.5 g of sample in a mixture of 5 ml of HNO_3 and 15 ml of water in a 100-ml Erlenmeyer flask. Add 3 ml of 30% H_2O_2 and gently heat on the steam bath until the solution is colorless. Do not heat any longer than necessary to decolorize the solution. Wash down the inside of the flask with a little water, add 1 ml of 30% H_2O_2, and digest on the steam bath for additional 15 minutes, washing down the sides of the flask with a little water once or twice during this digestion.   Cool, and dilute to 200 ml.   Dilute 5 ml of this solution to 20 ml, and add 1 ml of HNO_3 and 1 ml of $AgNO_3$ solution.   The turbidity so produced is not greater than that produced by treating 1 mg Cl^- (as NaCl) in the same manner as the sample.

Iodide: Dissolve 5 g in 20 ml of H_2O, add 1 ml of chloroform, 3 drops of ferric chloride, and 5 drops of 10% H_2SO_4 and shake gently.   No violet tint appears in the chloroform.

Nitrogen compounds: Dissolve 1 g in 50 ml of H_2O in a distillation flask, add 10 ml of 10% NaOH, and 0.5 g of powdered Devarda metal.   Allow to stand for 2 hours protected from loss or access of NH_3, then distill 40 ml, collecting the distillate in 5 ml of water containing 1 drop of dilute HCl.   Add to distillate 1 ml of 10% NaOH and 2 ml of Nessler solution.   The resulting color is not darker than that produced by treating 0.01 mg of nitrogen (0.04 mg NH_4Cl) in the same manner.

Sulfate: Dissolve 2 g in 10 ml of H_2O, add 1 ml of 0.1 N HCl and 2 ml of $BaCl_2$ Any resulting turbidity in 15 minutes is not more than in a blank to which 0.1 mg of SO_4 has been added.

Barium: Dissolve 2.0 g in 15 ml of water, add 2 drops of glacial acetic acid and filter if not clear.   Add to the solution 1.0 ml of potassium chromate solution and sufficient 10% NH_3 to make the color clear yellow.   Treat 15 ml of the water exactly as the solution of the reagent including filtration if the solution was filtered. After 5 minutes both are equally clear.

Calcium, Magnesium, and NH_4OH precipitate: To the filtrate from *Insoluble* add 5 ml of ammonium oxalate, 3 ml of ammonium phosphate, and 20 ml of NH_4OH, and allow to stand overnight.   If a precipitate is present, filter, wash it with 2.5% NH_3, and ignite.   The weight of the ignited precipitate does not exceed 1.0 mg.

Heavy metals: Dissolve 5 g in H_2O to make 50 ml.   To 10 ml add 0.015 mg of Pb, dilute 40 ml and 1 ml of 1 N acetic acid (*A*).   To the remaining 40 ml add 1 ml of 1 N acetic acid (*B*).   Then to each add 10 ml of H_2S.   *B* is not darker than *A*.

Iron: Dissolve 2 g in 40 ml of H_2O, add 2 ml of HCl, and dilute to 50 ml.   Add about 30 mg of ammonium persulfate and 3 ml of ammonium thiocyanate.   Any resulting red color is not darker than that in a blank to which 0.01 mg of Fe has been added.

Sodium: A 10% solution tested on a platinum wire imparts no distinct yellow color to a colorless flame.

Note: A quantitative estimation of sodium content may be readily achieved by Flame Photometry.

POTASSIUM CARBONATE, ANHYDROUS

K_2CO_3; mol. wt. 138.21; K—56.58%; CO_3—43.42%; CO_2—31.84%.

White, granular powder; readily absorbs up to 1.5 mols of H_2O on exposure to air.   Soluble in 1 part of water; insoluble in alcohol.   *Keep in tightly closed containers*.

Standards

Assay............99.8%–100.3% K_2CO_3	Aluminium (Al).............max 0.001%
Insoluble...................max 0.010%	Arsenic (As)................max 1 ppm
Moisture......................max 1.0%	Calcium and Magnesium
Chloride and Chlorate (as Cl)..max 0.003%	precipitate.................max 0.010%
Nitrogen compounds (as N)...max 0.001%	Heavy metals (as Pb).......max 0.0005%
Phosphate (PO_4)............max 0.001%	Iron (Fe)...................max 0.001%
Sulfur compounds (as SO_4)....max 0.005%	Sodium (Na)..........max about 0.02%
Ammonium hydroxide	
precipitate and Silica.......max 0.015%	

Assay and Moisture: Weigh accurately about 3 g and heat at 250°–300° to constant weight. The loss in weight does not exceed 1.0%. Dissolve the heated sample in 50 ml of water, add 2 drops of methyl orange and titrate with 1 N HCl to a brownish-yellow color. One ml of 1 N HCl = 0.06910 g K_2CO_3, log 83948. Calculate the percentage on the weight of the heated sample.

Insoluble: Dissolve 10 g in 100 ml of H_2O and heat on the steam bath for 30 minutes. Filter any undissolved matter on asbestos in a Gooch crucible, wash with water, and dry to contant weight at 105°. The weight of the insoluble residue does not exceed 1.0 mg.

Chloride and Chlorate: Ignite 1 g at a low red heat and allow to cool. Dissolve in 25 ml of H_2O, add 3 ml of HNO_3, filter if necessary, and dilute to 30 ml. To 10 ml add 1 ml of $AgNO_3$. The turbidity produced is not greater than that in a blank to which 0.01 mg of Cl has been added.

Nitrogen compounds: To a solution of 2 g in 50 ml of H_2O add 10 ml of 10% NaOH and 0.5 g of powdered Devarda metal; let stand for 2 hours protected from loss or access of ammonia. Dilute with water to 100 ml, decant 50 ml, and add 2 ml of Nessler solution. The color produced is not darker than is produced by treating 0.02 mg of nitrogen (0.08 mg NH_4Cl) in the same manner as the sample.

Phosphate: Dissolve 2 g in a mixture of 5 ml of H_2O and 6 ml of 25% H_2SO_4, evaporate, and heat to incipient sulfuric fumes. Add 20 ml of H_2O, filter, and add to the filtrate 1 ml each of phosphate reagents **A** and **B**; heat at 60° for 10 minutes. Any blue color produced is not darker than that of a control made with 0.02 mg of PO_4, 2 ml of 25% H_2SO_4, 1 ml of the phosphate reagents and in the same volume as with the sample.

Sulfur compounds: Dissolve 2 g in 15 ml of H_2O, add 5 drops of bromine water, and boil for 2 minutes; then add 5 ml of HCl and evaporate to dryness on the steam bath. Dissolve the residue in 1 ml of 0.1 N HCl and 10 ml of H_2O, filter if necessary, and add 2 ml of $BaCl_2$. If a turbidity is produced in 15 minutes it is not greater than that in a control made by evaporating to dryness on the steam bath 0.1 mg of SO_4, 5 drops of bromine water, and 5 ml of HCl, then treating the residue with the same quantities of the reagents and in the same final volume as the sample.

Ammonium hydroxide precipitate and Silica: Dissolve 10 g in 70 ml of water. Cautiously add 12 ml of H_2SO_4, evaporate, and heat to strong sulfuric fumes for 2–3 minutes. Cool, dissolve the residue in 130 ml of hot H_2O, and make just alkaline to methyl red with ammonium hydroxide. Heat to boiling, filter, wash with hot water, and ignite in a platinum crucible to constant weight. The weight of the ignited precipitate is not more than 1.5 mg. Treat the ignited precipitate with 5 drops each of sulfuric and hydrofluoric acids and ignite to constant weight. The loss in weight, SiO_2, is not more than 0.5 mg.

Aluminium: Dissolve 2 g in 20 ml of water, add 3 ml of glacial acetic acid, and 1 ml of a 0.1% aqueous solution of ammonium aurintricarboxylate (Aluminon). Allow to stand 5 minutes, then add 20 ml of ammonium carbonate solution. The red color produced is not darker than that of a control made as follows: To 20 ml of H_2O add 0.02 mg of aluminum, 1 g of ammonium acetate, 1.5 ml of glacial acetic acid, and 1 ml of the ammonium aurintricarboxylate solution. Allow to stand for 5 minutes, then add 20 ml of ammonium carbonate solution, and adjust to the same volume as with the sample.

Arsenic: Dissolve 2 g in 10 ml of H_2O, cautiously acidify with HCl and determine the arsenic by method on page 563. The stain is not greater than that from 0.002 mg of As.

Calcium and Magnesium: To the filtrate from the test for *Ammonium hydroxide precipitate and Silica* add 0.5 ml of HCl, 5 ml of ammonium oxalate, 2 ml of ammonium phosphate, and 15 ml of ammonium hydroxide; let stand overnight. Filter any precipitate present, wash with 2.5% NH_3, and ignite. The weight of the ignited precipitate does not exceed 1.0 mg.

Heavy metals: Dissolve 5 g of sample in 10 ml of water and *cautiously* add, in small portions, 10 ml of HCl (*A*). Dissolve 1 g of sample in 5 ml of water, add 10 ml of HCl and 0.02 mg of Pb (*B*). Evaporate both on the steam bath to dryness. Take up each in 25 ml of water, add a drop of phenolphthalein, and neutralize with 0.1 N NaOH. Add 1 ml of 1 N acetic acid to each, dilute to 40 ml, and add 10 ml of H_2S. *A* is not darker than *B*.

Iron: Dissolve 1 g in 20 ml of water, add 3 ml of HCl, bring to a boil, cool, and dilute to 50 ml. Add about 30 mg of ammonium persulfate and 3 ml of ammonium thiocyanate. Any red color produced is not darker than that of a blank to which 0.01 mg of Fe has been added.

Sodium: A 10% solution, tested on a platinum wire, imparts no distinct yellow color to a colorless flame.

Note: A quantitative determination of the sodium content may be readily achieved by Flame Photometry.

POTASSIUM CARBONATE, CRYSTALS

$K_2CO_3 \cdot 1\frac{1}{2}H_2O$; mol. wt. 165.24. Anhydrous—83.65%; H_2O—16.35%; K—47.32%.

Dull white crystals. Not hygroscopic; solubilities: the same as the anhydrous.

Standards

Loss on heating
  at 200°–250°............14.5%–16.5%
Assay (anhydrous basis)....99.7%–100.3%
Insoluble..................max 0.010%
Chloride and Chlorate
  (as Cl)..................max 0.003%
Nitrogen compounds (as N)...max 0.001%
Phosphate (PO_4)..........max 0.001%
Sulfur compounds (as SO_4)....max 0.005%

Ammonium hydroxide precipitate
  and Silica................max 0.015%
Aluminum (Al).............max 0.001%
Arsenic (As)..............max 1 ppm
Calcium and Magnesium
  precipitate..............max 0.010%
Heavy metals (as Pb).......max 0.0005%
Iron (Fe).................max 0.001%
Sodium (Na)..........max about 0.02%

Loss on heating: Weigh accurately 2.5 g to 3.0 g in a covered platinum crucible, uncover slightly and heat at 200°–250° to constant weight. The loss in weight corresponds to 14.5%–16.5%.

Assay: Place the crucible with its contents from the test for *Loss on heating* in a 300-ml beaker, add 75 ml of water and 2 drops (0.1 ml) of methyl orange, and titrate the solution with 1 N HCl to a brownish yellow color. One ml of 1 N HCl = 0.06910 g K_2CO_3, log 83948.

Insoluble; Chloride and Chlorate; Nitrogen compounds; Phosphate; Sulfur compounds; Ammonium hydroxide precipitate and Silica; Aluminum; Arsenic; Calcium and magnesium precipitate; Heavy Metals; Iron; Sodium: Test as described under the Anhydrous. The results should be as there required.

POTASSIUM CHLORATE

$KClO_3$; mol. wt. 122.56; K—31.90%; Cl—28.93%; available O—39.16%.

Colorless or white crystals or granules. Soluble in 17 parts of water; slowly soluble in 25 parts of glycerol; almost insoluble in alcohol.

Caution: Dangerous explosions may occur when potassium chlorate is rubbed with organic substances, sulfur, or other oxidizable substances. *Keep in well-closed containers, protected from organic matter.*

Standards

Insoluble.................max 0.005%	Calcium, Magnesium, and
Bromate (BrO_3).............max 0.015%	NH$_4$OH precipitate........max 0.005%
Chloride (Cl)...............max 0.001%	Heavy metals (as Pb).......max 0.0005%
Nitrogen compounds (as N)...max 0.001%	Iron (Fe).................max 0.0003%
Sulfate (SO_4).........max about 0.003%	Sodium (Na)................max 0.02%
Arsenic (As)...............max 0.5 ppm	*Assay*....................min 99.5%

Insoluble: Dissolve 20 g in 200 ml of hot H_2O and heat on the steam bath for 1 hour. Filter any insoluble residue, wash it with hot H_2O, and dry at 105°. Its weight does not exceed 1.0 mg.

Bromate: Dissolve 4 g in 200 ml of freshly boiled and cooled water in a glass-stoppered flask. Add 10 ml of 1 N HCl, mix, and add 10 ml of fresh potassium iodide solution and 5 ml of fresh starch solutions. Stopper immediately. Allow to stand for 1 hour, protected from light, then titrate with 0.1 N sodium thiosulfate to the disappearance of the blue color. Correct for a blank. Not more than 0.3 ml of the thiosulfate is consumed.

Chloride: Dissolve 1 g in 20 ml of warm H_2O, cool, add 5 drops of HNO_3 free from oxides of nitrogen, and 1 ml of $AgNO_3$. Any turbidity produced is not greater than that in a blank to which 0.01 mg of Cl has been added.

Nitrogen compounds: Dissolve 1 g in 50 ml of H_2O in a distillation flask, add 0.5 g of powdered Devarda metal, or 0.5 g aluminum wire in small pieces, and 10 ml of 10% NaOH. Allow to stand for 2 hours protected from loss or access of NH_3, then distill 40 ml, collecting the distillate in 5 ml of water containing 1 drop of dilute HCl. Add to the distillate 1 ml of 10% NaOH and 2 ml of Nessler solution. The resulting color is not darker than that produced by treating 0.01 mg of nitrogen (0.04 mg NH_4Cl) in the same manner as the sample.

Sulfate: Dissolve 5 g in 150 ml of H_2O, add 1 ml of 10% HCl and 5 ml of $BaCl_2$, and allow to stand overnight.   No turbidity or precipitate is formed.

Arsenic: Evaporate 4 g with 15 ml of HCl to dryness on the steam bath and test residue by method on page 563.   The stain is not more than that from 0.002 mg of As.

Calcium, Magnesium, and NH_4OH precipitate: Boil 10 g with 100 ml of H_2O and 25 ml of HCl until no more chlorine is evolved.   Dilute with water to 100 ml, heat to boiling, add 5 ml of ammonium oxalate, 3 ml of ammonium phosphate, and 20 ml of NH_4OH, and allow to stand overnight.   If a precipitate is present, filter, wash with 2.5% NH_3, and ignite.   The weight of the ignited precipitate does not exceed 0.5 mg.

Heavy metals: To 5 g of sample add 10 ml of H_2O and 15 ml of HCl (A).   To 1 g of the sample add 15 ml of HCl, 10 ml of water and 0.02 mg of Pb (B).   Evaporate both to dryness on the steam bath.   Add to each 10 ml more of HCl and re-evaporate to dryness.   Take up each in 25 ml of water, add a drop of phenolphthalein and neutralize with 0.1 N NaOH.   Add 1 ml of 1 N acetic acid to each, dilute to 40 ml and add 10 ml of H_2S. A is not darker than B.

Iron: To 3.5 g of sample add 5 ml of HCl and 5 ml of water and evaporate to dryness on the steam bath.   Add 5 ml of HCl and again evaporate to dryness.   Prepare a control by adding to 0.01 mg of Fe, 10 ml of HCl, and evaporating on the steam bath to dryness.   Take up each in 2 ml of HCl and water to make 50 ml.   Add to each 30 mg of ammonium persulfate and 3 ml of ammonium thiocyanate.   Any red color in the sample solution is not darker than that in the control.

Sodium: A 10% solution in hot water, tested on a platinum wire, imparts no distinct yellow color to a colorless flame.

Assay: Potassium chlorate may be assayed by the following method: Dry over sulfuric acid for 3 hours; then weigh accurately about 0.10 g and dissolve it in 10 ml of H_2O in a 250-ml flask.   Add exactly 35 ml of acid ferrous sulfate solution, close the flask with a valve stopper to prevent access of air, and boil for 10 minutes.   Cool, add 10 ml of 10% manganous sulfate solution and titrate the excess of ferrous sulfate with 0.1 N potassium permanganate.   Run a blank in the same manner with 35 ml of the acid ferrous sulfate solution.   The difference between the volume of permanganate consumed in the blank and the sample represents the $KClO_3$.   One ml of 0.1 N permanganate = 0.002043 g $KClO_3$, log 31027.

$$KClO_3 + 6FeSO_4 + 3H_2SO_4 \rightarrow 3Fe_2(SO_4)_3 + KCl + 3H_2O$$

Note: The acid ferrous sulfate solution is made by dissolving 7 g of clear crystals of ferrous sulfate in 90 ml of freshly boiled and cooled H_2O and adding sufficient H_2SO_4 to make 100 ml.

POTASSIUM CHLORIDE

KCl; mol. wt. 74.56; K—52.44%; Cl—47.56%.

Colorless or white crystals or granules.   Soluble in 3 parts of water; almost insoluble in alcohol.   This reagent, in crystal form, is substantially 99.9% pure.

Standards

Insoluble	max 0.005%	Sulfate (SO_4)	max 0.001%
Neutrality	to pass test	Barium (Ba)	max 0.001%
Bromide (Br)	max 0.01%	Calcium, Magnesium, and	
Iodide (I)	max 0.002%	NH_4OH precipitate	max 0.005%
Chlorate and Nitrate		Heavy metals (as Pb)	max 0.0005%
(as ClO_3)	max 0.002%	Iron (Fe)	max 0.0003%
Nitrogen compounds (as N)	max 0.001%	Sodium (Na)	max about 0.01%
Phosphate (PO_4)	max 0.0005%		

Insoluble: Dissolve 20 g in 100 ml of H_2O and heat on the steam bath for 1 hour. Should any insoluble residue remain, filter (retain filtrate), wash it well, and dry at 105°. Its weight is not more than 1 mg.

Neutrality: Dissolve 5 g in 50 ml of CO_2-free water and add 3 drops of phenolphthalein; no pink color is produced. Now add 0.2 ml of 0.02 N NaOH; a pink color is produced.

Bromide; Iodide: Dissolve 2 g in 7 ml of warm H_2O, slowly pour the solution into 30 ml of alcohol, cool, and filter. Evaporate the filtrate to dryness, dissolve the residue in 5 ml of H_2O, add to the solution 1 ml of chloroform, then add dropwise, with shaking, 5 drops of dilute chlorine water $(1+3)$. No yellow or violet color is produced in the chloroform.

Chlorate and Nitrate: Dissolve 0.5 g in water, add 0.2 ml of diphenylamine solution and dilute to 10 ml. Cool the solution in ice water for 2–3 minutes, then withdraw it from the cooling bath and, holding the beaker at an angle of about 45°, slowly run in along the sides of the beaker 10 ml of H_2SO_4 without agitation. Allow to stand for 15 minutes, then mix gently by swirling the contents of the beaker and allow to stand for 1 hour. No blue color appears.

Nitrogen compounds: Dissolve 1 g in 50 ml of H_2O in a distillation flask, add 10 ml of 10% NaOH and 0.5 g fine aluminum wire in small pieces. Allow to stand for 2 hours protected from loss or access of NH_3; then distill 40 ml into 5 ml of water containing 1 drop of dilute HCl. Add to the distillate 1 ml of 10% NaOH and 2 ml of Nessler solution. The color produced is not darker than that produced by treating 0.01 mg of nitrogen (0.04 mg NH_4Cl) in the same manner as the sample.

Phosphate: Dissolve 4 g in 20 ml of H_2O, add 2 ml of 25% H_2SO_4, 1 ml each of phosphate reagents **A** and **B**, and heat at 60° for 10 minutes. Any blue color produced is not darker than that of a blank to which 0.02 mg of PO_4 has been added.

Sulfate: Dissolve 10 g in 100 ml of water, add 2 ml of 1 N HCl, heat to boiling, add 5 ml of $BaCl_2$, and let stand overnight. No turbidity or precipitate appears.

Barium: Dissolve 4 g in 20 ml of H_2O, filter if necessary, and divide into two portions. To one portion add 2 ml of 10% H_2SO_4 and to the other add 2 ml of H_2O; they are equally clear after 2 hours.

Calcium, Magnesium, and NH_4OH precipitate: To the filtrate from the test for *Insoluble* add 5 ml of ammonium oxalate, 2 ml of ammonium phosphate, and 20 ml of NH_4OH, and allow to stand overnight. If a precipitate is present, filter, wash with 2.5% NH_3, and ignite. The weight of the ignited precipitate does not exceed 1 mg.

Heavy metals: Dissolve 5 g in H_2O to make 50 ml. To 10 ml add 0.015 mg of Pb, dilute to 40 ml, and add 1 ml of 1 N acetic acid (A). To the remaining 40 ml add 1 ml of 1 N acetic acid (B). Then to each add 10 ml H_2S; B is not darker than A.

Iron: Dissolve 3 g in 40 ml of H_2O, add 2 ml of HCl and dilute to 50 ml. Add 30 mg of ammonium persulfate and 3 ml of ammonium thiocyanate. Any resulting red color is not darker than that of a blank to which 0.01 mg of Fe has been added.

Sodium: A 10% solution, tested on a platinum wire, imparts no pronounced yellow color to a colorless flame.

Note: The quantitative evaluation of the sodium content is most advantageously accomplished by Flame Photometry (consult page 566 etc.). If, however, this method, owing to lack of the necessary equipment or other reason, is not available, the sodium can be quantitatively determined by the Uranyl Zinc (or magnesium) Acetate technique (page 577).

POTASSIUM CHROMATE

K_2CrO_4; mol. wt. 194.20; K—40.27%; CrO_3—51.49%; Cr—26.78%.

Lemon-yellow crystals. Soluble in about 2 parts water; insoluble in alcohol.

Standards

Insoluble...................max 0.005%	Calcium (Ca)...............max 0.005%
Free alkali..................to pass test	Sodium (Na)...........max about 0.01%
Chloride (Cl)................mas 0.002%	Assay.....................99.4–100.3%
Sulfate (SO_4)...............max 0.005%	

Insoluble: Dissolve 10 g in 100 ml of H_2O and heat on the steam bath for 30 minutes. Filter any insoluble residue (retain filtrate), wash it well, and dry at 105°. The weight of the residue does not exceed 0.5 mg.

Free alkali: Dissolve 2.0 g in 50 ml of CO_2-free water and add 0.1 ml of phenolphthalein. If a pink color is produced, not more than 0.4 ml of 0.1 N HCl is required to discharge it. Instead of using an indicator the titration can be made electrometrically to pH 9.3.

Chloride: Dissolve 2 g in 40 ml of water, add 20 ml of HNO_3, and divide into two equal portions. Heat both portions to 50°; to one portion add 1 ml of $AgNO_3$ and to the other portion add 1 ml of water. At the end of 5 minutes both portions are equally clear.

Sulfate: Dissolve 3 g in 100 ml H_2O, add 2 ml of HCl, heat to about 80°, and add 10 ml of a solution containing 1 g of $BaCl_2$ and 2 ml of HCl in 100 ml. No turbidity or precipitate is produced in 2 hours.

Calcium: To the filtrate from *Insoluble* add 2 ml of NH_4OH and 10 ml of ammonium oxalate and allow to stand overnight. Filter any precipitate present, wash it, and ignite. After cooling, add a few drops of H_2SO_4 and re-ignite. The weight of the residue ($CaSO_4$) is not more than 2.4 mg.

Sodium: A 10% solution, tested on a platinum wire, imparts no pronounced yellow color to a colorless flame.

Assay: Potassium chromate may be assayed as follows: Weigh accurately about 0.25 g and dissolve in 200 ml of freshly boiled and cooled H_2O in a glass-stoppered flask. Add 3 g of potassium iodide and 7 ml of HCl, allow to stand in the dark for 10 minutes, then titrate the liberated iodine with 0.1 N sodium thiosulfate, using starch toward the end. One ml of 0.1 N thiosulfate = 0.006473 g K_2CrO_4, log 81111. Correct for thiosulfate consumed by a blank.

$$K_2CrO_4 + 3KI + 8HCl \rightarrow 3I + CrCl_3 + 6KCl + 4H_2O$$

POTASSIUM CITRATE

$K_3C_6H_5O_7 \cdot H_2O$; mol. wt. 324.34; anhydrous—94.47%; H_2O—5.53%; K—36.15%; hydrated citric acid 64.79%.

Colorless or white crystals or granules. Soluble in 1 part of water; soluble in glycerol; almost insoluble in alcohol.

Its water content may be determined by the iodine (Fischer) method.

Standards

Insoluble.................max 0.010%		Ammonia (NH_3)............max 0.003%	
Free acid (as citric)..........max 0.15%		Heavy metals (as Pb).......max 0.0005%	
Free alkali......................none		Iron (Fe).................max 0.0005%	
Chloride (Cl)...............max 0.002%		Sodium (Na)..........max about 0.03%	
Phosphate (PO_4)...........max 0.001%		Assay, anhydrous bases.....99.4–100.5%.	
Sulfate (SO_4)...............max 0.005%			

Insoluble: Dissolve 10 g in 50 ml of H_2O and heat on steam bath for 30 minutes. Filter any undissolved matter, wash with hot water, and dry at 105°. The weight of the insoluble residue is not more than 1.0 mg.

Free acid; Free alkali: Dissolve 2 g in 50 ml of CO_2-free H_2O and add 0.20 ml of phenolphthalein. If a pink color is produced it is not more intense than that produced by adding 0.20 ml of phenolphthalein and 0.1 ml of 0.02 N NaOH to 50 ml of CO_2-free water. If no pink color is produced the addition of not more than 2.0 ml of 0.02 N NaOH would be required to produce a pink color.

Chloride: Dissolve 1 g in 20 ml of H_2O and add 1 ml of HNO_3 and 1 ml of $AgNO_3$. The turbidity produced is not greater than that in a blank to which 0.02 mg of Cl has been added.

Phosphate: Ignite 1 g in platinum until white or nearly so. Break up the residue well, add 25 ml of H_2O and 1 ml of 30% hydrogen peroxide, and boil for a few minutes. Neutralize with 25% H_2SO_4, add 2 ml excess of the acid, filter, and evaporate filtrate to incipient sulfuric fumes. Dilute to 20 ml, add 1 ml each of phosphate reagents **A** and **B**, and heat at 60° for 10 minutes. If a blue color is produced it is not darker than a control made with 0.01 mg of PO_4, 2 ml of 25% H_2SO_4, the same quantities of the phosphate reagents and in the same final volume as in the sample.

Sulfate: Ignite 2 g protected from sulfur, preferably in an electrical muffle furnace, until nearly free of carbon. Boil the residue with 20 ml of water and 2 ml of 30% H_2O_2 for 5 minutes; then add 10 mg of sodium carbonate and 5 ml of HCl and evaporate on the steam bath to dryness.   Prepare a control by evaporating 10 mg of sodium carbonate with 2 ml of the H_2O_2, 5 ml of HCl, and 0.1 mg of SO_4 to dryness on the steam bath.   Dissolve the residue from each in 10 ml of hot water, and filter, if necessary.   Then to each add 1 ml of 0.1 N HCl and 2 ml of $BaCl_2$.   Any turbidity appearing in 15 minutes in the solution of the sample is not greater than that in the control.

Ammonia: Dissolve 1 g in 50 ml of H_2O, add 2 ml of 10% NaOH and 2 ml of Nessler solution.   Any color produced is not darker than that of a blank to which 0.03 mg of NH_3 has been added.

Heavy metals: Dissolve 5 g in 30 ml of H_2O, add 5 ml of 1 N HCl, and dilute to 50 ml.   To 10 ml add 0.015 mg of Pb and dilute to 40 ml (A).   Then add to A and to the remaining 40 ml (B) 10 ml of H_2S. B is no darker than A.

Iron: Dissolve 2 g in 20 ml of water, add 5 ml of HCl, and dilute to 50 ml.   Add about 50 mg of ammonium persulfate and 3 ml of ammonium thiocyanate solution and mix.   Any resulting red color is not darker than that of a blank to which 0.01 mg of Fe has been added.

Sodium: Ignite 1 g, dissolve the residue in 20 ml of H_2O, neutralize with HCl, and filter.   The filtrate, tested on a platinum wire, imparts no pronounced yellow color to a colorless flame.

Note: The sodium may be quantitatively determined by Flame Photometry.

Assay: Potassium citrate may be assayed, after drying at 180°–200° to constant weight, by the general methods for Alkali Salts of Organic Acids, page 564.   One ml of 0.1 N acid = 0.01021 g $K_3C_6H_5O_7$ (anhydrous).   When so assayed not less than 99.4% and not more than 100.5% should be indicated.

POTASSIUM CYANATE

KCNO; mol. wt. 81.13 CN—32.08%; N—17.27%.

White crystalline.   Soluble in about 10 parts of cold water; soluble in methanol, dioxane, glycol; slightly in ethanol.   Hydrolyzed by H_2O to carbonate and NH_3.

Standards

Assay........................min 96%	Sulfate (SO_4)................max 0.03%
Solubility....................to pass test	Thiocyanate (CNS)...........to pass test
Carbonate (CO_3).............to pass test	Heavy metals (as Pb)........max 0.002%
Chloride (Cl)................max 0.02%	Iron (Fe)...................max 0.002%
Cyanide (CN)...............to pass test	
(max about 0.02%)	

Assay: Dry about 1 g at 105° for 2 hours.   Weigh accurately 0.35–0.40 g of the dried sample and dissolve in 30 ml of cold water.   Make the solution slightly acid (to litmus paper) with 10% HNO_3 and immediately transfer to a 200-ml volumetric flask.   Slowly add, while shaking the flask, 50.0 ml of 0.1 N $AgNO_3$.   Now add 1 ml of HNO_3, dilute with water to the 200-ml mark and mix thoroughly.   Filter through a dry filter into a dry flask.   Titrate the excess of $AgNO_3$ in 100 ml of the filtrate with 0.1 N thiocyanate and ferric ammonium sulfate solution as indicator. The percent of KCNO is calculated by the formula:

$$(V - (E \times 2) \times 0.008113)/\text{Wt} \times 100,$$

where V is the volume of the 0.1 N AgNO$_3$ added, E is the volume of 0.1 N thiocyanate consumed in the titration of excess of AgNO$_3$, 0.008112 is the KCNO equivalent per ml of 0.1 N AgNO$_3$, and Wt is the weight of the sample.

Solubility: Solution of 3 g in 50 ml of warm water is complete, clear and colorless.

Carbonate: To a solution of 1.0 g in 20 ml of water add 2 ml of calcium chloride and heat gently for 1 minute. Not more than a slight turbidity is produced.

Chloride: Dissolve 0.5 g in 25 ml of water in a small flask. Add 5 ml of 25% H$_2$SO$_4$ and gently boil the solution until the volume is reduced to about 15 ml. Add 25 ml of water and re-evaporate to 20 ml. Cool and dilute to 50 ml. To 10 ml of the solution add 1 ml of HNO$_3$ and AgNO$_3$. Any resulting turbidity is not greater than that in a control made with 0.01 mg Cl.

Cyanide: Dissolve 0.2 g in 10 ml of water. Add about 50 mg of sodium fluoride, 5 drops of a saturated solution of ferrous ammonium sulfate and 1 ml of 1 N NaOH. Mix and bring to a boil. Immediately add 25% H$_2$SO$_4$ until the precipitated ferrous hydroxide is dissolved; then add 5 more drops of the H$_2$SO$_4$. No pronounced blue or blue-green color is produced in 2 minutes.

Sulfate: Dissolve 0.5 g in 20 ml of water. Make the solution slightly acid with 1 N HCl, add 1 ml excess of the acid and 2 ml of BaCl$_2$ and mix well. Any turbidity produced in 15 minutes is not greater than that produced in a control containing 0.15 mg SO$_4$.

Thiocyanate: To a solution of 0.2 g in 25 ml of water and 2 ml of HCl and 2 drops of ferric ammonium sulfate solution. No red color of ferric thiocyanate is produced.

Heavy metals: Dissolve 4.0 g in water to make 40.0 ml. To 10 ml of the solution add 0.02 mg of Pb and 2 ml of 1 N acetic acid and dilute to 40 ml (A). To the remaining 30 ml add 3 ml of 1 N acetic acid and dilute to 40 ml. (B). Then to each add 10 ml of H$_2$S. B is not darker than A.

Iron: Dissolve 1.0 g in 20 ml of water and add 0.5 g of hydroxylamine hydrochloride. Add to the solution 5 ml of o-phenanthroline solution reagent for iron, mix and allow to stand for 1 hour. Any resulting color is not darker than that produced by treating 0.02 mg of Fe with the same quantities of reagents and in the same final volume as used with the sample.

POTASSIUM CYANIDE

KCN; mol. wt. 65.12; K—60.05%; CN—39.95%.

Colorless or white fragments or granules. Soluble in water; slightly soluble in alcohol. Decomposed by weak acids, even carbon dioxide; also affected by sunlight. *It is extremely poisonous! Keep in tightly closed containers, protected from light, moisture and acid fumes.*

Standards

Assay.................min 97% KCN	Sulfide (S″)................max 0.001%
Chloride (Cl)................max 0.20%	Thiocyanate (SCN)..........max 0.02%
Ferrocyanide [Fe(CN)$_6$].......max 0.05%	Lead (Pb)................max 0.0002%
Phosphate (PO$_4$)...........max 0.005%	Sodium (Na)................to pass test
Sulfate (SO$_4$)................max 0.02%	(max about 0.3%)

Caution: *Because of the extremely poisonous nature of cyanides, all tests are to be made under a hood with a strong draft. Pipettes should not be used for measuring solutions.*

Assay: Weigh accurately about 0.5 g and dissolve in 30 ml of water. Add 2 drops of potassium iodide and 1 ml of NH_4OH, and titrate with 0.1 N silver nitrate to a slight permanent turbidity. One ml of 0.1 N silver nitrate = 0.01302 g KCN, log 11461.

$$2KCN + AgNO_3 \rightarrow KAg(CN)_2 + KNO_3$$

Solution S: Dissolve 10.0 g in sufficient H_2O to make 200 ml; filter if necessary.

Chloride: Measure with a graduated cylinder 30 ml of *Solution S* into a 100-ml volumetric flask and dilute with 30 ml of water. Add 30 ml of formaldehyde, mix well, and allow to stand for 10 minutes. Then add 5 ml of nitric acid and exactly 5 ml of 0.1 N silver nitrate. Dilute with water to the 100-ml mark and mix well. Filter through a dry filter, rejecting the first filterful, and titrate the excess of silver nitrate in 50 ml of filtrate with 0.1 N ammonium thiocyanate, using 2 ml of ferric ammonium sulfate as indicator. Not less than 2.4 ml of the thiocyanate is required.

Ferrocyanide: To 20 ml of *Solution S* add 3 ml of HCl and 1 drop of freshly prepared ferric chloride solution. Any blue or green color produced in 30 minutes is not deeper than that in a control made with 1 mg of potassium ferrocyanide [= 0.5 mg Fe(CN)$_6$] and the same quantities of the reagents and in the same final volume as with the sample.

Phosphate: To 10 ml of *Solution S* add 3 ml of HCl and evaporate on the steam bath *under the hood* to dryness. Add 3 ml of HCl and 5 ml of water and re-evaporate to dryness. Dissolve the residue in 20 ml of water, add 2 ml of 25% H_2SO_4 and 1 ml of phosphate reagents **A** and **B**, and heat at 60° for 10 minutes. Any blue color produced is not darker than that in a control made with 0.025 mg of PO$_4$, 2 ml of 25% H_2SO_4, the same volumes of the phosphate reagents, and in the same final volume as with the sample.

Sulfate: Evaporate 10 ml of *Solution S* with 3 ml of HCl to dryness on the steam bath *under the hood*. Take up in 5 ml of water and re-evaporate with 2 ml of HCl. Dissolve the residue in 10 ml of water, add 1 ml of 0.1 N HCl and 2 ml of BaCl$_2$. If a turbidity is produced it is not greater than that produced when 0.10 mg of SO$_4$ in 10 ml of H_2O is treated with the same quantities of 0.1 N HCl and BaCl$_2$ as the sample.

Sulfide: Dissolve 1 g in 20 ml of H_2O and divide into two equal portions. To one portion add 3 drops of sodium plumbite solution (made by adding NaOH solution to 10% lead acetate until the precipitate redissolves). The solution exhibits no more color than the portion not treated with sodium plumbite solution.

Thiocyanate: To 20 ml of *Solution S, under hood*, add 4 ml of HCl and 4 drops of ferric ammonium sulfate. The solution is no more colored than a blank.

Lead: Dissolve 1.2 g in 10 ml of water in a separatory funnel. Add 5 ml of ammonium citrate solution, 2 ml of hydroxylamine hydrochloride solution for dithizone test, and 2 drops of phenol red; make the solution alkaline, if necessary, by the addition of NH_4OH. Add 5 ml of dithizone solution; shake gently but well for 1 minute and allow to separate. The color of the chloroform layer has no more red hue than that of a control made with 0.002 mg of Pb and 0.2 g of the sample dissolved in 10 ml of water and treated exactly as the solution of the 1.2-g sample.

Sodium: To about 0.1 g add 1 ml of HCl and evaporate to dryness *under hood.* The solution of the residue in 10 ml of H_2O tested on a platinum wire imparts no pronounced yellow color to a colorless flame.

A quantitative estimation of the sodium content of this reagent may be made either by (1) Flame Photometry or (2) gravimetrically by precipitation with uranyl magnesium or uranyl zinc acetate.

The solution for (1) is prepared by diluting 5 ml of *Solution S* (0.25 g) with 10 ml of water, cooling the solution in ice water, then gradually *adding under a hood with good ventilation,* 10 ml of HCl and *evaporating under the hood* to dryness. The residue of KCl is dissolved in water and 1 ml of HCl to 100 ml.

For the determination of the sodium by method (2) most of the potassium has to be removed. This is effected as follows: dissolve 1.0 g of sample in 15 ml of water, in a beaker, cool the solution in ice (to moderate the evolution of the HCN); then *under a well ventilated hood* gradually add 10 ml of 80% perchloric acid. After all the $HClO_4$ has been added, the solution is heated on the steam bath for 1–2 hours, *under the hood,* then cooled in ice water, and the potassium perchlorate is filtered off and washed with 20 ml of ice cold water. The filtrate and washings are evaporated nearly to dryness (to remove excess of $HClO_4$), 10 ml of ice cold H_2O is added while stirring, made slightly alkaline with NH_4OH, then 10 ml of alcohol is added and mixed. After allowing to stand for 15 minutes it is filtered and washed with a few ml of alcohol. The filtrate and washings are evaporated to about 10 ml and treated as described in paragragh (b) page 578, Precipitation as the Triple Acetate.

POTASSIUM DICHROMATE

$K_2Cr_2O_7$; mol. wt. 294.22; K—26.58%; CrO_3—67.98%; active O—16.32%; Cr—35.36%.

Dark orange-red crystals or granules. Soluble in 10 parts of water; insoluble in alcohol.

The reagent grade of this chemical is substantially 100% pure.

Standards

Insoluble and Ammonium hydroxide precipitate......max 0.005%	Sulfate (SO_4)................max 0.003%
	Calcium (Ca)................max 0.003%
Chloride (Cl)................max 0.002%	Sodium (Na)...........max about 0.02%

Insoluble and Ammonium hydroxide precipitate: Dissolve 10 g in 100 ml of warm H_2O, make alkaline with NH_4OH, and heat on the steam bath for 30 minutes. Should an insoluble residue remain, filter (retain filtrate), wash it well with hot H_2O, and dry at 105°. Its weight does not exceed 0.5 mg.

Chloride: Dissolve 2 g in 40 ml of water, add 20 ml of HNO_3, and divide into two equal portions. Heat both portions to 50°, then to one portion add 1 ml of $AgNO_3$ and to the other portion 1 ml of water. At the end of 5 minutes both portions are equally clear.

Sulfate: Dissolve 5 g in 150 ml of water. If any insoluble matter is present, filter through a filter which has been washed with diluted HCl (1+20). Add 15 ml of a solution, made by dissolving 1 g of $BaCl_2$ in 100 ml of H_2O and adding 2 ml of HCl, mix, and allow to stand overnight. The solution is clear and no precipitate is visible.

Calcium: To the filtrate from *Insoluble* add 2 ml of NH_4OH and 10 ml of ammonium oxalate and let stand overnight. Filter any precipitate present, wash well and ignite. After cooling, add a few drops of H_2SO_4 and re-ignite. The weight of the residue ($CaSO_4$) does not exceed 1.0 mg.

Sodium: A 10% solution in warm water, tested on a platinum wire, imparts no pronounced yellow color to a colorless flame.

POTASSIUM FERRICYANIDE

$K_3Fe(CN)_6$; mol. wt. 329.25; K—35.60%; $Fe(CN)_6$—64.60%; CN—47.41%.

Bright, ruby-red crystals. Soluble in about 2.5 parts of water; insoluble in alcohol. Reduced to ferrocyanide by light and reducing agents. *Keep protected from light.*

Standards

Insoluble..................max 0.010%	Ferrocyanide [Fe(CN)$_6$]........max 0.05%
Chloride (Cl)...............max 0.010%	*Assay*........................min 99%
Sulfate (SO$_4$)...........max about 0.01%	

Insoluble: Dissolve 10 g in 100 ml of H_2O and heat on the steam bath for 15 minutes. Filter any undissolved matter, wash it with water and dry at 105°. The insoluble residue does not exceed 1.0 mg.

Chloride: Dissolve 1 g in 75 ml of H_2O, add a solution of 1.3 g of chloride-free cupric sulfate in 25 ml H_2O, mix, and let stand for 15 minutes. Decant 20 ml of the clear liquid, add to it 2 ml of HNO_3 and 1 ml of $AgNO_3$. Any turbidity produced is not greater than that in a control made with 0.02 mg of Cl, 2 ml of HNO_3, 1 ml of $AgNO_3$, and sufficient cupric sulfate to match the color of the test with the sample.

Sulfate: Dissolve 5 g in 100 ml of H_2O without heating, filter, and add to the filtrate 5 drops of glacial acetic acid and 5 ml of $BaCl_2$. No turbidity is produced in 10 minutes.

Ferrocyanide: Mix 400 ml of H_2O with 20 ml of 10% H_2SO_4 and add, dropwise, 0.1 N permanganate until the pink color persists for 30 seconds. Dissolve in the solution 4 g of the sample and add 0.1 ml of the permanganate. The solution has a pink color in comparison with a similar solution of the sample without permanganate.

Assay: Potassium ferricyanide may be assayed as follows: Weigh accurately about 0.7 g and dissolve in 50 ml of water in a 300-ml glass-stoppered flask. Dissolve

3 g of potassium iodide in the solution, add 1 drop of glacial acetic acid, and a solution of 1.5 g of zinc sulfate in 10 ml of H_2O (see Note).   Stopper, mix, allow to stand for 30 minutes, then titrate the liberated iodine with 0.1 N sodium thiosulfate, using starch toward the end.   One ml of 0.1 N thiosulfate = 0.03292 g $K_3Fe(CN)_6$, log 51746.

$$(1)\quad 2K_3Fe(CN)_6 + 2KI \rightarrow 2K_4Fe(CN)_6 + 2I$$
$$(2)\quad 2I + 2Na_2S_2O_3 \rightarrow Na_2S_4O_6 + 2NaI$$

Note: The zinc serves to combine with the ferrocyanide as soon as the latter is formed, and by virtue of the insolubility of zinc ferrocyanide, the $Fe(CN)_6$ is removed from reaction and equation (1) is permitted to go to completion.

POTASSIUM FERROCYANIDE

$K_4Fe(CN)_6 \cdot 3H_2O$; mol. wt. 422.39; anhydrous—87.20%; H_2O—12.8%; $Fe(CN)_6$ —50.18%; CN—36.96%.

Yellow crystals or granules.   Soluble in 5 parts of water; insoluble in alcohol. Potassium ferrocyanide solutions rapidly deteriorate on exposure to air and light. In the presence of about 0.2% Na_2CO_3, however, the solutions are stable for several months.

Standards

Insoluble................max 0.010%	Sulfate (SO_4).........max about 0.010%
Chloride (Cl)..............max 0.010%	*Assay* (anhydrous basis).........min 99%

Insoluble: Dissolve 10 g in 100 ml of H_2O and heat on steam bath for 15 minutes. Filter any undissolved residue, wash it with water, and dry at 105°.   The weight of the insoluble residue does not exceed 1.0 mg.

Chloride: Dissolve 1 g in 75 ml of H_2O, add a solution of 13 g of chloride-free cupric sulfate in 25 ml of H_2O, mix, and let stand for 15 minutes.   Decant 20 ml of the clear liquid, add to it 2 ml of HNO_3 and 1 ml of $AgNO_3$.   Any resulting turbidity is not greater than that in a control made with 0.02 mg of Cl, 2 ml of HNO_3, 1 ml of $AgNO_3$, and sufficient cupric sulfate to match the color of the test with the sample.

Sulfate: Dissolve 5 g in 100 ml of H_2O without heating, filter, and add 5 drops of glacial acetic acid, and 5 ml of $BaCl_2$.   No turbidity is produced in 10 minutes.

Assay: Powder or crush well large crystals and dry at 100° to constant weight, or preferably at 70°–80° in a vacuum.   Weigh accurately about 1 g of the dried reagent and dissolve it in 200 ml of water in a porcelain dish.   Add 10 ml of H_2SO_4 and titrate with 0.1 N of potassium permanganate to slight reddish color.   One ml of the permanganate = 0.03683 g $K_4Fe(CN)_6$, log 56620.

$$5K_4Fe(CN)_6 + KMnO_4 + 4H_2SO_4 \rightarrow 5K_3Fe(CN)_6 + MnSO_4 + 3K_2SO_4$$

POTASSIUM FLUORIDE

$KF \cdot 2H_2O$; mol. wt. 94.13; anhydrous—61.72%; K—41.54%; F—20.18%.

White, crystalline powder; deliquescent.   Soluble in about 1 part of water; insoluble in alcohol.   The aqueous solution corrodes glass. *It is poisonous!   Keep in tightly closed containers.*

Standards

Insoluble.....................max 0.02%	Sulfite (SO_2)................max 0.005%
Free acid (as HF).............max 0.05%	Heavy metals (as Pb).........max 0.002%
Free alkali (as K_2CO_3).......max 0.15%	Iron (Fe)...................max 0.001%
Silicofluoride (K_2SiF_6)........max 0.10%	Sodium (Na)..........max about 0.02%
Chloride (Cl)................max 0.010%	*Assay*.......................min 98.5%
Sulfate (SO_4)...............max 0.020%	

Insoluble: Dissolve 5 g in 100 ml of H_2O in a platinum dish and heat on steam bath for 30 minutes. Filter any insoluble residue, wash it with water, and dry at 105°. Its weight does not exceed 1.0 mg.

Free acid; Free alkali: Dissolve 2 g in 40 ml of H_2O in a platinum dish, add 10 ml of saturated aqueous potassium nitrate solution, cool to 0°, and add 3 drops of phenolphthalein. If no pink color is produced, titrate with 0.1 N NaOH until a pink color persists for 15 seconds; not more than 0.5 ml of the NaOH is required. If a pink color is produced, titrate with 0.1 N HCl, stirring gently, until discharged; not more than 0.25 ml of the HCl is required (retain the solution).

Silicofluoride: Boil the solution from the preceding test and titrate while hot with 0.1 N NaOH to a permanent pink color. Not more than 0.4 ml of the NOH is required.

Chloride: Dissolve 0.3 g in 20 ml of H_2O, add 0.2 g of boric acid, 1 ml of HNO_3, and 1 ml of $AgNO_3$. Any turbidity produced is not greater than that in a blank to which 0.03 mg of Cl has been added.

Sulfate: Evaporate 0.5 g of the sample and 20 mg of sodium carbonate in platinum to dryness three times with 5-ml portions of HCl. Prepare a control by evaporating 20 mg of sodium carbonate with 15 ml of HCl and 0.1 mg of SO_4 to dryness on the steam bath. Dissolve the residue from each in 10 ml of water, filter if necessary, and to each add 1 ml of 0.1 N HCl and 1 ml of $BaCl_2$. Any turbidity in 15 minutes in the solution of the sample is not greater than that in the control.

Sulfite: Dissolve 6 g in 150 ml of H_2O, add 2 ml of HCl and 1 ml of starch solution, and titrate immediately with 0.1 N iodine. Not more than 0.1 ml of the iodine is required to produce a blue color.

Heavy metals: Dissolve 2 g in water to make 40 ml. To 10 ml add 0.02 mg of Pb and dilute to 40 ml (A). Dilute the remaining 30 ml to 40 ml (B). Then to each add 10 ml of H_2S. B is not darker than A.

Iron: Dissolve 1 g of sample in 15 ml of water, add 2 ml of HCl, and boil for 2 minutes. Cool, add 50 mg of ammonium persulfate and 15 ml of butanolic potassium thiocyanate solution, and shake well for about 30 seconds. Any red color in the butanol layer is not darker than that of a blank to which 0.01 mg of Fe has been added.

Sodium: A 10% solution, tested on a platinum wire, imparts no distinct yellow color to a colorless flame.

Assay: Potassium fluoride may be assayed as follows: Weigh accurately about 2 g of the sample previously dried at 120°, dissolve it in H_2O, and dilute to exactly 250 ml. Transfer 25 ml into a glass-stoppered flask, dilute with 25 ml of H_2O, add 1 ml of 0.05% sodium alizarin sulfonate, and adjust the acidity with 0.02 N NaOH until the pink color of the solution is just discharged. Add 0.4 ml of 1 N acetic acid and, while continuously stirring, titrate slowly with 0.1 N thorium nitrate to a permanent pink color.   One ml of 0.1 N thorium nitrate = 0.009413 g $KF \cdot 2H_2O$, log 97373.

Potassium fluoride may also be assayed gravimetrically by the method described under Sodium Fluoride.

POTASSIUM HYDROXIDE

KOH; mol. wt. 56.11; K—69.69%; K_2O—83.95%.

White pellets or sticks.   Rapidly deliquesces in the air and absorbs carbon dioxide.   Soluble in 1 part of water; soluble in alcohol.   When dissolved in water much heat is liberated.   *It is very caustic to organic matter.   Handle with rubber gloves.   Keep in tightly closed containers.*

Standards

Assay...................min 85.0% KOH		Ammonium hydroxide	
Carbonate (as K_2CO_3)..........max 2.0%		precipitate and Silica.......max 0.020%	
Chloride (Cl)...............max 0.010%		Silica (SiO_2)................max 0.010%	
Nitrogen compounds (as N)...max 0.001%		Heavy metals (as Ag).......max 0.001%	
Phosphate (PO_4)..........max 0.0005%		Iron (Fe)..................max 0.001%	
Sulfate (SO_4)..............max 0.003%		Nickel (Ni)................max 0.001%	
		Sodium (Na)...............max 0.05%	

Solution S: Weigh quickly 50 g of sample to within 0.1 g, dissolve it in carbon dioxide-free water, cool, and dilute to exactly 500 ml.

Assay; Carbonate: Dilute exactly 25 ml of *Solution* S (2.5-g sample) with 175 ml of cold, carbon dioxide-free water in a flask.   Add 5 ml of barium chloride stopper, and allow to stand for 5 minutes; then add 3 drops of phenolphthalein and titrate with 1 N HCl to the disappearance of the pink color.   The acid consumed in this titration indicates the KOH content.   One ml of 1 N HCl = 0.05611 g KOH, log 74904.   Now add 2 drops of methyl orange and titrate with the HCl to a permanent pink color.   The acid consumed with the methyl orange titration represents the carbonate.   One ml of 1 N HCl = 0.06910 g K_2CO_3, log 83948.

Chloride: Dilute 2.0 ml of *Solution* S with 15 ml of water, add 1 ml of HNO_3, cool, and add 1 ml of $AgNO_3$.   Any turbidity produced is not greater than that in the blank to which 0.02 mg of Cl has been added.

Nitrogen compounds: Dilute 20 ml of *Solution* S contained in a suitable distillation flask with 40 ml of ammonia-free water, add 1 g of powdered Devarda metal or 0.5 g of fine aluminum wire in small pieces and let stand for 2 hours protected from loss or access of ammonia.   Slowly distill 40 ml into 5 ml of water containing 1 drop of dilute HCl, then add to the distillate 1 ml of *Solution S* and 2 ml of Nessler solution.   The color produced is not darker than that produced by treating 0.02 mg of nitrogen (0.08 mg NH_4Cl), and 10 ml of *Solution S* in the same manner as the 30 ml of *Solution S*.

Phosphate: Render 20 ml of *Solution* S slightly acid with 25% H_2SO_4, then add 2 ml excess of the acid and evaporate in platinum to incipient sulfuric fumes. *Cautiously* add 20 ml of H_2O, filter, add to the filtrate 1 ml each of phosphate solutions **A** and **B**, and heat at 60° for 10 minutes. Any blue color produced is not darker than that of a control made with 0.02 mg of PO_4, 2 ml of 25% H_2SO_4, the same quantities of the phosphate reagent in the same final volume as used with the sample.

Sulfate: To 30 ml of *Solution S* add 8 ml of hydrochloric acid and evaporate to dryness on the steam bath. Dissolve the residue in 25 ml of water and re-evaporate to dryness on the steam bath. Dissolve the residue in 20 ml of warm water, add 1 ml of 0.1 N HCl and 2 ml of $BaCl_2$. Any turbidity produced in 20 minutes is not greater than that in a control made with 0.1 mg of SO_4, 1 ml of 0.1 N HCl, and 2 ml of $BaCl_2$ in the same volume as used with the sample.

Ammonium hydroxide precipitate and Silica: To 100 ml of *Solution S* cautiously add 12 ml of H_2SO_4 previously mixed with 15 ml of water, evaporate, and heat to evolution of copious sulfuric fumes for 2 to 3 minutes. Cool, dissolve the residue in 130 ml of hot water, and make just alkaline to methyl red with NH_4OH. Heat to boiling, filter if a precipitate is present; wash it with hot water and ignite in a platinum crucible to constant weight. The weight of the ignited precipitate is not more than 2.0 mg. Add to the weighed precipitate 5 drops each of H_2SO_4 and hydrofluoric acid, evaporate in platinum and ignite to constant weight. The loss in weight, SiO_2, is not more than 1.0 mg.

Note: A colorimetric procedure for the determination of small amounts of silica (5 to 100 micrograms) in alkali carbonates and hydroxides was reported by Kenyon and Bewick, *Anal. Chem.* **25**, 145 (1953). The method is based on the formation of the complex silica-molybdenum blue by the interaction of the silica with ammonium molybdate and a reducing agent.

Heavy metals: To 5.0 ml of *Solution S* add 15 ml of HNO_3. Evaporate on the steam bath to dryness, dissolve the residue in 40 ml of water, add a drop of phenolphthalein solution, then add 0.1 N NaOH until a pink color is just produced. Add 2 ml of 1 N acetic acid, and dilute to 50 ml. To 10 ml add 0.03 mg of Ag, and dilute to 40 ml (A). Then add to A, and to the remaining 40 ml (B), 10 ml of H_2S. B is not darker than A.

Iron: To 10 ml of *Solution S* add 3 ml of HCl and dilute to 50 ml. Add 30 mg of ammonium persulfate and 3 ml of ammonium thiocyanate. Any resulting red color is not darker than that of a blank to which 0.01 mg of Fe has been added.

Nickel: Dilute 20 ml of *Solution S* with 30 ml of water, neutralize with HCl and dilute to 80 ml. Make just alkaline to litmus paper (*p*H 8) with 10% NH_3, then add 5 ml of bromine water, 5 ml of dimethylglyoxime solution, 5 ml of 10% NaOH and dilute to 100 ml. Any resulting red color is not darker than that of a control made with 0.02 mg of nickel (Ni), the same quantities of the reagents as used in the test and in the same final volume.

Sodium: Neutralize 1 ml of *Solution S* with HCl, dilute to 20 ml, and test on platinum wire in a colorless flame. No distinct yellow color is imparted to the flame.

Note: The quantitative evaluation of the sodium content is most advantageously accomplished by Flame Photometry. If, however, this method, owing to lack of the necessary equipment or other reason, is not available, the sodium can be quantitatively determined by the uranyl zinc (or magnesium) acetate technique (page 577).

POTASSIUM IODATE

KIO_3; mol. wt. 214.01; K—18.27%; I—59.30%; active oxogen—18.7%.
White crystals or powder.   Soluble in 15 parts of water; insoluble in alcohol.

Standards

Insoluble..................max 0.005%	Sulfate (SO_4)...............max 0.003%
Neutrality...................to pass test	Heavy metals (as Pb).......max 0.0005%
Chlorate (ClO_3).........max about 0.01%	Iron (Fe)..................max 0.001%
Chloride and Bromide (as Cl)..max 0.010%	Sodium (Na)...........max about 0.02%
Iodide (I)..................max 0.002%	*Assay*....................99.8%–100.3%
Nitrogen compounds (as N)...max 0.003%	

Insoluble: Dissolve 10 g in 300 ml of hot H_2O and heat on the steam bath for 1 hour.   Filter any insoluble residue, wash it with hot water, and dry at 105°. Its weight does not exceed 0.5 mg.

Neutrality: Dissolve 3 g in 40 ml of warm H_2O and add 3 drops of phenolphthalein; no pink color is produced.   Now add 0.05 ml of 0.1 N NaOH; a pink color is produced.

Chlorate: To 2 g of the powdered sample add 2 ml of H_2SO_4.   The salt remains white and no odor or gas is evolved.

Chloride and Bromide: Dissolve 0.5 g in 15 ml of warm water, add 12 ml of sulfurous acid, and gently boil for 3 minutes.   Cool, add 5 ml of NH_4OH and 10 ml of H_2O, then slowly add, while stirring, 10 ml of 5% $AgNO_3$.   Filter, wash with about 10 ml of water, dilute filtrate to 100 ml, and mix.   To 20 ml add 2 ml of HNO_3.   Any resulting turbidity is not greater than that of a control made with 0.01 mg of chloride (Cl), 1 ml each of NH_4OH and $AgNO_3$ solution, and 2 ml of HNO_3.

Iodide: Dissolve 2 g in 40 ml of H_2O, and add 1 ml of chloroform and 1 ml of 1 N H_2SO_4.   The chloroform acquires no violet color in 1 minute.

Nitrogen compounds: Dissolve 1 g in 60 ml of H_2O, add 0.5 g powdered Devarda metal or 0.5 g of aluminum wire in small pieces and 10 ml of 10% NaOH. Allow to stand for 2 hours protected from loss or access of NH_3, then slowly distill about 40 ml into 5 ml of water containing 1 drop of dilute HCl.   Dilute to 50 ml; add 1 ml of 10% NaOH and 2 ml of Nessler solution.   The color is not darker than that produced by treating 0.02 mg of nitrogen (0.08 mg of NH_4Cl) in the same manner as the sample.

Sulfate: To 3 g of the sample add 20 mg of sodium carbonate and 10 ml of HCl, and evaporate on the steam bath to dryness.   Repeat the evaporation with 5 ml of HCl.   Dissolve the residue in 10 ml of H_2O, filter if necessary, and add to the filtrate 1 ml of 0.1 N HCl and 2 ml of $BaCl_2$.   Any resulting turbidity after 15 minutes is not greater than that in a control made as follows: Evaporate 20 mg of sodium carbonate and 15 ml of HCl to dryness.   Dissolve the residue and 0.1 mg of SO_4 in 10 ml of H_2O, and add 1 ml of 0.1 N HCl and 2 ml of $BaCl_2$.

Heavy metals: To 3 g of the sample add 10 ml of hot water and 10 ml of HCl (*A*).   To 0.5 g of sample add 15 ml of HCl and 0.01 mg of Pb(*B*).   Evaporate both to dryness on the steam bath. Add to (*A*) 5 ml of HCl and re-evaporate to dryness. Dissolve the residues in 20 ml of water, each, add a drop of phenolphthalein, and neutralize with 1 *N* NaOH. Add to each 1 ml of 1 *N* acetic acid, dilute to 25 ml, and add 5 ml of H_2S. *A* is not darker than *B*.

Iron: To 1 g of sample add 5 ml of H_2O and 5 ml of HCl and evaporate to dryness on steam bath. Repeat the evaporation with 5 ml of HCl. Prepare a control by adding to 0.01 mg of Fe, 10 ml of HCl, and evaporating on the steam bath to dryness. Take up each in 2 ml of HCl and water to make 50 ml. Add to each 30 mg of ammonium persulfate and 3 ml of ammonium thiocyanate. Any red color in the sample solution is not darker than that in the control.

Sodium: A 5% solution in hot H_2O, tested on a platinum wire, imparts no distinct yellow color to a colorless flame.

Assay: Potassium iodate may be assayed as Potassium Bromate. One ml of 0.1 *N* thiosulfate = 0.003567 g KIO_3, log 55230. When so assayed not less than 99.8% and not more than 100.3% should be indicated.

POTASSIUM IODIDE

KI; mol. wt. 166.01; K—23.55%; I—76.45%.

Colorless or white crystals or granules; slightly deliquescent. On long exposure to air it becomes yellowish from the formation of free iodine. Soluble in 1 part of water or in 20 parts of alcohol. *Keep in well-closed containers.*

Standards

Insoluble.................max 0.005%	Barium (Ba)...............max 0.002%
Drying loss.................max 0.20%	Calcium, Magnesium, and
Alkalinity (as K_2CO_3)........max 0.040%	NH₄OH precipitate........max 0.005%
Chloride and Bromide (as Cl)...max 0.01%	Heavy metals (as Pb).......max 0.0005%
Iodate (IO_3)........max about 0.0003%	Iron (Fe).................max 0.0003%
Nitrogen compounds (as N)...max 0.001%	Sodium (Na)..........max about 0.02%
Phosphate (PO_4)...........max 0.001%	*Assay*.......................min 99%
Sulfate (SO_4)...............max 0.005%	

Insoluble: Dissolve 20 g in 100 ml of H_2O and heat on the steam bath for 30 minutes. Filter any insoluble residue (retain filtrate), wash, and dry at 105°. Its weight does not exceed 1.0 mg.

Drying loss: Rapidly crush the large crystals, weigh accurately about 2 g, and dry at 150° for 6 hours. The loss corresponds to not more than 0.20%.

Alkalinity: A solution of 5 g in 50 ml of H_2O requires not more than 0.3 ml of 0.1 *N* HCl to neutralize it to methyl orange.

Chloride and Bromide: Dissolve 0.75 g of sample in a mixture of 5 ml of NH₄OH and 50 ml of H_2O; add slowly, with constant shaking, 20 ml of a 5% solution of $AgNO_3$. Allow to settle and filter. To 25 ml of filtrate add 3 ml of HNO_3. The turbidity is not greater than that produced by treating 0.25 g of sample and 0.05 mg of Cl in the same manner.

Iodate: Dissolve 1 g in 20 ml of oxygen-free water, add 1 ml of starch solution and 5 drops of 1 *N* H_2SO_4. No blue or violet color is produced in 1 minute.

Nitrogen compounds: Dissolve 2 g in 60 ml of H_2O, add 10 ml of 10% NaOH and 0.5 g of powdered Devarda metal. Allow to stand for 2 hours protected from loss or access of NH_3, then slowly distill 40 ml into 5 ml of water containing 1 drop of dilute HCl. Dilute the distillate to 50 ml and add 1 ml of 10% NaOH and 2 ml of Nessler solution. The resulting color is not darker than that produced by treating 0.02 mg of nitrogen (0.08 mg NH_4Cl) in the same manner as the sample.

Phosphate: Dissolve 2 g in 5 ml of H_2O, add 10 ml of nitric acid and 5 ml of HCl, and evaporate on the steam bath to dryness. Dissolve the residue in 2 ml of H_2O, add 3 ml of 25% H_2SO_4, evaporate and heat to incipient sulfuric fumes. Cool and dilute with H_2O to 20 ml. Add 1 ml each of phosphate reagents **A** and **B** and heat at 60° for 10 minutes. Any blue color produced is not darker than that of a control made with 0.02 mg of PO_4, 2 ml of 25% H_2SO_4, and the same quantities of the phosphate reagents and in the same volume as with the sample.

Sulfate: Dissolve 10 g in 100 ml of H_2O, add 1 ml of HCl, heat to boiling, add 5 ml of $BaCl_2$, and allow to stand overnight. If a precipitate is present, filter, wash until the washings cease to give a reaction for chloride, and ignite. The weight of the $BaSO_4$ so obtained is not more than 1.2 mg.

Barium: Dissolve 2.0 g in 10 ml of water, add 3 drops of glacial acetic acid and filter if necessary. Add 3 ml of a clear 10% of anhydrous Na_2SO_4, shake well and allow to stand for 15 minutes. No turbidity is visible.

Note: The solution may be yellow due to free iodine liberated by oxygen in the water, but this does not interfere with seeing any barium sulfate turbidity. If desired, however, the yellow color may be discharged by the addition of 5–10 mg of ascorbic acid or sodium sulfite.

Calcium, Magnesium, and NH_4OH precipitate: To the filtrate (without the washings) from *Insoluble* add 5 ml of ammonium oxalate, 3 ml of ammonium phosphate, and 20 ml of NH_4OH, and let stand overnight. Filter any precipitate present, wash it with 2.5% NH_3, and ignite. The weight of the ignited precipitate does not exceed 1.0 mg.

Heavy metals: Dissolve 5.0 g in water to 50 ml. To 10 ml add 0.015 mg of Pb ion, 30 mg of ascorbic acid, dilute to 40 ml and add 1 ml of 1 N acetic acid (A). To the remaining 40 ml add 30 mg of ascorbic acid and 1 ml of 1 N acetic acid (B). Then add to each 10 ml of H_2S. B is not darker than A.

Iron: Dissolve 3 g in 15 ml of water, add 3 ml of HCl and 2 ml of 30% H_2O_2 and evaporate to dryness on the steam bath until the iodine is completely volatilized. Dissolve the residue in 20 ml of water, add 2 ml of HCl, dilute to 50 ml and add 3 ml of ammonium thiocyanate. Any red color produced is not darker than that of a blank to which 0.01 mg of Fe has been added.

Sodium: A 10% solution, tested on a platinum wire, imparts no pronounced yellow color to a colorless flame.

Note: The sodium may be quantitatively estimated by Flame Photometry.

Assay: Potassium iodide may be assayed as follows: Weigh accurately about 0.5 g of the dried sample from the test for *Drying loss* and dissolve in 20 ml of H_2O in a glass-stoppered flask. Add 30 ml of HCl and 5 ml of chloroform, cool if necessary, and titrate with 0.05 M potassium iodate until the iodine color disappears from the aqueous layer. Stopper, shake vigorously for 30 seconds, and continue the titration, shaking vigorously after each addition of the iodate, until the iodine color in the chloroform is discharged. One ml of 0.05 M potassium iodate = 0.01660 g KI, log 22011.

$$2KI + KIO_3 + 6HCl \rightarrow 3ICl + 3KCl + 3H_2O$$

POTASSIUM METABISULFITE

Potassium Pyrosulfite

$K_2S_2O_5$; mol. wt. 222.32; K—35.18%; SO_2—57.63%.

Colorless or white crystals, having an odor of sulfur dioxide. Soluble in water, the solution having an acid reaction; insoluble in alcohol. *Keep in tightly closed containers.*

Standards

Assay................min 95.0% $K_2S_2O_5$	Heavy metals (as Pb)........max 0.002%
Insoluble...................max 0.010%	Iron (Fe)...................max 0.002%
Chloride (Cl)...............max 0.010%	Sodium (Na)................max 0.02%
Arsenic (As)................max 2 ppm	

Assay: Crush 1 g of the sample, then weigh accurately about 0.25 g and add it to exactly 50 ml of 0.1 N iodine. Allow to stand for 5 minutes, then add 1 ml of HCl and titrate the excess of iodine with 0.1 N sodium thiosulfate, using starch indicator. One ml of 0.1 N iodine = 0.005558 g $K_2S_2O_5$, log 74492.

Insoluble: Dissolve 10 g in 100 ml of warm H_2O and heat on the steam bath for 1 hour. Filter any undissolved residue, wash with water and dry at 105°. The weight of the insoluble residue does not exceed 1.0 mg.

Chloride: Dissolve 1 g in 10 ml of water, add 2 ml of 30% hydrogen peroxide, allow to stand for 30 minutes, then dilute to 100 ml. To 20 ml add 1 ml of HNO_3 and 1 ml of $AgNO_3$. The turbidity produced is not greater than that in a control made with 0.02 mg of Cl, 0.5 ml of the hydrogen peroxide, 1 ml of HNO_3, and 1 ml of $AgNO_3$ in the same volume as used with the sample.

Arsenic: Dissolve 1 g in 10 ml of H_2O, gradually add 5 ml of HNO_3, then add 3 ml of H_2SO_4, and evaporate to strong fumes. Cool, *cautiously* add 10 ml of water, then test for arsenic by the method described on page 563. The stain produced is not greater than that from 0.002 mg of As.

Solution S: Dissolve 5 g in 20 ml of hot H_2O, add 5 ml of HCl, and evaporate to dryness on the steam bath. Add 10 ml of hot H_2O and 2 ml of HCl and re-evaporate to complete dryness. Dissolve the residue in water and dilute to 50 ml.

Heavy metals: To 5 ml of *Solution S* add 0.02 mg of Pb, 1 ml of 1 N acetic acid, and dilute to 40 ml (A). To 15 ml of *Solution S* add 1 ml of 1 N acetic acid and dilute to 40 ml (B). Then to each add 10 ml of H_2S. B is not darker than A.

Iron: To 10 ml of *Solution S* add 2 ml of HCl and dilute to 50 ml. Add about 50 mg of ammonium persulfate and 3 ml of ammonium thiocyanate, and mix. Any resulting red color is not darker than that of a blank to which 0.01 mg of Fe has been added.

Sodium: A 10% solution tested on a platinum wire imparts no pronounced yellow color to a nonluminous flame.

POTASSIUM NITRATE

KNO_3; mol. wt. 101.10; K—38.67%; NO_3—61.33%; N—13.85%.

Colorless crystals or white granules; slightly hygroscopic. Melts at 339°. Soluble in 3 parts of water; in 500 parts of alcohol.

Standards

Insoluble.....................max 0.005%	Sulfate (SO_4)................max 0.003%
Neutrality....................to pass test	Calcium, Magnesium, and
Total chlorine (Cl)...........max 0.002%	NH_4OH precipitate........max 0.010%
Iodate (IO_3)...............max 0.0005%	Heavy metals (as Pb).......max 0.0005%
Nitrite (NO_2)..............max 0.001%	Iron (Fe)...................max 0.0003%
Phosphate (PO_4)...........max 0.0005%	Sodium (Na)................max 0.02%

Insoluble: Dissolve 20 g in 100 ml of H_2O and heat on steam bath 1 hour. Filter any undissolved matter (retain the filtrate), wash it, and dry at 105°. The weight of the insoluble residue does not exceed 1.0 mg.

Neutrality: To a solution of 5 g in 50 ml of CO_2-free water add 3 drops of phenolphthalein; no pink color is produced. Now titrate with 0.02 N NaOH to the production of a pink color; not more than 0.2 ml of the NaOH is required.

Total chlorine: Ignite 1 g, gently at first, then at low red heat. Cool, dissolve in 20 ml of H_2O, and add 1 ml of HNO_3 and 1 ml of $AgNO_3$. Any turbidity produced is not greater than that in a blank to which 0.02 mg of Cl has been added.

Iodate; Nitrite: Dissolve 1 g in 10 ml of H_2O, add 2 drops of 10% potassium iodide solution, 1 ml of chloroform, and 1 ml of glacial acetic acid; shake gently for 5 minutes. The chloroform is not colored pink or violet.

Phosphate: Dissolve 4 g in 25 ml of water and add 2 ml of 25% H_2SO_4. Add 1 ml each of phosphate reagents **A** and **B** and heat at 60° for 10 minutes. If a blue color is produced, it is not darker than that of a control made with 0.02 mg PO_4, 2 ml of 25% H_2SO_4, the same quantities of the phosphate reagents and in the same final volume as used with the sample.

Sulfate: Evaporate 3 g of the sample and 20 mg of sodium carbonate with 10 ml of H_2O and 10 ml of HCl to dryness. Take up with 10 ml of hot H_2O and re-evaporate to dryness with 5 ml of HCl. Dissolve the residue in 15 ml of H_2O, add 1 ml of 0.1 N HCl and 2 ml of $BaCl_2$, and allow to stand for 20 minutes. Any resulting turbidity is not greater than that in a control made as follows: Evaporate 20 mg of sodium carbonate with 15 ml of HCl to dryness. Dissolve the residue and 0.1 mg of SO_4 in water to make 15 ml and treat the solution with 1 ml of 0.1 N HCl and 2 ml of $BaCl_2$.

Calcium, Magnesium, and NH_4OH precipitate: To the filtrate from *Insoluble* add 5 ml of ammonium oxalate, 2 ml of ammonium phosphate, and 15 ml of NH_4OH; allow to stand overnight. If a precipitate is present, filter, wash with 2.5% NH_3, and ignite. The weight of the ignited precipitate does not exceed 2.0 mg.

Heavy metals: Dissolve 5 g in H_2O to make 50 ml. To 10 ml add 0.015 mg of Pb, dilute to 40 ml, and add 1 ml of 1 N acetic acid (A). To the remaining 40 ml add 1 ml of 1 N acetic acid (B). Then to each add 10 ml of H_2S. B is not darker than A.

Iron: Dissolve 3.0 g in 40 ml of water, add 2 ml of HCl, and dilute to 50 ml. Add about 30 mg of ammonium persulfate and 3 ml of ammonium thiocyanate, and mix. Any resulting red color is not darker than that in a blank to which 0.01 mg of Fe has been added.

Sodium: A 10% solution, tested on a platinum wire, imparts no pronounced yellow color to a colorless flame.

Note: The sodium content may be quantitatively determined by Flame Photometry.

POTASSIUM NITRITE

KNO_2; mol. wt. 85.10; K—45.94%; NO_2—54.06%.

Small, white or yellowish granules, or cylindrical sticks; deliquescent. Soluble in less than 0.5 part water; sparingly soluble in alcohol. *Keep in tightly closed containers.*

Standards

Assay...................min 94% KNO_2	Calcium (Ca)................max 0.010%
Insoluble....................max 0.010%	Heavy metals (as Pb)........max 0.001%
Chloride (Cl)................max 0.010%	Iron (Fe)...................max 0.001%
Sulfate (SO_4)..............max 0.010%	Sodium (Na)..........max about 0.02%

Assay: Weigh accurately about 1.5 g and dissolve in sufficient water to make exactly 100 ml. To 200 ml of water add 5 ml of sulfuric acid and immediately add 0.1 N potassium permanganate until a faint pink color persists for 2 minutes. Disregard this volume of permanganate. Now add 40 ml of the potassium permanganate, mix, and add slowly, with stirring, 10 ml of the potassium nitrite solution from a pipette, holding the tip of the pipette under the surface of the liquid. After 5 minutes add 15 ml of 0.1 N ferrous ammonium sulfate, allow to stand for 5 minutes and titrate the excess of ferrous ammonium sulfate with 0.1 N potassium permanganate. Each ml of 0.1 N permanganate consumed by the nitrite = 0.004255 g KNO_2, log 62890.

$$5KNO_2 + 2KMnO_4 + 3H_2SO_4 \rightarrow 5KNO_3 + K_2SO_4 + 2MnSO_4 + 3H_2O$$

Insoluble: Dissolve 10 g in 100 ml of water and heat on the steam bath for 30 minutes. Filter any undissolved matter, wash, and dry at 105°. The weight of the insoluble residue does not exceed 1.0 mg.

Solution S: Dissolve 10 g in water to make 100 ml.

Chloride: Dilute 2.0 ml of *Solution S* with 10 ml of water and add slowly 1 ml glacial acetic acid. Warm gently until no more gas is evolved, cool, dilute to 20 ml, and add 1 ml of nitric acid and 1 ml of silver nitrate. Any turbidity produced is not greater than that in a blank with 0.02 mg of Cl added.

Sulfate: To 10 ml of *Solution S* add 2 ml of hydrochloric acid and evaporate to dryness on the steam bath. Dissolve the residue in 10 ml of water and add 1 ml of 0.1 N HCl and 2 ml of barium chloride. Any turbidity produced is not greater than that in a control made with 0.1 mg of SO_4, 1 ml of 0.1 N HCl, 2 ml of barium chloride, and in the same volume as used with the sample.

Calcium: To 10 ml of *Solution S* add 1 ml of glacial acetic acid, heat to expel oxides of nitrogen. Cool, dilute to 10 ml, and add 2 ml of ammonium oxalate. Any turbidity produced in 15 minutes is not greater than that in a control made with 0.1 mg of Ca and 2 ml ammonium oxalate and in the same volume as with the sample.

Heavy metals: To 40 ml of *Solution S* add 5 ml of hydrochloric acid and evaporate to dryness on the steam bath. Dissolve the residue in 25 ml of water, add 1 drop of phenolphthalein, neutralize with 0.1 N NaOH and dilute to 40 ml. To 10 ml add 0.02 mg of Pb, 1 ml of 1 N acetic acid, and dilute to 40 ml (*A*). To the remaining 30 ml add 1 ml of 1 N acetic acid and dilute to 40 ml (*B*). Then to each add 10 ml of H_2S. *B* is not darker than *A*.

Iron: To 10 ml of *Solution S* add 3 ml of HCl and evaporate to dryness on the steam bath. Dissolve the residue in 10 ml of H_2O, add 2 ml of HCl and dilute to 50 ml. Add about 30 mg of ammonium persulfate and 3 ml of ammonium thiocyanate, and mix. Any resulting red color is not darker than that in a blank to which 0.01 mg of Fe has been added.

Sodium: A 10% solution, tested on a platinum wire, imparts no pronounced yellow color to a colorless flame.

Note: The sodium content may be quantitatively determined by Flame Photometry.

POTASSIUM OXALATE

$K_2C_2O_4 \cdot H_2O$; mol. wt. 184.24; anhydrous—90.22%; H_2O—9.78%; K—42.45%; hydrated oxalic acid—68.42%.

Colorless or white crystals; efflorescent in dry air. Soluble in 3 parts of water, slightly soluble in alcohol.

Standards

Insoluble.................max 0.010%	Heavy metals (as Pb).......max 0.002%
Acidity (as KHC$_2$O$_4$).........max 0.030%	Iron (Fe)...............max 0.001%
Alkalinity (as K$_2$CO$_3$).......max 0.020%	Sodium (Na)..........max about 0.02%
Chloride (Cl)..............max 0.002%	Substances darkened by
Nitrogen compounds (as N)...max 0.002%	H_2SO_4...................to pass test
Sulfate (SO$_4$)..............max 0.010%	Assay.....................min 99.5%

Insoluble: Dissolve 10 g in 100 ml of water and heat on the steam bath for 30 minutes. Filter any undissolved matter, wash it with water, and dry at 105°. The weight of the insoluble residue does not exceed 1.0 mg.

Acidity; Alkalinity: Dissolve 2.0 g in 100 ml of CO_2-free water. Add 0.2 ml of phenolphthalein and titrate with 0.01 N HCl or with 0.01 N NaOH, as is indicated by the indicator. Not more than 0.5 ml of the 0.01 N HCl, nor more than 0.4 ml of the 0.01 N NaOH is required to discharge a red color if any, or to impart a pink color if colorless.

Chloride: Ignite 1 g and dissolve the residue in 20 ml of water. Neutralize the solution with nitric acid and add 0.5 ml excess of the acid. Filter and add to the filtrate 1 ml of silver nitrate. Any turbidity produced is not greater than that in a blank to which 0.02 mg of Cl has been added.

Nitrogen compounds: Dissolve 1 g in 60 ml of water, add 10 ml of 10% NaOH and 0.5 g of fine aluminium wire in small pieces, and allow to stand 2 hours protected from loss or access of NH_3. Then slowly distill 40 ml into 5 ml of water containing 1 drop of dilute HCl, and add to the distillate 1 ml of 10% NaOH and 2 ml of Nessler solution. Any yellow color produced is not darker than that produced by treating 0.02 mg of nitrogen (0.08 mg NH_4Cl) in the same manner as the sample.

Sulfate: To 1.0 g of sample in a beaker, add 2 ml of water and 2 ml of HNO_3, mix, then add 2 ml of 30% H_2O_2. Cover the beaker and digest on steam bath until the reaction ceases, then remove the cover and evaporate to dryness. Add 5 ml of water and 3 ml of HCl, and re-evaporate to dryness. Dissolve the residue in 10 ml of water, add 1 ml of 1 N HCl, filter if necessary, add 2 ml of $BaCl_2$ and mix well. Any resulting turbidity in 15 minutes is not greater than that produced when 0.1 mg is treated exactly as the sample.

Solution S: Gently ignite 4 g in porcelain. Add to the residue 20 ml of H_2O and 5 ml of nitric acid, and evaporate to dryness on the steam bath. Add 20 ml of H_2O and re-evaporate. Dissolve the residue in 30 ml of H_2O, filter, add 1 drop of phenolphthalein, neutralize with 1 N NaOH, and dilute to 40 ml.

Heavy metals: To 5 ml of *Solution S* add 0.02 mg of Pb, 1 ml of 1 N acetic acid, and dilute to 40 ml (A).   To 15 ml of *Solution S* add 1 ml of 1 N acetic acid and dilute to 40 ml (B).   Then to each add 10 ml of H_2S. B is not darker than A.

Iron: To 10 ml of *Solution S* add 2 ml of HCl and dilute to 50 ml.   Add 30 mg of ammonium persulfate and 3 ml of ammonium thiocyanate, and mix. Any resulting red color is not darker than that of a control made with 0.01 mg of Fe, the same quantities of the reagents and in the same final volume as with the sample.

Sodium: Ignite 1 g in platinum and dissolve the residue in 10 ml of 10% HCl. The solution, tested on a platinum wire, imparts no pronounced yellow color to a colorless flame.

Note: The sodium content may be quantitatively determined by Flame Photometry.

Substances darkened by sulfuric acid: In a recently ignited test tube heat 1 g with 10 ml of H_2SO_4 to fumes of SO_3. Not more than a slight brownish tinge is produced.

Assay: Potassium oxalate may be assayed by the following method: Weigh accurately about 2.5 g, dissolve in water, and dilute to exactly 250 ml. Dilute 25 ml of the solution with 75 ml of water, add 20 ml of 25% sulfuric acid, then add slowly 20 ml of 0.1 N potassium permanganate. Now heat to 70° and complete the titration with the permanganate until a pale pink color persists for 15 seconds. One ml of 0.1 N permanganate = 0.009212 g $K_2C_2O_4 \cdot H_2O$, log 96435.

POTASSIUM PERCHLORATE

$KClO_4$; mol. wt. 138.55 K—28.22%; Cl—25.59%; O—46.19%.

Colorless or white crystals. Soluble in 65 parts of cold water, in 15 parts of boiling water, in about 4000 parts of alcohol.

Standards

Insoluble . . . . max 0.010%	Calcium (Ca) . . . . max 0.01%
Chloride (Cl) . . . . max 0.003%	Heavy metals (as Pb) . . . . max 0.001%
Chloride and Chlorate (as Cl) . . max 0.005%	Iron (Fe) . . . . max 0.001%
Chlorate and Nitrate . . . . max 0.002%	Sodium (Na) . . . . max about 0.02%
Nitrogen compounds (as N) . . . max 0.002%	Assay . . . . min 99%
Sulfate (SO_4) . . . . max 0.005%	

Insoluble: Dissolve 10 g in 200 ml of hot water, filter any insoluble residue wash it with hot water, and dry at 105°. Its weight is not more than 1.0 mg.

Chloride: Dissolve 0.5 g in 20 ml of hot H_2O, add 1 ml of HNO_3 and 1 ml of $AgNO_3$. Any resulting turbidity is not greater than that in a blank to which 0.015 mg of Cl has been added.

Chloride and Chlorate: Dissolve 0.5 g in 30 ml of hot H_2O and add 1 ml of fresh 10% ferrous sulfate. Allow to stand for 3 minutes, then add 2 ml of HNO_3 and 1 ml of $AgNO_3$. Any turbidity produced is not greater than that in a blank to which 0.025 mg of Cl has been added.

Chlorate and Nitrate: Dissolve 0.1 g in 10 ml of water, add 10 mg of NaCl, 0.2 ml of diphenylamine solution and 10 ml of sulfuric acid. No blue color is produced in 30 minutes.

Sulfate: Dissolve 8 g in 200 ml of hot H_2O, add 1 ml of HCl, heat to boiling, add 5 ml of $BaCl_2$, and let stand overnight. Warm to dissolve any potassium perchlorate that may crystallize out, filter, wash with hot H_2O, and ignite. The weight of the $BaSO_4$ is not more than 1.0 mg.

Calcium: Dissolve 1 g in 20 ml of hot H_2O, add 5 drops of ammonium hydroxide and 3 ml of ammonium oxalate and keep the solution hot. No turbidity is produced in 5 minutes.

Heavy metals: Dissolve 3 g in 60 ml of hot H_2O. To 10 ml of the solution add 0.02 mg of Pb, dilute to 50 ml, and add 0.5 ml of 1 N HCl (A). To the remaining 50 ml add 0.5 ml of 1 N HCl (B). Then to each add 10 ml of H_2S; B is not darker than A.

Iron: Dissolve 0.5 g in 20 ml of warm H_2O, add 0.5 ml of HCl and 15 ml of butanolic potassium thiocyanate, shake well, and allow to separate. Any red color in the butanol layer is not darker than that of a control made with 0.005 mg of Fe, 0.5 ml of HCl, and the same volumes of thiocyanate and water as with the sample.

Sodium: A 5% solution in hot water, tested on a platinum wire, imparts no pronounced yellow color to a colorless flame.

Assay: Mix 1 g, accurately weighed, of the dried and powdered sample with 5 g of powdered sodium nitrite in a nickel crucible, cover the crucible and heat it over a free flame until the mixture is well melted. Maintain it in this state, without raising the temperature much higher, for 30 minutes. Allow to cool, add 20 ml of hot water and digest until the fusion is dissolved.   Filter into a 200-ml volumetric flask and wash any undissolved matter thoroughly with hot water, cool, dilute to volume and mix.

$$KClO_4 + 4NaNO_2 \rightarrow 4NaNO_3 + 4KCl$$

Transfer 50.0 ml of the solution into a 250-ml, glass-stoppered flask, add an accurately measured volume of 25–30 ml of 0.1 N $AgNO_3$, then add slowly 6 ml of HNO_3 previously diluted with 30 ml of water and heat on steam bath to expel nitrous gases.   Cool, add 3 ml of nitrobenzene, shake well for 1–2 minutes, then add 3 ml of ferric ammonium sulfate solution and titrate the excess of $AgNO_3$ with 0.1 N thiocyanate.   Correct for any chloride derived from the $NaNO_2$.   One ml of 0.1 N $AgNO_3$ = 0.01386 g $KClO_4$, log 14176.

Potassium perchlorate may be assayed directly for its oxidizing efficiency by its reaction with titaneous trichloride.   This reagent is the only satisfactory reductant for perchlorate in solution available.   In outline the method is as follows: To a solution of about 0.2 g of the perchlorate, accurately weighed, in about 25 ml of water, contained in a flask in which the air has been displaced by an inert gas (CO_2 or N) 10 ml of H_2SO_4 is added, then a 100% excess of standardized (0.2 N) $TiCl_3$ solution run in from a pipette.   The mixture is now boiled for 10–15 minutes, cooled, and the unreacted $TiCl_3$ determined, after adding 1 g of thiocyanate, by titration with standardized ferric ammonium sulfate (0.1 N) to the production of ferric thiocyanate red brown color.   One ml of 0.1 N titaneous solution = 0.001732 g $KClO_4$.

$$ClO_4^- + 8Ti^{+3} + 4H_2O \rightarrow 8TiO^{+2} + 8H^+ + Cl^-$$

and

$$Ti^{+3} + Fe^{+3} + H_2O \rightarrow TiO^{+2} + Fe^{+2} + 2H^+$$

For the details of the method, consult Burns, E. A., and Muraca, R. F., *Anal. Chem.* 32 (1960), 1316.

POTASSIUM PERIODATE

Potassium Metaperiodate

KIO_4; mol. wt. 230.01; K—17.0%; I—55.18%; available O—27.8%.

Colorless crystals or a white, granular powder.   Soluble in about 80 parts of cold water, more soluble in hot water; insoluble in alcohol.

Standards

Assay..............99.8%–100.2% KIO_4	Iodide......................max 0.002%
Solubility....................to pass test	Manganese (Mn)............max 0.0002%
Chlorate...............max about 0.01%	Sodium (Na)...........max about 0.03%
Other halogens (as Cl).........max 0.01%	

Assay: Weigh accurately about 0.10 g (or use a portion of a stock solution corresponding to this quantity) of the sample dried over H_2SO_4, and dissolve it in 50 ml of H_2O in a glass-stoppered flask.   Add to the solution 3 g of potassium iodide and follow with a mixture of 3 ml of HCl and 5 ml of H_2O.   Allow to stand for 5 minutes, add 100 ml of cold H_2O, and titrate the liberated iodine with 0.1 N

sodium thiosulfate, adding starch toward the end. Correct for a blank. One ml of 0.1 N thiosulfate $= 0.002875$ g KIO_4, log 45864.

$$KIO_4 + 8KI + 8HCl \rightarrow 8I + 8KCl + 4H_2O$$

Solubility: Two grams dissolve completely in 75 ml of hot water.

Chlorate: To 1 g of the powdered sample add 1 ml of H_2SO_4. The salt remains white and no odor or gas is evolved.

Other halogens: Dissolve 0.5 g in a mixture of 25 ml of water and 15 ml of sulfurous acid and boil for 3 minutes. Cool, add 8 ml of 10% NH_3, then add, with stirring, 10 ml of 5% silver nitrate. Filter, wash with about 10 ml of water, and dilute to 100 ml. To 20 ml of the dilution add 1.5 ml of HNO_3. Any turbidity produced is not greater than that produced in a control with 0.01 mg of Cl, 2 ml of 10% NH_3, 1.5 ml of HNO_3, and 1 ml of $AgNO_3$ solution in the same volume as used with the sample.

Iodide: Dissolve 1 g in a mixture of 30 ml of warm H_2O and 5 ml of 10% H_2SO_4, add 1 ml of chloroform, and shake gently. The chloroform acquires no violet color in 1 minute.

Manganese: To 2.5 g of sample add 50 ml of 10% H_2SO_4 (A). To 0.5 g of sample add 50 ml of 10% H_2SO_4 and 0.004 mg of Mn (B). Add to each 5 ml of HNO_3 and 5 ml of phosphoric acid, boil gently for 10 minutes, and cool. Any pink color in A is not darker than that in B.

Sodium: A 4% solution in hot water, tested on a platinum wire, imparts no pronounced yellow color to a colorless flame.

POTASSIUM PERMANGANATE

$KMnO_4$; mol. wt. 158.04; K—24.74%; Mn—34.76%; active O—25.31%.

Dark purple or bronze crystals. Soluble in 15 parts of water; decomposed by alcohol and most other organic solvents.

Standards

Assay..............min 99.0% $KMnO_4$	Nitrogen compounds (as N)...max 0.002%
Insoluble....................max 0.20%	Sulfate (SO_4)...............max 0.005%
Chloride (Cl)................max 0.005%	

Assay: Weigh accurately about 1.5 g, dissolve in H_2O and dilute to exactly 500 ml. Weigh accurately about 0.25 g of dried sodium oxalate (primary standard), dissolve it in 100 ml of H_2O, and add 15 ml of 25% H_2SO_4. Then add slowly from a burette 30 ml of the potassium permanganate solution. Heat the solution to about 70° and complete the titration with the permanganate solution. One gram of sodium oxalate $= 0.4718$ g $KMnO_4$, log 67376.

$$2KMnO_4 + 5Na_2C_2O_4 + 8H_2SO_4 \rightarrow$$
$$10CO_2 + 5Na_2SO_4 + K_2SO_4 + 2MnSO_4 + 8H_2O$$

Insoluble: Dissolve 2 g in 100 ml of warm (about 50°) water in a 200-ml glass-stoppered flask. Filter through a washed and tared filtering crucible, previously dried at 105°. Wash until washings are colorless, and then dry at 105° for 2 hours. The insoluble weighs not more than 4.0 mg.

Chloride: Dissolve 1 g in 25 ml of warm water and slowly add this solution to a mixture of 15 ml of 10% HNO_3 and 3 ml of 30% hydrogen peroxide. When the solution is completely decolorized, dilute to 50 ml. To 20 ml add 1 ml of silver nitrate. The resulting turbidity is not greater than that in a blank to which 0.02 mg of Cl has been added.

Nitrogen compounds: Dissolve 1 g in 60 ml of H_2O in an ammonia distillation flask, add 1 ml of H_2SO_4 and 2.5 g of oxalic acid. When the solution has become colorless add 20 ml of 30% NaOH and 1 g of powdered Devarda metal or 0.5 g of aluminum wire in small pieces and let stand for 2 hours protected from loss or access of NH_3, then distill about 40 ml into 5 ml of water containing 1 drop of dilute HCl, and dilute to 100 ml. To 25 ml add 1 ml of 10% NaOH and 2 ml of Nessler solution. The resulting color is not darker than that produced by treating 0.02 mg of nitrogen (0.08 mg NH_4Cl) in the same manner as the sample.

Sulfate: Dissolve 2 g in 50 ml of warm water and add this solution slowly to a mixture consisting of 7 ml of hydrochloric acid, 30 ml of water, and 5 ml of 30% hydrogen peroxide. Add 20 mg of Na_2CO_3 and evaporate to dryness on the steam bath. Dissolve the residue in 1 ml of 0.1 N HCl and 10 ml of warm water, filter if necessary, add to the filtrate 2 ml of barium chloride solution, and allow to stand for 20 minutes. Any turbidity produced is not greater than that produced in a control made as follows: Evaporate to dryness on the steam bath 20 mg of Na_2CO_3, 7 ml of hydrochloric acid, and 5 ml of the hydrogen peroxide. Dissolve the residue and 0.1 mg of SO_4 in 10 ml of water, and add 1 ml of 0.1 N HCl and 2 ml of barium chloride solution.

POTASSIUM PERSULFATE

$K_2S_2O_8$; mol. wt. 270.32; active oxygen—5.92%.

Colorless, odorless crystals. Soluble in about 50 parts of water. It slowly decomposes, losing available oxygen; decomposition is accelerated by moisture. Potassium persulfate is especially useful in micro-Kjeldahl determinations of nitrogen. *Keep dry in a cool place.*

Standards

Assay................min 98% $K_2S_2O_8$		Ammonia (NH_3)............max 0.001%	
Insoluble...................max 0.010%		Heavy metals (as Pb)........max 0.002%	
Chloride (Cl)...............max 0.002%		Iron (Fe)..................max 0.001%	
Chlorate and Chloride (as Cl)..max 0.005%		Manganese (Mn)...........max 0.0003%	
Nitrate and Chlorate (as NO_3)..max 0.003%			

Assay: Weigh accurately about 0.5 g and dissolve it in a solution of 3 g of potassium iodide in 30 ml of water in a glass-stoppered flask. Add 10 ml of 10% H_2SO_4, allow to stand for 30 minutes, then titrate the liberated iodine with 0.1 N sodium thiosulfate. One ml of 0.1 N thiosulfate = 0.01352 g $K_2S_2O_8$, log 13098. Correct for a blank.

$$K_2S_2O_8 + 2KI \rightarrow 2K_2SO_4 + 2I$$

Chloride: Dissolve 1 g in 30 ml of hot H_2O. Cool and add 5 drops of $AgNO_3$ and 1 ml of HNO_3. The turbidity produced in 1 minute is not greater than that of a blank to which 0.02 mg of Cl has been added.

Chlorate and Chloride: Mix 1 g with 1 g of anhydrous sodium carbonate and ignite, gently at first, then strongly. Cool, dissolve the residue in 20 ml of H_2O, add 6 ml of HNO_3, dilute to 50 ml, and mix. To 20 ml add 1 ml of $AgNO_3$. Any turbidity produced is not greater than that produced when 1 ml of $AgNO_3$ solution is added to 20 ml of a solution containing 0.4 g of the ignited sodium carbonate, 0.02 mg of Cl and 1.5 ml of HNO_3.

Nitrate and Chlorate: Dissolve 0.1 g in 10 ml of water, add 2 ml of 10% NaOH and evaporate to dryness on the steam bath. Re-evaporate on the steam bath to dryness with 10 ml of water. Dissolve the cooled residue in 10 ml of water and neutralize with 25% H_2SO_4. Add 0.2 ml of diphenylamine solution, mix, add 12 ml of H_2SO_4 and allow to stand for 15 minutes. No blue color results.

Ammonia: To a solution of 1 g in 50 ml of water add 5 ml of 10% NaOH and 2 ml of Nessler solution. The resulting color is not darker than that of a blank to which 0.01 mg of NH_3 (0.04 mg NH_4Cl) has been added.

Heavy metals: Dissolve 1.5 g in 30 ml of hot water, add 5 ml of hydrochloric acid, and evaporate to about 5 ml. Add 25 ml of water, 2 drops of phenolphthalein, add dilute NH_4OH to a slight pink color, and dilute to 30 ml. To 5 ml of this solution add 0.02 mg of Pb, 1 ml of 1 N acetic acid and dilute to 40 ml (A). To the remaining 25 ml add 1 ml of 1 N acetic acid and dilute to 40 ml (B). Then to each add 10 ml of H_2S. B is not darker than A.

Iron: Dissolve 1 g in 20 ml of hot H_2O, add 3 ml of HCl and evaporate to dryness. Dissolve the residue in 20 ml of H_2O, add 2 ml of HCl and dilute to 50 ml. Add to the solution 50 mg of the potassium persulfate and 3 ml of ammonium thiocyanate, and mix. Any resulting red color is not darker than that in a control made with 0.01 mg of Fe, 50 mg of the potassium persulfate, 2 ml of HCl, and 3 ml of ammonium thiocyanate in the same final volume as with the sample.

Manganese: To 2 g of the sample add 2 g of ammonium nitrate and 30 ml of water, heat the solution to about 80°, and add 1.5 ml of silver nitrate solution. No pink color is produced in 1 minute.

POTASSIUM PHOSPHATE, DIBASIC

K_2HPO_4; mol. wt. 174.18; K—44.88%; PO_4—54.54%; P—17.80%.

White, somewhat hygroscopic powder. Very soluble in water; slightly soluble in alcohol.

Standards

Insoluble................max 0.010%	Sulfate (SO_4)..............max 0.005%
pH of 0.1 M solution..............9–9.3	Arsenic (As)................max 1 ppm
Carbonate (CO_3)........max about 0.2%	Heavy metals (as Pb)........max 0.001%
Mono- or Tribasic.............to pass test	Iron (Fe)..................max 0.001%
Chloride (Cl)................max 0.003%	Sodium (Na)..........max about 0.02%
Nitrate (NO_3)..............max 0.002%	Assay......................min 98.5%

Insoluble: Dissolve 10 g in 100 ml H_2O and heat on a steam bath for 1 hour. Filter any undissoved residue, wash it with water, and dry at 105°. Its weight does not exceed 1.0 mg.

pH: Dissolve 1.7 g in 100 ml of water and determine the pH potentiometrically with a glass electrode.

Carbonate: To 1 g add 3 ml of H_2O and follow with 2 ml of 10% HCl. Not more than a few bubbles are evolved.

Mono- or Tribasic: Dissolve 3 g in 30 ml of H_2O, cool to 20°, and add 3 drops of thymol blue. A blue color is produced which changes to yellow (with a greenish tinge) by the addition of not more than 0.4 ml of 1 N HCl.

Chloride: Dissolve 1 g in 25 ml of H_2O, add 5 ml of HNO_3, and 1 ml of silver nitrate. Any resulting turbidity is not greater than that in a blank to which 0.03 mg of Cl has been added.

Nitrate: Dissolve 0.5 g in 10 ml of water, add 50 mg of NaCl and 0.2 ml of diphenylamine solution, mix and slowly add 12 ml of H_2SO_4. Mix gently and allow to stand for 1 hour. No blue color results.

Sulfate: Dissolve 10 g in 100 ml of H_2O, add 6 ml of HCl, and filter. Heat the filtrate to boiling, add 5 ml of $BaCl_2$, and allow to stand overnight. If a precipitate is present, filter, wash it with hot H_2O and ignite. The weight of the precipitate of $BaSO_4$ is not more than 1.3 mg.

Arsenic: Determine in 2 g by the method on page 563. The stain is not greater than that from 0.002 mg of As.

Heavy metals: Dissolve 4 g in 20 ml of H_2O, add 8.5 ml of 10% HCl and dilute to 40 ml. To 10 ml of the solution add 0.02 mg of Pb and dilute to 40 ml (A). Dilute the remaining 30 ml of the solution to 40 ml (B). Then to each add 10 ml of H_2S. B is not darker than A.

Iron: Dissolve 1 g in 15 ml of H_2O, add 2 ml of HCl and boil for 2 minutes. Cool, add about 30 mg of ammonium persulfate and 15 ml of butanolic potassium thiocyanate, shake well, and allow to separate. Any red color in the butanol (upper) layer is not darker than that of a blank to which 0.01 mg of Fe has been added.

Sodium: A 10% solution, tested on a platinum wire, imparts no pronounced yellow color to a nonluminous flame.

Note: The sodium may be quantitatively estimated by Flame Photometry.

Assay: Dry about 5 g in a tared crucible to constant weight at 120°. Note the weight of the dried material. Place the crucible in a 300-ml beaker or flask, add 100 ml of water and 40.0 ml of 1 N H_2SO_4, and boil for 5 minutes. Cool to about 20° and titrate the solution, using a pH meter and glass electrodes, with 1 N NaOH to pH 9.2. The difference between the volumes of the 1 N H_2SO_4 added and the volume of the 1 N NaOH used × 0.1742 g represents the K_2HPO_4, log 24705. Not less than 5.65 ml nor more than 5.85 ml of the 1 N acid should be consumed per 1.000 g of the sample (theory 5.75) ml, corresponding to a minimum purity of 98.5% and to presence of a maximum of 1.0% of K_3PO_4.

POTASSIUM PHOSPHATE, MONOBASIC

Potassium Biphosphate; Sörensen's Potassium Phosphate

KH_2PO_4; mol. wt. 136.09; K—28.73%; PO_4—69.80%; P—22.76%.

Colorless or white crystals or granules. Soluble in 4 parts of water; almost insoluble in alcohol.

Standards

Insoluble, Calcium, and NH₄OH precipitate...............max 0.010%
pH of 0.1 M solution.............4.2–4.6
Drying loss..................max 0.20%
Chloride (Cl)................max 0.001%
Nitrogen compounds (as N)...max 0.001%

Sulfate (SO₄................max 0.003%
Arsenic (As).................max 1 ppm
Heavy metals (as Pb)........max 0.001%
Iron (Fe)...................max 0.002%
Sodium (Na)................max 0.02%
Assay...................99.5%–100.3%

Insoluble, Calcium, and NH₄OH precipitate: Dissolve 10 g in 100 ml of H_2O and add 5 ml of ammonium oxalate. Make the solution alkaline to litmus with NH_4OH, add 15 ml excess of NH_4OH, and allow to stand overnight. If a precipitate is present, filter, wash, and ignite at a low red heat. The weight of the ignited precipitate is not more than 1.0 mg.

pH: Dissolve 2.7 g in 100 ml of H_2O and determine the pH potentiometrically or by the use of indicators as follows:

To each of two 10-ml portions add 0.2 ml of 0.04% bromophenol blue. To one of them add 0.05 ml of 0.1 N HCl; a distinct change of color is produced. To each of two other 10-ml portions of the solution add 5 drops of a 0.02% solution of methyl red. To one of them add 0.05 ml of 0.1 N NaOH; a distinct change of color is produced.

Drying loss: Weigh accurately about 2 g and dry over H_2SO_4 overnight. The loss corresponds to not more than 0.2%.

Chloride: Dissolve 1 g in 20 ml of H_2O, add 2 ml of HNO_3 and 1 ml of $AgNO_3$. Any turbidity produced is not greater than that of a blank to which 0.01 mg of Cl has been added.

Nitrogen: To a solution of 2 g in 50 ml of H_2O add 20 ml of 10% NaOH and 0.5 g of powdered Devarda metal, and allow to stand for 2 hours protected from loss or access of NH_3. Then slowly distill 40–45 ml into 5 ml of H_2O containing a drop of diluted HCl, and add to the distillate 1 ml of 10% NaOH and 2 ml of Nessler solution. The color produced is not darker than that produced by treating 0.02 mg of nitrogen (0.08 mg NH_4Cl) in the same manner as the sample.

Sulfate: Dissolve 14 g in 150 ml of H_2O and 1 ml of HCl. Filter if necessary, heat the filtrate to boiling, add 5 ml of $BaCl_2$ and let stand overnight. If a precipitate is present, filter, wash well with water, and ignite. The weight of the barium sulfate so obtained does not exceed 1.0 mg.

Arsenic: Test 2 g by method on page 563. The stain is not more than that from 0.002 mg of As.

Heavy metals: Dissolve 4 g in 25 ml of H_2O, add 2 ml of 1 N HCl, and dilute to 40 ml. To 10 ml of the solution add 0.02 mg Pb and dilute to 40 ml (*A*). Dilute the remaining 30 ml of the solution to 40 ml (*B*). Then add to each 10 ml of H_2S. *B* is not darker than *A*.

Iron: Dissolve 1 g in 15 ml of water, add 2 ml of HCl, and boil gently for 2 minutes. Cool, add about 30 mg of ammonium persulfate and 15 ml of butanolic potassium thiocyanate, shake well for 30 seconds, and allow to separate. Any red color in the clear butanol (upper) layer is not darker than that of a blank to which 0.02 mg of Fe has been added.

Sodium: A 10% solution, tested on a platinum wire, imparts no pronounced yellow color to a nonluminous flame.

Note: The sodium may be quantitatively determined by Flame Photometry.

Assay: Dry about 5 g over a suitable desiccant to constant weight. Weigh accurately about 4 g of the dried sample and dissolve it in 150 ml of water in a conical flask. Boil for 5 minutes to expel CO_2, then cool to 20°–25° and titrate with 1 N NaOH to pH 9, using a pH meter and glass electrode. If an electrometric apparatus is not available, the titration may be made by using 0.5 ml of thymolphthalein indicator solution and titrating to the first appearance of a blue color. One ml of 1 N NaOH = 0.1361 g KH_2PO_4, log 13418. Not less than 7.30 ml and not more than 7.40 ml of 1 N NaOH is consumed by 1.000 g of the dried sample.

POTASSIUM PHOSPHATE, TRIBASIC

Tripotassium Phosphate

$K_3PO_4 \cdot 3H_2O$; mol. wt. 266.32; mol. wt. of anhydrous—212.27.

Colorless or white crystals; deliquescent. Freely soluble in water (about 2 in 2.5); insoluble in alcohol.

Standards

Assay, anhydrous basis	min 99%	Sulfate (SO_4)	max 0.01%
Ignition loss	max 20%	Arsenic (As)	max 2 ppm
Free (excess) KOH	max 0.6%	Heavy metals (as Pb)	max 0.002%
Insoluble	max 0.01%	Iron (Fe)	max 0.001%
Chloride (Cl)	max 0.005%	Sodium (Na)	max 0.03%
Nitrate (NO_3)	max 0.003%		

Ignition loss: Weigh accurately about 4 g in a tared crucible, cover loosely, and ignite at first gently then strongly (600°–800°) to constant weight. The loss in weight corresponds to not more than 20%.

Assay: After the final weighing in the test for *Ignition loss*, place the crucible with its contents in a 300–400 ml beaker, add sufficient water to cover it, then add slowly 40.0 ml of 1 N HCl, and warm until the K_3PO_4 is dissolved. Lift out the crucible from the beaker and rinse with water into the beaker. Boil the solution in the beaker for 5–7 minutes and then cool it to about 20°. Add 2 drops (0.1 ml) of methyl red and titrate with 1 N NaOH to a yellow color, then add from a burette just sufficient 1 N HCl to change the yellow color to red (pH 4.2). The difference between the total volume of 1 N HCl used and the volume of 1 N NaOH consumed represents the K_3PO_4 and any excess of KOH, and it should not be less than 9.3 ml and not more than 9.5 ml per gram of the anhydrous sample (theory 9.42 ml). One ml of 1 N HCl = 0.1061 g of K_3PO_4 and 0.056 g of KOH. The difference between 9.42 ml and the volume of 1 N HCl consumed by 1 g of the dehydrated sample is free (excess) KOH.

Note: In place of indicator the titration can be advantageously performed with an electrometric pH apparatus to pH 4.2.

Insoluble: Dissolve 10 g in 120 ml of water, cover and heat on the steam bath for 20 minutes. If an insoluble residue is present, filter it, wash well with water and dry at 105°. Its weight does not exceed 1.0 mg.

Chloride: Dissolve 1.0 g in 30 ml of water and add 4 ml of HNO_3 and 1 ml of $AgNO_3$ solution.   Any resulting turbidity is not greater than that in a blank to which 0.05 mg of Cl has been added.

Nitrate: Dissolve 0.5 g in 25 ml of water.   To 10 ml of the solution add 50 mg of NaCl and when it has dissolved add 0.2 m of diphenylamine solution, and slowly run in 10 ml of H_2SO_4.   Mix gently and allow to stand for 1 hour.   No blue color results.

Sulfate: To a solution of 10 g in 150 ml of H_2O, or to the filtrate from the test for *Insoluble,* add 8 ml of HCl, boil for a few minutes, filter if necessary, add 5 ml of $BaCl_2$ and let stand overnight.   If a precipitate is present, filter, wash and ignite it.   Its weight should not exceed 2.5 mg.

Arsenic: Test 2 g by the method on page 563.   The stain is not greater than that from 0.002 mg of As.

Heavy metals: Dissolve 4 g in 25 ml of water, add 8 ml of 10% HCl, boil for 5 minutes and dilute to 40 ml.   To 10 ml of the solution add 0.02 mg of Pb and dilute to 40 ml (*A*).   Dilute the remaining 30 ml of the solution to 40 ml (*B*).   Then to each add 10 ml of H_2S.   *B* is no darker than *A*.

Iron: To a solution of 1 g in 15 ml of water add 3 ml of HCl and boil gently for 5 minutes.   Cool, dilute to 15 ml, add 30 mg of ammonium persulfate and 15 ml of butanolic potassium thiocyanate solution, shake well and allow to separate.   Any red color in the butanol (upper) layer is not darker than that in a blank to which 0.01 mg of Fe has been added.

Sodium: A 2% solution tested on a platinum wire imparts no pronounced yellow color to a nonluminous flame.

POTASSIUM PYROSULFATE

$K_2S_2O_7$; mol. wt. 254.32; titratable acidity as H_2SO_4—38.6%.

Colorless or white fragments.   Hygroscopic, freely soluble in water.   The product of commerce is usually a mixture of approximately 70% $K_2S_2O_7$ and 30% of $KHSO_4$.

Standards

Assay—titratable acidity as	Arsenic (As) . . . . max 3 ppm
H_2SO_4 . . . . 37.6%–38.6%	Calcium precipitate . . . . max 0.01%
Insoluble and NH_4OH	Heavy metals (as Pb) . . . . max 0.001%
precipitate . . . . max 0.010%	Iron (Fe) . . . . max 0.001%
Chloride (Cl) . . . . max 0.002%	Sodium (Na) . . . . max about 0.02%
Phosphate (PO_4) . . . . max 0.001%	

Assay: Weigh accurately about 4.0 g, dissolve in 50 ml of water, add 1–2 drops of methyl orange and titrate with 1 N NaOH to yellow color.   One ml of 1 N NaOH = 0.04904 g H_2SO_4, log 69055.   Not less than 7.6 ml and not more than 7.8 ml of 1 N NaOH is consumed per 1.000 g of this pyrosulfate.

Insoluble and NH_4OH precipitate; Chloride; Phosphate; Arsenic; Ca and Mg precipitate; Heavy metals; Iron; Sodium: Test for these as described under Potassium Bilsulfate but omit addition of ammonium phosphate in the test for Ca.   The results should be as there required.

POTASSIUM RHODIZONATE

; mol. wt. 246.25.

Dark red, crystalline powder.   Soluble in water.   It is used for detection of barium.   Calcium does not interfere, nor does strontium in the presence of some free HCl.

The ammonium or sodium salts of rhodizonic acid are equally as satisfactory as the potassium salt if they comply with the test for sensitiveness to barium.

Sensitiveness to barium: (a) Dissolve 50 mg of the sample in 10 ml of water. (b) Dissolve 45 mg of barium chloride in H_2O to make 250 ml.

Dilute 1 ml of (b) (0.1 mg Ba) with 10 ml of water, add 0.1 ml of (a) and mix well.   A distinct turbidity is produced in 1 minute.

POTASSIUM SODIUM TARTRATE

Rochelle Salt

$KNaC_4H_4O_6 \cdot 4H_2O$;   mol.   wt.   282.23;   anhydrous—74.48%; H_2O—25.52%; K—13.86%; Na—8.15%; tartaric acid = 53.19%.

Colorless, clear crystals or a white powder; efflorescent in dry aid.   Soluble in less than 2 parts of water; almost insoluble in alcohol.   Its water content may be ascertained by the iodine (Fischer) method.

Standards

Insoluble	max 0.005%	Sulfate (SO_4)	max 0.005%
Free acid		Ammonia (NH_3)	max 0.003%
(as $KHC_4H_4O_6$)	max 0.12%	Calcium (Ca)	max 0.005%
Free alkali	none	Heavy metals	max 0.0005%
Chloride (Cl)	max 0.001%	Iron (Fe)	max 0.001%
Phosphate (PO_4)	max 0.002%	Assay	99–100.5%

Insoluble: Dissolve 20 g in 200 ml of H_2O and heat on the steam bath 1 hour. If an insoluble residue remains, filter (retain filtrate), wash, and dry at 105°.   Its weight does not exceed 1.0 mg.

Free acid; Free alkali: To a solution of 2 g in 25 ml of H_2O add 2 drops of phenolphthalein; no pink color is produced.   On the addition of 0.6 ml of 0.02 N NaOH a pink color is produced.

The pH of 0.2 M potassium sodium tartrate at 25° is 8.4.

Chloride: Dissolve 1 g in 20 ml of H_2O and add 2 ml of HNO_3 and 1 ml of $AgNO_3$.   Any turbidity produced is not greater than that in a blank to which 0.01 mg of Cl has been added.

Phosphate: Ignite 1 g in platinum until nearly white. Break up the residue well, add 20 ml of H_2O and 1 ml of hydrogen peroxide, and boil for a few minutes. Neutralize with 25% H_2SO_4, add 2 ml excess of the acid, filter, and evaporate filtrate to incipient acid fumes. Dilute to 20 ml, add 1 ml each of phosphate reagents **A** and **B** and heat at 60° for 10 minutes. If a blue color is produced, it is not darker than that of a control made with 0.02 mg PO_4, 2 ml of 25% H_2SO_4, the same quantities of the phosphate reagents and in the same final volume as used with the sample.

Sulfate: Ignite 2 g protected from sulfur in the flame, preferably in an electrical muffle furnace, until nearly free of carbon. Boil the residue with 20 ml of water and 2 ml of 30% H_2O_2 for 5 minutes, then add 10 mg of sodium carbonate and 5 ml of HCl and evaporate on the steam bath to dryness. Prepare a control by evaporating 10 mg of sodium carbonate with 2 ml of the H_2O_2, 5 ml of HCl and 0.1 mg of SO_4 to dryness on the steam bath. Dissolve the residue from each in 10 ml of hot water and filter. Then to each add 1 ml of 0.1 N HCl and 2 ml of $BaCl_2$. Any turbidity appearing in 15 minutes in the solution of the sample is not greater than that in the control.

Ammonia: Dissolve 1 g in 30 ml of H_2O. To 10 ml of the solution add 2 ml of 10% NaOH, dilute to 50 ml and add 2 ml of Nessler solution. The color produced is not darker than that in a blank to which 0.01 mg of NH_3 (0.03 mg NH_4Cl) has been added.

Calcium: Ignite 2 g in a spacious platinum crucible or dish until nearly free of carbon. Add 10 ml of water and 5 ml of HCl and evaporate to dryness on the steam bath. Dissolve the resulting chlorides in 7 to 8 ml of hot water, filter, and wash to 10 ml. Warm to about 50°, add 1 drop of acetic acid and 1 ml of ammonium oxalate solution, and allow to stand for 20 minutes. Any resulting turbidity is not greater than that produced by 0.1 mg of calcium (Ca) contained in a solution of 0.7 g of reagent potassium chloride in 10 ml of water and treated as the sample solution beginning with "Warm to about 50° . . . ."

Heavy metals: Dissolve 5 g in H_2O to make 50 ml. To 10 ml add 0.015 mg of Pb, dilute to 40 ml, and add 1 ml of 1 N HCl and 1 ml of H_2O (A). To the remaining 40 ml add 2 ml of 1 N HCl (B). Then to each add 10 ml of H_2S. B is not darker than A.

Iron: Dissolve 1 g in water, add 2 ml of HCl, and dilute to 50 ml. Add 50 mg of ammonium persulfate and 3 ml of ammonium thiocyanate, and mix. Any resulting red color is not darker than that of a blank to which 0.01 mg of Fe has been added.

Assay: Potassium Sodium Tartrate may be assayed, after drying to constant weight at 150°, by the general methods, preferably No. **1**, for Alkali Salts of Organic Acids, page 564. One ml of 0.1 N acid = 0.01051 g $KNaC_4H_4O_6$ (anhydrous).

POTASSIUM SULFATE

K_2SO_4; mol. wt. 174.26; K—44.88%; SO_4—55.12%.

Colorless or white crystals. Soluble in 10 parts of water; insoluble in alcohol.

The reagent grade in commerce occurs in the form of moderately large crystals and is about 99.9% pure.

Standards

Insoluble.................max 0.010%	Calcium, Magnesium, and NH$_4$OH
Neutrality.................to pass test	precipitate...............max 0.020%
Chloride (Cl)..............max 0.001%	Heavy metals (as Pb).......max 0.0005%
Nitrogen compounds (as N)..max 0.0005%	Iron (Fe)..................max 0.0005%
Phosphate (PO$_4$)...........max 0.0005%	Sodium (Na)...........max about 0.02%
Arsenic (As)................max 1 ppm	

Insoluble: Dissolve 10 g in 150 ml of hot H$_2$O and heat on the steam bath for 1 hour. Filter any insoluble residue (retain filtrate), wash it with hot H$_2$O, and dry at 105°. Its weight does not exceed 1.0 mg.

Neutrality: To a solution of 5 g in 75 ml of hot H$_2$O add 0.2 ml of phenolphthalein; no pink color is produced. Add 0.25 ml of 0.02 N NaOH; a pink color is produced.

Chloride: Dissolve 1 g in 20 ml of warm H$_2$O, add 1 ml of HNO$_3$ and 1 ml of AgNO$_3$. Any turbidity produced is not greater than that in a blank to which 0.01 mg of Cl has been added.

Nitrogen compounds: Dissolve 2 g in 60 ml of H$_2$O, add 10 ml of 10% NaOH and 1 g powdered Devarda metal, and let stand 2 hours protected from loss or access of NH$_3$. Then distill gently about 45 ml into 5 ml of H$_2$O containing 1 drop of dilute HCl, and add to the distillate 1 ml of 10% NaOH and 2 ml of Nessler solution. The color produced is not darker than that produced by treating 0.01 mg of nitrogen (0.04 mg NH$_4$Cl) in the same manner as the sample.

Phosphate: Dissolve 2 g in 20 ml of warm H$_2$O, add 2 ml of 25% H$_2$SO$_4$, 1 ml each of phosphate reagents **A** and **B**, and heat at 60° for 10 minutes. Any blue color produced is not darker than that in a blank to which 0.01 mg of PO$_4$ has been added.

Arsenic: Determine in 2 g by method on page 563. The stain is not more than that from 0.002 mg of As.

Calcium, Magnesium, and NH$_4$OH precipitate: Add to the filtrate from the test for *Insoluble* 5 ml of ammonium oxalate, 2 ml of ammonium phosphate, and 20 ml of NH$_4$OH, stir, and allow to stand overnight. If a precipitate is present, filter, wash it with 2.5% NH$_3$, and ignite. The weight of the ignited precipitate does not exceed 2.0 mg.

Heavy metals: Dissolve 5 g in warm H$_2$O to make 50 ml. To 10 ml add 0.015 mg of Pb, dilute to 40 ml and add 1 ml of 1 N acetic acid (A). To the remaining 40 ml add 1 ml of 1 N acetic acid (B). Then add to each 10 ml of H$_2$S. B is not darker than A.

Iron: Dissolve 2 g in 30 ml of warm H$_2$O and cool. Add 2 ml of HCl and dilute to 50 ml. Add about 30 mg of ammonium persulfate and 3 ml of ammonium thiocyanate, and mix. Any resulting red color is not darker than that of a blank to which 0.01 mg of Fe has been added.

Sodium: A 10% solution in warm water, tested on a platinum wire, imparts no pronounced yellow color to a colorless flame.

POTASSIUM TARTRATE

$K_2C_4H_4O_6 \cdot \frac{1}{2}H_2O$; mol. wt. 235.27; anhydrous—96.19%; H_2O—3.81%; K—33.23%; tartaric acid = 63.80%.

Small white crystals.   Soluble in 1 part of water; almost insoluble in alcohol.

Standards

Insoluble....................max 0.010%	Ammonia (NH₃)..............max 0.003%
Free acid (as KHC₄H₄O₆)......max 0.10%	Calcium (Ca)................max 0.005%
Free alkali (as K₂CO₃)........max 0.02%	Heavy metals (as Pb).......max 0.0005%
Chloride (Cl)................max 0.002%	Iron (Fe)...................max 0.001%
Phosphate (PO₄)............max 0.002%	Sodium (Na)...........max about 0.02%
Sulfate (SO₄)...............max 0.005%	Assay (anhydrous basis)......99%–100.5%

Insoluble: Dissolve 10 g in 100 ml of H_2O and heat on the steam bath for 1 hour. If an insoluble residue remains, filter (retain filtrate), wash, and dry at 105°.   Its weight does not exceed 1.0 mg.

Free acid; Free alkali: Dissolve 2 g in 25 ml of water and add 2 drops of phenolphthalein.   If a pink color is produced, it is discharged by 0.15 ml of 0.02 N HCl.   If no pink color is produced, it is produced by the addition of 0.5 ml of 0.02 N NaOH.

Chloride: Dissolve 1 g in 20 ml of H_2O and add 2 ml of HNO_3 and 1 ml of $AgNO_3$.   Any turbidity produced is not greater than that in a blank to which 0.02 mg of Cl has been added.

Phosphate: Apply the test described for Potassium Sodium Tartrate.   The result should be as there stated.

Sulfate: Ignite 2 g protected from sulfur in the flame, preferably in an electrical muffle furnace, until nearly free of carbon.   Boil the residue with 20 ml of water and 2 ml of 30% H_2O_2 for 5 minutes, then add 10 mg of sodium carbonate and 5 ml of HCl and evaporate to dryness on the steam bath.   Prepare a control by evaporating 10 mg of sodium carbonate with 2 ml of the H_2O_2, 5 ml of HCl, and 0.1 mg of SO_4 to dryness on the steam bath.   Dissolve the residue from each in 10 ml of hot water and filter.   Then to each add 1 ml of 0.1 N HCl and 2 ml of $BaCl_2$.   Any turbidity appearing in 15 minutes in the solution of the sample is not greater than that in the control.

Ammonia: Dissolve 1 g in 50 ml of H_2O, add 2 ml of 10% NaOH and 2 ml of Nessler solution.   The color produced is not darker than that in a blank to which 0.03 mg of NH_3 (0.12 mg NH_4Cl), has been added.

Calcium; Heavy metals; Iron: Apply the tests described for Potassium Sodium Tartrate.   The results conform to the requirements there stated.

Sodium: Ignite 1 g, dissolve the residue in 20 ml of H_2O, neutralize with HCl, and filter.   The filtrate, tested on a platinum wire, imparts no distinct yellow color to a colorless flame.   The sodium may be quantitatively determined by Flame Photometry, page 566.

Assay: Potassium tartrate may be assayed, after drying at 150° to constant weight, by method No. **1** for Alkali Salts of Organic Acids, page 564.   One ml of 0.1 N acid = 0.01131 g $K_2C_4H_4O_6$.

POTASSIUM THIOCYANATE

Potassium Sulfocyanate

KSCN; mol. wt. 97.18; K—40.23%; SCN—59.77%; CN—26.77%.

Colorless crystals; deliquescent. Soluble in 0.5 part of water; freely soluble in alcohol. *Keep in tightly closed containers.*

Standards

Insoluble.................max 0.005%	Ammonia (NH_3).............max 0.005%
Solubility in alcohol..........to pass test	Heavy metals (as Pb).......max 0.0005%
Iodine-consuming substances	Iron (Fe).................max 0.0003%
(Cyanide, Sulfide, etc.)......to pass test	Sodium (Na)..........max about 0.02%
Chloride (Cl)...............max 0.001%	*Assay* (dried).................min 99%
Sulfate (SO_4)...............max 0.005%	

Insoluble: Dissolve 20 g in 200 ml of H_2O and heat on the steam bath for 1 hour. Filter any insoluble residue, wash it with H_2O, and dry at 105°. Its weight is not over 1.0 mg.

Solubility in alcohol: One gram dissolves in 10 ml of alcohol, giving a clear solution with no insoluble residue remaining.

Iodine-consuming substances: Dissolve 2 g in a mixture of 20 ml of water and 1 ml of 10% H_2SO_4. Add 0.5 g of KI and 0.5 ml of starch solution and titrate with 0.1 N iodine. Not more than 0.15 ml of the iodine is required to produce a blue or reddish-blue color.

Chloride: Dissolve 1 g in 20 ml of H_2O in a small flask, add 10 ml of 25% H_2SO_4 and 7 ml of 30% hydrogen peroxide, and boil down gently *under hood* to 20 ml. Restore the volume with H_2O and again evaporate to 20 ml. Repeat this operation until all the cyanide has volatilized. Cool, dilute to 50 ml, and mix well. To 20 ml of this solution add 1 ml of nitric acid and 1 ml of silver nitrate. The turbidity produced is not greater than that in a control made with 0.01 mg of Cl, 1 ml of HNO_3, and 1 ml of silver nitrate in the same final volume as with the sample.

Sulfate: To a solution of 2 g in 10 ml of water add 1 ml of 0.1 N HCl and 2 ml of $BaCl_2$. Any turbidity produced in 15 minutes is not greater than that in a blank to which 0.10 mg of SO_4 has been added.

Ammonia: Dissolve 1 g in 60 ml of water in a distilling flask, add 10 ml of 10% NaOH, and distill over about 40 ml into 5 ml of water containing 1 drop of diluted HCl. Dilute the distillate to 100 ml. To 20 ml of this solution add 1 ml of 10% NaOH, dilute to 50 ml, and add 2 ml of Nessler solution. The color produced is not darker than that produced by treating 0.05 mg of NH_3 (0.15 mg NH_4Cl) in the same manner as the sample.

Heavy metals: Dissolve 5 g in water to make 50 ml. To 10 ml of the solution add 0.015 mg of Pb, dilute to 40 ml, and add 1 ml of 1 N acetic acid (*A*). To the remaining 40 ml add 1 ml of 1 N acetic acid (*B*). Then to each add 10 ml of H_2S. *B* is not darker than *A*.

Iron: Dissolve 4 g in water to make 40 ml. To 10 ml of the solution add 30 ml of water, 0.006 mg of Fe and dilute to 50 ml (*A*). Dilute the remaining 30 ml of the solution to 50 ml (*B*). Then to each add 2 ml of HCl and 50 mg of ammonium persulfate, and mix well. Any red color in *B* is not darker than that in *A*.

Sodium: A 10% solution tested on a platinum wire imparts no pronounced yellow color to a colorless flame.

Assay: Potassium thiocyanate may be assayed by the adsorption indicator method for Chloride and Thiocyanate, page 565. Use about 0.3 g of the dried sample, accurately weighed, previously dried over H_2SO_4. One ml of 0.1 *N* $AgNO_3$ = 0.009717 g KSCN, log 98753.

POTASSIUM XANTHATE

Potassium Xanthogenate

$KS_2COC_2H_5$; mol. wt. 160.32.

White or pale yellow crystals or a crystalline powder. Contains 8% to 10% water. Very soluble in water; soluble in 5 parts of alcohol. *Keep in tightly closed containers.*

Standards

Assay...........about 90% $KS_2COC_2H_5$	Chloride (Cl)................max 0.020%
Insoluble....................max 0.02%	Sulfate (SO_4).................max 0.10%
Alkalinity...................to pass test	Sulfide (S)...........max about 0.003%

Assay: Weigh accurately about 0.5 g and dissolve it in 50 ml of water. Add 50 ml of 0.1 *N* iodine, allow to stand for 5 minutes, then add 2 ml of glacial acetic acid and titrate the excess of iodine with 0.1 *N* sodium thiosulfate, adding starch toward the end. One ml of 0.1 *N* iodine = 0.01603 g $KS_2COC_2H_5$, log 20493.

Insoluble: Dissolve 5 g in 50 ml of H_2O, filter any undissolved matter, wash, and dry at 105°. The insoluble residue does not exceed 1.0 mg.

Alkalinity: Dissolve 1 g in 20 ml of H_2O, add 2 drops of phenolphthalein, and titrate with 0.1 *N* H_2SO_4. Not more than 2 ml of the acid is required to discharge the pink color.

Chloride: Dissolve 0.5 g in 20 ml of H_2O, add 2 ml of HNO_3, and let stand overnight. Filter and dilute the filtrate to 100 ml. To 20 ml of the filtrate add 2 ml of silver nitrate. Any turbidity produced is not greater than that of a control prepared with 0.02 mg of Cl, 0.5 ml of HNO_3 and 2 ml of $AgNO_3$, in the same final volume as used with the sample.

Sulfate: Dissolve 0.5 g in 20 ml of H_2O, add 3 ml of HCl, stopper, and let stand overnight. Filter and dilute the filtrate to 50 ml. To 10 ml of the filtrate add 2 ml of $BaCl_2$. The turbidity produced is not greater than that of a control made with 0.1 mg of SO_4, 1 ml of 1 *N* HCl and 2 ml of $BaCl_2$ in the same volume as used with the sample.

Sulfide: To 1 ml of lead acetate solution add 10% NaOH until the precipitate redissolves. Add 5 drops of this solution to a solution of 1 g of the sample in 20 ml of H_2O. No darkening is produced in 2 minutes.

PROPIONIC ACID

CH_3CH_2COOH; mol. wt. 74.08.

Colorless liquid; slightly pungent, acetic acid-like but somewhat disagreeable odor; solidifies at $-21°$; boils at $141°$; Sp. gr. about 0.987 at $25°/25°$; miscible with water, alcohol, acetone; soluble in chloroform, ether.

Standards

Assay....................99.5%–100.2%	Chloride (Cl)................max 0.001%
Boiling range................140°–141.5°	Heavy metals (as Pb).......max 0.0005%
Specific gravity (25°/25°)......0.984–0.988	Iron (Fe)...................max 0.001%
Miscibility with H_2O..........to pass test	Reaction with H_2SO_4.........to pass test
Evaporation residue..........max 0.01%	

Assay: Tare a weighing bottle with 10 ml of water. Quickly add about 3 ml of the sample, stopper and reweigh. Completely transfer the contents of the weighing bottle into a suitable beaker or flask and dilute with water to 75 ml. Add 2 drops of phenolphthalein and titrate with 1 N NaOH to a pink color. One ml of 1 N NaOH = 0.07408 g $C_3H_5O_2H$, log 36970.

Boiling range: Distill 50 ml. After the first 10 drops, all should distill between 140° and 141.5°. correction being made for barometric pressure.

Miscibility with water: Mix 10 ml of the acid with 25 ml of water. No turbidity is discernible after standing for 1 hour.

Evaporation residue: Evaporate 20.0 ml in a tared dish to dryness on the steam bath and dry at 120° for 1 hour. Any resulting residue weighs not more than 1.0 mg (retain).

Chloride: Dilute 2.0 ml to 20 ml and add 2 ml of HNO_3 and 1 ml of $AgNO_3$. Any resulting turbidity is not greater than that in a blank to which 0.02 mg of Cl has been added.

Solution R: Warm the residue obtained in the test for *Evaporation residue* with 2 ml of 1 N HCl and 10 ml of water and dilute to 50 ml.

Heavy metals: Dilute 10 ml of *Solution R* to 40 ml and add 10 ml of H_2S. Any darkening produced is not greater than that in a control made with 0.02 mg of Pb, 0.2 ml of 1 N HCl and 10 ml of H_2S, in the same final volume as with the sample.

Iron: To 5 ml of *Solution R* add 2 ml of HCl and 30 mg of ammonium persulfate, dilute to 50 ml and add 3 ml of ammonium thiocyanate. Any red color produced is not darker than that in a control made with 0.02 mg of Fe, the same quantities of the reagents and in the same final volume as with the sample.

Reaction with H_2SO_4: Slowly mix 10 ml of the acid with 5 ml of H_2SO_4 and allow to stand for 5 minutes. No darkening is produced.

PROPYLENE GLYCOL

1,2-Propanediol

$CH_3CHOH—CH_2OH$; mol. wt. 76.09.

Colorless, syrupy, odorless liquid. Miscible with water, acetone, alcohol, chloroform; soluble in ether.

Standards

Specific gravity (25°/25°)....1.0350–1.0370	Chloride (Cl)...............max 0.010%
Boiling range...................186°–188°	Sulfate (SO₄)...............max 0.002%
Miscibility...................to pass test	Heavy metals (as Pb).......max 0.0005%
Acid (as acetic).............max 0.006%	

Specific gravity: Determine with a pycnometer at 25°/25°.

Boiling range: Distill 50 ml. After the first 10 drops, not less than 48 ml distills between 186° and 188°, correction being made for the difference in the barometric pressure from 760 mm (see page 581).

Miscibility: Mix 10 ml of the propylene glycol with 30 ml of water. A clear solution results and it remains clear for 30 minutes.

Acid: Add 1 ml phenolphthalein solution to 50 ml of H_2O; then add 0.1 N NaOH dropwise until the pink color persists after shaking for a few seconds. Now add 10 ml of the sample and shake. If the pink color has disappeared, it is restored by the addition of not more than 0.1 ml of 0.1 N NaOH.

Chloride: Dilute 1.0 ml of sample with water to 100 ml. To 10 ml of the dilution add 1 ml of 10% HNO_3 and 1 ml of $AgNO_3$. Any turbidity produced is not greater than that in a blank to which 0.01 mg of Cl has been added.

Sulfate: Dilute 5 ml of sample to 15 ml; add 1 ml of 1 N HCl and 2 ml of $BaCl_2$. Any turbidity produced is not greater than that in a blank to which 0.1 mg of SO_4 has been added.

Heavy metals: Dilute 5.0 ml to 50 ml. To 10 ml add 0.015 mg of Pb, dilute to 40 ml, and add 2 ml of 1 N acetic acid (A). To the remaining 40 ml add 2 ml of 1 N acetic acid (B). Then to each add 10 ml of H_2S. B is not darker than A.

PYRIDINE

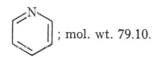 ; mol. wt. 79.10.

Colorless, clear liquid; characteristic odor; hygroscopic; flammable. Miscible with water, alcohol, chloroform, ether, and many other organic solvents. Sp. gr. 0.988 at 15°; boils at 115°.

Standards

Boiling range...................114°–116°	Copper (Cu)..................to pass test
Miscibility with water.........to pass test	(max about 0.0005%)
Evaporation residue.........max 0.002%	Permanganate-reducing
Chloride (Cl).................max 0.001%	substances.................to pass test
Sulfate (SO₄)................max 0.001%	Water......................max 0.10%
Ammonia (NH₃).............max 0.002%	Assay.........................min 99%

Boiling range: Distill 50 ml. After the first 10 drops, not less than 48 ml distills between 114° and 116°, correction being made for the barometric pressure (page 581).

Miscibility with water: To 10 ml of the sample add 40 ml of water.   A clear solution results.

Evaporation residue: Evaporate 50 ml on the steam bath and dry for 1 hour at 105°.   Not more than 1.0 mg of residue remains.

Chloride: Mix 2 ml with 25 ml of water, add 2 ml of HNO_3 and 1 ml of $AgNO_3$. Any turbidity produced in 30 seconds is not greater than that in a blank to which 0.02 mg Cl has been added.

Sulfate: To 5 ml add 10 mg of sodium carbonate and evaporate to dryness on the steam bath.   Treat the residue with 10 ml of water and 1 ml of 1 N HCl, filter, and add to the filtrate 2 ml of $BaCl_2$.   Any turbidity produced is not greater than that in a blank to which 0.05 mg of SO_4 has been added.

Ammonia: Mix 3 ml with 15 ml of CO_2-free water and add 2 drops phenolphthalein.   If a pink color is produced it is discharged by 0.20 ml of 0.02 N HCl.

Copper: Mix 5 ml with 15 ml water, add 2 ml of glacial acetic acid, 3 ml of ammonium thiocyanate and 5 ml of chloroform, shake vigorously, and allow to separate.   The chloroform layer is not green and, at most, only faintly yellow.

Permanganate-reducing substances: To 5 ml add 0.5 ml of 0.1 N potassium permanganate.   The pink color does not entirely disappear in 30 minutes.

Water: Determine by the iodine (Fischer) method.

Assay: Pyridine may be assayed as follows: Weigh accurately about 3 ml and dissolve in 25 ml of water.   Add a few drops of bromophenol blue indicator and titrate with 1 N HCl to the full yellow color.   One ml of 1 N HCl = 0.07940 g C_5H_5N, log 89982.

PYRIDOXINE HYDROCHLORIDE

Vitamin B_6 Hydrochloride

; mol. wt. 205.65; N—6.81%; Cl—17.24%.

Colorless or white crystals; melts at about 206°.   Sublimable; soluble in 5 parts of water, in about 75 of alcohol, and in glacial acetic acid; insoluble in chloroform or ether.

Standards

Melting range. . . . . .204°–208°	Solubility. . . . . .to pass test
Nitrogen (N) content. . . . . .6.8% ± 0.15%	Ignition residue. . . . . .max 0.030%
Absorptivity ($E_{1cm}^{1\%}$ in 0.1 N HCl). .422 ± 2	Heavy metals (as Pb). . . . . . . .max 0.002%
Drying loss. . . . . .max 0.20%	Iron (Fe). . . . . .max 0.002%

Melting range: Determine in a bath preheated to 190°.

Nitrogen content: Determine by the Kjeldahl method, using about 400 mg of the dried (over H_2SO_4) sample accurately weighed.

Chloride content: Proceed as described under *Assays for Chloride and Thiocyanate*, page 565.

Absorptivity: Dissolve 25.0 mg of the dried sample in 0.1 N HCl to make 100.0 ml. Dilute 5.0 ml of this solution with 0.1 N HCl to 100.0 ml. Measure the absorbance of the latter solution in a 1-cm cell in a suitable spectrophotometer at 291 mμ and divide the reading by the number of milligrams of sample per 100 mμ of the diluted solution.

Drying loss: Dry a suitable quantity to suffice for the four preceding tests in a vacuum over a desiccating agent for 2 hours. The loss in weight corresponds to not more than 0.2%.

Solubility: A solution of 1.0 g in 10 ml of water is clear, complete and practically colorless.

Ignition residue: Thoroughly char 3.0 g, then add 1 ml of H_2SO_4 and 1 ml of HNO_3, evaporate and ignite to constant weight. The weight of the residue does not exceed 1.0 mg.

Heavy metals: To the *Ignition residue* add 2 ml of HCl and 1 ml of HNO_3, and slowly evaporate to dryness over steam. Add to the residue 5 ml of 10% ammonium acetate solution and 2 ml of 10% NH_3, cover and digest over steam for 20 minutes. Neutralize the solution with acetic acid, add 0.5 ml of the acid in excess and dilute to 30 ml. Dilute 10 ml of this solution to 40 ml and add 10 ml of H_2S. Any resulting color is not darker than that of a control made with 0.02 mg of Pb, 2 ml of the ammonium acetate solution, 1 ml of the 10% NH_3 and 1 ml of the acetic acid.

Iron: To 10 ml of the solution from the preceding test add 2 ml of HCl, 30 mg of ammonium persulfate, dilute to 50 ml and add 3 ml of ammonium thiocyanate. Any red color produced is not darker than that of a control made with 0.02 mg of iron (Fe).

PYROGALLOL

Pyrogallic Acid; 1,2,3-Trihydroxybenzene

; mol. wt. 126.05.

White, lustrous crystals. Soluble in 2 parts of water, in 1 part of alcohol or in 2 parts of ether. *Darkens on exposure to air and sunlight.*

Standards

Melting range................131.5°–134°	Chloride (Cl)................max 0.001%
Solubility.....................to pass test	Sulfate (SO₄)................max 0.010%
Ignition residue.............max 0.05%	

Solubility: A solution of 1 g in 15 ml of water is complete and clear.

Ignition residue: Char well 2.0 g. Allow to cool, add 0.5 ml of H_2SO_4 and ignite at first gently to evaporate the acid, then strongly to constant weight. Not more than 1.0 mg of residue remains.

Chloride: Dissolve 1 g in 15 ml of cold H_2O, add 3 ml of 10% nitric acid and 1 ml of silver nitrate. Any turbidity produced is not greater than that in the blank to which 0.01 mg of Cl has been added.

Sulfate: Dissolve 1 g in 10 ml of water, add 1 ml of 1 N HCl and 1 ml of barium chloride. The turbidity is not greater than that in a blank to which 0.1 mg of SO_4 has been added.

QUINALDINIC ACID

—COOH; $C_{10}H_7NO_2 \cdot 2H_2O$; mol. wt. 209.20; H_2O—17.2%.

Quinoline-2-carboxylic acid

White to slightly yellow, crystalline. Slightly soluble in cold water; soluble in hot water, alcohol, methanol, benzene and solutions of alkali hydroxides and of carbonates. It darkens on exposure to sunlight. *Keep protected from light.*

Quinaldinic acid has been recommended for the separation and gravimetric determination of Cd, Cu, Zn[1,2,3,4], also for colorimetric determination of ferrous iron.[1] This reagent lends itself to the colorimetric determination of iron even in the presence of substantial amounts of Co, Cu, Ni and Zn.

Standards

Melting range..................156°–158°	Sensitiveness................to pass test
Solubility in Na_2CO_3..........to pass test	Ignition residue.............max 0.10%

Solubility in Na_2CO_3 solution: Add 50 mg of the sample to 5 ml of 1% sodium carbonate solution. A clear or practically clear solution results.

Sensitiveness: To a solution of 0.001 mg of Fe in 3 ml of water add in the sequence named, 1 ml of 5% hydroxylamine hydrochloride solution, 0.1 ml of the solution of the sample from the preceding test and 1 ml of 10% sodium cyanide solution. A distinct red color develops.

Ignition residue: To 1.0 g add 0.5 H_2SO_4 and ignite to constant weight. The residue, if any, weighs not more than 1.0 mg.

[1] Rây, P., and Bose, M. K., *Z. anal. Chem.* **95**, 400 (1933).
[2] Rây, P. and Bose M. K. *Mikrochemie* **18** 89 (1935).
[3] Alport N., and Moon, C. D. B., *Analyst*, **64**, 395 (1939).
[4] Lindsay, A. J., and Sherman, R. J., *ibid.* **65**, 636 (1940).

QUINALIZARIN
Tetrahydroxyanthraquinone

OH; mol. wt. 272.20.

Brown-red powder.   Insoluble in water; soluble in solutions of alkali hydroxides, forming a violet-colored solution which becomes yellow upon the addition of acid.   It is also soluble in concentrated sulfuric acid, producing a blue-violet color.

Quinalizarin as a 0.05% solution in dilute (about 0.2 N) sodium hydroxide is used for the colorimetric detection and estimation of small quantities of magnesium[1,2] and of beryllium.[3,4]   It is also used for the detection of borates.

Standards

Sensitiveness................to pass test   Ignition residue.............max 0.20%

Sensitiveness: (a) Dissolve 10 mg of the reagent in 100 ml of sulfuric acid. (b) Dissolve 10 mg of boric acid in 100 ml of water.   To 0.1 ml of (b) add 2 drops of 1 N NaOH and evaporate in a small dish or crucible to dryness on the steam bath. Then add to the residue 0.2 ml of (a).   The violet color of the quinalizarin solution changes to blue.

Ignition residue: To 0.5 g of the sample add 0.5 ml of sulfuric acid and ignite to constant weight.   The residue weighs not more than 1.0 mg.

[1] Hahn, Wolf, and Jaeger, *Ber.* **57**, 1394 (1924).
[2] Hahn, *Mikrochem. Pregl-Festschrift*, p. 127 (1929).
[3] Fischer, *Wiss. Veröff entl. Siemens-Konzern* **5**, 99 (1926).
[4] Kolthoff, *J. Am. Chem. Soc.* **50**, 224, 242 (1938).

QUINHYDRONE

$C_6H_4(OH)_2 \cdot C_6H_4O_2$; mol. wt. 218.20.

Quinhydrone is an addition compound of 1 mol hydroquinone and 1 mol quinone.
Bronze-green, crystalline, of a characteristic odor.   Slightly soluble in cold water; moderately soluble in hot water; soluble in alcohol and in ether.

Standards

Assay................49%–51% quinone	Ignition residue............max 0.050%
Melting range..................171°–173°	Sulfate (SO$_4$)................max 0.02%
Suitability for pH	Heavy metals (as Pb).......max 0.002%
determination.............to pass test	Iron (Fe)..................max 0.002%
Alcohol—insoluble..........max 0.010%	

Assay: Weigh accurately about 0.45 g, transfer to a glass-stoppered flask, add 25 ml of H_2O, 25 ml of 10% H_2SO_4 and 3 g of potassium iodide. Stopper, shake until dissolved, then titrate the liberated iodine with 0.1 N thiosulfate, using starch indicator toward the end. One ml of 0.1 N thiosulfate = 0.005403 g quinone, log 73263.

$$C_6H_4O_2 + 2KI + H_2SO_4 \rightarrow 2I + K_2SO_4 + C_6H_4(OH)_2$$
quinone   hydroquinone

Suitability for pH determination: To the lower part of a 10-ml graduated cylinder cut off at the 3-ml mark, add 2 ml of 0.1 N HCl. Add portionwise 1 g of the quinhydrone, tapping to make it sink. Add enough 0.1 N HCl to fill the cylinder without disturbing the quinhydrone. Place the cylinder in a 100-ml beaker and carefully add enough 0.1 N HCl to raise the level about 2 mm above the cylinder. To the acid outside the cylinder, add about 20 mg of the quinhydrone and stir gently.

Place two clean gold electrodes in the acid outside the cylinder and by means of a potentiometer, capable of reading accurately to 0.1 millivolt, measure the e.m.f. to determine any natural variation between the electrodes. This e.m.f. should not exceed 0.3 millivolt. Now carefully place one of the electrodes within the cylinder so that its metallic surface is completely covered by solid quinhydrone. Measure the e.m.f. after 5 minutes and again after 10 minutes. These two readings should agree within 0.5 millivolt, and the second reading should not exceed 1.0 millivolt after correcting for the natural variation in the electrodes found by the first reading.

Alcohol—insoluble: Dissolve 10 g in 100 ml of hot alcohol. Filter any undissolved matter, wash with hot alcohol until washings are colorless, and dry at 105°. The insoluble residue does not exceed 1.0 mg.

Ignition residue: Char well 2.0 g. Allow to cool, add 0.5 ml of H_2SO_4, and ignite gently at first, then strongly to constant weight. Any residue present does not exceed 1.0 mg.

Sulfate: To 1 g add 10 ml of hot H_2O and 0.5 g of sodium carbonate, evaporate in platinum and ignite, protection from access of sulfur until nearly white. Treat the residue with 20 ml of H_2O and 1 ml of 30% hydrogen peroxide, boil for a few minutes, then add 2 ml of HCl and evaporate to dryness on the steam bath. Dissolve the residue in 20 ml of H_2O, filter, and add 1 ml of 1 N HCl and 3 ml of $BaCl_2$. Any turbidity produced does not exceed that in a control made as follows: Evaporate 0.5 g of sodium carbonate, 1 ml of the hydrogen peroxide, and 2 ml of HCl to dryness on the steam bath. Dissolve the residue and 0.2 mg of SO_4 in 20 ml of H_2O, and then add 1 ml of 1 N HCl and 3 ml of $BaCl_2$.

Solution R: Evaporate the *ignition residue* with 2 ml of HCl and 0.5 ml of HNO_3 to dryness on the steam bath. Take up with 1 ml of 1 N HCl and 30 ml of hot water, cool, and dilute to 40 ml.

Heavy metals: Dilute 20 ml of *Solution R* to 40 ml and add 10 ml of H_2S. Any color produced is not darker than that of a control made wtih 0.02 mg of Pb, 0.5 ml of 1 N HCl and 10 ml of H_2S, in the same final volume as with sample.

Iron: To 10 ml of *Solution R* add 2 ml of HCl and dilute to 50 ml. Add about 30 mg of ammonium persulfate and 3 ml of ammonium thiocyanate. Any resulting red color is not darker than that in a blank to which 0.01 mg of Fe has been added.

QUINOLINE

C_9H_7N; mol. wt. 129.15.

Colorless, but rapidly discolors in air and light; hygroscopic, characteristic odor. Volatile with steam. Sp. gr. 1.090. Slowly soluble in about 60 parts of water; miscible with alcohol, carbon disulfide, chloroform, etc. It is a weak base, but forms water-soluble salts with strong acids.

Keep in full, tightly closed, light resistant containers. If it is pronouncedly colored, it should be redistilled, preferably over some NaOH pellets and in nitrogen.

Standards

Boiling range.................238° ± 2°	Ammonia, Isoquinoline, etc....to pass test
Refractive index.........1.6268 ± 0.0006	Water......................max 1.0%
Hydrocarbons, etc...........to pass test	

Shake about 75 ml of the quinoline with 10 g of anhydrous granular sodium sulfate several times during 1 hour, allow the Na_2SO_4 to settle and quickly decant into a bottle and stopper. Use this dehydrated quinoline for the determination of the boiling range and refractive index.

Boiling range: Distill 50 ml. Not less than 48 ml distills between 236° and 240°, correction being made for the barometric pressure.

Refractive index: Determine at 20°.

Hydrocarbons, etc.: To 5.0 ml add 25 ml of water and 5 ml of HCl. When the quinoline has dissolved, dilute with water to 50 ml. The solution is clear.

Ammonia, Isoquinoline, etc.: Place 2 ml in a 50-ml glass stoppered cylinder, fill to within about 1 cm from the neck with boiled out and cooled water (CO_2 and oxygen free) and shake frequently during 1 hour. Decant from the undissolved quinoline, and determine the pH of the decanted solution. It should not be above 9.3.

Water: The water content may be determined by the iodine (Fischer) method, adding to the methanol solution 5 ml of glacial acetic acid.

REINECKE SALT

Ammonium Reineckate

$NH_4[Cr(NH_3)_2(SCN)_4] \cdot H_2O$; mol. wt. 354.47.

Dark red crystals or red crystalline powder. Soluble in water, alcohol, or in 50% acetone.

It is used for the colorimetric determination of choline and other organic bases, with which it forms a water-insoluble but acetone-soluble, dark red compound.

It also forms sparingly soluble compounds with some other organic bases, e.g., alkaloids, and is used for their colorimetric determination.

Standards

Sensitiveness...............to pass test   Solubility..................to pass test
                                                Assay

Sensitiveness: Dissolve 10 mg in 2 ml of H_2O Add 0.2 ml of this solution to 1 ml of a solution of 10 mg of choline chloride in 20 ml of H_2O, and shake gently.   A distinct precipitate forms within 5 to 10 seconds.

Solubility: One gram gives a clear and complete solution with 50 ml of warm water.

Assay: Weigh accurately about 0.25 g of sample and dissolve it in 20 ml of water. Add 10 ml of 10% NaOH and gently boil until the Reineckate is decomposed and the mixture is green (about 10 minutes).   Cool, and add an excess of 10% HNO_3 (2.5 ml), filter if necessary and wash with hot water.   To the cooled filtrate add 40 ml of 0.1 N silver nitrate, and titrate the excess of silver nitrate with 0.1 N thiocyanate and ferric ammonium sulfate indicator.   One ml of 0.1 N $AgNO_3$ = 0.008862 g of ammonium Reineckate.

RESORCINOL

Resorcin; *m*-Dihydroxybenzene

$C_6H_4(OH)_2$; mol. wt. 110.11.

Colorless or white needles, with a slight aromatic odor.   Soluble in 1 part of water or alcohol; soluble in ether; soluble with difficulty in chloroform.

Standards

Melting range..................109°–111°   Ignition residue.............max 0.050%
Solubility......................to pass test   Acid........................to pass test
Diresorcin and Phenol.........to pass test   *Assay*......................99–100.5%

Solubility; Diresorcin and Phenol: Dissolve 1 g in 20 ml of water.   The solution is perfectly clear with no insoluble matter remaining and, when warmed, the odor of phenol is not perceptible.

Ignition residue: Char well 2.0 g.   Allow to cool, add 0.5 ml of H_2SO_4 and ignite at first gently to expel the acid, then strongly (600°–800°) to constant weight. Any residue does not exceed 1.0 mg.

Acid: Dissolve 1 g in 10 ml of CO_2-free water and add 0.1 ml of bromocresol green solution and 0.05 ml of 0.1 N NaOH.   A blue color is produced.

Assay: Resorcinol may be assayed as follows: Dry about 2 g to constant weight over H_2SO_4, then weigh accurately about 1.5 g, dissolve in H_2O and dilute to exactly 500 ml.   Transfer 25 ml to a 500-ml long-necked or iodine flask, add 50 ml of 0.1 N bromine and follow with 50 ml of H_2O and 5 ml of HCl.   Stopper at once, shake, and let stand for 2 minutes.   Add quickly 5 ml of potassium iodide, taking care to prevent loss of bromine, stopper at once, and shake.   Rinse the stopper and neck with 20 ml of H_2O and titrate the liberated iodine, representing the excess of bromine, with 0.1 N sodium thiosulfate, adding starch toward the end.   One ml of 0.1 N bromine = 0.001835 g $C_6H_4(OH)_2$, log 26364.

$$C_6H_4(OH)_2 + 6Br \rightarrow C_6HBr_3(OH)_2 + 3HBr$$

L-RHAMNOSE

Isodulcitol

$$\overset{\displaystyle \overline{\overset{O}{}}}{\underset{\underset{H\ \ H\ OH\ OH}{\cdots\ \cdots}}{\overset{\overset{OH\ H\ H}{\cdots\ \cdots}}{CH_3C{-}C{-}C{-}C{-}CH}}}\cdot OH \cdot H_2O; \text{ mol. wt. 182.17.}$$

Colorless or white crystals or powder.   Soluble in water; sparingly soluble in alcohol.

Standards

Melting range....................97°–99°	Ignition residue.............max 0.05%
(anhydrous basis)	Acid (as acetic)..............max 0.015%
Drying loss...................max 10.2%	Chloride (Cl)................max 0.004%
Specific rotation..........+8.5° to +8.8°	Sulfate (SO$_4$)................max 0.005%
(anhydrous basis)	Heavy metals (as Cu).......max 0.001%
Solubility.. ....to pass test	

Drying loss: Dry about 2.5 g, accurately weighed, at 80° to constant weight. The loss in weight is not more than 10.2% (retain).

Specific rotation: Dissolve 2000 g of the dried sample obtained in the test for *Drying loss* in about 15 ml H_2O, add 0.1 ml of ammonium hydroxide and sufficient H_2O to make exactly 25 ml.   Mix and allow to stand for 1 hour, then determine the angular rotation of this solution in a 200-mm tube at 25°, using sodium light.   The observed rotation, in degrees, multiplied by 6.25 = $[\alpha]_D^{25}$.

Solubility: A solution of 1 g in 20 ml of H_2O is complete, clear, and colorless.

Ignition residue: Char 2 g, add 0.5 ml of H_2SO_4, and ignite to constant weight. Not more than 1.0 mg of residue remains.

Acid: To 20 ml of CO_2-free water add 0.2 ml of phenolphthalein, then add dropwise 0.02 N NaOH until a pink color is produced.   Dissolve 2 g of the sample in this solution and titrate with 0.02 N NaOH until the pink color is restored.   Not more than 0.30 ml of the NaOH is required.

Chloride: Dissolve 0.5 g in 20 ml of H_2O, add 2 drops of HNO_3 and 0.5 ml of $AgNO_3$.   Any resulting turbidity is not greater than that of a blank to which 0.02 mg of Cl has been added.

Sulfate: Dissolve 1 g in 10 ml of H_2O, add 1 ml of 1 N HCl and 2 ml of $BaCl_2$. If a turbidity is produced it is not greater than that of a blank to which 0.05 mg of SO_4 has been added.

Heavy metals: Dissolve 2 g in water to make 20 ml.   To 5 ml of the solution add 1 ml of 1 N acetic acid and 0.01 mg of Cu, and dilute to 20 ml (A).   To the remaining 15 ml add 1 ml of 1 N acetic acid and dilute to 20 ml (B).   Then to each add 5 ml of H_2S. B is not darker than A.

RHODAMIN B

Tetraethylrhodamin

$(C_2H_5)_2N$ — — $N(C_2H_5)_2Cl$; $C_{28}H_{31}ClN_2O_3$; mol. wt. 479.0.

COOH

Dark green crystals with violet tint, or reddish-violet powder.   Soluble in about 70 parts water, 10 parts of ethanol, about 150 parts of chloroform.   It is an especially suitable reagent for the detection of small amounts of antimony[1] in the presence of large amounts of tin.   It has also been proposed for the colorimetric determination of antimony.[2]   It may also be used for the detection of thallium[3] and for the detection and estimation of small amounts of tungsten.[1]

For use with this reagent the antimony must be in the pentavalent state and in strongly acid solution.   In the suitably processed solution this reagent will detect 0.002 mg of Sb^{+5} by extraction of the solution (5 ml) with 5 ml of benzene or toluene.

Standards

Sensitiveness................to pass test   Ignition residue.............max 0.20%
Solubility....................to pass test

Sensitiveness: Solution (a) Dissolve 15 mg of antimony potassium tartrate (or 10 mg of antimony trichloride) in 1 ml of HCl and dilute to 250 ml of H_2O (0.02 mg Sb per ml).

Solution (b) Dissolve 10 mg of Rhodamin B in 100 ml of water.

Dilute 0.1 ml of solution (a) with 4 ml of water and add 3 drops of 10% sodium nitrite solution.   Add 1 ml of HCl and 1 ml of (b), and shake the mixture with 5 ml of benzene for about 1 minute.   The purplish-red color of the reagent passes into the benzene.

Solubility: A solution of 0.1 g of the reagent in 20 ml of water is clear and complete.

Ignition residue: Char 0.5 g, cool, add 0.5 ml of H_2SO_4, and ignite to constant weight.   The residue does not exceed 1.0 mg.

[1] Eergrive, E., *Z. anal. Chem.* **70**, 400 (1927).
[2] Frederic, W. G., *Ind. Eng. Chem., Anal. Ed.* **13**, 922 (1941).
[3] Miller, C. C., and Love, A. J., *J. Chem. Soc.* **143**, 1258, 1263 (1940).

RIBOFLAVIN

Vitamin B_2

; $C_{17}H_{20}N_4O_6$; mol. wt. 376.38; N—14.89%.

Yellow to orange-yellow, crystalline.   Maximum fluorescence at pH 6–7, and its pH is about 6.   Stable in air, slowly affected by direct sunlight; in alkaline solution it undergoes rapid oxidation in air and light.   Solubility in water varies (from 1 : 3000 to 1·12,000) according to crystal structure.   The available riboflavin consists of mixtures of two or three different structures.   Slightly soluble to practically insoluble in the usual organic solvents, but dissolves readily in dilute alkali hydroxide solutions.

Standards

Melting range................280°–285°	Ignition residue.............max 0.05%
Specific rotation.............−115°–120°	Chloride (Cl)...............max 0.005%
Nitrogen.................14.9% ± 0.3%	Sulfur compounds (as SO_4).....max 0.01%
Solubility in hot H_2O.........to pass test	Heavy metals (as Pb)........max 0.002%
Solubility in NaOH...........to pass test	Iron (Fe)..................max 0.002%
Lumiflavin..................to pass test	

Melting range: Determine in a bath preheated to 265°.

Specific rotation: Dry about 0.3 g at 105° for 1 hour.   Weigh accurately about 250 mg of the dried riboflavin, dissolve it in 5 ml of approximately 0.1 N alcoholic NaOH, dilute with water to exactly 25 ml. Determine the angular rotation in a 200- or 100-mm tube and calculate the specific rotation, page 582.

Nitrogen: Determine by the Dumas (gasometric) method or by suitable modification.

Solubility in hot H_2O: To 250 ml of hot water add 50 mg of the sample, shake well, and heat on the steam bath for 15 minutes shaking a few times.   No insoluble matter is noticeable after allowing to stand for 1 hour.

Solubility in NaOH: To 0.5 g add 5.0 ml of 1 N NaOH and 20 ml of water and shake gently.   When dissolved, dilute to 50 ml.   The solution is clear and no insoluble matter separates.

Lumiflavin: Prepare alcohol-free chloroform as follows:
Shake chloroform 3 times with an equal volume of water.   To the finally separated chloroform add 5 g of anhydrous sodium sulfate, shake, allow to stand for 1 hour, and filter.

To 25 mg of the riboflavin add 10 ml of the de-alcoholized chloroform, shake for 5 minutes, and filter.   The filtrate is colorless.

Ignition residue: Char thoroughly 2.0 g of sample, cool, add 2 ml of HNO_3 and 2 ml of H_2SO_4, evaporate, and ignite to constant weight.   The residue does not exceed 1.0 mg (retain).

Solution A: Mix 2.0 g with 2 g of anhydrous Na_2CO_3 and ignite at 550° to 650° until most of the carbon has burned off.   Boil the residue with 25 ml of water and 1 ml of 30% H_2O_2 for a few minutes, filter, and wash to 40 ml.

Chloride: To 10 ml of *Solution A* add a slight excess of HNO_3 and follow with 1 ml of $AgNO_3$.   Any turbidity produced is not greater than that produced in a control solution containing 0.5 g Na_2CO_3, 0.025 mg of Cl^- ion, etc., in the same final volume as with the sample.

Sulfur compounds: To 20 ml of *Solution A* add 3 ml of HCl and evaporate to dryness on the steam bath.   Dissolve residue in 10 ml of H_2O; add 1 ml of 0.1 N HCl and 2 ml of $BaCl_2$.   Any turbidity produced is not greater than that in a control made by evaporating 1 g of Na_2CO_3 and 0.1 mg of SO_4 with 3 ml of HCl, dissolving the residue on 10 ml of water and treating the solution as that of the sample.

Heavy metals: To the *Ignition residue* add 2 ml of HCl, and 1 ml of H_2O and slowly evaporate to dryness on the steam bath.   Digest the residue with 20 ml of hot water for 5 minutes, cool, and dilute to 40 ml.   Dilute 20 ml of the solution to 40 ml, add 1 ml of 1 N acetic acid and 10 ml of H_2S.   Any dark color produced is not deeper than that in 40 ml of H_2O containing 0.02 mg of Pb and 1 ml of the acetic acid.

Iron: To 10 ml of the solution of the *Ignition residue* obtained in the preceding test add 2 ml of HCl and 50 mg of ammonium persulfate, dilute to 50 ml, and add 3 ml of ammonium thiocyanate solution.   Any red color produced is not darker than that in a blank to which 0.01 mg of Fe has been added.

ROSOLIC ACID

Aurin; Corallin; Pararosolic Acid

HO—⟨⟩—C—⟨⟩—OH; mol. wt. 290.30.

Reddish-brown pieces with greenish metallic luster.   Almost insoluble in water; soluble in dilute alcohol. pH range: 6.8 yellow; 8.0 red.   It is usually used as a 1% solution in 50% alcohol.

Standards

Insoluble in 50% alcohol.......max 0.1%   Ignition residue.............max 0.20%
Sensitiveness.................to pass test

Insoluble in 50% alcohol: Dissolve 1 g in 100 ml of 50% alcohol, filter any undissolved matter, wash with 50% alcohol, and dry at 105°. The undissolved residue does not exceed 1.0 mg.

Sensitiveness: Dissolve 50 mg of the indicator in 10 ml of 50% alcohol. Add 0.3 ml of this solution to 100 ml of CO_2-free water; the water is colored pale yellow. On the addition of 0.05 ml of 0.1 N NaOH the color changes to red, which is changed to the original pale yellow by the addition of 0.05 ml of 0.1 N HCl.

Ignition residue: Char 0.5 g, cool, add 0.5 ml of H_2SO_4 and ignite to constant weight. The weight of the residue is not more than 1.0 mg.

R SALT

2-Naphthol-3,6-Sodium Disulfonate

; mol. wt. 348.27.

White or grayish-white granules or powder. Soluble in about 5 parts of water; insoluble in alcohol. Its solution is practically neutral to litmus.

Standards

Sensitiveness.................to pass test	Drying loss..................max 3.0%
Solubility....................to pass test	Sulfated ignition residue.....40.0%–42.0%

Sensitiveness: (a) Dissolve 10 mg of sample in 1 ml of H_2O.

(b) Dissolve 10 mg of sulfanilic acid in 50 ml of H_2O.

To one ml of (b) add 1 drop of HCl, mix, and add 0.1 ml of 5% sodium nitrite solution. Cool to about 15°, add 1 ml of 10% sodium carbonate solution, and follow with 0.1 ml of (a). An intense brown-red color is produced.

Solubility: A solution of 0.2 g in 5 ml of H_2O is clear or practically so.

Drying loss: Dry at 105° to constant weight. The loss in weight corresponds to not more than 3.0%.

Sulfated ignition residue: Weigh accurately about 1 g of the dried sample, add 2 ml of H_2SO_4, and heat gently until the H_2SO_4 is vaporized. Cool, add 2 ml of HNO_3, evaporate, then ignite to constant weight. The weight of the residue corresponds to from 40.0% to 42.0% of the weight of the dried sample taken (theory 40.8%).

RUBEANIC ACID

Dithio-oxamide

H_2N—C—C NH_2; mol. wt. 120.20.
‖ |
S S

Bright red crystals or crystalline powder. One hundred ml of water dissolves about 25 mg of rubeanic acid; 100 ml of alcohol dissolves about 0.5 g.

This reagent is used for the detection and colorimetric determination of small quantities of Co, Cu, and Ni, and of some other metals.[1,2,3,4] It is particularly sensitive toward Cu and Ni, forming with the metals inner complex compound of the di-imido form of rubeanic acid having the configuration

Standards

Solubility in alcohol..........to pass test	Sensitiveness.................to pass test
Ignition residue..............max 0.20%	

Solubility in alcohol: Dissolve 0.1 g in 20 ml of alcohol. The reagent dissolves completely and forms a clear solution.

Ignition residue: Char 0.5 g, cool, add 0.5 ml of H_2SO_4, and ignite to constant weight. The residue does not exceed 1.0 mg.

Sensitiveness: Dissolve 25 mg of the reagent in 5 ml of alcohol. Place 0.05 ml of a solution containing 0.02 mg of cupric sulfate per ml on a filter paper, hold over ammonia, then add 2 drops of the solution of the reagent. A black spot is formed.

Perform the above test with 0.05 ml of solution containing 0.02 mg of nickel sulfate per ml. A blue to violet-blue stain is produced.

[1] Rây, P., and Rây, R. M., *Quart. J. Indian Chem. Soc.* **3**, 118 (1926).

[2] Fiegl, F, and Kapulitzas, H. J., *Mikrochemie* **8**, 239 (1930).

[3] Alport, N. L., and Skrimshire, G. H., *Quart. J. Pharm.* **5**, 461 (1932).

[4] Thomson, T. A., *Mikrochemie* **15**, 295 (1934).

SALICYLALDOXIME

HO—⟨◯⟩—CH:N·OH; mol. wt. 137.13.

White to brownish, crystalline, pronounced aromatic odor. Slightly soluble in cold water; soluble in hot water; freely soluble in alcohol, benzene, ether, and in diluted hydrochloric acid.

Standards

Melting range...................57°–59°	Solubility in alcohol...........to pass test
Sensitiveness to copper.......to pass test	Solubility in 5% HCl..........to pass test
Sensitiveness to lead..........to pass test	Ignition residue..............max 0.20%

Solution S: Dissolve 0.10 g of sample in 1 ml of alcohol and add the solution slowly to 19 ml of water previously warmed to 80°. Cool, shaking gently if necessary to dissolve the oxime, and filter.

Sensitiveness to copper: To 0.20 mg of Cu in 10 ml of H_2O add 0.1 ml of 1 N acetic acid and 0.20 ml of *Solution S.* A distinct opalescence is produced in 1 minute.

Sensitiveness to lead: To 0.4 mg of Pb contained in 10 ml of H_2O add 0.1 ml of 10% NH_3 and 0.2 ml of *Solution S.* A distinct opalescence is produced in 1 minute.

Solubility in alcohol: A solution of 0.2 g in 5 ml of alcohol is not more than slightly turbid and not darker than pale brown.

Solubility in 5% HCl: A solution of 0.2 g in 10 ml of a mixture of equal volume of 10% HCl and water is practically clear.

Ignition residue: To 0.5 g add 0.5 ml of H_2SO_4 and ignite to constant weight. Not more than 1.0 mg of residue remains.

SALICYLIC ACID

OH; mol. wt. 138.12.

White, needle-like crystals. Soluble in 500 parts of water, more soluble in hot water; freely soluble in alcohol or ether. *Keep protected from light.*

Standards

Melting range . . . . 158.5°–160.5°	Heavy metals (as Pb) . . . . max 0.0005%
Solubility in alcohol . . . . to pass test	Iron (Fe) . . . . max 0.0003%
Ignition residue . . . . max 0.020%	Substances darkened
Chloride (Cl) . . . . max 0.002%	by H_2SO_4 . . . . to pass test
Sulfate (SO_4) . . . . max 0.005%	

Solubility in alcohol: A solution of 3 g in 20 ml of alcohol is clear and without insoluble matter.

Ignition residue: Char well 5.0 g. Allow to cool, add 0.5 ml of H_2SO_4 and ignite gently at first to expel the acid, then strongly (600°–800°) to constant weight. Any residue does not exceed 1.0 mg.

Chloride: Dissolve 0.5 g in 10 ml of alcohol, add 0.5 ml of HNO_3 and 0.5 ml of $AgNO_3$. If a turbidity is produced, it is not greater than that in a blank to which 0.01 mg of Cl has been added.

Sulfate: Mix 2 g with 30 ml of hot H_2O; add, in small portions, 0.5 g of sodium carbonate, evaporate, and ignite gently, protecting from access of sulfur, until white or nearly so. Add to the residue 15 ml of H_2O and 1 ml of 30% hydrogen peroxide, boil for 5 minutes, then add 2 ml of HCl and evaporate to dryness on the steam bath. Heat the residue with 5 ml of H_2O, filter, wash to 10 ml and add 1 ml of 0.1 N HCl and 2 ml of $BaCl_2$. Any turbidity produced is not greater than that in a control made as follows: Evaporate 0.5 g of sodium carbonate, 1 ml of hydrogen peroxide and 2 ml of HCl to dryness on the steam bath. Dissolve the residue and 0.1 mg of SO_4 in 10 ml of H_2O; add 1 ml of 0.1 N HCl and 2 ml of $BaCl_2$.

Solution R: To the *Ignition residue* add 2 ml of HCl and 2 ml of water, and slowly evaporate on the steam bath to dryness. Add 0.5 ml of 1 N HCl and 20 ml of hot water, digest for 2 minutes, cool and dilute to 50 ml.

Heavy metals: To 30 ml of *Solution R* add 10 ml of H_2S. Any darkening produced is not greater than that of a control made with 0.015 mg of Pb, 0.2 ml of 1 N HCl and 10 ml of H_2S in the same final volume as with the sample.

Iron: To 20 ml of *Solution R* add 2 ml of HCl and dilute to 25 ml. Add about 30 mg of ammonium persulfate and 2 ml of ammonium thiocyanate, and mix. Any resulting red color is not darker than that in a blank to which 0.006 mg of Fe has been added.

Substances darkened by H_2SO_4: Dissolve 0.5 g of the sample in 5 ml of sulfuric acid. The color of the resulting solution is not darker than pale yellow.

SEA SAND

Pale yellow to brownish-yellow, fine granules, usually with rounded off edges.

Standards

Hydrochloric acid—soluble....max 0.12%	Chloride (Cl)...............max 0.015%
Volatile substances...........max 0.10%	

Hydrochloric acid—soluble: Digest 20 g in a covered beaker with a mixture of 20 ml of HCl and 80 ml of H_2O on the steam bath for 2 hours. Restore the original volume with water, mix, and filter. Evaporate 50 ml of the filtrate and ignite. The weight of the residue does not exceed 12.0 mg.

Volatile substances: Dry about 6 g at 105° overnight, then weigh accurately 5 g and ignite to constant weight. The loss in weight on ignition does not exceed 5.0 mg.

Chloride: Shake 1 g with 100 ml of H_2O for 2 minutes and filter. To 20 ml of the filtrate add 1 ml of HNO_3 and 1 ml of $AgNO_3$. Any turbidity produced is not greater than that in a blank to which 0.03 mg of Cl has been added.

SELENIOUS ACID

Selenous Acid

H_2SeO_3; mol. wt. 128.98; Se—61.22%; SeO_2—86.03%.

Colorless or white crystals. Very soluble in water; freely soluble in alcohol. Exposure to 100° eliminates 1 mol of water and leaves SeO_2.

Standards

Assay.................min 98% H_2SeO_2	Ignition residue.............max 0.10%
Solubility....................to pass test	Selenate; Sulfate (as SO_4)......max 0.03%

Assay: Dissolve about 0.20 g, accurately weighed, in 50 ml of water in a glass-stoppered flask. Add a solution of 3 g of potassium iodide in 10 ml of water, follow with 5 ml of HCl, stopper and allow to stand for 10 minutes. Dilute with 50 ml of water and titrate the liberated iodine with 0.1 N sodium thiosulfate, using starch indicator, until the color is no longer diminished; then titrate back with 0.1 N iodine to a blue color. The volume of the thiosulfate less that of the iodine represents the selenious acid. One ml of 0.1 N sodium thiosulfate = 0.003225 g H_2SeO_3, log 50853.

$$H_2SeO_3 + 4KI + 4HCl \rightarrow Se + 4I + 4KCl + 3H_2O$$

Solubility: A solution of 1 g in 5 ml of water or in 5 ml of alcohol is complete and clear.

Ignition residue: Gently ignite 1 g to constant weight. Not more than 1.0 mg of residue remains.

Sulfate; Selenate: To 0.5 g in a small dish add 20 mg of Na_2CO_3 and 10 ml of HCl, and *slowly* evaporate on the steam bath *under hood* to dryness. Wash down the sides of the dish with 5 ml of HCl and re-evaporate to dryness on the steam bath. Dissolve the residue in 1 ml of 1 N HCl and 15 ml of hot water, filter if necessary, and add to filtrate 2 ml of $BaCl_2$. Any turbidity in 10 minutes is not greater than that in a control prepared by treating 0.15 mg of SO_4 exactly as the sample.

SELENIUM

Se; at. wt. 78.96.

Dark red amorphous, or bluish-black crystalline. Insoluble in water; soluble in solutions of the fixed alkali hydroxides or sulfides.

Selenium is used in the Kjeldahl determination of nitrogen in place of cupric sulfate or mercury; its use shortens the time of the digestion to about half. It is also used as a dehydrogenating agent inorganic synthesis.

Standards

Ignition residue	max 0.2%	Heavy metals (as Pb)	max 0.010%
Nitrogen (N)	max 0.005%	Iron (Fe)	max 0.005%
Sulfur (S)	max 0.050%		

Ignition residue: Ignite 1 g at a temperature not above 500° to constant weight. The weight of the residue does not exceed 2.0 mg (retain).

Nitrogen: Heat 1 g with 10 ml of H_2SO_4 in a Kjeldahl flask over a free flame until dissolved and the volume of the acid is reduced to about 5 ml. After cooling, *cautiously* dilute with 100 ml of H_2O, add an excess of 30% NaOH, and distill over about 75 ml into 5 ml of H_2O containing 2 drops of 1 N HCl. Dilute the distillate with H_2O to 250 ml and mix well. To 50 ml add 1 ml of 10% NaOH and 2 ml of Nessler solution. The resulting color is not darker than that produced by treating 0.05 mg of nitrogen (0.2 mg NH_4Cl) in the same manner as the sample.

Sulfur: To 1 g add first 5 ml of HNO_3, then 10 ml of HCl and evaporate to dryness on the steam bath. Add 10 ml of HCl and slowly re-evaporate to dryness.

Take up the residue with 30 ml of H_2O and 1 ml of HCl, filter and wash to 100 ml. Heat to boiling, slowly add, while stirring, 5 ml of $BaCl_2$ and digest on the steam bath for 4 hours or allow to stand overnight.   Filter, wash until free of chloride, ignite, and weigh.   The weight of the $BaSO_4 \times 0.1374$ represents sulfur (S) and does not exceed 0.05% of the weight of the selenium.

Solution R: To the *Ignition residue* add 3 ml of HCl and 2 ml of HNO_3 and evaporate to dryness on the steam bath.   Take up the residue with 2 ml of 10% HCl and 50 ml of hot H_2O, cool, make up to 100 ml with water, mix and filter.

Heavy metals: Dilute 30 ml of *Solution R* with H_2O to 40 ml and add 10 ml of H_2S.   Any resulting color is not darker than that of a control made with 0.03 mg of Pb, 0.2 ml of 1 N HCl and 10 ml of H_2S in the same volume as with the sample.

Iron: To 20 ml of *Solution R* add 2 ml of HCl and dilute to 50 ml.   Add 50 mg of ammonium persulfate and 3 ml of ammonium thiocyanate, and mix.   Any resulting red color is not darker than that of a control made with 0.01 mg of Fe, 2 ml of HCl and the same quantities of ammonium persulfate and thiocyanate and in the same final volume as with the sample.

SEMICARBAZIDE HYDROCHLORIDE

$NH_2CONHNH_2 \cdot HCl$; mol. wt. 111.54.

White crystals or crystalline powder.   Soluble in about 2 parts of water; almost insoluble in alcohol.

Standards

Melting range.................181°–184°	Solubility....................to pass test
Melting range of the acetone compound...........184°–187°	Ignition residue.............max 0.10%

Melting range of the acetone compound: Dissolve 1.5 g of sodium acetate in 10 ml of H_2O.   Add 1 ml of acetone and follow with 0.5 g of the sample.   Shake the mixture vigorously for 2 minutes and allow to stand for 15 minutes, with occasional vigorous shaking.   A white precipitate of the carbazone forms which, after filtering, washing with water, and drying over sulfuric acid, melts between 184° and 187°.

Solubility: One gram dissolves in 20 ml of water, yielding a clear and colorless or practically colorless solution.

Ignition residue: Char well 1.0 g.   Allow to cool, add 0.5 ml of H_2SO_4, and ignite gently at first, then strongly to constant weight.   Any residue present does not exceed 1.0 g.

SILICA GEL

Silica gel is amorphous, partly hydrated SiO_2.   It occurs as brownish glassy granules varying in size according to particular use.

Silica gel is used for the removal of water entrained in organic liquids, or for the absorption of water and other vapors. For use for water absorption from organic liquids, the mesh of the granules is preferably as follows:

All passes through a 20-mesh sieve; not more than 6% remains on the 30-mesh sieve; not less than 80% remains on a 150-mesh sieve; not more than about 6% passes through a 200-mesh sieve.

There is also available silical gel colored externally with a substance (usually cobalt chloride) to serve as an indicator when the silica gel has reached its water vapor absorption capacity. The test for alcohol-ether-soluble substances does not apply to this form of silica gel.

Standards

Capacity for water absorption....min 31%	Alcohol-ether-soluble
Ignition loss..................max 6%	substances...............max 0.025%

Capacity for water absorption: When the silica gel is exposed to air of 80% relative humidity (sulfuric acid of sp. gr. 1.19, or 27% H_2SO_4) it absorbs not less than 31% of its weight.

Ignition loss: Ignite 2 to 3 g, accurately weighed, at a temperature of 900° to 1000° to constant weight. The loss corresponds to not more than 6%.

Alcohol-ether-soluble substances: Place 5.0 g of sample in a glass-stoppered flask or cylinder, add 25 ml of a mixture of equal volumes of alcohol and ether, shake well, and allow to stand for 1 hour with frequent shaking. Measure 10 ml of the liquid, filter it through a small pledget of cotton if not clear, evaporate in a tared vessel on a steam bath, and dry at 105° for 30 minutes. The weight of the residue does not exceed 0.5 mg.

SILICIC ACID

Approximately H_2SiO_3.

White, amorphous powder. Insoluble in water or in acids, but readily soluble in hydrofluoric acid; soluble in hot solutions of potassium or sodium hydroxide.

Standards

Nonvolatile with hydrofluoric	Sulfate (SO_4)...............max 0.010%
acid.....................max 0.20%	Heavy metals (as Pb)........max 0.003%
Chloride (Cl)..............max 0.005%	Iron (Fe)..................max 0.003%

Nonvolatile with hydrofluoric acid: Place 0.5 g in a platinum crucible, add 1 ml of H_2SO_4 and 10 ml of hydrofluoric acid, evaporate to dryness, and ignite to constant weight. The residue does not exceed 1.0 mg. Correct for a blank.

Chloride: Digest 1 g with 50 ml of H_2O and 1 ml of HNO_3 for 15 minutes, filter, and add to the filtrate 1 ml of $AgNO_3$. The turbidity is not greater than that in the blank to which 0.05 mg of Cl has been added.

Sulfate: Boil 2 g with 20 ml of H_2O and 0.5 of HCl for 5 minutes and filter. Neutralize the filtrate with dilute NH_4OH and dilute to 20 ml. To 10 ml add 1 ml of 1 N HCl and 2 ml of $BaCl_2$.   The turbidity is not greater than that in the blank to which 0.1 mg of SO_4 has been added.

Heavy metals: Boil 2 g with 50 ml of H_2O and 5 ml of HCl for 5 minutes, filter hot and evaporate the filtrate on the steam bath to dryness.   Take up the residue with 0.5 ml of 1 N HCl and 20 ml of hot water, digest for 5 minutes, cool, and dilute to 100 ml.   Filter if necessary and to 50 ml add 10 ml of H_2S.   Any color produced is not darker than that of a control made with 0.03 mg of Pb, 0.2 ml of 1 N HCl, and 10 ml H_2S in the same final volume as with the sample.

Iron: To 25 ml of the solution prepared in the preceding test add 2 ml of HCl and 50 mg of ammonium persulfate, dilute to 50 ml, and add 3 ml of ammonium thiocyanate.   Any resulting red color is not darker than that in a blank to which 0.015 mg of Fe has been added.

SILICOTUNGSTIC ACID

Approximately: $SiO_2 \cdot 12WO_3 \cdot 26H_2O(14\%)$; in anhydrous: SiO_2—21%; WO_3—97.9%.

White or slightly yellow crystals; deliquescent.   Very soluble in water or alcohol. *Keep in tightly closed containers, in a cool place.*

Standards

Solubility in H_2O; in Alcohol...to pass test	Tungstate....................to pass test
Ammonia precipitate..........to pass test	Heavy metals (as Pb)........max 0.003%
Chloride (Cl)................max 0.005%	Ignition loss (water)...........max 15%
Nitrate (NO_3)...............max 0.002%	*Assay*
Sulfate (SO_4)................max 0.01%	

Solubility in H_2O; in Alcohol: 1.0 g dissolves completely in 10 ml of water, and in 10 ml of alcohol and the solutions are colorless.

Ammonia precipitate: To the water solution from the preceding test add a few drops of 10% NH_3.   No precipitation occurs, and the solution remains clear after the addition of 1 ml more of the ammonia.

Chloride: To a solution of 0.5 g in 20 ml of H_2O add 0.5 ml of HNO_3 and 1 ml of $AgNO_3$.   Any turbidity produced is not more than that in a blank to which 0.025 mg of Cl has been added.

Nitrate: Dissolve 0.5 g in 10 ml of H_2O, add 10 mg NaCl, 0.10 ml of indigo carmine and 10 ml of H_2SO_4.   The blue color remains for at least 2 minutes.

Sulfate: Dissolve 1.0 g in 10 ml of H_2O, add 1 ml of 1 N HCl and add 1 ml of $BaCl_2$.   If a turbidity is produced it is not greater than that in the blank to which 0.1 mg of SO_4 has been added.

Tungstate: To a filtered solution of 0.5 g in 5 ml of H_2O add 5 drops of HCl. The clarity of the solution is not affected.

Heavy metals: Dissolve 1 g in 15 ml of 10%, NaOH, add 2 ml of NH_4OH, and dilute with H_2O to 50 ml.   To 15 ml add 5 ml of H_2S.   Any color produced is not darker than that in a blank to which 0.01 mg of Pb has been added.

Ignition loss (water): Weigh accurately about 1 g into a tared small porcelain dish and expose it to a temperature of 120° for 2 hours, then ignite it gently (400°–500°) to constant weight.   The loss in weight does not exceed 14%.

Assay for WO₃: Transfer the residue obtained from the test for *Ignition loss* to a tared silica boat and weigh.   Place the boat in a short silica tube and ignite the tube at the site of the boat at a red heat, while passing into it simultaneously a stream of dry hydrogen chloride (HCl) and of air, until the residue in the boat is white or practically so.   After cooling reweigh the boat with its contents.   The loss in weight represents the WO₃ and it amounts to from 94% to 98%.

Assay for SiO₂: Transfer the residue completely from the *Assay for WO₃* to tared platinum crucible or dish and weigh.   Add 3 ml of hydrofluoric acid and evaporate on the steam bath.   Again add 2 ml of HF acid, re-evaporate and ignite gently.   Cool and weigh.   The loss in weight represents the SiO₂ and it should amount to not less than 1.9% and to not more than 2.2% (anhydrous basis.)   The ratio of (% WO₃)/(% SiO₂) is between 43 and 49.

SILVER, PRECIPITATED

Ag; at. wt. 107.88.

Fine, gray powder.   Insoluble in water; dissolves in nitric acid or in hot sulfuric acid, also in solutions of alkali cyanides in the presence of air.

Standards

Assay......................min 99.7%	Not precipitated by HCl.......max 0.03%
Nitric acid—insoluble.........max 0.01%	

Assay: Dry about 1 g for 1 hour at 120°.   Weigh accurately about 0.4 g of the dried sample and transfer it, with the aid of 15 to 20 ml of H₂O, into a 300-ml flask   Add in small portions nitric acid (about 5 ml) until the silver has dissolved.   Heat the solution gently until the oxides of nitrogen are expelled, cool, dilute with 100 ml of H₂O, add 2 ml of ferric ammonium sulfate, and titrate with 0.1 N thiocyanate to a permanent reddish color.   One ml of 0.1 N thiocyanate = 0.01079 g of Ag, log 03302.

Nitric acid—insoluble: To 10 g add 25 ml of H₂O, then add in small portions HNO₃ until the silver has dissolved.   Dilute the solution with 50 ml of water and heat on the steam bath for 1 hour.   Filter on a filtering crucible (retain filtrate), wash with H₂O until the washings no longer give an opalescence with a drop of HCl and dry at 105°.   The weight of the insoluble matter does not exceed 1.0 mg.

Substances not precipitated by HCl: Dilute the filtrate from the test for *Nitric acid—insoluble* to 250 ml, heat to boiling and add, dropwise, sufficient HCl (about 5 ml) to precipitate all of the silver, avoiding a great excess.   Cool, dilute to 300 ml and allow to stand overnight.   Filter, evaporate 200 ml of the filtrate to dryness in porcelain, and ignite gently.   The weight of the residue, after correcting for a blank with the same quantities of reagents and water, including filtration and evaporation, is not more than 2.0 mg.

SILVER ACETATE

$AgC_2H_3O_2$; mol. wt. 166.92; Ag—64.64%.

Small white or nearly white crystals.   Discolors on exposure to light.   Slowly soluble in 100 parts of water; soluble in about 35 parts of boiling water; soluble in dilute nitric acid.

Standards

Assay.............min 99.5% $AgC_2H_3O_2$	Nitrate (NO_3)...............max 0.01%
Insoluble and Chloride........max 0.02%	Not precipitated by HCl.......max 0.03%

Assay: Weigh accurately about 0.5 g and dissolve it in a mixture of 10 ml of H_2O and 5 ml of HNO_3.   Dilute the solution with 100 ml of water, add 2 ml of ferric ammonium sulfate and titrate with 0.1 N thiocyanate to a permanent reddish color.   One ml of 0.1 N thiocyanate = 0.01669 g $AgC_2H_3O_2$, log 22246.

Insoluble and Chloride: Boil gently 5 g with 100 ml of water and 5 ml of nitric acid until dissolved.   Filter hot (retain filtrate) on a filtering crucible, wash with hot water until the washings no longer give an opalescence with a drop of HCl, and dry at 105°.   The weight of the insoluble residue does not exceed 1.0 mg.

Nitrate: To 0.2 g of the powdered sample add 2 ml of phenoldisulfonic acid, and heat on the steam bath for 15 minutes.   Cool, add 25 ml of H_2O, cool, and make alkaline with ammonia.   Any yellow color produced is not darker than that produced from 0.02 mg of NO_3 treated in the same manner as the sample.

Not precipitated by HCl: Test the filtrate from *Insoluble and Chloride* as described for Silver, Precipitated.   The weight of the residue is not more than 1.0 mg.

SILVER CARBONATE

Ag_2CO_3; mol. wt. 275.77; Ag—78.24%; CO_2—15.96%.

Light yellow when freshly precipitated, but becomes grayish yellow on drying. Darkens in light.   Decomposes at about 220° into Ag_2O and CO_2.   Density 6.10. Practically insoluble in cold water, soluble in 2000 parts of boiling H_2O, in dilute HNO_3, acetic acid and in NH_4OH, NaCN.

Standards

Assay........................min 99%	Nitrate (NO_3)...............max 0.05%
Drying loss..................max 0.20%	Sulfate (SO_4)...............max 0.005%
Nitric acid—insoluble	Alkali carbonate (Na_2CO_3).....max 0.05%
(AgCl etc.)...............max 0.020%	Iron (Fe)...................max 0.001%
Not precipitated by HCl.......max 0.05%	

Assay: Weigh accurately about 0.5 g of the dried sample from the test for *Drying loss* and dissolve it, in a flask, in a mixture of 20 ml of water and 5 ml of

HNO_3.   Dilute with 75 ml of cold water, add 2 ml of ferric ammonium sulfate and titrate with 0.1 N thiocyanate to a permanent reddish color.   One ml of 0.1 N thiocyanate = 0.01384 mg Ag_2CO_3, log 14114.

Drying loss: Dry about 1 g at 105° for 2 hours.   The loss in weight corresponds to not more than 0.20%.

Nitric acid—insoluble: Dissolve 10 g in a mixture of 5 ml of HNO_3 and 20 ml of water and dilute to 50 ml.   If an insoluble residue is present, filter though a filtering crucible (retain filtrate).   Wash with H_2O until washings give no opalescence with a drop of diluted HCl and dry at 105°.   The weight of the insoluble matter does not exceed 2.0 mg.

Not precipitated by HCl: Dilute the filtrate from *Nitric acid—insoluble* to 200 ml, heat to boiling and dropwise add HCl (7 ml) to precipitate all the silver, avoiding a great excess of the HCl.   Cool, dilute to 250 ml and allow to stand overnight.   Filter and wash with water to make the filtrate 300 ml.   Evaporate 100 ml to dryness over steam and ignite gently.   The weight of the residue, after correcting for a blank with the same quantities of water and reagents, including filtration, does not exceed 1.7 mg.

Nitrate: To 0.6 g add 50 mg of Na_2CO_3 and 2 ml of warm phenoldisulfonic acid, mix well and heat on the steam bath for 15 minutes.   Cool, cautiously add 20 ml of water, then make alkaline with NH_4OH (S).   Prepare a control (C) as follows: Add 50 mg of Na_2CO_3 to 3 ml of standard nitrate solution (0.05 mg NO_3), evaporate on a steam bath to dryness and treat the dry residue as the sample. Dilute both to same volume.   The solution of the sample is no darker than that of the control.

The actual amount of NO_3 present in the sample may be quantitatively approximated by diluting the darker of the two solutions (S and C) with dilute NH_4OH (1 + 10) to match the lighter colored solution.   The % NO_3 is then calculated by the formula: V_s/V_c × mg NO_3 in control × 100/wt. V_s and V_c are the respective volumes, in ml, of the solutions and wt is the weight of the sample used.

Sulfate: Evaporate 100 ml of the filtrate from the test for *Not precipitated by HCl* to dryness on the steam bath.   Take up the residue with 10 ml of water and 1 ml of 0.1 N HCl, filter if not clear and add 2 ml of $BaCl_2$.   If a turbidity ensues it is not greater than that in a control made with 0.15 mg SO_4, 1 ml of 0.1 N HCl, and in the same final volume as with the sample.

Alkali carbonate: Digest 2 g with 25 ml of water in a covered beaker for 10 minutes, filter and add to the filtrate 1 drop of methyl orange.   If a yellow color is produced, it requires not more than 0.2 ml of 0.1 N HCl to change the color to pink.

Iron: To the residue from the test for *Not precipitated by HCl* add 2 ml of HCl and 5 ml of water, warm for a few minutes and dilute to 50 ml.   To 5.0 ml of the dilution add 2 ml of HCl, dilute to 50 ml and add 3 ml of ammonium thiocyanate. Any red color produced is not darker than that of a control made with 0.01 mg of Fe.

SILVER CHLORIDE

AgCl; mol. wt. 143.34; Ag—75.26%; Cl—24.74%.

Silver chloride is white, but it rapidly darkens in light; hence the product of commerce is usually grayish-white. Melts at 455°. Density 4.56. Solubility in H_2O: 1 mg in 500 ml; HCl increases its solubility in H_2O; soluble in cold NH_4OH more readily on heating; soluble in solutions of NaCN, thiosulfate and ammonium carbonate.

Standards

Insoluble in NH_4OH..........max 0.05%	Nitrate (NO_3)...............max 0.002%
Assay.................min 99.5% AgCl	Foreign heavy metals (Cu, Pb).max 0.003%
Soluble substances............max 0.05%	Iron (Fe)...................max 0.001%

Insoluble in NH_4OH: Weigh accurately 2.000 g of sample and transfer completely to a beaker. Add 20 ml of water and 1 ml of HNO_3, mix and heat for 10 minutes on the steam bath. Now add 5 ml of NH_4OH (28% NH_3), stir well, cover the beaker and heat at 70°–80°, adding more NH_4OH and H_2O if necessary until no more dissolves. Filter through a small, tared glass crucible, wash (retain filtrate and washings) with small volumes of water containing about 1% NH_3, and dry at 105°. The weight of the insoluble material does not exceed 1.0 mg.

Assay: Completely transfer the filtrate and washings from the preceding test to a 200-ml volumetric flask and dilute to the mark. Transfer 100 ml of this solution to a beaker, add 0.2 ml of HCl, heat to boiling and add, while stirring, HNO_3 until no more is precipitated on further addition of HNO_3, then add 5 drops of HCl. Allow to stand in the dark for 2–3 hours or overnight, then filter on a tared, sintered glass crucible and wash the silver chloride well with about 50 ml of water. Dry at 120° to constant weight. Not less than 99.5% of the sample taken is recovered.

Soluble substances: To 2.0 g add 50 ml of hot water and 2 ml of HNO_3 and stir well. Allow to stand with frequent stirring for 1 hour, then filter and wash with a little water. Evaporate the filtrate and washings to dryness over steam, dry at 120° for 1 hour and weigh. The weight of the residue does not exceed 1.0 mg.

Nitrate: To 0.5 g of sample add 5 ml of water, heat on the steam bath and add ammonium hydroxide (28% NH_3) a few drops at a time, shaking after addition, and warming, if necessary, to dissolve the AgCl. Cool to room temperature, add cold water to about 20 ml and reprecipitate the AgCl by the addition of just sufficient cold 25% H_2SO_4. Dilute with water to 25 ml and filter. To 10 ml of the filtrate add 10 mg of NaCl, 0.2 ml of diphenylamine solution, then add 10 ml of H_2SO_4. No blue color is produced after standing for 1 hour.

Foreign heavy metals: Digest the residue from the test for *soluble substances* with 0.5 ml of 1 N HCl and 20 ml of hot water for 10 minutes, filter and dilute to 50 ml. Dilute 25 ml of this solution to 40 ml and add 10 ml of H_2S. Any resulting color is not darker than that of a control made with 0.03 mg of Pb and 0.2 ml of 1 N HCl in 10 ml of water.

Iron: To the remaining 25 ml of the solution from the preceding test add 2 ml of HCl and 3 ml of ammonium thiocyanate. Any resulting red color is not darker than that of a control made with 0.01 mg of Fe and the same qualities of the reagents and in the same final volume as with the sample.

SILVER IODATE

$AgIO_3$; mol. wt. 282.8; Ag—38.15%; I—44.88%; O—16.97%.

White powder; slightly soluble in water; soluble in ammonium hydroxide and in solutions of KI or alkali cyanides.

Silver iodate is used for the determination of chloride in biological fluids, such as blood, urine, etc., by the method of Julius Sendroy.[1]

Standards

Insoluble in NH_4OH..........max 0.05%	Nitrogen compounds.........max 0.001%
Solubility in water............to pass test	

Insoluble in NH_4OH: Dissolve 2 g in a mixture of 20 ml of NH_4OH and 30 ml of H_2O. Filter any undissolved matter, wash with diluted ammonia $(1+3)$, and dry at 105°. Its weight does not exceed 1.0 mg.

Solubility in water: Shake 2 g with exactly 200 ml of H_2O in a glass-stoppered flask for 2 hours at 25° ± 1°. Filter through a small filter, rejecting the first 20 ml of filtrate, then evaporate exactly 100 ml of the subsequent filtrate to dryness on the steam bath, and dry at 105° to constant weight. The weight of the residue is not less than 5 mg and not more than 5.6 mg. (This amount of residue represents the solubility of silver iodate in water at 25°.)

Nitrogen compounds: Dissolve the residue from the preceding test in 40 ml of H_2O, add 10 ml of 10% NaOH and 0.5 g of fine aluminum wire in small pieces. Allow to stand for 2 hours protected from access or loss of NH_3, then distill about 40 ml into 5 ml of H_2O containing 1 drop of dilute HCl. Add to the distillate 1 ml of 10% NaOH and 2 ml of Nessler solution. Any color produced is not darker than that of a blank to which 0.01 mg of N (0.04 mg NH_4Cl) has been added.

[1] "Microdetermination of chloride in biological fluids with solid silver iodate," *J. Biol. Chem.* **120**, No. 2, Sept. 1937.

SILVER NITRATE

$AgNO_3$; mol. wt. 169.98; Ag—63.50%; NO_3—36.50%.

Colorless, transparent plates or white crystals. Melts at about 200°. It is stable in pure, dry air, but darkens in the presence of organic matter.

This reagent when thoroughly dried, preferably by fusion, is about 99.9% pure.

Standards

Insoluble....................to pass test	Sulfate (SO_4)................max 0.002%
Free acid...................to pass test	Not precipitated by HCl......max 0.010%
Chloride (Cl)...............max 0.001%	Foreign metals (as Cu, Fe, Pb).max 0.002%

Insoluble: Dissolve 10 g in 15 ml of water. A clear and complete solution results (retain the solution).

Free acid: Dissolve 5 g in 50 ml of water, add 5 drops of 0.04% bromocresol green solution and mix well.   The solution has a blue color, not green or yellow.

Chloride: To a solution of 2 g of the sample in 25 ml of water add 1 ml of HNO_3. Any resulting turbidity is not greater than that produced by adding 1 ml each of silver nitrate solution and of HNO_2 to 25 ml of water containing 0.01 mg of Cl.

Sulfate: Dissolve 6 g in 150 ml of water, heat to boiling, and gradually add 5 ml of HCl previously diluted with 15 ml of water.   Allow to stand overnight, add water to make 180 ml, mix, and filter.   Evaporate 150 ml of the filtrate to dryness on the steam bath.   Take up the residue with 5 ml of water and 0.5 ml of 1 N HCl, filter, wash to 10 ml, and add 1 ml of $BaCl_2$.   Any resulting turbidity is not greater than that in a control made with a solution of 0.1 mg of SO_4 in 10 ml of water treated with 0.5 ml of 1 N HCl and 1 ml of $BaCl_2$ solution.

Not precipitated by HCl: Dilute the solution from the test for *Insoluble* to about 250 ml, heat to boiling, and add slowly, with constant stirring, 10 ml of HCl previously diluted with 20 ml of water.   Allow to stand overnight, filter, and wash with about 50 ml of water.   Evaporate the filtrate, in porcelain or silica, to dryness on the steam bath.   Heat the residue with 10 ml of water and 2 drops of HCl, filter, and wash with 10 ml of water.   Evaporate the filtrate to dryness on the steam bath and dry at 105° for 2 hours.   (Retain this residue and also that from the blank).   Run a blank with the same quantities of water and reagents, including filtrations and evaporation.   The corrected weight of the residue from the sample is not more than 1.0 mg.

Foreign metals: To each of the residues obtained in the test for *Not precipitated by HCl* add 1 ml of 10% HCl and 10 ml of hot water.   To the residue from the blank add 0.2 mg of Cu, and dilute both to 100 ml.   Then to 20 ml of each add 10 ml of H_2S.   The solution from the residue of the sample is not darker than that from the blank.

SILVER OXIDE

Ag_2O; mol. wt. 231.76%; Ag—93.10%; O—6.90%.

Heavy, brownish-black powder; slowly decomposing on exposure to light. Very slightly soluble in water; easily soluble in dilute nitric acid.   *Keep away from ammonia fumes and easily oxidizable substances, and also keep protected from light.*

Standards

Assay . . . . min 99.7% Ag_2O	Nitrate (NO_3) . . . . max 0.01%
Drying loss . . . . max 0.25%	Alkalinity (as NaOH) . . . . max 0.012%
Nitric acid—insoluble . . . . max 0.02%	Not precipitated by HCl . . . . . . max 0.05%

Assay: Weigh accurately about 0.5 g of the dried sample from the test for *Drying loss* and dissolve it in a mixture of 20 ml of water and 5 ml of HNO_3.   Dilute the solution with 100 ml of H_2O, add 2 ml of ferric ammonium sulfate, and titrate with 0.1 N thiocyanate to a permanent reddish color.   One ml of 0.1 N thiocyanate = 0.01159 g Ag_2O, log 06408.

Drying loss: Weigh accurately about 1 g and dry for 3 hours at 120°. The loss corresponds to not more than 0.25%.

Nitric acid—insoluble: Dissolve 5 g in a mixture of 5 ml of nitric acid and 10 ml of water and dilute with 50 ml of water. Filter any undissolved residue on a filtering crucible (retain the filtrate), wash with water until the washing gives no opalescence with a drop of HCl, and dry at 105°. The weight of the insoluble residue does not exceed 1.0 mg.

Nitrate: To 0.5 g add 30 mg of Na_2CO_3 and 2 ml of warm phenoldisulfonic acid, mix well and heat on the steam bath for 15 minutes. Cool, *cautiously* add 20 ml of water, then make alkaline with NH_4OH (S). Prepare a control (C) as follows: Add 30 mg of Na_2CO_3 to 5 ml of standard nitrate solution (0.05 mg NO_3), evaporate on a steam bath to dryness and treat the dry residue as the sample. Dilute both to same volume. The solution of the sample is no darker than that of the control.

Alkalinity: Digest 2 g with 40 ml of H_2O on the steam bath for 15 minutes, cool, and dilute to 50 ml. Filter, rejecting the first 10 ml. To 25 ml of the filtrate add 2 drops of phenolphthalein, and if a pink color is produced titrate with 0.02 N HCl. Not more than 0.2 ml of the HCl is required to discharge the pink color.

Not precipitated by HCl: Test the filtrate from the test for *Nitric acid—insoluble* as described for Silver, Precipitated. The weight of the residue does not exceed 1.7 mg.

SILVER SULFATE

Ag_2SO_4; mol. wt. 311.83; Ag—69.19%; SO_4—30.81%.

Colorless or white crystals, or crystalline powder. Slowly soluble in 150 parts of cold water, soluble in 70 parts of boiling water; soluble in nitric acid and in hot concentrated sulfuric acid. *Keep protected from light and organic matter.*

Standards

Assay.................min 99.7% Ag_2SO_4	Not precipitated by HCl......max 0.030%
Insoluble and Chloride.......max 0.020%	Iron (Fe)..................max 0.001%
Nitrate (NO_3)...............max 0.001%	

Assay: Dry about 1 g for 2 hours at 120°. Weigh accurately about 0.5 g of the dried sample and dissolve, by warming if necessary, in a mixture of 20 ml of H_2O and 5 ml of HNO_3. Cool the solution, dilute with 100 ml of H_2O, add 2 ml of ferric ammonium sulfate, and titrate with 0.1 N thiocyanate to a permanent reddish color. One ml of 0.1 N thiocyanate = 0.01559 g Ag_2SO_4, log 19285.

Insoluble and Chloride: Powder 5 g and boil it gently with 300 ml of water and 5 ml of HNO_3 until dissolved. Filter any undissolved residue (retain filtrate) on a filtering crucible, wash with hot water, and dry at 105°. The weight of the undissolved residue does not exceed 1.0 mg.

Nitrate: To 1.0 g of sample contained in a small beaker add 10 mg of Na_2CO_3 (A). For a control place in a similar beaker 1.0 ml of standard nitrate solution (0.01 mg NO_3), add 10 mg Na_2CO_3 and evaporate to dryness on the steam bath (B). Then to each add 3 ml of warm phenoldisulfonic acid, mix and heat on the steam bath for 15 minutes.   Cool, add 20 ml of water and sufficient ammonia to produce a full yellow color, and dilute both to the same volume with ammonia.   The color of A is not darker than that of B.

The actual amount (%) of NO_3 present in the sample may be quantitatively approximated by diluting the darker of the two solutions with dilute ammonia to match the color intensity of the lighter colored one, and the NO_3 then calculated by the formula: $V_A/V_B \times$ mg NO_3 in the control, $\times$ 100/wt, V_A and V_B representing the volumes, in ml, of the respective solution, and wt the weight of the sample used.

Not precipitated by HCl: Heat to boiling the filtrate from the test for *Insoluble and Chloride* and add, dropwise with stirring, sufficient HCl (about 3.5 ml) to precipitate all of the silver, avoiding a great excess.   Cool, dilute to 300 ml, and allow to stand overnight.   Filter, evaporate to dryness 200 ml of the filtrate in porcelain, and ignite to constant weight.   The weight of the residue, after correcting for a blank with the same quantities of reagents and water, including filtration and evaporation, is not more than 1.0 g (retain).

Iron: To the residue from the preceding test add 2 ml of HCl and 2 ml of H_2O, and slowly evaporate on the steam bath to dryness.   Take up in 1 ml of HCl and 20 ml of water, filter if necessary, and dilute to 50 ml.   To 10 ml of this solution add 2 ml of HCl and dilute to 50 ml.   Now add about 30 mg of ammonium persulfate and 3 ml of ammonium thiocyanate, and mix.   Any resulting red color is not darker than that of a control made with 0.01 mg of Fe, 2 ml of HCl and the same quantities of the reagents and in the same final volume as with the sample.

SODA LIME

Sodium Hydroxide with Lime

Soda lime is a mixture of variable proportions of sodium hydroxide and/or potassium hydroxide with calcium oxide.   It usually is in the form of white or slightly colored granules.   It absorbs carbon dioxide from the air.   *Keep in tightly closed containers*.   It may contain an indicator to show by change in color when it reaches maximum absorption of water.

Standards

Carbon dioxide absorption capacity....................min 25%	Drying loss....................max 8%

Carbon dioxide absorption capacity: Insert a pledget of cotton in the bottom of a U-tube, fill one side of the tube with anhydrous calcium chloride, stopper, and weigh.   Now place about 10 g of the sample in the other side of the tube, stopper, and reweigh.   Connect the side of the tube containing the soda lime with a wash bottle containing concentrated sulfuric acid and which in turn is connected with a cylinder of CO_2.   Slowly pass the CO_2 for 3 hours, weigh the U-tube, then pass CO_2 for 1-hour periods until the gain in weight between two successive weighings is not over 1% of the weight of the soda lime.

Drying loss: Weigh accurately about 5 g and dry at 200° for 18 hours.   The loss in weight does not exceed 8%.

SODIUM

Na; at. wt. 23.00.

Soft, waxy.   Freshly cut surface is silvery-white, but rapidly becomes dull gray in the air.   Melts at 97.6°.   Decomposes water with the evolution of hydrogen and much heat.   Dissolves in alcohols, forming sodium alcoholate.   *Keep in tightly closed containers, suitably protected from air and moisture.*

Standards

Chloride (Cl).............max 0.0015%   Sulfate (SO_4).............max 0.002%
Nitrogen (N).............max 0.002%   Heavy metals (as Pb)........max 0.001%
Phosphate (PO_4)..........max 0.0005%   Iron (Fe)..................max 0.001%

Solution S: Free the metal from oil, etc., if any, by shaving off a thin layer. Weigh 20 g, cut it into *small* pieces and add them, one at a time, to 400 ml of ice-cold water.   When all the sodium has dissolved, dilute to 500.0 ml and use for the following tests:

Chloride: Neutralize 25 ml of *Solution S* with HNO_3, add 1 ml excess acid and 1 ml of $AgNO_3$.   The resulting turbidity is not greater than that in the blank to which 0.015 mg of Cl has been added.

Nitrogen: Add 2 ml of Nessler solution to 13 ml of *Solution S* previously diluted to 50 ml.   The color is not darker than that of a control made with 0.01 mg nitrogen (0.04 mg NH_4Cl), 2.5 ml of *Solution S* and 2 ml of Nessler solution in the same volume as the sample.

Phosphate: *Cautiously* neutralize to litmus paper 50 ml of *Solution S* with 25% H_2SO_4, then add 5 ml more of the acid, evaporate, and heat to the evolution of copious sulfuric fumes.   Cool, dissolve the residue in 20 ml of water, filter, and wash with 5 ml of water.   Add to the filtrate 1 ml each of phosphate reagents **A** and **B** and heat at 60° for 10 minutes.   If a blue color is produced, it is not darker than that of a control made with 0.01 mg PO_4, 2 ml of 25% H_2SO_4 and the same quantities of the reagents (and in the same volume) as with the sample, and treated in the same manner as the sample.

Sulfate: Neutralize 125 ml of *Solution S* with HCl and evaporate to 90 ml.   Add 0.5 ml of HCl and 5 ml of $BaCl_2$, and allow to stand overnight.   No turbidity or precipitate is produced.

Heavy metals: To 25 ml of *Solution S*, cautiously add 15 ml of HCl and 0.02 mg of Pb (*A*).   To 75 ml of *Solution S* add 15 ml of HCl (*B*) and treat each as follows: Evaporate on the steam bath to dryness.   Dissolve the residue in 30 ml of water, add 1 drop of phenolphthalein solution, then add 0.1 N NaOH until the solution is just pink.   Add 1 ml of 1 N acetic acid, dilute to 40 ml, and add 10 ml of H_2S. *B* is not darker than *A*.

Iron: Neutralize 25 ml of *Solution S* with HCl, add 2 ml of the acid in excess, and dilute to 50 ml.   Add about 30 mg of ammonium persulfate and 3 ml of ammonium thiocyanate.   Any red color produced is not darker than that of a control made with 0.01 mg of Fe, 2 ml of HCl, and the same quantities of the reagents and in the same final volume as with the sample.

SODIUM ACETATE

$NaC_2H_3O_2 \cdot 3H_2O$; mol. wt. 136.09; anhydrous—60.28%; H_2O—39.72%; Na—16.90%; acetic acid—44.12%.

Colorless or white crystals, or fused lumps.   Efflorescent in dry air.   Soluble in 1 part of water; sparingly soluble in alcohol.

Standards

Insoluble....................max 0.005%	Calcium, Magnesium, and
Free acid (as acetic)..........max 0.012%	NH₄OH precipitate........max 0.010%
Free alkali..................to pass test	Heavy metals (as Pb).......max 0.0005%
Chloride (Cl)................max 0.001%	Iron (Fe)..................max 0.0005%
Phosphate (PO₄)...........max 0.0005%	Permanganate-reducing
Sulfate (SO₄)...............max 0.002%	substances................to pass test
	Assay, anhydrous basis.......99.0–100.3%

Insoluble: Dissolve 20 g in 150 ml of H_2O and heat on steam bath for 1 hour. Filter any undissolved matter, wash with water, and dry at 105°.   The insoluble residue does not exceed 1.0 mg.

Free acid; Free alkali: Dissolve 5 g in 100 ml of CO_2-free water and add 0.2 ml of phenolphthalein.   If a pink color is produced it requires not more than 0.05 ml of 0.1 N HCl to discharge it.   If no pink color is produced, not more than 0.1 ml of 0.1 N NaOH is required to produce a pink color.

Chloride: Dissolve 2 g in 20 ml of H_2O, add 2 ml of HNO_3 and 1 ml of $AgNO_3$. Any turbidity is not greater than that in a blank to which 0.02 mg of Cl has been added.

Phosphate: Dissolve 4 g in 20 ml of H_2O.   Add 2 ml of 25% H_2SO_4 and 1 ml each of phosphate reagents **A** and **B**, and heat at 60° for 10 minutes.   If a blue color is produced, it is not darker than that of a control made with 0.02 mg PO_4, 2 ml of 25% H_2SO_4, the same quantities of the phosphate reagents and in the same final volume as with the sample.

Sulfate: Dissolve 5 g in 25 ml of H_2O.   Add 2 ml of 10% HCl and 3 ml of $BaCl_2$, and heat at about 75° for 5 minutes.   Any turbidity produced is not greater than that in the blank with 0.15 mg of SO_4 added.

Calcium, Magnesium, and NH₄OH precipitate: Dissolve 10 g in 100 ml of H_2O, add 5 ml of ammonium oxalate, 2 ml of ammonium phosphate, and 15 ml of NH_4OH, allow to stand overnight.   If a precipitate is present filter, wash with 2.5% NH_3, and ignite.   The weight of the ignited precipitate does not exceed 1.0 mg.

Heavy metals: Dissolve 5 g in 15 ml of water, add 5 ml of 10% HCl, and dilute to 25 ml.   To 5 ml add 0.015 mg of Pb and dilute to 40 ml (A).   To the remaining

20 ml add water to make 40 ml (*B*).   Then to each add 10 ml of H_2S.   *B* is not darker than *A*.

Iron: Dissolve 2 g in water, add 3 ml of HCl, and dilute to 50 ml.   Add about 50 mg of ammonium persulfate and 3 ml of ammonium thiocyanate.   Any resulting red color is not darker than that of a blank to which 0.01 mg of Fe has been added.

Permanganate-reducing substances: Dissolve 5 g in 50 ml of H_2O, add 2 ml of H_2SO_4 and 0.1 ml of 0.1 *N* potassium permanganate.   The pink color is not entirely discharged within 30 minutes.

Assay: Sodium acetate may be assayed, after drying at 150° to constant weight, by the general methods for Alkali Salts of Organic Acids, page 564.   One ml of 0.1 *N* acid = 0.008204 g of $NaC_2H_3O_2$.

SODIUM ACETATE, ANHYDROUS

$NaC_2H_3O_2$; mol. wt. 82.04; Na—28.04%; acetic acid—73.19%.

White crystals.   Soluble in 2 parts of water.   *Keep in tightly closed containers.*

Standards

Insoluble.....................max 0.01%	Sulfate (SO_4)...............max 0.003%
Alkalinity (as Na_2CO_3)........max 0.02%	Calcium, Magnesium, and
Drying loss (water)............max 1.0%	NH$_4$OH precipitate.........max 0.02%
Chloride (Cl)................max 0.002%	Heavy metals (as Pb)........max 0.001%
Phosphate (PO_4).............max 0.001%	Iron (Fe)...................max 0.001%

Insoluble: Dissolve 10 g in 100 ml of water.   If insoluble matter is present, filter, wash it well with warm water, and dry at 105°.   Its weight does not exceed 1.0 mg.

Alkalinity: Dissolve 5 g in 50 ml of H_2O and add 3 drops of phenolphthalein. If a pink color is produced, not more than 0.2 ml of 0.1 *N* HCl is required to discharge it.

Drying loss: Weigh accurately about 2 g and dry to constant weight at 120°. The loss corresponds to not more than 1.0%.

Chloride: Dissolve 1 g in 20 ml of water, add 1 ml of HNO_3 and 1 ml of $AgNO_3$. Any turbidity produced is not greater than that of a blank to which 0.02 mg of Cl has been added.

Sulfate: Dissolve 3 g in 20 ml of H_2O, neutralize with 1 *N* HCl, then add 1 ml excess of the acid and 2 ml of $BaCl_2$.   Any turbidity is not greater than that in a control made with 0.15 mg of SO_4, 1 ml of 1 *N* HCl, and 2 ml of $BaCl_2$ in the same volume as with the sample.

Calcium, Magnesium, and NH$_4$OH precipitate: Determine as in Sodium Acetate.   The residue does not exceed 2.0 mg.

Phosphate; Heavy metals; Iron: Test as described for Sodium Acetate, using one-half of the quantities of sample.   The results conform to the requirements there stated.

SODIUM ALIZARINSULFONATE

Alizarin Carmine; Alizarin Red; Alizarin S

$\cdot H_2O$; mol. wt. 360.28.

Yellowish-brown or orange-yellow powder.   Freely soluble in water with a yellow color; sparingly soluble in alcohol. pH range: 3.7 yellow; 5.2 violet. Usually used as a 1% aqueous solution, as an indicator and for the determination of aluminum, fluorine.

Sensitiveness: Add 0.2 ml of a 1% aqueous solution of the sodium alizarin-sulfonate to 100 ml of water and follow with 0.05 ml of 0.1 N NaOH; a violet-red color is produced.   Upon the subsequent addition of 0.05 ml of 0.1 N HCl the original yellow color returns.

SODIUM AMMONIUM PHOSPHATE

Microcosmic Salt

$NaNH_4HPO_4 \cdot 4H_2O$; mol. wt. 209.08; anhydrous—65.53%; H_2O—34.47%; NH_3—8.14%; PO_4—45.44%.

Colorless or white crystals or granules.   Efflorescent; loses ammonia on prolonged exposure to the air.   Soluble in 6 parts of water; insoluble in alcohol.

Standards

Insoluble, Calcium, and	Sulfate (SO_4)...............max 0.010%
NH_4OH precipitate........max 0.010%	Arsenic (As)................max 1 ppm
Chloride (Cl)...............max 0.002%	Heavy metals (as Pb)........max 0.001%
Nitrate (NO_3)..............max 0.002%	Iron (Fe)...................max 0.001%

Insoluble, Calcium, and NH_4OH precipitate: Dissolve 10 g in 100 ml of H_2O.   Add to the solution 5 ml of ammonium oxalate and 15 ml of NH_4OH, and allow to stand overnight.   Filter if any precipitate is present, wash it with H_2O, and ignite at a low red heat.   The weight of the ignited precipitate is not more than 0.0010 g.

Chloride: Dissolve 1 g in 20 ml of water, add 2 ml of HNO_3 and 1 ml of $AgNO_3$. Any turbidity produced is not greater than that in the blank to which 0.02 mg of Cl has been added.

Nitrate: Dissolve 0.2 g in 10 ml of water, add 25 mg of NaCl, 0.2 ml of diphenyl-amine solution and 10 ml of sulfuric acid.   No blue color is produced in 30 minutes.

Sulfate: Dissolve 10 g in 100 ml of H_2O, add 5 ml of hydrochloric acid, and filter.   Heat the filtrate to boiling, add 5 ml of $BaCl_2$, and allow to stand overnight.

Filter if a precipitate is present, wash it with hot H_2O, and ignite.   The weight of the precipitate ($BaSO_4$) does not exceed 2.5 g.

Arsenic: Determine in 2 g by the method on page 563.   The stain is not greater than from 0.002 mg of As.

Heavy metals: Dissolve 4 g in 30 ml of H_2O, add 6.0 ml of 10% HCl and dilute to 40 ml.   To 10 ml of the solution add 0.02 mg of Pb and dilute to 40 ml (A). Dilute the remaining 30 ml of the solution to 40 ml (B).   Then to each add 10 ml of H_2S. B is not darker than A.

Iron: Dissolve 1 g in 15 ml of water, add 2 ml of HCl, and boil for 2 minutes. Cool, add about 50 mg of ammonium persulfate and 15 ml of butanolic potassium thiocyanate, and shake well   Any red color in the butanol layer is not darker than that of a blank to which 0.01 mg of Fe has been added.

SODIUM ARSENATE, DIBASIC

$Na_2HAsO_4 \cdot 7H_2O$; mol. wt. 312.00; anhydrous—59.6%; H_2O—40.4%; As— 24.01%; As_2O_5—36.83%.

Colorless crystals.   Soluble in about 1.5 parts of water; insoluble in alcohol.

Standards

Assay...........99%–100.5% Na_2HAsO_4	Mono- or Tribasic............to pass test
(anhydrous basis)	Nitrate (NO_3)..............max 0.010%
Drying loss....................39%–41%	Sulfate (SO_4)...............max 0.015%
Insoluble....................max 0.010%	Heavy metals (as Pb).......max 0.002%
Arsenite (As_2O_3)............max 0.003%	Iron (Fe)...................max 0.002%
Chloride (Cl)...............max 0.003%	

Assay; Drying loss: Weigh accurately about 1 g of the quickly crushed crystals and dry at 105° to constant weight (about 4 hours).   The loss in weight is not less than 38% and not more than 41%.

Dissolve an accurately weighed quantity of about 0.5 g of the dried sample from the preceding test in 50 ml of H_2O in a glass-stoppered flask.   Heat the solution to 80°, add 10 ml of HCl and 3 g of potassium iodide, stopper, and let stand for 15 minutes.   Cool, and titrate the liberated iodine with 0.1 N sodium thiosulfate, using starch indicator toward the end.   One ml of 0.1 N thiosulfate = 0.01560 g Na_2HAsO_4, log 19312.   Correct for any iodine liberated in a blank.

Insoluble: Dissolve 10 g in 100 ml of H_2O and heat on the steam bath 1 hour. Filter any undissolved residue, wash it with water, and dry at 105°.   Its weight does not exceed 1.0 mg.

Arsenite: Dissolve 10 g in 75 ml of cold H_2O and make the solution just acid with dilute H_2SO_4.   Add 2 g of sodium bicarbonate and, when it has dissolved, add starch solution and titrate with 0.02 N iodine to a blue color.   Not more than 0.30 ml of the iodine is consumed.   Correct for any iodine consumed by a blank.

Chloride: To a solution of 1 g in 25 ml H_2O add 2 ml of HNO_3, and 1 ml of $AgNO_3$.   Any resulting turbidity is not greater than that in a blank to which 0.03 mg of Cl has been added.

Mono- or Tribasic: Dissolve 1 g in 30 ml of H_2O, cool to 20° and add 3 drops of thymol blue. A blue color is produced which changes to yellow (with a greenish tinge) by the addition of not more than 0.5 ml of 1 N HCl.

Nitrate: Dissolve 0.1 g in 10 ml of water, add 20 mg of NaCl and 0.10 ml of indigo carmine solution, then slowly run in 10 ml of H_2SO_4. The blue color does not entirely disappear in 5 minutes.

Sulfate: Dissolve 5 g in 50 ml of H_2O, add 2 ml of HCl, heat to boiling, add 5 ml of $BaCl_2$, and allow to stand overnight. If a precipitate is present, filter, wash it with hot H_2O, ignite, and weigh. Its weight is not more than 2.0 mg.

Heavy metals: Dissolve 1.1 g of sample in 20 ml of H_2O in a small dish. Add 2 g of potassium iodide, 10 ml of HBr, and 2 drops of H_2SO_4, and evaporate on the steam bath. Wash down the sides of the dish with a few ml of H_2O, add 5 ml of HBr, and re-evaporate on the steam bath. Take up with 20 ml of hot water, neutralize to litmus paper with dilute NH_4OH, add 2 ml of 1 N acetic acid, dilute to 40 ml, and add 10 ml of H_2S. Any color produced is not darker than that produced by treating 0.1 of sample with 0.02 mg of Pb, with the same quantities of the reagents and in exactly the same manner as the sample.

Iron: Dissolve 1 g in 15 ml of water, add 2 ml of HCl, and boil for 2 minutes. Cool, add about 50 mg of ammonium persulfate and 15 ml of butanolic potassium thiocyanate, and shake well. Any red color in the butanol layer is not darker than that of a blank to which 0.02 mg of Fe has been added.

SODIUM ARSENITE

Sodium Metarsenite

Approx. $NaAsO_2$; mol. wt. 130.

White powder. Very soluble in water; slightly soluble in alcohol. Absorbs carbon dioxide from the air, forming arsenic trioxide. *Keep in tightly closed containers.*

Standards

Assay.................min 95% $NaAsO_2$	Sulfate (SO_4)...............max 0.020%
Insoluble....................max 0.01%	Antimony...................max 0.05%
Carbonate (as CO_2)......max about 0.15%	Lead and other metals........to pass test
Chloride (Cl)...............max 0.005%	(max about 0.03% as Pb)

Assay: Dry about 1 g over H_2SO_4 for 24 hours. Weigh accurately 0.2 g of the dried sodium arsenite and dissolve in 30 ml of water. Make the solution just acid with HCl, add 40 ml of a cold 5% solution of sodium bicarbonate, and titrate with 0.1 N iodine, using starch as indicator, to a permanent blue color. One ml of 0.1 N iodine = 0.006497 g $NaAsO_2$, log 81271.

$$NaAsO_2 + 2I + 3NaHCO_3 \rightarrow Na_2HAsO_4 + 2NaI + 3CO_2 + H_2O$$

Insoluble: Dissolve 10 g in 100 ml of CO_2-free water, filter any undissolved residue, wash it with water, and dry at 105°. The weight of the insoluble residue does not exceed 1.0 mg.

Carbonate: Dissolve 1 g in 2 ml of H_2O and add 1 ml of 10% HCl. No distinct effervescence is produced.

Chloride: To a solution of 0.4 g of the sample in 20 ml of water add 2 ml of nitric acid, filter, and add to the filtrate 1 ml of silver nitrate. Any turbidity produced is not greater than that in a blank to which 0.02 mg of Cl has been added.

Sulfate: Dissolve 1 g in 15 ml of water, add 3 ml of 10% HCl, filter if necessary, and add to the filtrate 2 ml of $BaCl_2$. Any resulting turbidity is not greater than that in a control made with 0.2 mg of SO_4, 1 ml of 1 N HCl and 2 ml of $BaCl_2$ in the same final volume as with the sample.

Antimony; Lead and other metals: Dissolve 0.2 g in 3 ml of H_2O, add 5 ml of HCl and 0.3 ml of H_2SO_4 and evaporate on the steam bath, *under hood*, until all the HCl is driven off. Add 2 ml of H_2O and 2 ml of HCl and re-evaporate. Take up the residue in 10 ml of hot H_2O and neutralize to litmus with ammonium hydroxide. Add 2 ml of 1 N HCl, dilute to 40 ml, and add 10 ml of H_2S. No brown color is produced. If a yellow or orange color is present, it is not darker than that of a control made with 0.10 mg of Sb, 2 ml of 1 N HCl and 10 ml of H_2S in the same volume as with the sample.

SODIUM BICARBONATE

$NaHCO_3$; mol. wt. 84.01; Na—27.38%; CO_2—52.37%; Na_2O—36.90%.

White, crystalline powder. Soluble in 12 parts of water; insoluble in alcohol. In moist, warm air it slowly loses carbon dioxide and water, thereby changing to the normal carbonate. In aqueous solutions it begins to lose carbon dioxide at about 20° and, on boiling the solution, it is entirely converted into the normal carbonate.

Standards

Assay...........99.8%–100.3% $NaHCO_3$	Sulfur compounds (as SO_4)....max 0.003%
Normal carbonate...........to pass test	Calcium, Magnesium, and
Insoluble...................max 0.015%	NH$_4$OH precipitate........max 0.020%
Chloride (Cl)...............max 0.003%	Heavy metals..............max 0.0005%
Iodine consuming substances...to pass test	Iron (Fe).................max 0.0005%
Nitrogen compounds (as N)..max 0.0005%	Potassium (K)..............max 0.02%
Phosphate (PO_4)...........max 0.001%	

Assay; Normal carbonate: Dry about 3 g over H_2SO_4 for 3 hours, then weigh accurately, dissolve in 50 ml of water, add 2 drops of methyl orange, and titrate with 1 N HCl to a brownish-yellow color. One ml of 1 N HCl = 0.0840 g $NaHCO_3$, log 92428. The total alkalinity so determined corresponds to not less than 99.8% and to not more than 100.3% as $NaHCO_3$.

Insoluble: Dissolve 10 g in 100 ml of hot H_2O and heat on steam bath for 15 minutes. Filter any undissolved residue, wash it with water, and dry at 105°. Its weight does not exceed 1.5 mg.

Chloride: Dissolve 1 g in 30 ml of water, add a slight excess of HNO_3, filter if necessary, and add 2 ml of $AgNO_3$. The resulting turbidity is not greater than that in a blank to which 0.03 mg of Cl has been added.

Iodine consuming substances: Dissolve 2 g in 50 ml of cold water. Add to the solution 5 drops of starch solution and 1 drop of 0.1 N iodine. The solution becomes blue.

Nitrogen compounds: Dissolve 4 g in 45 ml of H_2O, add 25 ml of 10% NaOH and 1 g powdered Devarda metal, and let stand for 3 hours protected from loss or access of NH_3.   Decant 35 ml, dilute to 50 ml, and add to it 2 ml of Nessler solution. The resulting color is not darker than that produced by treating 0.02 mg of nitrogen (0.08 mg NH_4Cl) in the same manner.

Phosphate: Dissolve 2 g in a mixture of 15 ml of H_2O and 7 ml of 25% H_2SO_4, add 1 ml each of phosphate reagents **A** and **B**, and heat at 60° for 10 minutes. Any blue color produced is not darker than that of a control made with 0.02 mg of PO_4, 2 ml of 25% H_2SO_4, 1 ml each of the phosphate reagents and in the same volume as with the sample.

Sulfur compounds: Dissolve 3 g of sample and 10 mg of sodium carbonate in 20 ml of water, add 5 drops of bromine water, boil for 2 minutes, then add 5 ml of HCl and evaporate to dryness on the steam bath.   Prelare a control by evaporating 10 mg of sodium carbonate, 5 drops of bromine water, 5 ml of HCl and 0.1 mg of SO_4 to dryness on the steam bath.   Dissolve the residue from each in 1 ml of 0.1 N HCl and sufficient water to make 15 ml, and add to each 2 ml of $BaCl_2$.   Any turbidity appearing in 20 minutes in the solution of the sample is not greater than that in the control.

Calcium, Magnesium, and NH_4OH precipitate: Mix 10 g with 100 ml of water, add 12 ml of HCl, and filter if necessary.   Add to the filtrate 5 ml of ammonium oxalate, 2 ml of ammonium phosphate, and 20 ml of ammonium hydroxide and let stand overnight.   Filter any precipitate present, wash it with 2.5% NH_3, and ignite.   Its weight, after ignition, does not exceed 2.0 mg.

Heavy metals: Dissolve 5 g of sample in 10 ml of water and *cautiously* add, in small portions, 7 ml of HCl.   Evaporate on the steam bath to dryness, take up in 25 ml of water, add a drop of phenolphthalein, and neutralize with 0.1 N NaOH. Add 3 ml of 1 N acetic acid and dilute to 40 ml.   To 10 ml add 0.015 mg of Pb and dilute to 40 ml (A).   Add to A and to the remaining 40 ml (B) 10 ml of H_2S. A is not darker than B.

Iron: Dissolve 2 g in 30 ml of water, add 3 ml of HCl, bring to a boil, cool, and dilute to 50 ml.   Add about 30 mg of ammonium persulfate and 3 ml of ammonium thiocyanate.   Any red color produced is not darker than that of a blank to which 0.01 mg of Fe has been added.

Potassium: Dissolve 1 g in 15 ml of H_2O, add 3 ml of HCl, evaporate to dryness, and heat at 120° for 30 minutes.   Dissolve the residue in 10 ml of H_2O, filter if necessary, and add 10 ml of sodium cobaltinitrite solution; then, while stirring, add 10 ml of alcohol and allow to stand for 2 hours.   Any turbidity or precipitate formed is not greater than that formed by treating 10 ml of water containing 0.2 mg of potassium (K) with the same volumes of the reagents.

Note: A more accurate quantitative determination of the potassium may be accomplished by Flame Photometry.

SODIUM BISMUTHATE

$NaBiO_3$; mol. wt. 280.0; active oxygen—5.07%.

Yellowish-brown powder of somewhat variable composition.   It is not a true bismuthate. Theoretically, sodium bismuthate, $NaBiO_3$, contains 5.7% active oxygen. It is insoluble in water, decomposed by boiling water, and is rapidly decomposed by acids. Loses oxygen on keeping. *Keep in well-stoppered bottles.*

Standards

Assay.................min 85% $NaBiO_3$	Manganese.................max 0.0005%
Chloride (Cl)................max 0.002%	

Assay: Dissolve 7 g of clear crystals of ferrous sulfate in 90 ml of freshly boiled and cooled H_2O, add sufficient H_2SO_4 to make 100 ml. Cool and standardize by titration of 25 ml with 0.1 N potassium permanganate. Weigh accurately about 0.7 g of the sodium bismuthate, add 25 ml of the standardized ferrous sulfate solution, stopper, and let stand for 30 minutes with frequent shaking. Then titrate the excess of ferrous sulfate with 0.1 N potassium permanganate. The difference in the volume of permanganate consumed in the two titrations represents $NaBiO_3$. One ml of 0.1 N permanganate − 0.01400 g $NaBiO_3$, log 14613.

$$2NaBiO_3 + 4FeSO_4 + 6H_2SO_4 \rightarrow 2Fe_2(SO_4)_3 + Bi_2(SO_4)_3 + Na_2SO_4 + 6H_2O$$

Chloride: To 2 g of the bismuthate add 40 ml of H_2O and boil for 10 minutes. Cool, dilute with water to 50 ml, mix, and filter. To 25 ml of the filtrate add 1 ml of HNO_3 and 1 ml of $AgNO_3$. Any turbidity produced is not greater than that in a blank to which 0.02 mg of Cl has been added.

Manganese: Boil 2 g with 35 ml of dilute HNO_3 (2+3), then add 0.5 ml of sulfurous acid and boil to expel oxides of nitrogen. Cool the solution to 15°, add 0.5 g of the sodium bismuthate, and allow to stand for 5 minutes without stirring. Add 25 ml of water, and filter through asbestos. The filtrate has no more color than that obtained by treating 0.01 mg of Mn in the same manner as the sodium bismuthate, using 0.5 g of the sodium bismuthate to produce the pink color.

SODIUM BISULFATE, FUSED

$NaHSO_4$; mol. wt. 120.06; Na_2SO_4—59.15%; free H_2SO_4—50.84%.

White fragments; hygroscopic. Usually contains more or less pyrosulfate. Soluble in 2 parts of water. *Keep in well-closed containers.*

Standards

Assay (% acidity)......40%–42% H_2SO_4	Arsenic (As)................max 1 ppm
Insoluble and NH_4OH	Calcium and Magnesium
precipitate...............max 0.010%	precipitate...............max 0.010%
Chloride (Cl)...............max 0.001%	Heavy metals (as Pb).......max 0.001%
Nitrate (NO_3)..............max 0.001%	Iron (Fe)..................max 0.001%
Phosphate (PO_4)...........max 0.001%	

Assay: Weigh accurately about 4 g, dissolve it in 50 ml of H_2O, and titrate with 1 N NaOH, using methyl orange indicator. One ml of 1 N NaOH = 0.04904 g H_2SO_4, log 69055.

Insoluble and NH_4OH precipitate: Dissolve 10 g in 100 ml of water and make alkaline to methyl red with ammonium hydroxide. Boil the solution for

1 minute and, if a precipitate is present, filter hot (retain filtrate), wash it with H_2O, and dry at 105°. Its weight does not exceed 1.0 mg.

Chloride: To a solution of 1 g in 10 ml of H_2O add 1 ml of HNO_3 and 1 ml of $AgNO_3$. Any turbidity produced is not greater than that in the blank to which 0.01 mg of Cl has been added.

Nitrate: Dissolve 0.5 g in 10 ml of water. Add to the solution 20 mg of NaCl, 0.2 ml diphenylamine solution and follow slowly with 10 ml of H_2SO_4. No blue color appears after 30 minutes.

Phosphate: Dissolve 2 g in 20 ml of H_2O, add 1 ml each of phosphate reagents **A** and **B**, and heat at 60° for 10 minutes. Any blue color produced is not deeper than that of a control made by treating 0.02 mg of PO_4 with 2 ml of 25% H_2SO_4, 1 ml each of the phosphate reagents in the same volume and in the same manner as the sample.

Arsenic: Determine in a 2-g sample by method on page 563. The stain is not more than that from 0.002 mg of As.

Calcium and Magnesium precipitate: To the filtrate (without the washings) from *Insoluble* add 5 ml of ammonium oxalate, 3 ml of ammonium phosphate, and 20 ml of NH_4OH; allow to stand overnight. If a precipitate is formed, filter, wash it with 2.5% NH_3 and ignite. Its weight, after ignition, is not more than 1.0 mg.

Heavy metals: Dissolve 4 g in 25 ml of water, neutralize the solution to phenolphthalein with NH_4OH, and dilute to 40 ml. To 10 ml add 0.02 mg of Pb and 2 ml of 1 N acetic acid and dilute to 40 ml (A). To the remaining 30 ml add 2 ml of 1 N acetic acid and dilute to 40 ml (B). Then to each add 10 ml of H_2S. B is not darker than A.

Iron: Dissolve 2 g in 25 ml of H_2O, add 2 ml of HCl, and boil gently for 5 minutes. Cool, and dilute to 40 ml. Dilute 20 ml of the solution to 50 ml; add about 30 mg of ammonium persulfate and 3 ml of ammonium thiocyanate. Any red color produced is not darker than that in a control made with 0.01 mg of Fe, 2 ml of HCl, the same quantities of the ammonium persulfate and thiocyanate and in the same final volume as with the sample.

SODIUM BISULFATE, HYDRATED

$NaHSO_4 \cdot H_2O$; mol. wt. 138.08; anhydrous—86.95%; free H_2SO_4—35.52%.

Colorless, slightly hygroscopic crystals. Soluble in about 1.5 parts of water. *Keep in well-closed containers.*

Standards

Assay...............35%–36.5% H_2SO_4	Arsenic (As).................max 1 ppm
Insoluble and NH_4OH	Calcium and Magnesium
precipitate................max 0.010%	precipitate................max 0.010%
Chloride (Cl)................max 0.001%	Heavy metals (as Pb)........max 0.010%
Nitrate (NO_3)..............max 0.001%	Iron (Fe)...................max 0.001%
Phosphate (PO_4)............max 0.001%	

Assay: Determine the titratable H_2SO_4 by the method described for Sodium Bisulfate, Fused.

Insoluble and NH₄OH precipitate; Chloride; Nitrate; Phosphate; Arsenic; Calcium and Magnesium precipitate; Heavy metals; Iron: Apply the tests described for Sodium Bisulfate, Fused. The results conform to the requirements there stated.

SODIUM BISULFITE

Sodium Hydrogen Sulfite

$NaHSO_3$; mol. wt. 104.07; Na—22.10%; SO_2—61.56%.

Usually contains some pyrosulfite ($Na_2S_2O_5$) which, however, for all purposes possesses the same properties as the bisulfite.

White granular powder, having an odor of sulfur dioxide. In the air it slowly oxidizes to sulfate. Soluble in 4 parts of water, in about 100 parts of alcohol. *Keep in tightly closed containers.*

Standards

Assay..............min 95% as $NaHSO_3$	Arsenic (As)................max 2 ppm
Insoluble..................max 0.010%	Heavy metals (as Pb)........max 0.001%
Chloride (Cl)...............max 0.010%	Iron (Fe)..................max 0.001%

Assay: Weigh accurately about 0.2 g and add it to exactly 50 ml of 0.1 N iodine contained in a glass-stoppered flask. Allow to stand for 5 minutes, add 1 ml of HCl and titrate the excess of iodine with 0.1 N sodium thiosulfate, using starch indicator. One ml of 0.1 N iodine = 0.005203 g $NaHSO_3$, log 71625.

Insoluble: Dissolve 10 g in 100 ml of H_2O and heat on the steam bath for 1 hour. Filter any undissolved matter, wash it with water, and dry at 105°. The weight of the insoluble residue does not exceed 1.0 mg.

Chloride: Dissolve 1 g in 10 ml of water, add 2 ml of 30% hydrogen peroxide, allow to stand for 30 minutes, then dilute to 100 ml. To 20 ml add 1 ml of HNO_3 and 1 ml of $AgNO_3$. The turbidity produced is not greater than that in a control made with 0.02 mg of Cl, 0.5 ml of the hydrogen peroxide, 1 ml of HNO_3, and 1 ml of $AgNO_3$ in the same volume as with the sample.

Arsenic: Dissolve 2 g in 10 ml of H_2O, gradually add 3 ml of HNO_3, then add 3 ml of H_2SO_4 and evaporate to strong fumes. Cool, cautiously add 10 ml of water, and test for arsenic by the method described on page 563. The stain produced is not greater than that from 0.002 mg of As.

Solution S: Dissolve 5 g in 20 ml of hot H_2O, add 5 ml of HCl, and evaporate to dryness on the steam bath. Add 10 ml of hot H_2O and 2 ml of HCl, and reevaporate to complete dryness. Dissolve the residue in water and dilute to 50 ml.

Heavy metals: To 5 ml of *Solution S* add 0.02 mg of Pb, 1 ml of 1 N acetic acid, and dilute to 40 ml (*A*). To 25 ml of *Solution S* add 1 ml of 1 N acetic acid and dilute to 40 ml (*B*). Then to each add 10 ml of H_2S. *B* is not darker than *A*.

Iron: To 10 ml of *Solution S* add 2 ml of HCl and dilute to 50 ml. Add about 30 mg of ammonium persulfate and 3 ml of ammonium thiocyanate, and mix. Any resulting red color is not darker than that of a blank to which 0.01 mg of Fe has been added.

SODIUM BITARTRATE

$NaHC_4H_4O_6 \cdot H_2O$; mol. wt. 190.09; anhydrous—90.52%; H_2O—9.48%; Na—12.1%; tartaric acid = 78.95%.

Colorless crystals or white crystalline powder. Soluble in 9 parts of water, in 2 parts of boiling water; almost insoluble in alcohol.

Standards

Assay.........99%–100.5% $NaHC_4H_4O_6$ (anhydrous basis)	Sulfate (SO_4)...............max 0.005%
	Ammonia (NH_3)..............max 0.02%
Ammonium hydroxide—	Calcium (Ca)................max 0.005%
insoluble................max 0.010%	Heavy metals (as Pb).......max 0.001%
Chloride (Cl)...............max 0.002%	Iron (Fe)..................max 0.001%
Phosphate (PO_4)...........max 0.001%	

Assay: Dry about 1 g to constant weight at 120°. Weigh accurately about 0.7 g of the dried sample, dissolve it in 40 ml of water, and titrate with 0.1 N NaOH, using phenolphthalein indicator. One ml of 0.1 N NaOH = 0.01720 g $NaHC_4H_4O_6$, log 23553.

Ammonium hydroxide—insoluble: Dissolve 10 g in a mixture of 100 ml of H_2O and 4 ml of NH_4OH. Filter any insoluble residue, wash it with hot H_2O, and dry at 105°. Its weight does not exceed 1.0 mg.

Chloride: Dissolve 1 g in 20 ml of water, add 2 ml of HNO_3 and 1 ml of $AgNO_3$. Any resulting turbidity is not greater than that of a blank to which 0.02 mg of Cl has been added.

Phosphate: Ignite 2 g in platinum until nearly white. Break up the residue well, add 25 ml of H_2O, 1 ml HNO_3, and 1 ml of 30% hydrogen peroxide, and boil for a few minutes. Neutralize with 25% H_2SO_4, add 2 ml excess of the acid, filter, and evaporate filtrate to incipient fumes of SO_3. Dilute to 20 ml, add 1 ml each of phosphate reagents **A** and **B**, and heat at 60° for 10 minutes. If a blue color is produced, it is not darker than that of a control made with 0.02 mg PO_4, 2 ml of 25% H_2SO_4, the same quantities of the phosphate reagents and in the same final volume as with the sample.

Sulfate: Ignite 2 g protected from sulfur in the flame, preferably in an electrical muffle furnace, until nearly free of carbon. Boil the residue with 20 ml of water and 2 ml of 30% H_2O_2 for 5 minutes, then add 10 mg of sodium carbonate and 5 ml of HCl and evaporate to dryness on the steam bath. Prepare a control by evaporating 10 mg of sodium carbonate with 2 ml of the H_2O_2, 5 ml of HCl, and 0.1 mg of SO_4 to dryness on the steam bath. Dissolve the residue from each in 10 ml of hot water and filter. Then to each add 1 ml of 0.1 N HCl and 2 ml of $BaCl_2$. Any turbidity appearing in 15 minutes in the solution of the sample is not greater than that in the control.

Ammonia: Dissolve 1 g in 50 ml of H_2O. To 10 ml of the solution add 2 ml of 10% NaOH, dilute to 50 ml and add 2 ml of Nessler solution. The color produced is not darker than that in a blank to which 0.02 mg of NH_3 (0.08 mg NH_4Cl) has been added.

Calcium: Test as described under Potassium Bitartrate. The result should be as there stated.

Heavy metals: Dissolve 4 g in 30 ml of warm water, add 2 drops of phenolphthalein, and follow with just sufficient dilute NH_4OH to produce a slight pink color. Add 2 ml of 1 N HCl and dilute with water to 40 ml. To 10 ml add 0.02 mg of Pb, dilute to 30 ml, and add 1 ml of 1 N HCl (A). Dilute the remaining 30 ml of the solution to 40 ml (B). Then to each add 10 ml H_2S. B is not darker than A.

Iron: Dissolve 1 g in water, add 2 ml of HCl, and dilute to 50 ml. Add 50 mg of ammonium persulfate and 3 ml of ammonium thiocyanate, and mix. Any resulting red color is not darker than that of a blank to which 0.01 mg of Fe has been added.

SODIUM BORATE

Borax; Sodium Tetraborate

$Na_2B_4O_7 \cdot 10H_2O$; mol. wt. 381.42; anhydrous—52.77%; H_2O—47.23%; boric acid = 64.87%; B—11.33%.

Hard, white crystals or powder; soluble in about 20 parts of water, 1 part of boiling water or about 2 parts of glycerol; insoluble in alcohol.

Standards

Insoluble....................max 0.005%	Arsenic (As)................max 1 ppm
Carbonate (CO_2)..............to pass test	Calcium (Ca)................max 0.005%
Chloride (Cl)................max 0.001%	Heavy metals (as Pb)........max 0.001%
Phosphate (PO_4)............max 0.001%	Iron (Fe)...................max 0.001%
Sulfate (SO_4)...............max 0.005%	*Assay*

Insoluble: Dissolve 20 g in 300 ml of hot H_2O and heat on steam bath for 1 hour Filter any undissolved residue, wash it with hot H_2O, and dry at 105°. Its weight does not exceed 1.0 mg.

Carbonate: Powder 1 g, add sufficient water to cover the sample, then add 5 ml of 10% HCl. No effervescence is noticeable.

Chloride: Dissolve 2 g in 30 ml of warm H_2O, add 2 ml of HNO_3 and 1 ml of $AgNO_3$. Any resulting turbidity in 15 minutes is not greater than that in a blank with 0.02 mg of Cl added.

Phosphate: To 1 g add 10 ml of hot H_2O and 2.5 ml of 25% H_2SO_4 and evaporate in platinum as far as possible on the steam bath. Treat the residue with 20 ml of H_2O, add 1 ml each of phosphate reagents **A** and **B**, and heat at 60° for 10 minutes. Any blue color produced is not darker than that of a blank to which 0.01 mg of PO_4 has been added.

Sulfate: Dissolve 2 g in 10 ml of hot H_2O, add 1.0 ml of HCl, 75 ml of methanol, cover and evaporate on the steam bath to about 10 ml. Filter, and wash with cold H_2O to 15 ml, and add 2 ml of barium chloride. Any turbidity produced is not greater than that in a control made with 0.1 mg of SO_4, 1 ml of 1 N HCl, and 2 ml of barium chloride in the same volume as with the sample.

Arsenic: Determine in 2 g by method on page 563. The stain is not greater than that from 0.002 mg of As.

Calcium: Dissolve 2 g in 30 ml of warm H_2O, add 1 ml of glacial acetic acid, and 3 ml ammonium oxalate. No turbidity is produced in 15 minutes.

Note: If desired the calcium may be quantitatively determined by Flame Photometry.

Heavy metals: Dissolve 4 g in 30 ml of hot H_2O, add 4 ml of glacial acetic acid, and dilute to 40 ml. To 10 ml add 0.02 mg of Pb and dilute to 40 ml (A). Dilute the remaining 30 ml to 40 ml (B). Then heat both to 80° and add 10 ml of H_2S to each. B is not darker than A.

Iron: Dissolve 1 g in 20 ml of hot water, add 3 ml of HCl, and boil for 2 minutes. Cool, add about 30 mg of ammonium persulfate and 15 ml of butanolic potassium thiocyanate (page 4), shake well, and allow to separate. Any red color in the butanol layer is not darker than that of a blank to which 0.01 mg of Fe has been added.

Assay: Sodium borate may be assayed as follows, and it should assay not less than 99% $Na_2B_4O_7.10H_2O$. Weigh accurately about 0.4 g, dissolve in 15 ml of H_2O, add 1 drop of methyl orange, and titrate with 0.1 N HCl just to a pink color. Now add 80 ml of neutralized glycerol and 0.2 ml of phenolphthalein, and titrate with 0.1 N NaOH to a pink color. One ml of 0.1 N NaOH = 0.009536 g borax, log 97937. The volume of 0.1 N HCl required should be within 0.1 ml of half of the 0.1 N NaOH used up.

Note: Neutralized glycerol is made by mixing 80 ml of glycerin with 20 ml of water and 4 drops of phenolphthalein and adding 0.1 N NaOH until the pink color persists after shaking for 30 seconds.

SODIUM BORATE, FUSED

Anhydrous Sodium Borate; Borax Glass; Fused Borax

$Na_2B_4O_7$; mol. wt. 201.25; B—21.50%; B_2O_3—69.20%.

White, granular powder. It absorbs moisture from the air. Soluble in water, a small amount of undissolved matter usually remaining. *Keep in tightly closed containers.*

Standards

Assay	Ignition loss
min 97% $Na_2B_4O_7$	max 1.0%

Assay: Weigh accurately about 0.3 g, dissolve it in 15 ml of water, add 1 drop of methyl orange, and titrate with 0.1 N HCl to just a pink color. Now add 80 ml of neutralized glycerol (for its preparation see Note in the *Assay* of the preceding article) and 0.2 ml of phenolphthalein, and titrate with 0.1 N NaOH to a pink color. One ml of 0.1 N NaOH = 0.01005 g $Na_2B_4O_7$, log 00217.

Ignition loss: Ignite about 1 g, accurately weighed, to constant weight. The loss in weight corresponds to not more than 1%.

SODIUM BROMATE

NaBrO$_3$; mol. wt. 150.90; Na—15.24%; Br—52.96%; active O—31.8%.

Colorless or white crystals, or crystalline powder. Soluble in 4 parts of water.

Caution! *When rubbed with organic substances, sulfides or other readily oxidizable substances, it may react with explosive violence.*

Standards

Assay............99.7%–100.3% NaBrO$_3$	Nitrogen compounds (as N)...max 0.002%
Insoluble...................max 0.005%	Sulfate (SO$_4$)...............max 0.005%
Neutrality..................to pass test	Heavy metals (as Pb)......max 0.0005%
Bromide (as Br)..............max 0.01%	Iron (Fe).................max 0.001%

Assay: Powder about 0.5 g and dry to constant weight over H$_2$SO$_4$. Weigh accurately about 0.1 g (or use a portion of a stock solution corresponding to this quantity) of the dried sample and dissolve in 50 ml of H$_2$O in a glass-stoppered flask. Add 3 g of potassium iodide and 3 ml of HCl, previously diluted with 10 ml of H$_2$O. Allow to stand for 5 minutes, then add 50 ml of cold water and titrate the liberated iodine with 0.1 N thiosulfate. Correct for a blank. One ml of 0.1 N thiosulfate = 0.002515 g NaBrO$_3$, log 40054.

Insoluble: Dissolve 10 g in 100 ml of hot H$_2$O and heat on the steam bath for 1 hour. Should an insoluble residue remain, filter, wash it with hot H$_2$O, and dry at 105°. Its weight does not exceed 0.5 mg.

Neutrality: Dissolve 5 g in 60 ml of warm H$_2$O and add 0.2 ml of phenol-phthalein; no pink color is produced. Now add 0.02 N NaOH to the production of a pink color; not more than 0.2 ml of the NaOH is required.

Bromide: Dissolve 4 g in 80 ml of H$_2$O. To 40 ml add 0.25 ml of 1 N H$_2$SO$_4$. At the end of 2 minutes the liquid is not darker than the remaining 40 ml.

Nitrogen compounds: Dissolve 1 g in 40 ml of H$_2$O in a distilling flask, then add 1 g of powdered Devarda metal and 10 ml of 10% NaOH. Allow to stand 2 hours protected from loss or access of NH$_3$, then distill 40 ml into 5 ml of water containing 1 drop of dilute HCl. Add to the distillate 1 ml of 10% NaOH, dilute to 50 ml and add 2 ml of Nessler solution. The resulting color is not darker than that produced by treating 0.02 mg of nitrogen (0.08 mg NH$_4$Cl) in the same manner as the sample.

Sulfate: To 2 g add 20 mg of sodium carbonate, 10 ml of water and 10 ml of HCl and evaporate to dryness on the steam bath. Take up the residue with 10 ml of water, and add to the solution 1 ml of 0.1 N HCl and 2 ml of BaCl$_2$. Any turbidity produced is not greater than that in a control prepared as follows: To 10 ml of water add 20 mg of sodium carbonate, 0.1 mg of SO$_4$, and 10 ml of HCl, and evaporate to dryness on the steam bath. Dissolve the residue in 10 ml of water, and add 1 ml of 0.1 N HCl and 2 ml of BaCl$_2$.

Heavy metals: To 2.5 g of the sample add 10 ml of hot water and 10 ml of HCl (A). To 0.5 g of sample add 15 ml of HCl and 0.01 mg of Pb (B). Evaporate both to dryness on the steam bath. Add to A 5 ml of HCl and re-evaporate to dryness. Dissolve the residues in 20 ml of water each, add a drop of phenolphthalein and neutralize with 1 N NaOH. Add to each 1 ml of 1 N acetic acid, dilute to 25 ml and add 5 ml of H_2S. A is not darker than B.

Iron: To 1.2 g of sample add 5 ml of H_2O and 5 ml of HCl and evaporate to dryness on the steam bath. Repeat the evaporation with 5 ml of HCl. Prepare a control by adding 0.01 mg of Fe, 10 ml of HCl to 0.2 g of sample and evaporating to dryness on the steam bath. Take up each in 2 ml of HCl and water to make 50 ml. Add to each 30 mg of ammonium persulfate and 3 ml of ammonium thiocyanate. Any red color in the sample solution is not darker than that in the control.

SODIUM CARBONATE, ANHYDROUS

Na_2CO_3; mol. wt. 106.00; Na—43.40%; CO_2—41.51%; Na_2O—58.49%.

White, granular powder; hygroscopic; on exposure to air it will gradually absorb about 15% water, corresponding to 1 mol. Soluble in 5 parts of water; insoluble in alcohol. *Keep in tightly closed containers.*

Standards

Insoluble . . . . max 0.010%	Aluminium (Al) . . . . max 0.001%
Drying loss . . . . max 1.0%	Arsenic (As) . . . . max 1 ppm
Chloride (Cl) . . . . max 0.002%	Calcium and Magnesium
Nitrogen compounds (as N) . . . max 0.001%	precipitate . . . . max 0.010%
Phosphate (PO_4) . . . . max 0.001%	Heavy metals (as Pb) . . . . max 0.0005%
Sulfur compounds (as SO_4) . . . . max 0.003%	Iron (Fe) . . . . max 0.0005%
Ammonium hydroxide	Potassium (K) . . . . max 0.02%
precipitate and Silica . . . . max 0.010%	

Insoluble: Dissolve 10 g in 100 ml of water and heat the solution on the steam bath for 30 minutes. Filter any undissolved residue on asbestos in a Gooch crucible, wash it with hot water, and dry at 105°. Its weight does not exceed 1.0 mg.

Drying loss: Weigh accurately about 2 g and heat at 250°–300° to constant weight. The loss in weight corresponds to not more than 1.0%.

Chloride: To a solution of 1 g in 25 ml of water add 2 ml of nitric acid, and 1 ml of silver nitrate. Any resulting turbidity is not greater than that in a blank to which 0.02 mg of Cl has been added.

Nitrogen compounds: Dissolve 2 g in 50 ml of water, add 10 ml of 10% NaOH and 0.5 g of powdered Devarda metal or aluminum wire in small pieces and let stand for 3 hours protected from loss or access of ammonia. Dilute with water to 100 ml, decant 50 ml, and add to it 2 ml of Nessler solution. The color produced is not darker than that produced by treating 0.02 mg of nitrogen (0.08 mg NH_4Cl) in the same manner as the sample.

Phosphate: Dissolve 2 g in a mixture of 15 ml of H_2O and 10 ml of 25% H_2SO_4, evaporate and heat to incipient fumes of SO_3. Add 20 ml of H_2O, filter, add to the filtrate 1 ml each of phosphate reagents **A** and **B** and heat at 60° for 10 minutes. Any blue color produced is not darker than that of a control made with 0.02 mg of PO_4, 2 ml of 25% H_2SO_4, 1 ml each of the phosphate reagents and in the same volume as with the sample.

Sulfur compounds: Dissolve 3 g in 20 ml of water, add 5 drops of bromine water, and boil for 2 minutes.   Add 7 ml of hydrochloric acid and evaporate to dryness on the steam bath.   Dissolve the residue in 15 ml of water, and add 1 ml of 0.1 N HCl and 3 ml of barium chloride.   Any turbidity produced in 15 minutes is not greater than that of a control made as follows: To 10 mg of the sample add 5 drops of the bromine water, 7 ml of hydrochloric acid, and 0.1 mg of SO_4.   Evaporate to dryness on the steam bath.   Dissolve the residue in sufficient water to make 15 ml and treat the solution with 1 ml of 0.1 N HCl and 3 ml of barium chloride.

Ammonium hydroxide precipitate and Silica: Dissolve 10 g in 80 ml of water in a platinum dish, *cautiously* add 15 ml of sulfuric acid, evaporate, and heat to strong sulfuric fumes for 2 to 3 minutes.   Cool, dissolve the residue in 130 ml of hot water, and make just alkaline to methyl red with ammonium hydroxide.   Heat to boiling, filter (retain filtrate), wash, and ignite in platinum.   The weight of the ignited precipitate is not more than 1.0 mg.   Treat the ignited precipitate with 5 drops each of sulfuric and hydrofluoric acids, ignite, and weigh.   The loss in weight is not more than 0.5 mg.

Note: A colorimetric procedure for the determination of small amounts of silica in alkali carbonates and hydroxides was reported by Kenyon and Bewick, *Anal. Chem.* **25**, 145 (1953).   The method is based on the formation of the complex silicomolybdenum blue by the interaction of the silica with ammonium molybdate and a reducing agent.

Aluminium: Dissolve 2 g in 20 ml of water, add 3 ml of glacial acetic acid, and 1 ml of a 0.1% aqueous solution of aluminon (ammonium aurintricarboxylate). Allow to stand for 5 minutes, then add 10 ml of ammonium carbonate solution. The red color produced is not darker than that produced in a control made as follows: To 20 ml of water add 0.02 mg of aluminum, 1 g of ammonium acetate, 1.5 ml of glacial acetic acid, and 1 ml of the aluminon solution; allow to stand for 5 minutes; then add 10 ml of ammonium carbonate solution, and adjust to the same volume as with the sample.

Arsenic: Dissolve 2 g in 15 ml of water, cautiously acidify with H_2SO_4, and determine by the method on page 563.   The stain is not greater than that from 0.002 mg of As.

Calcium and Magnesium precipitate: To the filtrate from the test for *Ammonium hydroxide precipitate and Silica* add 0.5 ml of HCl, 5 ml of ammonium oxalate, 2 ml of ammonium phosphate, 20 ml of NH_4OH and let stand overnight. Filter if a precipitate is present, wash it with 2.5% NH_3, and ignite.   The weight of the ignited precipitate does not exceed 1.0 mg.

Heavy metals: Dissolve 5 g of sample in 20 ml of water and cautiously add in small portions 10 ml of HCl (A).   Dissolve 1 g of sample in 5 ml of water, then add 10 ml of HCl and 0.02 mg of Pb (B).   Evaporate both on the steam bath to dryness. Take up each in 25 ml of water, add a drop of phenolphthalein, and neutralize with 0.1 N NaOH.   Add 1 ml of 1 N acetic acid to each, dilute to 40 ml and add 10 ml of H_2S. A is not darker than B.

Iron: Dissolve 2 g in 20 ml of water, add 5 ml of HCl, bring to a boil, cool, and dilute to 50 ml.   Add about 30 mg of ammonium persulfate and 3 ml of ammonium thiocyanate. Any red color produced is not darker than that of a control made with 0.01 mg of Fe and 2 ml of HCl.

Potassium: Dissolve 1 g in 10 ml of H_2O, add 3 ml of HNO_3, evaporate to dryness, and heat at 120° for 30 minutes. Dissolve the residue in 5 ml of H_2O, filter if necessary, add 10 ml of sodium cobaltinitrite solution; then, while stirring, add 5 ml of alcohol and allow to stand for 2 hours. Any turbidity or precipitate formed is not greater than that formed by treating 10 ml of water containing 0.2 mg of potassium (K) with the same volumes of the reagents.

Note: A more accurate, quantitative determination of small amounts of potassium in sodium reagents can be accomplished by Flame Photometry.

SODIUM CARBONATE, DECAHYDRATE

Sodium Carbonate Crystals

$Na_2CO_3 \cdot 10H_2O$; mol. wt. 286.15; anhydrous—37.04%; H_2O—62.96%; Na—16.07%; Na_2O—21.67%; CO_2—15.37%.

Colorless, transparent crystals. Effloresces in air, and melts, when fully hydrated, at 32°. Soluble in 1.6 parts of water. *Keep in well-closed containers, in a cool place.*

Standards

Assay (anhydrous basis) min 99.7% Na_2CO_3

Insoluble	max 0.005%
Chloride (Cl)	max 0.001%
Nitrogen compounds (as N)	max 0.0005%
Phosphate (PO_4)	max 0.0005%
Ammonium hydroxide precipitate	max 0.005%
Sulfur compounds (as SO_4)	max 0.0015%
Aluminum (Al)	max 0.0005%
Arsenic	max 0.5 ppm
Calcium and Magnesium precipitate	max 0.005%
Heavy metals (as Pb)	max 0.0005%
Iron (Fe)	max 0.0003%
Potassium (K)	max 0.01%

Assay: Weigh accurately about 8 g, heat it first at about 70°, then gradually raise the temperature and finally heat at 250°–300° to constant weight. The loss in weight corresponds to not more than 63.5%. Dissolve the dehydrated sample in 50 ml of H_2O and titrate with 1 N HCl, using methyl orange indicator. One ml of 1 N HCl = 0.05300 g Na_2CO_3, log 72428.

Chloride: To a solution of 3 g in 25 ml of water add 2 ml of nitric acid and 2 ml of silver nitrate. Any resulting turbidity is not greater than that in a blank to which 0.03 mg of Cl has been added.

Ammonium hydroxide precipitate: Dissolve 20 g in 50 ml of water, *cautiously* add 10 ml of sulfuric acid, evaporate, and heat to strong sulfuric fumes for 2 to 3 minutes. Cool, dissolve the residue in 130 ml of hot water, and make just alkaline to methyl red with ammonium hydroxide. Heat to boiling, filter (retain filtrate), wash, and ignite in platinum. The weight of the ignited precipitate is not more than 1.0 mg.

Calcium and Magnesium precipitate: To the filtrate from the test for *Ammonium hydroxide precipitate* add 0.5 ml of HCl, 5 ml of ammonium oxalate,

2 ml of ammonium phosphate, and 20 ml of NH_4OH and let stand overnight. Filter if a precipitate is present, wash it with 2.5% NH_3, and ignite. The weight of the ignited precipitate does not exceed 1.0 mg.

Heavy metals: Dissolve 5 g of sample in 10 ml of water and cautiously add, in small portions, 4 ml of HCl (*A*). Dissolve 1 g of sample in 5 ml of water and add 4 ml of HCl and 0.02 mg of Pb (*B*). Evaporate both on the steam bath to dryness. Take up each in 25 ml of water, add a drop of phenolphthalein, and neutralize with 0.1 *N* NaOH. Add 1 ml of 1 *N* acetic acid to each, dilute to 40 ml, and add 10 ml of H_2S. *A* is not darker than *B*.

Iron: Dissolve 3 g in 20 ml of water, add 4 ml of HCl, and dilute to 50 ml. Add about 30 mg of ammonium persulfate and 3 ml of ammonium thiocyanate. Any red color produced is not darker than that of a blank to which 0.01 mg of Fe has been added.

Insoluble; Nitrogen compounds; Phosphate; Sulfur compounds; Aluminum; Arsenic; Potassium: Apply the tests described for Sodium Carbonate, Anhydrous, using twice the quantity of sample indicated there. The results conform to the requirements there stated.

SODIUM CARBONATE, MONOHYDRATE

$Na_2CO_3 \cdot H_2O$; mol. wt. 124.01; anhydrous—85.47%; H_2O—14.53%; Na—37.10%; Na_2O—50.00%; CO_2—35.48%.

White, crystalline powder. Soluble in 5 parts of water; insoluble in alcohol.

Standards

Drying loss................max 15.0%	Aluminum (Al).............max 0.001%
Insoluble..................max 0.010%	Arsenic.....................max 1 ppm
Chloride (Cl)..............max 0.003%	Calcium and Magnesium
Nitrogen compounds (as N)...max 0.001%	precipitate...............max 0.010%
Phosphate (PO_4)...........max 0.001%	Heavy metals (as Pb).......max 0.0005%
Sulfur compounds (as SO_4)....max 0.003%	Iron (Fe).................max 0.0005%
Ammonium hydroxide	Potassium (K).............max 0.02%
precipitate...............max 0.010%	

Drying loss: Weigh accurately about 2 g and heat at 250°–300° to constant weight. The loss in weight corresponds to not more than 15%.

Insoluble; Chloride; Nitrogen compounds; Phosphate; Ammonium hydroxide precipitate; Sulfur compounds; Aluminium; Arsenic; Calcium and Magnesium precipitate; Heavy metals; Iron; Potassium: Apply the tests described for Sodium Carbonate, Anhydrous. The results conform to the requirements there indicated.

SODIUM CHLORATE

$NaClO_3$; mol. wt. 106.45; Na—21.6%; Cl—33.31% active O—45.09%.

Colorless or white crystals, or granules. Soluble in about 1 part of water; slightly soluble in alcohol.

Caution! *Dangerous explosions are liable to occur when sodium chlorate is triturated with organic substances, sulfur, and other readily oxidizable substances. Keep in well-closed containers, protected from organic matter.*

Standards

Insoluble.................max 0.005%	Calcium, Magnesium, and
Bromate (BrO₃)..............max 0.03%	NH₄OH precipitate........max 0.010%
Chloride (Cl)...............max 0.001%	Heavy metals (as Pb)........max 0.001%
Nitrogen compounds (as N)...max 0.001%	Iron (Fe)..................max 0.0005%
Sulfate (SO₄)..........max about 0.003%	*Assay*......................min 99.5%

Insoluble: Dissolve 20 g in 100 ml of hot H_2O and heat on the steam bath for 1 hour.   Filter any insoluble residue, wash it with hot H_2O, and dry at 105°.   The weight of the insoluble residue is not more than 1.0 mg.

Bromate: Dissolve 3 g in 150 ml of freshly boiled and cooled water in a glass-stoppered flask.   Add 10 ml of 1 N HCl, 10 ml of fresh potassium iodide and add 5 ml of fresh starch.   Stopper immediately, allow to stand for 1 hour protected from light, then titrate with 0.1 N sodium thiosulfate.   Not more than 0.45 ml of the 0.1 N thiosulfate is consumed.   Correct for a blank.

Chloride: Dissolve 3 g in 40 ml of H_2O, cool, add 5 drops of HNO_3 free from oxides of nitrogen, and 2 ml of $AgNO_3$.   Any turbidity produced is not greater than that in a blank to which 0.03 mg of Cl has been added.

Nitrogen Compounds: Dissolve 1 g in 40 ml of H_2O in a distillation flask and add 1 g of powdered Devarda metal and 10 ml of 10% NaOH.   Allow to stand for 2 hours protected from loss or access of NH_3, then distill 40 ml, collecting the distillate in 5 ml of water containing 1 drop of dilute HCl.   Add to the distillate 1 ml of 10% NaOH and 2 ml of Nessler solution.   The resulting color is not darker than that produced by treating 0.01 mg of nitrogen (0.04 mg NH_4Cl) in the same manner as the sample.

Sulfate: Dissolve 3 g in 50 ml of H_2O, add 1 ml of 10% HCl, and 5 ml of $BaCl_2$; allow to stand overnight.   No turbidity or precipitate is formed.

Calcium, Magnesium, and NH₄OH precipitate: Boil 10 g with 50 ml of water and 15 ml of HCl until no more chlorine is evolved.   Dilute with water to 120 ml, heat to boiling, add 5 ml of ammonium oxalate, 3 ml of ammonium phosphate, and 20 ml of NH_4OH; allow to stand overnight.   If a precipitate is present, filter, wash with 2.5% NH_3, and ignite.   The weight of the ignited precipitate does not exceed 1.0 mg.

Heavy metals: To 3 g of sample add 10 ml of H_2O and 10 ml of HCl (*A*).   To 1 g of the sample add 10 ml of HCl, 10 ml of water, and 0.02 mg of Pb (*B*).   Evaporate both to dryness on the steam bath.   Add to each 5 ml more of HCl and re-evaporate to dryness.   Take up each in 25 ml of water, add a drop of phenolphthalein, and neutralize with 0.1 N NaOH.   Add 1 ml of 1 N acetic acid to each, dilute to 40 ml, and add 10 ml of H_2S.   *A* is not darker than *B*.

Iron: To 2 g of sample add 10 ml of H_2O and 10 ml of HCl and evaporate to dryness on the steam bath.   Add 5 ml of HCl and again evaporate to dryness.   Prepare a control by adding to 0.01 mg of Fe, 15 ml of HCl, and evaporating on the steam bath to dryness.   Take up each in 2 ml of HCl and water to make 50 ml.

Add to each about 30 mg of ammonium persulfate and 3 ml of ammonium thiocyanate. Any red color in the sample solution is not darker than that in the control.

Assay: Sodium chlorate may be assayed by the method described under Potassium Chlorate, and not less than 99.5% of $NaClO_3$ should be found. One ml of 0.1 N potassium permanganate = 0.001774 g $NaClO_3$, log 24895.

SODIUM CHLORIDE

$NaCl$; mol. wt. 58.45; Na—39.34% Cl—60.66%.

Colorless or white crystals; slightly hygroscopic. Soluble in 3 parts of water; almost insoluble in alcohol.

The reagent grade of this chemical, when in the form of moderately large crystals, is substantially 99.9% pure.

Standards

Insoluble................max 0.005%	Phosphate (PO_4)...........max 0.0005%
Neutrality..................to pass test	Sulfate (SO_4)..............max 0.001%
Bromide and Iodide	Barium (Ba)..........max about 0.001%
(as Br)...................max 0.01%	Calcium, Magnesium, and
Chlorate and Nitrate	NH_4OH precipitate........max 0.005%
(as ClO_3)................max 0.002%	Heavy metals (as Pb)............0.0005%
Nitrogen compounds	Iron (Fe).......................0.0002%
(N).....................max 0.001%	Potassium (K)....................0.01%

Insoluble: Dissolve 20 g in 150 ml of H_2O and heat on the steam bath for 1 hour. Should any undissolved residue remain, filter (retain filtrate), wash it with water, and dry at 105°. Its weight does not exceed 1.0 mg.

Neutrality: Dissolve 5 g in 50 ml of CO_2-free water and add 3 drops of phenolphthalein and bring to a boil; no pink color is produced. Now add 0.20 ml of 0.02 N NaOH; a pink color is produced.

Bromide and Iodide: Dissolve 2 g in 7 ml of warm water, slowly pour the solution into 30 ml of alcohol, cool, and filter. Evaporate the filtrate to dryness on the steam bath, dissolve the residue in 5 ml of water and add to the solution 1 ml of chloroform; then add, dropwise, with shaking, 5 drops of diluted chlorine water (1+3). No yellow or violet color appears in the chloroform.

Chlorate and Nitrate: Dissolve 0.5 g in 10 ml of water and add 0.2 ml of diphenylamine solution. Cool in ice water for 1–2 minutes, then withdraw from the cooling bath, and, holding the beaker at an angle of about 45°, add slowly 12 ml of H_2SO_4 without agitation. Allow to stand for 10–15 minutes, then mix the liquids by gently swirling and allow to stand for 1 hour. No blue color appears.

Nitrogen compounds: Dissolve 1 g in 50 ml of H_2O, add 10 ml of 10% NaOH and 0.5 g fine aluminum wire in small pieces. Allow to stand for 2 hours protected from loss or access of NH_3, then distill 40 ml into 5 ml of water containing 1 drop of dilute HCl. Add to the distillate 1 ml of 10% NaOH and 2 ml of Nessler solution. The color produced is not darker than that produced by treating 0.01 mg of nitrogen (0.04 mg NH_4Cl) in the same manner as the sample.

Phosphate: Dissolve 4 g in 25 ml of H_2O, add 2 ml of 25% H_2SO_4, 1 ml each of phosphate reagents **A** and **B**, and heat at 60° for 10 minutes. Any resulting blue color is not darker than that of a blank with 0.02 mg of PO_4 added.

Sulfate: Dissolve 10 g in 100 ml of water, add 2 ml of 1 N HCl, heat to boiling, add 5 ml of $BaCl_2$, and let stand overnight. No turbidity or precipitate appears.

Barium: Dissolve 4 g in 20 ml of water, filter if necessary and divide into two portions. To one portion add 2 ml of 10% H_2SO_4 and to the other 2 ml of H_2O; they are equally clear after 2 hours.

Calcium, Magnesium, and NH_4OH precipitate: To the filtrate from the test for *Insoluble* add 5 ml of ammonium oxalate, 2 ml of ammonium phosphate, and 30 ml of ammonium hydroxide; allow to stand overnight. Filter any precipitate formed, wash it with 2.5% NH_3, and ignite. The weight of the ignited precipitate is not more than 1.0 mg.

Heavy metals: Dissolve 5 g in H_2O to make 50 ml. To 10 ml add 0.015 mg of Pb, dilute to 40 ml, and add 1 ml of 1 N acetic acid (A). To the remaining 40 ml add 1 ml of 1 N acetic acid (B). Then to each add 10 ml of H_2S; B is not darker than A.

Iron: Dissolve 5 g in 40 ml of H_2O, add 2 ml of HCl, and dilute to 50 ml. Add about 30 mg of ammonium persulfate and 3 ml of ammonium thiocyanate. Any resulting red color is not darker than that of a blank to which 0.015 mg of Fe has been added.

Potassium: Dissolve 2 g in 15 ml of H_2O, add 10 ml of sodium cobaltinitrite, then add, while stirring, 5 ml of alcohol, let stand for 2 hours. Any precipitate formed is not more than that formed by treating 10 ml of water containing 0.2 mg of potassium (0.64 mg KCl) with 10 ml of sodium cobaltinitrite and allowing to stand overnight.

Note: A more exact estimation of the potassium may be achieved by Flame Photometry, page 566.

SODIUM CITRATE

$Na_3C_6H_5O_7 \cdot 2H_2O$; mol. wt. 294.12; anhydrous—87.75%; H_2O—12.25%; Na—23.46%; hydrated citric acid = 71.44%.

Small colorless or white crystals. Soluble in 2 parts of water; insoluble in alcohol.

Its water content may be determined by the iodine (Fischer) method.

Standards

Insoluble	max 0.005%	Sulfate (SO_4)	max 0.005%
Free acid (as citric)	max 0.15%	Ammonia (NH_3)	max 0.003%
Free alkali	none	Heavy metals (as Pb)	max 0.0005%
Chloride (Cl)	max 0.002%	Iron (Fe)	max 0.001%
Phosphate (PO_4)	max 0.001%	*Assay*	99%–100.3%

Insoluble: Dissolve 20 g in 100 ml of water and heat on the steam bath for 30 minutes. Filter any undissolved matter, wash with hot water, and dry at 105°. The weight of the insoluble residue is not more than 1.0 mg.

Free acid; Free alkali: Dissolve 2 g in 50 ml of CO_2-free H_2O and add 0.20 ml of phenolphthalein. If a pink color is produced it is not more intense than that produced by adding 0.20 ml of phenolphthalein and 0.1 ml of 0.02 N NaOH to 50 ml of CO_2-free water. If no pink color is produced, the addition of not more than 2.0 ml of 0.02 N NaOH should produce a pink color.

The pH of neutral sodium citrate at 25° is 8.2.

Chloride: Dissolve 1 g in 20 ml of H_2O and add 1 ml of HNO_3 and 1 ml of $AgNO_3$. The turbidity produced is not greater than that in the blank to which 0.02 mg of Cl has been added.

Phosphate: Ignite 1 g in platinum until nearly free of carbon. Break up the residue well, add 25 ml of H_2O and 1 ml of hydrogen peroxide, and boil for a few minutes. Neutralize with 25% H_2SO_4, add 2 ml excess of the acid, filter, and evaporate filtrate to incipient fumes of SO_3. Dilute to 20 ml, add 1 ml each of phosphate reagents A and B and heat at 60° for 10 minutes. If a blue color is produced, it is not darker than that of a control made with 0.01 mg PO_4, 2 ml of 25% H_2SO_4, the same quantities of the phosphate reagents and in the same final volume as with the sample.

Sulfate: Ignite 2 g in platinum protected from sulfur in the flame until nearly free of carbon. Boil the residue with 20 ml of H_2O and 1 ml of 30% hydrogen peroxide, then add 10 mg of sodium carbonate and 5 ml of HCl and evaporate to dryness on the steam bath. Prepare a control by evaporating 10 mg of sodium carbonate and 1 ml of the H_2O_2, 5 ml of HCl and 0.1 mg of SO_4 to dryness on the steam bath. Dissolve the residue from each in 10 ml of water and filter, if necessary. Then to each add 1 ml of 0.1 N HCl and 2 ml of $BaCl_2$. Any turbidity appearing in 15 minutes in the solution of the sample is not greater than that in the control.

Ammonia: Dissolve 1 g in 50 ml of H_2O, add 1 ml of 10% NaOH and 2 ml of Nessler solution. Any color produced is not darker than that of a blank to which 0.03 mg of NH_3 (0.10 mg NH_4Cl) has been added.

Heavy metals: Dissolve 5 g in 30 ml of H_2O, add 5 ml of 1 N HCl, and dilute to 50 ml. To 10 ml add 0.015 mg of Pb and dilute to 50 ml (A). Then add to A and to the remaining 40 ml (B) 10 ml of H_2S. B is not darker than A.

Iron: Dissolve 1 g in 20 ml of water, add 3 ml of HCl, and dilute to 50 ml. Add about 50 mg of ammonium persulfate and 3 ml of ammonium thiocyanate solution, and mix. Any resulting red color is not darker than that of a blank to which 0.01 mg of Fe has been added.

Assay: Sodium citrate may be assayed, after drying at 180° to constant weight, by the general methods for Alkali Salts of Organic Acids, page 564. One ml of 0.1 N acid = 0.008604 g of $Na_3C_6H_5O_7$ (anhydrous).

SODIUM COBALTINITRITE

Sodium Cobaltic Nitrite

Approx.: $Na_3CO(NO_2)_6$; mol. wt. 404; Co—14.6%; NO_2—68.3%.

Yellow to brownish-yellow powder. Freely soluble in water; slightly soluble in alcohol.

Standards

Solubility . . . . to pass test	*Assay* for CO content . . . . min 95%
Sensitiveness . . . . to pass test	*Assay* for NO_2 content . . . . min 95%
Drying loss . . . . max 1.0%	

Solubility: A solution of 2 g in 20 ml of water is clear or not more than faintly turbid.

Sensitiveness: Dissolve 3 g in 10 ml of water, filter if necessary, and add the solution to a mixture of 1 ml of glacial acetic acid and 5 ml of water containing 0.5 mg of potassium (1.0 mg KCl) and shake well. A distinct precipitate is produced in 1 hour.

Drying loss: When dried at 105°, the loss in weight does not exceed 1.0%.

Assay for Cobalt: Weigh accurately 1.0 to 1.2 g of the dried sample and transfer completely with the aid of 10–15 ml of water to a tall beaker. When dissolved slowly add 10 ml of HCl. Wash down the inside of the beaker with a stream of water and evaporate to dryness on the steam bath. Moisten the residue with a few drops of HCl and dissolve it in 25 ml of water. Transfer the solution completely to a 250-ml glass stoppered flask. While swirling the flask slowly add 15 ml of 10% NaOH, then add 5–7 ml of 3% H_2O_2 and 25 ml of water, mix well and boil gently to expel excess of H_2O_2 and reduce the volume to about 25 ml. Cool, add 3 g of KI and follow with 20 ml of 25% H_2SO_4. Immediately stopper the flask and rotate it until a clear solution results. Titrate the liberated iodine with 0.1 N thiosulfate, adding starch indicator toward the end. Correct for a blank with the same quantities of NaOH solution, H_2SO_4 and KI. One ml of 0.1 N thiosulfate = 0.005894 g of cobalt (Co), log 77041. Not less than 13.8% of Co should be found, corresponding to 95% of sodium cobaltinitrite.

Assay for Nitrite: Dissolve about 0.5 g of the dried sample, accurately weighed, in 25 ml of water in a 250-ml volumetric flask. While swirling the flask add through a funnel in the neck of the flask 10 ml of 10% NaOH. Digest on the steam bath for 15 minutes, cool, dilute to volume, mix well and allow to stand for 2 hours or longer. Filter through a dry filter or fritted glass crucible, rejecting the first 20–30 ml.

Mix in a beaker 150 ml of water, 10 ml of H_2SO_4 and add 40.0 ml of 0.1 N $KMnO_4$; then add from a pipette 50.0 ml of the filtrate from the preceding paragraph, keeping the tip of the pipette well below the surface of the liquid, but without stirring. Allow to stand for 5 minutes, then add 20.0 ml of 0.1 N ferrous ammonium sulfate (or an accurately weighed quantity of about 0.80 g of uneffloresced ferrous ammonium sulfate crystals). Titrate the excess of the ferrous iron with 0.1 N $KMnO_4$. The total volume of the $KMnO_4$ used, less the volume of the 0.1 N ferrous solution (or its equivalent if crystals of the ferrous salt is used) represents the NO_2. One ml of 0.1 N $KMnO_4$ = 0.002300 g of NO_2, log 36173. Not less than 65% and not more than 69% NO_2 should be found.

SODIUM CYANIDE

NaCN; mol. wt. 49.01; Na—46.92%; CN—53.08%.

Colorless or white fragments or a granular powder; deliquescent. Soluble in water; slightly soluble in alcohol. Decomposed by weak acids, even CO_2; also affected by sunlight. *Extremely poisonous.* It usually contains about 1% of Na_2CO_3 and some NaOH. *Keep in tightly closed containers, protected from acid fumes, light and moisture.*

Standards

Assay.................min 96% NaCN	Sulfate (SO_4)...............max 0.010%
Chloride (Cl)...............max 0.015%	Sulfide (S).................max 0.001%
Ferrocyanide [$Fe(CN)_6$]..max about 0.01%	Thiocyanate (SCN)..........max 0.020%
Phosphate (PO_4)............max 0.020%	Lead (Pb)................max 0.0004%

Caution! *Because of the extremely poisonous nature of cyanides, all tests are to be made under a hood with a strong draft. Pipettes are not to be used in measuring solutions.*

Assay: Weigh accurately about 0.4 g and dissolve in 30 ml of water. Add 2 drops of potassium iodide and 1 ml of NH_4OH; titrate with 0.1 N silver nitrate to a slight permanent turbidity. One ml of 0.1 N silver nitrate = 0.009801 g NaCN, log 99127.

Solution S: Dissolve 10 g in sufficient water to make 200 ml, filter if necessary, and use for the following tests.

Chloride: To 2.0 ml of *Solution S* add 5 ml of formaldehyde, mix, and allow to stand for a few minutes. Add 10 ml of water and 1 ml nitric acid, mix well, then add 1 ml of silver nitrate. Any turbidity produced is not greater than that produced by treating 4 ml of water containing 0.03 mg of Cl with the same quantities of the reagents as the sample.

Ferrocyanide: To 20 ml of *Solution S* add, *under the hood*, 3 ml of HCl and 1 drop of freshly prepared ferric chloride solution. No blue or green color is produced in 1 hour.

Phosphate: To 2.0 ml of *Solution S* add 2 ml of HCl and evaporate on the steam bath *in the hood* to dryness. Add 2 ml of HCl and 5 ml of water and re-evaporate to dryness. Dissolve the residue in 20 ml of water, add 2 ml of 25% H_2SO_4 and 1 ml each of phosphate reagents **A** and **B**, and heat at 60° for 10 minutes. Any blue color produced is not darker than that in a control made with 0.02 mg of PO_4, 2 ml of 25% H_2SO_4, and the same volumes of the phosphate reagents and in the same final volume as with the sample.

Sulfate: Evaporate 20 ml of *Solution S* with 5 ml of HCl to dryness on the steam bath *under the hood*. Take up the residue in 5 ml of water and re-evaporate with 2 ml of HCl. Dissolve the residue in 10 ml of water, add 1 ml of 0.1 N HCl and 2 ml of $BaCl_2$. If a turbidity is produced it is not greater than that produced when 0.1 mg of SO_4, dissolved in 10 ml of H_2O, is treated with the same quantities of 0.1 N HCl and $BaCl_2$ as the sample.

Sulfide: Dissolve 1 g in 20 ml of water and divide into two equal portions. To one portion add 3 drops of sodium plumbite solution (made by adding 10% NaOH solution to 10% lead acetate solution until the precipitate first formed redissolves). The treated solution exhibits no more color than the portion not treated with the sodium plumbite.

Thiocyanate: To 20 ml of *Solution S* add, *under the hood,* 4 ml of HCl and 4 drops of ferric ammonium sulfate. The solution is no more colored than the blank.

Lead: Dissolve 0.6 g in 10 ml of water in a separatory funnel. Add 5 ml of ammonium citrate solution, 2 ml of hydroxylamine hydrochloride solution for dithizone test, and 2 drops of phenol red; make the solution alkaline, if necessary, by the addition of NH_4OH. Add 5 ml of dithizone in chloroform solution, shake gently but well for 1 minute, and allow to separate. The color of the chloroform layer has no more red hue than that of a control made with 0.002 mg of Pb and 0.1 g of the sample dissolved in 10 ml of water and treated exactly as the solution of the 0.6-g sample.

SODIUM DIETHYLTHIOCARBAMATE

Sodium Diethyldithiocarbamate

$(C_2H_5)_2N \cdot CS_2Na$; mol. wt. 171.27; N—8.18%; S—37.45%.

White or brownish or slightly pink crystals; contains variable amounts of water. Freely soluble in water or in alcohol. Its solution is alkaline and when acidified a white turbidity is produced due to the formation of carbon disulfide.

It is used for the determination of copper[1,2,3] and for its separation from other metals, such as lead. This reagent will detect the presence of 0.001 mg of copper in 100 ml of solution.

Standards

Solubility............... to pass test   Sensitiveness............... to pass test

Solubility: Dissolve 0.5 g of the sample in 25 ml of water. A clear or practically clear solution results.

Sensitiveness: Dilute 1.0 ml of the solution from the test for *Solubility* to 10 ml. Add 2 ml of this solution to an aqueous solution containing 0.002 mg of Cu and 1 ml of 10% NH_3 in a volume of 50 ml. Add 5 ml of isoamyl alcohol, shake gently but well for 1 minute and allow to separate. The isoamyl alcohol layer has a distinct yellow color, compared with a blank without copper.

[1] Delepine, M., *Compt. rend.* **146**, 981 (1908).
[2] Thatcher, R. W., *J. Am. Chem. Soc.* **55**, 4524 (1933).
[3] Conn, L. W. Johnson, A. H., Trebler, H. A., and Karpenko, V., *Ind. Eng. Chem., Anal. Ed.* **7**, 15 (1934). (Copper in milk.)

SODIUM ETHYLENEDIAMINE TETRAACETATE, *see*
DISODIUM ETHYLENEDIAMINE TETRAACETATE

SODIUM FLUORIDE

NaF; mol. wt. 41.99% Na—54. 76%; F—45.24%.

White powder. Soluble in 25 parts of water; insoluble in alcohol. The aqueous solution corrodes glass. *Poisonous!*

Standards

Insoluble.................... max 0.02%	Sulfate (SO_4)..................... 0.030%
Drying loss.................. max 0.30%	Sulfite (SO_2)..................... 0.005%
Free acid (as HF)................ 0.05%	Heavy metals (as Pb)............ 0.003%
Free alkali (as Na_2CO_3)........... 0.10%	Iron (Fe)....................... 0.002%
Silicofluoride (as Na_2SiF_6).......... 0.10%	*Assay*....................... min 98.5%
Chloride (Cl)................... 0.005%	

Insoluble: Dissolve 5 g in 100 ml of warm H_2O in a platinum dish and heat the solution on the steam bath for 1 hour. Filter any undissolved matter on a tared platinum Gooch crucible, wash it with hot H_2O, and dry at 105°. Its weight does not exceed 1.0 mg.

Drying loss: Weigh accurately about 2 g and dry to constant weight at 150°. The loss in weight corresponds to not more than 0.30%.

Free acid; Free alkali: Dissolve 2 g in 40 ml of water in a platinum dish and add 10 ml of a saturated, aqueous potassium nitrate solution. Cool to 0° and add 0.2 ml of phenolphthalein. If no pink color is produced, titrate with 0.1 N NaOH until a pink color persists for 15 seconds; no more than 0.5 ml of the NaOH is required. If a pink color is produced, titrate with 0.1 N HCl, stirring gently, until the pink color is discharged; not more than 0.2 ml of the HCl is required (retain the solution).

Silicofluoride: Boil the solution from the preceding test and titrate it while hot with 0.1 N NaOH to a permanent pink color. Not more than 0.45 ml of the 0.1 N NaOH is required to produce the color.

Chloride: Dissolve 0.4 g in 20 ml of H_2O, add 0.2 g of boric acid, 1 ml of nitric acid, and 1 ml of silver nitrate. Any resulting turbidity is not greater than that in a blank to which 0.02 mg of Cl has been added.

Sulfate: Evaporate 0.5 g of the sample and 20 mg of sodium carbonate to dryness five times with 5-ml portions of HCl in a platinum dish. Dissolve the residue in 10 ml of water, add 1 ml of 1 N HCl, filter if necessary, and add 2 ml of $BaCl_2$. The resulting turbidity is not greater than that of a control made as follows: Evaporate 25 ml of HCl with 20 mg of sodium carbonate to dryness on the steam bath. Dissolve the residue and 0.15 mg of SO_4 in 10 ml of water and add 1 ml of 1 N HCl and 2 ml of $BaCl_2$.

Sulfite: Dissolve 6 g in 150 ml of water, add 2 ml of HCl and 0.5 ml of starch solution and titrate immediately with 0.1 N iodine to a blue color. Not more than 0.1 ml of the iodine is required to produce the blue color.

Heavy metals: Dissolve 1.5 g in 40 ml of hot water, filter, and dilute to 60 ml. To 10 ml add 0.03 mg of Pb, dilute to 50 ml, and add 1 ml of 1 N acetic acid (*A*). To the remaining 50 ml add 1 ml of 1 N acetic acid (*B*). Then to each add 10 ml of H_2S. *B* is not darker than *A*.

Iron: To 1 g of sample contained in a platinum dish add 20 ml of water and 2 ml of HCl and boil for 5 minutes. Cool, and transfer to a separatory funnel; add about 50 mg of ammonium persulfate and 15 ml of butanolic potassium thiocyanate, shake well, and allow to separate. Any red color in the butanol layer is not darker than that of a blank to which 0.02 mg of Fe has been added.

Assay: Sodium fluoride may be assayed by the following method: Dry about

1 g at 150° for 3 hours.　Weigh accurately about 0.6 g of the dried sample and dissolve it in 50 ml of H_2O in platinum.　Add 2 drops of methyl orange and 3 drops of bromocresol green, then add, dropwise, with constant stirring, sufficient 5% thorium nitrate solution to produce a maximum pink color.　Finally add 1 ml of glacial acetic acid and allow to stand overnight.　Filter, wash with hot H_2O, and ignite in platinum to thorium oxide.　The weight of the thorium oxide (ThO_2) × 0.6316 = NaF, log 80353.

SODIUM FORMATE

$NaCHO_2$; mol. wt. 68.02; Na—33.81%; formic acid = 67.67%.

Colorless or white crystals, having a slight odor of formic acid.　Soluble in 2 parts of water; slightly soluble in alcohol; soluble in glycerol.

Standards

Assay................min 99% $NaCHO_2$		Phosphate (PO_4)............max 0.001%	
Insoluble...................max 0.010%		Sulfate (SO_4)..............max 0.005%	
Free acid (as HCOOH)........max 0.05%		Calcium (Ca)................max 0.005%	
Free alkali.........................none		Heavy metals (as Pb)........max 0.001%	
Chloride (Cl)................max 0.002%		Iron (Fe).................max 0.0005%	
Oxalate (C_2O_4)...............to pass test			

Assay: Dry about 1 g for 18 hours over H_2SO_4.　Weigh accurately about 0.4 g of the dried sample, dissolve in H_2O, and dilute to exactly 100 ml.　Transfer 20 ml of the dilution in a glass-stoppered flask, add 2 ml of 10% NaOH and 50 ml of 0.1 N potassium permanganate.　Heat on the steam bath for 20 minutes, cool, add 3 ml of HCl and 3 g of potassium iodide, and titrate the liberated iodine, representing the excess of permanganate, with 0.1 N thiosulfate, using starch at the end.　Determine the value of the permanganate in terms of 0.1 N thiosulfate by running a blank with the same quantities of permanganate and the other reagents and in the same manner as with the sample.　One ml of 0.1 N $KMnO_4$ = 0.003400 g $NaCHO_2$, log 53148.

$$3NaCHO_2 + 2KMnO_4 + NaOH \rightarrow 2Na_2CO_3 + K_2CO_3 + 2MnO_2 + 2H_2O$$

Sodium formate may also be assayed by the "calomel" method which is based on the reaction $HCOOH + 2HgCl_2 \rightarrow 2HgCl + CO_2 + 2HCl$.

An aliquot of a stock solution equivalent to not more than 100 mg of sodium formate is transferred to a conical flask and diluted with water to about 50 ml. Twenty ml of a solution, containing 5 g of sodium acetate and 2.5 g of NaCl in 100 ml of H_2O, is added, followed by 30 ml of 5% mercuric chloride solution.　The flask is connected with an air condenser and heated on the steam bath for 2.5 to 3 hours.　The precipitated calomel is filtered on a tared filtering crucible previously dried at 105°, washed with water, then with alcohol, dried at 105°, and weighed. The weight of the calomel × 0.1449 = HCOONa.

Insoluble: Dissolve 10 g in 100 ml of H_2O and heat on the steam bath for 30 minutes.　Filter any undissolved residue, wash it with water, and dry at 105°. Its weight does not exceed 1.0 mg.

Free acid; Free alkali: Dissolve 2 g in 20 ml of water and add 2 drops of phenolphthalein. No pink color is produced, and the addition of not more than 0.25 ml of 0.1 N NaOH is required to produce a pink color.

Chloride: Dissolve 1 g in 20 ml of water, add 2 ml of HNO_3 and 1 ml of silver nitrate. Any turbidity produced is not greater than that in the blank to which 0.02 mg of Cl has been added.

Oxalate: To a solution of 1 g in 10 ml of H_2O add 1 drop of glacial acetic acid and 1 ml of calcium chloride solution. No turbidity is formed in 10 minutes.

Phosphate: Ignite 2 g in platinum. Break up the residue well, add 25 ml of H_2O and 1 ml of hydrogen peroxide and boil for a few minutes. Neutralize with 25% H_2SO_4, add 2 ml excess of the acid, filter, and evaporate filtrate to incipient sulfuric fumes. Dilute to 20 ml, add 1 ml each of phosphate reagents **A** and **B**, and heat at 60° for 10 minutes. If a blue color is produced, it is not darker than that of a control made with 0.02 mg PO_4, 2 ml of 25% H_2SO_4, and the same quantities of the phosphate reagents in the same final volume as with the sample.

Sulfate: Dissolve 2 g in 15 ml of water, add 1 ml of 1 N HCl and 2 ml of $BaCl_2$. Any resulting turbidity is not greater than that in a blank to which 0.1 mg of SO_4 has been added.

Calcium: Dissolve 1 g in 10 ml of H_2O and add 1 ml of ammonium oxalate. No turbidity appears in 10 minutes.

Heavy metals: Dissolve 4 g in water to make 40 ml. To 10 ml add 0.02 mg of Pb, dilute to 30 ml, and add 2 ml of 1 N HCl (A). To the remaining 30 ml add 2 ml of 1 N HCl (B). Then add to each 10 ml of H_2S; B is not darker than A.

Iron: Dissolve 2 g in 15 ml of H_2O, add 4 ml of HCl, 50 mg of ammonium persulfate, and 15 ml of butanolic potassium thiocyanate, shake vigorously for 30 seconds and allow to separate. Any red color in the clear butanol layer is not darker than that of a control made with 0.01 mg of Fe, 1 ml of HCl, the same amounts of persulfate and thiocyanate as with the sample.

SODIUM HYDROSULFITE

"Sodium Dithionate"

$Na_2S_2O_4$; mol. wt. 174.13.

White or grayish, crystalline. Soluble in water; slightly soluble in alcohol. It gradually oxidizes in the air, more readily so when in solution, to bisulfite and bisulfate and acquiring an acid reaction. It is also affected by light. It generally contains sodium bisulfite or sulfite. *Keep in well-closed containers, protected from light.*

Sodium hydrosulfite is a very powerful reducing agent. It reduces many metallic salts to the metal.

Standards

Assay...............min 90% $Na_2S_2O_4$	Heavy metals...............max 0.002%	
Solubility....................to pass test	Iron (Fe)...................max 0.002%	
Sulfide......................to pass test		

Assay: Weigh accurately about 1 g of sodium hydrosulfite, dissolve it in a mixture of 10 ml of formaldehyde and 10 ml of water contained in a small, glass-stoppered flask, and allow to stand for 30 minutes with frequent agitation. Transfer the solution to a 250-ml volumetric flask, add 150 ml of oxygen-free water and 3 drops of methyl orange and follow, dropwise, with 1 N H_2SO_4 to a slight acid reaction. Dilute with water to 250 ml and mix well. To 50 ml of the dilution add 2 drops of phenolphthalien and just sufficient 0.1 N NaOH to produce a slightly pink color. Finally, titrate with 0.1 N iodine, using starch indicator. One ml of 0.1 N iodine = 0.004353 g $Na_2S_2O_4$, log 63877.

$$Na_2S_2O_4 + 4I + 3H_2O \rightarrow NaHSO_4 + NaHSO_3 + 4HI$$

Now discharge the blue color of the solution with a drop of 0.1 N sodium thiosulfate and then titrate with 0.1 N NaOH to a pink color. One ml of 0.1 N NaOH = 0.003482 g $Na_2S_2O_4$, log 54185.

$$NaHSO_4 + 4HI + 5NaOH \rightarrow Na_2SO_4 + 4NaI$$

Note: Neutralization with acid toward methyl orange converts any sodium sulfite present to bisulfite. This bisulfite, as well as any bisulfite originally present and that formed in the titration with iodine, combines with the formaldehyde to sodium formaldehyde bisulfite which reacts neither with iodine nor with alkali hydroxide.

Solubility: A solution of 2 g in 50 ml of oxygen-free water is clear and complete, or practically so.

Sulfide: Add 10% NaOH to lead acetate solution until the precipitate redissolves. Add 5 drops of this solution to a solution of 1 g sample in 10 ml of H_2O; there should be no immediate darkening.

Solution S: Dissolve 2 g in 25 ml of water, *cautiously* add 5 ml of 30% hydrogen peroxide, then add 5 ml of HCl and evaporate to dryness on the steam bath. Dissolve the residue in 25 ml of water, filter if necessary, add 1 drop of phenolphthalein solution, and neutralize with 0.1 N NaOH. Discharge the pink color with 5 drops of 0.1 N HCl and dilute to 40 ml.

Heavy metals: To 5 ml of *Solution S* add 0.02 mg of Pb and dilute to 40 ml (A). Dilute 25 ml of *Solution S* to 40 ml (B). Then to each add 10 ml of H_2S. B is not darker than A.

Iron: To 10 ml of *Solution S* add 2 ml of HCl, dilute to 50 ml, and add 50 mg of ammonium persulfate and 3 ml of ammonium thiocyanate. Any resulting red color is not darker than that of a blank to which 0.01 mg of Fe has been added.

SODIUM HYDROXIDE

NaOH; mol. wt. 40.00; Na—57.48%; Na_2O—77.48%.

White pellets or sticks; deliquesces and readily absorbs carbon dioxide from the air. Melts at 320°. Soluble in about 1 part of water; soluble in alcohol. When dissolved in water or alcohol much heat is liberated. It is very caustic to organic tissue. *Handle with rubber gloves! Keep in tightly closed containers.*

Standards

Assay................min 97% NaOH		Ammonium hydroxide	
Carbonate (as Na_2CO_3).........max 2.0%		precipitate and Silica.......max 0.020%	
Chloride (Cl)................max 0.005%		Silica (SiO_2)................max 0.010%	
Nitrogen compounds (as N)...max 0.001%		Heavy metals (as Ag)........max 0.002%	
Phosphate (PO_4)...........max 0.001%		Iron (Fe)...................max 0.001%	
Sulfate (SO_4)...............max 0.005%		Nickel (Ni)................max 0.001%	

Solution S: Weigh quickly 50 g of sample to within 0.1 g, dissolve in CO_2-free water, cool, and dilute to exactly 500 ml.

Assay; Carbonate: Dilute exactly 20 ml of *Solution S* (2-g sample) with 175 ml of cold, CO_2-free water in a flask.   Add 5 ml of $BaCl_2$ solution, stopper, and allow to stand for 5 minutes.   Add 3 drops of phenolphthalein and titrate with 1 N HCl to the disappearance of the pink color.   The acid consumed in this titration indicates the NaOH content.   One ml of 1 N HCl = 0.04001 g NaOH, log 60206. Now add 2 drops of methyl orange and titrate with the HCl to a permanent pink color.   The acid consumed with the methyl orange titration represents the carbonate.   One ml of 1 N HCl = 0.05300 g Na_2CO_3, log 72428.

Chloride: Dilute 4.0 ml of *Solution S* with 20 ml of water, add 2 ml of HNO_3, cool, and add 1 ml of $AgNO_3$.   Any turbidity produced is not greater than that in a blank to which 0.02 mg of Cl has been added.

Nitrogen compounds: Dilute 30 ml of *Solution S* contained in a suitable distillation flask with 40 ml of ammonia-free water, add 1 g of powdered Devarda metal or 0.5 g of aluminum wire in small pieces and let stand for 7 hours protected from loss or access of ammonia.   Slowly distill 40 ml into 5 ml of water containing 1 drop of dilute HCl, then add to the distillate 1 ml of *Solution S* and 2 ml of Nessler solution.   The color produced is not darker than that produced by treating 0.02 mg of nitrogen (0.08 mg NH_4Cl), and 10 ml of *Solution S* in the same manner as the 30 ml of *Solution S*.

Phosphate: Render 20 ml of *Solution S* slightly acid with 25% H_2SO_4, then add 3 ml excess of the acid and evaporate in platinum to incipient sulfuric fumes. Cautiously add 20 ml of H_2O, filter, then add to the filtrate 1 ml each of phosphate solutions **A** and **B**, and heat at 60° for 10 minutes.   Any blue color produced is not darker than that of a control made with 0.02 mg of PO_4, 2 ml of 25% H_2SO_4, the same quantities of the phosphate reagent and in the same final volume as with the sample.

Sulfate: To 30 ml of *Solution S* add 3 ml of hydrochloric acid and evaporate to dryness on the steam bath.   Dissolve the residue in 25 ml of water and re-evaporate to dryness.   Dissolve in 20 ml of warm water, add 1 ml of 0.1 N HCl and 2 ml of $BaCl_2$.   Any turbidity produced in 20 minutes is not greater than that in a control made with 0.1 mg of SO_4, 1 ml of 0.1 N HCl, and 2 ml of $BaCl_2$ in the same volume as with the sample.

Ammonium hydroxide precipitate and Silica: To 100 ml of *Solution S* *cautiously* add 15 ml of H_2SO_4 previously mixed with 15 ml of water, evaporate in a platinum dish, and heat to evolution of copious sulfuric fumes for 2 to 3 minutes. Cool, dissolve the residue in 130 ml of hot water, and make just alkaline to methyl red with NH_4OH.   Heat to boiling, filter if a precipitate is present, wash it with hot water, and ignite in a platinum crucible to constant weight. The weight of the ignited precipitate is not more than 2.0 mg. Add to the weighed precipitate 5 drops each of H_2SO_4 and hydrofluoric acid, evaporate, and ignite to constant weight. The loss in weight, SiO_2, is not more than 1.0 mg.

Note: A colorimetric procedure for the determination of small amounts of silica in alkali carbonates and hydroxides was reported by Kenyon and Bewick, *Anal. Chem.* **25**, 145 (1953). The method is based on the formation of the complex silicomolybdenum blue by the interaction of the silica with ammonium molybdate and a reducing agent.

Heavy metals: To 25 ml of *Solution S* add 5 ml of HNO_3 and evaporate on the steam bath to dryness. Dissolve the residue in 20 ml of water, add a drop of phenolphthalein solution, and then add 0.1 N NaOH until a pink color is just produced. Add 3 ml of 1 N acetic acid and dilute to 50 ml. To 10 ml add 0.03 mg of Ag and dilute to 40 ml (*A*). Then add to *A* and to the remaining 40 ml (*B*) 10 ml of H_2S. *B* is not darker than *A*.

Iron: To 10 ml of *Solution S* add 5 ml of HCl and dilute to 50 ml. Add 30 mg of ammonium persulfate and 3 ml of ammonium thiocyanate. Any resulting red color is not darker than that of a blank to which 0.01 mg of Fe has been added.

Nickel: Dilute 20 ml of *Solution S* with 30 ml of water, neutralize with HCl and dilute to 80 ml. Make just alkaline to litmus paper (*p*H 8.5) with 10% NH_3, then add 5 ml of bromine water, 5 ml of dimethylglyoxime solution, 5 ml of 10% NaOH and dilute to 100 ml. Any resulting red color is not darker than that of a control made with 0.02 mg of nickel (Ni), the same quantities of the reagents as used in the test and in the same final volume.

SODIUM HYPOPHOSPHITE

$NaH_2PO_2 \cdot H_2O$; mol. wt. 106.00; anhydrous—83.0%; H_2O—17.0%.

Colorless crystals or a white, granular powder; effloresces in dry air; slightly deliquescent in damp air. Soluble in 1 part of water; soluble in alcohol or glycerin. Sodium hypophosphite is a strong reducing agent.

Standards

Assay...........min 99% $NaH_2PO_2H_2O$	Arsenic (As)................max 2 ppm
Insoluble...................max 0.010%	Calcium (Ca)...............max 0.050%
Chloride (Cl)...............max 0.010%	Heavy metals (as Pb).......max 0.0005%
Sulfate (SO_4)...............max 0.010%	Iron (Fe)..................max 0.001%

Assay: Weigh accurately about 0.3 g, dissolve in water, and dilute to exactly 200 ml. Transfer 50 ml to a 500-ml glass-stoppered, volumetric flask, add 50 ml of 0.1 N bromine, 120 ml of water, then add quickly to 20 ml of 10% H_2SO_4 and immediately stopper. Shake gently and allow to stand for 3 hours. Add quickly a solution of 2 g of potassium iodide in 10 ml of water and titrate the liberated iodine, representing the excess of bromine, with 0.1 N thiosulfate, adding starch toward the end. One ml of 0.1 N bromine = 0.002651 g $NaH_2PO_2 \cdot H_2O$, log 42341.

$$NaH_2PO_2 + 4Br + 2H_2O \rightarrow NaH_2PO_4 + 4HBr$$

Note: Carry out standardization of the 0.1 N bromine in same manner as the assay.

Insoluble: Dissolve 10 g in 100 ml of H_2O and heat on steam bath for 1 hour. Filter if an undissolved residue is present (retain filtrate), wash it with H_2O, and dry at 105°. The weight of the insoluble residue does not exceed 1.0 mg.

Chloride: Dissolve 5 g in 20 ml of water, add 5 ml of silver nitrate and 10 ml of HNO_3, and heat gently to expel oxides of nitrogen. Allow to stand for 2 hours, filter the precipitate of silver chloride, wash it well with water, and dry at 120°. The weight of the silver chloride is not more than 2.0 mg.

Sulfate: To the filtrate from the test for *Insoluble* add 1 ml of HCl, heat to boiling, add 5 ml of $BaCl_2$, and allow to stand overnight. Filter any precipitate of $BaSO_4$, wash it with hot H_2O, and ignite. The weight of the ignited precipitate does not exceed 2.5 mg.

Arsenic: Dissolve 1 g in 10 ml of water, add 5 ml of nitric acid, and evaporate to dryness on the steam bath. Re-evaporate with 10 ml of H_2O and 5 ml of nitric acid. Take up the residue with 10 ml of water, add 5 ml of sulfuric acid, and evaporate to strong sulfuric fumes. *Cautiously* add 10 ml of water and test for arsenic by method on page 563. The stain is not greater than that from 0.002 mg of As.

Calcium: Dissolve 1 g in 15 ml of H_2O, warm to 50°, and add 1 ml of ammonium hydroxide and 2 ml of ammonium oxalate. Any turbidity produced in 10 minutes is not greater than that produced by adding 1 ml of ammonium hydroxide and 2 ml of ammonium oxalate to 15 ml of water containing 0.5 mg of Ca.

Heavy metals: Dissolve 4 g in H_2O to make 40 ml. To 10 ml add 0.01 mg of Pb, dilute to 30 ml, and add 1 ml of 1 N HCl (A). To the remaining 30 ml add 1 ml of 1 N HCl (B). Then to each add 10 ml of H_2S. B is not darker than A.

Iron: Dissolve 1 g in 10 ml of water, add 5 ml of HNO_3, and evaporate on the steam bath to dryness. Take up the residue with 2 ml of HCl and 15 ml of water, add 50 mg of ammonium persulfate and 15 ml of butanolic potassium thiocyanate; shake well and allow to separate. Any red color in the butanol layer is not darker than that of a control made with 0.01 mg of Fe, 2 ml of HCl, and the same quantities of the reagents, and in the same final volume as with the sample.

SODIUM IODATE

$NaIO_3$; mol. wt. 197.90; Na—11.62%; I—64.13%; active oxygen—20.2%.

White, crystalline powder. Soluble in 20 parts of water; insoluble in alcohol.

Standards

Assay.............99.7%–100.2% $NaIO_3$	Iodide (I)...................max 0.002%
Insoluble...................max 0.005%	Nitrogen compounds (as N)...max 0.003%
Neutrality..................to pass test	Sulfate (SO_4)...............max 0.005%
Chlorate (ClO_3)..............max 0.01%	Heavy metals (as Pb).......max 0.0005%
Chloride and Bromide (as Cl)..max 0.020%	Iron (Fe)..................max 0.001%

Assay: Weigh accurately between 0.1 and 0.12 g (or a portion of a stock solution corresponding to this quantity) of the sample previously dried at 105° for 1 hour, and dissolve it in 50 ml of H_2O in a glass-stoppered flask. Add to the solution 3 g of potassium iodide and 3 ml of HCl, previously diluted with 10 ml of H_2O. Allow to stand for 5 minutes, then add 100 ml of cold water and titrate the liberated iodine with 0.1 N sodium thiosulfate, adding starch toward the end. Correct for 0.1 N thiosulfate consumed by a blank. One ml of 0.1 N thiosulfate = 0.003299 g $NaIO_3$, log 51838.

$$NaIO_3 + 5KI + 6HCl \rightarrow 6I + 6KCl + 3H_2O$$

Insoluble: Dissolve 20 g in 300 ml of hot H_2O and heat on the steam bath for 1 hour. Filter any insoluble residue, wash it with hot water, and dry at 105°. Its weight does not exceed 1.0 mg.

Neutrality: Dissolve 3 g in 40 ml of warm water and add 2 drops of phenolphthalein solution; no pink color is produced. Now add 0.05 ml of 0.1 N NaOH; a pink color is produced.

Chlorate: To 2 g of the powdered sample add 2 ml of H_2SO_4. The salt remains white and no odor or gas is evolved.

Chloride and Bromide: Dissolve 0.5 g in 15 ml of hot water, add 12 ml of sulfurous acid, and gently boil for 3 minutes. Cool, add 5 ml of NH_4OH and 10 ml of H_2O, then slowly add with stirring 10 ml of 5% $AgNO_3$. Filter, wash with about 10 ml of water, dilute filtrate to 100 ml, and mix. To 20 ml add 2 ml of HNO_3. Any resulting turbidity is not greater than that in a control made with 0.01 mg of chloride (Cl), 1 ml each of NH_4OH and $AgNO_3$ solution, and 2 ml of HNO_3.

Iodide: Dissolve 2 g in 40 ml of H_2O, and add 1 ml of chloroform and 0.5 ml of 1 N H_2SO_4. The chloroform acquires no violet color in 1 minute.

Nitrogen compounds: Dissolve 1 g in 60 ml of H_2O in an ammonia distillation flask, add 0.5 g powdered Devarda metal or 0.5 g of aluminum wire in small pieces and 10 ml of 10% NaOH. Allow to stand for 2 hours protected from loss or access of NH_3; then slowly distill about 40 ml into 5 ml of water containing 1 drop of dilute HCl. Dilute to 50 ml and mix well. To 20 ml of the solution add 1 ml of 10% NaOH, dilute to 50 ml, and add 2 ml of Nessler solution. The color is not darker than that produced by treating 0.03 mg of nitrogen (0.12 mg NH_4Cl) in the same manner as the sample.

Sulfate: To 2 g of the sample add 20 mg of sodium carbonate and 10 ml of HCl and evaporate on the steam bath to dryness. Repeat the evaporation with 5 ml of HCl. Dissolve the residue in 10 ml of H_2O, filter if necessary, and add to the filtrate 1 ml of 0.1 N HCl and 2 ml of $BaCl_2$. Any resulting turbidity is not greater than that in a control made as follows: Evaporate 20 mg of sodium carbonate and 15 ml of HCl to dryness. Dissolve the residue and 0.1 mg of SO_4 in 10 ml of H_2O, then add 1 ml of 0.1 N HCl and 2 ml of $BaCl_2$.

Heavy metals: To 2.5 g of the sample add 10 ml of hot water and 10 ml of HCl (A). To 0.5 g of sample add 15 ml of HCl and 0.01 mg of Pb (B). Evaporate both to dryness on the steam bath. Add to A 5 ml of HCl and re-evaporate to dryness. Dissolve the residues in 20 ml of water each, add a drop of phenolphthalein and neutralize with 1 N NaOH. Add to each 1 ml of 1 N acetic acid, dilute to 25 ml, and add 5 ml of H_2S. A is not darker than B.

Iron: To 1 g of sample add 5 ml of H_2O and 5 ml of HCl and evaporate to dryness on steam bath. Repeat the evaporation with 5 ml of HCl. Prepare a control by adding to 0.01 mg of Fe, 10 ml of HCl, and evaporating on the steam bath to dryness.   Take up each in 2 ml of HCl and water to make 50 ml.   Add to each about 30 mg of ammonium persulfate and 3 ml of ammonium thiocyanate.   Any red color in the sample solution is not darker than that in the control.

SODIUM MOLYBDATE

$Na_2MoO_4 \cdot 2H_2O$; mol. wt. 241.98; anhydrous—85.12%; H_2O—14.88%; MoO_3—59.50%; Mo—39.67%.

Colorless or white crystals, or a powder.   Soluble in 2 parts of water.

Standards

Assay, anhydrous basis........min 98.5%	Phosphate (PO_4)............max 0.001%
Insoluble...................max 0.010%	Sulfate (SO_4)................max 0.02%
Chloride (Cl)...............max 0.005%	Ammonia (NH_3).............max 0.01%
Nitrate (NO_3)..............max 0.003%	Heavy metals (as Pb)........max 0.003%

Assay: Weigh accurately about 0.5 g of the sample previously dried to constant weight at 105°, and dissolve it in 200 ml of H_2O and 1 ml of acetic acid.   Heat the solution to boiling, add a clear solution of 1.5 g of lead acetate in 20 ml of water and boil gently until the precipitate becomes granular.   Wash several times by decantation with water, then filter, wash, dry and ignite.   The weight of the lead molybdate, $PbMoO_4$, so obtained multiplied by 0.5609 = Na_2MoO_4, log 74899.

Insoluble: Dissolve 10 g in 200 ml of water and heat on the steam bath for 30 minutes.   Filter any undissolved residue (retain filtrate), wash it with water and dry at 105°.   Its weight does not exceed 1.0 mg.

Chloride: Dissolve 0.4 g in 40 ml of water and add the solution to 5 ml of HNO_3. Filter, if necessary, and add 1 ml of $AgNO_3$.   Any resulting turbidity is not greater than that in a blank to which 0.02 mg of Cl has been added.

Nitrate: Dissolve 0.5 g in 10 ml of H_2O, add 10 mg of NaCl and 0.1 ml of indigo carmine, then follow with 10 ml of H_2SO_4.   The blue color is not entirely discharged in 5 minutes.

Phosphate: To the filtrate from the test for *Insoluble* add 5 ml of NH_4OH and pour the solution into a mixture of 30 ml of HNO_3 and 15 ml of H_2O.   Shake at 40° for 5 minutes and allow to stand for 1 hour.   Any yellow precipitate formed is not more than that produced when a mixture of 1 g of sample and 0.04 mg of PO_4 is treated in the same manner.

Sulfate: Dissolve 1 g in 5 ml of hot H_2O, add 5 ml of HNO_3, and evaporate to dryness.   Digest the residue with 1 ml of HCl and 10 ml of water, dilute to 20 ml, and filter.   Add to the filtrate 2 ml of $BaCl_2$.   Any resulting turbidity is not greater than that in a control made with 0.2 mg of SO_4, 1 ml of 1 N HCl, and 2 ml of $BaCl_2$ in the same volume as with the sample.

Ammonia: Dissolve 0.2 g in 40 ml of H_2O, add 3 ml of 10% NaOH and 2 ml of Nessler solution.   The resulting color is not darker than that of a blank to which 0.02 mg of HN_3 (0.06 mg NH_4Cl) has been added.

Heavy metals: Dissolve 2 g in 20 ml of H_2O, add 10 ml of 10% NaOH and 2 ml of ammonium hydroxide, and dilute to 40 ml.   To 10 ml of the solution add 0.03 mg of Pb and dilute to 40 ml (*A*).   Dilute the remaining 30 ml of the solution to 40 ml (*B*).   Then add to each 10 ml of H_2S.   *B* is not darker than *A*.

SODIUM NITRATE

$NaNO_3$; mol. wt. 85.00; Na—27.06%; NO_3—72.94%; N—16.48%.

Colorless crystals; moderately deliquescent in moist air.   Melts at 316°. Soluble in 1.2 parts of water; in 100 parts of alcohol.   When dissolved in water the temperature of the solution is lowered.   *Keep in tightly closed containers.*

Standards

Insoluble....................max 0.005%	Sulfate (SO_4)...............max 0.003%
Neutrality...................to pass test	Calcium, Magnesium, and
Total chlorine (Cl)..........max 0.002%	NH_4OH precipitate........max 0.010%
Iodate (IO_3)..............max 0.0005%	Heavy metals (as Pb).......max 0.0005%
Nitrite (NO_2)..............max 0.001%	Iron (Fe).................max 0.0003%
Phosphate (PO_4)...........max 0.0005%	

Insoluble: Dissolve 20 g in 100 ml of H_2O and heat on steam bath for 1 hour. Filter any undissolved residue (retain the filtrate), wash it with water, and dry at 105°.   Its weight does not exceed 1.0 mg.

Neutrality: To a solution of 5 g in 50 ml of CO_2-free water add 3 drops of phenolphthalein; no pink color is produced.   Now add 0.02 N NaOH to the production of a pink color; not more than 0.2 ml is required to produce a pink color.

Total chlorine: Ignite 1 g, gently at first, then at low red heat for a few minutes. Cool, dissolve in 20 ml of water, and add 1 ml HNO_3 and 1 ml of silver nitrate.   Any turbidity produced is not greater than that in a blank to which 0.02 mg of Cl has been added.

Iodate; Nitrite: Dissolve 1 g in 10 ml of H_2O, add 2 drops of 10% potassium iodide solution, 1 ml of chloroform and 1 ml of glacial acetic acid, and shake gently for 5 minutes.   The chloroform is not colored pink or violet.

Phosphate: Dissolve 4 g in 25 ml of water and add 2 ml of 25% H_2SO_4.   Add 1 ml each of phosphate reagents **A** and **B**, and heat at 60° for 10 minutes.   If a blue color is produced, it is not darker than that in a control made with 0.02 mg PO_4, 2 ml of 25% H_2SO_4, the same quantities of the phosphate reagents and in the same final volume as with the sample.

Sulfate: Evaporate 3 g of the sample and 20 mg of sodium carbonate with 10 ml of H_2O and 10 ml of HCl to dryness.   Take up with 10 ml of hot H_2O and re-evaporate to dryness with 5 ml of HCl.   Dissolve the residue in 15 ml of H_2O, then add 1 ml of 0.1 N HCl and 2 ml of $BaCl_2$.   Any resulting turbidity is not greater than that in a control made as follows: Evaporate 20 mg of sodium carbonate with 15 ml of HCl to dryness.   Dissolve the residue and 0.1 mg of SO_4 in water to make 15 ml, then treat the solution with 1 ml of 0.1 N HCl and 2 ml of $CaCl_2$.

Calcium, Magnesium, and NH_4OH precipitate: To the filtrate from the test for *Insoluble* add 5 ml of ammonium oxalate, 2 ml of ammonium phosphate and 15 ml of NH_4OH and allow to stand overnight.   If a precipitate is present filter, wash it with 2.5% NH_3, and ignite.   Its weight does not exceed 1.0 mg.

Heavy metals: Dissolve 5 g in H_2O to make 50 ml.   To 10 ml add 0.015 mg of Pb, dilute to 40 ml, and add 1 ml of 1 N acetic acid (A).   To the remaining 40 ml add 1 ml of 1 N acetic acid (B).   Then to each add 10 ml of H_2S; B is not darker than A.

Iron: Dissolve 3 g in 40 ml of water, add 2 ml of HCl, and dilute to 50 ml.   Add about 30 mg of ammonium persulfate and 3 ml of ammonium thiocyanate, and mix well.   Any resulting red color is not darker than that in a blank to which 0.01 mg of Fe has been added.

SODIUM NITRITE

$NaNO_2$; mol. wt. 69.00; Na—33.33%; NO_2—66.67%.

White or slightly yellow granules, or cylindrical rods.   It is hygroscopic; melts at about 250°.   Soluble in about 1.2 parts of water; sparingly soluble in alcohol. *Keep in tightly closed containers.*

Standards

Assay................min 98% $NaNO_2$	Calcium (Ca)...............max 0.010%	
Insoluble...................max 0.010%	Heavy metals (as Pb)........max 0.001%	
Chloride (Cl)...............max 0.005%	Iron (Fe)...................max 0.001%	
Sulfate (SO_4)...............max 0.010%	Potassium (K).............max 0.005%	

Assay: Weigh accurately about 1.2 g, dissolve in water, and dilute to exactly 100 ml.   To 300 ml of water add 5 ml of sulfuric acid, and then immediately add 0.1 N potassium permanganate until a faint pink color persists for 2 minutes.   Disregard this volume of permanganate.   Now add, from a pipette, exactly 50 ml of the potassium permanganate, mix and add slowly, with stirring, 10 ml of the sodium nitrite solution, holding the tip of the pipette under the surface of the liquid.   After 5 minutes add 15 ml of 0.1 N ferrous ammonium sulfate, allow to stand for 5 minutes, and titrate the excess of ferrous ammonium sulfate with 0.1 N permanganate. Each ml of the 0.1 N permanganate consumed by the nitrite = 0.003451 g $NaNO_2$, log 53794.

Insoluble: Dissolve 10 g in 100 ml of H_2O and heat on the steam bath for 10 minutes.   Filter any undissolved residue, wash it with water and dry at 105°. Its weight does not exceed 1.0 mg.

Solution S: Dissolve 10 g in sufficient water to make exactly 100 ml.

Chloride: Dilute 4 ml of *Solution S* with 10 ml of water and add slowly 1 ml of glacial acetic acid.   Warm gently until no more gas is evolved, cool, dilute to 20 ml and add 1 ml of HNO_3 and 1 ml of $AgNO_3$.   Any turbidity produced is not greater than that in a blank to which 0.02 mg of Cl has been added.

Sulfate: To 10 ml of *Solution S* add 2 ml of HCl and evaporate to dryness on the steam bath.   Dissolve the residue in 10 ml of H_2O, add 1 ml of 0.1 N HCl and 2 ml of $BaCl_2$.   The resulting turbidity is not greater than that in a control made with 0.1 mg of SO_4, 1 ml of 0.1 N HCl and 2 ml of $BaCl_2$ in the same volume as with the sample.

Calcium: To 10 ml of *Solution S* add 1 ml of glacial acetic acid, heat to expel oxides of nitrogen, cool, dilute to 10 ml, and add 2 ml of ammonium oxalate.   Any turbidity produced in 10 minutes is not greater than that in a control made with 0.1 mg of Ca and 2 ml of ammonium oxalate in the same volume as with the sample.

Heavy metals: To 40 ml of *Solution S* add 6 ml of hydrochloric acid and evaporate to dryness on the steam bath.   Dissolve the residue in 25 ml of water, add 1 drop of phenolphthalein, neutralize with 0.1 N NaOH and dilute to 40 ml. To 10 ml add 0.02 mg of Pb, 1 ml of 1 N acetic acid, and dilute to 40 ml (A).   To the remaining 30 ml add 1 ml of 1 N acetic acid and dilute to 40 ml (B).   Then to each add 10 ml of H_2S. B is not darker than A.

Iron: To 10 ml of *Solution S* add 3 ml of HCl and evaporate to dryness on the steam bath.   Dissolve the residue in 10 ml of H_2O, add 2 ml of HCl, and dilute to 50 ml.   Add about 30 mg of ammonium persulfate, and 3 ml of ammonium thiocyanate, and mix.   Any resulting red color is not darker than that in a blank to which 0.01 mg of Fe has been added.

Potassium: Dissolve 2 g in 10 ml of water and filter, if necessary.   Add 10 ml of sodium cobaltinitrite solution, then add slowly, with stirring, 2 ml of glacial acetic acid and 10 ml of alcohol, shake well, and allow to stand for 1 hour.   Any turbidity or precipitate formed is not greater than that produced by 0.10 mg of potassium (K) contained in 10 ml of water and treated with the same volumes of the reagents.

Note: A more accurate quantitative evaluation of the potassium content may be achieved by Flame Photometry.

SODIUM NITROFERRICYANIDE

Sodium Nitroprusside

$Na_2Fe(CN)_5NO \cdot 2H_2O$;   mol. wt.   297.97;   anhydrous—87.9%; H_2O—12.1%; CN—43.65%.

Dark-red, transparent crystals.   Soluble in about 2.5 parts of water.

Standards

Insoluble . . . . max 0.010%	Sulfate (SO_4) . . . . max 0.01%
Chloride (Cl) . . . . max 0.020%	*Assay*
Ferricyanide . . . . max about 0.05%	

Insoluble: Dissolve 10 g in 50 ml of water and heat the solution on the steam bath for 30 minutes.   Filter any undissolved residue, wash it with water, and dry at 105°.   The weight of the insoluble residue is not more than 1.0 mg.

Chloride: Dissolve 1 g in 85 ml of water, add a solution of 1.25 g of cupric sulfate in 15 ml of water, mix, and let stand until settled.   Filter, discarding the first 25 ml of filtrate.   To 10 ml of the subsequent filtrate add 2 ml of HNO_3 and 1 ml of $AgNO_3$.   Any resulting turbidity is not greater than that in a control made with 0.02 mg of Cl, 2 ml of HNO_3, and sufficient cupric sulfate to match the color of the test with the sample.

Ferricyanide: To a solution of 0.5 g of the sample in 10 ml of water add 1 ml of 10% ferrous ammonium sulfate.   The turbidity formed is reddish-brown, and not greenish-gray by reflected light.

Sulfate: Dissolve 5 g in 100 ml of water without heating, filter, and add 5 drops glacial acetic acid and 5 ml $BaCl_2$. No turbidity is produced in 10 minutes.

Assay: Dissolve 1.0 of sodium nitroferricyanide, accurately weighed, in water to make 100.0 ml. Transfer 25.0 ml to a 200–300 ml porcelain dish, add 50 ml of water and 1 ml of potassium chromate solution and titrate, while stirring well, with 0.1 N $AgNO_3$ until the color change to brownish persists after stirring. One ml of 0.1 N $AgNO_3$ = 0.01490 g $Na_2Fe(CN)_5NO \cdot 2H_2O$, log 17319.

SODIUM OXALATE, PRIMARY STANDARD

Sörensen's Oxalate

$Na_2C_2O_4$; mol. wt. 134.00; Na—34.32%; anhydrous oxalic acid = 67.18%.

White, crystalline. Soluble in 30 parts of cold water, in 16 parts of boiling water; insoluble in alcohol.

Standards

Insoluble....................max 0.005%	Sulfate (SO_4)................max 0.002%
Drying loss.................max 0.010%	Heavy metals (as Pb)...... max 0.001%
Acidity (as $NaHC_2O_4$)........max 0.022%	Iron (Fe)...................max 0.001%
Alkalinity (as Na_2CO_3).......max 0.040%	Potassium (K)...............max 0.01%
Chloride (Cl)................max 0.002%	Substances darkened
Nitrogen compounds (as N)...max 0.002%	by H_2SO_4.................to pass test

Insoluble: Dissolve 20 g in 500 ml of water and heat on the steam bath for 1 hour. Filter any undissolved residue, wash it with hot water; and dry at 105°. The weight of the insoluble residue does not exceed 1.0 mg.

Drying loss: Dry 5 g to constant weight at 105°. The loss in weight does not exceed 0.5 mg.

Acidity; Alkalinity: Dissolve 2 g in 150 ml of CO_2-free water, add 0.2 ml of phenolphthalein, and boil for 10 minutes while passing through the solution a current of CO_2-free air. Restore the volume to 150 ml with CO_2-free water. Prepare a color standard as follows: Dilute 10 ml of 0.1 N NaOH to 150 ml with CO_2-free water and add 0.2 ml of phenolphthalein. Dilute 6 ml of the red liquid to 150 ml with CO_2-free water. Titrate the hot sodium oxalate solution with 0.01 N NaOH or HCl until the color matches that of the standard. Not more than 0.4 ml of 0.01 N NaOH nor more than 0.8 ml of 0.01 N HCl is required.

Chloride: Ignite 1 g in platinum and dissolve the residue in 20 ml of water. Neutralize the solution with HNO_3 and add 0.5 ml excess of the acid. Filter, and add to the filtrate 1 ml of $AgNO_3$. Any turbidity produced is not greater than that in a blank to which 0.02 mg of Cl has been added.

Nitrogen compounds: Dissolve 1 g in 60 ml of warm H_2O in a suitable distillation flask and cool. Add 10 ml of 10% NaOH and 0.5 g of fine aluminum wire in small pieces and allow to stand for 2 hours protected from loss or excess of NH_3. Slowly distill about 40 ml in 5 ml of H_2O containing 1 drop of dilute HCl; then add to the distillate 1 ml of 10% NaOH and 2 ml of Nessler solution. The color produced is not darker than that produced by treating 0.02 mg of nitrogen (0.08 mg NH_4Cl) in the same manner as the sample.

Sulfate: To 5.0 g of sample in a beaker, add 15 ml of water and 10 ml of HNO_3, and mix. Add 10 ml of 30% H_2O_2, cover the beaker and digest on steam bath until the reaction ceases, then remove the cover and evaporate to dryness. Add 5 ml of water and 5 ml of HCl, and re-evaporate to dryness. Dissolve the residue in 10 ml of water, add 1 ml of 1 N HCl, filter if necessary, add 2 ml of $BaCl_2$ and mix well. Any resulting turbidity in 20 minutes is not greater than that produced when 0.1 mg is treated exactly as the sample.

Solution S: Gently ignite 5 g in porcelain. Add to the residue 10 ml of H_2O, 10 ml of HCl, and 1 ml of HNO_3 and evaporate to dryness on the steam bath. Add 20 ml of H_2O and re-evaporate. Dissolve the residue in 30 ml of H_2O, filter, add 1 drop phenolphthalein, neutralize with 1 N NaOH, and dilute to 50 ml.

Heavy metals: To 5 ml of *Solution S* add 0.01 mg of Pb, 1 ml of 1 N acetic acid and dilute to 40 ml (A). To 25 ml of *Solution S* add 1 ml of 1 N acetic acid and dilute to 40 ml (B). Then to each add 10 ml of H_2S. B is not darker than A.

Iron: To 10 ml *Solution S* add 2 ml of HCl and dilute to 50 ml. Add 30 mg of ammonium persulfate and 3 ml of ammonium thiocyanate, and mix. Any resulting red color is not darker than that of a control made with 0.01 mg of Fe and the same quantities of the reagents and in the same final volume as with the sample.

Potassium: Ignite 2 g in platinum until nearly free from carbon. Dissolve the residue in 10 ml of H_2O, add 3 ml of HNO_3, evaporate to dryness on the steam bath, and heat the residue at 120° for 2 hours. Take up with 10 ml of water, filter, and add to the filtrate 5 ml of sodium cobaltinitrite solution; then add, with constant stirring, 10 ml of alcohol, and allow to stand for 2 hours. Any turbidity or precipitate formed is not greater than that produced by 0.2 mg of potassium (K) contained in 10 ml of water and treated with the same volumes of the reagents.

Note: The potassium can be more accurately determined by Flame Photometry.

Substances darkened by H_2SO_4: In a recently ignited test tube heat 1 g of the sodium oxalate with 10 ml of H_2SO_4 to evolution of sulfuric fumes. The acid acquires not more than a faint brownish tinge.

SODIUM PERCHLORATE

$NaClO_4 \cdot H_2O$; mol. wt. 140.47; H_2O—12.83%; in anhydrous; Cl—28.96%; oxygen—52.37%.

Colorless, deliquescent crystals. Decomposes at about 150°. Soluble in 1 part of water and in 20 parts of alcohol.

This perchlorate is preferred to the potassium compound when solutions of greater concentration are required than are attainable with the latter.

Standards

Insoluble.....................max 0.010%	Calcium (Ca).................max 0.020%
Chloride (Cl).................max 0.005%	Heavy metals (as Pb).........max 0.001%
Chloride and Chlorate (as Cl)..max 0.020%	Iron (Fe)....................max 0.001%
Chlorate and Nitrate (as ClO_3)..max 0.003%	*Assay*
Sulfate (SO_4)...............max 0.005%	

Insoluble: Dissolve 10 g in 75 ml of warm water and allow the solution to cool at about 20° for 1 hour. If an insoluble residue is present filter, wash with cold water, and dry at 100°. The weight of the insoluble matter does not exceed 1.0 mg.

Chloride: Dissolve 1.0 g in 50 ml of H_2O. Dilute 10 ml of the solution to 20 ml, and add 1 ml of HNO_3 and 1 ml of $AgNO_3$. Any resulting turibdity is not greater than that in 20 ml of H_2O containing 0.02 mg of Cl and treated with the same quantities of HNO_3 and $AgNO_3$ as the solution of the sample.

Chloride and Chlorate: To 10 ml of the solution prepared in the test for *Chloride* add 1 ml of freshly prepared 10% ferrous sulfate solution and warm for 2 minutes. Allow to stand for 3 minutes, dilute to 20 ml, then add 2 ml of HNO_3 and 1 ml of $AgNO_3$. Any turbidity produced is not greater than that in a blank to which 0.04 mg of Cl has been added.

Chlorate and Nitrate: Dissolve 0.1 g in 10 ml of water. Add 10 mg of NaCl, 0.2 ml of diphenylamine solution and 10 ml of H_2SO_4. No blue color is produced in 30 minutes.

Calcium: Using 0.5 g of the reagent dissolved in 10 ml of water, make the test as described under Potassium Perchlorate. The result should be as there stated.

Sulfate; Heavy metals; Iron: Apply the tests given for Potassium Perchlorate. The results should be as there stated.

Assay: Dry about 1.5 g at 80° in a vacuum desiccator to constant weight. Using 75 mg of the dried sample, proceed as described under Potassium Perchlorate. One ml of 0.1 N $AgNO_3$ = 0.01224 g of $NaClO_4$. By the titanium method 1 ml of 0.1 N titanous solution = 0.001531 g of anhydrous $NaClO_4$.

SODIUM PERIODATE

Sodium Metaperiodate

$NaIO_4$; mol. wt. 213.90.

Colorless or white crystals or white crystalline powder. Soluble in 40 parts of water, freely soluble in the presence of HCl; insoluble in alcohol.

Sodium periodate is principally used for the colorimetric determination of small amounts of manganese, and also for the quantitative estimation of glycols.

Standards

Assay..............99.7%–100.3% $NaIO_4$	Other halogens (as Cl)........max 0.02%
Solubility....................to pass test	Iodide (I)..................max 0.002%
Chlorate (ClO_3)..............to pass test	Manganese (Mn)...........max 0.0002%
(limit about 0.01%)	

Assay: Weigh accurately about 0.10 g of the sample previously dried over H_2SO_4 for 4 hours (or a portion of a stock solution corresponding to this quantity) and dissolve it in 50 ml of H_2O in a glass-stoppered flask. Add to the solution 3 g of potassium iodide and follow with a cool mixture of 3 ml of HCl and 5 ml of H_2O. Allow to stand for 5 minutes, add 100 ml of cold H_2O, then titrate the liberated iodine with 0.1 N sodium thiosulfate, adding starch toward the end. Correct for a blank. One ml of 0.1 N thiosulfate = 0.002674 g $NaIO_4$. Correct for a blank.

Solubility: Two grams dissolve completely in 50 ml of hot water.

Chlorate: To 1 g of the powdered sample add 1 ml of H_2SO_4. The salt remains white and no odor or gas is evolved.

Other halogens: Dissolve 0.2 g in a mixture of 10 ml of water and 7 ml of sulfurous acid and boil for 3 minutes. Cool, add 6 ml of 10% NH_3 and 4 ml of 5% silver nitrate. Filter, wash with about 10 ml of H_2O, and dilute the filtrate to 100 ml. To 25 ml of the diluted filtrate add 1 ml of HNO_3. Any turbidity produced is not greater than that produced in a control with 0.01 mg of Cl, 1 ml of 10% NH_3, 1 ml of HNO_3, and 0.5 ml of the silver nitrate solution in the same volume as with the sample.

Iodide: Dissolve 1 g in a mixture of 20 ml of H_2O and 5 ml of 10% H_2SO_4, add 1 ml of chloroform, and shake gently. The chloroform acquires no violet color in 1 minute.

Manganese: To 2.5 g of sample add 50 ml of 10% H_2SO_4 (*A*). To 0.5 g of sample add 50 ml of 10% H_2SO_4 and 0.004 mg of Mn (*B*). Add to each 5 ml of HNO_3 and 5 ml of phosphoric acid, boil gently for 10 minutes, and cool. Any pink color in *A* is not darker than that in *B*.

SODIUM PEROXIDE

Na_2O_2; mol. wt. 77.98; Na—58.97%; active oxygen 20.51%.

Pale yellow, granular powder. Rapidly absorbs water and CO_2 from the air. Freely soluble in water, with the liberation of oxygen and formation of sodium hydroxide. When brought in contact with organic matter, ignition and explosion may take place. *Keep in tightly closed containers, in a cool place, protected from contact with organic matter.*

Standards

Assay....................	min 93% Na_2O_2	Ammonium hydroxide	
Chloride (Cl)................	max 0.002%	precipitate................	max 0.02%
Nitrogen compounds (as N)...	max 0.002%	Heavy metals (as Pb)........	max 0.002%
Phosphate (PO₄)...........	max 0.0005%	Iron (Fe)..................	max 0.003%
Sulfate (SO₄)................	max 0.001%		

Caution! *Sodium peroxide must be added to water slowly and in small portions; also, when neutralizing, the acid must be added cautiously and in small portions.*

Assay: Weigh accurately about 0.7 g, add it gradually to a mixture of 400 ml of water and 5 ml of H_2SO_4, previously cooled to 10°, and dilute with water to exactly 500 ml. Mix well and titrate 100 ml with 0.1 N potassium permanganate. One ml of 0.1 N permanganate = 0.003900 g Na_2O_2, log 59106.

$$5Na_2O_2 + 2KMnO_4 + 8H_2SO_4 \rightarrow 5O_2 + 8H_2O + 5Na_2SO_4 + K_2SO_4 + 2MnSO_4$$

Chloride: Dissolve 1 g in 20 ml of cold water, and *cautiously* add 5 ml of HNO_3. Filter if necessary, cool, and add 1 ml of $AgNO_3$. Any resulting turbidity is not greater than that in a blank to which 0.02 mg of Cl has been added.

Nitrogen: Dissolve 1.25 g of sample in 30 ml of ice-cooled water, neutralize with acetic acid and add a few drops excess of the acid. Boil down to 15 ml, cool and add it to 50 ml of water contained in an ammonia distillation flask connected through a spray trap to a condenser the end of which dips beneath the surface of 5 ml of water containing 1 drop of 10% HCl. Add to the flask 10 ml of 10% HaOH and 0.5 g fine aluminum wire in small pieces. Allow to stand for 1 hour, then distill over 35 ml. Dilute the distillate to 50 ml and add to it 1 ml of 10% NaOH and 2 ml of Nessler solution. The color produced should not be darker than that resulting when 0.25 g of sample, the same volume of acetic acid as used with the sample and 0.02 mg of N (0.08 mg NH_4Cl) are treated as the sample beginning with "Boil down . . . ."

Phosphate: Dissolve 2 g in 30 ml of cold water, and *cautiously* add 12 ml of 25% H_2SO_4. Evaporate as far as possible on the steam bath, then heat, with frequent stirring, to incipient evolution of sulfuric fumes. Dissolve the cooled residue in 20 ml of water, add 1 ml each of phosphate reagents **A** and **B** and heat at 60° for 10 minutes. Any blue color is not darker than that of a control made with 0.01 mg of PO_4, 2 ml of 25% H_2SO_4 and the same quantities of the other reagents and in the same volume as with the sample.

Sulfate: Dissolve 10 g in 150 ml of cold water, cautiously neutralize the solution with HCl, add 1 ml excess of the HCl, and boil it down to 100 ml. Filter if necessary, heat the filtrate to boiling, add 5 ml of $BaCl_2$, and allow to stand overnight. No precipitate is formed.

Ammonium hydroxide precipitate: Dissolve 5 g in 40 ml of water, cool in ice, add 40 ml of 25% H_2SO_4, evaporate, and heat to copious evolution of sulfuric fumes. Cool, *cautiously* add 100 ml of H_2O, and make just alkaline with NH_4OH. Boil to remove free NH_3, filter any precipitate if present, wash it with hot water, and ignite. The weight of the ignited precipitate is not more than 1.0 mg.

Heavy metals: Add cautiously 2.5 g of sample to a cooled mixture of 15 ml of water and 5 ml of HCl. Evaporate on the steam bath to dryness, dissolve the residue in 10 ml of water, add 2 ml of HCl, and re-evaporate on the steam bath to dryness. Take up with 20 ml of water, add a drop of phenolphthalein solution, and run in 0.1 N NaOH until a pink color is just produced. Add 2 ml of 1 N acetic acid and dilute to 50 ml. To 10 ml add 0.03 mg of Pb and dilute to 40 ml (A). Add to A and to the remaining 40 ml (B) 10 ml of H_2S. A is not darker than B.

Iron: Dissolve 1 g in 25 ml of water, add 3 ml of HCl and boil until reduced to about 5 ml. Transfer the solution to a Nessler tube, add 1 ml of HCl, dilute to 50 ml, and add 3 ml of ammonium thiocyanate. Any resulting red color is not darker than that of a control made with 0.03 mg of Fe and 2 ml of HCl.

SODIUM PHOSPHATE, DIBASIC, ANHYDROUS

Disodium Hydrogen Phosphate

For pH Buffer Solutions

Na_2HPO_4; mol. wt. 141.96; Na—32.40%; PO_4—66.90%; P—21.82%.

White, hygroscopic powder. On exposure to air it will gradually absorb the equivalent of 7 mols of water. Soluble in 12 parts of water; insoluble in alcohol. *Keep in tightly closed containers.*

Standards

pH in 0.1 M solution.............9.1–9.3	Total Nitrogen (N)...........max 0.001%
Insoluble...................max 0.010%	Sulfate (SO_4)................max 0.005%
Drying loss..................max 0.2%	Arsenic (As)................max 1 ppm
Chloride (Cl)...............max 0.002%	Heavy metals (as Pb).......max 0.001%
Nitrate (NO_3)..............max 0.002%	Iron (Fe)..................max 0.002%

pH: Dissolve 1.4 g in 100 ml of water and determine the pH potentiometrically with a glass electrode.

Insoluble: Dissolve 10 g in 100 ml of hot water and heat on the steam bath for 30 minutes.   Filter any undissolved residue, wash it with water, and dry at 105°. Its weight does not exceed 1.0 mg.

Drying loss: Weigh accurately about 2 g and dry to constant weight at 105°. The loss in weight corresponds to not more than 0.2%.

Chloride: Dissolve 1 g in 20 ml of warm water, add 3 ml of nitric acid and 1 ml of silver nitrate.   Any resulting turbidity is not greater than that in a blank to which 0.02 mg of Cl has been added.

Nitrate: Dissolve 0.2 g in 10 ml of water, add 50 mg of NaCl and 0.2 ml of diphenylamine solution, and slowly run in 10 ml of H_2SO_4.   Mix gently and allow to stand for 1 hour.   No blue color results.

Total Nitrogen: Dissolve 1 g in 50 ml of water in a distillation flask connected through a spray trap to a condenser, the end of which dips beneath the surface of 10 ml of water containing 2 drops of 10% HCl.   Add to the flask 10 ml of 10% NaOH and 0.5 g of fine aluminium wire in small pieces.   Allow to stand for 1 hour, then distill over 30–35 ml.   Add to the distillate 2 ml of 10% NaOH and 2 ml of Nessler solution.   Any resulting dark color is not more intense than that produced by treating 0.01 mg of N (0.04 mg NH_4Cl) in the same manner as the sample.

Sulfate: Dissolve 10 g in 100 ml of water and add 7 ml of HCl.   Filter, heat the filtrate to boiling, add 5 ml of $BaCl_2$, and allow to stand overnight.   If a precipitate is formed, filter, wash it with hot water, and ignite.   The weight of the precipitate of $BaSO_4$ is not more than 1.2 mg.

Arsenic: Determine in 2 g by method on page 563.   The stain is not greater than that from 0.002 mg of As.

Heavy metals: Dissolve 4 g in 20 ml of H_2O, add 10.0 ml of 10% HCl and dilute to 40 ml.   To 10 ml of the solution add 0.02 mg of Pb and dilute to 40 ml (A).   Dilute the remaining 30 ml of the solution to 40 ml (B).   Then to each add 10 ml of H_2S. B is not darker than A.

Iron: Dissolve 1 g in 15 ml of H_2O, add 2 ml of HCl, and boil gently for 2 minutes. Cool, add about 30 mg of ammonium persulfate and 15 ml of butanolic potassium thiocyanate, shake well, and allow to separate.   Any red color in the butanol layer is not darker than that in a blank to which 0.02 mg of Fe has been added.

SODIUM PHOSPHATE, DIBASIC HEPTAHYDRATE

$Na_2HPO_4 \cdot 7H_2O$; mol. wt. 268.08; H_2O—47.04%; PO_4—35.43%; P—11.56%.

White crystals.   Relatively stable in the air.   Soluble in about 4 parts of water; insoluble in alcohol.

Standards

pH of 0.1 M solution.............8.8–9.3	Total nitrogen (N)..........max 0.001%
Water of hydration...........44%–50%	Sulfate (SO$_4$)...............max 0.005%
Insoluble...................max 0.005%	Arsenic (As)................max 1 ppm
Mono- or Tribasic............to pass test	Heavy metals (as Pb) max....max 0.001%
Chloride (Cl)...............max 0.001%	Iron (Fe)...................max 0.001%
Nitrate (No$_3$)..............max 0.002%	

Water of hydration: Weigh accurately about 1 g and dry it to constant weight at 105°. The loss in weight corresponds to not less than 44% and to not more than 50%.

Insoluble: Dissolve 20 g in 200 ml of water and heat on the steam bath for 1 hour. Filter any undissolved residue, wash it with water, and dry at 105°. Its weight does not exceed 1.0 mg.

Mono- or Tribasic: Dissolve 3 g in 30 ml of H$_2$O, cool to 20°, and add 3 drops of thymol blue. A blue color is produced which changes to yellow (with a greenish tinge) by the addition of not more than 0.4 ml of 1 N HCl.

Chloride: Dissolve 2 g in 20 ml of water, add 3 ml of HNO$_3$ and 1 ml of silver nitrate. Any resulting turbidity is not greater than that in a blank to which 0.02 mg of Cl has been added.

Nitrate: Dissolve 0.2 g in 10 ml of water, add 50 mg of NaCl, 0.2 ml of diphenyl-amine solution and slowly run in 10 ml of H$_2$SO$_4$. Mix by gently swirling and allow to stand. No blue color is produced in 1 hour.

Total Nitrogen: To a solution of 2 g in 50 ml of H$_2$O, add 20 ml of 10% NaOH and 1 g of powdered Devarda metal, and let stand for 2 hours protected from access or loss of NH$_3$. Then slowly distill about 40 ml into 5 ml of H$_2$O containing 1 drop of 10% HCl. Add to the distillate 1 ml of 10% NaOH and 2 ml of Nessler solution. The color is not darker than that produced by treating 0.02 mg of nitrogen (0.08 mg NH$_4$Cl) in the same manner as the sample.

Sulfate: Dissolve 10 g in 100 ml of water and add 5 ml of HCl. Filter, heat the filtrate to boiling, add 5 ml of BaCl$_2$, and allow to stand overnight. If a precipitate is formed, filter, wash it with hot water, and ignite. The weight of the ignited precipitate is not more than 1.2 mg.

Arsenic: Determine in 2 g by method on page 563. The stain is not greater than that from 0.002 mg of As.

Heavy metals: Dissolve 4 g in 20 ml of H$_2$O, add 6.0 ml of 10% HCl, and dilute to 40 ml. To 10 ml of the solution add 0.02 mg of Pb and dilute to 40 ml (A). Dilute the remaining 30 ml of the solution to 40 ml (B). Then to each add 10 ml of H$_2$S. B is not darker than A.

Iron: Dissolve 1 g in 15 ml of H$_2$O, add 2 ml of HCl, and boil gently for 2 minutes. Cool, add about 30 mg of ammonium persulfate and 15 ml of butanolic potassium thiocyanate, shake well, and allow to separate. Any red color in the butanol (upper) layer is not darker than that of a blank to which 0.01 mg of Fe has been added.

SODIUM PHOSPHATE, MONOBASIC

Sodium Biphosphate; Sodium Dihydrogen Phosphate

$NaH_2PO_4 \cdot H_2O$; mol. wt. 138.00; anhydrous—86.95%; H_2O—13.05%; PO_4—68.82%; P—22.45%.

Colorless or white crystals; somewhat hygroscopic.   Soluble in 1 part of water; slightly soluble in alcohol.

Standards

Assay............99%–100.5% NaH_2PO_4	Chloride (Cl)................max 0.005%
(anhydrous basis)	Nitrate (NO_3)..............max 0.003%
pH of 0.2 mol solution............4.2–4.6	Sulfate (SO_4)...............max 0.005%
Drying loss..................10%–14%	Arsenic (As).................max 2 ppm
Insoluble, Calcium, and	Heavy metals (as Pb)........max 0.001%
NH₄OH precipitate........max 0.010%	Iron (Fe)..................max 0.002%

Assay; Drying loss: Dry about 5 g at 105° to constant weight.   The loss corresponds to 10% to 14%.   Weigh accurately about 4 g of the dried sample and dissolve it in 100 ml of H_2O.   Add 0.5 ml of thymolphthalein indicator and titrate with 1 N NaOH to the appearance of a blue color.   One ml of 1 N NaOH = 0.1200 g of NaH_2PO_4, log 07918.

$$NaH_2PO_4 + NaOH \rightarrow Na_2HPO_4 + H_2O$$

p**H:** Dissolve 2.8 g in 100 ml of water and determine the pH, preferably potentiometrically or by the use of indicators as follows: To each of two 10-ml portions of the solution, add 0.2 ml of 0.04% bromophenol blue, and to one of them add 0.1 ml of 0.1 N HCl; a distinct change of color is produced.   To each of two other 10-ml portions of the solution add 5 drops of a 0.02% solution of methyl red, and to one of them add 0.1 ml of 0.1 N NaOH; a distinct change of color is produced.

Insoluble, Calcium, and NH₄OH precipitate: Dissolve 10 g in 100 ml of water and add 5 ml of ammonium oxalate.   Make the solution alkaline to litmus with NH₄OH, add 15 ml excess of NH₄OH, and allow to stand overnight.   Filter any precipitate formed, wash it with water, and ignite at a low red heat.   The weight of the ignited precipitate is not more than 0.0010 g.

Chloride: Dissolve 0.2 g in 10 ml of water, add 2 ml of HNO_3 and 1 ml of silver nitrate.   Any turbidity produced is not greater than that of a blank to which 0.01 mg of Cl has been added.

Nitrate: Dissolve 0.2 g in 10 ml of water, add to the solution 50 mg of NaCl and 0.2 ml of diphenylamine solution and follow with 10 ml of H_2SO_4.   No blue color appears in 30 minutes.

Sulfate: Dissolve 10 g in 100 ml of water and 2 ml of HCl.   Filter if necessary, heat the filtrate to boiling, add 5 ml of $BaCl_2$, and allow to stand overnight.   If a precipitate is present, filter, wash it with hot water, and ignite.   The weight of the ignited precipitate does not exceed 1.2 mg.

Arsenic: Test 1 g by the method on page 563.   The stain is not greater than that from 0.002 mg of As.

Heavy metals: Dissolve 4 g in 25 ml of H_2O, add 2 ml of 1 N acetic acid, and dilute to 40 ml.   To 10 ml of the solution add 0.02 mg of Pb and dilute to 40 ml (A). Dilute the remaining 30 ml of the solution to 40 ml (B).   Then add to each 10 ml of H_2S. B is not darker than A.

Iron: Dissolve 2 g in 15 ml of H_2O, add 3 ml of HCl and boil gently for 2 minutes. Cool, add about 30 mg of ammonium persulfate and 15 ml of butanolic potassium thiocyanate, shake well, allow to separate.   Any red color in the butanol (upper) layer is not darker than that of a blank to which 0.02 mg of Fe has been added.

SODIUM PHOSPHATE, TRIBASIC

Trisodium Phosphate

$Na_3PO_4 \cdot 12H_2O$; mol. wt. 380.14; anhydrous—43.14%; H_2O—56.86%; PO_4—24.99%; P—8.16%.   The article of commerce usually contains only about 45% H_2O (about 8 mols).

Colorless or white crystals.   It absorbs gaseous acids.   Soluble in about 2.5 parts of water; insoluble in alcohol.

Standards

Assay (anhydrous basis) min 98% Na_3PO_4	Sulfate (SO_4)...............max 0.010%
Insoluble....................max 0.010%	Arsenic (As).................max 3 ppm
Free (excess) NaOH...........max 1.6%	Heavy metals (as Pb)........max 0.001%
Chloride (Cl)...............max 0.002%	Iron (Fe)...................max 0.001%
Nitrate (NO_3)..............max 0.002%	

Assay: Dry about 6 g in a tared platinum crucible at 105° for 2 hours, then ignite *gently* to constant weight.   Place the crucible with its contents in a beaker, add 100 ml of water and 40.0 ml of 1 N HCl.   Heat gently to effect solution of the phosphate and then boil for about 5 minutes.   Cool to about 20°, and 2 drops of methyl red and titrate with 1 N NaOH to a yellow color.   Now add from a burette just sufficient 1 N HCl to change the color to pink (pH 4.2) and note the volume used.   The titration can be advantageously performed potentiometrically to pH 4.2.   The difference between the total volume of the 1 N HCl used and the volume of the 1 N NaOH consumed for the back titration represents the sodium phosphate plus any excess of NaOH, and it should not be less than 11.95 ml per 1.0 g of the ignited sample and not more than 12.60 ml (theory for Na_3PO_4 is 12.20 ml).   One ml of 1 N acid = 0.0820 g Na_3PO_4.

$$Na_3PO_4 + 2HCl \rightarrow NaH_2PO_4 + 2NaCl$$

The difference between 12.20 ml and the volume of the 1 N HCl consumed by 1 g of the dehydrated sample × 0.04001 g represents excess NaOH per 1 g of sample.

Insoluble: Dissolve 10 g in 100 ml of water and warm the solution for 15 minutes on the steam bath.   Filter any undissolved residue, wash it with water, and dry at 105°.   Its weight does not exceed 1.0 mg.

Chloride: Dissolve 1 g in 20 ml of water, add 3 ml of HNO_3 and 1 ml of silver nitrate.   Any turbidity produced is not greater than that in a blank to which 0.02 mg Cl has been added.

Nitrate: Dissolve 0.5 g in 25 ml of water.   To 10 ml of the solution add 50 mg of NaCl and when it has dissolved add 0.2 ml of diphenylamine solution.   Mix, and slowly run in, without agitation, 10 ml of H_2SO_4.   After a few minutes mix gently and allow to stand for 1 hour.   No blue color results.

Sulfate: Dissolve 10 g in 150 ml of water and add 8 ml of hydrochloric acid. Filter, heat the filtrate to boiling, add 5 ml of $BaCl_2$, and allow to stand overnight. If a precipitate has formed, filter, wash it with hot H_2O, and ignite.   The weight of the ignited precipitate of $BaSO_4$ does not exceed 2.5 mg.

Arsenic: Test 1 g by method on page 563.   The stain is not greater than that from 0.003 mg of As.

Heavy metals: Dissolve 4 g in 25 ml of H_2O, add 8.0 ml of 10% HCl, boil for 5 minutes, cool, and dilute to 40 ml.   To 10 ml of the solution add 0.02 mg Pb and dilute to 40 ml (A).   Dilute the remaining 30 ml of the solution to 40 ml (B).   Then add to each 10 ml of H_2S. B is not darker than A.

Iron: Dissolve 1 g in 15 ml of water, add 3 ml of HCl, and boil gently for 5 minutes.   Cool, dilute to 15 ml, add about 30 mg of ammonium persulfate and 15 ml of butanolic potassium thiocyanate, shake well, and allow to separate.   Any red color in the butanol (upper) layer is not darker than that in a blank to which 0.01 mg of Fe has been added.

SODIUM PYROPHOSPHATE

$Na_4P_2O_7 \cdot 10H_2O$; mol. wt. 446.1; anhydrous salt—59.62%; H_2O—40.38%.

Colorless or white crystals; effloresces in dry air.   Soluble in 10 parts cold water or in 2 parts of boiling water; insoluble in alcohol.

Standards

Insoluble, Calcium, and	Sulfate (SO_4)................max 0.010%
NH_4OH precipitate........max 0.010%	Arsenic (As).................max 3 ppm
Carbonate...................to pass test	Heavy metals (as Pb)........max 0.001%
Chloride (Cl)...............max 0.003%	Iron (Fe)....................max 0.001%
Nitrate (NO_3)...............max 0.003%	*Assay*.........................min 98%
Orthophosphate (Na_2HPO_4)......max 2%	

Insoluble, Calcium, and NH_4OH precipitate: Dissolve 10 g in 150 ml of water, add 5 ml of ammonium oxalate and 20 ml of NH_4OH, and allow to stand overnight.   Filter any precipitate formed, wash it with H_2O, and ignite.   The ignited precipitate is not more than 1.0 mg.

Carbonate: Powder 2 g, add 5 ml of water and follow with 5 ml of 10% HCl. No effervescence is produced.

Chloride: Dissolve 1 g in 20 ml of water, add 3 ml of HNO_3 and 1 ml of silver nitrate.   Any turbidity produced is not greater than that in a blank to which 0.03 mg of Cl has been added.

Nitrate: Dissolve 0.2 g in 10 ml of water. Add to the solution 50 mg of NaCl, 0.2 ml diphenylamine solution, and follow slowly with 10 ml of H_2SO_4. No blue color appears after 30 minutes.

Orthophosphate: To 1 g of the powdered sample add 2 ml of silver nitrate. No yellow color is produced.

Sulfate: Dissolve 10 g in 150 ml of water and add 5 ml of HCl. Filter, heat the filtrate to boiling, add 5 ml of $BaCl_2$, and allow to stand overnight. If a precipitate is formed, filter, wash it with hot H_2O, and ignite. The weight of the ignited precipitate is not more than 2.5 mg.

Arsenic: Test 1 g by method on page 563. The stain is not greater than that from 0.003 mg of As.

Heavy metals: Dissolve 4 g in 25 ml of H_2O, add 8.0 ml of 10% HCl, boil for 5 minutes, cool, and dilute to 40 ml. To 10 ml of the solution add 0.02 mg Pb and dilute to 40 ml (A). Dilute the remaining 30 ml of the solution to 40 ml (B). Then add to each 10 ml of H_2S. B is not darker than A.

Iron: Dissolve 1 g in 15 ml of water, add 3 ml of HCl, and boil gently for 5 minutes. Cool, dilute to about 15 ml, add about 30 mg of ammonium persulfate and 15 ml of butanolic potassium thiocyanate, shake well, and allow to separate. Any red color in the butanol (upper) layer is not darker than that in a blank to which 0.01 mg of Fe has been added.

Assay: Dry about 5 g in shallow layer at 150° to constant weight, then weigh accurately and dissolve it in 100 ml of water in a conical flask. Add 50.0 ml of 1 N H_2SO_4 and boil gently for 10 minutes. Cool to room temperature and titrate the solution with 1 N NaOH to pH 4.0 with a pH meter and glass electrode system. The difference between the volume of acid added and the volume of the 1 N NaOH used represents $Na_4P_2O_7$. One ml of 1 N acid = 0.1329 g $Na_4P_2O_7$. One gram of the anhydrous should consume not less than 7.40 ml (98%) and not more than 7.65 ml of the 1 N acid (theory 7.52 ml).

SODIUM SALICYLATE

$HO \cdot C_6H_4CO_2Na$; mol. wt. 160.11; Na—14.36%; salicylic acid = 86.26%.

Fine, white, crystalline scales. Soluble in 1 part of water, in 10 parts of alcohol, in 4 parts of glycerol.

Standards

Insoluble . . . . max 0.005%	Ammonia (NH_3) . . . . max about 0.03%
Chloride (Cl) . . . . max 0.003%	Heavy metals (as Pb) . . . . max 0.001%
Sulfate (SO_4) . . . . max 0.010%	$Assay$ . . . . min 99.5%

Insoluble: Dissolve 20 g in 150 ml of water, and heat the solution on the steam bath for 15 minutes. Filter if an undissolved residue is present, wash with water, and dry at 105°. The insoluble residue does not exceed 1.0 mg.

Chloride: Ignite 1 g thoroughly in platinum. Heat the residue with 30 ml of water, cool, and acidify with nitric acid. Filter, and add to the filtrate 1 ml of $AgNO_3$. Any resulting turbidity is not greater than that in a blank to which 0.03 mg of Cl has been added.

Sulfate: Ignite 2 g in platinum protected from sulfur in the flame, preferably in an electric muffle furnace until nearly free from carbon. Boil the residue with 20 ml of H_2O and 1 ml of 30% hydrogen peroxide, then add 10 mg of sodium carbonate and 3 ml of HCl and evaporate to dryness on the steam bath. Prepare a control by evaporating 10 mg of sodium carbonate and 1 ml of the H_2O_2, 3 ml of HCl and 0.2 mg of SO_4 to dryness on the steam bath. Dissolve the residue from each in 20 ml of water and filter if necessary. Then to each add 1 ml of 0.1 N HCl and 2 ml of $BaCl_2$. Any turbidity appearing in 15 minutes in the solution of the sample is not greater than that in the control.

Ammonia: To a solution of 1 g in 10 ml of water add 2 ml of sodium hydroxide and boil gently. No odor of ammonia is perceptible.

Heavy metals: Dissolve 4.0 g in 65 ml of water, add to the solution 10 ml of 10% HCl while stirring well and filter with moderate suction. Add to filtrate 2 drops of phenolphthalein and just sufficient 1 N NaOH to produce a pink color, discharge the pink color with 4 ml of 1 N acetic acid and dilute to 80 ml. To 20 ml add 0.02 mg of Pb and dilute to 60 ml (A). Then to 60 ml of the solution (B) and to A add 10 ml of H_2S. B is not darker than A.

Assay: Sodium salicylate may be assayed by titration in glacial acetic acid solution as described under Assays of Alkali Salts of Organic Acids, page 564, or by the following method:

Dry about 1 g at 105° for 2 hours. Weigh about 0.5 g, transfer to a glass-stoppered Erlenmeyer flask, and dissolve in 20 ml of water. Add 50 ml of ether and 0.5 ml of bromophenol blue and titrate with 0.1 N HCl with constant agitation, until a permanent pale green color appears in the aqueous layer. Transfer the contents of the flask to a separatory funnel and draw off the aqueous layer into another flask. Wash the ether layer with 5 ml of water and add the washing to the aqueous layer. Now add to the aqueous solution 20 ml of ether and continue with the titration, with vigorous agitation, until a permanent pale green color appears in the water layer. One ml of 0.1 N HCl = 0.01601 g of $NaC_6H_5O_3$.

SODIUM SELENITE

Na_2SeO_3; mol. wt. 172.94; Se—45.65%.

White, odorless, crystalline; soluble in water. It usually contains some water of crystallization.

Standards

Assay...............min 98% Na_2SeO_3	Chloride (Cl).................max 0.01%
Solubility....................to pass test	Nitrate (NO_3)................max 0.01%
Carbonate (CO_2).............about 0.3%	Selenate and Sulfate (as SO_4)...max 0.05%

Assay: Dry about 0.5 g at 120° to constant weight, then weigh accurately about 0.2 g and dissolve it in 50 ml of H_2O in a glass-stoppered flask. Add 3 g of potassium iodide, follow with 5 ml of HCl, and allow to stand for 10 minutes. Dilute with 50 ml of H_2O and titrate the liberated iodine with 0.1 N sodium thiosulfate, using starch indicator, until the color is no longer diminished; then titrate back with 0.1 N iodine to a blue color. The volume of the sodium thiosulfate less that consumed by a blank represents the sodium selenite. One ml of the 0.1 N sodium thiosulfate = 0.004330 g Na_2SeO_3, log 63649.

$$Na_2SeO_3 + 4KI + 6HCl \rightarrow 4I + Se + 2NaCl + 4KCl$$

Solubility: A solution of 1 g in 10 ml of water is complete and clear or nearly so.

Carbonate: To 0.5 g add 1 ml of water and 2 ml of 10% HCl. No effervescence is produced.

Chloride: Dissolve 0.5 g in 40 ml of water, add 2 ml of HNO_3 and 1 ml of silver nitrate. Any turbidity produced is not greater than that in the blank to which 0.05 mg Cl has been added.

Nitrate: Dissolve 0.2 g in 10 ml of water. Add 10 mg of HaCl, 0.1 ml of indigo carmine and 10 ml of H_2SO_4. The blue color persists for 5 minutes.

Selenate and Sulfate: To 0.5 g in a small dish add 20 mg of Na_2CO_3 and 10 ml of HCl, and *slowly* evaporate on the steam bath *under hood* to dryness. Wash down the sides of the dish with 5 ml of HCl and re-evaporate to dryness on the steam bath. Dissolve the residue in 1 ml of 1 N HCl and 15 ml of hot water, filter if necessary, and add to filtrate 2 ml of $BaCl_2$. Any turbidity in 10 minutes is not greater than that in a control prepared by treating 0.15 mg of SO_4 exactly as the sample.

SODIUM SULFATE, ANHYDROUS

Na_2SO_4; mol. wt. 142.06; Na—32.38%; SO_4—67.62%; S—22.57%.

White powder, or granular. Readily takes up moisture to the extent of one molecule. Soluble in 6 parts of water; insoluble in alcohol. *Keep in tightly closed containers.*

Standards

Insoluble.................max 0.010%	Arsenic (As).................max 1 ppm	
Ignition loss.................max 0.50%	Calcium, Magnesium, and	
Neutrality.................to pass test	NH$_4$OH precipitate........max 0.020%	
Chloride (Cl).................max 0.002%	Heavy metals (as Pb).......max 0.0005%	
Nitrogen compounds (as N)..max 0.0005%	Iron (Fe).................max 0.001%	
Phosphate (PO$_4$)...........max 0.0005%		

Insoluble: Dissolve 10 g in 150 ml of hot water and heat on the steam bath for 1 hour. Filter any insoluble residue (retain filtrate), wash it with hot H_2O, and dry at 105°. Its weight does not exceed 1.0 mg.

Ignition loss: Ignite gently 1 g; the loss in weight corresponds to not more than 0.5%.

Neutrality: Dissolve 5 g in 60 ml of CO_2-free water, and add 3 drops of phenolphthalein; no pink color is produced. Add 0.5 ml of 0.02 N NaOH; a pink color is produced.

Chloride: Dissolve 1 g in 20 ml of water, add 1 ml of HNO_3 and 1 ml of silver nitrate. Any resulting turbidity is not greater than that of a blank to which 0.02 mg of Cl has been added.

Nitrogen compounds: Dissolve 4 g in 60 ml of water in a suitable distillation flask.   Add 20 ml of 10% NaOH and 1 g of powdered Devarda metal, and let stand for 2 hours protected from loss or access of NH_3.   Then slowly distill about 45 ml into 5 ml of water containing 1 drop of dilute HCl and add to the distillate 1 ml of 10% NaOH and 2 ml of Nessler solution.   The color produced is not darker than that produced by treating 0.02 mg of nitrogen (0.08 mg NH_4Cl) in the same manner as the sample.

Phosphate (and silica): Dissolve 2 g in 20 ml of water, add 2 ml of 25% H_2SO_4 and 1 ml each of phosphate reagents **A** and **B** and heat at 60° for 10 minutes. Any blue color produced is not darker than that in a blank to which 0.01 mg of PO_4 has been added.

Arsenic: Determine in 2 g of the sample by method on page 563.   The stain is not more than that from 0.002 mg As.

Calcium, Magnesium, and NH_4OH precipitate: To the filtrate from the test for *Insoluble* add 5 ml of ammonium oxalate, 2 ml of ammonium phosphate, and 15 ml of NH_4OH, and let stand overnight.   If a precipitate is formed, filter, wash it with 2.5% NH_3, and ignite.   The weight of the ignited precipitate does not exceed 2.0 mg.

Heavy metals: Dissolve 5 g in sufficient water to make 50 ml.   To 10 ml add 0.015 mg of Pb, dilute to 40 ml, and add 1 ml of 1 N acetic acid (A).   To the remaining 40 ml add 1 ml of 1 N acetic acid (B).   Then to each add 10 ml of H_2S; B is not darker than A.

Iron: Dissolve 1 g in 20 ml of H_2O, add 2 ml of HCl and dilute to 50 ml.   Add about 30 mg of ammonium persulfate and 3 ml of ammonium thiocyanate, and mix. Any resulting red color is not darker than that of a blank to which 0.01 mg of Fe has been added.

SODIUM SULFATE, ANHYDROUS

For Drying of Liquids

For the intended use, this sodium sulfate should be in the form of a fine *granular* material and not a fine powder.

Standards

Insoluble....................max 0.01%	Ignition loss.................max 0.5%	
Free acid....................to pass test	Alcohol-ether-soluble	
Free alkali..................to pass test	substances................max 0.05%	

Insoluble: Determine as described under Sodium Sulfate, Anhydrous, using 10 g of sample.   The result should be as there stated.

Free acid; Free alkali: Dissolve 5 g in 75 ml of CO_2-free water and add 3 drops of phenolphthalein solution; no pink color is produced.   Now add 0.5 ml of 0.02 N NaOH; a pink color is produced.

Alcohol-ether-soluble substances: Shake in a glass-stoppered cylinder 2 g of sample with a mixture of 20 ml of alcohol and 10 ml of ether for 5 minutes and allow to stand for 1 hour with frequent shaking.   Filter through a filter paper moistened with alcohol, evaporate the filtrate on the steam bath, and dry at 105° for 1 hour.   The weight of the residue does not exceed 1.0 mg.

SODIUM SULFATE, DECAHYDRATE

$Na_2SI_4 \cdot 10H_2O$; mol. wt. 322.21; anhydrous—44.09%; H_2O—55.91%; Na—14.28%; SO_4—29.81%; S—9.95%.

Colorless, odorless crystals.   Melts at 32.5°; effloresces on exposure to the air. Soluble in 2 parts water at 25°; insoluble in alcohol.   *Keep in well-closed containers in a cool place.*

Standards

Insoluble	max 0.005%	Arsenic (As)	max 1 ppm
Neutrality	to pass test	Calcium, Magnesium, and	
Chloride (Cl)	max 0.001%	NH₄OH precipitate	max 0.010%
Nitrate (NO₃)	max 0.001%	Heavy metals (as Pb)	max 0.0005%
Phosphate (and silica)	max 0.0003%	Iron (Fe)	max 0.0005%

Insoluble: Twenty grams dissolved in 150 ml of hot water yield not more than 1.0 mg of insoluble matter.

Neutrality: Dissolve 5 g in 60 ml of CO_2-free water, add 3 drops of phenolphthalein; no pink color is produced.   Add 0.25 ml of 0.02 N NaOH; a pink color is produced.

Chloride: Dissolve 2 g in 25 ml of water, add 1 ml of HNO_3 and 1 ml of silver nitrate.   Any resulting turbidity is not greater than that of a blank to which 0.02 mg of Cl has been added.

Nitrate: Dissolve 0.5 g in 10 ml of H_2O, add 10 mg of NaCl and 0.2 ml of diphenylamine solution, and slowly run in 10 ml of H_2SO_4.   After 5 minutes mix by gently swirling and allow to stand for 1 hour.   No blue color appears.

Phosphate (and silica): Dissolve 3 g in 20 ml of water, add 2 ml of 25% H_2SO_4 and 1 ml each of phosphate reagents **A** and **B**, and heat at 60° for 10 minutes. Any blue color produced is not darker than that in a blank to which 0.01 mg of PO_4 has been added.

Arsenic: Determine in 2 g of the sample by method on page 563.   The stain is not greater than that from 0.002 mg of As.

Calcium, Magnesium, and NH₄OH precipitate: To the filtrate from the test for *Insoluble* add 5 ml of ammonium oxalate, 2 ml of ammonium phosphate, and 15 ml of NH_4OH, and let stand overnight.   If a precipitate is formed, filter, wash it with 2.5% NH_3, and ignite.   The weight of the ignited precipitate does not exceed 2.0 mg.

Heavy metals: Dissolve 5 g in sufficient water to make 50 ml.   To 10 ml add 0.015 mg of Pb, dilute to 40 ml, and add 1 ml of 1 N acetic acid (A).   To the remaining 40 ml add 1 ml of 1 N acetic acid (B).   Then to each add 10 ml of H_2S; B is not darker than A.

Iron: Dissolve 2 g in 20 ml of H_2O, add 2 ml HCl and dilute to 50 ml.   Add about 30 mg of ammonium persulfate and 3 ml of ammonium thiocyanate, and mix. Any resulting red color is not darker than that of a blank to which 0.01 mg of Fe has been added.

SODIUM SULFIDE

$Na_2S \cdot 9H_2O$; mol. wt. 240.20; anhydrous salt—32.5%; H_2O—67.5%; Na—19.15%; S—13.35%.

Colorless, very deliquescent crystals. Melts at about 50°. Turns yellow on exposure to air and light with the formation of carbonate, polysulfide, etc. It is decomposed by acids, even by carbonic acid. Soluble in 0.5 part water; soluble in alcohol. *Keep in tightly closed containers in a cool place, protected from light.*

Standards

Ammonia (NH_3)............max 0.002%	Iron (Fe)....................to pass test
Sulfite and Thiosulfate	*Assay*........................min 96%
(as SO_2)...................max 0.1%	

Ammonia: Dissolve 1 g in 80 ml of water, add a solution of 2 g of lead acetate in 20 ml of H_2O and allow the precipitate to settle. Decant 50 ml into a suitable distillation flask, add to it 20 ml of 10% NaOH, and distill about 40 ml into 5 ml of water containing a drop of dilute HCl. Dilute to 50 ml, then add 1 ml of 10% NaOH and 2 ml of Nessler solution. The color is not darker than that produced by treating 0.02 mg of NH_3 (0.06 mg NH_4Cl) in the same manner as the sample.

Sulfite and Thiosulfate: Dissolve 3 g in 200 ml of oxygen-free water, and add a solution of 5 g of zinc sulfate in 100 ml of oxygen-free water. Shake well and allow to stand for 30 minutes. Filter, and titrate 100 ml of the filtrate with 0.1 N iodine to a blue color, using starch as indicator. Not more than 0.3 ml of the iodine is required. Correct for any iodine consumed by a blank.

Iron: A fresh solution of 5 g of sodium sulfide in 100 ml of H_2O is clear and colorless.

Assay: Sodium sulfide may be assayed as follows: Weigh accurately about 0.5 g and dissolve in 30 ml of oxygen-free water, in a glass-stoppered flask. Immediately run in with agitation exactly 50 ml of 0.1 N iodine, then add 2 ml of HCl and titrate the excess of iodine with 0.1 N thiosulfate, using starch indicator. One ml of 0.1 N iodine = 0.01201 g $Na_2S \cdot 9H_2O$, log 07954.

$$Na_2S + I_2 \rightarrow 2NaI + S$$

SODIUM SULFITE, ANHYDROUS

Na_2SO_3; mol. wt. 126.05; Na—36.49%; SO_2—50.82%; S—25.43%.

Small crystals or white crystalline powder; gradually oxidizes to sulfate on exposure to air. Soluble in 4 parts of water; slightly soluble in alcohol. *Keep in tightly closed containers.*

Standards

Assay..............min 98% Na_2SO_3	Thiosulfate.................to pass test
Insoluble...................max 0.005%	Arsenic (As).................max 1 ppm
Free acid...........................none	Heavy metals (as Pb)........max 0.001%
Free alkali (as Na_2CO_3).......max 0.15%	Iron (Fe)...................max 0.001%
Chloride (Cl)...............max 0.020%	

Assay: Weigh accurately about 0.25 g and add it to exactly 50 ml of 0.1 N iodine.   Allow to stand for 5 minutes, then add 1 ml of HCl and titrate the excess of iodine with 0.1 N sodium thiosulfate, using starch as indicator.   One ml of 0.1 N iodine = 0.006303 g Na_2SO_3, log 79955.

Insoluble: Dissolve 20 g in 200 ml of water and heat on the steam bath for 1 hour.   Filter any undissolved matter, wash it with water, and dry at 105°.   The weight of the insoluble residue does not exceed 1.0 mg.

Free acid: Dissolve 1 g in 10 ml of water and add 2 drops of phenolphthalein; a pink color is produced.

Free alkali: Dissolve 1 g in 15 ml of water and add 2 ml of neutral 30% hydrogen peroxide.   Mix well and evaporate on the steam bath to half the volume.   Cool, dilute with 10 ml of water, add a drop of methyl red, and titrate with 0.1 N HCl. Not more than 0.3 ml of the HCl is required to produce a pink color.

Chloride: Dissolve 1 g in 10 ml of water, add 3 ml of 30% hydrogen peroxide, allow to stand for 30 minutes, then dilute to 100 ml.   To 10 ml add 10 ml of water, 2 ml of nitric acid, and 1 ml of silver nitrate.   Any turbidity produced is not greater than that in a control made with 0.02 mg of Cl, 0.3 ml of the hydrogen peroxide, the same quantities of nitric acid and silver nitrate and in the same volume as with the sample.

Thiosulfate: Dissolve 1 g in 15 ml of water and slowly add 5 ml of hydrochloric acid.   No turbidity is produced in 5 minutes.

Arsenic: Dissolve 2 g in 10 ml of water and gradually add 4 ml of nitric acid. Then add 3 ml of sulfuric acid and evaporate to strong sulfuric fumes.   Cool, *cautiously* add 10 ml of water, and test for arsenic by the method described on page 563.   The stain formed is not greater than that from 0.002 mg of As.

Heavy metals: Dissolve 3 g of sample in 20 ml of H_2O and add 5 ml of HCl (A). Dissolve 1 g of the sample in 20 ml of H_2O, then add 0.02 mg of Pb and 5 ml of HCl (B).   Evaporate both to dryness on the steam bath.   Add to each 5 ml more of HCl and re-evaporate to dryness on the steam bath.   Take up each in 25 ml of water, add a drop of phenolphthalein, and neutralize with 0.1 N NaOH.   Add 1 ml of 1 N acetic acid to each, dilute to 40 ml and add 10 ml of H_2S. A is not darker than B.

Iron: Dissolve 1 g in 10 ml of water, add 3 ml of HCl and evaporate to dryness on the steam bath.   Dissolve the residue in 5 ml of water, add 2 ml of HCl, and again evaporate to dryness.   Take up in 2 ml of HCl and water to make 50 ml, and add about 50 mg of ammonium persulfate and 3 ml of ammonium thiocyanate.   Any red color in the sample solution is not darker than that in a control made with 0.01 mg of Pb, 2 ml of HCl and the same quantities of the reagents and in the same final volume as with the sample.

SODIUM TARTRATE

$Na_2C_4H_4O_6 \cdot 2H_2O$;   mol. wt. 230.09%;   anhydrous—84.34%; H_2O—15.66%; tartaric acid = 65.22%.

Colorless, odorless crystals.   Soluble in 3 parts of water; insoluble in alcohol. Sodium tartrate retains its full water content even when exposed at 100° for several hours, and has been, therefore, recommended as a standard for standardizing the Fischer reagent for determination of water.

Standards

Drying loss.............15.60%–15.70%		Sulfate (SO_4)...............max 0.005%	
Insoluble..................max 0.005%		Ammonia (NH_3)............max 0.003%	
Free acid (as $NaHC_4H_4O_6$).....max 0.08%		Calcium (Ca)...............max 0.005%	
Free alkali (as Na_2CO_3).......max 0.03%		Heavy metals (as Pb).......max 0.0005%	
Chloride (Cl)...............max 0.001%		Iron (Fe)..................max 0.001%	
Phosphate (PO_4)..........max 0.0005%			

Drying loss at 150°: Weigh accurately about 2 g in a shallow weighing bottle and dry at 150° to constant weight. The loss in weight corresponds to not less than 15.60% and not more than 15.70%.

Insoluble: Dissolve 20 g in 200 ml of H_2O and heat on the steam bath 1 hour. If an insoluble residue remains, filter, wash, and dry at 105°. Its weight does not exceed 1.0 mg.

The pH of 0.2 M solution at 25° is about 8.4.

Free acid; Free alkali: Dissolve 2 g in 20 ml of water and add 0.1 ml of phenolphthalein. If a pink color is produced, it is discharged by 0.3 ml of 0.02 N HCl. If no pink color is produced, add 0.02 N NaOH until it is produced; not more than 0.5 ml of the NaOH is required to produce a pink color.

Chloride: Dissolve 1 g in 10 ml of water and add 3 ml of HNO_3 and 1 ml of $AgNO_3$. Any turbidity produced is not greater than that in a blank to which 0.01 mg has been added.

Phosphate: Ignite 2.0 g in platinum, preferably in an electric muffle furnace, until the ash is nearly white. Cool, add 25 ml of water and 2 ml of 30% H_2O_2 and boil for a few minutes, neutralize with 25% H_2SO_4 and add 3 ml excess of the acid. Filter and evaporate the filtrate to incipient sulfuric fumes, dilute to 20 ml, add 1 ml each of phosphate reagents **A** and **B**, and heat at 60° for 10 minutes. Any blue color produced is not darker than that of a control made with 0.02 mg of PO_4.

Sulfate: Ignite 2 g protected from sulfur in the flame (or preferably in an electric muffle furnace) until nearly free of carbon. Boil the residue with 20 ml of H_2O and 2 ml of 30% hydrogen peroxide, then add 20 mg of sodium carbonate and 5 ml of HCl and evaporate to dryness on the steam bath. Prepare a control by evaporating 20 mg of sodium carbonate, 2 ml of the H_2O_2, 5 ml of HCl and 0.1 mg of SO_4 to dryness on the steam bath. Dissolve the residue from each in 10 ml of water and filter. Then to each add 1 ml of 0.1 N HCl and 2 ml of $BaCl_2$. Any turbidity appearing in 15 minutes in the solution of the sample is not greater than that in the control.

Ammonia: Dissolve 1 g in 25 ml of H_2O, add 1 ml of 10% NaOH and 2 ml of Nessler solution. The color produced is not darker than that of a blank to which 0.03 mg of NH_3 (0.1 mg NH_4Cl) has been added.

Calcium: Ignite 2 g in a spacious platinum crucible or dish until nearly free of carbon. Add 15 ml of water and 5 ml of HCl and evaporate to dryness on the steam bath. Dissolve the resulting chloride in 7 to 8 ml of hot water, filter, and wash to 10 ml. Warm to about 50°, add 1 drop of acetic acid and 2 ml of ammonium oxalate solution and allow to stand for 20 minutes. Any resulting turbidity is not greater than that produced by 0.1 mg of calcium (Ca) contained in a solution of 1 g of reagent sodium chloride in 10 ml of water and treated as the sample solution beginning with "Warm to about 50° . . . ."

Heavy metals: Dissolve 5 g in 30 ml of H_2O, add 5 ml of 1 N HCl, and dilute to 50 ml. To 10 ml add 0.015 mg of Pb and dilute to 40 ml (A). Then add to A and to the remaining 40 ml (B) 10 ml of H_2S. B is not darker than A.

Iron: Dissolve 1 g in 20 ml of water, add 3 ml of HCl, and dilute to 50 ml. Add about 50 mg of ammonium persulfate and 3 ml of ammonium thiocyanate solution, and mix. Any resulting red color is not darker than that of a blank to which 0.01 mg of Fe has been added.

SODIUM TETRAPHENYLBORON

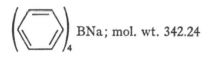 BNa; mol. wt. 342.24

Colorless or white crystals, slightly hygroscopic. Soluble in about 4 parts of water, in 1.8 parts of absolute alcohol, in about 1 part of methanol at 25°; soluble in acetone; slightly soluble in benzene. In aqueous solution it gradually decomposes, manifested by turbidity; mineral acids accelerate decomposition. Decomposition may be retarded by addition of a few drops of dilute sodium hydroxide solution. In acetonitrile solution sodium tetraphenylboron exhibits two peaks: at 266 microns and 274 microns.

Sodium tetraphenylboron is used principally for the determination of potassium. It is not specific, however, for potassium, since ammonium, organic nitrogen bases (alkaloids, amines), cesium and rubidium are also precipitated by this reagent in relatively dilute aqueous solution. Alkaline earths and lithium in moderate amounts, Al, Mg, and PO_4 do not interfere.

Standards

Sensitiveness. . . . . .to pass test   Solubility. . . . . .to pass test
Suitability for potassium
  determination. . . . . .to pass test

Sensitiveness: (*a*) Dissolve 25 mg of the sodium tetraphenylboron in 25 ml of water. (*b*) Dissolve 30 mg of potassium chloride in 50 ml of water (1 ml of this solution = 0.32 mg of K).

Dilute 1.0 ml of (*b*) with 4 ml of water. Add 1 drop of 0.1 N HCl, then add 5 ml of (*a*) and shake well. A slight but distinct turbidity or precipitate is produced in 3 minutes.

Note: The solubility of potassium tetraphenylboron in water at about 25° is 0.065 mg per ml, corresponding to 0.007 mg of potassium (K).

Suitability for determination of potassium: (*a*) Weigh accurately 200 to 220 mg of dried potassium chloride and dissolve it in water to make 100 ml. (*b*) Dissolve 300 mg of the sodium tetraphenylboron in 25 ml of water.

Measure exactly 20 ml of (a) into a 200-ml beaker, add 0.5 ml of 0.1 N HCl, dilute with 30 ml of H_2O, and warm to about 50°. While stirring, add solution (b), then place the beaker with the precipitate in cold water for 30 minutes. Filter the precipitate on a small filtering crucible, previously dried at 120° and weighed, and wash first with small portions of a cold 0.5% solution of the sample, then with small portions of cold water until free of chloride, dry at 120° for 2 hours, and weigh. The weight multiplied by 0.218 represents KCl, and it should correspond to not less than 99.0% and not more than 100.5% of the KCl used.

Solubility: Freshly prepared solutions of 0.2-g portions of the sample in 5 ml of water and in 5 ml of acetone are colorless, clear, and complete.

SODIUM THIOCYANATE

Sodium Sulfocyanate

NaSCN; mol. wt. 81.08; Na—28.37%; SCN—71.63%.

Colorless or white crystals; slightly deliquescent. Very soluble in water; soluble in alcohol. *Keep in tightly closed containers.*

Standards

Solubility in alcohol...........to pass test	Ammonia (NH_3).........max about 0.02%
Iodine-consuming substances	Heavy metals (as Pb).......max 0.0005%
(Cyanide, Sulfide, etc.).......to pass test	Iron (Fe)..................max 0.0003%
Chloride (Cl)................max 0.010%	*Assay*.......................min 99.0%
Sulfate (SO_4)................max 0.010%	

Solubility in alcohol: Heat 2 g with 25 ml of alcohol on the steam bath under reflux condenser. Not more than a trace of undissolved residue remains on cooling.

Iodine-consuming substances: Dissolve 2 g in a mixture of 20 ml of H_2O and 1 ml of 10% H_2SO_4. Add 0.5 g of potassium iodide and 0.5 ml of starch solution, and titrate with 0.1 N iodine. Not more than 0.4 ml of the iodine is required to produce a blue or reddish-blue color.

Chloride: Dissolve 1 g in 20 ml H_2O in a small flask, add 10 ml of 25% H_2SO_4 and 7 ml of 30% hydrogen peroxide, then boil down gently *under hood* to 20 ml. Restore the volume with H_2O and again evaporate to 20 ml. Repeat this operation until all the cyanide has volatilized. Cool, dilute to 50 ml and mix well. Dilute 10 ml of this solution to 20 ml and add 1 ml of nitric acid and 1 ml of silver nitrate. The turbidity produced is not more than that in a control made with 0.02 mg of Cl and 1 ml each of HNO_3 and silver nitrate in the same final volume as with the sample.

Sulfate: Dissolve 1 g in 10 ml of H_2O, add 1 ml of 0.1 N HCl and 2 ml of $BaCl_2$. Any turbidity produced is not greater than that in a blank to which 0.1 mg of SO_4 has been added.

Ammonia: Dissolve 1 g in 10 ml of H_2O, add 5 ml of 10% NaOH and heat on the steam bath for 5 minutes. The vapors do not affect moist red litmus paper.

Heavy metals: Dissolve 5 g in H_2O to make 50 ml. To 10 ml add 0.015 mg of Pb, dilute to 40 ml and add 1 ml of 1 N acetic acid (A). To the remaining 40 ml add 1 ml of 1 N acetic acid (B). Then to each add 10 ml of H_2S. B is not darker than A.

Iron: Dissolve 4 g in water to make 40 ml. To 10 ml of the solution add 0.006 mg of Fe and dilute to 50 ml (A). Dilute the remaining 30 ml of the solution to 50 ml (B). Then to each add about 50 mg of ammonium persulfate and 2 ml of HCl, and mix well. Any red color in B is not darker than that in A.

Assay: Sodium thiocyanate may be assayed by the adsorption indicator method for Chloride and Thiocyanate, page 565, using about 0.3 g, accurately weighed, of the sample previously dried over H_2SO_4. One ml of 0.1 N $AgNO_3$ = 0.008108 g NaSCN.

SODIUM THIOGLYCOLLATE

$HS \cdot CH_2 \cdot COONa$; mol. wt. 114.1; S—28.1%.

White, crystalline powder having, when fresh, only a slight odor. Very soluble in water; slightly soluble in alcohol. The aqueous solution (1:10) has a slight acid reaction. It is hygroscopic and oxidizes in the air. *Keep in tightly closed containers, protected from light. It should not be used if it is yellowish or darker.*

Standards

Assay.........min 80% $HS \cdot CH_2 \cdot COONa$ Sulfide (S)............max about 0.05%
Solubility....................to pass test

Assay: Weigh accurately about 0.25 g of the sample and dissolve it in about 5 ml of oxygen-free water in the weighing bottle. Promptly add the solution to 50 ml of 0.1 N iodine contained in a glass-stoppered flask, and rinse out the weighing bottle into the iodine solution with a few ml of water. Allow to stand for 5 minutes, then add 5 ml of 10% HCl and titrate the excess of iodine with 0.1 N thiosulfate, adding starch toward the end. One ml of 0.1 N iodine = 0.01141 g of $HS \cdot CH_2 \cdot COONa$, log 05729.

For the chemistry of their assay see Thioglycollic Acid.

Solubility: A solution of 2 g in 10 ml of water is colorless and complete or practically complete.

Sulfide: Dissolve 0.5 g in 10 ml of H_2O in a small flask, add 2 ml of HCl, then place a strip of paper moistened with lead acetate solution over the mouth of the flask and bring the solution to a boil. The leaf acetate paper is not markedly darkened.

SODIUM THIOSULFATE

$Na_2S_2O_3 \cdot 5H_2O$; mol. wt. 248.19; anhydrous—63.71%; H_2O—36.29%; S—25.84%; SO_2—51.62%.

Colorless crystals or white granules. Efflorescent above 33°. Loses all of its H_2O at 100°. Soluble in less than 1 part of water; insoluble in alcohol. Its aqueous solution decomposes slowly, more rapidly on boiling.

Standards

Insoluble.................max 0.005%
Neutrality.................to pass test
Nitrogen compounds (as N)...max 0.002%
Sulfate and Sulfite (as SO_4)....max 0.05%
Heavy metals (as Pb)........max 0.001%
Assay.......................min 99.5%

Insoluble: Dissolve 20 g in 200 ml of water, filter any undissolved residue, wash it with water, and dry at 105°. The weight of the undissolved matter does not exceed 1.0 mg.

Neutrality: Dissolve 5 g in 50 ml of CO_2-free water and add 2 drops of phenolphthalein; no pink color is produced. Now add 0.05 ml of 0.1 N NaOH; a pink color is produced.

Nitrogen compounds: Dissolve 0.5 g of salicylic acid in 7 ml of H_2SO_4 in a Kjeldahl flask, add 1 g of the sample, and digest over a low flame until the liquid is colorless or nearly so. *Cautiously* dilute with 60 ml of water and connect with a condenser and a receiver containing 5 ml of water and 1 drop of dilute HCl. Add to the liquid in the Kjeldahl flask 30 ml of 30% NaOH, or sufficient to make strongly alkaline, and distill over about 40 ml. Dilute to 50 ml and add 1 ml of 10% NaOH and 2 ml of Nessler solution. The color produced is not darker than that produced by treating 0.02 mg of nitrogen (0.08 mg NH_4Cl) in the same manner.

Sulfate and sulfite: Dissolve 0.5 g in 15 ml of water, add approximately 0.1 N iodine until the solution is faintly yellow, and dilute to 50 ml. To 20 ml add 2 ml of 0.1 N HCl and 2 ml of $BaCl_2$. Any resulting turbidity in 15 minutes is not greater than that of a control made with 0.10 mg of SO_4, 2 ml of 0.1 N HCl, 2 ml of $BaCl_2$, and sufficient H_2O to give the same volume as in the test with the sample.

Heavy metals: Dissolve 5 g in 20 ml of water and add 6 ml of HCl. Evaporate to dryness on the steam bath and heat for 1 hour at about 150°. Take up with 25 ml of water, filter, add to the filtrate 1 drop of phenolphthalein solution and just sufficient 0.1 N NaOH to produce a pink color. Add 2 ml of 1 N acetic acid and dilute to 50 ml. To 10 ml add 0.03 mg of Pb and dilute to 40 ml (*A*). Add to *A* and to the remaining 40 ml (*B*) 10 ml of H_2S. *B* is not darker than *A*.

Assay: Sodium thiosulfate may be assayed by dissolving about 0.7 g, accurately weighed, in 50 ml of H_2O, and titrating with 0.1 N iodine and starch indicator. One ml of 0.1 N iodine = 0.02482 g $Na_2S_2O_3 \cdot 5H_2O$, log 39480.

To determine the "absolute" purity, about 1 g is first dried at about 40° for 1 hour, then to constant weight at 105°. About 0.5 g of the dried sample is weighed, dissolved in 50 ml of water, and titrated with 0.1 N iodine and starch indicator. One ml of 0.1 N iodine = 0.02482 g $Na_2S_2O_3$, log 39480. When so assayed, a purity of 99.5% to 100.2% should be indicated.

$$2Na_2S_2O_3 + 2I \rightarrow Na_2S_4O_6 + 2NaI$$

SODIUM TUNGSTATE

$Na_2WO_4 \cdot 2H_2O$; mol. wt. 329.87; anhydrous—89.08%; H_2O—10.92%; WO_3—70.30%; W—55.75%.

Colorless crystals or a white crystalline powder. Soluble in about 1.1 parts of water; insoluble in alcohol.

Standards

Assay, anhydrous basis........min 98.5%	Sulfate (SO_4)................max 0.010%
Alkalinity (as Na_2CO_3).........max 0.2%	Arsenic (As)..................max 2 ppm
Insoluble....................max 0.010%	Heavy metals................max 0.001%
Chloride (Cl)................max 0.005%	Iron (Fe)....................max 0.001%
Nitrate (NO_3)..............max 0.003%	Molybdenum (Mo)...........max 0.001%

Assay: Weigh accurately about 0.5 g of sample previously dried to constant weight at 105° and dissolve in 50 ml of water. If the solution is not clear, filter, and wash well with water. Add to the solution 10 to 15 ml of HCl, boil, and evaporate to 10 ml. Dilute to about 150 ml and add 10 ml of cinchonine hydrochloride solution (made by dissolving 2.5 g of cinchonine in 25 ml of a mixture of equal volumes of HCl and H_2O), and heat on the hot plate for 30 minutes, stirring occasionally. Allow the cinchonine tungstate acid to settle, decant through a filter paper, preferably containing some paper pulp, then filter the precipitate, wash it well with the diluted cinchonine solution (1:100), dry, and ignite in platinum to constant weight at a relatively low temperature. Cool and weigh. Now add to the WO_3 0.5 ml of HF and 5 drops of H_2SO_4, evaporate, and ignite to constant weight. Any loss in weight (silica) corresponds to not more than 0.20%. The weight of the $WO_3 \times 1.267 = Na_2WO_4$, log 10278.

Alkalinity: Dissolve 2 g in 50 ml of cold H_2O and add 2 drops of thymol blue. A blue color is produced which is changed to yellow by not more than 0.4 ml of 0.1 N acid.

Insoluble: Dissolve 10 g in 100 ml of water and heat the solution on the steam bath for 30 minutes. If an undissolved residue remains, filter, wash it with hot water, and dry at 105°. Its weight does not exceed 1.0 mg.

Chloride: Dissolve 1 g in 20 ml of H_2O, add 3 ml of phosphoric acid, and dilute to 50 ml. Dilute 10 ml of the solution to 20 ml and add 1 ml of HNO_3 and 1 ml of $AgNO_3$. Any turbidity produced is not greater than that in a blank to which 0.01 mg of Cl has been added.

Nitrate: Dissolve 1.0 g in 15 ml of water and add 5 ml of 25% H_2SO_4. Allow the precipitate ($WO_3 + H_2O$) to settle and filter, or preferably centrifuge and decant. To 10 ml of the filtrate (which need not be entirely clear), add 10 mg of NaCl and 0.1 ml of indigo carmine solution, then add 10 ml of H_2SO_4. The blue (or green) color does not entirely disappear in 5 minutes.

Sulfate: Dissolve 2 g in 100 ml of water, add slowly, with stirring, 5 ml of HCl, evaporate to dryness, and heat at 120° for 20 minutes. Add to the residue 30 ml of H_2O, 2.5 ml of HCl, and 2 ml of the cinchonine solution prepared as described under *Assay*, and heat just below the boiling point for 30 minutes. Cool, dilute to 30 ml, and filter. To 15 ml of the filtrate add ammonium hydroxide until a slight permanent precipitate is formed, then add just sufficient HCl to redissolve it and follow with 2 ml of $BaCl_2$ and allow to stand for 20 minutes. Any resulting turbidity is not greater than that in a control made as follows. To 1 ml of the cinchonine solution add 0.1 mg of SO_4, dilute to 16 ml, and add 2 ml of $BaCl_2$.

Arsenic: Test 1.0 g by the method on page 563 without previous treatment. The stain is not greater than that produced by 0.002 mg of As.

Heavy metals; Iron: Dissolve 1 g in 20 ml of H_2O, add 2 ml of NH_4OH and

5 ml of H_2S. At most only a slight greenish color, but not a brown color, is produced.

Molybdenum: Dissolve 2 g in 15 ml of water and make the solution slightly alkaline, if it is not so, with NaOH. Dissolve in this solution, without warming, 0.5 g of potassium xanthate, add 10 ml of chloroform, and then add, drop by drop, 25% H_2SO_4, shaking after each addition, until the color in the chloroform is no longer intensified. The resulting color is not darker than that of a blank to which 0.03 mg of MoO_2 (0.02 mg Mo) has been added.

STANNIC CHLORIDE, ANHYDROUS

Fuming Stannic Chloride; Tin Tetrachloride

$SnCl_4$; mol. wt. 260.53; Sn—45.57%; Cl—54.43%.

Colorless, fuming, caustic liquid. Forms the crystalline pentahydrate with about one-third its weight of water. Freely soluble in water and in alcohol. Boils at 115°. Sp. gr. 2.2. *Keep in tightly stoppered bottles.*

Standards

Solubility....................to pass test	Arsenic (As)................max 5 ppm
Free chlorine.................to pass test	Substances not precipitated
Sulfate (SO$_4$)................max 0.005%	by H$_2$S....................max 0.05%
Antimony (Sb)..............max 0.005%	Iron (Fe)....................max 0.001%
	Other heavy metals (as Pb)...max 0.010%

Caution! *Dilution of stannic chloride must be done with care because of the heat produced.*

Solubility: A solution of 2 ml (4.4 g) in 100 ml of water is clear and colorless.

Free chlorine: Dissolve 1 ml of sample in 20 ml of water, cool, add 1 ml of chloroform and 2 drops of potassium iodide, and shake. No violet color appears in the chloroform in 1 minute.

Sulfate: Dissolve 1 ml (2.2 g) in 50 ml of water, add 1 ml of HCl and 50 ml of H_2O and filter if necessary. Heat the filtrate to boiling, add 5 ml of barium chloride, and let stand overnight. No turbidity or precipitate is formed.

Antimony: Dilute 1.0 ml of sample with water to 55 ml. Transfer 5 ml of the dilution to a small separatory funnel and add 3 ml of HCl. In a similar separatory funnel place a volume of standard antimony solution corresponding to 0.01 mg of Sb, dilute to 5 ml, and add 3 ml of HCl, then treat both as follows:

Add 3 drops of 10% sodium nitrite solution, mix, and warm at about 50° for 1 minute. Cool, add 5 ml of H_2O and 5 ml of a solution of 10 mg of rhodamin B in 100 ml of H_2O, and 15 ml of toluene. Shake well for about 1 minute, allow to separate, draw off and discard the aqueous (lower) layer. Shake the toluene layer with 5 ml of 10% HCl, allow to separate and discard the aqueous layer. Add to the toluene about 1 g of granular anhydrous sodium sulfate (sodium sulfate for drying of liquids, page 486) and shake until the liquid is clear (about 1 minute). Pour off the toluene into a graduated cylinder, wash the funnel and the sodium sulfate with 5 ml of toluene, add the washing to the cylinder, then add sufficient toluene to measure 25 ml, and mix. The red color in the cylinder with the sample is not darker than that with the antimony standard.

Arsenic: Test 0.5 ml by the method on page 563. The stain is no greater than that from 0.0025 mg of As.

Substances not precipitated by H_2S: Dilute 2.0 ml with 220 ml of H_2O, warm to 70°, precipitate the tin completely with H_2S, and filter. To 100 ml of filtrate add 0.5 ml of H_2SO_4, evaporate to dryness, and ignite. The residue weighs not more than 1.0 mg (retain residue).

Iron: To the residue from *Substances not precipitated by H_2S* add 2 ml of HCl and 0.5 ml of nitric acid and slowly evaporate to dryness on the steam bath. Take up with 2 ml of HCl and dilute to 50 ml. Add 30 mg of ammonium persulfate and 3 ml of ammonium thiocyanate, and mix. Any resulting red color is not darker than that of a blank to which 0.02 mg of Fe has been added.

Other heavy metals: Dissolve 1.0 ml in a mixture of 5 ml of HCl, 5 ml of HNO_3 and 15 ml of water. Boil until brown fumes are no longer evolved, cool and dilute to 100 ml. To 10 ml add 10% NaOH until the precipitate first formed redissolves. Dilute to 40 ml and add 10 ml of H_2S. Any resulting dark color is not darker than that of a control made with 0.02 mg of Pb, the same volumes of NaOH and H_2S as used in the test with the sample and in the same final volume.

STANNIC CHLORIDE, CRYSTALS

Tin Tetrachloride Crystals

$SnCl_4 \cdot 5H_2O$; mol. wt. 350.61; anhydrous—74.31%; H_2O—25.69%; Sn—33.86%.

White to slightly yellow crystals, or fused small pieces. Freely soluble in water and in alcohol.

Standards

Solubility in HCl.............to pass test	Iron (Fe)...................max 0.001%
Sulfate (SO_4)...............max 0.005%	Substances not precipitated
Antimony (Sb).............max 0.005%	by H_2S....................max 0.05%
Arsenic (As)................max 5 ppm	Other heavy metals (as Pb)...max 0.010%

Apply the tests described under Stannic Chloride, Anhydrous, using 2 g of sample for each 1 ml of sample there directed. The results should be as there stated.

STANNOUS CHLORIDE

$SnCl_2 \cdot 2H_2O$; mol. wt. 225.65; anhydrous—84.03%; H_2O—15.97%; Sn—52.60%; Cl—31.43%.

Colorless crystals. Soluble in less than 1 part of water when slightly acidified with hydrochloric acid; soluble in alcohol. With much water it forms an insoluble basic salt. The salt or its solution absorbs oxygen from the air, forming a basic stannic salt. The oxidation of the solution may be prevented by the presence of metallic tin. *Keep in tightly closed containers.*

Standards

Solubility in HCl..............to pass test	Iron (Fe)...................max 0.003%
Sulfate (SO$_4$).........max about 0.003%	Other heavy metals
Alkalies, Earths, etc...........max 0.05%	(as Pb)..................max 0.010%
Ammonia (NH$_3$).......max about 0.01%	*Assay*........................min 96%
Arsenic (As)................max 2 ppm	

Solubility in HCl: Five grams dissolve completely in a mixture of 5 ml of hydrochloric acid and 5 ml of water at 40°.

Sulfate: Dissolve 5 g in 5 ml of hydrochloric acid and dilute with water to 50 ml. Heat the solution to boiling, add 5 ml of BaCl$_2$, and let stand overnight. No precipitate forms.

Alkalies, Earths, etc.: Dissolve 4 g in 5 ml of HCl, dilute with water to 200 ml, completely precipitate the tin with H$_2$S, and filter. To 100 ml of the filtrate add 5 drops of H$_2$SO$_4$, evaporate to dryness, and ignite. The residue does not exceed 1.0 mg (retain residue).

Ammonia: To 1 g in a small flask add 10 ml of 10% NaOH and heat on the steam bath. The escaping vapors do not affect moist red litmus paper.

Arsenic: Dissolve 5 g in 10 ml of HCl, heat to boiling, and let stand for 1 hour. The solution has no more color than a similar solution when freshly prepared.

Iron: To the residue from *Alkalies, Earths, etc.*, add 2 ml of HCl, 2 ml of H$_2$O and 0.5 ml of HNO$_3$, and slowly evaporate to dryness on the steam bath. Dissolve the residue in 1 ml of HCl and make up to 40 ml. To 10 ml add 2 ml of HCl and dilute to 50 ml. Add about 30 mg of ammonium persulfate and 3 ml of ammonium thiocyanate, and mix. Any resulting red color is not darker than that of a blank to which 0.015 mg of Fe has been added.

Other heavy metals: Dissolve 1 g in a mixture of 3 ml of HCl, 3 ml of HNO$_3$ and 5 ml of H$_2$O. Boil gently until brown fumes are no longer evolved, cool, and dilute to 50 ml. To 10 ml add 10% NaOH until the precipitate first formed redissolves, cool, dilute to 40 ml and add 10 ml of H$_2$S. Any resulting color is not darker than that of a control made with 0.02 mg of Pb, 10 ml of H$_2$S, the same volume of the NaOH and in the same final volume as with the sample.

Assay: Stannous chloride may be assayed by the following method: Weigh accurately about 0.4 g and dissolve in 3 ml of hydrochloric acid. Dilute immediately with 50 ml of water, add 5 g of potassium sodium tartrate and a cold saturated solution of sodium bicarbonate until slightly alkaline to litmus paper, then titrate at once with 0.1 N iodine, using starch as indicator. One ml of 0.1 N iodine = 0.01128 g SnCl$_2 \cdot$ 2H$_2$O, log 05231.

STARCH SOLUBLE

For Diastatic Power Determination

Fine, white powder. Soluble in water; insoluble in alcohol.

Standards

Sensitiveness.................to pass test	Reducing sugars (as maltose)...max 0.75%
Solubility.....................to pass test	Drying loss....................max 12%
pH............................4.8–5.5	Ignition residue...............max 0.7%

Sensitiveness: Add 1 ml of the solution obtained in the test for solubility and 50 mg of KI to 100 ml of water and add 0.05 ml of 0.1 N iodine. A blue color is produced which is discharged by 0.05 ml of 0.1 N thiosulfate.

Solubility: Mix 2 g with a little H_2O, then add 100 ml of hot water and boil gently for 2 minutes. The solution is not more than opalescent and it remains mobile on cooling.

pH: Determine the pH in a 2% aqueous solution, preferably potentiometrically.

Reducing sugars: Vigorously shake 10 g with 100 ml of H_2O for 15 minutes at room temperature. Allow to settle, and then filter through a dry filter, rejecting the first 10 ml of filtrate. Add 50 ml of Fehling solution to 50 ml of the filtrate, bring to a boil in 4 minutes, and continue boiling for 2 minutes. Immediately filter through a tared filtering crucible, wash with hot water, then with 10 ml of alcohol, and finally with 15 ml of ether, dry at 105° for 30 minutes, cool, and weigh. The weight of the cuprous oxide so obtained is not more than 47.0 mg.

Drying loss: Dry about 1 g, accurately weighed, for 4 hours at 105°. The loss in weight corresponds to not more than 12%.

Ignition residue: Char 1 g, cool, add 1 ml of H_2SO_4, and ignite to constant weight. Not more than 7.0 mg of residue remains.

STARCH SOLUBLE

For Iodometry

Fine, white powder. Soluble in water; insoluble in alcohol.

Standards

Sensitiveness................to pass test	pH............................4.5–6.0
Solubility...................to pass test	Ignition residue.............max 0.30%

Sensitiveness: Make a paste of 1 g with a little cold water and add to it, with stirring, 200 ml or boiling water. Add 5 ml of this solution to 100 ml of water containing 50 mg of potassium iodide, and then add 0.05 ml of 0.1 N iodine. A deep blue color is produced which is discharged by 0.05 ml of 0.1 N thiosulfate.

Solubility: Dissolve 2 g in 100 ml of hot H_2O; the solution is not more than opalescent and it remains perfectly mobile in cooling.

pH: Determine the pH in a 2% solution, preferably potentiometrically.

Ignition residue: Char 1 g, cool, add 1 ml of H_2SO_4 and ignite to constant weight. Not more than 3.0 mg of residue remains.

STRONTIUM ACETATE

$Sr(CH_3CO_2)_2 \cdot \frac{1}{2}H_2O$; mol. wt. 214.73; Sr—40.18%; acetic acid—55.93%; H_2O—4.20%.

White, crystalline. Soluble in 3 parts of water; slightly soluble in alcohol.

Standards

Insoluble	max 0.010%	Barium (Ba)	max 0.02%
Free acid (as acetic)	max 0.060%	Calcium (Ca)	max 0.20%
Chloride (Cl)	max 0.005%	Heavy metals (as Pb)	max 0.001%
Nitrate (NO_3)	max 0.003%	Iron (Fe)	max 0.001%
Alkali and Magnesium			
(Mg + Na)	max 0.15%		

Insoluble: Dissolve 10 g in 150 ml of H_2O and 2 ml of glacial acetic acid, and heat on the steam bath for 1 hour. Filter any undissolved residue, wash with water and dry at 105°. The insoluble residue does not exceed 1.0 mg.

Free acid: Dissolve 2 g in 30 ml of water and add 2 drops of phenolphthalein, and titrate with 0.1 N NaOH to the production of a pink color. Not more than 0.2 ml of the NaOH is required.

Chloride: Dissolve 1 g in 50 ml of water. To 20 ml add 1 ml of HNO_3 and 1 ml of silver nitrate. Any resulting turbidity is not more than that in the blank with 0.02 mg of added Cl ion.

Nitrate: Dissolve 0.5 g in 22 ml of water, add 3 ml of 25% H_2SO_4, shake well and let stand for 15 minutes, shaking a few times during this period. Filter or centrifuge and decant. To 10 ml of the filtrate add 20 mg of NaCl and 0.2 ml of diphenylamine solution, then run in slowly, without agitation, 10 ml of H_2SO_4. Mix the contents of the beaker by gently swirling it and allow to stand for 30 minutes. No blue color appears.

Alkali and Magnesium: Dissolve 2 g in 80 ml of water, and add 2 drops of HCl. Heat to boiling, add 10 ml of 25% H_2SO_4 and allow to cool to room temperature. Dilute to 100 ml, add 100 ml of alcohol and allow to stand overnight. Filter through a dry filter, evaporate 100 ml of the filtrate to dryness in a tared dish and ignite to constant weight. The weight of the residue does not exceed 5.0 mg.

Barium: Dissolve 1 g in 10 ml of water, add 1 drop of glacial acetic acid and 0.5 ml of 10% potassium dichromate. No turbidity is produced in 2 minutes.

Calcium: Ignite 1 g until nearly white. Warm the residue with a mixture of 20 ml of H_2O and 3 ml of HNO_3, filter, wash with 5 ml of H_2O and evaporate the filtrate to dryness on the steam bath. Powder the residue and dry it at 120° for 3 hours. Reflux the powder with 15 ml of alcohol for 10 minutes, cool on ice and filter. Repeat the extraction with 10 ml of alcohol. Evaporate the combined filtrate to dryness, add a few drops of H_2SO_4 and ignite to constant weight. The weight of the residue does not exceed 5 mg.

Note: The calcium may be more advantageously determined by Flame Photometry.

Heavy metals: Dissolve 4 g in 40 ml of H_2O. To 10 ml add 0.02 mg of Pb, dilute to 30 ml and add 1 ml of 1 N acetic acid (A). To the remaining 30 ml add 1 ml of 1 N acetic acid (B). Then to each add 10 ml of H_2S; B is not darker than A.

Iron: Dissolve 1 g in 20 ml of H_2O, add 3 ml of HCl and 0.5 ml of HNO_3, and boil for 1 minute, cool, dilute to 50 ml, and add 3 ml of ammonium thiocyanate. Any resulting red color is not darker than that of a blank to which 0.01 mg of Fe has been added.

STRONTIUM CARBONATE

$SrCO_3$, mol. wt. 147.64; Sr—59.36%; CO_3—40.64%; CO_2—29.81%.

White powder. Almost insoluble in water; soluble in dilute nitric and hydrochloric acids or in acetic acid.

Standards

Acetic acid—insoluble........max 0.010%
Chloride (Cl)...............max 0.005%
Nitrate (NO_3)..............max 0.003%
Phosphate (PO_4)...........max 0.001%
Alkali carbonate (as Na_2CO_3)...max 0.05%

Alkali and Magnesium
  (Mg + Na)...............max 0.30%
Barium (Ba)...........max about 0.03%
Calcium (Ca)................max 0.20%
Heavy metals (as Pb).......max 0.001%
Iron (Fe)..................max 0.001%

Acetic acid—insoluble: Gently heat 10 g with 100 ml of H_2O and add in small portions 20 ml of glacial acetic acid. When no more dissolves, filter, wash with hot water, and dry at 105°. The insoluble residue does not exceed 1.0 mg.

Chloride: Dissolve 1 g in a mixture of 30 ml of H_2O and 3 ml of HNO_3, filter, and dilute to 50 ml. To 20 ml add 1 ml of $AgNO_3$. Any turbidity produced is not greater than that in a blank to which 0.02 mg of Cl has been added.

Nitrate: Suspend 0.5 g in 5 ml of water and add, a few drops at a time, glacial acetic acid, shaking after each addition, until dissolved. Dilute to 20 ml and add 5 ml of 25% H_2SO_4. Shake well and allow to stand for 15–20 minutes, shaking several times during this period. Filter or, preferably centrifuge, and decant. To 10 ml of the filtrate add 20 mg of NaCl, 0.2 ml of diphenylamine solution, mix, then run in slowly 10 ml of H_2SO_4, mix gently and allow to stand for 30 minutes. No blue color results.

Phosphate: To 2 g add 20 ml of H_2O, then add HCl dropwise until dissolved. Dilute with 20 ml of H_2O, heat to boiling, add 6 ml of 25% H_2SO_4, and allow to stand for 30 minutes. Filter, and wash to 50 ml. To 25 ml of the filtrate add 1 ml each of phosphate reagents **A** and **B** and heat at 60° for 10 minutes. Any blue color produced is not darker than that of a control made with 0.01 mg of PO_4, 2 ml of 25% H_2SO_4, the same amounts of the reagents **A** and **B** in the same volume of solution and heated as with the sample.

Alkali carbonate: Boil 2 g with 50 ml of H_2O for 5 minutes, cool, dilute to 50 ml, and filter. To 25 ml of the filtrate add 2 drops of phenolphthalein. If a pink color is produced, it is discharged by not more than 0.05 ml of 0.1 N HCl.

Alkali and Magnesium: To 2 g add 15 ml of water and follow dropwise with HCl until just dissolved (about 2 ml). Dilute with 75 ml of water, heat to boiling and add 10 ml of 25% H_2SO_4. Allow to cool to room temperature, then add 100 ml of alcohol, add water to make 200 ml. Mix and filter through a filtering crucible or dry paper filter. Evaporate 100 ml of the filtrate in a tared dish to dryness, then heat gently at first to expel excess of H_2SO_4 and finally ignite to constant weight. The weight of the residue does not exceed 8.0 mg.

Barium: To 0.7 g add 10 ml of H_2O and 2 ml of HCl and evaporate to dryness on the steam bath. Dissolve the residue in 10 ml of water, filter, dissolve in the filtrate 1 g of sodium acetate, then add 1 drop of glacial acetic acid and 0.5 ml of 10% potassium dichromate.   No turbidity is produced in 2 minutes.

Calcium: Evaporate 1 g with 10 ml of water and 2 ml of nitric acid to dryness on the steam bath.   Powder the residue well and dry it at 120° for 3 hours.   Reflux the dried powder with 15 ml of absolute alcohol for 10 minutes, cool on ice, and filter.   Repeat the extraction with 10 ml of absolute alcohol.   Evaporate the combined filtrates to dryness, add 0.5 ml of H_2SO_4 and ignite.   The weight of the residue ($CaSO_4$) is not more than 5.0 mg.

Note: The calcium in strontium compounds may be more advantageously determined by Flame Photometry.

Heavy metals: Evaporate 4 g with a mixture of 20 ml of water and 5 ml of HCl to dryness on the steam bath, then dissolve the residue in water to make 40 ml. To 10 ml add 0.02 mg of Pb, 1 ml of 1 N acetic acid, and dilute to 40 ml (A).   To the remaining 30 ml add 1 ml of 1 N acetic acid and dilute to 40 ml (B).   Then to each add 10 ml of H_2S; B is not darker than A.

Iron: To 1 g add 20 ml of water, 3 ml of HCl, and 5 drops of HNO_3, and bring to a boil.   Cool, filter if necessary, and dilute to 50 ml.   Add 3 ml of ammonium thiocyanate and mix.   Any resulting red color is not darker than that of a blank to which 0.01 mg of Fe has been added.

STRONTIUM CHLORIDE

$SrCl_2 \cdot 6H_2O$; mol. wt. 266.64; anhydrous salt—59.46%; H_2O—40.54%; Sr— 32.86%; Cl—26.60%.

Colorless or white crystals or granules.   Soluble in 1 part of water; soluble in alcohol.   Loses all its water at 150°.

Standards

Insoluble	max 0.005%	Barium (Ba)	max about 0.02%
Neutrality	to pass test	Calcium (Ca)	max 0.10%
Nitrate (NO_3)	max 0.003%	Heavy metals (as Pb)	max 0.0005%
Sulfate (SO_4)	max 0.01%	Iron (Fe)	max 0.001%
Alkali and Magnesium			
(Mg + Na)	max 0.15%		

Insoluble: Dissolve 20 g in 150 ml of water and heat on the steam bath for 1 hour.   Filter any undissolved matter, wash with hot water, and dry at 105°. Not more than 1.0 g of insoluble matter is obtained.

Neutrality: Dissolve 5 g in 50 ml of water and add 3 drops of phenolphthalein; no pink color is produced.   Add 0.2 ml of 0.02 ml of 0.02 N NaOH, a pink color is produced.

Nitrate: Dissolve 1.0 g in 22 ml of water, add 3 ml of 25% H_2SO_4, shake well and let stand for 15 minutes, shaking a few times during this period.   Filter or centrifuge and decant.   To 10 ml of the filtrate add 0.2 ml of diphenylamine solution, then run in slowly, without agitation, 10 ml of H_2SO_4.   After 10 minutes mix the contents of the beaker by gently swirling it and allow to stand for 1 hour. No blue color appears.

Sulfate: Dissolve 1 g in 10 ml of water, add 1 ml of 0.1 N HCl and 2 ml of $BaCl_2$. No turbidity appears in 10 minutes.

Alkali and Magnesium: Dissolve 2 g in 80 ml of water, and add 2 drops of HCl. Heat to boiling, add 10 ml of 25% H_2SO_4 and allow to cool to room temperature. Dilute to 100 ml, then add 100 ml of alcohol and allow to stand overnight. Filter through a dry filter, evaporate 100 ml of the filtrate to dryness in a tared dish and ignite to constant weight. The weight of the residue does not exceed 4.0 mg.

Barium: Dissolve 1 g of sample and 1 g of sodium acetate in 10 ml of water, add 1 drop of glacial acetic acid and 0.5 ml of 10% potassium dichromate. No turbidity appears in 2 minutes.

Calcium: Evaporate 1 g with 5 ml of HNO_3 to dryness on the steam bath and re-evaporate with another 5 ml of the same acid. Powder the residue well and dry it at 120° for 3 hours. Reflux the powder with 15 ml of alcohol (absolute) for 10 minutes, cool on ice, and filter. Repeat the extraction with 10 ml of absolute alcohol. Evaporate the combined filtrates to dryness, add 0.5 ml of H_2SO_4 and ignite. The weight of the residue ($CaSO_4$) is not more than 2.5 mg.

Note: The calcium may be more advantageously determined by Flame Photometry.

Heavy metals: Dissolve 5 g in water to make 50 ml. To 10 ml add 0.015 mg of Pb, dilute to 40 ml, and add 1 ml of 1 N acetic acid (A). To the remaining 40 ml add 1 ml of 1 N acetic acid (B). Then to each add 10 ml of H_2S. B is not darker than A.

Iron: Dissolve 1 g in 10 ml of water, add 2 drops of HNO_3, bring to boil, cool, add 2 ml of HCl and dilute to 50 ml. Add 3 ml of ammonium thiocyanate and mix. Any resulting red color is not darker than that of a blank to which 0.01 mg of Fe has been added.

STRONTIUM NITRATE, ANHYDROUS

$Sr(NO_3)_2$; mol. wt. 211.65; Sr—41.40%; NO_3—58.60%.

Colorless or white crystals or granules. Soluble in 1.5 parts of water; slightly soluble in alcohol or in acetone; almost insoluble in absolute alcohol.

Standards

Insoluble...................max 0.005%	Barium (Ba)................max 0.02%
Neutrality...................to pass test	Calcium (Ca)................max 0.10%
Chloride (Cl)................max 0.002%	Heavy metals (as Pb).......max 0.0005%
Sulfate (SO_4)................max 0.005%	Iron (Fe)...................max 0.001%
Alkali and magnesium	Drying loss.................max 0.20%
(Na + Mg)................max 0.10%	

Insoluble: Dissolve 20 g in 150 ml of H_2O and heat on the steam bath for 1 hour. Filter any undissolved residue, wash with water, and dry at 105°. Insoluble residue does not exceed 1.0 mg.

Neutrality: Dissolve 5 g in 50 ml of H_2O and add 3 drops of phenolphthalein; no pink color is produced. Add 0.2 ml of 0.02 N NaOH; a pink color is produced.

Chloride: Dissolve 1 g in 15 ml of water, add 1 ml of HNO_3, and dilute to 20 ml.

To 10 ml add 1 ml of silver nitrate. Any resulting turbidity is not more than that in the blank with 0.01 mg of Cl added.

Sulfate: Dissolve 1 g in 5 ml of hot water, add 10 ml of HCl, and evaporate to dryness on the steam bath. Dissolve the residue in 10 ml of water, add 1 ml of 0.1 N HCl and 2 ml of $BaCl_2$. No turbidity results in 10 minutes.

Alkali and Magnesium: Dissolve 2 g in 80 ml of water, and add 2 drops of HCl. Heat to boiling, add 10 ml of 25% H_2SO_4 and allow to cool to room temperature. Dilute to 100 ml, then add 100 ml of alcohol and allow to stand overnight. Filter through a dry filter, evaporate 100 ml of the filtrate to dryness in a tared dish and ignite to constant weight. The weight of the residue does not exceed 4.0 mg.

Barium: Dissolve 1 g of sample and 1 g of sodium acetate in 10 ml of water, add 1 drop of glacial acetic acid and 0.5 ml of 10% potassium dichromate. No turbidity is produced in 2 minutes.

Calcium: Powder well 1 g of the sample and dry at 120° for 2 hours. Reflux the dried powder with 15 ml of absolute alcohol for 10 minutes, cool on ice, and filter. Repeat the extraction with 10 ml of absolute alcohol. Evaporate the combined filtrates to dryness, add 0.5 ml of H_2SO_4, and ignite. The weight of the residue ($CaSO_4$) does not exceed 2.5 mg.

Note: The calcium may be more advantageously determined by Flame Photometry.

Heavy metals: Dissolve 5 g in water to make 50 ml. To 10 ml add 0.015 mg of Pb, dilute to 40 ml, and add 1 ml of 1 N acetic acid (A). To the remaining 40 ml add 1 ml of 1 N acetic acid (B). Then to each add 10 ml of H_2S. B is not darker than A.

Iron: Dissolve 1 g in 20 ml of water, add 15 ml of butanolic potassium thiocyanate and 1 ml of HCl, shake vigorously for 30 seconds, and allow to separate. Any red color in the clear butanol layer is not darker than that in a blank to which 0.01 mg of Fe has been added.

Drying loss: Weigh accurately about 2 g and dry at 105° for 4 hours. The loss in weight corresponds to not more than 0.2%.

SUCCINIC ACID

HOOC—CH_2—CH_2—COOH; mol. wt. 118.09.

Colorless crystals. Soluble in 20 parts water, 2 parts boiling water, 10 parts alcohol or 80 parts ether.

Standards

Melting range.................185°–187°	Sulfate (SO_4)................max 0.005%
Insoluble...................max 0.010%	Ammonia (NH_3).............max 0.002%
Ignition residue.............max 0.020%	Heavy metals (as Pb).......max 0.0005%
Chloride (Cl)...............max 0.002%	Iron (Fe)...................max 0.001%
Phosphate (PO_4)...........max 0.001%	*Assay*...................99.8%–100.2%

Insoluble: Dissolve 10 g in 150 ml of hot water and heat on the steam bath for 30 minutes. Filter any undissolved matter, wash with hot water, and dry at 105°. The insoluble residue is not more than 1.0 mg.

Ignition residue: Thoroughly char 5.0 g. Cool, then add 0.5 ml of H_2SO_4 and ignite at first gently to evaporate the acid, then strongly to constant weight. Not more than 1.0 mg of residue remains.

Chloride: Dissolve 1 g in 20 ml of warm water and add 1 ml of HNO_3 and 1 ml of $AgNO_3$. Any turbidity produced is not greater than that in a blank to which 0.02 mg of Cl has been added.

Phosphate: Dissolve 2 g in 10 ml of hot H_2O in a platinum crucible, add 0.3 g of magnesium nitrate, evaporate, and ignite. Warm the residue with 2 ml of 25% H_2SO_4 and 5 ml of H_2O, then add 15 ml of H_2O, and filter. Add to filtrate 1 ml each of phosphate reagents **A** and **B** and heat at 60° for 10 minutes. Any blue color produced is not deeper than that in a blank to which 0.02 mg of PO_4 has been added.

Sulfate: Dissolve 2 g in 15 ml of hot H_2O and add 1 ml of 0.1 N HCl. Heat the solution to about 80°, add 2 ml of $BaCl_2$ and allow to stand at 80° for 15 minutes. Any turbidity produced is not greater than that in a blank to which 0.1 mg of SO_4 has been added.

Ammonia: Dissolve 1 g in 40 ml of H_2O, add 10 ml of 10% NaOH and 2 ml of Nessler solution. The color is not darker than that of a blank to which 0.02 mg of NH_3 (0.06 mg NH_4Cl) has been added.

Heavy metals: Dissolve 5 g in 40 ml of hot water and neutralize with NH_4OH to litmus paper. Cool, add 5 ml of 1 N HCl, and dilute with water to 50 ml. To 10 ml of the solution add 0.015 mg of Pb and dilute with H_2O to 40 ml (A). Then add 10 ml of H_2S to A and to the remaining 40 ml of the solution (B). B is not darker than A.

Iron: Dissolve 1 g in 40 ml of water, add 2 ml of HCl, and dilute to 50 ml. Add about 30 mg of ammonium persulfate and 3 ml of ammonium thiocyanate, and mix. Any resulting red color is not darker than that in a blank to which 0.01 mg of Fe has been added.

Assay: Succinic acid may be assayed alkalimetrically as follows: Dry about 0.5 g of the acid over H_2SO_4 overnight, then weigh accurately about 0.3 g, dissolve in 25 ml H_2O, and titrate with 0.1 N NaOH, using phenolphthalein indicator. One ml of 0.1 N NaOH = 0.005905 g $(CH_2CO_2H)_2$, log 77122.

SUCROSE

Cane Sugar; Saccharose

$C_{12}H_{22}O_{11}$; mol. wt. 342.30.

Colorless crystals or white granules. Soluble in 0.5 part of water or in 200 parts of alcohol.

Standards

Specific rotation $[\alpha]_D^{25}$.... +66.4° to +66.8°	Nitrogen (N)...............max 0.005%
Solubility....................to pass test	Sulfate (SO_4)...............max 0.003%
Ignition residue.............max 0.010%	Heavy metals (as Cu).......max 0.0005%
Acid (as acetic)..............max 0.005%	Iron (Fe)..................max 0.0005%
Chloride (Cl)................max 0.002%	

Specific rotation: Determine the moisture by drying 5 g to constant weight at 105°. Weigh accurately a quantity of the original sample equivalent to 12.5 g of the anhydrous sucrose, dissolve in water, and dilute to 100 ml. Observe the rotation of this solution in a 200-mm tube at 25°, using sodium light. The observed rotation in degrees multiplied by $5 = [\alpha]_D^{25}$.

Solubility: A solution of 10 g of the sugar in 100 ml of water is clear, colorless, and free from insoluble matter.

Ignition residue: Char well 10 g. Allow to cool, add 1.0 ml of H_2SO_4 and ignite gently at first, then strongly (600°–800°) to constant weight. The weight of the residue, if any, does not exceed 1.0 mg.

Acid: To 100 ml of CO_2-free water add 2 drops of phenolphthalein and add, dropwise, 0.02 N NaOH until a pink color is produced. Dissolve 10 g of the sample in the solution and add 0.02 N NaOH to reproduce the same pink color. Not more than 0.4 ml of the NaOH is required.

Chloride: Dissolve 1 g in 20 ml of water, add 5 drops of HNO_3 and 1 ml of $AgNO_3$. Any turbidity produced is not greater than that in a blank with 0.02 mg of Cl added.

Nitrogen: Place 1 g in a 500-ml Kjeldahl flask, add 50 mg of salicylic acid and 15 ml of H_2SO_4, and let stand for 30 minutes. Then add 0.2 g of sodium thiosulfate and 10 g of potassium sulfate and heat over a small flame until the liquid is colorless or nearly so. Cool, *cautiously* add 100 ml of H_2O and 80 ml of 30% NaOH, and distill over about 75 ml into 5 ml of water containing 1 drop of dilute HCl. Dilute to 100 ml and mix well. To 40 ml add 1 ml of 10% NaOH and 2 ml of Nessler solution. The resulting color is not darker than that produced by 0.05 mg of nitrogen (0.2 mg NH_4Cl) treated in the same manner as the sample.

Sulfate: Dissolve 2 g in 20 ml of H_2O, add 1 ml of 1 N HCl and 2 ml of $BaCl_2$. No turbidity is produced in 15 minutes.

Heavy metals: Dissolve 5 g in water to make 50 ml. To 10 ml of the solution add 0.015 mg of Cu, dilute to 40 ml, and add 1 ml of 1 N acetic acid (*A*). To the remaining 40 ml add 1 ml of 1 N acetic acid (*B*). Then to each add 10 ml of H_2S; mix, and observe in 3 to 5 minutes. *B* is not darker than *A*.

Iron: Dissolve 2 g in water, add 2 ml of HCl, and dilute to 50 ml. Add about 50 mg of ammonium persulfate and 3 ml of 30% ammonium thiocyanate, and mix. Any resulting red color is not darker than that in a blank to which 0.01 mg of Fe has been added.

SULFAMIC ACID

$HO \cdot SO_2NH_2$; mol. wt. 97.10; N—14.43%.

Colorless or white crystals. Freely soluble in water; sparingly in alcohol.

Standards

Assay.....................99.5%–100.3%		Sulfate (SO_4)................max 0.030%	
Insoluble....................max 0.010%		Heavy metals (as Pb)........max 0.001%	
Ignition residue.............max 0.010%		Iron (Fe)...................max 0.0005%	
Chloride (Cl)................max 0.001%			

Assay: Dissolve 1.0 g to 1.2 of sulfamic acid, previously dried over H_2SO_4 or other suitable desiccator for 2 hours and accurately weighed in water to 100.0 ml. Transfer 25.0 ml to a conical flask, add 75 ml of water and 10 ml of 25% H_2SO_4, and titrate slowly, at room temperature, with 0.1 M sodium nitrite.

$$HNO_2 + HO \cdot SO_2 \cdot NH_2 \rightarrow N_2 + H_2SO_4 + H_2O$$

After the addition of each 5 ml or so of the nitrite solution the flask is stoppered and shaken vigorously to aid in the removal of the nitrogen evolved. Near the end point, the titration must be carried out drop by drop with shaking after each addition. The end point is reached when a drop of the titrated solution added to starch-iodide solution on a spot plate produces a blue color, which persists for 30 seconds. One ml of 0.1 M $NaNO_2$ = 0.009710 g $HO \cdot SO_2 \cdot NH_2$, log 98717.

Insoluble: Dissolve 10 g in 100 ml of H_2O and heat on the steam bath for 30 minutes. If an insoluble residue remains, filter, wash well with hot water, dry at 105°. Not over 1.0 mg of insoluble is found.

Ignition residue: Ignite 10 g until well charred. Allow to cool, add 0.5 ml of H_2SO_4 and reignite to constant weight. The weight of the residue, if any, does not exceed 1.0 mg.

Chloride: To a solution of 1 g in 10 ml of H_2O add 1 ml of HNO_3 and 1 ml of $AgNO_3$. Any turbidity produced is not greater than that in a blank to which 0.01 mg of Cl has been added.

Sulfate: Dissolve 1 g in 20 ml of H_2O, add 2 ml of 0.1 N HCl and 2 ml of $BaCl_2$. If a turbidity is produced, it is not greater than that in a blank to which 0.3 mg of SO_4 has been added.

Heavy metals: Dissolve 4 g in 30 ml of H_2O, neutralize with ammonium hydroxide to litmus paper, and dilute to 40 ml. To 10 ml add 0.02 mg of Pb, 2 ml of 1 N acetic acid and dilute to 40 ml (A). To the remaining 30 ml add 2 ml of 1 N acetic acid and dilute to 40 ml (B). Then to each add 10 ml of H_2S. B is not darker than A.

Iron: Dissolve 2 g in 20 ml of H_2O, add 2 ml of HCl and dilute to 50 ml. Add about 50 mg of ammonium persulfate and 3 ml of ammonium thiocyanate, and mix. Any resulting red color is not darker than that of a blank to which 0.01 mg of Fe has been added.

SULFANILIC ACID

Anilinesulfonic acid

SO₃H

$\cdot H_2O$; mol. wt. 191.21; H_2O—9.42%.

NH₂

White crystals or granules. Soluble in 150 parts of water; more soluble in hot water; very slightly soluble in alcohol or ether.

Standards

Assay (anhydrous basis)
99.0%–100.3% $H_2NC_6H_4SO_3H$
Drying loss..................max 10.0%
Insoluble in Na_2CO_3 solution..max 0.020%

Ignition residue.............max 0.020%
Chloride (Cl)................max 0.002%
Nitrite (NO_2).............max 0.00005%
Sulfate (SO_4)..............max 0.010%

Assay; Drying loss: Dry about 0.7 g at 105° for 4 hours.   The loss does not exceed 10%.   Transfer the dried sample to an Erlenmeyer flask, add 75 ml of hot water, and heat on the steam bath until completely dissolved.   Cool to room temperature and titrate with 0.1 N NaOH, using phenolphthalein as indicator. One ml of 0.1 N NaOH = 0.01732 g $H_2NC_6H_4SO_3H$, log 23855.

Insoluble in sodium carbonate: Dissolve 5 g in 50 ml of clear 5% sodium carbonate solution and let stand for 1 hour.   Filter any undissolved residue, wash with water, and dry at 105°.   The weight of the insoluble residue is not more than 1.0 mg.

Ignition residue: Char well 5.0 g.   Allow to cool, add 0.5 ml of H_2SO_4 and ignite gently at first, then strongly (600°–800°) to constant weight.   The weight of the residue, if any, does not exceed 1.0 mg.

Chloride: Boil 5 g with 100 ml of water until dissolved, dilute to 100 ml, cool, and filter.   To 10 ml of the filtrate add 0.5 ml of nitric acid and 1 ml of silver nitrate. Any turbidity produced is not greater than that in the blank to which 0.01 mg of Cl has been added.

Nitrite: Add 0.5 g to 50 ml of water, then add 5 ml of sulfanilic-α-naphthyl-amine solution (page 560) and warm on the steam bath until dissolved.   The solution has no more color than the same volume of water with 5 ml of the reagent.

Sulfate: Evaporate 40 ml of the filtrate from the test for *Chloride* to 20 ml, cool on ice, filter, and add to the filtrate 1 ml of 0.1 N HCl and 2 ml of $BaCl_2$.   Any turbidity produced is not greater than that in a control made with 0.2 mg of SO_4, 1 ml of HCl and 2 ml of $BaCl_2$ in the same volume as the sample.

SULFOSALICYLIC ACID

$OH \cdot 2H_2O$; mol. wt. 254.22; H_2O—14.17%.

White, or nearly white, crystals or crystalline powder.   Very soluble in water; in about 1 part of alcohol.   *Keep protected from light.*

Standards

Assay (anhydrous basis)...99.5%–100.5%
Solubility....................to pass test
Ignition residue..............max 0.05%
Chloride (Cl)................max 0.002%
Drying loss...................max 15%

Salicylic acid................max 0.020%
Sulfate (SO_4)..............max 0.020%
Heavy metals (as Pb)........max 0.001%
Iron (Fe)....................max 0.001%

Assay; Drying loss: Dry about 0.5 g first at 60°–70°, then at 110° to constant weight; the loss does not exceed 15%. Dissolve the dried sample in 50 ml of H_2O and titrate with 0.1 N NaOH, using phenolphthalein as indicator. One ml of 0.1 N NaOH = 0.01091 g of $C_7H_6O_6S$, log 03782.

Solubility: Two grams of the acid dissolve completely in 20 ml of water, forming a clear and colorless solution.

Ignition residue: Char well 4.0 g. Allow to cool, add 0.5 ml of H_2SO_4 and ignite gently at first to expel the acid, then strongly (600°–800°) to constant weight. Any residue does not exceed 2.0 mg.

Chloride: Dissolve 1 g in 20 ml of water, add 1 ml of HNO_3 and 1 ml of silver nitrate. Any turbidity produced is not more than that in the blank with 0.02 mg of Cl added.

Salicylic acid: Dissolve 5 g in 25 ml of water in a separatory funnel, add 0.5 ml of HCl and 25 ml of chloroform, and shake for 5 minutes. Draw off the chloroform, wash it twice with 5 ml of water. Filter the chloroform through paper wetted with chloroform and evaporate at room temperature. Dissolve the residue in 50 ml of warm water, cool, and add 0.5 ml of freshly prepared ferric ammonium sulfate solution. The color is not darker than that produced by adding 0.5 ml of the ferric ammonium sulfate to 50 ml of water containing 1 mg of salicylic acid.

Sulfate: To a solution of 1.0 g in 20 ml of water add 1 ml of 0.1 N HCl and 2 ml of $BaCl_2$. The turbidity produced in 10 min is not greater than that in the blank to which 0.2 mg of SO_4 has been added.

Heavy metals: Evaporate the residue from test for *Ignition residue* with 2 ml of hydrochloric acid and 0.5 ml of nitric acid to dryness on the steam bath. Take up with 1 ml of 1 N HCl and 30 ml of hot water, cool, and dilute to 80 ml. To 40 ml add 10 ml of H_2S. Any darkening is not greater than that produced in a control made with 0.02 mg of Pb, 0.5 ml of 1 N HCl and 10 ml of H_2S in the same volume as with the sample.

Iron: To the remaining 20 ml of the solution from the preceding test add 2 m of HCl and dilute to 50 ml. Add 50 mg of ammonium persulfate and 3 ml of ammonium thiocyanate, and mix. Any resulting red color is not darker than that of a blank to which 0.01 mg of Fe has been added.

SULFURIC ACID

H_2SO_4; mol. wt. 98.08; S—32.69%; SO_3—81.63%; SO_4—97.96.

Colorless, odorless, viscous liquid. Sp. gr. 1.84. Miscible with water or alcohol with evolution of much heat. *When diluting, the acid should always be added to the diluent and not the diluent to the acid.* Rapidly absorbs moisture from the air. *Keep protected from moisture and organic matter.*

Standards

Assay.......................min 95%	Permanganate-reducing substances
Nonvolatile...............max 0.0005%	(as SO_2)...........max about 0.0003%
Chloride (Cl)..............max 0.00002%	Ammonia (NH_3)............max 0.0002%
Nitrate (No₃)...............to pass test	Arsenic (As)...............max 0.01 ppm
(max about 0.00005%)	Heavy metals (as Pb).......max 0.0001%
	Iron (Fe)................max 0.00002%

Assay: Weigh a glass-stoppered flask, quickly add about 1 ml of sample, stopper immediately, and reweigh. Add 50 ml of H_2O and titrate with 1 N NaOH, using methyl orange as indicator. One ml of 1 N NaOH = 0.04904 g H_2SO_4, log 69055.

Nonvolatile: Evaporate 55 ml (100 g) to dryness in a platinum dish and ignite at cherry redness for 5 minutes. Not more than 0.5 mg of residue remains (retain residue).

Chloride: Add 14 ml (25 g) of the acid to 40 ml of water, cool, add 1 ml of nitric acid and 1 ml of silver nitrate. Any turbidity produced is not greater than that in the blank to which 0.005 mg of Cl has been added.

Nitrate: Dissolve 3 to 5 mg of diphenylbenzidine in a mixture of 2 ml of the acid and 1 ml of water, then add 5 ml of the acid and mix gently. No blue coloration is produced in 10 minutes.

Permanganate-reducing substances: Add 30 ml (55 g) of the acid to 60 ml of ice-cold water, cool to 25°, and add 0.05 ml of 0.1 N potassium permanganate. The mixture remains pink for 5 minutes.

Ammonia: Add 2.8 ml of the acid (5 g) to 50 ml of cold water contained in a flask suitable for ammonia distillation, cool in ice, and slowly add 30 ml of 10% NaOH. Cool, add 25 ml more of the NaOH and distill about 40 ml into 5 ml of water containing 1 drop of dilute HCl. Add to the distillate 1 ml of 10% NaOH and 2 ml of Nessler solution. Any color produced is not darker than that produced by treating 0.01 mg of NH_3 (0.03 mg of NH_4Cl) in the same manner as the sample.

Arsenic: Cautiously add 3 ml of nitric acid to 110 ml (200 g of the acid in a beaker and evaporate to 10 ml. Cool, cautiously dilute with 20 ml of water, and re-evaporate to strong sulfuric fumes and until the volume has been reduced to 5 ml. Cool, dilute with 15 ml of water, and test by method on page 563. The stain is not greater than that from 0.002 mg of As.

Heavy metals: Add 11 m of the acid (20 g) to 10 mg of sodium carbonate dissolved in a few drops of water and evaporate over a free flame nearly to dryness. Add 1 ml of HNO_3 and evaporate on the steam bath. Add to the residue 20 ml of hot water and 2 drops of phenolphthalein, neutralize with 1 N NaOH, add 1 ml of 1 N acetic acid, and dilute to 40 ml. Prepare a control with 0.02 mg of Pb, 1 ml of 1 N acetic acid in a volume of 40 ml. Then add to each 10 ml of H_2S. Any color in the solution of the sample is not darker than that of the control.

Iron: To the residue from the test for *Nonvolatile* add 2 ml of H_2O and 3 ml of HCl and slowly evaporate on the steam bath. Add to the residue 5 ml of HCl and 25 ml of water, filter, if necessary, and dilute to 150 ml. To 50 ml add 30 mg of ammonium persulfate and 3 ml of ammonium thiocyanate solution. Any red color is not darker than that of a control made with 0.01 mg of Fe, 2 ml of HCl, and in the same final volume as with the sample.

SULFURIC ACID, FUMING

$H_2SO_4 + xSO_3$.

Colorless, or only slightly colored, viscous liquid, emitting choking fumes of SO_3. Sp. gr. of the 20% acid is about 1.9. *Handle with great caution! Keep in tightly closed, glass-stoppered bottles protected from moisture and organic matter.*

Standards

Assay (free SO_3)	Nitrogen compounds
within 2% ± of claimed %	$(NH_3, NO_3$ as N) . . . . max 0.0005%
Nonvolatile . . . . max 0.002%	Arsenic (As) . . . . max 0.03 ppm
	Iron (Fe) . . . . max 0.0002%

Assay: Quickly transfer about 1 ml of the acid into a small, tared, glass-stoppered weighing bottle, stopper immediately, and reweigh. Cautiously loosen the stopper and place the weighing bottle and stopper in 100 to 120 ml CO_2-free water contained in a casserole or beaker of suitable capacity. Swirl the beaker until the acid is dispersed through the liquid, add 2 to 3 drops of methyl orange and titrate with 1 N NaOH to a yellow color. Each ml of 1 N sodium hydroxide consumed in excess of 20.39 ml per 1 g of the acid represents 21.45% of "free" SO_3.

Nonvolatile: Evaporate 13 ml (25 g) of the acid in a platinum dish to dryness and ignite at cherry redness for 5 minutes. Not more than 0.5 mg of residue remains (retain residue).

Nitrogen compounds: Add 1.0 ml (2 g) of the acid to 50 ml of water contained in a flask suitable for ammonia distillation. Cool in ice and slowly add 15 ml of 10% NaOH. Add 1 g of powdered Devarda metal or 0.5 g of fine aluminum wire in small pieces, cool, add 10 ml more of the NaOH, and allow to stand, protected from access of NH_3, for 2 hours. Distill about 40 ml into 5 ml of water containing 1 drop of diluted hydrochloric acid. Add to the distillate 1 ml of 10% NaOH and 2 ml of Nessler solution. Any color produced is not darker than that produced by treating 0.01 mg of N (0.04 mg of NH_4Cl) in the same manner as the sample.

Arsenic: Cautiously add 3 ml of HNO_3 to 37 ml (70 g) of the acid and evaporate to about 10 ml. Cool, cautiously dilute with 20 ml of water, and evaporate to strong acid fumes until the volume is reduced to about 5 ml. Cool, dilute with 20 ml of water, and determine the arsenic by the method on page 563. The stain is not greater than that from 0.002 mg of As.

Iron: To the residue from the test for *Nonvolatile* add 3 ml of HCl and 2 ml of H_2O and slowly evaporate to dryness on the steam bath. Take up with 2 ml of HCl and water and dilute to 100 ml. To 20 ml add 2 ml of HCl, dilute to 50 ml, and add 30 mg of ammonium persulfate and 3 ml of ammonium thiocyanate. Any resulting red color is not darker than that of a blank to which 0.01 mg of Fe has been added.

SULFUROUS ACID

A 6% solution of SO_2 in water; mol. wt. of SO_2 = 64.07; S—50.05%.

Colorless, clear liquid; suffocating odor. Miscible with water. Loses strength on keeping, due to oxidation. Sp. gr. about 1.03. *Keep in well-closed containers.*

Standards

Assay . . . . min 6.0% SO_2	Arsenic (As) . . . . max 0.3 ppm
Nonvolatile . . . . max 0.005%	Heavy metals (as Pb) . . . . max 0.0002%
Chloride (Cl) . . . . max 0.0003%	Iron (Fe) . . . . max 0.0005%

Assay: Weigh a glass-stoppered flask containing 50 ml of 0.1 N iodine, quickly add 2 ml of the sample, stopper, and reweigh. Then titrate the excess iodine with 0.1 N thiosulfate. One ml of 0.1 N iodine = 0.003203 g SO_2, log 50556.

Nonvolatile: Evaporate 20 ml to dryness and ignite for 5 minutes. Not more than 1.0 mg of residue remains.

Chloride: Digest 10 ml with 2 ml of 30% hydrogen peroxide in a small flask on the steam bath for 1 hour, cool, and dilute to 30 ml. To 20 ml add 1 ml of nitric acid and 1 ml of $AgNO_3$. Any turbidity produced is not more than that in a blank with 0.02 mg of Cl added.

Arsenic: Evaporate 7 ml with 0.5 ml of H_2SO_4 on the steam bath to about 1 ml, dilute to 5 ml, and test by method on page 563. The stain produced is not more than that from 0.002 mg of As.

Heavy metals: Dilute 10 ml with 15 ml of H_2O and boil to remove SO_2. Neutralize with dilute NaOH, add 2 ml of 1 N acetic acid, dilute to 40 ml and add 10 ml of H_2S. Any darkening produced is not more than that in a control made with 0.02 mg of Pb, 2 ml of 1 N acetic acid, and 10 ml of H_2S in the same volume as with the sample.

Iron: Evaporate 2 ml of the acid in glass or porcelain to dryness on the steam bath. Add to the residue 1 ml of HCl and 5 drops of HNO_3 and re-evaporate on the steam bath to dryness. Take up with 2 ml of HCl and dilute to 50 ml. Add 50 mg of ammonium persulfate and 3 ml of ammonium thiocyanate, and mix. Any resulting red color is not darker than that of a blank to which 0.01 mg of Fe has been added.

TANNIC ACID

Gallotannic Acid; Tannin

$C_{14}H_{10}O_9 + xH_2O$; mol. wt. of anhydrous acid = 322.

Yellowish to brownish powder. Soluble in 1 part of water or alcohol; soluble in acetone; almost insoluble in chloroform or ether. *Keep protected from light.*

Standards

Solubility in H_2O............to pass test	Sugar; Dextrin...............no reaction
Ignition residue...............max 0.10%	Drying loss..................max 12.0%
Heavy metals (as Pb)........max 0.002%	

Solubility in water: A solution of 2 g in 10 ml of warm water is clear or practically so.

Ignition residue: Thoroughly char 1 g of sample, cool, add 1 ml of H_2SO_4, and ignite to constant weight. Not more than 1.0 mg of residue remains.

Heavy metals: Evaporate the residue from the preceding test with 2 ml of HCl and 0.5 ml of HNO_3 to dryness on the steam bath. Take up with 2 ml of 0.1 N HCl and 40 ml of H_2O, and add 10 ml of H_2S. Any color produced is not darker than that of a control made with 0.02 mg of Pb; 2 ml of 0.1 N HCl and 10 ml of H_2S in the same volume as with the sample.

Sugar; Dextrin: Dissolve 2 g in 10 ml of water and add 10 ml of alcohol. The solution remains clear for 1 hour, and the subsequent addition of 5 ml of ether causes no turbidity.

Drying loss: Dry 1 g to constant weight at 105°. The loss in weight corresponds to not more than 12.0 %.

Note: The water content of tannic acid may be determined by the iodine (Fischer) method.

TARTARIC ACID

$$HOOC \cdot \underset{\underset{H}{|}}{\overset{\overset{OH}{|}}{C}} \text{——} \underset{\underset{OH}{|}}{\overset{\overset{H}{|}}{C}} \cdot COOH; \text{ mol. wt. } 150.09.$$

Colorless crystals or white powder. Soluble in 1 part of water; 5 parts of alcohol.

Standards

Insoluble....................max 0.005%	Phosphate (PO_4)............max 0.001%
Ignition residue.............max 0.020%	Sulfate (SO_4)................max 0.005%
Chloride (Cl).....................0.000%	Heavy metals (as Pb).......max 0.0005%
Oxalate (C_2O_4)...............to pass test	Iron (Fe)...................max 0.0005%
(limit about 0.1%)	*Assay*....................99.8%–100.3%

Insoluble: Dissolve 20 g in 100 ml of water and heat on the steam bath for 1 hour. Filter any undissolved matter, wash with H_2O, and dry at 105°. The weight of the insoluble residue does not exceed 1.0 mg.

Ignition residue: Place 5.0 g in a tared dish or crucible, and ignite slowly until it is well charred. Allow to cool, add 0.5 ml of H_2SO_4, heat to evaporate excess of H_2SO_4, then ignite strongly to constant weight. Any residue remaining does not exceed 1.0 mg.

Chloride: To a solution of 1 g in 20 ml of water add 1 ml of nitric acid and 1 ml of silver nitrate. No opalescence is reproduced.

Oxalate: Dissolve 5 g in 30 ml of water, neutralize one-half of the solution with NH_4OH, using litmus paper as indicator, then add the other half of the solution and sufficient H_2O to make 40 ml. Shake well, cool at about 15° for 15 minutes, and filter. To 20 ml of the filtrate add 20 ml of a saturated aqueous calcium sulfate solution. No turbidity or precipitate is produced in 2 hours.

Phosphate: Dissolve 2 g in 5 ml of H_2O in a platinum crucible, add 0.3 g of magnesium nitrate, evaporate, and ignite. Warm the residue with 2 ml of 25% H_2SO_4 and 5 ml of H_2O, then add 15 ml of H_2O, and filter. Add to filtrate 1 ml each of phosphate reagents **A** and **B** and heat at 60° for 5 minutes. Any blue color produced is not deeper than that of a blank to which 0.02 mg of PO_4 has been added.

Sulfate: Dissolve 2.5 g in 10 ml of H_2O and add 0.2 ml of 1 *N* HCl. Heat the solution to about 65°, add 2 ml of $BaCl_2$ solution and allow to stand for 15 minutes.

Any turbidity produced is not greater than that in a control made with 0.1 mg of SO_4 and 0.5 g of the tartaric acid.

Heavy metals: Dissolve 5 g in 30 ml of H_2O, add 3 drops of phenolphthalein and follow with 28% NH_3 until the solution is faintly pink. Cool, add 1 ml of 10% HCl and dilute with water to 50 ml. To 10 ml of the solution add 0.015 mg of Pb and dilute with H_2O to 40 ml (A). Then add 10 ml of H_2S to A, and to the remaining 40 ml of the solution (B). B is not darker than A.

Iron: Dissolve 2 g in 30 ml of H_2O, add 2 ml of HCl and about 30 mg ammonium persulfate and dilute to 50 ml. Add 3 ml of ammonium thiocyanate and mix. Any resulting red color is not darker than that of a blank to which 0.01 mg of Fe has been added.

Assay: The assay serves to establish the identity of the acid, thus eliminating confusion with other similar organic acids.

Dry about 3 g of the powdered acid for 3 hours over an efficient desiccant. Weigh accurately about 3 g of the dried reagent and dissolve it in 50 ml of water. Add 0.1 ml of phenolphthalein solution and titrate with 1 N NaOH. One ml of 1 N NaOH = 0.07505 g of $C_4H_4O_6$. One g (1.000) of the acid requires not less than 13.28 ml and not more than 13.38 ml of 1 N NaOH (theory 13.32).

TERTIARY BUTYL ALCOHOL

Tertiary Butanol

$(CH_3)_3COH$; mol. wt. 74.12.

Colorless crystals, liquid above 25.5°; camphoraceous odor. Sp. gr. 0.781 (25°/25°). Boils at 83°. Miscible with water and the usual organic solvents including benzene and carbon disulfide.

Standards

Boiling range. . . . . .82.5°–83.5°	Evaporation residue. . . . . .max 0.005%
Freezing temperature. . . . . . .not below 25°	Acid (as acetic). . . . . .max 0.003%
Miscibility with H_2O,CS_2. . . . . .to pass test	Alkalinity (as NH_3). . . . . .max 0.001%

Boiling range: Distill 50 ml. After the first 10 drops not less than 48 ml distills between 82.5° and 83.5°, correction being made for the barometric pressure (page 581).

Freezing temperature: Determine as described on page 581. It should not be below 25°.

Miscibility: Dilute 5-ml portions with 15 ml of water and with 15 ml of carbon disulfide and allow to stand for 30 minutes. The mixtures are as clear as the diluents.

Evaporation residue: Evaporate 25 ml of the steam bath and dry at 105° for 1 hour. The weight of the residue does not exceed 1.0 mg.

Acid: To 20 ml of water add 0.2 ml of phenolphthalein and 0.02 N NaOH until a slight pink color persists after shaking. Disregard the volume of the alkali so consumed. Now add 20 ml of the sample mix, and titrate with the 0.02 N NaOH until the pink color is restored. Not more than 0.4 ml of the NaOH is required.

Alkalinity: Dilute 10 ml with 20 ml of water and add 1 drop of methyl red. If the solution is yellow, not more than 0.25 ml of 0.02 N H_2SO_4 is required to change it to pink.

TETRAETHYLAMMONIUM HYDROXIDE

$(C_2H_5)_4N \cdot OH$; mol. wt. 147.26.

This base is known only in solution or as solid tetra- or hexahydrate. In commerce it is usually available as a 10% aqueous solution. This solution is clear, colorless and has a strong ammonia-like odor. Tetraethylammonium hydroxide is a strong base, absorbing CO_2 from the air. Sp. gr. of the 10% solution is about 1.01. *Keep in tightly closed containers.*

Standards

Assay............min 98% of labeled %	Evaporation residue..........max 0.02%
Other amines................to pass test	Heavy metals (as Pb).......max 0.0005%

Assay: Accurately weigh a glass-stoppered flask with about 15 ml of water. Add a quantity of the solution equivalent to about 0.3 g of $(C_2H_5)_4N \cdot OH$ and re-weigh. Titrate the solution with 0.1 N HCl, using methyl red indicator. One ml of 0.1 N acid = 0.01473 g of $(C_2H_5)_4N \cdot OH$, log 16820.

Other amines: Weigh accurately a quantity of the solution corresponding to about 0.5 g of the amine in a wide weighing bottle tared with 5 ml of water. Add a slight excess of 1 N HCl (about 5 ml), evaporate to dryness on the steam bath, and dry at 105° for 2 hours. The weight of the tetraethylammonium chloride so obtained multiplied by 0.8883 represents the quantity of $(CH_3)_4N \cdot OH$ in the weight of the sample taken for the test, and it corresponds to within 1% of that found in the assay, the percentage found in the assay representing 100%.

Evaporation residue: Evaporate 5 ml on the steam bath and dry at 105° for 1 hour. The weight of the residue does not exceed 1.0 mg.

Heavy metals: To the residue obtained in the test for *Evaporation residue* add 5 drops of HNO_3 and 1 ml of H_2O, and evaporate to dryness on the steam bath. Take up the residue with 1 ml of 1 N acetic acid and 5 ml of hot H_2O, dilute to 40 ml, and add 10 ml of H_2S. Any color produced is not darker than that of a control made with 0.025 mg of Pb, 1 ml of 1 N acetic acid and in the same final volume as with the sample.

TETRAHYDROFURAN

Tetramethylene Oxide

H$_2$C——CH$_2$
| |
H$_2$C   CH$_2$; mol. wt. 72.10.
\ /
O

Colorless liquid; characteristic, somewhat pungent odor; sp. gr. 0.885; boils at 66°. Miscible with water and the usual organic solvents, including petroleum ether and carbon disulfide.   When mixed with water $(1+1)$ some heat is generated and the volume contracts to the extent of about 7% of the tetrahydrofuran.   Considerable heat is generated when it is mixed with chloroform.

Tetrahydrofuran upon exposure to air is extremely prone to form peroxide, and is hence usually preserved with not over 0.1% of a suitable preservative. The name of the preservative and amount should be stated on the label.   *Keep in small, well-filled containers and protect from light.*

Standards

Specific gravity (25°/25°).....0.884–0.8860
Boiling range...................65°–66°
Evaporation residue,
    including preservative........max 0.1%

Acid.......................to pass test
Water.......................max 0.1%

Specific gravity: Determine with a suitable pycnometer at 25°/25°.

Boiling range: Distill 50 ml.   After the first 10 drops, not less than 49 ml distills between 65° and 66°, correction being made for barometric pressure.

Evaporation residue: Evaporate 12 ml (10 g) to dryness on the steam bath, and dry the residue at 105° for 1 hour.   The weight of the residue is not more than 2.0 mg if a preservative is present, but not more than 1.0 mg if no preservative is declared on the label.

Acid: Mix 5 ml of sample with 10 ml of water and add 1 drop of methyl red.   If a pink color is produced, not more than 0.05 ml of 0.1 N NaOH is required to change it to yellow.

Water: Determine by the iodine (Fischer) method.

TETRAMETHYLAMMONIUM HYDROXIDE

$(CH_3)_4N \cdot OH$; mol. wt. 91.15.

This base is known only in solution or as a solid pentahydrate.   In commerce it is usually available as a 10% aqueous solution.   This solution is clear, colorless and has a strong ammonia-like odor.   Tetramethylammonium hydroxide is a stronger base than ammonia and rapidly absorbs CO_2 from the air.   Sp. gr. of the 10% solution is about 1.00.   *Keep in tightly closed containers.*

Standards

Assay............min 98% of labeled %
Other amines................to pass test

Evaporation residue.........max 0.02%
Heavy metals (as Pb).......max 0.0005%

Assay: Accurately weigh a glass-stoppered flask with about 15 ml of water. Add a quantity of the solution equivalent to about 0.2 g of $(CH_3)_4N \cdot OH$, and reweigh.   Titrate the solution with 0.1 N HCl, using methyl red indicator.   One ml of 0.1 N acid = 0.009115 g of $(CH_3)_4NO \cdot H$, log 95976.

Other amines: Weigh accurately a quantity of the solution corresponding to about 0.3 g of the amine in a wide weighing bottle tared with 5 ml of water.   Add a slight excess of 1 N HCl (about 4 ml), evaporate to dryness on the steam bath, and dry at 105° for 2 hours. The weight of the tetramethylammonium chloride so obtained multiplied by 0.8317 represents the quantity of $(CH_3)_4N \cdot OH$ in the weight of the sample taken for the test, and it corresponds to within 1% of that found in the assay; the percentage found in the assay representing 100%.

Evaporation residue: Evaporate 5 ml to dryness on the steam bath and dry at 105° for 1 hour. The weight of the residue does not exceed 1.0 mg.

Heavy metals: To the residue obtained in the test for *Evaporation residue* add 5 drops of HNO_3 and 1 ml of water, and evaporate to dryness on the steam bath. Take up the residue with 1 ml of 1 N acetic acid and 5 ml of hot H_2O, dilute to 40 ml and add 10 ml of H_2S. Any color produced is not darker than that of a control made with 0.025 mg of Pb, and 1 ml of 1 N acetic acid and in the same final volume as with the sample.

THALLIUM NITRATE

Thallous Nitrate

$TlNO_3$; mol. wt. 266.40; Tl—76.72%; NO_3—23.28%.

White or colorless crystals. Soluble in about 10 parts of water; insoluble in alcohol. *Poisonous.*

It is useful for the determination of iodide in the presence of chloride or bromide, thallium iodide being practically insoluble in water.

Standards

Solubility....................to pass test	Alkalies, Earths, etc.
Chloride.....................to pass test	(as sulfates)...............max 0.20%
Sulfate......................to pass test	Iron (Fe)...................max 0.002%
Ammonium hydroxide	Other metals (as Pb).........max 0.005%
precipitate................to pass test	

Solubility: Dissolve 2 g in 50 ml of warm water and cool. No insoluble matter remains and the solution is clear. Retain the solution as *Solution S.*

Chloride: Dilute 5 ml of *Solution S* to 10 ml, add 0.5 ml of HNO_3 and 1 ml of $AgNO_3$ solution. No turbidity is produced in 2 minutes.

Sulfate: To 5 ml of *Solution S* add 2 drops of acetic acid and 5 drops of 5% barium nitrate solution. No turbidity is produced in 10 minutes.

Ammonium hydroxide precipitate: Heat 25 ml of *Solution S* to boiling and add 5 drops of NH_4OH. No turbidity is produced.

Alkalies, Earths, etc.: Dilute the solution from the preceding test to 90 ml add 1 ml of NH_4OH, and completely precipitate with H_2S. Dilute to 100 ml, mix, and filter without washing. Evaporate 50 ml of the filtrate to a few ml, add 5 drops of H_2SO_4, and ignite. The weight of the ignited residue does not exceed 1.0 mg.

Iron: Dissolve 0.5 g in 15 ml of water and add 1 ml of HCl. Filter off the precipitate of thallium chloride and wash it with a few ml of water. Add to the filtrate 15 ml of butanolic potassium thiocyanate, shake well, and allow to separate. Any red color in the butanol layer is not darker than that of a blank to which 0.01 mg of Fe has been added.

Other metals: Dissolve 1 g in water to make 40 ml. To 10 ml of the solution add 0.025 mg of Pb and 2.0 ml of 1 N acetic acid and dilute to 40 ml (A). To the remaining 30 ml add 2.0 ml of 1 N acetic acid and dilute to 40 ml (B). Then to each add 10 ml of H_2S. B is not darker than A.

THIAMINE HYDROCHLORIDE

Vitamin B_1 Hydrochloride; Aneurin Hydrochloride

$C_{12}H_{17}ClN_4OS \cdot HCl$;
mol. wt. 337.28;
Cl (Total)—21.03%;
N—16.61%; S—9.51%.

Small, colorless or white crystals. Odorless, but with age a slight thiazole (sulfidic) odor develops. It is chemically quite stable in air, but the anhydrous product on exposure to air absorbs the equivalent of about 1 mol of H_2O (about 4%). The pH of its H_2O solution is 3. It is not affected by dilute acids, but at pH above 5.5, and especially in alkaline solutions, it is attacked by air or mild oxidizing agents. Soluble in 1 part of water, 80 parts of alcohol; insoluble in ether or chloroform.

Standards

Melting range	246°–249°	Drying loss	max 5.0%
Chloride (Cl), total	21.0% ± 0.4%	Color of solution	to pass test
Sulfur (S)	9.50% ± 0.30%	Ignition residue	max 0.03%
pH	2.7–3.4	Heavy metals (as Pb)	max 0.002%

Melting range: Dry at 105° for 2 hours, then determine the melting range, preheating the bath to 230°.

Chloride, total: Accurately weigh about 0.2 g of the sample, previously dried at 105° to constant weight, and dissolve it in 50 ml of water. Add to the solution 5 ml of 10% HNO_3 and exactly 20 ml of 0.1 N $AgNO_3$. Allow to stand, protected from light for 1 to 2 hours, then filter and wash the precipitate with several 5-ml portions of water. Determine in the combined filtrate and washings the excess of $AgNO_3$ by titration with 0.1 N ammonium thiocyanate using ferric ammonium sulfate or ferric nitrate as indicator. The volume of 0.1 N $AgNO_3$ consumed for the precipitation of the Cl in the sample multiplied by 0.003546 g represents the total Cl.

Sulfur: Using about 0.2 g of the previously dried (at 105°) and accurately weighed sample, determine the sulfur (S) by the Parr bomb method, page 578.

pH: The pH of thiamine hydrochloride determined in a 5% solution is 2.7 to 3.3.

Drying loss: Dry about 1 g accurately weighed at 105° to constant weight. The loss in weight does not exceed 5%.

Color of solution: A solution of 1.0 g in 10 ml of water is colorless.

Ignition residue: Thoroughly char 3.0 g.   Cool, then add 0.5 ml of H_2SO_4 and ignite at first gently to evaporate the acid, then strongly to constant weight. Not more than 1.0 mg of residue remains.

Heavy metals: To the *Ignition residue* add 2 ml of HNO_3 and evaporate on the steam bath.   Add to the residue 5 ml of 10% ammonium acetate solution and 2 ml of 10% NH_3, cover and digest on the steam bath for 20 minutes.   Neutralize to litmus paper with acetic acid, add a few drops excess, and dilute to 40 ml.   Dilute 20 ml of the solution to 40 ml and add 10 ml of H_2S.   Any color produced is not darker than that of a control made with 0.03 mg of Pb, half the quantities of ammonium acetate solution and 10% NH_3, and treated in the same manner as the sample.

THIAZOLE YELLOW

Clayton Yellow; Titan Yellow

; mol wt. 695.73; N—10.07; S—18.44%.

Yellowish-brown powder.   Soluble in water or in alcohol.   Dilute aqueous solutions are used for colorimetric determination of magnesium.   *Keep protected from light.*

Standards

Sensitiveness..................to pass test   Ignition residue (Na_2SO_4)....19.8%–21.5%
Solubility....................to pass test

Sensitiveness: To 10 ml of H_2O containing 0.005 mg of Mg, add 0.2 ml of a 0.01% solution (10 mg in 100 ml) of thiazole yellow and 2 ml of 1 N NaOH.   A distinct pink color is produced in 5 to 10 minutes.

Solubility: A solution of 0.2 g in 50 ml of water is clear or practically so.

Ignition residue (Na_2SO_4): Dry about 1.5 g at 105° for 2 hours.   Weigh accurately the dried material into a tared porcelain crucible and ignite until thoroughly charred.   Allow to cool, add 2 ml each of HNO_3 and H_2SO_4 and ignite at first gently to expel excess of the acids, then strongly (600°–800°) to constant weight.   The residue of Na_2SO_4 so obtained amounts to not less than 19.8% and to not more than 21.5% (theory 20.4%).

THIOACETAMIDE

$CH_3 \cdot CS \cdot NH_2$; mol. wt. 75.14; N—18.64%; S—42.7%; H_2S—45.4%.

Colorless or white, slightly hygroscopic crystals; becomes slightly yellow on exposure to air.   When fresh, it is practically odorless, but after the container has been opened several times an odor of H_2S develops.   Freely soluble in water or alcohol, very slightly in benzene.

In aqueous solution and in the presence of hydrogen ions (acids) thiocetamide readily yields H_2S; $CH_3 \cdot CS \cdot NH_2 + H_2O \rightarrow H_2S + CH_3CONH_2$, and because of convenience in handling it may be preferred for many analytical operations where H_2S is required.

Thioacetamide in aqueous solution is quite stable even at moderately higher than room temperatures (50°–60°) but in presence of acid it rapidly hydrolyzes at room temperature.

Standards

Melting range..................107°–109°	Solubility....................to pass test
Assay........................min 99%	Ignition residue..............max 0.1%
Sensitiveness................to pass test	

Assay: (a) Place exactly 50 ml of 0.1 N iodine in a 250-ml glass-stoppered flask, add 10 ml of diluted HCl (1 + 2) and 10 ml of chloroform, stopper, and mix gently.   (b) Weigh accurately 0.5 to 0.55 g of the thioacetamide and dissolve in boiled out and cooled water to make 100.0 ml.

While rotating (a), add to it exactly 25 ml of (b), holding the tip of the pipette about 1 cm below the surface of the iodine solution.   Rinse the tip of the pipette with a few drops of water into the iodine solution, stopper, mix, and allow to stand for 10 minutes.   At the end of this period titrate the excess of iodine with 0.1 N thiosulfate to the disappearance of the iodine color from the chloroform.   Run a blank and make any necessary correction.   One ml of 0.1 N iodine = 0.003751 g CH_3CSNH_2, log 57415.

Sensitiveness: Dilute 0.1 ml of lead acetate solution to 25 ml, add 3 drops of acetic acid and mix.   Add to this mixture 0.05 ml of the aqeuous solution of the thioacetamide resulting from the test for *Solubility* and shake well.   A black color or precipitate is produced within 1 to 2 minutes.

Solubility: Solutions of 0.5-g portions in 5 ml of water and in 5 ml of alcohol are clear and complete.

Ignition residue: To 1.0 g add a few drops of H_2SO_4 and ignite to constant weight.   The weight of the residue does not exceed 1.0 mg.

THIOGLYCOLLIC ACID

$CH_2SHCOOH$; mol. wt. 92.11.

Colorless or nearly colorless liquid, with a strong, unpleasant odor.   Sp. gr. 1.32.   It is miscible with water and soluble in alcohol.   Boils at about 105° at 15 mm pressure.

Thioglycollic acid produces with iron, in strongly ammoniacal solution, a pink or a reddish-purple color, according to the amount of iron present.   It is sensitive to Fe in 1 part in 5 million parts of solution.

Standards

Assay...........min 88% CH$_2$SHCOOH	Solubility.....................to pass test
Sensitiveness.................to pass test	Ignition residue..............max 0.10%
Iron (Fe)....................to pass test	

Assay: (*a*) Dissolve about 0.3 g, accurately weighed, in 20 ml of water and titrate with 0.1 N sodium hydroxide, using solution of cresol red as indicator.   One ml of 0.1 N sodium hydroxide = 0.00921 g of C$_2$H$_4$O$_2$S.

(*b*) To the above neutralized solution 3 drops of HCl, dissolve in it 2 g of sodium bicarbonate and titrate with 0.1 N iodine using starch solution as indicator.   One ml of 0.1 N iodine = 0.00921 g of C$_2$H$_4$O$_2$S.

$$2HS \cdot CH_2COOH + 2I \rightarrow \begin{array}{l} S \cdot CH_2COH \\ | \\ S \cdot CH_2COOH \end{array} + 2HI$$

The purity found by (*b*) is the more correct.

Sensitiveness: Mix 1 ml of thioglycollic acid with 2 ml of ammonium hydroxide and dilute with water to 10 ml.   Add 0.5 ml of this solution to 20 ml of water containing 0.005 mg of Fe, mixed with 5 ml of ammonium hydroxide.   A distinct pinkish color should be produced.

Iron: Mix 0.1 ml with 20 ml of water and render strongly alkaline with ammonia.   No pink color is produced.

Solubility: One ml gives a clear and colorless solution with 5 ml of water and with 20 ml of alcohol.

Ignition residue: Ignite 1 g with 0.5 ml of H$_2$SO$_4$.   The residue does not exceed 1.0 mg.

THIONALIDE

Thioglycollic-β-aminonaphthalide

—NH·CO·CH$_2$SH; mol. wt. 217.28.

White to slightly cream-colored crystals or crystalline powder.   Insoluble in water; soluble in about 10 parts of alcohol; also soluble in glacial acetic acid and in most of the usual organic solvents.

This reagent, under suitable conditions, forms precipitates with many of the heavy metals, functioning essentially as hydrogen sulfide.   The precipitates are quite pure and of definite composition, the metal replacing the hydrogen of the SH-group.[1,2,3,4]

From acetic or mineral acid solutions thionalide precipitates Ag, Au, As, Bi, Cu, Hg, Pd, Pt, Sb, Sn; from acetic acid solutions, Cd, Co, Mn, Ni, Pb, Tl.

Standards

Melting range.................110°–112°	Solubility in acetic acid.......to pass test
Sensitiveness................to pass test	Ignition residue.............max 0.10%

Sensitiveness: (a) Dissolve 50 mg of the reagent in 10 ml of glacial acetic acid.

(b) Dilute 1.0 ml of standard antimony solution to 100 ml. To 1 ml of the dilution add 1 drop of 10% HCl, 0.2 ml of glacial acetic acid, and 0.1 ml of (a). A distinct white turbidity is produced.

Dilute 1.0 ml of standard copper solution to 25 ml. To 1 ml of the dilution add 2 drops of 10% HCl, 0.2 ml of glacial acetic acid and 0.2 ml of (a). A yellowish precipitate is formed.

Solubility in acetic acid: A solution of 0.2 g in 5 ml of hot 50% acetic acid is clear.

Ignition residue: Char 1.0 g, cool, add 0.5 ml of H_2SO_4, and ignite to constant weight. The residue weighs not more than 1.0 mg.

[1] Berg, R., and Roebling, W., *Ber.* **68**, 403 (1935).
[2] Berg, R., and Fakrenkamp, E. S. Z., *Anal. Chem.* **112**, 161 (1938).
[3] Rogers, W. J., Beanush, F. E., and Russell, D. S., *Ind. Eng. Chem., Anal. Ed.* **12**, 561 (1940).
[4] Fiegl, F., and daSelva, C. P. J., *ibid.* **14**, 316 (1942).

THIOSEMICARBAZIDE

$NH_2CSNHNH_2$; mol. wt. 91.14; N—46.12%; S—35.18%.

White, crystalline powder. Soluble in water or in alcohol.

Standards

Melting range.................181°–184°	Ignition residue.............max 0.10%
Solubility...................to pass test	

Solubility: One g dissolves in 25 ml of warm water, giving a clear and colorless or practically colorless solution.

Ignition residue: Char 1 g, cool, then add 0.5 ml of H_2SO_4 and ignite to constant weight. The weight of the residue is not more than 1.0 mg.

THIOUREA

$(NH_2)_2CS$; mol. wt. 76.12; N—36.80%; S—42.12%.

White, odorless crystals or crystalline powder. Soluble in about 12 parts of water; soluble in alcohol; sparingly soluble in ether. It is an excellent reagent for detection and estimation of bismuth and some other metals, such as osmium and palladium.

With this reagent the presence of 1 part of bismuth in 100,000 parts of solution is readily detectable.

Standards

Melting range.................175°–179°   Solubility....................to pass test
Sensitiveness to bismuth.......to pass test   Ignition residue..............max 0.10%

Sensitiveness to bismuth: (a) Dissolve 0.23 g bismuth nitrate in 8 ml of HNO_3 and dilute with water to 200 ml. (b) Dissolve 0.1 g of sample in 10 ml of H_2O.

Dilute 0.2 ml of (a) (= 0.1 mg of Bi) with H_2O to 10 ml, and add 1 ml of (b). A distinct yellow color is produced at once.

Solubility: A solution of 1 g in 20 ml of water is complete, clear, and colorless.

Ignition residue: Char well 1.0 g. Allow to cool, add 0.5 ml of H_2SO_4 and ignite gently at first, then strongly (600°–800°) to constant weight. The weight of the residue, if any, does not exceed 1.0 mg.

THORIUM NITRATE

$Th(NO_3)_4 \cdot 4H_2O$; mol. wt. 552.15; anhydrous—86.95%; H_2O—13.05%; Th—42.03%; ThO_2—47.83%. It may contain less than 4 mols of water.

Colorless or white crystals. Slightly deliquescent. Very soluble in water, the solution having a strong acid reaction.

Standards

Solubility....................to pass test   Heavy metals (as Pb)........max 0.002%
Chloride (Cl)................max 0.002%   Iron (Fe)...................max 0.003%
Sulfate (SO$_4$)...............max 0.005%   Titanium....................to pass test
Alkali and Earths (as Sulfates).max 0.20%   (max about 0.01%)
Aluminum (Al), etc...........to pass test   *Assay*
          (max about 0.2% as Al)

Solubility: Two grams dissolve completely in 20 ml of water.

Chloride: Dissolve 1 g in 20 ml of water, add 1 ml of HNO_3 and 1 ml of $AgNO_3$. Any resulting turbidity is not greater than that in a blank to which 0.02 mg of Cl has been added.

Sulfate: Dissolve 2 g in a few ml of water, add 5 ml of HCl, and evaporate to dryness on the steam bath. Re-evaporate with 5 ml of HCl. Dissolve the residue in 100 ml of H_2O, heat the solution to boiling, add 20 ml of a hot 10% aqueous solution of oxalic acid. Cool, filter, and wash with water to 150 ml. To 75 ml of the filtrate add 1 ml of hydrochloric acid, heat to boiling, add 5 ml of barium chloride, and allow to stand overnight. Filter any precipitate present, wash it with hot water, and ignite. The weight of the ignited precipitate ($BaSO_4$) does not exceed 1.3 mg.

Alkali and Earths: Dissolve 2 g in 100 ml of water, add a slight excess of NH_4OH, boil to remove free NH_3, dilute to 100 ml, and filter. To 50 ml of the filtrate add 5 drops of H_2SO_4, evaporate, and ignite. The weight of the residue does not exceed 2.0 mg.

Aluminum: To 50 ml of the filtrate from the precipitated oxalate in the test for *Sulfate* add a slight excess of NH_4OH and heat to boiling. No precipitate is formed.

Heavy metals: Dissolve 2 g in water to make 40 ml. To 10 ml add 0.02 mg of Pb and a solution of 0.5 g of sodium acetate in 20 ml of water, and dilute to 40 ml (*A*). To the remaining 30 ml add a solution of 0.5 g of sodium acetate in 10 ml of water (*B*). Then dilute both to the same volume and add to each 10 ml of H_2S. *B* is not darker than *A*.

Iron: Dissolve 1 g in 15 ml of H_2O, add 0.5 ml of HCl and 10 ml of butanolic potassium thiocyanate, shake vigorously for 30 seconds, and allow to separate. Any red color in the clear butanol layer is not darker than that of a blank to which 0.03 mg of Fe has been added.

Titanium: To 10 ml of a 5% solution of the thorium nitrate in water add 0.5 ml of 30% hydrogen peroxide. No yellow color is produced.

Assay: Weigh accurately about 1.0 g, dissolve it in 100 ml of H_2O, and add 2 ml of 10% H_2SO_4. Heat the solution to boiling and add 20 ml of hot 10% solution of oxalic acid. Cool, filter, wash with a little water and ignite to constant weight. The weight of the thorium oxide multiplied by 1.818 = $Th(NO_3)_4$, log 25959, or, multiplied by 2.090 = $Th(NO_3)_4 \cdot 4H_2O$.

THYMOL

Methyl *iso*-propylphenol

OH

$(CH_3)_2CH$⟨⟩CH_3; mol. wt. 150.21.

Colorless, usually large, crystals; characteristic odor. Almost insoluble in water; soluble in 1 part of alcohol or chloroform, or 1.5 parts of ether; also soluble in glacial acetic acid and in moderately concentrated aqueous solutions of fixed alkali hydroxides.

Standards

Melting range....................49°–51°	Solubility in alcohol
Evaporation residue.........max 0.030%	or ether...................to pass test

Evaporation residue: Volatilize 5 g on the steam bath. Not more than 1.5 mg of residue remains.

Solubility in alcohol or ether: Two grams dissolve completely in 20 ml of alcohol or ether and the solutions are colorless.

THYMOL BLUE

Thymolsulfonphthalein

$(C_{10}H_{13}O)_2 : C \cdot C_6H_4 \cdot O \cdot SO_2$; mol. wt. 466.58.

Brownish-green, crystalline powder. Slightly soluble in water; soluble in alcohol and in dilute alkali solutions. Its pH color changes are: acid, 1.2 red, 2.8 yellow; alkaline, 8 yellow, 9.4 blue.

Standards

Solubility in alcohol..........to pass test	pH range
Sensitiveness................to pass test	Acid: 1.2 red; 2.8 yellow
Ignition residue.............max 0.10%	Alkaline: 8.0 yellow; 9.4 blue

Solubility in alcohol: One-tenth gram dissolves completely in 100 ml of alcohol, yielding a clear solution.

Sensitiveness: To 100 ml of CO_2-free water add 0.3 ml of the solution from the test for Solubility. The water should become yellow with not more than a slight hue of green (pH 6). Now titrate with 0.01 N NaOH. When 0.3 to 0.5 ml of the NaOH has been added the color should be blue.

Ignition residue: Char 1.0 g, cool, add 0.5 ml of H_2SO_4, evaporate the acid and ignite to constant weight. The residue is not more than 1.0 mg.

pH—Acid range: To 25 ml each of pH buffer solutions (page 584) pH 1.2 (a) and 2.8 (b) add 0.3 ml of the solution from the test for Solubility in alcohol: (a) is red; (b) is yellow.

pH—Alkaline range: To 25 ml each of pH buffer solutions pH 8.0 (c) and 9.4 (d) add 0.3 ml of the solution from the test for Solubility in alcohol. (c) becomes yellow and (d) becomes blue-green.

THYMOLPHTHALEIN

$C_6H_4COOC[C_6H_2$-2-CH_3-4-OH—5CH$(CH_3)_2]_2$; mol. wt. 430.52.

White or slightly yellow, crystalline powder. Insoluble in water; freely soluble in alcohol; also soluble in acetone and dilute solutions of alkali hydroxides. pH range: 8.8 colorless; 10.2 blue.

Standards

Melting range................251°–254°	Solubility in NaOH solution...to pass test
Sensitiveness................to pass test	Ignition residue.............max 0.10%
Solubility in alcohol..........to pass test	

Sensitiveness: To 100 ml of CO_2-free water and 0.3 ml of the solution from the test for Solubility in alcohol. The water remains colorless. On the subsequent addition of 0.5 ml of 0.01 N NaOH the water becomes light blue (pH about 9), and it becomes intensely blue on the further addition of 0.3 ml of the NaOH (pH-10).

Solubility in alcohol: A solution of 0.1 g in 10 ml of alcohol is clear and colorless.

Solubility in NaOH solution: Dissolve 0.1 g in 10 ml of 0.1 N sodium hydroxide and dilute with water to 50 ml. The solution is clear.

Ignition residue: Char 10 g, cool, add 0.5 ml of H_2SO_4, and ignite to constant weight. Any residue does not exceed 1.0 mg.

TIN

Sn; at. wt. 118.70.

Soft, almost silver white; in the form of granules, irregular thin pieces, or rods. Melts at about 232°. Very slowly soluble in cold hydrochloric acid but readily soluble in the hot acid; also soluble in boiling sulfuric acid. Nitric acid converts it into insoluble metastannic acid.

Standards

Antimony (Sb)..............max 0.010%	Lead (Pb)..................max 0.020%
Arsenic (As).................max 1 ppm	Copper (Cu)................max 0.004%
Total foreign metals..........max 0.10%	Iron (Fe)...................max 0.005%
(as oxides)	

Antimony: Place 1 g of sample in a small beaker. Add 5 ml of water and 15 ml of aqua regia (made by mixing 18 ml of HNO_3 with 82 ml of HCl), cover with a watch glass, and warm until the metal is dissolved, adding more of the aqua regia if necessary. Evaporate on the steam bath or boil down to about 3 ml. Cool, add 5 ml of water, and 1 g of urea and dilute to 50 ml. Transfer 5 ml of the solution to a small separatory funnel and add 3 ml of HCl.

In a similar separatory funnel place a volume of standard antimony solution corresponding to 0.01 mg of Sb, and dilute to 5 ml. Add 3 ml of HCl and 3 drops of 10% sodium nitrite solution, mix, heat at 50°–60° for 1–2 minutes, and cool. Then treat each of the solutions as follows:

Add 5 ml of a solution of 10 mg of rhodamine B in 100 ml of H_2O and 15 ml of toluene. Shake well for about 1 minute, allow to separate, draw off and discard the aqueous (lower) layer. Shake the toluene layer with 5 ml of 10% HCl, allow to separate and discard the aqueous layer. Add to the toluene about 0.5 g of granular anhydrous sodium sulfate (sodium sulfate for drying of liquids) and shake until the liquid is clear (about 1 minute). Pour off the toluene into a graduated cylinder, wash the funnel and the sodium sulfate with 5 ml of toluene, add the washing to the cylinder, then add sufficient toluene to measure 25 ml, and mix. The red color in the cylinder with the sample is not darker than that with the antimony standard.

Solution S: To 15 g of the tin in small pieces add 20 ml of H_2O and 60 ml of HNO_3 and digest on the steam bath with frequent stirring until the metal is completely oxidized; then evaporate to dryness. Add to the residue 7 ml of HNO_3 and 75 ml of water and heat on steam bath for 15 minutes. Filter, wash with a few ml of water, and dilute filtrate to 150 ml.

Arsenic: To 20 ml of *Solution S* add 3 ml of H_2SO_4 and evaporate to copious sulfuric fumes. Cool, cautiously add 10 ml of water and re-evaporate to evolution of copious sulfuric fumes. Determine the arsenic in the residual liquid by the method on page 563. The stain is not greater than that obtained from 0.002 mg of As.

Total foreign metals: Evaporate 20 ml of *Solution S* to dryness and ignite to constant weight. Not more than 2.0 mg of residue remains.

Lead: To 50 ml of *Solution S* add 2 ml of H_2SO_4 and carefully evaporate to sulfuric fumes. Cool, cautiously add 10 ml of water and 5 ml of alcohol, and allow to stand for 1 hour. If a precipitate is present, filter on asbestos in a Gooch crucible, wash with a few ml of 10% H_2SO_4, and ignite. The weight of the precipitate ($PbSO_4$) does not exceed 1.5 mg.

Copper: Dilute the filtrate from the lead sulfate in the preceding test with an equal volume of water and pass in H_2S. If a dark precipitate is formed, filter (retain filtrate), wash with a few ml of hydrogen sulfide water, and ignite the precipitate. Cool, add 1 ml of HCl and 0.5 ml of HNO_3, and evaporate to dryness on the steam bath. Warm the residue with 1 ml of glacial acetic acid and add sufficient water to make 100 ml. To 10 ml add 1 g of ammonium acetate, 1 ml of glacial acetic acid, 0.3 ml of pyridine, 1 ml of ammonium thiocyanate, and 5 ml of chloroform, shake vigorously, and allow to separate. Any color produced in the chloroform does not exceed that produced by 0.02 mg of Cu in 10 ml of water treated in the same manner as the sample beginning with "add 1 g ammonium acetate...."

Iron: Boil the filtrate from the preceding test to expel the hydrogen sulfide. Add a few drops of bromine water, boil again to expel excess bromine, cool, and dilute with H_2O to 250 ml. To 20 ml add 2 ml HCl, dilute to 50 ml, add 50 mg of ammonium persulfate and 3 ml of ammonium thiocyanate, and mix. Any resulting red color is not darker than that of a blank to which 0.02 mg of Fe has been added.

TITANIUM DIOXIDE

TiO_2; mol. wt. 79.90; Ti—59.95%.

White, amorphous. Insoluble in water, HCl, HNO_3 or dilute H_2SO_4. Dissolves in HF acid, and in concentrated H_2SO_4. After having been heated at 500° or over it is difficultly soluble in sulfuric acid. It is converted to the sulfate by heating with potassium bi- or pyrosulfate. Fusion with alkali hydroxides or carbonates yields water-soluble titanates.

Standards

Drying loss (at 110°)...........max 0.5%	Sulfate (SO_4)................max 0.01%
Ignition loss.................max 0.5%	Heavy metals (as Pb)........max 0.003%
Assay, dried basis.............min 99%	Iron (Fe)....................max 0.02%
Dilute HCl—soluble...........max 0.3%	H_2SO_4—insoluble (SiO_2)........max 0.1%
Phosphate (PO_4).............max 0.02%	

Drying loss: Accurately weigh about 2 g of sample and dry at 110° to constant weight. Any loss in weight amounts to not more than 0.5%.

Ignition loss: Weigh accurately about 1 g of the dried TiO_2 obtained in the preceding test and ignite it at 700°–800° to constant weight. The loss in weight, if any, amounts to not more than 0.5%.

Assay: Weigh accurately 350–400 mg of the dried (not the ignited) sample obtained in the test for *Drying loss* and transfer it completely into a 250-ml beaker. Add 1 ml of water, then add with stirring 20 ml of H_2SO_4 and 7–8 g of ammonium sulfate. Mix well and heat on a hot plate to evolution of sulfuric fumes. Raise the temperature and continue heating until solution of sample is complete, or if undissolved matter is present it is apparent that no more will dissolve on further heating.   Cool well and cautiously pour the contents of the beaker into 100 ml of cold water, rinsing out the beaker well with 25 ml of water into the main solution. Heat the final solution carefully to boiling while stirring; then allow to settle. Filter, if necessary, on a fritted glass crucible and wash the beaker and crucible thoroughly with 10% H_2SO_4.   Dilute the combined filtrates to 150 ml and add *slowly* 6–8 ml of NH_4OH with continuous stirring to reduce the acidity of the solution to about 7% free H_2SO_4.

Place a pledget of glass wool at the bottom of a 25-cm Jones reductor tube and fill the tube with amalgamated zinc to the reservoir.   Wash the amalgamated zinc with several 100-ml portions of 10% H_2SO_4 until 100 ml of the washing does not decolorize 1 drop (0.05 ml) of 0.1 N potassium permanganate.

Place 50 ml of ferric ammonium sulfate solution in a 500-ml suction flask and add to it dropwise 0.1 N $KMnO_4$ until a slight pink color persists for 5 minutes. Attach the reductor tube to the neck of the suction flask, turn on a moderate vacuum, and pass 50 ml of 10% H_2SO_4 through the reductor at the rate of about 30 ml per minute, regulating the rate by means of the vacuum.   Now pass the titanium solution at the same rate and follow with 100 ml of 10% H_2SO_4 and then with 100 ml of water.   During these operations the reductor tube should be kept filled with the solution or with water above the upper level of the amalgamated zinc.   Gradually release the suction, wash down the outlet tube of the reductor and the sides of the receiving flask, and immediately titrate the Fe^{II} formed with 0.1 N potassium permanganate to a slight pink color persisting for 2 minutes.   Correct for any permanganate consumed by a blank of 200 ml of the same lot of 10% H_2SO_4.   One ml of 0.1 N $KMnO_4$ = 0.00799 g of TiO_2, log

$$2Ti^{IV} + Zn \rightarrow 2Ti^{III} + Zn^{II}; \qquad Ti^{III} + Fe^{III} \rightarrow Ti^{IV} + Fe^{II}$$

Dilute HCl (and water)—soluble: Suspend 4 g in 90 ml of water.   Add with stirring 10 ml of HCl, cover and heat on the steam bath for 30 minutes with occasional stirring.   Filter on a Gooch crucible having a mat of 2 layers: first of medium coarse, acid-washed asbestos, then a layer of *fine* acid-washed asbestos. If the filtrate is not clear, refilter.   The filtration may be facilitated by adding 1 or 2 g of HCl washed fine asbestos and centrifuging for 30 minutes, or decanting the clear liquid and filtering the residual matter.   Wash 3 times with 10-ml portions of diluted HCl (1+9). Evaporate the filtrate and wash to dryness on a steam bath and dry at 150° for 2 hours.   Any residue remaining does not exceed 12.0 mg (retain).

Solution R: Add to the residue obtained in the test for *Dilute HCl soluble* 2 ml of 1 N HCl, swirl to moisten the residue and heat on the steam bath for 2–3 minutes.   Add 25 ml of hot water, digest for 10 minutes, then dilute to 200 ml and mix.

Phosphate: To 5.0 ml of *Solution R* add 1 ml of HNO_3 and evaporate to dryness on the steam.   Dissolve the residue in 1 ml of HNO_3 and water to make 50 ml.   To 20 ml of the solution add 2 ml of 25% H_2SO_4 and 1 ml each of phosphate reagents **A** and **B**, and heat at 60° for 10 minutes.   Any blue color produced is not darker than that of a control made with 0.02 mg of PO_4 contained in 20 ml of water, and treated exactly as the sample, beginning with "add 2 ml of 25% H_2SO_4 . . . ."

Sulfate: Evaporate 50 ml of *Solution R* to dryness on the steam bath. Add to the residue 0.2 ml of 1 N HCl and 10 ml of hot water, filter if necessary, and add to filtrate 2 ml of $BaCl_2$ solution. Any turbidity resulting in 10 minutes is not greater than that in a control made with 0.1 mg of SO_4.

Heavy metals: Evaporate 50 ml of *Solution R* in a porcelain dish to dryness on the steam bath. Digest the residue with 1 ml of 1 N HCl and 20 ml of hot water for a few minutes, cool, dilute to 40 ml and add 10 ml of H_2S. Any resulting dark color is not more intense than a control made with 0.03 mg of Pb.

Iron: Add 2 ml of HCl to 5.0 ml of *Solution R* and dilute to 50 ml. Now add 50 mg of ammonium persulfate, shake to dissolve it and add 3 ml of ammonium thiocyanate solution. Any red color produced is not darker than that of a control made by treating 0.02 mg of Fe^{III} exactly as the solution of the sample.

H_2SO_4—insoluble: Transfer 1.0 g of the sample to a 250-ml beaker, add 1 ml of water, mix, then add with stirring 25 ml of H_2SO_4 and 5–8 g of ammonium sulfate. Heat on hot plate, with frequent stirring, to evolution of sulfuric fumes. Raise the temperature and continue heating until all of the sample is dissolved, or, if undissolved matter is present, it is apparent that no more will dissolve on further heating. Cool well and slowly pour the solution into 100 ml of cold water. Filter the cooled solution on a small filter paper and wash beaker and filter with several 10-ml portions of 10% H_2SO_4. Place the filter paper in a tared platinum crucible and ignite to constant weight. The residue does not exceed 1.0 mg.

To ascertain whether or not the undissolved matter is silica (SiO_2), add to the crucible 5 drops of H_2SO_4, 1 ml of hydrofluoric acid, evaporate on the steam bath, ignite and weigh. If it is SiO_2, the loss in weight should be close to the weight of the H_2SO_4 insoluble found.

TITAN YELLOW, *see* THIAZOLE YELLOW

TITANIUM TRICHLORIDE

Titanous Chloride

$TiCl_3$; mol. wt. 154.27; Ti—31.05%; Cl—68.95%.

Dark-violet, hygroscopic, and rapidly oxidizes in the air. Soluble in water, the solution depositing titanic acid on exposure to air.

Titanium trichloride is usually available as a dark violet-blue, 20% aqueous solution. *Keep in small, tightly closed, glass-stoppered bottles and protected from sunlight.*

Titanium trichloride solution should assay not less than 95% of the labeled percentage of $TiCl_3$.

Assay: Place about 1 g of sodium bicarbonate in a 100-ml volumetric flask, add 20 ml of oxygen-free water, then gradually add 10 ml of HCl.

Quickly transfer about 6 ml of the titanium trichloride solution to a small, tared weighing bottle and weigh. Through a small funnel transfer the solution into the 100-ml volumetric flask and completely wash the content of the weighing bottle into the volumetric flask with 10 to 15 ml of 10% HCl. Make up to volume with oxygen-free water and mix.

Weigh accurately 1.2 to 1.25 g of clear crystals of ferric ammonium sulfate and dissolve, in a 300-ml flask, in 50 ml of oxygen-free water (made by boiling water for 15 to 20 minutes and cooling). Add 2 ml of sulfuric acid, previously diluted with 10 ml of water, and follow in small portions with about 1.5 g of sodium bicarbonate. Now run in from a burette 30 ml of the titanium trichloride dilution, then add a solution of 1 g of ammonium thiocyanate in 5 ml of water and complete titration with the titanium solution until the red color just disappears. One g of ferric ammonium sulfate = 0.3126 g of $TiCl_3$.

o-TOLIDINE

H_2N—⬡(CH₃)—⬡(CH₃)—NH_2; mol. wt. 212.28.

White or pale pink, crystalline powder, with an odor resembling aniline. It is almost insoluble in water; soluble in dilute acids; also soluble in alcohol or in ether. o-Tolidine is used for the detection of free chlorine in water.

Standards

Melting range . . . . .129°–131°	Solubility in dilute acid . . . . . . .to pass test
Sensitiveness . . . . .to pass test	Ignition residue . . . . .max 0.10%

Sensitiveness: Place 50 mg of the sample in a mortar, add 0.5 ml of water and 0.5 ml of hydrochloric acid and grind well. Add 20 ml of water and transfer completely to a 50-ml cylinder, then add 5 ml of hydrochloric acid and dilute with water to 50 ml. Add 1 ml of this solution to 20 ml of water containing 2.5 mg of chlorine. A distinct yellow color is produced.

Note: A chlorine solution for the test can be prepared by diluting sodium hypochlorite solution of known hypochlorite content with sufficient water to make 1 ml contain 0.01 mg of active chlorine.

Solubility in dilute acid: Add 1 ml of HCl to 0.1 g of the sample, then add 20 ml of water. The resulting solution is colorless and complete or practically so.

Ignition residue: Thoroughly char 1.0 g. Cool, then add 0.5 ml of H_2SO_4 and ignite at first gently to evaporate the acid, then strongly to constant weight. Not more than 1.0 mg of residue remains.

TOLUENE

Toluol

⬡(CH₃); mol. wt. 92.14.

Colorless, clear, highly refractive, flammable liquid. Insoluble in water; miscible with alcohol, ether, chloroform and many other organic solvents. Sp. gr. about 0.865 at 25°/25°.

Standards

Boiling range.................110°–111°	Sulfur compounds (as S)......max 0.003%
Evaporation residue.........max 0.001%	Water......................max 0.05%
Neutrality...................to pass test	Substances darkened by H_2SO_4.to pass test

Boiling range: Distill 50 ml. After the first 10 drops, all distills between 110° and 111°, correction being made for the difference of the barometric pressure from 760 mm.

Evaporation residue: Evaporate 120 ml on the steam bath and dry at 105° for 20 minutes. Not more than 1.0 mg of residue remains.

Neutrality: Shake 20 ml with 10 ml of CO_2-free water, draw off the aqueous layer, and add to it 1 drop of methyl red. If a red color is produced, it is changed to yellow by 0.1 ml of 0.02 N NaOH. If a yellow color is produced, it is changed to red by 0.1 ml of 0.02 N HCl.

Sulfur compounds: To 10 ml of the sample add 1 ml of absolute alcohol and 3 ml of potassium plumbite solution. Gently boil the mixture under a reflux condenser for 15 minutes, agitating well the contents of the flask several times during the heating, and then set aside for 5 minutes. The aqueous layer is colorless.

Note: The sulfur may be determined quantitatively by the method described on page 579.

Water: The water in toluene may be determined by the iodine (Fischer) method.

Substances darkened by H_2SO_4: Shake 15 ml with 5 ml of sulfuric acid for 20 seconds and allow to stand for 15 minutes. The toluene layer is colorless and the acid is not darker than a mixture of 2 volumes of water and 1 volume of a color standard containing 5 g of cobalt chloride, 40 g of ferric chloride and 20 ml of HCl in a liter.

TRICHLOROACETIC ACID

CCl_3CO_2H; mol. wt. 163.40; Cl—65.10%.

Colorless crystals, characteristic odor; rapidly deliquescent. Soluble in 0.1 part of water; soluble in alcohol or ether. *Keep in tightly stoppered bottles, in a cool place, protected from light.*

Standards

Assay.........99.0%–100.2% CCl_3CO_2H	Phosphate (PO_4)............max 0.001%
Less chlorinated acids.........to pass test	Sulfate (SO_4)................max 0.02%
Solubility....................to pass test	Heavy metals (as Pb)........max 0.002%
Ignition residue..............max 0.03%	Iron (Fe)...................max 0.001%
Chloride (Cl)................max 0.001%	Substances darkened
Nitrate (NO_3)..............max 0.002%	by H_2SO_4................to pass test

Assay; Less chlorinated acids: Dry about 6 g to constant weight over H_2SO_4. Weigh accurately about 5 g of the dried sample, taking care to prevent absorption of moisture, dissolve in 40 ml of water, add 3 drops of phenolphthalein, and titrate with 1 N NaOH. One ml of 1 N NaOH = 0.1634 g CCl_3CO_2H, log 21325. Each gram of sample consumes not less than 6.06 ml and not more than 6.12 ml 1 N NaOH.

Solubility: Dissolve 5 g in 25 ml of water. No insoluble residue remains.

Ignition residue: Place 5 g ($\pm$ 0.1 g) in a tared porcelain dish and ignite slowly until most has volatilized. Allow to cool, add a few drops of H_2SO_4 and then ignite strongly to constant weight. Any residue remaining is not over 1.5 mg.

Chloride: Dissolve 1 g in 20 ml of water. To 30 ml add 0.5 ml of HNO_3 and 1 ml of $AgNO_3$. Any turbidity produced is not greater than that in a blank to which 0.02 mg of Cl has been added.

Nitrate: Dissolve 0.30 g in 10 ml of water, add about 20 mg of NaCl and 0.2 ml of diphenylamine solution. Mix and slowly add, without agitation, 10 ml of H_2SO_4. After 5–10 minutes mix by swirling and allow to stand for 30 minutes. No blue color appears.

Phosphate: Dissolve 2 g in 25 ml of H_2O, add 1 ml of 25% H_2SO_4, and 1 ml each of phosphate reagents **A** and **B**, and heat at 60° for 10 minutes. Any blue color produced is not greater than that of a blank to which 0.02 mg of PO_4 has been added.

Sulfate: Dissolve 1 g in 20 ml of water, add 1 ml of 0.1 N HCl and 3 ml of $BaCl_2$. Any turbidity produced is not greater than that in a blank to which 0.2 mg of SO_4 has been added.

Heavy metals: To the *Ignition residue* add 2 ml of HCl and 0.5 ml of HNO_3, and slowly evaporate on the steam bath to dryness. Take up the residue with 1 ml of 1 N HCl and 20 ml of hot water, cool, and dilute to 50 ml. Dilute 10 ml of the solution to 40 ml and add 10 ml of H_2S. Any color produced is not darker than a control made with 0.02 mg of Pb, 0.2 ml of 1 N HCl and 10 ml of H_2S in the same final volume as with the sample.

Iron: Dissolve 1 g in water, add 1 ml of HCl and dilute to 50 ml. Add 30 mg of ammonium persulfate and 3 ml of ammonium thiocyanate, and mix. Any resulting red color is not darker than that of a blank to which 0.01 mg of Fe has been added.

Substances darkened by H_2SO_4: To 1 g add 10 ml of sulfuric acid and heat on the steam bath for 10 minutes. Only a slight darkening develops.

TRIPHENYLTETRAZOLIUM CHLORIDE

Red Tetrazolium

; mol. wt. 334.80.

White to yellowish crystalline powder.   Soluble in about 10 parts of water or alcohol; slightly soluble in acetone; insoluble in ether.   Usually contains solvent of crystallization, and when freed from solvent by drying (at 105°) it melts with decomposition at about 240°.

Standards

Sensitiveness.................to pass test	Solubility....................to pass test
Drying loss...................max 5%	Ignition residue...............max 0.2%

Sensitiveness: (*a*) Dissolve 10 mg of sample in 10 ml of absolute alcohol.

(*b*) Dissolve 10 mg of dextrose in 20 ml of absolute alcohol.

To 0.2 ml of (*b*) add 1 ml of absolute alcohol and 0.5 ml of diluted tetramethylammonium hydroxide (1+9 absolute alcohol), then add 0.2 ml of (*a*).   A pronounced red color develops in about 10 minutes.

Drying loss: Dry a suitable quantity at 105° to constant weight.   The loss in weight does not exceed 5%.

Solubility: 100-mg portions of sample yield complete or practically complete and clear solution with 10 ml of water or 10 ml of alcohol.

Ignition residue: Ignite 0.5 g until well charred.   Allow to cool, add 0.5 ml of H_2SO_4 and reignite to constant weight.   The weight of the residue, if any, does not exceed 1.0 mg.

L-TRYPTOPHAN

Indol-aminopropionic Acid

$-CH_2CH \cdot NH_2 \cdot COOH$; mol. wt. 204.22; N—13.72%.

Colorless or white crystals, or white, crystalline powder.   Soluble in about 100 parts of water at 25°, in about 20 parts of boiling water.   Soluble in hot alcohol; also soluble in diluted HCl and in alkali hydroxide solutions.

Nitrogen (N).............13.7% $\pm$ 0.25%	Chloride (Cl)................max 0.005%
Specific rotation in H_2O......31.2° $\pm$ 0.7°	Phosphate (PO_4)............max 0.002%
Solubility....................to pass test	Sulfate (SO_4)................max 0.015%
Drying loss...................max 0.3%	Ammonium salts (as NH_3)....max 0.010%
Ignition residue..............max 0.05%	Heavy metals (as Pb)........max 0.001%
Tyrosine.....................to pass test	Iron (Fe)...................max 0.002%
(max about 0.05%)	

Nitrogen: Determine by the Kjeldahl method, using about 0.2 g of dried sample.

Specific rotation; Drying loss: Dry about 1.0 g of sample, accurately weighed, at 105° for 3 hours: the loss in weight corresponds to not more than 0.3%.

Weigh 0.25 g of the dried sample, dissolve it in water to make exactly 25 ml.   Measure the rotation of the solution at $25° \pm 2°$ in a 200-mm tube in sodium light and calculate the specific rotation (page 582).

Solubility: Separate solutions of 0.5 g in 20 ml of warm water and in 10 ml of 10% HCl are clear and colorless.

Ignition residue: Moisten 2.0 g with 1 ml of H_2SO_4 and ignite to constant weight.   The weight of the residue does not exceed 1.0 mg (retain residue).

Tyrosine: Dissolve 0.10 g in 3 ml of 10% H_2SO_4 and add 10 ml of 10% solution of mercuric sulfate in 10% H_2SO_4.   Heat the solution on the steam bath for 10 minutes, filter, and wash with 5 ml of the mercuric sulfate solution.   Add to the filtrate 0.5 ml of 5% sodium nitrite solution.   No pink or red color is produced in 10 minutes.

Chloride: To a solution of 0.40 g of sample in 20 ml of water add 1 ml of HNO_3 and 1 ml of 0.1 N $AgNO_3$.   Any resulting turbidity is not greater than that in a blank to which 0.02 mg of Cl has been added.

Phosphate: Place 0.5 g of sample in a platinum crucible, add an equal quantity of magnesium nitrate and 5 ml of H_2O.   Evaporate to dryness on the steam bath, and ignite at a low temperature until the residue is nearly white.   Add to the residue 5 ml of water and 3 ml of 25% H_2SO_4, heat for 5 minutes, then add 10 ml of hot water, filter, and wash to 20 ml.   Add to the filtrate 1 ml each of phosphate reagents **A** and **B** and heat at 60° for 10 minutes.   Any resulting blue color is not darker than that of a blank to which 0.01 mg of PO_4 has been added.

Sulfate: To a solution of 0.65 g in 15 ml of hot water add 3 ml of 1 N HCl and 2 ml of $BaCl_2$.   If a turbidity is produced in 10 minutes it does not exceed that of a blank to which 0.1 mg of SO_4 has been added.

Ammonium Salts: Dissolve 0.5 g in 60 ml of water in a small distilling flask, add 1.0 g of magnesium oxide, and distill about 40 ml into 5 ml of water containing 1 drop of diluted (1+3) HCl.   Dilute the distillate to 50 ml.   Dilute 20 ml of this solution to 50 ml, and add 2 ml of 10% NaOH and 2 ml of Wessler solution.   Any color produced is not darker than that of a control made with 0.05 mg of NH_3 (0.15 mg NH_4Cl) and treated in the same manner as the sample.

Heavy metals: To the *Ignition residue* add 2 ml of HCl, 2 ml of H_2O, and 0.5 ml of HNO_3, and evaporate to dryness on the steam bath.   Digest the residue with 0.5 ml of 1 N HCl and 10 ml of hot water for 5 minutes, cool, and dilute to 50 ml.   To 25 ml add 5 ml of H_2S.   Any resulting coloration is not darker than that of a control made with 0.01 mg Pb, 0.2 ml of 1 N HCl and 5 ml H_2S in the same final volume as with the sample.

Iron: To the remaining 25 ml of solution from the preceding test add 2 ml of HCl, dilute to 50 ml, add about 30 mg of ammonium persulfate and 3 ml of ammonium thiocyanate solution, and mix.   Any resulting red coloration is not darker than that of a blank to which 0.02 mg of Fe has been added.

TURMERIC PAPER

Yellow strips or sheets, made by impregnating filter paper with turmeric solution (see page 560).

Sensitiveness: Mix 5 ml of water with 1 ml of HCl and 1 ml of an aqueous solution of 0.10 g of boric acid in 100 ml of water. Immerse a strip of the paper in this solution for 1 minute and allow to dry. The paper acquires a brown color. Now moisten the paper with ammonium hydroxide; the color changes to a greenish-brown.

L-TYROSINE

β-(p-Hydroxyphenyl) Alanine

$HO \cdot C_6H_4CH_2CH(NH_2)COOH$; mol. wt. 181.19; N—7.73%.

Colorless, silky needles, or white crystalline powder. One gram dissolves in about 230 ml of water at 25°; very slightly soluble in alcohol; soluble in dilute mineral acids and in alkaline solutions.

Standards

Nitrogen (N)...............7.7% ± 0.2%	Phosphate (PO₄) max 0.002%
Specific rotation in 1 N HCl.. −10.5° ± 0.5°	Sulfate (SO₄)...............max 0.015%
Solubility....................to pass test	Ammonium salts (as NH₃)....max 0.010%
Drying loss..................max 0.2%	Heavy metals (as Pb).......max 0.001%
Ignition residue.............max 0.05%	Iron (Fe)..................max 0.002%
Chloride (Cl)........ max 0.005%	

Nitrogen: Determine by the Kjeldahl method, using about 0.3 g of the dried sample accurately weighed.

Specific rotation; Drying loss: Dry about 1 g of the sample, accurately weighed, at 105° for 2 hours. The loss in weight corresponds to not more than 0.2%. Weigh accurately about 0.75 g of the dried sample and dissolve it in 10% HCl to make exactly 25 ml. Measure the rotation of the solution at 25° ± 2° in a 200-mm tube and calculate the specific rotation (page 582).

Solubility: Separate solutions of 0.5 g in 10 ml of 10% HCl, and 10 ml of 5% Na_2CO_3 solution are clear and colorless.

Ignition residue; Chloride; Phosphate; Sulfate; Ammonium salts; Heavy metals; Iron: Apply the respective tests described under L-Tryptophan. The results should be as there stated.

URANYL ACETATE

Uranium Acetate

$UO_2(CH_3CO_2)_2 \cdot 2H_2O$; mol. wt. 424.19; anhydrous—91.5%; H_2O—8.5%; U—56.16%.

Yellow, crystalline. Soluble in 10 parts of water, usually incompletely, due to presence of basic salt which dissolves on addition of acetic acid.

Standards

Insoluble...............max 0.010%
Chloride (Cl)...............max 0.003%
Nitrate (NO_3)...............max 0.005%
Sulfate (SO_4)...............max 0.01%
Alkalies, Earths (as sulfates)...max 0.05%

Ammonia (NH_3)...............to pass test
(max about 0.05%)
Heavy metals (as Pb)........max 0.002%
Iron (Fe)...............max 0.001%
Uranous salt (as U^{IV})........max 0.06%
Assay...............min 99%

Insoluble: Dissolve 10 g in a mixture of 100 ml of H_2O and 5 ml of glacial acetic acid, heating if necessary to aid solution. Filter any undissolved matter (retain the filtrate but not the washings), wash with H_2O, and dry at 105°. The insoluble residue does not exceed 1.0 mg.

Solution S: To the filtrate from the test for *Insoluble* add 50 ml of water and 8 ml of 30% hydrogen peroxide. Heat until the precipitate is coagulated, filter through a sintered glass filter, wash with about 25 ml of water, and dilute the filtrate to 200 ml.

Chloride: Dilute 10 ml of *Solution S* to 20 ml, add 1 ml of HNO_3 and 1 ml of $AgNO_3$ solution. Any resulting turbidity is not greater than that of a blank to which 0.015 mg of Cl has been added.

Nitrate: Dissolve 0.5 g in 20 ml of water. Heat the solution almost to boiling and add it, with stirring, to a mixture of 25 ml of water and 2 ml of NH_4OH free from carbonate. Heat for a few minutes, dilute to 50 ml, and decant through a sintered glass filter without washing. Evaporate 20 ml of the filtrate to about 10 ml, cool, and refilter if necessary.

Add 10 mg NaCl, 0.10 ml of indigo carmine solution, then add slowly 10 ml of H_2SO_4. The blue color does not entirely disappear in 5 minutes.

Sulfate: To 20 ml of *Solution S* add 1 ml of 0.1 N HCl and 2 ml of $BaCl_2$. Any turbidity produced is not greater than that in a control made with 10 ml of water containing 0.1 mg of SO_4 and treated with the same volumes of the reagents as the solution of the sample.

Alkalies, Earths, etc.: Evaporate 40 ml of *Solution S* to about 10 ml and make alkaline with ammonia. If no turbidity develops in 3 minutes, add 3 drops of sulfuric acid, evaporate to dryness, and ignite. If a turbidity develops after alkalinization, filter, add to the filtrate 3 drops of H_2SO_4, evaporate, and ignite. The weight of the residue does not exceed 1.0 mg.

Ammonia: Dissolve 0.25 g in 5 ml of water, add 5 ml of 5% NaOH solution, and boil gently. The escaping vapor does not turn red litmus paper blue.

Heavy metals: Evaporate 20 ml of *Solution S* on the steam bath to dryness. Take up in 1 ml of 1 N acetic acid and 10 ml of hot water, digest for 2 minutes, dilute to 40 ml, and add 10 ml of H_2S. Any color produced is not darker than that of a control made with 0.02 mg of Pb, 1 ml of 1 N acetic acid and 10 ml of H_2S in the same final volume as with the sample.

Iron: To 20 ml of *Solution S* add 2 ml of HCl, dilute to 50 ml, and add 3 ml of ammonium thiocyanate. Any resulting red color is not darker than that of a blank to which 0.01 mg of Fe has been added.

Uranous salt: Dissolve 4 g in 400 ml of water, add 4 ml of H_2SO_4, and divide the solution into two equal portions. Titrate one portion with 0.1 N potassium permanganate to the production of a slight pink color in comparison with the other portion. Not more than 0.20 ml of the permanganate is required to produce the change in color.

Assay: Weigh accurately about 0.5 g and dissolve it in 100 ml of water. Heat the solution to boiling and add ammonium hydroxide, free from carbonate, until no further precipitation is produced. Filter, wash with a 1% aqueous solution of ammonium nitrate, then ignite gently with free access of air to constant weight. The weight of the U_3O_8 so obtained multiplied by 1.511 = $UO_2(C_2H_3O_2)_2$, log 17926.

URANYL COBALT ACETATE SOLUTION—page 560

URANYL MAGNESIUM ACETATE SOLUTION—page 558

URANYL ZINC ACETATE SOLUTION—page 561

URANYL NITRATE

Uranium Nitrate

$UO_2(NO_3)_2 \cdot 6H_2O$; mol. wt. 502.18; anhydrous—78.5%; H_2O—21.5%; U—47.4%.

Yellow crystals; slight greenish fluorescence. Soluble in 1.5 parts of water; soluble in alcohol or ether.

Standards

Insoluble ....max 0.010%	Heavy metals (as Pb) ....max 0.002%
Chloride (Cl) ....max 0.002%	Iron (Fe) ....max 0.002%
Sulfate (SO₄)................max 0.005%	Uranous salt (as U^IV)........max 0.06%
Alkalies, Earths (as sulfates)...max 0.10%	*Assay*
Ammonia (NH₃)..............to pass test	
(max about 0.05%)	

Insoluble: Dissolve 10 g in 100 ml of H_2O and heat on the steam bath for 30 minutes. Filter any undissolved residue (retain the filtrate but not the washings), wash, and dry at 105°. The weight of the insoluble residue does not exceed 1.0 mg.

Solution S: To the filtrate from the test for *Insoluble* add 50 ml of water, 5 g of ammonium acetate, and 8 ml of 10% hydrogen peroxide. Heat until the precipitate is coagulated, and filter through a sintered glass filter. Wash with about 30 ml of water and dilute the filtrate to 200 ml.

Chloride: To 10 ml of *Solution S*, add 1 ml of HNO_3 and 1 ml of $AgNO_3$ solution. Any resulting turbidity is not greater than that in a blank to which 0.01 mg of Cl has been added.

Sulfate: Concentrate 40 ml of *Solution S* to about 10 ml, add 1 ml of 0.1 N HCl and 1 ml of $BaCl_2$, and allow to stand for 20 minutes. Any turbidity produced is not greater than that in a blank to which 0.1 mg of SO_4 has been added.

Alkalies, Earths, etc.: Evaporate 20 ml of *Solution S* to about 10 ml and make alkaline with ammonia. If no turbidity develops in 3 minutes, add 3 drops of sulfuric acid, evaporate to dryness, and ignite. If a turbidity develops after alkalinization, filter, add to the filtrate 3 drops of H_2SO_4, evaporate, and ignite. The weight of the residue does not exceed 1.0 mg.

Ammonia: Dissolve 0.25 g in 5 ml of water, add 5 ml of 5% NaOH solution, and boil gently. The escaping vapor does not turn red litmus paper blue.

Heavy metals: Evaporate 20 ml of *Solution S* on the steam bath to dryness. Take up in 1 ml of 1 N acetic acid and 10 ml of hot water, digest for 2 minutes, dilute to 40 ml, and add 10 ml of H_2S. Any color produced is not darker than that of a control made with 0.02 mg of Pb, 1 ml of 1 N acetic acid, and 10 ml of H_2S in the same final volume as with the sample.

Iron: To 10 ml of *Solution S* add 2 ml of HCl, dilute to 50 ml, and add 3 ml of ammonium thiocyanate. Any resulting red color is not darker than that of a blank to which 0.01 mg of Fe has been added.

Uranous salt: Dissolve 4 g in 400 ml of water, add 4 ml of H_2SO_4, and divide the solution into two equal portions. Titrate one portion with 0.1 N potassium permanganate to the production of a slight pink color in comparison with the other portion. Not more than 0.20 ml of the permanganate is required to produce the change in color.

Assay: As for uranyl acetate. The weight of the U_3O_8 multiplied by 1.789 = $UO_2(NO_3)_2 \cdot 6H_2O$, log 25261.

URANYL ZINC ACETATE, CRYSTALS

Uranium Zinc Acetate

$UO_2(CH_3COO)_2 \cdot 2Zn(CH_3OO)_2 \cdot 2H_2O$; mol. wt. 791.1; U—30.0%; Zn—16.5%; H_2O—4.5%.

Yellow crystals. Soluble in about 10 parts of water, 50 parts of alcohol, 100 parts of acetone.

Standards

Assay (uranium content)......min 29.0%	Sulfate (SO_4)................max 0.02%
Insoluble....................max 0.02%	Alkali, etc. (as Sulfates).......max 0.10%
Sensitiveness................to pass test	Foreign heavy metals (Pb)....max 0.003%
Nitrate (NO_3)...............to pass test	

Assay: The uranium content of this reagent may be determined titrimetrically as follows:

A quantity of the sample equivalent to 75–100 mg of uranium (U) is dissolved in 100 ml of 10% H_2SO_4 (approx. 2 N) and just enough permanganate solution added to impart to the solution a distinct pink color. The solution is then passed through a Jones reductor at the rate of 50–75 ml per minute. The reductor is washed into the receiving flask with some 50 ml or more of the 10% H_2SO_4 until the uranyl solution is all displaced from the tube into the receiving flask and finally with 75–100 ml of water. Since a small amount of the uranium may be reduced to U^{+3} (instead of U^{+4}), air is bubbled through the solution by means of a long tube inserted into it for 5–10 minutes. The air (oxygen) oxidizes any U^{+3} to U^{+4}. After rinsing the tube with water into the flask the solution is titrated with 0.1 N

KMnO$_4$ to a pink color. A correction for a blank is made by passing through the reductor an equal volume of the H$_2$SO$_4$ as used with the sample and titrating the solution with the KMnO$_4$ to the same intensity of pink color. One ml of 0.1 N KMnO$_4$ = 0.01190 g of U, log 07555.

Insoluble: Dissolve 5.0 g in 50 ml of water and 2 ml of glacial acetic acid, heating, if necessary, to aid solution and cool. If undissolved matter is present filter (retain filtrate, but not washings). Wash with small volumes of cold water until the washings are practically colorless and dry at 105°. The weight of the insoluble does not exceed 1.0 mg.

Sensitiveness: Dissolve 1.0 g of sample in 10 ml of water and 0.5 ml of glacial acetic acid. If the solution is not clear, filter. Add all of the clear solution to 1.0 ml of a solution of sodium chloride containing 1.3 mg NaCl (0.5 mg Na). Shake well and let stand 15–20 minutes. A distinct, crystalline precipitate of sodium uranyl zinc acetate is produced.

Solution S: To the filtrate from the test for *Insoluble* add 25 ml of water and 7 ml of 30% hydrogen peroxide and heat until the precipitate is coagulated. Filter through a sintered glass, filter and wash with water to make filtrate measure 150 ml.

Nitrate: Test as prescribed for Uranyl Acetate. The result should be as there stated.

Sulfate: To 15 ml of *Solution S* add 1 ml of 0.1 N HCl and 2 ml of BaCl$_2$. Any resulting turbidity is not greater than in a control made with 0.1 mg of SO$_4$ in 10 ml of water and the same volumes of the reagents as with sample.

Alkali, etc.: Dilute 30 ml of *Solution S* to 50 ml, add 1 ml of NH$_4$OH and boil gently to expel H$_2$O$_2$. Dilute to about 75 ml and completely precipitate the Zn with H$_2$S. Filter, without washing, and evaporate filtrate to about 10 ml, refiltering if necessary. Add to filtrate 3 drops of H$_2$SO$_4$, evaporate and ignite. The weight of the residue does not exceed 1.0 mg.

Foreign heavy metals: Evaporate 30 ml of *Solution S* to dryness over steam. Digest the residue with 10 ml of hot water and 2 ml of 0.1 N HCl for 5 minutes and dilute to 20 ml. To 5 ml add 0.015 mg of Pb; then *under hood* add with stirring 15 ml of 10% sodium cyanide solution and dilute to 25 ml (A). To the remaining 15 ml of the solution add with stirring 15 ml of the sodium cyanide solution (B). Then to each add 0.5 ml of freshly prepared approximately 5% sodium sulfide solution. B is not darker than A.

UREA

Carbamide

(NH$_2$)$_2$CO; mol. wt. 60.06; N—46.65%.

Colorless crystals. Soluble in 2 parts of water, in 6 parts of cold alcohol.

Standards

Melting range.................132°–133°	Chloride (Cl)...............max 0.001%
Solubility in water............to pass test	Sulfate (SO$_4$)...............max 0.002%
Insoluble in alcohol...........max 0.02%	Heavy metals (as Pb).......max 0.0005%
Ignition residue.............max 0.020%	Iron (Fe).................max 0.0005%

Solubility in water: A solution of 5 g in 100 ml of water is clear and colorless.

Insoluble in alcohol: Dissolve 5 g in 40 ml of warm alcohol, filter any undissolved matter, wash with alcohol, and dry at 105°. The insoluble residue does not exceed 1.0 mg.

Ignition residue: To 5 g add 1 ml of H_2SO_4 and ignite gently to constant weight. The weight of the residue does not exceed 1.0 mg (retain).

Chloride: Dissolve 1 g in 10 ml of water, add 1 ml of HNO_3 and 1 ml of $AgNO_3$. Any resulting turbidity is not greater than the blank with 0.01 mg of Cl added.

Sulfate: Dissolve 5 g in 20 ml of hot water, add 5 ml of 1 N HCl and 2 ml of $BaCl_2$. Any turbidity produced in 15 minutes is not greater than that in the blank to which 0.10 mg of SO_4 has been added.

Heavy metals: Dissolve 6 g in 30 ml of warm water. To 5 ml of the solution add 0.02 mg of Pb, 1 ml of 1 N acetic acid, and dilute to 40 ml (A). To the remaining 25 ml add 1 ml of 1 N acetic acid and dilute to 40 ml (B). Then to each add 10 ml of H_2S. B is not darker than A.

Iron: Dissolve 2 g of sample in water, add 2 ml of HCl, and dilute to 50 ml. Add 30 mg of ammonium persulfate and 3 ml of ammonium thiocyanate, and mix. Any red color produced is not darker than that of a control made with 0.01 mg of Fe, 2 ml of HCl, the same quantities of ammonium persulfate and thiocyanate and in the same final volume as with the sample.

URIC ACID

; mol. wt. 168.11; N—33.33%.

White or slightly yellow crystals, or crystalline powder; odorless. Almost insoluble in water or alcohol; soluble in alkali hydroxides, in glycerol and in solutions of sodium acetate or sodium phosphate.

Standards

Identity....................to conform	Ignition residue.............max 0.20%
Nitrogen content (N)........32.7%–33.5%	Ammonium compounds.......to pass test
Solubility in NaOH solution....to pass test	(limit about 0.05% NH_3)

Identity: To about 1 mg of sample in a small porcelain dish or crucible add 1 ml of HCl and about 50 mg of potassium chlorate, then evaporate on the steam bath to dryness and absence of an HCl odor. Invert the dish over another dish or small beaker containing a few drops of NH_4OH. A violet color is produced which disappears on the addition of aqueous NaOH.

(a) Dissolve 10 mg of the uric acid by heating with 1 ml of 1 N NaOH and dilute to 10 ml.

(*b*) Dissolve 0.5 g of molybdic acid (85%) and 1 g of dibasic sodium phosphate crystals by heating with 20 ml of water, neutralize to litmus paper with dilute HNO, and dilute to 25 ml.

To 0.5 ml of (*a*) add 4 ml of water and 0.5 ml of 10% HCl, then add 1 ml of (*b*) and boil the mixture for a few seconds. A strong green color develops in 2 to 5 minutes.

Nitrogen content: Powder the sample and dry to constant weight over H_2SO_4. Weigh accurately about 0.15 g of the dried sample and determine the nitrogen by the Kjeldahl method. One ml of 0.1 N HCl = 0.00141 mg of N = 0.004202 g $C_5H_4N_4O_3$, log 62346.

Ignition residue: Char well 1.0 g. Allow to cool; then add 0.5 ml H_2SO_4 and ignite at first gently to evaporate the acid, then strongly to constant weight. Not more than 2.0 mg of residue remains.

Solubility in NaOH; Ammonium compounds: To 1 g in a test tube add 10 ml of water and 10 ml of 10% NaOH and, while agitating, heat gently. The solution while hot is clear and colorless or nearly colorless, and the odor of ammonia is not perceptible during and after the heating.

VANADYL SULFATE

$VOSO_4 \cdot xH_2O$; in anhydrous: V—31.56%; SO_4—58.93%.

Vanadyl sulfate of commerce has a somewhat variable amount of water of hydration, up to about 50%. About 20% of the water is eliminated at 100°; complete dehydration can only be effected at about 200°.

Blue crystals; solubility in water difficult and usually incomplete.

Standards

Drying loss (water).............max 50%	Substances not precipitated
Assay.................min 97% $VOSO_4$	by NH_4OH.................max 1.0%
(anhydrous basis)	Iron (Fe)...................max 0.003%
Pentavalent vanadium (V^{+5})....max 0.5%	
(anhydrous basis)	

Drying loss: Dry about 1 g accurately weighed at 220° to constant weight. The loss in weight corresponds to not more than 50%.

Assay: Weigh accurately about 0.4 g of the dried sample obtained in the test for *Drying loss*, and transfer it completely with 15 to 20 ml of water into a beaker. Add 3 ml of H_2SO_4, cover beaker with a watch glass, and heat on the steam bath until all is dissolved. Cool, dilute with 125 ml of water, and titrate with 0.1 N potassium permanganate to the production of a pinkish color which persists for 1 minute. One ml of 0.1 N permanganate = 0.01630 g $VOSO_4$, log 21219.

Pentavalent vanadium: Dissolve 1 g by heating with 50 ml of H_2O and 5 ml HCl in a glass-stoppered flask, cool, add 2 g of potassium iodide, and allow to stand for 30 minutes. Add 50 ml of water and titrate the liberated iodine with 0.1 N thiosulfate, using starch as indicator. Correct for the volume of thiosulfate consumed by a blank. One ml of 0.1 N thiosulfate = 0.005095 g of vanadium.

Substances not precipitated by NH₄OH: Dissolve 1 g by heating with 20 ml of water and 2 ml of HCl. Dilute to about 75 ml and neutralize to litmus paper with NH₄OH. Transfer to a cylinder, slowly add an excess of 5 ml of the ammonium hydroxide and sufficient water to make 100 ml, and allow to stand overnight. Decant 50 ml of the supernatant liquid through a filter, evaporate to dryness, and ignite. The weight of the residue does not exceed 5.0 mg.

Iron: Dissolve 0.5 g by warming with 20 ml of H_2O and 1 ml of HCl. Dilute with 20 ml of H_2O and slowly add 10% NaOH, with stirring, until no more dissolves upon the further addition of the NaOH. Filter, and wash with hot water until the washings are colorless. Pour on the filter, about 1 ml at a time, 5 ml of hot hydrochloric acid (1 + 2) and wash well with hot water. Cool the filtrate, dilute to 50 ml, and add 50 mg of ammonium persulfate and 3 ml of ammonium thiocyanate. Any resulting red color is not darker than that of a control made with 0.015 mg of Fe, 2 ml of HCl, and the same quantities of ammonium persulfate and thiocyanate and in the same final volume as with the sample.

VANILLIN

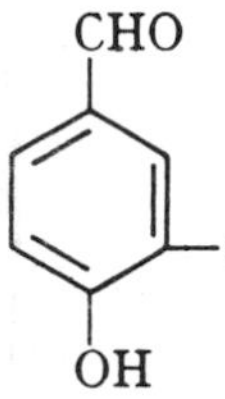

CHO

—OCH₃; mol. wt. 152.15.

OH

Fine, white crystals; characteristic odor. Gradually turns yellow in light. Soluble in about 100 parts of cold water, in 15 parts of boiling water; freely soluble in alcohol, chloroform, or ether. *Keep protected from light.*

Standards

Melting range................81.5°–82.5°	Ignition residue.............max 0.05%
Solubility in alcohol..........to pass test	Solubility in NaOH solution....to pass test

Solubility in alcohol: A solution of 1 g in 10 ml of alcohol is colorless and clear or practically so.

Solubility in NaOH solution: One gram dissolves completely upon warming with 15 ml of 1 N sodium hydroxide.

Ignition residue: Moisten 2 g with 1 ml of H_2SO_4 and ignite to constant weight. Not more than 1.0 mg of residue remains.

XYLENE

Xylol

$C_6H_4(CH_3)_2$; mol. wt. 106.17.

Xylene of commerce may be a mixture of the *m*- and *o*-isomers of dimethylbenzene.

Colorless, clear liquid. Insoluble in water; miscible with alcohol, ether, and chloroform. Sp. gr. about 0.86 at 25°.

Standards

Boiling range.................137°–140°

Evaporation residue.........max 0.002%

Neutrality....................to pass test

Substances darkened by

H_2SO_4....................to pass test

Sulfur compounds (S).........max 0.003%

Water...........to pass test (max 0.05%)

Boiling range: Distill 50 ml. After the first 10 drops, all distills between 137° and 140°, applying correction for barometric pressure, page 581.

Evaporation residue: Evaporate 60 ml on the steam bath and dry at 105° for 30 minutes. Not more than 1.0 mg of residue remains.

Neutrality: Shake 20 ml with 10 ml of CO_2 free water, draw off the aqueous layer, and add to it 1 drop of methyl red. If a red color is produced it is changed to yellow by 0.1 ml of 0.02 N NaOH. If a yellow color is produced it is changed to red by 0.1 ml of 0.02 N HCl.

Substances darkened by H_2SO_4: Shake 15 ml with 5 ml of sulfuric acid for 20 seconds and allow to stand for 15 minutes. The xylene layer is colorless, and the acid is not darker than a mixture of 1 volume of water and 3 volumes of a color standard containing 5 g of cobalt chloride, 40 g ferric chloride, and 20 ml of HCl in a liter.

Sulfur compounds: To 10 ml of the sample add 1 ml of absolute alcohol and 3 ml of potassium plumbite solution. Gently boil the mixture under a reflux condenser for 15 minutes, agitating well the contents of the flask several times during the heating, and then set aside for 5 minutes. The aqueous layer is colorless.

Note: The sulfur may be quantitatively determined by the method on page 579.

Water: Introduce 10 ml of the sample into a dry cylinder, stopper immediately, and cool in crushed ice. No cloudiness is produced. Care must be exercised in this test to avoid absorption of moisture from the air.

The actual H_2O content of xylene may be determined by the iodine (Fischer) method.

D-XYLOSE

Wood Sugar

$$H_2C-\overset{\overset{\displaystyle H}{|}}{C}-\overset{\overset{\displaystyle OH}{|}}{C}-\overset{\overset{\displaystyle H}{|}}{C}-CH\cdot OH; \quad \text{mol. wt. } 150.13.$$

White, needle-like crystals or crystalline powder. Soluble in water; sparingly in cold alcohol.

Standards

Melting range....................145°–150°	Acid (as acetic)...............max 0.015%
Specific rotation........+18.5° to +19.5°	Chloride (Cl)................max 0.002%
Solubility.....................to pass test	Sulfate (SO$_4$)................max 0.005%
Ignition residue..............max 0.05%	Heavy metals (as Cu).......max 0.001%

Specific rotation: Dissolve 1.000 g of the dried sample in about 15 ml H_2O, add 0.1 ml of ammonium hydroxide and sufficient H_2O to make exactly 25 ml. Determine the rotation of this solution in a 200-mm tube at 25°, using sodium light. The observed rotation in degrees multiplied by 12.5 = $[\alpha]_D^{25}$.

Solubility: A solution of 1 g in 10 ml of H_2O is complete, clear and colorless.

Ignition residue: Char 2 g, then add 0.5 ml of H_2SO_4 and ignite to constant weight. Not more than 1.0 mg of residue remains (retain).

Acid: To 20 ml of CO_2-free water add 2 drops of phenolphthalein, then add dropwise 0.02 N NaOH until a pink color is produced. Dissolve 2 g of the sample in this solution and titrate with 0.02 N NaOH until the pink color is restored. Not more than 0.25 ml of the NaOH is required.

Chloride: Dissolve 0.5 g in 10 ml of H_2O, add 5 drops of HNO_3 and 1 ml of $AgNO_3$. Any resulting turbidity is not greater than that in a blank to which 0.01 mg of Cl has been added.

Sulfate: Dissolve 1 g in 10 ml of H_2O, add 1 ml of 0.1 N HCl and 2 ml of $BaCl_2$. If a turbidity is produced, it is not greater than that in a blank to which 0.05 mg of SO_4 has been added.

Heavy metals: Evaporate the *Ignition residue* with 2 ml of HCl and 0.5 ml of HNO_3 to dryness on the steam bath. Take up the residue with 0.5 ml of 1 N HCl and 10 ml of hot water, dilute to 40 ml and add 10 ml of H_2S. Any brown color produced is not darker than that of a control made with 0.02 mg of Cu, 0.5 ml of 1 N HCl, and 10 ml of H_2S, and in the same volume as with the sample.

ZINC

Zn; at. wt. 65.38.

Lustrous, bluish-white cylindrical rods, shot, granules or mossy pieces. Soluble in dilute acids or in solutions of alkali hydroxides.

Standards

Arsenic (As)...............max 0.1 ppm	Permanganate-reducing
Iron (Fe)....................max 0.01%	substances.................to pass test
Lead (Pb)..................max 0.01%	

Arsenic: Test 22 g by the method on page 563, using 25 ml of sulfuric acid or 45 ml of HCl diluted with about 75 ml of water. Any stain produced is not greater than that produced in a control made with 0.002 mg of As, 2 g of the zinc, and the same quantities of acid and water as with the sample.

Solution S: To 2 g in a flask add 15 ml of water and 15 ml of HCl and allow to stand or heat gently on a steam bath until the zinc is nearly all dissolved. Then add 1 ml of nitric acid and boil gently until all is dissolved.   Cool, dilute to 100 ml, and mix well.

Iron: To 5 ml of *Solution S* add 2 ml of HCl and dilute to 15 ml.   Add 50 mg of ammonium persulfate and 15 ml of butanolic potassium thiocyanate, shake well, and allow to separate.   Any resulting red color in the butanol layer is not darker than that of a blank to which 0.01 mg of Fe has been added.

Lead: To 20 ml of *Solution S* add NH_4OH dropwise until a slight permanent precipitate is produced, then add just sufficient HCl to dissolve the precipitate and dilute to 40 ml.   To 10 ml add 0.02 mg of Pb, and while stirring, add 30 ml of 10% sodium cyanide solution, and dilute to 60 ml (*A*).   To the remaining 30 ml add, with stirring, 30 ml of 10% sodium cyanide solution (*B*).   Then to each add 0.5 ml of freshly prepared approximately 5% sodium sulfide solution.   *B* is not darker than *A*.

Permanganate-reducing substances: Heat 20 g with a mixture of 25 ml of H_2SO_4 and 150 ml of water in a flask provided with a Bunsen valve to prevent access of air.   Add 1 ml of 10% cupric sulfate solution to accelerate solution of the zinc.   When the zinc has dissolved, titrate the solution with 0.1 N potassium permanganate until a faint pink color persists for 30 seconds.   Not more than 0.20 ml of the permanganate is required, after correcting for blank and end point.

ZINC ACETATE

$Zn(CH_3CO_2)_2 \cdot 2H_2O$; mol. wt. 219.50; anhydrous—83.58%; H_2O—16.42%; Zn—29.79%; acetic acid = 54.71%.

White, crystalline plates, having a slight odor of acetic acid.   Soluble in 3 parts of water, in 30 parts of alcohol.

Standards

Insoluble	max 0.010%	Alkalies, Earths, etc.	max 0.20%
Chloride (Cl)	max 0.001%	Arsenic (As)	max 1 ppm
Nitrate (NO_3)	max 0.003%	Iron (Fe)	max 0.001%
Sulfate (SO_4)	max 0.005%	Lead (Pb)	max 0.005%

Insoluble: Dissolve 10 g in 100 ml of water and 1 ml of glacial acetic acid. Filter any undissolved residue, wash it with water, and dry at 105°.   Its weight does not exceed 1.0 mg.

Chloride: Dissolve 1 g in 10 ml of water, add 1 ml of HNO_3 and 1 ml of silver nitrate.   Any resulting turbidity is not greater than that in a blank to which 0.01 mg of Cl has been added.

Nitrate: Dissolve 0.2 g in 20 ml of water, add 20 mg of NaCl and 0.2 ml of diphenylamine solution, mix and slowly add 10 ml of H_2SO_4.   Mix gently and allow to stand for 30 minutes.   No blue color results.

Sulfate: Dissolve 2 g in 15 ml of water, add 1 ml of 1 N HCl and 2 ml of $BaCl_2$. If any turbidity is produced, it is not greater than that in a blank to which 0.1 mg of SO_4 has been added.

Alkalies, Earths, etc.: Dissolve 2 g in 140 ml of water, add 10 ml of NH_4OH, precipitate the zinc with H_2S, and filter without washing.   To 75 ml of the filtrate add 5 drops of H_2SO_4, evaporate, and ignite.   Not more than 2.0 mg of residue remains.

Arsenic: Test 2 g by the method on page 563.   The stain is not more than that from 0.002 mg of As.

Iron: Dissolve 1 g in 15 ml of water, then add 2 ml of HCl, about 50 mg of ammonium persulfate, and 15 ml of butanolic potassium thiocyanate.   Shake well and allow to separate.   Any red color in the butanol layer (upper) is not darker than that of a blank to which 0.01 mg of Fe has been added.

Lead: Dissolve 1 g in sufficient water to make 25 ml.   To 5 ml of the solution add 0.02 mg of Pb, then add, with stirring, 25 ml of 10% sodium cyanide solution and dilute to 50 ml (A).   To 15 ml of the solution add, with continuous stirring, 25 ml of the sodium cyanide solution and dilute to 50 ml (B).   Then to each add 0.5 ml of freshly prepared, approximately 5% sodium sulfide solution. B is not darker than A.

ZINC CARBONATE

A basic carbonate of zinc of somewhat variable composition.   It is a white powder.   Insoluble in water; soluble in dilute acids with effervescence; also soluble in ammonium hydroxide and alkali hydroxide solutions.

Standards

Assay.....................min 70% ZnO	Alkali carbonate
Sulfuric acid—insoluble......max 0.010%	(as Na_2CO_3)...............max 0.05%
Chloride (Cl)...............max 0.002%	Alkalies, Earths (as Sulfates)...max 0.30%
Nitrate (NO_3)..............max 0.003%	Arsenic (As)................max 2 ppm
Sulfate (SO_4)...............max 0.010%	Iron (Fe)..................max 0.002%
	Lead (Pb)..................max 0.01%

Assay: Weigh accurately about 2 g and add 50 ml of 1 N H_2SO_4.   When dissolved, add methyl orange and titrate the excess of acid with 1 N NaOH.   One ml of 1 N H_2SO_4 = 0.04069 g ZnO, log 60949.

Sulfuric acid—insoluble: To 10 g add, in small portions, a mixture of 100 ml of H_2O and 7 ml of H_2SO_4, then heat on the steam bath for 1 hour.   If an insoluble residue remains, filter, wash it well with H_2O, and dry at 105°.   Its weight does not exceed 1.0 mg.

Chloride: Dissolve 1 g in a mixture of 2 ml of HNO_3 and 20 ml of H_2O and add 1 ml of silver nitrate.   Any resulting turbidity is not greater than that in a blank to which 0.02 mg of Cl has been added.

Nitrate: Mix 0.2 g of sample with 10 ml of water, add 20 mg of NaCl and 0.2 ml of diphenylamine solution and slowly run in 10 ml of H_2SO_4.   Mix gently and let stand for 30 minutes.   No blue color appears.

Sulfate: To 1 g add 5 ml of water and sufficient HCl to dissolve.   Evaporate the solution to about 2 ml, take up with 1 ml of 1 N HCl and 20 ml of water, and add 2 ml of $BaCl_2$.   Any resulting turbidity is not greater than that in a control made with 0.2 mg of SO_4, 1 ml of 1 N HCl, and 2 ml of $BaCl_2$ in the same volume as with the sample.

Alkali carbonate: Boil 3 g with 30 ml of water for 5 minutes, cool, dilute with water to 30 ml, and filter.   To 20 ml of the filtrate add 1 drop of methyl orange and titrate with 0.1 N HCl to a pink color.   Not more than 0.2 ml of the acid is required.

Alkalies, Earths, etc.: Dissolve 1 g in a mixture of 10 ml of water and 2 ml of H_2SO_4 and dilute to 90 ml.   Add 10 ml of NH_4OH and precipitate the zinc with H_2S.   Filter without washing, evaporate 50 ml of the filtrate, and ignite.   Not more than 1.5 mg of residue remains.

Arsenic: Test 1 g by the method on page 563.   The stain is not more than that from 0.003 mg of As.

Iron: Heat 1.0 g with 5 ml of water and add HCl dropwise until just dissolved. Cool and dilute to 50 ml.   Add 2 ml of HCl, 30 mg of ammonium persulfate and 3 ml of ammonium thiocyanate.   Any resulting red color is not darker than that of a control made with 0.02 mg of Fe, 2 ml of HCl and the same quantities of the other reagents as with the sample.

Lead: Heat 0.5 g with 10 ml of H_2O, then add dropwise HNO_3 until just dissolved.   Add NH_4OH dropwise until a slight permanent precipitate is produced, then add just sufficient HNO_3 to dissolve the precipitate and dilute to 25 ml.   To 5 ml add 0.015 mg of Pb and, while stirring, add 30 ml of 10% sodium cyanide solution and dilute to 50 ml (A).   To the remaining 20 ml add, with stirring, 30 ml of the sodium cyanide solution (B).   Then to each add 0.5 ml of freshly prepared, approximately 5% sodium sulfide solution. B is not darker than A.

ZINC CHLORIDE

$ZnCl_2$; mol. wt. 136.29; Zn—47.96%; Cl—52.04%.

White or nearly white granules or cylindrical rods; rapidly deliquescent. Soluble in less than 1 part of H_2O, in about 1 part of alcohol, in 2 parts of glycerol. *Keep in tightly closed containers.*

Standards

Assay...................min 97% $ZnCl_2$	Alkalies, Earths, etc...........max 0.20%
Oxychloride..................to pass test	Ammonia (NH_3).............max 0.005%
Insoluble.....................max 0.005%	Iron (Fe)...................max 0.001%
Nitrate (NO_3)..... ....max 0.003%	Lead (Pb).................max 0.005%
Sulfate (SO_4)...............max 0.010%	

Assay: Zinc chloride may be assayed by either of the methods for assay of chlorides or thiocyanates, page 565.   One ml of 0.1 N $AgNO_3$ = 0.006815 g of $ZnCl_2$.   It may also be assayed by determining the Zn according to the mercuric ammonium thiocyanate procedure under Zinc Nitrate.

Oxychloride: Dissolve 20 g in 200 ml of H_2O.   On adding 6 ml of 1 N HCl to the solution the flocculent precipitate entirely dissolves.

Insoluble: Add a few drops of HCl to the solution from the preceding test, filter any undissolved residue, wash it with water containing 1 ml of HCl per 100 ml, and dry at 105°.   Its weight does not exceed 1.0 mg.

Nitrate: Dissolve 0.2 in 10 ml of water, add 0.2 ml of diphenylamine solution, then add slowly and without agitation 10 ml of H_2SO_4. After 10 minutes mix by gentle swirling and allow to stand for 1 hour. No blue color appears.

Sulfate: Dissolve 2 g in 20 ml of water and 1 ml of 1 N HCl, and add 2 ml of barium chloride. Any turbidity produced is not greater than that in a blank to which 0.2 mg of SO_4 has been added.

Alkalies, Earths, etc.: Dissolve 2 g in 140 ml of water, add 10 ml of NH_4OH, precipitate the zinc with H_2S, and filter without washing. To 75 ml of the filtrate add 5 drops of H_2SO_4, evaporate, and ignite. Not more than 2.0 mg of residue remains.

Ammonia: Dissolve 1 g in 50 ml of water. To 10 ml of the solution add 10 ml of 10% NaOH, dilute to 50 ml, and add 2 ml of Nessler solution. The color is not darker than that in a blank to which 0.01 mg of NH_3 (0.03 mg NH_4Cl) has been added.

Iron: Dissolve 1 g in 15 ml of water, add 1 ml of HCl, 30 mg of ammonium persulfate, and 15 ml of butanolic potassium thiocyanate; shake well and allow to separate. Any red color in the butanol layer is not darker than that in a blank to which 0.01 mg of Fe has been added.

Lead: Dissolve 1 g in 10 ml of H_2O with the aid of 1 drop of HCl and dilute to 20 ml. To 5 ml of the solution add 0.025 mg of Pb and 25 ml of 10% sodium cyanide solution and dilute with water to 40 ml (A). To the remaining 15 ml of the solution add 25 ml of the sodium cyanide solution (B). Then to each add 0.5 ml of approximately 5% sodium sulfide solution. B is not darker than A.

ZINC DUST

Zinc Powder

Fine, gray powder. Usually contains some zinc oxide. It absorbs nitrogen from the air and, in moist condition, readily occludes oxygen. *Keep in well-closed containers.*

Standards

Assay.............min 95% metallic Zn   Nitrogen (N)...............max 0.002%

Assay: Weigh accurately about 0.1 g, transfer it into a 300 ml flask with the aid of 25 ml of water, and add a freshly prepared solution of 2.5 g of ferric ammonium sulfate in 25 ml of water. Add a few glass beads, allow to stand, shaking frequently, until the zinc has dissolved. Then add promptly a mixture of 5 ml of H_2SO_4 and 50 ml of water, and titrate the ferrous salt formed with 0.1 N potassium permanganate. Correct for a blank. One ml of 0.1 N permanganate = 3.269 mg Zn, log 51441.

Nitrogen: Dissolve 12 g in a mixture of 10 ml of H_2SO_4 and 100 ml of water in a Kjeldahl flask, heating gently if necessary. Cool, connect the flask with a condenser carrying an efficient trap bulb and a receiver containing 10 ml of 0.02 N HCl. Add to the flask 50 ml of 30% NaOH, and distill about 60 ml into the receiver. Titrate the excess of acid with 0.02 N NaOH, using methyl red as the indicator. Not more than 0.75 ml of the 0.02 N HCl is neutralized by the ammonia in the distillate. Correct for any nitrogen in the reagents by conducting a blank with 2 g of the zinc and the same quantities of H_2SO_4 and NaOH and in the same manner as with the sample.

ZINC NITRATE

$Zn(NO_3)_2 \cdot 6H_2O$; mol. wt. 297.49; anhydrous—63.67%; H_2O—36.33%; Zn—21.97%; NO_3—41.70%; ZnO—27.36%.

When in the form of fragments it usually contains less water than indicated by the formula.

Colorless or white crystals, or fragments. Soluble in 1 part of water; soluble in alcohol. *Keep in well-closed containers.*

Standards

Insoluble	max 0.005%	Ammonia (NH_3)	max 0.01%
Free acid (as HNO_3)	max 0.02%	Iron (Fe)	max 0.001%
Chloride (Cl)	max 0.002%	Lead (Pb)	max 0.005%
Sulfate (SO_4)	max 0.010%	Assay	
Alkalies, Earths, etc.	max 0.20%		

Insoluble: Dissolve 20 g in 150 ml of water and a few drops of HNO_3, and heat on the steam bath for 30 minutes. Filter any undissolved residue, wash it well, and dry at 105°. Its weight does not exceed 1.0 mg.

Free acid: Dissolve 2 g in 20 ml of water and add 2 drops of methyl orange. If a pink color is produced, it is changed to yellow by 0.5 ml of 0.02 N NaOH.

Chloride: Dissolve 1 g in 25 ml of H_2O, add 1 ml of HNO_3 and 1 ml of $AgNO_3$. Any turbidity produced is not greater than that in a blank to which 0.02 mg of Cl has been added.

Sulfate: Evaporate 2 g with 5 ml of HCl on the steam bath. Take up the residue with 1 ml of 1 N HCl and 20 ml of H_2O, and add 2 ml of $BaCl_2$. Any resulting turbidity is not greater than that in a control made with 0.2 mg of SO_4, 1 ml of 1 N HCl, and 2 ml of $BaCl_2$ in the same volume as with the sample.

Alkalies, Earths, etc.; Ammonia; Lead: Apply the tests described under *Zinc Chloride*, but use only 0.5 g of sample in the test for *Ammonia*. The results should be as there stated.

Iron: To a solution of 1 g in 15 ml of H_2O add 0.5 ml of HCl and 15 ml of butanolic potassium thiocyanate, shake well, and allow to separate. Any red color in the butanol layer is not darker than that in a blank to which 0.01 mg of Fe has been added.

Assay: Zinc nitrate may be assayed by cautiously igniting it to ZnO. The weight of the ZnO multiplied by 3.655 represents zinc nitrate.

Zinc nitrate may also be assayed by the following method: Weigh accurately about 2 g, dissolve it in 2 ml of HCl and sufficient water to make exactly 250 ml. Dilute 50 ml with 50 ml of water, add 5 ml of HCl, then add, with vigorous stirring, 40 ml of mercuric ammonium thiocyanate solution (page 558), and allow to stand for 2 hours. Filter on a tared crucible, wash first with a solution containing 20 ml of the mercury-thiocyanate solution per liter, then with 20 ml of cold water and dry to constant weight at 105°. The weight of the precipitate multiplied by $0.5971 = Zn(NO_3)_2 \cdot 6H_2O$, log 77605.

ZINC OXIDE

ZnO; mol. wt. 81.38; Zn—80.34%.

White, amorphous powder. Insoluble in water; soluble in dilute acids or in ammonium hydroxide or ammonium carbonate solution, also in solutions of alkali hydroxides.

Standards

Sulfuric acid—insoluble......max 0.010%
Alkali carbonate..............to pass test
Chloride (Cl)................max 0.001%
Nitrate (NO_3)..............max 0.002%
Sulfur compounds (as SO_4)....max 0.010%
Alkalies, Earths, etc..........max 0.10%

Arsenic (As)................max 1 ppm
Iron (Fe)..................max 0.001%
Lead (Pb)..................max 0.005%
Manganese (Mn)...........max 0.0005%
Permanganate-reducing
    substances................to pass test

Sulfuric acid—insoluble: Mix 10 g with 150 ml of water, add 10 ml of H_2SO_4 and heat on the steam bath for 30 minutes. If an undissolved residue remains, filter, wash it well with water, and dry at 105°. Its weight does not exceed 1.0 mg.

Alkali carbonate: Boil 2 g with 20 ml of water for 1 minute and filter. Cool the filtrate and add 2 drops of phenolphthalein; no pink color is produced.

Chloride: Dissolve 1 g in a cold mixture of 2 ml of HNO_3 and 10 ml of water and add 1 ml of silver nitrate. Any resulting turbidity is not greater than that in a blank to which 0.01 mg of Cl has been added.

Nitrate: Suspend 0.5 g in 5 ml of water, add 25% H_2SO_4 until dissolved and dilute to 20 ml. To 10 ml add 20 mg of NaCl and 0.2 ml of diphenylamine solution, mix and then add 10 ml of H_2SO_4. No blue color is produced in 30 minutes.

Sulfur compounds: Mix 2 g with 25 ml of H_2O, add 20 mg sodium carbonate and 0.5 ml of bromine water. Boil for 5 minutes, then add just sufficient HCl to dissolve the oxide. Filter, if necessary, dilute with H_2O to 20 ml and add 2 ml of $BaCl_2$. If a turbidity is produced, it is not greater than that in a control made with 0.2 mg of SO_4, 2 ml of 1 N HCl, and the same quantities of sodium carbonate, bromine water and $BaCl_2$ and in the same volume as with the sample.

Alkalies, Earths, etc.: Dissolve 2 g by heating with a mixture of 15 ml of water and 5 ml of glacial acetic acid. Dilute to 140 ml and pass in H_2S to precipitate most of the zinc; then make alkaline with NH_4OH and pass in H_2S for 5 minutes longer. Dilute with water to 150 ml and filter without washing. To 75 ml of the filtrate add 5 drops of H_2SO_4, evaporate, and ignite. Not more than 1.0 mg of residue remains.

Arsenic: Dissolve 2 g in 15 ml of water and just sufficient H_2SO_4 to dissolve and test the solution for arsenic by the method on page 563. The stain is not greater than that from 0.002 mg of As.

Iron: Dissolve 1 g in a mixture of 4 ml of HCl and 10 ml of H_2O. Add to the solution 50 mg of ammonium persulfate and 15 ml of butanolic potassium thiocyanate, shake well, and allow to separate. Any red color in the butanol layer is not darker than that of a control made with 0.01 mg of Fe, 1 ml of HCl and the same quantities of the other reagents and in the same volume as with the sample.

Lead: Heat 1.0 g with 10 ml of H_2O and add HCl dropwise, with stirring, until just dissolved. Add NH_4OH dropwise until a slight permanent precipitate is produced, then add just sufficient HCl to dissolve the precipitate and dilute to 20 ml. To 5 ml add 0.025 mg of Pb and, while stirring, 30 ml of 10% sodium cyanide solution and dilute to 50 ml (A). To the remaining 15 ml add, with stirring, 30 ml of 10% sodium cyanide solution (B). Then to each add 0.5 ml of freshly prepared, approximately 5% sodium sulfide solution. B is not darker than A.

Manganese: Dissolve 2 g in 30 ml of water and 10 ml of HNO_3. Add 5 ml each of H_2SO_4 and of phosphoric acid and boil for 5 minutes. Cool, add 0.25 g of potassium periodate and again boil for 5 minutes. Any pink color produced is not darker than that produced by treating 0.01 mg of Mn exactly as the sample.

Permanganate-reducing substances: Carefully triturate in a mortar 5 g of the zinc oxide with 40 ml of water containing in solution 0.25 g of ferric ammonium sulfate (free from ferrous). Transfer the mixture with the aid of 75 ml of oxygen-free water into a flask, add in small portions 5 ml of H_2SO_4 and warm, if necessary, to dissolve the oxide. Cool the solution and add 0.15 ml of 0.1 N potassium permanganate. The solution acquires a pink color which persists for 15 seconds. Correct for a blank made with the reagents.

ZINC SULFATE

$ZnSO_4 \cdot 7H_2O$; mol. wt. 287.56; anhydrous—56.14%; H_2O—43.86%; Zn—22.74%; SO_4—33.41%.

Colorless or white crystals. Efflorescent in dry air. At 200° it loses all of its H_2O. Soluble in 1 part of water; slowly soluble in glycerol; insoluble in alcohol. The water in zinc sulfate may be determined by the iodine (Fischer) method.

Standards

Insoluble..................max 0.010%	Ammonia (NH_3)............max 0.002%	
Free acid...................to pass test	Arsenic (As)................max 1 ppm	
Chloride (Cl)..............max 0.0005%	Iron (Fe)...................max 0.001%	
Nitrate (NO_3)..............max 0.002%	Lead (Pb).................max 0.002%	
Alkalies, Earths, etc..........max 0.20%	Manganese (Mn)...........max 0.0003%	

Insoluble: Dissolve 10 g on 100 ml of water and heat on the steam bath for 1 hour. Filter any undissolved residue, wash it with water, and dry at 105°. Its weight does not exceed 1.0 mg.

Free acid: Dissolve 2 g in 30 ml of water and add 1 drop of methyl orange; no pink color is produced.

Chloride: To a solution of 2 g in 10 ml of water add 1 ml of HNO_3 and 1 ml of silver nitrate. Any resulting turbidity is not greater than that in a blank to which 0.01 mg Cl has been added.

Nitrate: Dissolve 0.25 g in 10 ml of water, add 20 mg of NaCl and 0.2 ml of diphenylamine solution and slowly run in 10 ml of H_2SO_4. Mix gently and allow to stand for 30 minutes. No blue color results.

Alkalies, Earths, etc.: Dissolve 2 g in 150 ml of water, pass in H_2S to precipitate most of the zinc, then add 1 ml of NH_4OH and pass more H_2S to precipitate the zinc completely, and filter without washing. Evaporate 75 ml of the filtrate and ignite. Not more than 2.0 mg of residue remains.

Ammonia: To a solution of 1 g in 20 ml of H_2O add sufficient 10% NaOH to redissolve the precipitate first formed, dilute to 50 ml and add 2 ml of Nessler solution. The color is not darker than that of a blank to which 0.02 mg of NH_3 (0.06 mg NH_4Cl) has been added.

Arsenic: Test 2 g by the method on page 563. The stain is not greater than that from 0.002 mg of As.

Iron: Dissolve 1 g in 10 ml of H_2O, add 1 ml of HCl, about 30 mg of ammonium persulfate and 15 ml of butanolic potassium thiocyanate (page 4). Shake vigorously for 30 seconds and allow to separate. Any red color in the clear butanol layer is not darker than that in a blank to which 0.01 mg of Fe has been added.

Lead: Dissolve 2 g in sufficient water to make 20 ml. To 5 ml of the solution add 0.02 mg of Pb, then add, while stirring, 30 ml of 10% sodium cyanide solution and dilute to 50 ml (A). To the remaining 15 ml add, with stirring, 30 ml of 10% sodium cyanide solution and dilute to 50 ml (B). Then to each add 0.5 ml of freshly prepared, approximately 5% sodium sulfide solution. B is not darker than A.

Manganese: Dissolve 5 g in 50 ml of water, add 5 ml of H_2SO_4, 10 ml of HNO_3, and 5 ml of phosphoric acid, and boil for 5 minutes. Cool, add 0.25 g of potassium periodate, and again boil for 5 minutes. Any pink color in the filtrate is not darker than that resulting from treating 0.015 mg of Mn in the same manner as the sample.

ZIRCONIUM NITRATE

$Zr(NO_3)_4 \cdot 5H_2O$; mol. wt. 429.33; H_2O—20.98%; Zr—21.25%; NO_3—57.73%.

Colorless or white crystals, pieces or scales, usually having a strong acid odor. Freely soluble in water; soluble in alcohol.

Standards

Solubility....................to pass test	Heavy metals (as Pb)........max 0.003%
Chloride (Cl)................max 0.002%	Iron (Fe)....................max 0.010%
Sulfate (SO$_4$)................max 0.005%	Thorium (Th)................to pass test
Alkalies, Earths, etc...........max 0.10%	(max about 0.1%)
Aluminum (Al)...............to pass test	
(max about 0.1%)	

Solubility: A solution of 2 g in 25 ml of H_2O is complete and clear, or not more than slightly opalescent.

Chloride: To a solution of 1 g in 20 ml of H_2O, filtered if not clear, add 1 ml of HNO_3 and 1 ml of $AgNO_3$. Any turbidity produced is not greater than that in a blank to which 0.02 mg of Cl has been added.

Solution S: Dissolve 2 g in 75 ml of hot water and pour the solution slowly, with stirring, into a mixture of 5 ml of ammonium hydroxide and 50 ml of H_2O. Boil for 10 minutes, cook, add sufficient water to make 100 ml and filter.

Sulfate: Boil down 20 ml of *Solution S* to about 10 ml, neutralize with HCl, dilute to 20 ml, add 1 ml of 1 N HCl and 2 ml of $BaCl_2$. If a turbidity is produced, it is not greater than that of a control made with 0.2 mg of SO_4, 1 ml of 1 N HCl and 2 ml of $BaCl_2$ in the same final volume as with the sample.

Alkalies, Earths, etc.: Evaporate 50 ml of *Solution S* to about 10 ml, refilter if necessary, add to the filtrate a few drops of H_2SO_4, evaporate and ignite to constant weight. The residue amounts to not more than 1.0 mg.

Aluminium: Dissolve 1 g in 20 ml of water, pour the solution with stirring into 10 ml of 10% NaOH diluted with an equal volume of water, and filter. To 20 ml of the filtrate add 1 g of ammonium chloride and boil for 2 minutes. No turbidity is produced.

Heavy metals: Dissolve 2 g in water to make 50 ml and filter if not clear. To 5 ml of the solution add 0.03 mg of Pb and a solution of 0.5 g of sodium acetate in 10 ml of water, and dilute to 40 ml (*A*). To 30 ml of the solution add a solution of 1 g of sodium acetate in 10 ml of water (*B*). Then to each add 10 ml of H_2S. *B* is not darker than *A*.

Iron: To 5 ml of the solution from the preceding test add 0.5 ml of HCl and 15 ml of butanolic potassium thiocyanate, shake well, and allow to separate. Any red color in the butanol layer is not darker than that in a blank to which 0.02 mg of Fe has been added.

Thorium: Dissolve 1 g in 25 ml of water, filter if not clear, warm to about 50°, and add 2 ml of a 10% potassium fluoride solution. No turbidity is produced in 10 minutes.

REAGENT SOLUTIONS OR FORMULATIONS

(Frequently used in Analytical Chemical Work)

A

Alkaline Lead Solution: see POTASSIUM PLUMBITE SOLUTION.

Amalgamated Zinc: Place 300 g of 20–30 mesh pure granular zinc in a beaker, and add to it 300 ml of a 2% solution of mercuric chloride (or nitrate) and 1 ml of HCl. Stir the mixture thoroughly for 5–10 minutes, then decant the liquid, and wash the amalgamated zinc several times by decantation with water. The amalgamated zinc should have a bright silvery color.

Ammonio-Silver Nitrate Solution: see SILVER AMMONIUM NITRATE SOLUTION.

Ammonium Mercuric Thiocyanate Solution: see MERCURIC AMMONIUM THIOCYANATE SOLUTION.

Ammonium Molybdate Solution for the *gravimetric* or *volumetric* determination of Phosphorus (phosphate), *see* page 4.

Aqua Regia is a mixture of 1 volume of nitric acid (sp. gr. 1.4) with 3 volumes of hydrochloric acid (sp. gr. 1.18).

B

Barfoed's Reagent for Glucose (Dextrose) is a solution of 13.3 g of cupric acetate in a mixture of 198 ml of water and 2 ml of glacial acetic acid.
Ref.: *Z anal. Chem.* **12**, 27 (1873); *J. Am. Chem. Soc.* **29**, 1744 (1907).

Benedict Solutions for Reducing Sugar: (*a*) For *quantitative* determination: Dissolve 200 g of sodium carbonate decahydrate (or 75 g of anhydrous), 170 g of sodium citrate ($2H_2O$) and 125 g of potassium thiocyanate in about 800 ml of warm water and filter if necessary. Dissolve 18.0 g of crystal cupric sulfate in about 100 ml of water and slowly pour this solution into the preceding one, while stirring. Now add 5 ml of 5% potassium ferrocyanide solution, cool, and dilute to exactly 1 liter; 25 ml of this solution = 50 mg of glucose.
Ref.: *J. Biol. Chem.* **5**, 485 (1909).

(*b*) For *qualitative* detection: dissolve 17.3 g of crystalline cupric sulfate, 144 g of sodium citrate ($2H_2O$) and 100 g of anhydrous sodium carbonate in water to make 1 liter. It is used like Fehling solution.

Benzidine-Cupric Acetate Solution for Cyanide: (*a*) Prepare a saturated solution of benzidine acetate and dilute 47.5 ml of this solution to 100 ml. (*b*) Dissolve 0.286 g of cupric acetate in water; dilute to 100 ml.

When the mixture of the two reagents is spotted on filter paper exposed to HCN gas, a blue color is produced.

C

Cadmium Iodide Linear Starch: Used in the colorimetric determination of microgram quantities of iodine, especially in biologic fluids, it may be prepared as follows: Dissolve

12.0 g of CdI_2 in 400 ml of water and boil gently for 10–15 minutes to expel any free iodine. Dilute to 800 ml, and while stirring add 15 g of the amylase potato starch fraction ("superlose" Stein Hall Co., New York) to the gently boiling solution and boil for 10 minutes longer. Filter with suction through a fine filter while maintaining the solution at about 65°. Dilute the filtrate with water to one liter. If a high-speed centrifuge is available, the time-consuming filtration can be eliminated.

Ref.: Lambert, J. L., and Zotomer, F., *Anal. Chem.* **35**, No. 3, 405 (1963).

Chromous Sulfate ($CrSO_4$) Standard Solution (0.1 N):

(1) Mercury amalgam: Stir 250 g of 20-mesh zinc with 125 ml of 10% HCl (1 conc. HCl + 3 water) for about 1 minute. Add a solution of 3 g of mercuric chloride in 100 ml of water and stir for 3 to 5 minutes. Decant and wash the amalgamated zinc thoroughly by decantation with water.

(2) Mix 3 ml of concentrated H_2SO_4 with 1 liter of H_2O, cool by the addition of ice if necessary to 20°–25°, then dissolve in it 52 g of chromium potassium sulfate.

Place the amalgamated zinc in a Jones reductor suitably connected with a burette, a reservoir bottle for the Cr_2 solution placed above the top level of the burette, and a source of CO_2 to displace the air from the system and to pressure the chrome alum solution upward through the reductor into the reservoir bottle at the rate of about 50 ml per minute (for details see the publication of the authors indicated under Ref.). The Cr^2 solution in the reservoir is finally standardized as follows: Siphon the solution into the burette, then run an accurately measured volume 20–30 ml into 40 ml of 0.1 N iodine (KI_3) and determine the excess of iodine with 0.1 N sodium thiosulfate.

Ref.: Stone, H. W., and Beeson, C., *Anal. Chem.* 188 (1936).

Cochineal Solution is prepared by macerating 1 g of cochineal with 80 ml of 25% alcohol for 4 days in a loosely stoppered flask, and then filtering. Yellowish-red with acid, violet with alkalies.

Curcumin Indicator Solution for Beryllium determination is a solution of 0.1 g of curcumin in 100 ml of alcohol. pH range: 6.0 yellow; 8.0 brown-red.

D

Decolorized Magenta: *see* FUCHSINE-SULFUROUS ACID SOLUTION.

Diazotized Sulfanilic Acid Solution (Diazobenzenesulfonic Acid Solution): Dissolve 0.2 g of sulfanilic acid in 20 ml of 1 N HCl, cool well in ice, add sufficient 10% (W/V) sodium nitrite solution until an immediate blue color is produced with starch iodide paper, then add 50 mg of sulfamic acid.

Ref.: *British Pharmacopœia*, 1953.

F

Fehling Solution for Glucose consists of 2 solutions: (*a*) A solution of 34.64 g crystalline cupric sulfate in water to make 500 ml. (*b*) 173 g Rochelle salt and 150 ml of KOH solution, sp. gr. 1.14, with water to make 500 ml. For use, equal volumes of (*a*) and (*b*) are mixed.

Ref.: *Ann.* **72**, 106 (1849); **106**, 75 (1858).

Folin-Denis Reagent for Phenols: Heat 20 g phosphomolybdic acid,

100 g sodium tungstate and 50 ml 85% phosphoric acid with 750 ml of water for 2 hours under a reflux condenser and, after cooling, add water to make 1 liter. This reagent is colored blue by phenols.

Ref.: *J. Biol. Chem.* **12**, 239 (1912).

Fröhde Reagent for Alkaloids is a freshly prepared solution of 100 mg of ammonium or sodium molybdate in 100 ml of concentrated H_2SO_4.

Fuchsine-Sulfurous Acid Solution for Aldehyde is made by dissolving 0.2 g of basic fuchsine in 120 ml of warm water and then, after cooling, adding 2 g of sodium bisulfite, 2 ml of HCl and diluting to 200 ml.

H

Hanus Solution for determining the Iodine Number of fats and oils.

Dissolve 13.2 g iodine in 1000 ml of glacial acetic acid with the aid of gentle heat. Cool the solution to 25° and determine the iodine content in a 25-ml portion by titration with 0.1 N sodium thiosulfate. Add to the remainder of the solution a quantity of bromine equivalent to that of the iodine present. The solution must be kept in glass-stoppered bottles, protected from light.

Ref.: *Z. Untersuch. Nahr. u. Genussm.* 1901, p. 913.

Hubl Solution for determining the Iodine Number of fats and oils: (*a*) A solution of 25 g iodine in 500 ml 90% alcohol. (*b*) A solution of 30 g mercuric chloride in 500 ml 90% alcohol.

Hubl states that the reagent is preserved in the mixed form, but the reagent should not be used until 48 hours after the mixing.

Ref.: *Z. anal. Chem.* **25**, 432 (1886); **39**, 654 (1900).

I

Iodeosin Indicator Solution is a solution of 0.1 g of iodeosin in 100 ml of ether saturated with water.

Iodine Monochloride Solution is prepared as follows: Dissolve 4.3 g of potassium iodate and 6.7 g of potassium iodide in 50 ml of water, add 50 ml of HCl and shake until solution results. Add 5 ml of chloroform, then add dilute (*M*/20) potassium iodate until the chloroform becomes colorless.

Iodobromide Solution for determining the Iodine Number of fats and oils: *see* HANUS SOLUTION.

K

Kraut Reagent for Alkaloids (Bismuth-Potassium Iodide Solution): Dissolve 8 g of $Bi(NO_3)_3 \cdot 5H_2O$ in 20 ml of 20–25% HNO_3 (1 vol. conc. HNO_3 + 3 water). Dissolve 27.5 g of KI in 50 ml of H_2O. Mix the solutions and dilute to 100 ml.

L

Litmus Indicator Solution: Digest 25 g of powdered litmus with 3 successive 100-ml volumes of boiling alcohol, continuing each extraction for about 1 hour. Filter, wash with alcohol, and discard the alcohol filtrate. Macerate the residue with about 25 ml of cold water for 4 hours; filter, wash with 15 ml of water, and discard the filtrate. Digest the resulting residue with 125 ml of boiling water for 1 hour and filter.

Logwood Solution: Pour 100 ml of boiling water over 2 g of fresh logwood chips, allow to stand for a few hours, and filter.

M

Magnesia Mixture for Phosphate or Arsenate determination: Dissolve 55 g of magnesium chloride and 70 g of ammonium chloride in 650 ml of water, then add 120 ml of 28% ammonia and sufficient water to make 1 liter.

Magnesium Uranyl Acetate (Uranium Magnesium Acetate):

(a) Dissolve 50 g of uranyl acetate in water, add 25 ml of glacial acetic acid and dilute with water to 500 ml.

(b) Dissolve 300 g of magnesium acetate in water, add 25 ml of glacial acetic acid and dilute to 500 ml.

Mix the two solutions, allow to stand overnight and filter if necessary.

Marme Reagent for alkaloids: Dissolve 6 g of KI in 18 ml of H_2O, then dissolve in this solution 3 g of CdI_2.

Marquis Reagent for Alkaloids is concentrated H_2SO_4 mixed with 1 drop of formaldehyde solution for each ml of the acid.

Mayer's Reagent for Alkaloids (Mercuric Potassium Iodide Solution): Dissolve 1.358 g of mercuric chloride in 60 ml of water. Dissolve 5 g of potassium iodide in 10 ml of water. Mix the two solutions and add water to make 100 ml.

Ref.: *Am. J. Pharm.* **35**, 20 (1863).

Mercuric Ammonium Thiocyanate Solution is made by dissolving 30 g of ammonium thiocyanate and 27 g of mercuric chloride in water to make 1 liter.

Mercury Iodocyanide Reagent for Organic Acids: Dissolve 1.6 g of mercuric cyanide in 25 ml of water and add to it 25 ml of a solution containing 0.9 g of iodine and 1.6 g of potassium iodide.

Ref.: *C. A.* **34**, 958 (1950).

Millon's Reagent: To 3 ml (40 g) of mercury contained in a flask and under the hood, slowly add 30 ml of HNO_3 (sp. gr. 1.4) and frequently shake the contents (but do not heat) until the reaction has ceased. Allow to stand for one hour or longer, and as crystals separate warm *slightly* to dissolve them and add 10–20 ml of $1+4$ HNO_3. Pour off the liquid from any unreacted mercury, and dilute with an equal volume of H_2O containing 2 ml of HNO_3 per 100 ml.

Murexide-Naphthol Green Indicator: To 5 g of powdered KCl or K_2SO_4 add 50 mg of murexide and 125 mg of naphthol green, and grind in a mortar to a homogeneous mixture.

N

Nessler Solution (reagent): *see* p. 6.

Nitro-chromic Acid Solution: Mix 1 volume of 5% potassium chromate solution with 133 volumes of water and 66 volumes of nitric acid (sp. gr. 1.4). This solution should not be used if more than one month old.

P

Pavy Solutions for glucose: (a) To 120 ml of Fehling Solution add 300 ml of ammonia, sp. gr. 0.89, and dilute with water to 1 liter. Glucose reduces this solution with decolorization and without precipitation of cuprous oxide. Ten ml is equivalent to 0.005 g of glucose.

(b) Dissolve 4.158 g of cupric sulfate in 250 ml water and add 10 g of mannite, 50 ml of glycerin, and a solution of 20.4 g of KOH in 100 m water. Finally add 300 ml of ammonia, sp. gr. 0.89, filter, and dilute the filtrate to 1 liter with water.

Twenty-five ml of this solution is equivalent to 15 mg of glucose.

Ref.: *Z. anal. Chem.* **19**, 98 (1880); *Pharm. Zentralhalle*, 1901, p. 618.

o-**Phenanthroline Solution** as a Redox Indicator: Dissolve 0.5 g of *o*-Phenanthroline in a freshly prepared solution of 0.5 g of crystalline ferrous sulfate in 100 ml of water containing 2 drops of H_2SO_4.

Phosgene Test Paper: Dissolve without heat 5 g of dimethylaminobenzaldehyde and 5 g of colorless diphenylamine in 100 ml of absolute alcohol. Impregnate strips of unsized paper (filter paper) with the solution, drain and dry by suspending them vertically in the dark in air free from acid fumes. Discard 3–5 cm from the top and bottom of each strip.

Potassium Plumbite Solution for the detection of Sulfidic Sulfur in organic compounds: Dissolve 1.7 g of lead acetate, 3.4 g of potassium citrate and 50 g of potassium hydroxide in water to make 100 ml.

Pyridine Bromide Solution for determination of Iodine Number of fats and oils: Dissolve 8 g (8.2 ml) of pyridine and 20 ml of H_2SO_4 in 50 ml of glacial acetic acid, keeping the mixture cool. Add 8 g of bromine dissolved in 20 ml of glacial acetic acid and dilute to 1 liter with glacial acetic acid.

Pyrogallol Solution Alkaline, Potassium Pyrogallate Solution: Dissolve 1 g of pyrogallol in 4 ml of water. Dissolve 24 g of potassium hydroxide in 16 ml of water. Mix the two solutions immediately before use.

S

Sanchis Zirconium-Alizarin Indicator for Fluorine: (*a*) Dissolve 0.17 g of alizarin sodium sulfonate in 100 ml of water. (*b*) Dissolve 0.87 g of zirconium nitrate in 100 ml of water.

Slowly add (*a*) to (*b*), shake, and allow to stand overnight. For use, dilute 20 ml with water to 100 ml.

Ref.: *Ind. Eng. Chem., Anal. Ed.* **6**, 184 (1934).

Schiff Reagent for Aldehydes: Dissolve 0.25 g of fuchsine in 1 liter of water and decolorize by passing in the solution sulfur dioxide. Aldehydes give a violet-red color with this reagent.

Ref.: *Ann.* **140**, 93 (1866); Caro, *Ber.* **13**, 2342 (1880).

Silver-Ammonium Nitrate Solution: Dissolve 1 g of silver nitrate in 20 ml of water, add 10% ammonia, dropwise and with stirring, until the precipitate first formed is almost but not entirely dissolved, then filter. Keep this solution in dark-amber bottles.

Sodium Cobaltinitrite Solution for detection and determination of Potassium: Dissolve 25 g of sodium nitrite in 50 ml of water, add 5 ml of glacial acetic acid and 3 g of cobalt nitrate dissolved in 15 ml of water, then dilute with water to 100 ml.

Starch Solution: Triturate 0.5 g of starch, preferably arrowroot, with 10 ml of cold water, and slowly pour it, with constant stirring, into 100 ml of boiling water. Boil gently until the liquid is thin and translucent. Allow to settle and use only the clear supernatant liquid. Keep in the refrigerator.

Starch-Iodate Paper is prepared by impregnating unglazed (filter) paper with STARCH-IODIDE SOLUTION (see below) diluted with an equal volume of a 5% solution of potassium iodate.

Starch-Iodide Paste: Heat 100 ml of water to boiling, add a solution of 0.75 g of KI in 5 ml of water, then follow with a solution of 2 g of zinc chloride in 10 ml of water. While the solution is boiling, add, with stirring, a smooth suspension of 5 g of potato starch in 30 ml of water.   Continue to boil for 2 minutes and then cool.

Starch-Iodide Solution (Starch-Potassium Iodide Solution): Dissolve 0.5 g of potassium iodide and 1 g of zinc chloride in 100 ml of STARCH SOLUTION.   Starch-iodide paper is made by impregnating filter paper with this solution.

Sulfanilic-α-Naphthylamine Solution: Dissolve 0.5 g of sulfanilic acid in 150 ml of 6% acetic acid.   Dissolve 0.1 g of α-naphthylamine in 100 ml of 6% acetic acid and mix the two solutions.   If a pink color develops on standing it may be discharged with a little zinc powder.

T

Tollens Reagent for Aldehydes: Dissolve 1 g of silver nitrate in 10 ml of a mixture of equal volumes of water and ammonium hydroxide, then add 10 ml of 10% NaOH and mix.   The reagent yields a mirror with solutions containing aldehydes.

Ref.: *Ber.* **15**, 1635 (1882).

Turmeric Solution for Borate is prepared as follows: Digest 20 g of ground turmeric root with four 100-ml portions of water, decanting the clear liquid each time and discarding it.   Dry the residue at a temperature not above 100°, then macerate it with 100 ml of alcohol for several days and filter.

U

Uranyl Cobalt Acetate Solution (Cobalt Uranyl Acetate Solution): (*a*) Dissolve 40 g of uranyl acetate in water, add 25 ml of glacial acetic acid, and dilute to 500 ml.

(*b*) Dissolve 200 g of cobalt acetate in water, add 25 ml of glacial acetic acid and dilute to 500 ml.

Mix the two solutions, allow to stand overnight, and filter if necessary.

Uranium (or Uranyl) Magnesium Acetate Solution, *see* page 558.

Uranium (or Uranyl) Zinc Acetate Solution, *see* page 561.

V

Valser Reagent for alkaloids: slowly add a 10% solution of potassium iodide to red mercuric iodide until a small quantity of the mercuric iodide remains undissolved after thorough stirring, and filter.   One-hundred ml of 100% KI solution dissolves approximately 15 g of red mercuric iodide.

W

Wijs Solution for determining the Iodine Number of fats and oils: Dissolve 13 g of iodine in 1 liter of glacial acetic acid that meets the dichromate test.   Set aside 25 ml of the solution and pass dry chlorine into the solution until the color of iodine just disappears.   Add the 25 ml that have been set aside to take up any excess of free chlorine.

Ref.: *Ber.* 1898, p. 750; Dubavetz, *Chem. Ztg.* 1914, p. 114.

Z

Zimmermann-Reinhardt Solution for titrating iron with permanganate in the presence of HCl is prepared as follows: Dissolve 70 g of manganese sulfate (MnSO$_4$·4H$_2$O) or 53 g of MnSO$_4$·H$_2$O in 500 ml of water, add, with constant stirring, 125 ml of H$_2$SO$_4$ (93%–97%) and 125 ml of 85% phosphoric acid and dilute with water to 1 liter.

Ref.: Kolthoff and Sundell, *Quantitative Inorganic Analysis*, p. 572.

Zinc Amalgam: Add 25 g of granular or mossy zinc to 50 ml of mercury in a beaker. Heat with continuous stirring on a hot plate or sand bath *under hood* at about 150° until the zinc has dissolved completely or practically so. Allow to cool to room temperature, add, if necessary, sufficient mercury to prevent solidification at room temperature and mix. Place the amalgam in a glass-stoppered flask and shake a few times with diluted HCl (1+3$_3$) to remove any zinc oxide formed. The amalgam thus prepared contains about 3.5% Zn.

Zinc Iodide Starch Solutions: *see* STARCH-IODIDE SOLUTION.

Zinc Uranyl Acetate (Uranium Zinc Acetate): (*a*) Dissolve 50 g of uranyl acetate in water, add 15 ml of glacial acetic acid and dilute to 500 ml.

(*b*) Dissolve 150 g of zinc acetate in water, add 15 ml of glacial acetic acid and dilute to 500 ml.

Mix the two solutions, allow to stand overnight and filter if necessary.

Or dissolve 50 g of crystalline uranyl zinc acetate in water, add 15 ml of glacial acetic acid, dilute to 500 ml and filter if necessary after standing overnight.

Zirconium Alizarin Sulfonate Indicator Solutions for determination of fluorine: *see* SANCHIS ZIRCONIUM-ALIZARIN INDICATOR.

ARSENIC TEST

The generator (A) is a 50-ml bottle; (B) and (C) are glass tubes of the dimensions shown in the accompanying cut. Connections are made as indicated by tightly fitting, rubber stoppers. At least two generators should be prepared.

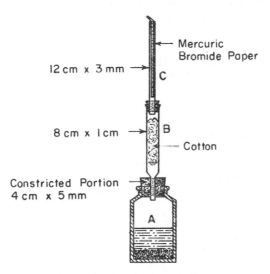

Apparatus for the Arsenic Test

To prepare the generator for use, insert in the middle portion of (B) a pledget of purified cotton about 5 cm long. Moisten the cotton with diluted lead acetate solution $(1+1)$ and remove the excess by applying gentle suction to the constricted end of the tube. Immediately before beginning the test, place a strip of mercuric bromide paper in (C) as indicated, bending the upper end to secure its position, and connect (B) and (C) as shown.

The mercuric bromide paper is prepared as follows: Immerse strips of heavy quantitative filter paper, 2.5 mm $\times$ 12 cm, for 1 hour in a solution of 5 g of mercuric bromide in 100 ml of alcohol. Remove the strips with a glass rod and suspend on glass rods until dry. Keep them in tightly closed bottles, protected from light.

Dissolve the specified quantity of the sample or the residue after special treatment directed in the text, in 10 ml of H_2O. (No water, however, should be added when the addition of water to the final residue is directed in the text.) Transfer the solution to the generator, add 3 ml of HCl or H_2SO_4, 5 ml of 20% potassium iodide solution, 0.2 ml of stannous chloride solution, (made by dissolving 2 g $SnCl_2 \cdot 2H_2O$ in 100 ml of hydrochloric acid), and allow to stand for 10 minutes. Then add 15 ml of water and 2–3 g of granulated zinc (about 30 mesh) and immediately insert the stopper carrying (B) and (C). Immerse the bottle in water at 25° and maintain at 25° for 1 hour.

The stain on the mercuric bromide paper, compared immediately, does not exceed, in depth or intensity, that produced when a volume of standard arsenic solution (page 563), containing the quantity of arsenic specified in the test, is diluted to 10 ml and treated in exactly the same manner as the sample, beginning with "Transfer the solution to the generator . . . ."

ASSAYS FOR ALKALI AND ALKALI EARTH SALTS OF ORGANIC ACIDS

For either Method I or Method II the salt to be assayed, if it is hydrous, should be rendered anhydrous by drying at a temperature of 120°–160°, or the water determined in a separate portion of the sample by drying or by the iodine (Fischer) method and the assay results calculted on the anhydrous basis.

Method I—*Pyrolytic Method:* A weighed quantity of 0.001 to 0.002 mol equivalent of the sample (corresponding to 25–35 ml of 0.1 N acid) is placed in a platinum crucible or small dish and ignited, gently at first, then at a red heat until the residue is white or only slightly gray.   It is more convenient and efficient to do the ignition in an electric muffle furnace at 500°–600°; it is recommended, however, to char the material with a burner prior to putting it in the furnace, since some salt may spatter when exposed at once to a high temperature.

When the ignition is completed as indicated by the white or nearly white color of the resulting ash, the crucible is allowed to cool and then put in a 300-ml beaker or casserole and about 50 ml of water added.   Exactly 40 or 50 ml of 0.1 N sulfuric acid is then slowly and cautiously added.   As soon as the effervescence subsides, the inside of the beaker is washed down with a spray of water, and the contents of the beaker boiled gently for 15 to 20 minutes to expel all CO_2.   To ensure the presence of an excess of acid, a drop of methyl orange is added to the liquid after the CO_2 has been expelled.   If the solution turns yellow, a measured volume more of the H_2SO_4 is added to make it red.   The solution is then allowed to cool to room temperature and the excess acid is determined by titration with 0.1 N NaOH using phenolphthalein as indicator.   Equivalents of the salts per ml of volumetric acid are given in the tables of equivalents of normal acids, *see* pages 603 etc.

When assaying barium, calcium, or strontium salts by this method, 0.1 N HCl should be used in place of H_2SO_4, and after the addition of the acid 30 to 50 ml of water is added and the solution boiled down to 60 to 70 ml.   This extra water is to prevent volatilization of HCl if the solution becomes excessively concentrated by evaporation.

Note: This method is not applicable when the organic acid contains halogen or acidic substituents (e.g., chloro-, nitro-, sulfo-acids) because the carbonate or oxide first formed will react with the substituents and thus become "neutralized."

Method II—*Nonaqueous Titration:* This method is much simpler and more expedient than the foregoing and is now more favored.   The preferred solvent is glacial acetic acid and the titrant is 0.1 N perchloric acid in dioxane.   Methylrosaniline chloride (crystal violet, gentian violet, methyl violet), pH 3.3 to 1.5, is the indicator of choice.

A quantity of the carboxylic acid salt corresponding to 25 to 35 ml of 0.1 N acid is dissolved in a 250- to 300-ml flask in 40 to 50 ml of glacial acetic acid, warming if necessary or adding 20 to 25 ml of neutral dioxane to aid solution.   After cooling, 1 to 2 drops of a 1% solution of methylrosaniline is added, then titrated with 0.1 N perchloric acid to a color change from violet to blue or bluish-green.   The change in color is readily observed by comparison with the color of 60 ml of glacial acetic acid to which the same volume of the indicator has been added.   If the $HClO_4$ has been standardized by applying a correction for the volume of acid consumed by the end point, a similar correction should be made in the assay.

Somewhat more precise and accurate results are obtained by potentiometric titration to an electrometric end point.

The acetates of cadmium, calcium, and magnesium may be satisfactorily titrated potentiometrically but not with indicator.[1]

When treated with acetic acid, tartrates containing potassium form potassium bitartrate, which is but slightly soluble in the acid; hence for such compounds the pyrolytic method (No. 1) is preferable.

[1] Casey, A. T., and Starke, K., *Anal. Chem.* **31**, 1060 (1959).

ASSAYS FOR CHLORIDE AND THIOCYANATE

1. The Volhard Method: A previously dried and accurately weighed quantity of the chloride or thiocyanate equivalent to 25 to 35 ml of 0.1 N silver nitrate is dissolved in a 250- to 300-ml conical flask in 50 ml of water.   About 3 ml of colorless nitric acid is added and, while agitating the solution, an accurately measured volume of 30 to 45 ml of 0.1 N AgNO$_3$ is slowly run in.   Then 3 to 5 ml of nitrobenzene is added and the mixture vigorously shaken for 1 minute (the nitrobenzene causes the AgCl to agglomerate and is withdrawn from the reacting with the thiocyanate).   Now 3 ml of ferric alum or ferric nitrate solution is added and the excess of silver nitrate is back-titrated with 0.1 N thiocyanate until the liquid phase remains reddish after shaking.

For thiocyanate the nitrobenzene is omitted.

2. Adsorption Indicator Method: This method has in its favor the fact that only one standard solution—the 0.1 N AgNO$_3$—is required.   It is applicable to organic chlorides which exert a reducing action on silver nitrate.

Procedure: Weigh accurately a quantity of the chloride or thiocyanate equivalent to 25 to 35 ml of 0.1 N AgNO$_3$ and transfer it to a 250- to 300-ml conical flask. Add 5 ml of water, then add 5 ml of glacial acetic acid and 50 ml of methanol, and agitate until the chloride is dissolved.   Add 2 to 3 drops of an 0.5% eosin solution (an excess of indicator renders the end point less sharp) and slowly titrate with 0.1 N AgNO$_3$, adding the latter dropwise toward the end, until the color suddenly changes to intense, slightly fluorescent red.

COPPER AND ZINC—

ESTIMATION OF SMALL AMOUNTS IN IRON SALTS

Dissolve 1.0 g in 30 ml of water.   Transfer 10 ml of the solution to a small separatory funnel and add a solution of 5 g of tartaric acid in a mixture of 45 ml of water and 8 ml of NH_4OH (a solution of 6 g of ammonium tartrate in 45 ml of water and 6 ml of NH_4OH may be used). Add 15 ml of dithizone-chloroform solution (10 mg per liter) and shake gently for 2 to 3 minutes. Allow the liquids to separate completely and draw off the dithizone solution into a small separatory funnel. Repeat the extracts twice with 10 ml of dithizone solution.

Copper: Extract the dithizone solution twice with 15-ml portions of approximately 0.05 N HCl (1 ml of HCl + 220 ml H_2O) to remove zinc—retain the HCl extract if zinc is also determined—and compare the pink color of the dithizone solution with that of a control made with the quantity of copper (Cu) indicated under the specific iron compound and treated with the same quantities of the reagents and in same manner as the 10-ml solution of sample.

If zinc is known to be absent, the extraction with hydrochloric acid is omitted.

Zinc: Adjust the combined HCl extract from the dithizone solution in the test for Copper to pH 5 to 5.5 with approximately 0.5 N (7%) sodium acetate solution, add 1 ml of 0.1 N sodium thiosulfate, and shake the liquid with 15 ml of dithizone-carbonate tetrachloride solution for 2 minutes and allow to separate. The pink color of the dithizone solution is compared with that of a control prepared with the quantity of zinc (Zn) indicated under the specific iron salt and the same volume of sodium acetate solution, etc.

The actual amounts of copper and zinc present may be ascertained by diluting the dithizone solution of sample or control, whichever is darker, with chloroform for copper or with carbon tetrachloride for the zinc until the colors match, noting the exact volume of the diluent required. The quantity of copper or of zinc is then calculated from the dilution.

For the application of the foregoing method to ferrous salts, the iron must first be oxidized to ferric. This is accomplished by adding in small portions, and with stirring, 2 to 3 ml of HNO_3 to a solution of 1.0 g of sample in 20 ml of H_2O and continue boiling gently until nitrous gases are no longer evolved. After cooling, the solution is diluted to 30 ml.

FLAME PHOTOMETRY

Theodore C. Rains*

"For the determination of microgram quantities of individual alkali and alkaline-earth metals in the presence of macro quantities of the other alkali or alkaline earth metals."

The principles of flame emission photometry have been known for more than a century; however, only since the 1930's has flame photometry been established as a quantitative method. Lundegårdh in the early thirties published a two-volume treatise[1] in which flame emission photometry received its proper recognition as a reliable analytical method. Since his early work, vast improvements have been made in flame photometry due to new techniques, burners, electronic and optical systems. At present more than 76 elements can be determined.

* National Bureau of Standards, Washington, D.C.
[1] Lundegårdg, H., *Die Quantitative Spektralanalyse der Elemente*, Vols. 1 and 2, Gustav Fischer Verlagsbuchhandlung, Jena, 1929, 1934.

Currently there are a number of instruments available. The various models range from instruments which are equipped with absorption or interference filters to the more sophisticated type which contain monochromators of high resolution and dispersion. The basic apparatus consists of a gas regulator, atomizer-burner, optical system, photodetector, amplifier and the instrument of indicating or recording the output of the detector. These basic components are described in the following paragraphs.

Gas Regulator. Gas regulators are available from all major companies that sell flame photometers. However, to maintain a flame that is steady, it is imperative that the oxygen and fuel pressure, as well as the flow, be maintained at a constant value while the instrument is in use. Slight changes in the pressure or flow of gas will produce erratic flame results. A thorough discussion is presented by Dean[2] on the use of gas regulators.

The two fuels which are predominantly used in flame photometry are hydrogen or acetylene. The choice is up to each individual user. The oxyhydrogen flame is preferred by many workers because of the low flame background and a cleaner burning flame. For most elements including the alkali and alkaline-earth metals, the oxyhydrogen flame will yield a lower detection limit. The oxyacetylene flame produces a higher temperature flame and consequently better excitation of the line; however, the flame background is more intense. If one is working at high concentrations, the background contribution becomes less of a factor and oxyacetylene will be preferred for its greater line intensity and economy of fuel.

Atomizer-burner. The main objective of the atomizer is to introduce the sample into the flame as an aerosol at a uniform rate while the burner supplies the fuel and oxygen at a constant pressure to produce a steady flame. There are two general types of atomizers. One type is an integral, atomizer-burner constructed to introduce all of the sample solution directly into the flame as droplets. Another type has a spray chamber where only a small percentage of the sample consisting of the fine droplets is introduced into the flame. This latter type is hazardous to use with organic solvents. Perhaps the one major factor which limits high precision in flame photometry is the effect produced by the atomizer-burner. It is difficult to obtain a precision of less than 0.5% because of the turbulent nature of the flame by these burners.

Optical Systems. The function of the optical system is to collect the radiation from the steadiest portion of the flame, disperse it spectrally, and then focus it on the photodetector. Instruments using light filters are adequate for some routine analyses. Instruments equipped with prisms or diffraction gratings are preferred because of their much wider versatility, since interferences of spectral nature are minimized with instruments having a high degree of resolution and dispersion.

Another parameter one should consider is the slit width. The entrance and exit slits must be adjusted properly. The narrowest possible slit width is important because it will give a higher ratio of line intensity to flame background and consequently a lower detection limit. It also minimizes spectral interferences and stray light. The optimum slit width for the alkali and alkaline-earth metals will depend upon the instrument. For example, the optimum slit width for the Beckman DU is 0.03 mm.

---

[2] Dean, John A., *Flame Photometry*, McGraw-Hill Book Co., Inc., New York, 1960.

Photodetector. A variety of multiplier phototubes are available commercially to detect the radiation or emitted light. A few of these multiplier phototubes are listed in Table 1. The gain of a multiplier phototube depends upon the power supply, which should provide a very stable d.c. supply of 500–2500 volts, depending on the type of multiplier phototube and the desired sensitivity. It is essential for good control that the voltage applied to the system be regulated in steps of 25 to 50 volts.

At the start of the work period to stabilize the phototube and thus to minimize any drift of its output, open the shutter between the multiplier phototube and the flame at least 15 minutes before aspiration of samples.

TABLE 1

Multiplier Phototube	Spectral Response	Range, mμ	Suitable for these Elements
RCA-1P28	S-5	200-700	Li, Na, Mg, Ca, Sr
RCA-6217	S-10	300-800	Li, Na, Ca, Sr, K
EMI-6286	S-13	200-650	Li, Na, Mg, Ca, Sr
EMI-9558Q	S-20	200-880	All alkali and alkaline earths
FW-118	S-1	800-1000	Li, Na, K, Rb, Cs

Amplifier. The photocurrent from the multiplier phototube is fed to the amplifier which can enhance the current by a factor of 10^6. A good amplifier is essential for maximum sensitivity and reproducibility. A more complete discussion of amplifiers is presented by Herrmann and Alkemade.[3]

Indicating Circuit. The indicating circuit may be a simple galvanometer. However, a recording potentiometer is preferred. The recording of the data gives a permanent record and permits one to scan automatically the wavelength region under investigation. A 10-mv recorder with a pen speed of 1 sec for full-scale deflection is best suited for this type of data collecting.

General Operations

A thorough understanding of the operation of the flame photometer is essential. It is suggested that one follow the instructions provided by the manufacturer for the start up of the instrument.

In Table 2 the wavelength, detection limit and a practical concentration for the alkalies and alkaline-earth metals are listed. The detection limits were obtained in the author's laboratory using a Jarrell-Ash Ebert scanning spectrometer together with flame attachment and the modified ORNL—1887A power supply.[4] The practical concentrations are intended only as a guide. The concentration best suited for a particular instrument will depend upon such factors as sensitivity, precision, matrix and solvents.

[3] Herrmann, R. and Alkemade, C. T. J., translated by Paul T. Gilbert, Jr., *Chemical Analysis by Flame Photometry*, 2nd ed., Interscience, New York, 1963.

[4] Kelly, M. T., Fisher, D. J., and Jones, H. C., "High-sensitivity, Recording Scanning Flame Spectrophotometer," *Anal. Chem.* **31**, 178 (1959).

TABLE 2

Element	Wavelength, mμ	Detection Limit,[a] μg/ml	Practical Concentration, μg/ml
Li	670.8	0.0002	1–5
Na	589.0	0.0001	1–5
K	766.5	0.0002	1–5
Rb	794.8	0.001	1–5
Cs	852.1	0.002	1–5
Mg	285.2	0.2	5–25
Ca	422.7	0.001	2–10
Sr	460.7	0.002	2–10
Ba	553.6	0.05	1–5

[a] The detection limit is defined as concentration detected at twice the standard deviation of the flame background. (Rains, T. C., Ferguson, Marion, and Feldman, Cyrus, unpublished work.)

Interferences. There are numerous types of interferences in flame photometry, but due to limited space, only a few basic ones will be discussed. The major interferences are spectral, condensed-phase, anions and flame background.

Spectral interference is due to the inability of the monochromator to isolate the desired radiant energy from the rest of the spectra. The degree to which this type of interference is encountered will depend upon the monochromator and the slit width. Fortunately, flame photometers are available in which this type of interference is eliminated when dealing only with the alkali and alkaline-earth metals. It is suggested that to minimize this type of interference one read the discussion on each element in the latter part of the chapter.

Condensed-phase is a type of interference encountered when an element (such as calcium) forms a compound of low volatility with an element (such as aluminum) in the flame. Since in this type of reaction the concentration of calcium atoms or molecules capable of emitting in the flame are reduced, the emission intensity of calcium will drop. Condensed-phase interference is observed with all alkaline-earth metals from a number of elements; such as, aluminum, chromium, iron, and titanium. When these elements are present with the alkali or alkaline-earth metals, the use of a radiation buffer (e.g., glycerol and perchloric acid)[5,6,7] is recommended.

The emission intensity of the alkaline-earth metals is also severely affected by the often encountered anions—e.g., phosphate and sulfate. The effect of phosphate depends on the form in which it is present; the effect of the monohydrogen phosphate on the emission intensity of strontium is more pronounced than its effect on the other alkaline-earth metals. Glycerol,[5,6] lanthanum[8] and ethylenediamine

5 Rains, T. C., Zittel, H. E., and Ferguson, Marion, "Flame Spectrophotometric Determination of Micro Concentrations of Strontium in Calcareous Material," *Anal. Chem.* **34**, 778 (1962).

6 Rains, T. C., Zittel, H. E., and Ferguson, Marion, "Elimination of Anion Interferences in the Flame Spectrophotometric Determination of Calcium: Use of Glycerol as a Releasing Agent," *Talanta* **10**, 367 (1963).

7 Dean, John A., Burger, J. C., Rains, T. C., and Zittel, H. E., "Flame Spectrophotometric Study of Barium," *Anal. Chem.* **33**, 1722 (1961).

8 Yofe, J., and Finkelstein, R., "Elimination of Anionic Interference in Flame Photometric Determination of Calcium in the Presence of Phosphate and Sulfate," *Anal. Chim. Acta* **19**, 166 (1958).

tetraacetic acid (EDTA)[9] are used to inhibit the effect of phosphate and sulfate. Studies with glycerol and perchloric acid as a releasing agent have shown that concentrations of 1.0 and 0.1 M of sulfate and phosphoric acid, respectively, can be present without interference with the determination of calcium or strontium. Of the common anions, chloride or perchlorate are preferred for most flame photometric analyses.

Flame background emission becomes a major interference only if improper background measurements are made. Failure to correct properly for the background reading can lead to serious errors. This is especially true if manual operation is employed instead of the scanning technique. The wavelength at which the background measurement is to be made can be obtained by slowly scanning the wavelength region on both sides of the emission line or band. If the background emission intensity is the same on both sides of the line or band, a background reading can be taken on either side of the base (Fig. 1-A). If the background emission

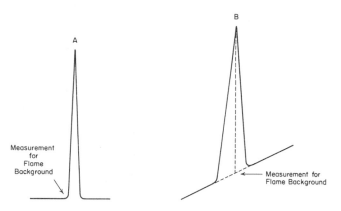

Figure 1. Typical Examples for the Determination of Flame Background.

intensity of either side of the line or band is different, the background reading can be obtained by constructing a line across the base of the line or band, as shown in Fig. 1-B, and subtracting the background value at the point of intersection with the perpendicular line drawn from the peak of the curve. By scanning the wavelength region of interest, slight variation due to carbon bands, or continuum due to the major element can be detected. At no time should one assume the flame background of the sample to be the same as a distilled water blank.

Evaluation of Data. When one is trying to determine trace quantities of any element in the presence of macro quantities of another element, even with the best possible instrumentation and technique, the data can lead to erroneous results if it is improperly evaluated. The first requirement is that one be familiar with the spectrum of the element of interest. Although flame spectrograms of many elements are available in the literature,[3] one should determine the spectrum of each element under his own instrumental conditions. If there is a spectral interference which the monochromator is unable to resolve, a chemical separation should be

[9] Wirtschafter, J. D., "Suppression of Radiation Interference in Flame Photometry by Protective Chelation," *Science* **125**, 603 (1957).

considered.   On the other hand, if the interference is of a chemical nature, the following method should be used to correct for this type of interference.

Calibration in the Presence of Chemical Interference: A calibration curve using 4 to 5 different concentrations of a standard stock solution should be first prepared.   It is suggested that the standard solutions to be aspirated in the flame for the alkalies be prepared in a 0.01 to 0.001 N HCl.   The best medium for the alkaline-earth metals is a solution of 10% glycerol and 0.1 N HClO$_4$.   As a check for any enhancement or suppression due to the various types of interference, aliquots of a standard stock solution are added to the unknown solution and all solutions diluted to the same volume.   The samples containing the standard additions should give emission intensities that are approximately twice the value of the same unknown without the standard additions.   The emission intensity of each sample is then measured and the concentration for each sample determined using the calibration curve.   The calibration curve must be essentially linear.   If subtracting the quantity of unknown found in sample X from that found in sample A gives a concentration equal to the standard solution added, there is no depression or enhancement.   If the recovery of the standard solutions is either less or greater than the standards added, the true concentration of the solution can be then determined by the following equation as suggested by Dean.[7]

$$X \cdot \frac{S}{A - X} = C \qquad\qquad (1\text{-}1)$$

where $X = $ μg/ml of element in unknown as determined from the calibration curve
   $S = $ amount of standard added, μg/ml
   $A = $ μg ml of element found in unknown with standard added as determined from the calibration curve
   $C = $ concentration actually present, μg/ml.

Preparation of Samples.   Weigh a 1-g test portion of the sample and dissolve it by a suitable procedure.   Transfer the solution to a clean 100-ml volumetric flask and dilute to calibrated volume with distilled or deionized water.   (**Note:** Hydrochloric, nitric or perchloric acids are preferred for dissolving samples in which flame photometric analyses are to be performed.   All glassware should be cleaned with 1:1 HCl or aqua regia and rinsed with distilled water before use.)   Prepare a reagent blank along with the sample.

Preparation of a Sodium Calibration Curve.   Prepare a standard stock solution of sodium to contain 1.00 mg of Na per ml by dissolving 2.542 g of reagent-grade NaCl in water and dilute the solution to 1 liter with water.   Prepare dilute solutions from this standard stock solution as needed.

Prepare a series of standard solutions of sodium that contain 1 to 5 μg of Na per ml.   (See Table 2.)   Aspirate into the flame the standard that contains 5 μg of Na per ml while scanning the wavelength region of 588 to 590 mμ.   Adjust the voltage to the multiplier phototube until a reading of 80% of full scale of the recorder or indicating instrument is obtained.   Aspirate each of the series of standard solutions.   Aspirate distilled water between each standard solution.   Always aspirate distilled water through the burner last.   Measure the emission intensity of the atomic sodium line and of the flame background at wavelengths of 589.0 and 588.0 mμ, respectively.   (The wavelength at which the background can be measured will depend upon the resolution of the instrument.)   To obtain the net emission intensity of each standard, subtract the emission intensity of the flame background from the total emission intensity of the sodium line.   Plot on rectilinear graph paper the net emission intensity as ordinate versus the concentration of the standards, expressed in µg of Na per ml as abscissa.   The calibration curve should pass through the origin.   A typical calibration curve is shown in Fig. 2.

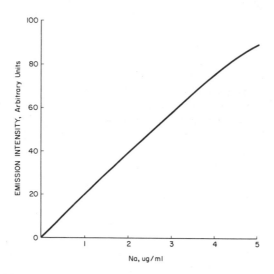

Figure 2.   Typical Calibration Curve for the Flame Photometric Determination of Sodium.

Analysis of Samples.   Transfer three equal aliquots of the sample, which are estimated to contain 10 to 20 µg of Na, to 10-ml volumetric flasks.   Add two different known quantities—e.g., 10 and 20 µg of sodium—of the standard solution to two of the volumetric flasks.   (The highest standard addition should give an emission reading that is twice the value of the unknown.)   Dilute the resulting solution to calibrated volume with distilled water.   (The acid concentration of the sample to be aspirated should be from 0.01 to 0.001 N.)   Aspirate the sample and the samples with the standard additions into the flame and measure the emission intensity as directed in the procedure for the calibration curve.   Follow the sample with distilled water and a standard solution of Na.   Determine the Na concentration of the sample by referring to the calibration curve.   If the standard additions were not completely recovered, correct for the true sodium concentration by Eq. 1-1.

Note: Recheck a point on the calibration curve by aspirating a standard solution after every three or four samples or any adjustment of the instrument.   If the value does not coincide within the experimental error with the calibration curve, prepare a new calibration curve using a series of standard solutions.

Preparation of a Calcium Calibration Curve.   Prepare a standard stock solution of calcium to contain 1.00 mg of Ca per ml by dissolving 2.497 g of reagent grade $CaCO_3$ in 1 N HCl and dilute the solution to 1 liter with water.   Prepare dilute solutions from this standard stock solution as needed.

Prepare a series of standard solutions of calcium that contain 2 to 10 µg of Ca per ml as follows (see Table 2): To a series of 50-ml volumetric flask, add 1 to 5 ml of a standard solution of calcium (100 µg per ml). Add 5 ml of 1 N $HClO_4$ and 10 ml of 50 vol./vol.% aqueous solution of glycerol; dilute the resulting solution to 50 ml with water. Aspirate into the flame the standard that contains 10 µg of Ca per ml while scanning the wavelength region of 422.0 to 423.0 mµ. Adjust the voltage to the multiplier phototube until a reading of 80% of full scale of the recorder or indication instrument is obtained. Aspirate each of the series of standard solutions. Measure the emission intensity of Ca at 422.7 mµ and the flame background at 422.2 mµ. Plot the net emission intensity of each standard as described in the preparation of a Na calibration curve.

Analysis of Samples. Transfer three identical aliquots of the sample, which are estimated to contain 20 to 40 µg of Ca, to 10-ml volumetric flasks. Add 1 ml of 1 N $HClO_4$ and 2 ml of a 50 vol./vol.% aqueous solution of glycerol. Add two different known quantities—e.g., 20 and 40 µg of calcium—of the standard solution to two of the volumetric flask. Dilute the resulting solution to calibrated volume with distilled water. Measure the emission intensity of the atomic calcium line as described previously. If the standard additions are not completely recovered, correct to obtain the true calcium concentration by Eq. 1-1.

Lithium. Lithium has a strong resonance line at 670.8 mµ which is relatively free of spectral interference from the other alkali and alkaline-earth metals. However, strontium has a weak band system in this region with a peak at 672 mµ, and if an instrument of poor resolution is used, this band would cause spectral interference. Lithium is not affected by the common anions. The procedure as outlined for sodium can be followed for the determination of lithium in the presence of the other alkali and alkaline-earth metals.

Sodium. Sodium has a very strong doublet at 589.0 and 589.6 mµ. This doublet appears as a single line in the average flame photometer. The calibration curve of sodium will show strong self-absorption above 10 µg per ml. Therefore, one should work below this concentration level to minimize this effect. The most difficulty encountered in the determination of sodium is contamination. The utmost care must be taken to keep all containers free of foreign ions and one must avoid any disturbance of the air around the flame housing while the sample is being aspirated. The sodium resonance line at 589.0 mµ encounters no spectral interference from the other alkali or alkaline-earth metals. Only by using an instrument of poor resolution will the interference of a high concentration of calcium whose oxide band peak is at 622 mµ be observed.

Potassium. The flame emission spectrum of potassium consists of a strong doublet at 766.5 and 769.9 mµ and a much weaker doublet at 404.4 and 404.7 mµ. The 766.5 mµ line is approximately twice as sensitive as the 769.9 mµ line, and therefore is preferred for flame photometry. Also potassium emits a continuum which extends from 350 to 1000 mµ. The potassium doublet at 766.5 and 769.9 mµ suffers serious spectral interference from the rubidium line at 780.0 mµ, if an instrument of poor resolution and dispersion is used.

Potassium emission is observed to be enhanced by a large excess of rubidium or cesium. This enhancement is due to the repression of the ionization of potassium by electrons produced in the flame by the rubidium or cesium.[10] This type of enhancement can be corrected by the use of the standard addition method. (It is

[10] Foster, W. H., and Hume, D. N., "Mutual Cation Interference Effects in Flame Photometry," *Anal. Chem.* **31**, 2033 (1959).

worth noting that the concentration of the standard additions must be smaller than those suggested for Na or Ca so that the readings will fall on the calibration curve.)

For best results it is suggested that a red sensitive multiplier phototube be used. (See Table 1.)   This will allow the use of a narrow slit width, 0.03 mm, and provide for a lower detection limit of potassium.

Rubidium.   The major lines of interest for rubidium are at 780.0 and 794.8 mμ. The line at 794.8 mμ is preferred as the spectral interference of K is minimized. Elements that are easily ionized, such as K and Cs, repress the ionization of rubidium, and therefore enhance the atomic lines.   The standard addition method as described previously will correct this type of interference.

Cesium.   The major line of interest of cesium is at 852.1 mμ.   Although there is a pair of lines at 455.5 and 459.3 mμ, these lines are less sensitive and suffer more direct spectral interference.   Since the ionization potential of cesium is 3.89 electron volts, potassium whose ionization potential is 4.34 electron volts is often used to enhance the emission intensity of cesium.   Care should be used in adding potassium to solutions in which cesium is to be determined.   One should previously test the effect with pure solution, and especially test for cesium contamination in the potassium salt.

Magnesium.   Magnesium is one of the most difficult elements to determine flame photometrically.   The 285.2 mμ resonance line of magnesium lies near the OH band system.   Therefore, correction for the flame background emission is difficult.   To make the proper background correction, one should use the baseline technique[2] with as narrow slit width as feasible.   If a grating monochromator is used, better resolution can be obtained by going to the second order and measuring the magnesium peak and flame background at 570.4 and 570.3 mμ, respectively. Since magnesium emission intensity is inhibited by various anions, glycerol and perchloric acid have been shown to act as a releasing agent to overcome this difficulty.

Calcium.   The preferred line for calcium is a resonance line at 422.7 mμ. Calcium also has a strong oxide band whose peak is 554 mμ.   The major spectral interference to the oxide band is barium, and the resonance line is relatively free of spectral interferences.   Serious inhibition is encountered with sulfate and phosphate which can be eliminated by the addition of glycerol and perchloric acid as a releasing agent.[6]   Calcium, like sodium, is always present as dust particles in the air, and extreme caution must be used when determining trace quantities.

Strontium.   The major spectral interference encountered with the strontium resonance line at 460.7 mμ is that from lithium.   The interference of the lithium 460.3-mμ arc line with the emission intensity of strontium is instrumental.   This difficulty can be overcome with a spectrometer of high resolution if the scanning of the strontium 460.7-mμ line is approached from the longer wavelength side and if the background is measured at a wavelength of 460.9 mμ.   Also, the ionic line of barium at 455.4 mμ and the resonance line of cesium at 455.5 mμ may cause spectral interference.

The emission intensity of strontium is enhanced by the presence of calcium. The strontium emission intensity becomes constant over the range of calcium concentration from 200 to 5000 μg per ml.   Strontium-free calcium can be prepared[5] and used as a radiation buffer or the standard addition method can be applied to correct for this type of enhancement.

The procedure outlined for calcium should be followed to overcome the inhibition of sulfate and phosphate and the condensed-phase type of interference.

Barium. The flame emission spectrum of barium consists of the ionic resonance doublet at 455.4 and 493.4 mμ, the atomic resonance line at 553.6 mμ and a series of oxide bands ranging from 450 to 610 mμ and from 730 to 1000 mμ. The atomic resonance line at 553.6 mμ provides the greatest sensitivity, but serious interference is usually encountered from the strong calcium emission bandhead at 554 mμ. The ionic lines are strongly affected by the presence of elements with low ionization potentials, such as the alkali metals, and are not recommended.

To determine trace quantities of barium in the presence of macro quantities of the alkalies or other alkaline-earth metals, the following separation has been used with quantitative results.[11]

Procedure for the Determination of Barium. Transfer an aliquot estimated to contain 10–50 μg of barium to a 50-ml glass centrifuge tube. Dilute the solution to 25 ml with water and add 3 ml of 5 M ammonium acetate solution. Add 1 drop of a 1% solution of phenolphthalein. Adjust the basicity of the sample with ammonium hydroxide to a faint red color as indicated by the phenolphthalein. Add 5 ml of a 5% solution of $K_2Cr_2O_7$. With vigorous agitation, slowly add 1 ml of a lead stock solution (5 mg of Pb per ml); stir the sample for an additional 30 seconds. Centrifuge the sample and add 1 ml of a lead stock solution (2 mg of Pb per ml) with vigorous agitation. Repeat the centrifugation and decant the supernate. Wash the precipitate with 20 ml of a wash solution. (Prepare wash solution by dissolving 2 g of $K_2Cr_2O_7$ in 800 ml of water. Add 20 ml of 5 M ammonium acetate solution, and adjust pH to 6.2. Dilute to 1 liter.) Centrifuge the sample and decant the supernate. Dissolve the $PbCrO_4$ precipitate with 5 drops of nitric acid and 10 drops of 30% hydrogen peroxide. To a 25-ml volumetric flask add 2.5 ml of 1 M perchloric acid and 5 ml of glycerol solution (50 vol./vol.%). Then add 5 ml of acetone to the sample in the glass centrifuge tube and transfer the sample to the previously prepared 25-ml volumetric flask. Wash the glass centrifuge tube with two 5-ml portions of acetone and combine the supernatant liquids. Dilute the sample with water to the calibrated volume. Measure the emission intensity of the barium resonance line and the flame background at 553.6 and 553.4 mμ, respectively.

Prepare a series of barium standard solutions using the above procedure and prepare a calibration curve as described previously. This separation will quantitatively remove barium from the alkalies and other alkaline-earth metals.

NITRATE—ESTIMATION OF SMALL AMOUNTS IN INORGANIC REAGENTS

Sample Solution (S): A quantity of the reagent containing 0.01 to 0.03 mg of NO_3 is dissolved in about 5 ml of water, or an aliquot of a solution prepared as described under the respective reagent and equivalent to these amounts of NO_3 is taken. Two ml of brucine sulfate solution is added and then diluted to 10 ml, preferably in a 100-ml glass-stoppered, graduated cylinder.

Control Solution (C): An accurately measured volume of standard nitrate

[11] Rains, T. C., Ferguson, Marion, and Feldman, Cyrus, unpublished work.

solution, corresponding to the quantity of NO_3, in mg, presumed to be present in the weight of the sample used or in the aliquot of solution is placed in a similar cylinder as used for (S), 2 ml of brucine sulfate is added and the solution diluted to 10 ml.   If the sample being tested is a chloride, about 50 mg of NaCl is added to the control solution.

Blank (B): Dilute 2 ml of the same brucine sulfate solution as used for S and C to 10 ml.   The blank is used only when the intensity of the colors of S and C is measured spectrophotometrically.

Procedure: To Solutions S and C add slowly and with constant stirring 25 ml of H_2SO_4.   Allow any transient pink color to change to yellow, and cool immediately in ice water to room temperature.   After the solutions have cooled, dilute both to 50 ml for any other definite volume, with H_2SO_4.   If S is of lighter color than C, the reagent tested meets the standard limit of NO_3.

Should a quantitative determination of the actual amount of the NO_3 be desired, it can readily be achieved.

Spectrophotometrically: Set a spectrophotometer at 410 mμ, and adjust it to zero (0) absorbance with the blank in the light path; then determine the absorbancies of S and C.   The percentage of NO_3 is calculated as follows: (As/Ac) × mg NO_3 in control × (100/wt), wherein As and Ac are the respective absorbancies of the sample and control solutions, and wt is the weight of the sample, in mg, used or present in the aliquot of solution taken.

Note: If the color of either S or C is too intense to read accurately, all of the 3 solutions, S, C, B, should be diluted with H_2SO_4 to the same, suitable, volume.

Visually: In the absence of a spectrophotometer the amount of NO_3 can be quantitatively approximated as follows: Dilute Solution S or C, whichever is darker, with H_2SO_4 until it matches the lighter color.   The %NO_3 is calculated by the formula: (V_S/V_C) × mg NO_3 in control × (100/wt), where V_S and V_C are the final volumes, in ml, of S and C, respectively, and wt is the weight, in mg, of the sample used or present in the aliquot of solution taken.

NITROGEN DETERMINATION
BY THE KJELDAHL METHOD

The quantity of sample to be taken for this determination should, preferably, contain from 30 to 40 mg of nitrogen.

The weighed sample, or a measured volume of a stock solution, is introduced into a 500- to 800-ml Kjeldahl flask in such a manner that all of the sample is in the bottom of the flask.   Then 10 g of powdered potassium sulfate or anhydrous sodium sulfate and 0.5 g of powdered cupric sulfate or 0.3 g of reagent (mercuric oxide) selenium (catalyst) are added and followed with 20 ml of sulfuric acid, which is poured slowly down the neck so that any of the sample adhering to the neck of the flask is washed down.   The flask is inclined to an angle of about 45° and gently heated over a free flame or electrically until frothing has ceased.   If the substance under test is sublimable at a temperature above 100°, the flask with its contents is heated in boiling water with frequent shaking for 30 minutes before being heated over a free flame.   The heat is then increased until the acid boils briskly and the heating is continued until the liquid has been clear green in color, or nearly colorless, for 45 minutes or longer.   If necessary, an addition of a few 1- to 2-ml portions of reagent hydrogen peroxide during the digestion will frequently shorten the time of digestion. After allowing to cool, 150 ml of water is *cautiously* added and then 100 ml of 30% sodium hydroxide poured down the side of the flask so that it does not mix at once with the acid solution. A few pieces of granulated zinc are added and the flask at once connected by means of a Kjeldahl connecting bulb with a water-cooled condenser, the delivery tube of which dips under the surface of 50 ml of 0.1 N hydrochloric acid contained in a 500-ml Erlenmeyer flask. The contents of the Kjeldahl flask are mixed by gentle rotation, then distilled until about two-thirds of the liquid has distilled over. To ensure complete recovery of the nitrogen, it is advisable to add now to the distilling flask 50 ml of water and distill it over. The excess of acid in the receiving flask is titrated with 0.1 N sodium hydroxide, using as indicator 2 to 3 drops of methyl red solution. A blank test should be made with all the reagents and any necessary correction applied.

When mercuric oxide is used as a catalyst, before commencing distillation sufficient sodium sulfide solution should be added to the solution in the flask to precipitate all the mercury as sulfide.

When *nitrate* or NO_2 compounds are present, add to the sample contained in the flask 25 ml of sulfuric acid in which 1 g of salicylic acid has been dissolved. After thoroughly mixing the contents, allow to stand for 30 minutes with frequent gentle shaking, then add 5 g of powdered sodium thiosulfate, mix well, add 0.5 g of powdered cupric sulfate or 0.3 g of selenium metal, and proceed as described before, beginning with "The flask is inclined . . . ."

Instead of 0.1 N acid, the receiver may be charged with 50 to 100 ml of saturated (5%) aqueous boric acid solution. After the distillation is completed 2 drops of methyl red is added and the yellow solution titrated with 0.1 N acid.

The use of boric acid thus permits direct titration of the NH_3, and is particularly advantageous when only a few milligrams of nitrogen are to be determined.

SODIUM—DETERMINATION OF SMALL AMOUNTS IN PRESENCE OF LARGE AMOUNTS OF OTHER ALKALI METALS BY THE URANIUM TRIPLE ACETATE METHOD

The quantitative determination of small amounts of sodium (Na), and especially in the presence of large amounts of other alkali metals (K,Li), is expeditiously and satisfactorily achieved by flame photometry. When, however, this facility is not available, the sodium may be satisfactorily evaluated by the *triple acetate method*. When a solution of uranyl magnesium or zinc acetate is added to a solution containing sodium ions, a triple acetate of the composition $NaC_2H_3O_2 \cdot Mg(C_2H_3O_2)_2 \cdot UO_2(C_2H_3O_2)_2 \cdot 6H_2O$ is formed. This compound is soluble in water, but is insoluble in the presence of a large excess of the uranyl magnesium or zinc acetate solution.

In general, other alkali metals, especially Li and K, but also cesium and rubidium, interfere and must be removed. Moderately large amounts of Ba or Ca offer no serious interference, but strontium does. Arsenate and/or phosphate cause high results for the sodium and must be removed.

In this book the principal application of the method is for the estimation of the sodium content of potassium reagents wherein the maximum permissible amount of sodium (Na) is 0.1% and often less, and the sodium, therefore, must be separated from the potassium.

Procedure for Sodium in Potassium Salts:

(a) *Separation from the potassium:* A quantity of the potassium salt presumably containing, as figured from the permissible amount of the sodium, at least 0.25 mg of Na, and preferably double this, is dissolved in 10–15 ml of water, heating if necessary, and, with stirring, 5–7 ml of 70% perchloric acid is slowly added, cooled on ice and allowed to stand for 30 minutes. The precipitated potassium perchlorate is filtered on a sintered glass crucible, well drained with suction, and washed with 10–15 ml of ice cold water. The filtrate and washings are evaporated to about 2 ml to eliminate excess of $HClO_4$, 3 ml of water is added and the solution is made slightly alkaline with NH_4OH. It is then filtered through a glass crucible and washed with 1 ml of cold water. The total filtrate should not exceed about 6 ml and should be clear.

(b) *Precipitation of the sodium:* One-hundred ml of magnesium or zinc uranyl acetate solution is now added to the filtrate with vigorous stirring; it is allowed to stand for 30 minutes, but is stirred vigorously several times during this period. The precipitate is then collected in a tared Gooch or sintered glass crucible, the beaker washed with several 1-ml portions of the uranium solution to collect any adhering precipitate, each washing being passed through the precipitate in the crucible. The precipitate is now washed with several small portions of alcohol saturated with dry sodium magnesium uranyl acetate, and finally with a few ml of ether to displace any adhering alcohol. Air is then drawn through the precipitate for 3–5 minutes, the crucible wiped dry, placed in the balance case for 10 minutes and weighed as:

$$NaMg(C_2H_3O_2)_3 \cdot 3UO_2(C_2H_3O_2)_2 \cdot 6H_2O \text{ containing } 1.54\% \text{ Na}$$

or if zinc uranyl acetate reagent was used the precipitate would be weighed as:

$$NaZn(C_2H_3U_2)_3 \cdot 3UO_2(C_2H_3O_2)_2 \cdot 6H_2O \text{ containing } 1.49\% \text{ Na}$$

For the separation of sodium from lithium one should consult the literature.

Arsenate can be readily removed by evaporating the solution of the arsenate once or twice with 1–2 g of Kl and 10–15 ml of hydrobromic acid.

The elimination of phosphate is accomplished by adding to the solution magnesia mixture, filtering, and evaporating the filtrate, and igniting gently. The sodium will be in the ignition residue.

SULFUR DETERMINATION BY THE PARR BOMB METHOD

This method is readily applicable to the determination of sulfur in all solid organic compounds. By being heated with sodium peroxide the organic substance is completely oxidized (burned) and the sulfur converted into sulfate which is determined as barium sulfate.

The quantity of sample to be taken for the determination will vary according to the sulfur content. It should preferably not be more than is equivalent to 25 mg of S. In no instance, however, should the weight of the sample exceed 0.5 g. If less than this quantity of sample is used, sufficient sucrose is added to the weighed sample to make the total 0.5 g. The addition of the sucrose is to produce sufficient heat by the combustion of the additional carbon to effect complete combustion of the sample. Likewise, when the carbon content of the sample is less than 60%, 0.25 g of sucrose is added to furnish additional carbon. In order to accelerate ignition of the mixture, 1 g of powdered, lump-free potassium chlorate or perchlorate is incorporated in the mixture.

Procedure: Place 1 g of powdered potassium chlorate or perchlorate in the fusion cup of a Parr peroxide bomb, then add the weighed sample, and the sucrose if required. Mix intimately with a glass rod; then add 15 g of sodium peroxide free from lumps. Seal the cup, mix the contents by thorough shaking for 1 to 2 minutes, then ignite the charge by means of ignition wires attached to the terminals of the cover before assembling the unit. If a gas flame is used for the ignition, the pointed flame from a blast lamp is allowed to impinge on the bottom of the fusion cup for a brief period.

Caution! *To prevent possible injury to the operator, the bomb should be placed inside a piece of steel pipe or within a wire enclosure before the charge is ignited.*

The bomb is allowed to cool, its outer surface is rinsed with distilled water, the cup opened, placed in a beaker, and enough hot water added to cover the cup. The cup cover is rinsed with a jet of hot water into the beaker. The fused mass is allowed to disintegrate, and solution is facilitated by stirring with a glass rod. The cup is lifted out of the beaker and rinsed well with hot water into the beaker. Hydrochloric acid is slowly added until the solution is slightly acid, then 2 ml more of the acid added and diluted with water, if necessary, to 200 to 250 ml. If insoluble matter is present, the solution is filtered and the insoluble washed with hot water. The solution is brought to a boil and the sulfate precipitated with barium chloride in the usual manner.

Sulfur—Determination of Small Amounts in Liquid Volatile Hydrocarbons:

Introduce 40 ml of KOH solution in alcohol—approximately 0.5 N, into a ground neck conical flask, avoiding rubber stopper or connection. Add 10.0 ml of the sample, attach an efficient condenser and boil the mixture gently for 30 minutes. Detach the condenser, add to the flask 50 ml of water and heat on the steam bath until the alcohol (from the KOH solution) and the sample have evaporated. Add 50 ml of bromine water and heat on the steam bath for 15 minutes. Transfer the solution to a beaker, neutralize to litmus paper with 10% HCl and add 1 ml excess of HCl. Concentrate the solution to about 50 ml, filter if necessary, heat to boiling, add 5 ml of $BaCl_2$ solution, cover, heat on the steam bath for 2 hours and allow to stand overnight. If a precipitate is present, filter, wash and ignite. From the weight of the precipitate ($BaSO_4$) deduct the weight of $BaSO_4$ obtained from a blank made with the same quantities of the reagents and in the same manner as with the sample. Barium sulfate contains 13.74% sulfur (S). Calculate the percentage of sulfur on the weight—10 × sp. gr.—of the sample.

WATER DETERMINATION BY THE IODINE (FISCHER) METHOD

The iodine (Karl Fischer) method for the determination of water is based on the fact that the reaction between iodine and sulfur dioxide takes place only in the presence of water. The methanol and pyridine used in preparing the reagent solution, besides acting as solvent and buffer, also partake in the reaction as expressed in the following equations. They should, therefore, be as free from water as practicable; otherwise much of the iodine will be inactivated by the water in these solvents.

$$H_2O + I_2 + SO_2 + 3C_5H_5N \rightarrow 2C_5H_5N \cdot HI + C_5H_5NSO_3$$
$$C_5H_5NSO_3 + CH_3OH \rightarrow C_5H_5NH \cdot SO_4CH_3$$

Preparation of the Fischer Reagent: (a) Add 125 g of iodine to a mixture of 650 ml of methanol and 200 ml of pyridine contained in a flask, and immediately close the flask tightly. (b) Pass dry sulfur dioxide into 100 ml of pyridine, contained in a 250-ml graduated cylinder and cooled in an ice bath, until the volume reaches 200 ml.

Slowly add (b) with agitation to the cooled (a), stopper immediately, and shake well until the iodine is dissolved. Transfer the solution to an automatic pipette, protected from absorption of moisture by a drying agent such as anhydrous calcium chloride or silica gel, and allow to stand for 24 hours before standardizing. One ml of the reagent when freshly prepared should be, theoretically, equivalent to about 8 mg of water, but, owing to the invariable presence of some water in the reagents, 1 ml is usually equivalent to 5 mg of water.

The reagent deteriorates continuously, and it should be standardized within 1 hour before use, or daily if in continuous use.

The replacement of the methanol in the formulation of the Fischer reagent with methyl Cellosolve-monomethyl ether of ethylene glycol is advocated by E. L. Peters and J. L. Jungnickel, *Anal. Chem.* **27**, 450 (1955). The solution so prepared appears to be more stable and consequently retains its titer for a longer time.

Water Standards: (1) *Water Solution:* Take a dry, glass-stoppered 100-ml volumetric flask, add about 0.5 ml of water, and reweigh. Make to volume with anhydrous methanol and mix well.

(2) *Sodium Tartrate:* $Na_2C_4H_4O_6 \cdot 2H_2O$, is very suitable as a water standard, because it retains practically its full water content, 15.66%, even at a temperature of about 50°. For use as a water standard its water content is ascertained by drying at 150° to constant weight.

Apparatus: The titration with the Fischer method is carried out in a 60 to 75-ml flask fitted with a rubber stopper with accommodation for the burette tip, a vent tube protected with a desiccant, and two platinum electrodes. The stirring of the solution during titration must be continuous and efficient, and can be accomplished by magnetic stirring, or by means of a propeller stirrer.

For many purposes the end point can be detected visually by the change from a light brownish-yellow to an amber color.

For colored substances or when the end point is not clearly defined, the electrometric method for indicating the end point is recommended. This method makes use of the "dead stop" end point.

The circuit consists of two bright platinum electrodes which are externally polarized by means of a 1.5-volt dry cell connected through a potentiometer of resistance 2000 ohms. The potentiometer is adjusted so that when a small excess (about 0.02 ml) of the reagent is present, a current of 50 to 150 microamperes is recorded. At the beginning of a titration, if the system is correctly adjusted, a current of only a few microamperes will flow between the polarized electrodes. After each addition of reagent the pointer of the microammeter is deflected but rapidly returns to its original position.   At the end point a deflection is obtained which endures for a longer period.

Standardization of the Iodine (Fischer) Reagent: Pipette exactly 10 ml of the methanol into a dry titration flask and titrate with the Fischer reagent to the end point.   Record the volume of ml consumed as A.   Now pipette exactly 10 ml of the standard water solution into the flask and titrate again.   Record the volume of ml used for the second titration as B.   Instead of the standard water solution, about 200 mg of sodium tartrate, accurately weighed, may be transferred into the flask and titrated in the same manner.

The equivalency of 1 ml of the reagent in terms of mg of water is then calculated by the formula $W/(B - A)$, the W representing the quantity, in mg, of water in the 10 ml of the standard water solution or in the number of mg of sodium tartrate used.

Procedure with the sample: Transfer about 25 ml of the reagent methanol to the titration flask and titrate to the end point with the Fischer reagent.   Do not record the volume consumed.   Now quickly transfer to the titrated liquid an accurately weighed quantity of the sample containing 10 to 50 mg of water, stir vigorously, and titrate with the Fischer reagent.

BAROMETRIC PRESSURE CORRECTION
and remarks about
BOILING RANGE, OR TEMPERATURE, DETERMINATION

The temperature data for the boiling range requirements are for normal, 760-mm atmospheric pressure.   A small deviation of 2 to 3 mm, either way, in the pressure during the boiling range determination may be ignored.   If, however, the deviation is greater, a correction to the observed temperature should be applied.

The correction is 0.1° for each 2.7 mm deviation from 760 mm, adding it if the pressure is lower, or subtracting if higher than 760.

Remarks: The thermometer used for boiling range determination should be either one calibrated for "emergent stem" or a short-stemmed one, permitting the desired temperature range to extend within the neck of the flask.

The flame, the flask, including the neck, and the thermometer, if more than a few degrees below the boiling range extend above the stopper, should be well shielded against air currents: otherwise the results may be erratic and notably so with low-boiling liquids.

FREEZING POINT DETERMINATION

The freezing point of liquids, also frequently designated as the congealing or crystallization point, is determined in the following manner:

About 10 ml of the liquid is placed in a thoroughly dry test tube, about 20 mm diameter, and cooled in water or other suitable medium, the temperature of which is about 5° below the supposed freezing point of the liquid. The tube is then promptly suspended, through a cork stopper or other suitable arrangement, to at least three-quarters of its length, in a larger test tube or narrow bottle to form an insulating air jacket and thus prevent too rapid a rise in temperature. The liquid is then gently stirred with a standardized thermometer until it begins to solidify. The stirring is then discontinued and the temperature rise noted every 5 to 10 seconds. Solidification may frequently be induced by rubbing the inner walls of the tube with the thermometer. The highest temperature remaining constant for about 1 minute is the freezing point.

MELTING RANGE, OR TEMPERATURE, DETERMINATION

The melting range data given in this book are determined by the "capillary tube" method.

Either a thermometer calibrated for "emergent stem" or a short-stemmed thermometer permitting the desired temperature range to extend within the liquid of the bath is to be used.

The "bath" is preheated to 10° below the lower figure of the melting range; then the capillary tube with the substances being tested is attached to the thermometer so that the closed end of the capillary is near the middle of the bulb of the thermometer. Adjust the thermometer so that the immersion mark is at the level of the surface of the liquid in the bath or, if a short-stemmed thermometer is used, so that the mercury column up to the higher point in the range is immersed. Now heat the bath at such a rate that the temperature rises 2.5° to 3.5° per minute, and note the temperature at which the substance begins definitely to melt and when it is completely melted.

The temperature at the beginning of the melting is regarded as the lower point and that at the complete melting as the higher point of the melting range.

SPECIFIC ROTATION

The extent of the specific rotation of an optically active substance is, among other conditions, more or less affected by the concentration of the substance in the solution. A variation, however, of only 10% to 20% in the concentration will usually not appreciably affect the specific rotation.

If the quantity of the substance available is insufficient to make 10 ml of the specified concentration, the rotation may be taken in a semimacro polariscope tube which requires only about 2 ml of solution, thus affording a concentration closer to the one specified.

The solution for determining the rotation is prepared and the rotation observed, unless otherwise stated, at 25° ± 2°.

Calculation of Specific Rotation: The specific rotation of the substance in the solvent used is calculated from the formula $(a \times 100)/(l \times c)$, where a is the observed angular rotation, l is the length of the tube in decimeters, and c is the number ⁴ g of the substance in 100 ml of solution.

*p*H DETERMINATION

For the measurement of the *p*H the use of *p*H electrometers (*p*H meters) is to be preferred. Such meters eliminate the need for buffer solutions, give a direct reading, and the results are more accurate. When, however, a *p*H meter is not available, the colorimetric method described below can be used with an accuracy of about 0.2 point.

The given *p*H values for indicators hold for determinations in aqueous solutions only. When alcohol or any other solvent is used to dissolve a substance, the *p*H values of the indicators change and, if used with such solvents, their values must be ascertained under the same conditions.

pH of Chemicals: Prepare a solution of the chemical, of the concentration indicated in the text, in water freed from carbon dioxide by boiling in resistant glass, and cooled to room temperature, protecting it during cooling from access of acid or alkaline gases.

Usually fifth-molar solutions are used for *p*H determinations. If the chemical composition of a sample is unknown, use an approximately 2% solution in water. If the chemical is slightly soluble in water, an aqueous solution saturated at room temperature is used.

An approximation to within one *p*H point or less can readily be made with *p*H paper strips available for this purpose.

Place 5 ml of the solution to be tested in a hard glass test tube of about 10-ml capacity. Add a suitable quantity, accurately measured, of the proper indicator solution and mix thoroughly. Usually 0.5 ml of the indicator solution is used.

Place in 4 to 6 similar test tubes 5-ml portions of buffer mixtures (page 584), the *p*H values of which overlap the *p*H value of the solution under examination and differ from each other by not more than 0.2 *p*H unit. To each of these buffer mixtures add exactly the same quantity of the indicator solution as was added to the solution under examination, and mix thoroughly. Now compare the color of the unknown solution with the colors of the buffer mixtures. The *p*H of the unknown is that represented by the *p*H of the buffer mixture it most closely matches in color.

The colors of the solutions are preferably compared by holding the test tubes against a white background.

Smaller or larger quantities of the solution under examination may be used, but in any case the volume of this solution, the volume of the buffers, the quantity of indicator, and the dimensions of the test tubes must be the same for the solution under examination and for the buffer solutions.

pH of Indicators: Prepare a solution of the indicator as described under *Indicators for pH Determinations*, pages 586 etc.

Select a set of 3 buffer mixtures, differing by 0.2 *p*H unit from each other, the *p*H of the middle one coinciding with the assumed *p*H of the indicator at the lowest point of the range. Similarly, select a set of 3 buffer mixtures, differing by 0.2 *p*H unit from each other, the *p*H of the middle one coinciding with the assumed *p*H of the indicator at the highest point of the range. Select also a buffer mixture of a *p*H lying approximately in the middle of the *p*H range of the indicator.

Place 5 ml of each of the buffer mixtures in test tubes of hard glass, and to each add exactly the same volume of the indicator solution, usually 0.3 to 0.5 ml. The color of each of the buffer mixtures lying outside of the pH range at either end should be the same as that of the buffer mixture at the given pH; while the color of the buffer mixtures in the test tubes of either end within the range should be slightly tinted with the color of the other end. The color of the middle tube should be distinctly different from the color of the other tubes and have a tint of the colors at either end of the pH range.

For example: The pH range of methyl red is: 4.2 red; 6.2 yellow. Select 7 buffer mixtures having a pH range of 4.0, 4.2, 4.4, 5.2, 6.0, 6.2, and 6.4. To 5 ml of each of the mixtures add 0.5 ml of the indicator solution. There should be no difference in the color of the buffer mixtures of 4.0 and 4.2, and of 6.4 and 6.2. The color of the mixture of 4.4 should be slightly paler than 4.2. Similarly, buffer mixture pH 6.0 should have a slight reddish tint as compared with 6.2. The mixture 5.2 should be reddish-yellow and distinctly different from either 4.2 or 6.2.

BUFFER SOLUTIONS AND MIXTURES

Solutions for the Preparation of Buffer Mixtures
(According to Clark and Lubs)

The water used for making Buffer Solutions or Mixtures should be thoroughly freed from carbon dioxide by boiling in "nonsoluble" glass, or in porcelain. As soon as the solution or mixture has been prepared it should be transferred to glass-stoppered bottles of resistant glass.

Boric Acid and Potassium Chloride, M/5: Dissolve 6.184 g of boric acid and 7.455 g of potassium chloride in sufficient water to make exactly 500 ml.

Hydrochloric Acid, 0.1 N: Prepare as described on page 592.

Potassium Biphthalate, M/5: Dissolve 20.414 g of potassium biphthalate, previously dried for 24 hours over sulfuric acid, in sufficient water to make exactly 500 ml.

Potassium Phosphate Monobasic, M/5: Dissolve 13.616 of potassium phosphate monobasic in sufficient water to make exactly 500 ml.

Potassium Chloride, M/5: Dissolve 7.455 g of potassium chloride in sufficient water to make exactly 500 ml.

Sodium Hydroxide, 0.1 N: Prepare as described on page 594.

HCl-KCl Mixtures

Each mixture is diluted with sufficient water to make 100 ml.

pH	0.1 N HCl	$\frac{M}{5}$KCl	pH	0.1 N HCl	$\frac{M}{5}$KCl
	ml	ml		ml	ml
1.1	94.56	2.70	1.7	23.76	38.10
1.2	75.10	12.45	1.8	18.86	40.60
1.3	59.68	20.15	1.9	14.98	42.50
1.4	47.40	26.30	2.0	11.90	44.05
1.5	37.64	31.20	2.1	9.46	45.30
1.6	29.90	35.00	2.2	7.52	46.25

Potassium Biphthalate-HCl Mixtures

Each mixture is diluted with sufficient water to make 100 ml.

pH	0.1 N HCl	$\frac{M}{5}$KHC$_8$H$_4$O$_4$	pH	0.1 N HCl	$\frac{M}{5}$HKC$_8$H$_4$O$_4$
	ml	ml		ml	ml
2.2	46.60	25	3.2	14.80	25
2.4	39.60	25	3.4	9.95	25
2.6	33.00	25	3.6	6.00	25
2.8	26.50	25	3.8	2.65	25
3.0	20.40	25	....	....	....

Potassium Biphthalate-NaOH Mixtures

Each mixture is diluted with sufficient water to make 100 ml.

pH	0.1 N NaOH	$\frac{M}{5}$KHC$_8$H$_4$O$_4$	pH	0.1 N NaOH	$\frac{M}{5}$KHC$_8$H$_4$O$_4$
	ml	ml		ml	ml
4.0	0.40	25	5.2	29.75	25
4.2	3.65	25	5.4	35.25	25
4.4	7.35	25	5.6	39.70	25
4.6	12.00	25	5.8	43.10	25
4.8	17.50	25	6.0	45.40	25
5.0	23.65	25	6.2	47.00	25

KH$_2$PO$_4$-NaOH Mixtures

Each mixture is diluted with sufficient water to make 100 ml.

pH	0.1 N NaOH	$\frac{M}{5}$ KH$_2$PO$_4$	pH	0.1 N NaOH	$\frac{M}{5}$KH$_2$PO$_4$
	ml	ml		ml	ml
5.8	3.66	25	7.0	29.54	25
6.0	5.64	25	7.2	34.90	25
6.2	8.55	25	7.4	39.34	25
6.4	12.60	25	7.6	42.74	25
6.6	17.74	25	7.8	45.17	25
6.8	23.60	25	8.0	46.85	25

H_3BO_3-KCl-NaOH Mixtures

Each mixture is diluted with sufficient water to make 100 ml.

pH	0.1 N NaOH	$\frac{M}{5}H_3BO_3$—KCl	pH	0.1 N NaOH	$\frac{M}{5}H_3BO_3$—KCl
	ml	ml		ml	ml
7.8	2.65	25	9.0	21.40	25
8.0	4.00	25	9.2	26.70	25
8.2	5.90	25	9.4	32.00	25
8.4	8.55	25	9.6	36.85	25
8.6	12.00	25	9.8	40.80	25
8.8	16.40	25	10.0	43.90	25

INDICATORS FOR pH DETERMINATIONS

and for Acid-Base Titration

The "pH" in the column "Preparation" designates that the indicator solution prepared as directed is recommended for measuring the hydrogen ion concentration only. The designation "vol." signifies that the indicator solution is intended for volumetric analysis; the designation "pH, vol." indicates that the solution is applicable for the determination of hydrogen ion concentration as well as for volumetric analysis.

The water used for preparing indicator solutions is to be freed from carbon dioxide by thoroughly boiling it out in resistant glass or in porcelain. Similarly, the alcohol used for making the indicator solution should be neutral.

When the indicator solution is to be prepared with the aid of 0.02 N sodium hydroxide, triturate well the quantity of the indicator material with the volume of the 0.02 N NaOH in an agate mortar, and then dilute with carbon-dioxide-free water to the volume indicated.

Indicator	Mol. Wt.	Range	Preparation
METACRESOL PURPLE.......... m-Cresolsulfonphthalein (acid range)	382	Red 1.2–2.5 yellow	pH: 0.10 g in 13.6 ml of 0.02 N NaOH and dilute with water to 250 ml
p-XYLENOL BLUE............. 1,4-dimethyl-5-hydroxyben-zenesulfonphthalein (acid range)	410	Red 1.2–2.8 yellow	pH: 0.10 g in 250 ml of alcohol
THYMOL BLUE................ Thymolsulfonphthalein (acid range)	466	Red 1.2–2.8 yellow	pH: 0.10 g in 10.75 ml of 0.02 N NaOH, and dilute with water to 250 ml
TROPAEOLIN 00............... Sodium-p-diphenylamine-azo-benzene-sulfonate	375	Red 1.3–3.0 yellow	pH, vol.: 0.10 g in 100 ml of water
BENZOPURPURINE 4B..........	690	Blue-violet 1.3–4.0 red	pH, vol.: 0.10 g in 100 ml of water

Indicator	Mol. Wt.	Range	Preparation
METHYLROSANILINE CHLORIDE... Methyl Violet, Crystal Violet	408	Blue 1.5–3.2 violet	pH, vol.: 0.25 g in 100 ml of water
ALIZARIN YELLOW R (p)........ Sodium-p-nitrobenzene-azo-salicylate	309	Red 1.9–3.3 yellow	pH, vol.: 0.10 g in 100 ml of warm water
2,6-DINITROPHENOL (β).........	184	Colorless 2.4–4.0 yellow	pH, vol.: 0.1 g in a few ml of alcohol, then dilute with water to 100 ml
p-DIMETHYLAMINOAZOBENZENE... Methyl Yellow	225	Red 2.9–4.0 yellow	pH, vol.: 0.10 g in 200 ml of alcohol
BROMOPHENOL BLUE............ Tetrabromophenolsulfon-phthalein	670	Yellow 3.0–4.6 blue	pH: 0.10 g in 7.45 ml of 0.02 N NaOH and dilute with water to 250 ml vol.: 0.1 g in 250 ml of alcohol
CONGO RED.................	696	Blue 3.0–5.2 red	pH, vol.: 0.10 g in 100 ml of water
METHYL ORANGE.............. Sodium-p-dimethylamino-benzenesulfonate, Helianthin	327	Red 3.2–4.4 yellow	vol.: 0.1 g in 100 ml of water
BROMOCHLOROPHENOL BLUE..... Dibromo-dichlorophenol-sulfonphthalein	580	Yellow 3.2–4.8 blue	pH: 0.10 g in 8.6 ml of 0.02 N NaOH, then dilute with water to 250 ml vol.: 0.1 g in 250 ml alcohol
SODIUM ALIZARIN SULFONATE....	360	Yellow 3.7–5.2 violet	pH, vol.: 1.0 g in 100 ml of water
IODEOSIN.................... Tetraiodofluorescein	836	Yellow 0–about 4 rose red	vol.: 0.10 g in 100 ml of ether saturated with water
2,5-DINITROPHENOL (γ).........	184	Colorless 4–5.8 yellow	pH, vol.: 0.1 g in 20 ml of alcohol, then dilute with water to 100 ml
BROMOCRESOL GREEN.......... Tetrabromo-m-cresolsulfon-phthalein, Bromocresol Blue	698	Yellow 4.0–5.4 blue	pH: 0.10 g in 7.15 ml of 0.02 N NaOH and dilute with water to 250 ml vol.: 0.1 g in 250 ml alcohol
METHYL RED................ Dimethylamino-azo-benzene-o-carboxylic acid	269	Red 4.2–6.2 yellow	pH: 0.10 g in 18.6 ml of 0.02 N NaOH and dilute with water to 250 ml vol.: 0.10 g in 100 ml alcohol
LACMOID....................		Red 4.4–6.2 blue	vol.: 0.5 g in 100 ml alcohol
AZOLITMIN..................		Red 4.5–8.3 blue	vol.: 0.5 g in 80 ml of warm water, then add 20 ml of alcohol
COCHINEAL..................		Red 4.8–6.2 violet	vol.: Triturate 1 g with 25 ml alcohol and 75 ml of water, let stand for 2 days and filter
HEMATOXYLIN................	302	Yellow 5.0–6.0 violet	vol.: 0.5 g in 100 ml alcohol
CHLOROPHENOL RED............ Dichlorophenol-sulfon-phthalein	423	Yellow 5.0–6.6 red	pH: 0.10 g in 11.8 ml of 0.02 N NaOH and dilute with water to 250 ml vol.: 0.1 g in 250 ml of alcohol
p-NITROPHENOL...............	139	Colorless 5.0–7.6 yellow	pH, vol.: 0.25 g in 100 ml water

Indicator	Mol. Wt.	Range	Preparation
BROMOCRESOL PURPLE Dibromo-o-cresolsulfon-phthalein	540	Yellow 5.2–6.8 purple	pH: 0.10 g in 9.25 ml of 0.02 N NaOH and dilute with water to 250 ml vol.: 0.05 g in 250 ml alcohol
BROMOPHENOL RED Dibromophenolsulfonphthalein	512	Yellow 5.2–7.0 red	pH: 0.10 g in 9.75 ml of 0.02 N NaOH and dilute with water to 250 ml vol.: 0.1 g in 250 ml alcohol
ALIZARIN Dioxyanthraquinone	240	Yellow 5.5–6.8 red	vol.: 0.1 g in 100 ml alcohol
BROMOTHYMOL BLUE Dibromothymolsulfonphthalein	624	Yellow 6.0–7.6 blue	pH: 0.10 g in 8.0 ml of 0.02 N NaOH and dilute with water to 250 ml vol.: 0.10 g in 100 ml of 50% alcohol
CURCUMIN		Yellow 6–8.0 brownish red	A saturated aqueous solution
PHENOL RED Phenolsulfonphthalein	354	Yellow 6.8–8.4 red	pH: 0.10 g in 14.20 ml of 0.02 N NaOH and dilute with water to 250 ml vol.: 0.1 g in 100 ml alcohol
ROSOLIC ACID Aurin; Corallin	304	Yellow 6.8–8.2 red	pH, vol.: 1.0 g in 100 ml of 50% alcohol
CYANIN	115	Colorless 7.0–8.0 violet-blue	pH: 1.0 g in 100 ml alcohol
CRESOL RED o-Cresolsulfonphthalein	382	Yellow 7.2–8.8 red	pH: 0.10 g in 13.1 ml of 0.02 N NaOH and dilute with water to 250 ml vol.: 0.1 g in 100 ml alcohol
α-NAPHTHOLPHTHALEIN	418	Rose 7.3–8.7 green	pH, vol.: 0.10 g in 100 ml of 50% alcohol
METACRESOL PURPLE m-Cresolsulfonphthalein (alkaline range)	382	Yellow 7.4–9.0 purple	pH: 0.10 g in 13.1 ml 0.02 N NaOH and dilute with water to 250 ml vol.: 0.1 g in 100 ml alcohol
THYMOL BLUE Thymolsulfonphthalein (alkaline range)	466	Yellow 8.0–9.4 blue	pH: 0.10 g in 10.75 ml of 0.02 N NaOH and dilute with water to 250 ml vol.: 0.1 g in 100 ml alcohol
p-XYLENOL BLUE 1,4-Dimethyl-5-hydroxy-benzenesulfonphthalein (alkaline range)	410	Yellow 8.0–9.4 blue	pH, vol.: 0.10 g in 250 ml alcohol
TROPAEOLIN 000 Sodium-α-naphthol-azo-benzenesulfonate	350	Yellow 7.6–8.9 red	vol.: 0.1 g in 100 ml water
o-CRESOLPHTHALEIN	346	Colorless 8.2–10.4 red	pH: 0.10 g in 250 ml alcohol
α-NAPHTHOLBENZEIN	767	Yellow 8.5–9.8 green	pH: 1.0 g in 100 ml alcohol
PHENOLPHTHALEIN	318	Colorless 8.2–10 red	vol.: 1.0 g in 100 ml alcohol
THYMOLPHTHALEIN	430	Colorless 8.6–10.2 blue	pH, vol.: 0.10 g in 100 ml alcohol
POIRRIER BLUE C4B		Blue 11–13.0 red	pH: 0.2 g in 100 ml water
NITRAMINE 2,4,6-Trinitrophenyl-methyl-nitroamine	287	Yellow 11.0–13.0 orange-brown	pH: 0.10 g in 100 ml 70% alcohol
SODIUM INDIGO DISULFONATE Indigo Carmine	466	Blue 11.6–14.0 yellow	pH: 0.25 g in 100 ml of 50% alcohol

*p*H TABLE

The greater part of the *p*H values in the following table were determined in the author's laboratory. The chemicals used were of reagent or similar high quality; the *p*H of the water ranged between 6.7 and 6.85 and the temperature was 25° ± 2°.

Solution	Concentration	*p*H	Solution	Concentration	*p*H
Acetic Acid	1 M	2.4	Dextrose	0.5 M	5.9
Acetic Acid	0.1 M	2.9	Dimethylformamide	0.5 M	6.7
Acetic Acid	0.01 M	3.4	Disodium EDTA	0.05 M	4.7
Aluminum Chloride	0.2 M	3.0			
Aluminum Potassium			Ephedrine	0.05 M	10.9
Sulfate	0.2 M	3.3	Ephedrine Hydrochloride	0.1 M	5.8
Aminoacetic Acid	0.2 M	4	Ethanolamine (mono)	0.2 M	11.3
p-Aminobenzoic Acid	0.05 M*	3.5			
saturated solution					
Ammonium Acetate	0.5 M	7	Ferric Ammonium Sulfate	0.1 M	2–2.5
Ammonium Bicarbonate	0.2 M	7*	Ferric Chloride	0.1 M	1.5–2.0
Ammonium Chloride	0.2 M	4.6	Formamide	0.5 M	5.1
Ammonium Citrate	0.1 M	4.3			
Dibasic					
Ammonium Hydroxide	1 M	11.8	Hexamethylenetetramine	0.2 M	8.4
Ammonium Hydroxide	0.1 M	11.3	(Methenamine)		
Ammonium Hydroxide	0.01 M	10.8	Hydrazine Sulfate	0.2 M	1.3
Ammonium Nitrate	0.2 M	5.6	Hydrochloric Acid	1 M	0.1
Ammonium Oxalate	0.2 M	6.6	Hydrochloric Acid	0.1 M	1.1
Ammonium Phosphate	0.2 M	4.2	Hydrochloric Acid	0.01 M	2.0
Monobasic			Hydroxylamine	0.2 M	3.2
Ammonium Sulfamate	0.2 M	4.9	Hydrochloride		
Ammonium Sulfate	0.2 M	5.6	Hypophosphorous Acid	0.1 M	1.5
Ammonium Tartrate	0.2 M	6.5			
Aniline	0.2 M	8.1	Isoquinoline	0.1 M	9.7
Barbital Sodium	0.1 M	9.4	Lead Monoxide (saturated)		7.7
Barium Acetate	0.2 M	8.1	Lead Nitrate	0.2 M	4.1
Barium Chloride	0.2 M	6.4			
Barium Nitrate	0.2 M	6.4	Magnesium Acetate	0.2 M	7.5
Benzoic Acid	0.03 M*	2.8	Magnesium Chloride	0.2 M	5.6–6.2
saturated solution			Magnesium Oxide		10.3
Boric acid	0.1 M	5.1	saturated solution		
Borax	0.1 M	9.2	Magnesium Sulfate	0.2 M	6.0
			Manganese Chloride	0.2 M	5.5
			Mercuric Chloride	0.2 M	3.2
			Mercuric Oxide Yellow		5.6
Cadmium Acetate	0.2 M	7.1	saturated solution		
Cadmium Chloride	0.2 M	5.1	Methenamine—*see*		
Caffeine	0.1 M*	6.5	Hexamethylenamine		
Calcium Acetate	0.2 M	7.6			
Calcium Chloride	0.2 M	6.1	Nickel Ammonium	0.1 M	4.6
Calcium Hydroxide	0.02 M*	12.3	Sulfate		
saturated solution			Nickel Nitrate	0.2 M	4.2
Chromic Chloride	0.2 M	2.4	Nicotinamide	0.2 M	6.8
Citric Acid	0.1 M	2.1	Nicotinic Acid	0.1 M	2.7
Cobalt Acetate	0.2 M	6.8			
Cobalt Chloride	0.2 M	4.6	Phenylhydrazine	0.1 M	9.2
Cupric Chloride	0.2 M	3.6	Potassium Bicarbonate	0.1 M	8.2
Cupric Nitrate	0.2 M	4.0	Potassium Biphthalate	0.05 M	4.0
Cupric Sulfate	0.2 M	4.0	Potassium Bisulfate	0.1 M	1.4

* Approximate.

Solution	Concentration	pH	Solution	Concentration	pH
Potassium Bitartrate saturated solution	0.02 M	3.6	Sodium Citrate, Tribasic	0.2 M	8.2
			Sodium Hydroxide	1 M	14.0
Potassium Bromate	0.1 M	6.0	Sodium Hydroxide	0.1 M	12.7
Potassium Bromide	0.2 M	7.3	Sodium Hydroxide	0.01 M	11.8
Potassium Carbonate	0.1 M	11.6	Sodium Molybdate	0.2 M	8.2
Potassium Chlorate	0.1 M	6.2	Sodium Nitrite	0.2 M	7.6
Potassium Chloride	0.2 M	6.5	Sodium Oxalate	0.2 M	7.0
Potassium Chromate	0.2 M	9.2	Sodium Perchlorate	0.1 M	6.3
Potassium Ferricyanide	0.2 M	6.7	Sodium Phosphate Dibasic	0.1 M	9.3
Potassium Ferrocyanide	0.2 M	9.0			
Potassium Hydroxide	0.1 M	13.0*	Sodium Pyrophosphate	0.1 M	10.3
Potassium Iodate	0.1 M	6.1	Sodium Salicylate	0.2 M	5.5
Potassium Iodide	0.2 M	7.6	Sodium Sulfate	0.2 M	6.1
Potassium Nitrate	0.2 M	6.3	Sodium Sulfite	0.2 M	9.8
Potassium Nitrite	0.2 M	8.2	Sodium Tartrate	0.2 M	8.2
Potassium Oxalate	0.2 M	7.6	Sodium Tetraphenylboron	0.2 M	7.8
Potassium Perchlorate	0.1 M	6.8	Sodium Thiosulfate	0.2 M	7.4
Potassium Periodate	0.05 M	6.3	Sodium Thiosulfate	0.2 M	7.4
Potassium Permanganate	0.2 M	8.1	Sodium Tungstate	0.2 M	9*
			Strontium Nitrate	0.2 M	6.1
Potassium Phosphate Dibasic	0.2 M	9.3	Sulfamic Acid	0.1 M	1.2
			Sulfanilic Acid	0.05 M	2.2
Potassium Phosphate Monobasic	0.2 M	4.4	Sulfosalicylic Acid	0.1 M	1.0
Potassium Sodium Tartrate	0.2 M	8.0			
Potassium Thiocyanate	0.2 M	6.2			
Pyridine	0.2 M	8.5	Tartaric Acid	0.1 M	1.9
			Tetramethyl Ammonium Hydroxide	0.1 M	12.9
Quinoline	0.1 M	9.3			
			Trichloroacetic Acid	0.1 M	1.2
Salicylic Acid saturated solution	0.015 M*	2.4			
			Trisodium EDTA	0.05	8.5
Silver Nitrate	0.1 M	6*			
Sodium Acetate	0.2 M	8.4			
Sodium Arsenate, Dibasic	0.2 M	9*	Urea	0.2 M	6.8
Sodium Benzoate	0.2 M	8.0			
Sodium Bicarbonate	0.1 M	8.2			
Sodium Borate—see Borax			Zinc Acetate	0.2 M	7*
			Zinc Oxide, Amer. Process saturated solution		6.9
Sodium Carbonate	0.1 M	11.6			
Sodium Chloride	0.2 M	6.4	Zinc Sulfate	0.2 M	4.6

VOLUMETRIC SOLUTIONS AND TABLES
OF THEIR EQUIVALENTS

INTRODUCTORY REMARKS

The exact normality value of the volumetric solutions is of fundamental importance in volumetric analysis.

When large volumes of the solutions are made, particular attention must be paid to the proper and thorough mixing of the solutions. Except when making a liter or two, the bottle in which the solution is contained should not be filled more than four-fifths of its capacity to permit mixing. After the solution has been prepared and mixed it should be allowed to stand for several days, being mixed or agitated three to four times a day, then thoroughly mixed again before portions are withdrawn for the standardization.

At least 20 ml of a 1 N solution should be used for the standardization. With 0.1 N and lower normalities, 35–45 ml should be used.

When a "primary standard" substance is used for the determination of the normality, the quantity of the substance should be such that 30–40 ml of the solution will be required. Also, somewhat different weights should be taken for each determination.

Unless the burettes to be used with the solutions are very accurately calibrated, it is advisable to standardize the solution with the same burette with which it will be used.

The solutions should be standardized at average room temperature. If it is necessary to standardize when the temperature of the laboratory is above normal, it should be restandardized when the normal temperature is restored. It is good practice to check the normality value of volumetric solutions frequently. Some solutions, such as sodium thiosulfate, potassium permanganate, etc., because of their relatively rapid deterioration, should be redetermined quite frequently, at least once a month, preferably more often.

Volumetric solutions should be kept in containers of "nonsoluble" glass. When kept in ordinary glass, dilute solutions of alkali hydroxides have been known to increase in normality due to alkali dissolved from the glass.

When volumetric solutions of alkali hydroxide are lifted in the burette by means of vacuum or pressure, a soda-lime tube should be inserted in the proper place of the closure to absorb carbon dioxide or other acids from the air.

To ensure greater accuracy and to guard against error, the determination of the normality value should be repeated, using for the check a few ml more, or a few ml less, than for the first determination. It is better still to standardize volumetric solutions by two different methods. The two determinations should agree to within 0.3% and the mean taken for the final value.

PRIMARY STANDARDS

The term "Primary Standard" designates a substance of constant composition and of sufficient purity and stability to be used for standardizing volumetric solutions. Such a substance may also be used for the preparation of volumetric solutions, and when made up to an exact volume the solution requires no further standardization.

Many substances have been proposed for primary standards. From the author's experience the following are reliable:

Arsenic Trioxide—reduction; standardization of iodine solution.

Iodine—oxidation; standardization of sodium thiosulfate solution.

Potassium Biphthalate—alkalimetry.

Potassium Bitartrate—alkalimetry.

Potassium Dichromate—oxidation; standardization of sodium thiosulfate solution.

Potassium Iodate—oxidation.

Silver Nitrate—argentometry.

Sodium Carbonate, Anhydrous—acidimetry.

Sodium Oxalate—standardization of permanganate solution.

PREPARATION AND STANDARDIZATION
OF VOLUMETRIC SOLUTIONS

NORMAL ACIDS

Normal (1 N) Hydrochloric Acid (36.46 g HCl in a liter): For each liter of the solution to be prepared dilute 90 ml of hydrochloric acid (35%–38%) with 920 ml of water and mix thoroughly. (See Introductory Remarks.) Standardize the solution by the following methods:

Method I—Measure from a burette 20 ml of the solution into a 250-ml beaker and dilute with 100 ml of water. Add 5 drops of nitric acid, then add, slowly, with constant stirring, sufficient of a 10% silver nitrate solution to precipitate all the chloride, avoiding a large excess. Usually 40 ml of the silver nitrate will suffice. After the silver nitrate has been added, boil the mixture for 5 minutes, cover the beaker, and allow it to stand in the dark until the precipitate has settled, the supernatant liquid has become clear and the mixture has cooled to the temperature of the room. Decant the supernatant liquid through a Gooch crucible with an asbestos pad or a sintered glass crucible, which has been previously washed with water acidulated with nitric acid, and dried at 120° to constant weight. Transfer the precipitate completely onto the filter with the aid of small portions of water acidulated with nitric acid. Wash the silver chloride with small portions of water acidulated with nitric acid until 5 ml of the washings give no opalescence on the addition of a drop of diluted hydrochloric acid. Finally dry the crucible with the precipitate to constant weight at 120°. The weight of the silver chloride multiplied by 0.2544 represents the weight of HCl in the volume of solution taken for the determination.

To prevent the discoloration of the silver chloride, the operation, and especially the filtration, should be carried out in subdued light and away from direct sunlight.

Method II—Weigh accurately, in a covered platinum crucible previously ignited and tared, about 1.8 g of reagent anhydrous sodium carbonate and heat at 225°–275° in a sand bath, or any other suitable bath, until of constant weight. Transfer the sodium carbonate completely with the aid of water into a beaker or flask and add sufficient water to make about 75 ml.   After the sodium carbonate has dissolved, add 2–3 drops of methyl orange and slowly run in from a burette, with constant agitation, the solution to be standardized, until the yellow color of the solution changes to a brownish pink.   One gram of anhydrous sodium carbonate is equivalent to 0.6882 g HCl.

Normal (1 N) Sulfuric Acid (49.04 g H_2SO_4 in a liter): For each liter of normal sulfuric acid to be prepared dilute 30 ml of sulfuric acid (95% H_2SO_4 or over) with 1 liter of water, allow to cool to room temperature, and mix thoroughly. Standardize the solution by the following methods:

Method I—Measure from a burette 20 ml of the solution into a 500-ml beaker and dilute with 250 ml of water.   Add 1 ml of hydrochloric acid, heat to boiling and add gradually, with continuous stirring, sufficient hot barium chloride solution until precipitation is complete, avoiding an undue excess of barium chloride.   Heat the mixture on the steam bath for 2 hours or allow to stand overnight.   Decant the clear liquid through a filter and wash the barium sulfate several times by decantation with 74-ml portions of hot water.   Then transfer the precipitate with the aid of hot water completely onto the filter and wash with hot water until 10 ml of the washings remain unaffected by the addition of a few drops of silver nitrate.   Dry the barium sulfate with the filter at about 100°, then ignite to constant weight.   If the barium sulfate has been collected on a paper filter, a few drops of sulfuric acid should be added to the ignited and cooled precipitate, then re-ignited to constant weight.   This treatment converts into barium sulfate any barium sulfide that may have been formed by the ignition with the paper.   One gram of barium sulfate is equivalent to 0.4202 g of H_2SO_4.

Method II—Determine the normality of the solution against anhydrous sodium carbonate as described for hydrochloric acid.   One gram of anhydrous sodium carbonate is equivalent to 0.9253 g H_2SO_4.

Method III—The normality of the acid is also conveniently determined as follows: Accurately measure from a burette 30–40 ml of the acid to be standardized into a platinum dish, add, *cautiously*, freshly prepared ammonium hydroxide (made by distilling reagent ammonium hydroxide into freshly distilled water) until a strong odor of NH_3 is perceptible, and evaporate on the steam bath to dryness. Moisten the residue with a few ml of the ammonium hydroxide, re-evaporate on the steam bath and dry at 100° to constant weight.   One gram of the ammonium sulfate so obtained is equivalent to 0.7422 g H_2SO_4.

TENTH-NORMAL ACIDS

Tenth-normal (0.1 N) Hydrochloric or Sulfuric Acid is prepared by diluting, for each liter, 10 ml of hydrochloric acid or 3 ml of sulfuric acid with 1 liter of water.   The dilutions should be thoroughly mixed.   Their normality is determined in the same manner as described for Normal Acids, using 35–45 ml.

For the standardization against anhydrous sodium carbonate use 0.2 g of the Na_2CO_3 dissolved in about 40 ml of water.

The normality of 0.1 N acids may conveniently be checked against carefully standardized 0.1 N alkali hydroxides.

Fiftieth (0.02 N) or lower normality acids are best prepared by diluting the required volume of N or 0.1 N acid with water to exactly 1 liter.

NORMAL ALKALI HYDROXIDE

The following description for the preparation of normal and other normalities of sodium hydroxide is applicable to the preparation of potassium hydroxide solutions. For a normal solution use 65 g of potassium hydroxide, and one-tenth of this quantity for 0.1 N.

Normal (1 N) Sodium Hydroxide (40.00 g NaOH in a liter): For every liter of the solution dissolve 45 g of sodium hydroxide in 950 ml of water. Add, in small portions, a freshly prepared saturated solution of barium hydroxide until no more precipitate forms. The barium hydroxide precipitates the sodium carbonate, releasing its equivalent of sodium hydroxide. Mix thoroughly (see *Introductory Remarks*) and allow to stand protected from access of carbon dioxide until the precipitate has thoroughly subsided, then decant quickly into a suitable bottle, and stopper. The stopper should be provided with soda-lime tubes (see *Introductory Remarks*). The solution so prepared is standardized by the following methods:

Method I—Accurately measure from a burette 30–40 ml of 1 N hydrochloric or sulfuric acid into a flask, and dilute with 50 ml of carbon dioxide-free water. Add 3 drops of phenolphthalein and titrate with the sodium hydroxide from a burette to the production of a slight but permanent pink color.

Method II—Dry about 5 g of potassium biphthalate at 100° for 2 hours and weigh accurately. If the potassium biphthalate is in the form of larger crystals they should be crushed before drying. Dissolve it in 75 ml of CO_2-free water, add 3 drops of phenolphthalein and titrate with the sodium hydroxide solution from a burette to a slight pink color, persisting for 15 seconds. One gram of potassium biphthalate is equivalent to 0.1959 g of NaOH or 0.2747 g KOH.

In place of the biphthalate, reagent potassium bitartrate may be used. For 1 N alkali, 5–6 g previously powdered and dried for 2 hours at 105° and then accurately weighed is treated with 75–100 ml of hot water and the alkali is run in. The potassium bitartrate will dissolve as the alkali is added. For 0.1 N NaOH, 0.5–0.6 g of the bitartrate is employed. One gram of potassium bitartrate = 0.2126 g of NaOH or 0.2981 g of KOH.

Sodium hydroxide solution, even when entirely free from carbonate, will have slightly different normality values with different indicators, such as methyl orange or phenolphthalein. This is due to the different pH of these indicators. The normality of the solution should, therefore, be determined separately for each indicator with which the sodium hydroxide is used.

Tenth-normal (0.1 N) Sodium Hydroxide (4.000 g NaOH in a liter): This solution is prepared in the same manner as N sodium hydroxide, using a proportionate quantity of NaOH. It is also standardized in the same manner with 0.1 N hydrochloric or sulfuric acid, or with about 0.5 g of potassium biphthalate.

Fiftieth (0.02N) or Lower Normalities of Sodium Hydroxide are best prepared by diluting the required volume of N or 0.1 N sodium hydroxide with carbon-dioxide-free water to 1 liter, and mixing well. In alkali hydroxide solutions of these lower normalities, the normality changes rather quickly due to absorption of carbon dioxide and solubility of the glass. Therefore, they should not be prepared in more than 1-liter quantities.

TENTH-NORMAL AMMONIUM OR POTASSIUM THIOCYANATE

7.611 g NH_4SCN in a Liter

For each liter of the solution to be prepared dissolve 8 g of ammonium thiocyanate or 10 g of the potassium salt in 1 liter of water. Standardize the solution thus prepared as follows:

Measure accurately from a burette 35–40 ml of 0.1 N silver nitrate into a glass-stoppered 300–400 ml flask and dilute it with 75 ml of water. Add 2 ml of ferric ammonium sulfate and 2–3 ml of nitric acid, and slowly run in from a burette, with constant agitation, the solution to be standardized until a brownish-red color persists after shaking for 30 seconds.

The solution may also be standardized by the Adsorption Indicator Method, page 565.

TENTH-NORMAL BROMINE

7.992 g Br in a Liter

For each liter of the solution dissolve 3 g of potassium bromate and 25 g of potassium bromide in a liter of water. Determine the exact normality as follows:

Measure accurately from a burette 30–35 ml of the solution into a 500-ml glass-stoppered, volumetric flask and dilute with 120 ml of water. Add, quickly, 5 ml of hydrochloric acid, immediately stopper the flask and shake the contents gently. Cool the flask for a few minutes in cold water, then add, quickly, 7 ml of 10% potassium iodide and immediately stopper the flask. Shake gently for a few minutes, open the stopper slightly and wash it and the neck of the flask with a little water. Now run in slowly from a burette 0.1 N sodium thiosulfate until the solution is pale yellow, then add starch solution and continue with the addition of the thiosulfate until the blue color is just discharged.

TENTH-NORMAL CERIC SULFATE OR CERIC AMMONIUM SULFATE

66.8 g $Ce(CO_4)_2 \cdot 2(NH_4)_2SO_4 \cdot 4H_2O$ or 40.4 g $Ce(SO_4)_3 \cdot 4H_2O$ in a Liter

Place about 40 g of ceric sulfate or 67 g of ceric ammonium sulfate in a mortar, add 30 ml of water, then add *cautiously* 30 ml of sulfuric acid. Triturate the mixture well, transfer it with the aid of water into a flask or beaker, add about 300 ml of water, and heat until no more dissolves. Dilute with water to about 800 ml and filter if necessary into a 1-liter volumetric flask, add water to make exactly 1 liter, mix well and standardize the solution as follows:

Method I—Weigh accurately about 0.2 g of sodium oxalate, primary standard, previously dried for 2 hours at 105°, and dissolve it in 75 ml of water in a beaker. Add, with stirring, 2 ml of sulfuric acid which has previously been mixed with 5 ml of water and follow with 10 ml of HCl. Heat to 70°–75° and titrate with the ceric sulfate solution until a permanent slight yellow color is produced.   One gram of sodium oxalate $= 149.3$ ml of $0.1 \ N$ ceric sulfate.

$$2Ce(SO_4)_2 + Na_2C_2O_4 \rightarrow 2CO_2 + Ce_2(SO_4)_3 + Na_2SO_4$$

Method II—Weigh accurately about 0.15 g of arsenic trioxide, primary standard, previously dried at 105° for 2 hours, and dissolve it in a conical flask in 5 ml of N sodium hydroxide and 25 ml of water by gentle warming.   Cool, add 30 ml of water, 40 ml of HCl, 0.1 ml of osmium tetroxide solution in 10% H_2SO_4 (1 in 100) or 5 ml of iodine monochloride solution (see page 557) and 0.1 ml of *o*-phenanthroline indicator. Titrate with the ceric sulfate solution until the red color remains discharged for 30 seconds and the solution acquires a bluish color.   Toward the end the reaction is slow and the last 3 or 4 ml of the ceric sulfate solution should be added in small portions, each portion being allowed to react before the next one is added.   Correct for a blank with the same volume of the reagents and the indicator.   Usually 0.1 ml of indicator will require 0.1 ml of the ceric sulfate solution.   One gram of arsenic trioxide $= 202.2$ ml of $0.1 \ N$ ceric sulfate.

$$4Ce(SO_4)_2 + As_2O_3 + 2H_2O \rightarrow As_2O_5 + 2Ce_2(SO_4)_3 + 2H_2SO_4$$

TENTH NORMAL FERROUS AMMONIUM SULFATE

39.216 g $FeSO_4 \cdot (NH_4)_2SO_4 \cdot 6H_2O$ in a Liter

Dissolve 40 g of ferrous ammonium sulfate in a cooled mixture of 300 ml of water and 30 ml of sulfuric acid, dilute with water to 1 liter and mix well.   Dilute an accurately measured volume of 35–40 ml of the solution with 25 ml of water, and titrate with $0.1 \ N$ potassium permanganate to a permanent, slight pink color.

Note: This solution is also used where $0.1 \ N$ ferrous sulfate is called for.

TENTH-MOLAR ETHYLENEDIAMINE TETRAACETATE, EDTA

29.22 g $C_{16}H_{16}N_2O_8$, or 33.62 g $C_{16}H_{14}N_2O_8 \cdot Na_2$ in a Liter

Dissolve 34 g of the dihydrate of the disodium salt, which is the form generally preferred, in water to make 1 liter.   If the solution is to be made from the acid EDTA, 29.5 g of the ethylenediamine tetraacetic acid is placed in liter flask, 500–600 ml of water added, then 200 ml of 1 N NaOH gradually added while the contents are being mixed.   When the EDTA has dissolved, the solution is allowed to cool to room temperature, diluted with water to 1 liter, and well mixed.

The solutions are standardized against a standard calcium (chloride) solution prepared as follows:

Dry in a shallow layer about 12 g of powdered, reagent grade Iceland spar, or reagent *Calcium Carbonate, Precipitated, Low in Alkalies* at a temperature of 200°–250° for 4 hours.   Weigh 10.02 g of the dried carbonate and quantitatively transfer it to a 500-ml wide-mouthed flask.   Add 50 ml of water through a funnel, then add in small portions hydrochloric acid (about 20 ml), warming the solution toward the end, until dissolved.   Heat gently to expel CO_2, filter into a 1-liter volumetric flask.   Wash well the 500-ml flask and filter with water, allow to cool, dilute to mark with water, and mix well. The solution so prepared contains 4.000 mg Ca per ml.

Dilute exactly 25 ml of the calcium solution with 75 ml of water, add 50 mg of murexide-naphthol green indicator, page 588, and 15 ml of approximately 1 N NaOH, and titrate with the EDTA solution to a blue color.

TENTH-NORMAL IODINE

12.692 g I in a Liter

If only 1 liter of the solution is desired, it is best prepared in the following manner. Weigh a small, glass-stoppered flask with 35 g of potassium iodide; then add about 13 g of reagent iodine and reweigh accurately. Open the flask and pour in quickly about 50 ml of water; stopper and gently rotate until all is dissolved. Transfer the solution, quickly and completely, with the aid of water, through a funnel into a 1-liter volumetric flask. Rinse down the funnel and the stem with water, add 3 drops of hydrochloric acid, dilute to exactly 1 liter and mix well. From the weight of the iodine used calculate the normality of the solution.

Note: Potassium iodide frequently contains small amounts of alkali carbonate or hydroxide. These alkalies may react with the iodine, forming iodate. Such a solution will give slightly different values when used in acid or neutral solutions. The addition of hydrochloric acid prevents the formation of iodate, or reliberates the iodine from the iodate.

For larger volumes of 0.1 N iodine dissolve for every liter 13 g of iodine and 35 g of potassium iodide in 100 ml of water. Dilute with 900 ml water and add 3 drops of HCl for every liter, then determine the normality as follows:

Weigh accurately in a glass-stoppered weighing bottle from 0.20 to 0.22 g of reagent arsenic trioxide previously dried overnight over sulfuric acid. Add to the bottle 5 ml of water and 5 ml of 10% sodium hydroxide and stir gently with a small glass rod until the arsenic trioxide is dissolved. Transfer the solution completely, with the aid of some water, into a 400-ml beaker or flask and dilute with sufficient water to make about 100 ml. Drop into the solution a small piece of litmus paper and add 10% sulfuric acid until the paper turns slightly red. Cool the solution, if necessary, to about 20°–35° and dissolve in it, with only gentle agitation, 2 g of sodium bicarbonate. Then add some starch solution and run from a burette, slowly and with continuous agitation, the iodine solution until the blue color persists for 30 seconds. One gram of As_2O_3 is equivalent to 2.5663 g of iodine.

TENTH-NORMAL OXALIC ACID

6.303 g $H_2C_2O_4 \cdot 2H_2O$ in a Liter

Dissolve 6.5 g of oxalic acid in a liter of water and mix well. Measure accurately 35–40 ml of the solution into a 300-ml flask and dilute with 50 ml of water. Slowly add 5 ml of sulfuric acid, mix well, and run in slowly, with agitation, about 75% of the volume of 0.1 N potassium permanganate required for the quantity of oxalic acid taken.   Then heat the solution to 70° and complete the titration with permanganate until the pink color persists for 30 seconds.

As a check the oxalic acid solution can be titrated with 0.1 N sodium hydroxide, using phenolphthalein as indicator.   The results by the two methods should agree quite closely, but the normality found by the permanganate method should be taken as the final value.

TENTH-NORMAL PERCHLORIC ACID

10.046 g $HClO_4$ in a Liter

Dilute 8.5 ml of 70%–72% $HClO_4$ with redistilled dioxane to 1 liter and standardize as follows:

Dry about 0.6 g of potassium biphthalate at 105° for 2 hours.   Potassium bitartrate, anhydrous sodium acetate or sodium salicylate may be used instead of the biphthalate.   Weigh accurately 0.5–0.6 g of the dried standard and dissolve in 50 ml of glacial acetic acid in a 300-ml flask.   Warming and/or addition of 20–25 ml of dioxane will facilitate solution.   Cool the solution, if necessary, to room temperature, add 0.1 ml of 1% methylrosaniline chloride solution in glacial acetic acid, and titrate with the perchloric acid solution until the violet color changes to bluish-green.   Deduct the volume of perchloric acid required to produce the end point by 50 ml of the glacial acid to which the same volume of dioxane, if any, and the same volume of the indicator have been added.   Each 0.02042 g of potassium biphthalate is equivalent to 1 ml of 0.1 N perchloric acid.

Some authorities prefer to use acetous perchloric acid—that is, a solution of $HClO_4$ in glacial acetic acid.   It is prepared by diluting the same volume of $HClO_4$ as above with 500 ml of glacial acetic acid, adding 20 ml of acetic anhydride (to counterbalance the water from the perchloric acid), then diluting with the glacial acid to 1 liter and standardizing as above described.

TENTH-NORMAL POTASSIUM BROMATE

2.783 g $KBrO_3$ in a Liter

Dry about 3 g of reagent potassium bromate at 105° to constant weight, then dissolve 2.785 g of the dried reagent in water to make exactly 1 liter and mix thoroughly.

TENTH-NORMAL POTASSIUM DICHROMATE

4.9035 g $K_2Cr_2O_7$ in a Liter

Carefully pulverize a sufficient quantity of reagent potassium dichromate and dry at 120° to constant weight.   Dissolve 4.904 g of the dried reagent in sufficient water to make exactly 1 liter and mix thoroughly.

For the preparation of large volumes of the solution, for use in the analysis of ferruginous materials, dissolve 5 g of the potassium dichromate for every liter of solution and standardize it against a standard steel or a standard iron ore obtained from the Bureau of Standards, Washington, D.C.

TWENTIETH-MOLAR POTASSIUM IODATE

10.701 g KIO$_3$ in a Liter

Dry about 11 g of reagent potassium iodate to constant weight at 105°, then dissolve 10.701 g of the dried reagent in sufficient water to make exactly 1 liter and mix thoroughly.

TENTH-NORMAL POTASSIUM IODATE

3.567 g KIO$_3$ in a Liter

Dry about 4 g of reagent potassium iodate at 105° to constant weight. Dissolve 3.567 g of the dried reagent in water to make exactly 1 liter and mix.

TENTH-NORMAL POTASSIUM PERMANGANATE

3.161 g KMnO$_4$ in a Liter

Dissolve 3.3 g of potassium permanganate in about 1050 ml water and boil the solution gently in a flask for 20–30 minutes. Stopper and allow to stand for several days in the dark. Decant through an asbestos filter into a bottle protected from light, but do not wash the undissolved residue, and determine the exact normality of the solution in the following manner:

Method I—Dry a suitable quantity of reagent sodium oxalate at 105° to constant weight. Weigh accurately about 0.25 g of the dried sodium oxalate and transfer it into a mixture of 10 ml sulfuric acid and 250 ml of water, which has been previously boiled for 10 minutes and cooled to room temperature. After the sodium oxalate has dissolved add, from a burette at the rate of 25–35 ml per minute and with stirring, a volume of the permanganate solution corresponding to about 75% (about 30 ml) of the total volume of the permanganate solution required for the quantity of sodium oxalate weighed. Allow to stand until the pink color disappears, then heat the contents of the beaker to about 60° and complete the titration by adding the permanganate solution until a slight pink color persists for 30 seconds. The last ml or so should be added dropwise, allowing each drop to become decolorized before the next is added.

Determine the volume of permanganate required to produce the same pink color in the same volume of solution, and deduct it from the volume of the permanganate used with the sodium oxalate. One gram of sodium oxalate is equivalent to 0.4718 g of KMnO$_4$.

Method II—As a check, the normality of the permanganate solution can be determined as follows:

Measure from the burette 35–40 ml of the permanganate solution into a 300-ml glass-stoppered flask and dilute with 50 ml of water. Add 10 ml of 10% H$_2$SO$_4$ and a solution of 3 g of potassium iodide in 20 ml of water, and allow to stand, protected from light, for 5 minutes. Titrate the liberated iodine with 0.1 N thiosulfate, adding starch toward the end. Determine the volume of thiosulfate consumed in a blank test made with the same quantities of the reagents, and deduct from the volume of thiosulfate consumed with the permanganate.

The results by the two methods should agree quite closely, but the normality found by the sodium oxalate should be taken as the final value.

For the preparation of larger volumes of this volumetric solution, dissolve about 33 g of potassium permanganate in a liter of water and boil gently in a flask for 20–30 minutes. Stopper and allow to stand for several days. Decant through an asbestos filter, but do not wash the undissolved residue. Dilute the filtrate with water to about 10 liters in a bottle protected from light, mix thoroughly, and let stand for several days (to mix well and to allow any reducible substances in the water to be oxidized). Standardize the solution so prepared by *Method I* and preferably check by *Method II*.

Potassium permanganate solution will gradually become "weaker" and its normality value should, therefore, be frequently checked.

The addition of 10 g of potassium hydroxide per liter of 0.1 N potassium permanganate is claimed to preserve the solution for a longer time.

TENTH-NORMAL SILVER NITRATE

16.989 g AgNO$_3$ in a Liter

When only 1 liter of 0.1 N silver nitrate is required it is best prepared as follows:

Carefully crush 18–20 g of reagent silver nitrate, and dry it overnight at 105°. Care should be taken to avoid the silver nitrate from coming in contact with dust or organic matter which will discolor it. Weigh accurately 17.000 g of the dried silver nitrate, dissolve it in water to make exactly 1 liter, and mix well.

For the preparation of larger volumes of 0.1 N silver nitrate dissolve, for each liter to be made, 17.5 g of silver nitrate in 1 liter of water. After having made sure that the solution is thoroughly and uniformly mixed it is standardized as follows:

Method I—Measure accurately from a burette about 40 ml of the silver nitrate solution into a 250-ml beaker and dilute with 50 ml of water. Heat the solution to boiling and add slowly, with continuous stirring, approximately normal hydrochloric acid until no more precipitate is produced on the further addition of a drop of the hydrochloric acid. Cover the beaker and boil the mixture cautiously for 5 minutes, and then allow it to stand in the dark until the precipitate has settled, the supernatant liquid has become clear, and the mixture has cooled to room temperature. Decant the supernatant liquid through a Gooch crucible with an asbestos pad or a sintered class crucible which has been previously washed with water acidulated with nitric acid and dried at 120° to constant weight; then transfer the precipitate completely on to the filter with the aid of small portions of water acidulated with nitric acid, and dry the crucible with the precipitate to constant weight at 120°. The weight of the silver chloride multiplied by 1.1852 represents the weight of silver nitrate in the volume of solution taken for the determination.

To prevent the discoloration of the silver chloride the determination, and especially the filtration, should be carried out in subdued light and away from direct sunlight.

Method II (electrolytically)—Measure accurately 40–45 ml of the silver nitrate solution into a weighed platinum dish and add a solution of 2 g of sodium cyanide in 10 ml of water. Electrolyze the solution, using a rotating anode making about 500 r.p.m., by passing through it an electric current, gradually increasing it to 2.5 amperes and to from 5–7 volts. After the current has been passed for 20 minutes, remove a few drops of the liquid into a test tube and add a drop of diluted hydrochloric acid. If a turbidity is produced, continue with the electrolysis until the liquid, tested as described, gives no turbidity with hydrochloric acid. After all the silver has settled, siphon off the liquid without interrupting the current, and wash the deposited silver by siphoning with water until the current drops to nearly 0°. Rinse the deposited silver with alcohol, then with ether, and dry the dish at about 100° for a few minutes, cool and weigh. Dry again for another 5 minutes and reweigh. If the weight has changed, dry again until the weight is constant. The weight of the silver multiplied by 1.5748 represents the weight of the silver nitrate in the volume of the solution used for the determination.

Solution of silver nitrate should be kept in bottles protected from light.

TENTH-MOLAR SODIUM NITRITE

6.90 g $NaNO_2$ in a Liter

Dissolve about 7.3 g of sodium nitrite in sufficient water to make 1 liter. Determine the $NaNO_2$ in 20 ml of the solution by the method described for the assay of *Sodium Nitrite*, page 471, using 50 ml of 0.1 N potassium permanganate. One ml of 0.1 N permanganate corresponds to 0.0034501 g $NaNO_2$.

The solution may be standardized by diazotization as follows: Dissolve in a beaker or casserole an accurately weighed quantity of about 0.4 g of reagent sulfanilic acid, previously rendered anhydrous by drying at 105° to constant weight, in 50 ml of water, and 5 ml of hydrochloric acid. Cool to 15°, add about 30 g of crushed ice, then titrate slowly with the sodium nitrite solution, stirring vigorously until a pale blue or a grayish-blue color is produced immediately when a glass rod dipped in the titrated solution is streaked on starch-iodide paper. When the titration is complete, the end point should be reproducible after the solution has been standing for 1 minute. One gram of anhydrous sulfanilic acid is equivalent to 0.3984 g of $NaNO_2$.

TENTH-NORMAL SODIUM THIOSULFATE

24.819 g $Na_2S_2O_3 \cdot 5H_2O$ in a Liter

For every liter of the solution dissolve about 26 g of sodium thiosulfate and 0.2 g of anhydrous sodium carbonate in 1 liter of water, and after thoroughly mixing standardize the solution by the following methods:

Method I—Measure accurately 35–40 ml of 0.1 N potassium dichromate into a glass-stoppered flask and dilute it with 50 ml of water. Add 2 g of potassium iodide and 5 ml of hydrochloric acid, immediately stopper the flask and allow to stand for 10 minutes. Dilute with 100 ml of water and run in slowly from a burette, with constant agitation, the sodium thiosulfate solution until the liquid in the flask has assumed a yellowish-green color. Then add starch solution and continue with the addition of the sodium thiosulfate until the blue color is just discharged.

Method II—Weigh accurately a glass-stoppered flask containing a solution of 2 g potassium iodide in 10 ml of water. Quickly introduce into the flask from 0.40 to 0.50 g of reagent iodine, stopper the flask, and reweigh. Gently rotate the liquid in the flask until the iodine has dissolved. Open the stopper a little and rinse it and the sides of the flask with about 50 ml of water. Then add the sodium thiosulfate solution from a burette, while continuously agitating, until the liquid in the flask is a pale yellow color. Add starch solution and continue the titration until the blue color is just discharged. One gram of iodine is equivalent to 1.9555 g of sodium thiosulfate ($Na_2S_2O_3 \cdot 5H_2O$).

The normality of solutions of sodium thiosulfate will change on keeping. The solution will usually become weaker, but occasionally it may become somewhat stronger. This volumetric solution should accordingly be frequently restandardized.

INDICATORS FOR VOLUMETRIC DETERMINATIONS

Indicator solutions should be kept in tightly stoppered bottles, protected from light.

Bromocresol Green: Dissolve 100 mg in 100 ml of alcohol.

Bromophenol Blue: Dissolve 100 mg in a mixture of 50 ml of water and 50 ml of alcohol.

Bromothymol Blue: Dissolve 100 mg in a mixture of 50 ml of water and 50 ml of alcohol.

Crystal Violet (Methylrosaniline Chloride, Methyl Yellow): Dissolve 100 mg of crystal violet in 10 ml of glacial acetic acid.

Eosin: Dissolve 50 mg in 10 ml of water.

Ferric Ammonium Sulfate: Dissolve 10 g of ferric ammonium sulfate in sufficient water to make 100 ml.

Ferric Nitrate: Dissolve 7 g of ferric nitrate in a mixture of 98 ml H_2O and 2 ml HNO_3. This solution may be used as an indicator instead of ferric ammonium sulfate.

Methyl Orange: Dissolve 100 mg in 100 ml of water.

Methyl Red: Dissolve 100 mg in 100 ml of alcohol.

Phenolphthalein: Dissolve 1 g in 100 ml of alcohol.

Phenol Red: Dissolve 100 mg in 100 ml of alcohol.

Starch: Triturate 1 g of starch with 10 ml of cold water and pour, with constant stirring, into 200 ml of boiling water. Allow to settle and use the clear supernatant liquid.

Thymol Blue: Dissolve 100 mg in 100 ml of alcohol.

Thymolphthalein: Dissolve 100 mg in 100 ml of alcohol.

EQUIVALENTS OF VOLUMETRIC SOLUTIONS
NORMAL ACID

For half, fifth, tenth or other normalities, the equivalents given for Normal Acid are multiplied by 0.5, 0.2, 0.1 or any other number expressing the normality.
The equivalents of alkaloids and of some other bases are given under Tenth-Normal Acid.

One ml of normal acid
is equivalent to:

	Gram	Logarithm
Aminoacetic Acid, $NH_2CH_2CO_2H$	0.07507	87547
Ammonia, NH_3	0.01703	23121
Ammonium, NH_4	0.01804	26482
Ammonium Acetate, $NH_4C_2H_3O_2$	0.07708	88694
Ammonium Bicarbonate, NH_4HCO_3	0.07905	89790
Ammonium Bisulfate, NH_4HSO_4	0.1151	06108
Ammonium Carbamate, $NH_4NH_2CO_2$	0.03903	59140
Ammonium Carbonate, $(NH_4)_2CO_3$	0.04804	68160
Ammonium Chloride, NH_4Cl	0.05350	72835
Ammonium Citrate, Dibasic, $(NH_4)_2HC_6H_5O_7$, from ammonia	0.07544	87760
Ammonium Nitrate, NH_4NO_3, from total nitrogen	0.04003	60239
Ammonium Phosphate, Dibasic, $(NH_4)_2HPO_4$ (direct titration)	0.1321	12090
Ammonium Phosphate, Dibasic, $(NH_4)_2HPO_4$, from NH_3	0.06604	81981
Ammonium Phosphate, Monobasic, $NH_4H_2PO_4$, from NH_3	0.1151	06108
Ammonium Salicylate, $NH_4C_7H_5O_3$	0.1552	19089
Ammonium Sulfate, $(NH_4)_2SO_4$	0.06607	82000
Ammonium Sulfide, $(NH_4)_2S$	0.03407	53237
Ammonium Tartrate, $(NH_4)_2C_4H_4O_6$	0.09208	96417
Barium, Ba	0.06869	83689
Barium Acetate, $Ba(C_2H_3O_2)_2 \cdot H_2O$	0.1369	13640
Barium Acetate, Anhydrous	0.1279	10687
Barium Carbonate, $BaCO_3$	0.09868	99423
Barium Hydroxide, $Ba(OH)_2$	0.08569	95293
Barium Hydroxide, $Ba(OH)_2 \cdot 8H_2O$	0.1578	19811
Barium Oxide, BaO	0.07669	88474
Calcium, Ca	0.02004	30190
Calcium Acetate, $Ca(C_2H_3O_2)_2H_2O$	0.08809	94493
Calcium Acetate, Anhydrous	0.07908	89807
Calcium Carbonate, $CaCO_3$	0.05005	69940
Calcium Citrate, $Ca_3(C_6H_5O_7)_2 \cdot 4H_2O$	0.09508	97809
Calcium Citrate, Anhydrous, $Ca_3(C_6H_5O_7)_2$	0.04984	69758
Calcium Formate, $Ca(HCO_2)_2$	0.06505	81325
Calcium Glycerophosphate, $CaC_3H_7PO_6 \cdot H_2O$	0.2282	35832
Calcium Hydroxide, $Ca(OH)_2$	0.03705	56879
Calcium Lactate, $Ca(C_3H_5O_3)_2 \cdot 5H_2O$	0.1542	18808
Calcium Lactate, Anhydrous	0.1091	03782
Calcium Mandelate, $Ca(C_8H_7O_3)_2$	0.1712	23350
Calcium Oxide, CaO	0.02804	44799
Calcium Propionate, $Ca(C_3H_5O_2)_2$	0.09311	96900
Calcium Stearate, $Ca(C_{18}H_{35}O_2)_2$	0.3035	48216
Calcium Tartrate, $CaC_4H_4O_6 \cdot 4H_2O$	0.1308	11611
Calcium Tartrate, Anhydrous	0.09406	97340

NORMAL ACID—*Continued*

One ml of normal acid
is equivalent to:

	Gram	Logarithm
Citric Acid, $C_6H_8O_7 \cdot H_2O$	0.07005	84819
Citric Acid, Anhydrous	0.06404	80645
Ethyl Cyanoacetate, $NC \cdot CH_2 \cdot COOC_2H_5$	0.1131	05729
Guanidine, CH_5N_3	0.05907	77137
Guanidine Carbonate, $(NH:C[NH_2]_2)_2 \cdot H_2CO_3$	0.09009	95458
Hexamethylenetetramine, $(CH_2)_6N_4$	0.03505	54469
Lead, Pb	0.1036	01536
Lead Acetate, $Pb(C_2H_3O_2)_2 \cdot 3H_2O$	0.1897	27807
Lead Acetate, Anhydrous	0.1676	22427
Lead Oxide, PbO	0.1116	04766
Lead Subacetate (mono-), $Pb(CH_3CO_2)_2, Pb(OH)_2$	0.02833	45225
Lithium, Li	0.006940	84136
Lithium Acetate, Anhydrous, $LiC_2H_3O_2$	0.06596	81928
Lithium Carbonate, Li_2CO_3	0.03694	56750
Lithium Citrate, $Li_3C_6H_5O_7 \cdot 4H_2O$	0.09399	97308
Lithium Hydroxide, LiOH	0.02395	37931
Lithium Oxide, Li_2O	0.01494	17435
Magnesium, Mg	0.01216	08493
Magnesium Acetate, $Mg(C_2H_3O_2)_2 \cdot 4H_2O$	0.1072	03019
Magnesium Acetate, Anhydrous	0.07117	85230
Magnesium Carbonate, $MgCO_3$	0.04216	62490
Magnesium Carbonate, Basic, $(MgCO_3)_4Mg(OH)_2 \cdot 5H_2O$	0.04858	68646
Magnesium Hydroxide, $Mg(OH)_2$	0.02917	46494
Magnesium Lactate, $Mg(C_3H_5O_3)_2 \cdot 3H_2O$	0.1282	10789
Magnesium Nitrate, $Mg(NO_3)_2 \cdot 6H_2O$	0.1282	10789
Magnesium Nitrate, Anhydrous	0.1483	17114
Magnesium Oxide, MgO	0.02016	30449
Magnesium Salicylate, $Mg(C_7H_5O_3)_2 \cdot 4H_2O$	0.1853	26788
Magnesium Salicylate, Anhydrous	0.1493	17377
Methenamine—*see* Hexamethyleneamine		
Nitric Acid, HNO_3	0.06302	79948
Nitric Anhydride, N_2O_5	0.05401	73247
Nitrogen, N	0.01401	14644
Nitrous Anhydride, N_2O_3	0.03801	57990
Nitrate, NO_3	0.06201	79246
Potassium, K	0.03920	59218
Potassium Acetate, $KC_2H_3O_2$	0.09814	99185
Potassium Bicarbonate, $KHCO_3$	0.1001	00043
Potassium Bitartrate, $KHC_4H_4O_6$	0.1881	27439
Potassium Borate, Anhydrous, $K_2B_4O_7$	0.1171	06856
Potassium Carbonate, $K_2CO_3 \cdot 1\frac{1}{2}H_2O$	0.08261	91703
Potassium Carbonate, Anhydrous	0.0691	83948
Potassium Citrate, $K_3C_6H_5O_7 \cdot H_2O$	0.1081	03383
Potassium Citrate, Anhydrous	0.1021	00903
Potassium Formate, $KHCO_2$	0.08412	92490

NORMAL ACID—*Continued*

One ml of normal acid
is equivalent to:

	Gram	Logarithm
Potassium Hydroxide, KOH	0.05611	74904
Potassium Lactate, KC₃H₅O₃	0.1281	10755
Potassium Nitrate, KNO₃	0.1011	00475
Potassium Oxide, K₂O	0.0471	67302
Potassium Phosphate, Dibasic, K₂HPO₄	0.1742	24105
Potassium Sodium Tartrate, KNaC₄H₄O₆·4H₂O	0.1411	14953
Potassium Sodium Tartrate, Anhydrous	0.1051	02160
Potassium Tartrate, K₂C₄H₄O₆·½H₂O	0.1176	07041
Potassium Tartrate, Anhydrous	0.1131	05346
Potassium Phosphate, Tribasic, K₃PO₄, methyl orange indicator	0.1062	02612
Pyridine, C₅H₅N	0.07910	89818
Sodium, Na	0.02300	36173
Sodium Acetate, NaC₂H₃O₂·3H₂O	0.1361	13386
Sodium Acetate, Anhydrous	0.08202	91392
Sodium Ammonium Phosphate, NaNH₄HPO₄·4H₂O	0.2091	32035
Sodium Ammonium Phosphate, Anhydrous	0.1371	13704
Sodium Benzoate, NaC₇H₅O₂	0.1440	15836
Sodium Bicarbonate, NaHCO₃	0.08402	92438
Sodium Borate, Na₂B₄O₇·10H₂O	0.1907	28035
Sodium Borate, Anhydrous	0.1006	00260
Sodium Cacodylate, Anhydrous	0.1600	20412
Sodium Carbonate, Anhydrous, Na₂CO₃	0.0530	72428
Sodium Carbonate, Monohydrate, Na₂CO₃·H₂O	0.06201	79246
Sodium Carbonate, Decahydrate, Na₂CO₃·10H₂O	0.1431	15564
Sodium Cinnamate, NaC₉H₇O₂	0.1701	23070
Sodium Citrate, Anhydrous, Na₃C₆H₅O₇	0.08602	93460
Sodium Citrate, Dihydrate, Na₃C₆H₅O₇·2H₂O	0.09804	99140
Sodium Citrate, Na₃C₆H₅O₇·5½H₂O	0.1191	07591
Sodium Formate, NaHCO₂	0.06802	83264
Sodium Glycerophosphate, Na₂C₃H₇PO₆·5½H₂O	0.3152	49859
Sodium Glycerophosphate, Anhydrous	0.2161	33465
Sodium Hydroxide, NaOH	0.04001	60206
Sodium Lactate, NaC₃H₅O₃	0.1120	04922
Sodium Malate, Na₂C₄H₄O₅·½H₂O	0.09353	97923
Sodium Mandelate, C₆H₅CHOHCOONa	0.1742	24105
Sodium Nitrate, NaNO₃, from nitrogen	0.08501	92947
Sodium Oleate, NaC₁₈H₃₃O₂	0.3045	48359
Sodium Oxalate, Na₂C₂O₄	0.0670	82607
Sodium Oxide, Na₂O	0.0310	49136
Sodium Phosphate, Dibasic, Na₂HPO₄·7H₂O	0.2681	42830
Sodium Phosphate, Dibasic, Anhydrous	0.1420	15235
Sodium Phosphate, Dibasic, Na₂HPO₄·12H₂O	0.3582	55413
Sodium Phosphate Tribasic Anhydrous, Na₃PO₄ (methyl orange indicator)	0.08200	91381
Sodium Propionate, NaC₃H₅O₂	0.09607	98259
Sodium Salicylate, NaC₇H₅O₃	0.1601	20439
Sodium Sulfide, Na₂S·9H₂O	0.1201	07954
Sodium Sulfide, Anhydrous, Na₂S	0.03903	59140
Sodium Stearate, NaC₁₈H₃₅O₂	0.3065	48643
Sodium Succinate, Na₂C₄H₄O₄·6H₂O	0.1351	13066
Sodium Succinate, Anhydrous	0.08102	90859

NORMAL ACID—*Continued*

One ml of normal acid
is equivalent to:

	Gram	Logarithm
Sodium Tartrate, $Na_2C_4H_4O_6 \cdot 2H_2O$	0.1150	06070
Sodium Tartrate, Anhydrous	0.09702	98686
Strontium, Sr	0.04382	64167
Strontium Acetate, Anhydrous, $Sr(C_2H_3O_2)_2$	0.1028	01199
Strontium Carbonate, $SrCO_3$	0.07382	86817
Strontium Hydroxide, $Sr(OH)_2 \cdot 8H_2O$	0.1329	12352
Strontium Hydroxide, Anhydrous	0.06083	78412
Strontium Oxide, SrO	0.05182	71450
Strontium Salicylate, $Sr(C_7H_5O_3)_2 \cdot 2H_2O$	0.1989	29863
Strontium Salicylate, Anhydrous	0.1809	25744
Urea, $(NH_2)_2CO$ (from N)	0.03003	48144
Uric Acid, $C_5H_4N_4O_3$ (from N)	0.04202	62346
Zinc, Zn	0.03269	51441
Zinc Carbonate, $ZnCO_3$	0.06269	79720
Zinc Hydroxide, $Zn(OH)_2$	0.04970	69636
Zinc Nitrate, $Zn(NO_3)_2 \cdot 6H_2O$	0.1487	17231
Zinc Nitrate, Anhydrous	0.09470	97635
Zinc Oxide, ZnO	0.04069	60949

TENTH-NORMAL ACID

One ml of tenth-normal acid
is equivalent to:

	Gram	Logarithm
Amine, NH_2	0.001602	20466
Ammonia, NH_3	0.001703	23121
Apomorphine, $C_{17}H_{17}O_2N$	0.02673	42700
Apomorphine Hydrochloride, $C_{17}H_{17}O_2N \cdot HCl \cdot \frac{1}{2}H_2O$	0.03128	49527
Apomorphine Hydrochloride, Anhydrous	0.03038	48259
Arecoline, $C_8H_{13}O_2N$	0.01552	19089
Arecoline Hydrobromide, $C_8H_{13}O_2N \cdot HBr$	0.02361	37310
Arginine, $C_6H_{13}N_4O_2$ (from N)	0.004355	63899
Arginine Hydrochloride, $C_6H_{13}N_4O_2 \cdot HCl$ (from N)	0.005265	72140
Asparagine, $C_4H_8N_2O_3 \cdot H_2O$ (from N)	0.007507	87547
Atropine, $C_{17}H_{23}O_3N$	0.02894	46150
Atropine Sulfate, $(C_{17}H_{23}O_3N)_2 \cdot H_2SO_4 \cdot H_2O$	0.03474	54083
Barbital Sodium, $C_8H_{11}N_2O_3Na$	0.02062	31429
Berberine, Anhydrous, $C_{20}H_{17}O_4N$	0.03353	52543
Brucine, Anhydrous, $C_{23}H_{26}O_4N_2$	0.03944	59594
Brucine Sulfate $(C_{23}H_{26}O_4N_2)_2 \cdot H_2SO_4 \cdot 7H_2O$	0.05065	70458
Brucine Sulfate, Anhydrous	0.04434	64680
Bulbocapnine, $C_{19}H_{19}O_4N$	0.02522	40175
Caffeine, $C_8H_{10}O_2N_4 \cdot H_2O$ (from N)	0.005305	72469
Caffeine, Anhydrous (from N)	0.004855	68619
Cephaeline, $C_{14}H_{19}O_2N$	0.02333	36791
Choline, $C_5H_{15}O_2N$	0.01212	08350
Choline Chloride, $C_5H_{14}ONCl$	0.01396	14489
Cinchonidine, $C_{19}H_{22}ON_2$	0.02944	46894
Cinchonidine Sulfate, $(C_{19}H_{22}ON_2)_2 \cdot H_2SO_4 \cdot 3H_2O$	0.03705	56879
Cinchonidine Sulfate, Anhydrous	0.03434	53580
Cinchonine, $C_{19}H_{22}ON_2$	0.02944	46894
Cinchonine Sulfate, $(C_{19}H_{22}ON_2)_2 \cdot H_2SO_4 \cdot 2H_2O$	0.03614	55799
Cinchonine Sulfate, Anhydrous $(C_{19}H_{22}ON_2)_2 \cdot H_2SO_4$	0.03434	53580
Cocaine, $C_{17}H_{21}O_4N$	0.03034	48202
Cocaine Hydrochloride, $(C_{17}H_{21}O_4N) \cdot HCl$	0.03398	53122
Codeine, $C_{18}H_{21}O_3N \cdot H_2O$	0.03174	50161
Codeine, Anhydrous	0.02994	47625
Codeine Hydrochloride, $C_{18}H_{21}O_3N \cdot HCl \cdot 2H_2O$	0.03718	57031
Codeine Hydrochloride, Anhydrous	0.03356	52582
Codeine Phosphate, $C_{18}H_{21}O_3NH_3PO_4 \cdot 1\frac{1}{2}H_2O$	0.04244	62778
Codeine Phosphate, Anhydrous	0.03975	59934
Codeine Sulfate, $(C_{18}H_{21}O_3N)_2 \cdot H_2SO_4 \cdot 5H_2O$	0.03934	59483
Codeine Sulfate, Anhydrous	0.03484	54208
Coniine, $C_8H_{17}N$	0.01272	10449
Cotarnine, $C_{12}H_{15}O_4N$	0.02373	37530
Cotarnine Chloride, $C_{12}H_{14}O_3NCl \cdot H_2O$	0.02737	43737
Cupreine, Anhydrous, $C_{19}H_{22}O_2N_2$	0.03104	49192
Cystine, $C_6H_{12}N_2O_4S_2$ (from N)	0.01203	08027
Diethylamine, $(C_2H_5)_2NH$	0.007309	86386
Dihydromorphinone, $C_{17}H_{19}O_3N$	0.02854	45545
Dihydromorphinone Hydrochloride, $C_{17}H_{19}O_3N \cdot HCl$	0.03218	50759
Dimethylamine, $(CH_3)_2NH$	0.004508	65398
Diethanolamine, $HN(CH_2 \cdot CH_2OH)_2$	0.01051	02160

TENTH-NORMAL ACID—*Continued*

One ml of tenth-normal acid
is equivalent to:

	Gram	Logarithm
Ecgonine, Anhydrous, $C_9H_{15}O_3N$	0.01853	26788
Ecgonine Hydrochloride, $C_9H_{15}O_3N \cdot HCl$	0.02218	34596
Emetine, $C_{29}H_{40}O_4N_2$	0.02403	38075
Emetine Hydrochloride, Anhydrous, $C_{29}H_{40}O_4N_2 \cdot 2HCl$	0.02768	44217
Ephedrine, $C_{10}H_{15}ON$	0.01652	21801
Ephedrine Hydrochloride, $C_{10}H_{15}ON \cdot HCl$	0.02017	30471
Ephedrine Sulfate $(C_{10}H_{15}ON)_2 \cdot H_2SO_4$	0.02143	33102
Ergonovine, $C_{10}H_{23}N_3O_2$	0.03254	51242
Ethanolamine, $H_2NCH_2 \cdot CH_2OH$	0.06110	78604
Ethylamine, $(C_2H_5)NH_2$	0.004508	65398
Ethylenediamine, $NH_2(CH_2)_2NH_2$	0.003005	47784
Ethylhydrocupreine, $C_{19}H_{22}N_2 \cdot OH \cdot OC_2H_5$	0.03404	53199
Ethylhydrocupreine Hydrochloride, $C_{19}H_{22}N_2 \cdot OH \cdot OC_2H_5 \cdot HCl$	0.03769	57623
Ethylmorphine, $C_{17}H_{18}O_2N(OC_2H_5)$	0.03134	49610
Ethylmorphine Hydrochloride, $C_{17}H_{18}O_2N(OC_2H_5) \cdot HCl_{12}H_2O$	0.03859	58647
Eucaine, $C_{15}H_{21}O_2N$	0.02474	39340
Eucaine Hydrochloride, $C_{15}H_{21}O_2N \cdot HCl$	0.02838	45301
Glutamic Acid, Anhydrous, C_5H_9NO (from N)	0.01652	21801
Glyceryl Trinitrate (from N)	0.007567	87892
Histidine, $C_6H_9N_3O_2$ (from N)	0.005171	71357
Histidine Hydrochloride, $C_6H_9N_3O_2 \cdot HCl$ (from N)	0.006990	84448
Homatropine, $C_{16}H_{21}O_3N$	0.02753	43981
Homatropine Hydrobromide, $C_{16}H_{21}O_3N \cdot HBr$	0.03563	55182
Hydrastine, $C_{21}H_{21}O_6N$	0.03834	58365
Hydrastine Hydrochloride, $C_{21}H_{21}O_6N \cdot HCl$	0.04198	62304
Hydrastinine, $C_{11}H_{13}NO_3$	0.02072	31639
Hydrastinine Hydrochloride, $C_{11}H_{11}O_2N \cdot HCl$	0.02256	35334
Hydroquinine, Anhydrous, $C_{20}H_{26}O_2N_2$	0.03264	51375
Hyoscyamine, $C_{17}H_{23}O_3N$	0.02894	46150
Hyoscyamine Hydrobromide, $C_{17}H_{23}O_3N \cdot HBr$	0.03703	56855
Hyoscyamine Sulfate, $(C_{17}H_{23}O_3N)_2 \cdot H_2SO_4 \cdot 2H_2O$	0.03565	55182
Isoleucine, $C_6H_{13}O_2N$ (from N)	0.01312	11793
Leucine, $C_6H_{13}O_2N$ (from N)	0.01312	11793
Lysine, $C_6H_{14}O_2N$ (from N)	0.01462	16495
Lysine Hydrochloride, $C_6H_{14}O_2N \cdot HCl$ (from N)	0.01826	26150
Methionine, $(C_5H_{11}NO_2S)$ (from N)	0.1492	17377
Methylamine, CH_3NH_2	0.003106	49220
Morphine, $C_{17}H_{19}O_3N \cdot H_2O$	0.03033	48187
Morphine, Anhydrous, $C_{17}H_{19}O_3N$	0.02853	45530
Morphine Hydrobromide, $C_{17}H_{19}O_3N \cdot HBr \cdot 2H_2O$	0.04203	60455
Morphine Hydrobromide, Anhydrous	0.03663	56384
Morphine Hydrochloride, $C_{17}H_{19}O_3N \cdot HCl \cdot 3H_2O$	0.03758	57496
Morphine Hydrochloride, Anhydrous	0.03218	50759
Morphine Sulfate, $(C_{17}H_{19}O_3N)_2 \cdot H_2SO_4 \cdot 5H_2O$	0.03794	57910
Morphine Sulfate, Anhydrous	0.03344	52427
Narceine, Anhydrous, $C_{23}H_{27}O_8N$	0.04455	64885
Narceine Hydrochloride, Anhydrous, $C_{23}H_{27}O_8N \cdot HCl$	0.04819	68296

One ml of tenth-normal acid
is equivalent to:

	Gram	Logarithm
Narceine Sulfate, $C_{23}H_{27}O_8N \cdot H_2SO_4$	0.07237	85956
Nicotinamide, $C_5H_4NCONH_2$ (from NH_2)	0.01221	08672
Nicotine, $C_{10}H_{14}N_2$	0.01622	21005
Nicotine Sulfate, $C_{10}H_{14}N_2 \cdot H_2SO_4$	0.02602	41531
Nitrogen, N	0.001401	14644
Papaverine, $C_{20}H_{21}O_4N$	0.03394	53071
Papaverine Hydrochloride, $C_{20}H_{21}O_4N \cdot HCl$	0.03758	57496
Pelletierine, $C_8H_{15}ON$	0.01412	14983
Phenacaine Hydrochloride, $C_{18}H_{22}N_2O_2 \cdot HCl \cdot H_2O$	0.03529	54765
Phenobarbital Sodium, $C_{12}H_{11}N_2O_3Na$	0.02542	40518
Phenylalanine, $CaH_{11}NO_2$ (from N)	0.01652	21801
Physostigmine, $C_{15}H_{21}O_2N_3$	0.02753	43981
Physostigmine Salicylate, $C_{15}H_{21}O_2N_3 \cdot C_7H_6O_3$	0.04134	61637
Physostigmine Sulfate, $(C_{15}H_{21}O_2N_3)_2 \cdot H_2SO_4$	0.03243	57322
Procaine, $C_{13}H_{20}O_2N_2$	0.02364	37365
Procaine Hydrochloride, $C_{13}H_{20}O_2N_2 \cdot HCl$	0.02728	43584
Quinidine, Anhydrous, $C_{20}H_{24}O_2N_2$	0.03244	51108
Quinidine Sulfate, $(C_{20}H_{24}O_2N_2)_2 \cdot H_2SO_4 \cdot 2H_2O$	0.03915	59273
Quinine, $C_{20}H_{24}O_2N_2 \cdot 3H_2O$	0.03785	57807
Quinine, Anhydrous	0.03244	51108
Quinine Bisulfate, $C_{20}H_{24}O_2N_2 \cdot H_2SO_4 \cdot 7H_2O$	0.05485	73918
Quinine Ethylcarbonate, $C_{20}H_{23}O_2N_2 \cdot CO \cdot OC_2H_5$	0.03964	59813
Quinine Hydrobromide, $C_{20}H_{24}O_2N_2 \cdot HBr \cdot H_2O$	0.04232	62655
Quinine Hydrochloride, $C_{20}H_{24}O_2N_2 \cdot HCl \cdot 2H_2O$	0.03968	59857
Quinine Phosphate, $(C_{20}H_{24}O_2N_2)_3 \cdot 2H_3PO_4 \cdot 5H_2O$	0.04197	62294
Quinine Phosphate, Anhydrous	0.03683	56620
Quinine Salicylate, $C_{20}H_{24}O_2N_2 \cdot C_7H_6O_3 \cdot H_2O$	0.04804	68160
Quinine Sulfate, $(C_{20}H_{24}O_2N_2)_2 \cdot H_2SO_4 \cdot 7H_2O$	0.04364	63988
Quinine Sulfate, $(C_{20}H_{24}O_2N_2)_2 \cdot H_2SO_4 \cdot 2H_2O$	0.03914	59262
Quinine Sulfate, Anhydrous, $(C_{20}H_{24}O_2N_2)_2 \cdot H_2SO_4$	0.03733	57206
Scopolamine, $C_{17}H_{21}O_4N$	0.03033	48187
Scopolamine Hydrobromide, $C_{17}H_{21}O_4N \cdot HBr \cdot 3H_2O$	0.04382	64167
Strychnine, $C_{21}H_{22}O_2N_2$	0.03344	52427
Strychnine Nitrate, $C_{21}H_{22}O_2N_2 \cdot HNO_3$	0.03972	59901
Strychnine Phosphate, $C_{21}H_{22}O_2N_2 \cdot H_3PO_4 \cdot 2H_2O$	0.04684	67062
Strychnine Phosphate, Anhydrous	0.04324	63589
Strychnine Sulfate, $(C_{21}H_{22}O_2N_2)_2 \cdot H_2SO_4 \cdot 5H_2O$	0.04285	63195
Strychnine Sulfate, Anhydrous	0.03834	58365
Tetracaine Hydrochloride (Pantocaine), $C_{15}H_{24}N_2O_2 \cdot HCl$	0.03007	47813
Thebaine, $C_{19}H_{21}O_3N$	0.03113	49318
Thebaine Hydrochloride, Anhydrous, $C_{19}H_{21}O_3N \cdot HCl$	0.03478	54133
Theobromine, $C_7H_8O_2N_4$ (from N)	0.004504	65360
Theophyllin, $C_7H_8O_2N_4$ (from N)	0.004504	65360
Threonine, $C_3H_8ON \cdot COOH$ (from N)	0.01191	07591
Triethanolamine, $N(CH_2 \cdot CH_2OH)_3$	0.01492	17377
Tropine, $C_8H_{15}ON$	0.01412	14983
Tryptophane, $C_{11}H_{12}N_2O_2$ (from N)	0.01021	00903
Tyrosine, $C_9H_{11}NO_3$ (from N)	0.1812	25816
Valine, $C_4H_{10}N \cdot COOH$ (from N)	0.01172	06893

NORMAL ALKALI HYDROXIDE

For half, fifth, tenth or other normalities, the equivalents given for normal alkali hydroxide are multiplied by 0.5, 0.2, 0.1 or any other number expressing the normality.

One ml of normal alkali hydroxide
is equivalent to:

	Gram	Logarithm
Abietic Acid, $HC_{20}H_{29}O_2$	0.3024	48058
Acetaldehyde, CH_3CHO	0.04405	64395
Acetic Acid, CH_3CO_2H	0.06005	77837
Acetic Anhydride, $(CH_3CO)_2O$	0.05105	70800
Acetyl, CH_3CO	0.04304	63387
Acetyl Chloride, C_2H_3OCl	0.03924	59373
Acetylsalicylic Acid, $C_8H_7O_3COOH(\frac{1}{2})$	0.09008	95463
Aminoacetic Acid, $NH_2C_2H_4O_2$	0.07507	87547
Aminobenzoic Acid, $C_7H_7O_2N_7$	0.1371	13704
Aminosalicylic Acid, $NH_2C_7H_5NO_3$	0.1531	18498
Ammonium Acetate, $NH_4C_2H_3O_2$	0.07708	88694
Ammonium Biphosphate, $NH_4H_2PO_4$	0.1151	06108
Ammonium Bisulfate, NH_4HSO	0.1151	06108
Ammonium Chloride, NH_4Cl	0.05350	72835
Ammonium Sulfate, $(NH_4)_2SO_4$	0.06607	82000
Ammonium Tartrate, $(NH_4)_2C_4H_4O_6$	0.09206	96407
Amyl Acetate, $CH_3CO_2 \cdot C_5H_{11}$	0.1302	11461
Amyl Butyrate, $C_9H_{18}O_2$	0.1582	19921
Amyl Formate, $C_6H_{12}O_2$	0.1161	06483
Amyl Valerate, $C_{10}H_{20}O_2$	0.1723	23629
Arsenic Acid, H_3AsO_4, phenolph. indicator	0.07099	85120
Benzaldehyde, $C_6H_5 \cdot CHO$	0.1061	02572
Benzoic Acid, C_6H_5COOH	0.1221	08672
Benzoyl Chloride, $C_6H_5 \cdot COCl$	0.07025	84665
Boric Acid, H_3BO_3	0.06184	79127
Boric Anhydride, B_2O_3	0.03482	54183
Borneol, $C_{10}H_{18}O$	0.1542	18808
Bornyl Acetate, $C_{10}H_{17}C_2H_3O_2$	0.1963	29270
Boron, B	0.01084	03423
Butyric Acid, $C_4H_8O_2$	0.0881	94478
Carbon Dioxide, CO_2	0.0220	34242
Chloral Hydrate, $CCl_3CHO \cdot H_2O$	0.1654	21854
Chlorine, Cl	0.03546	54970
Chromium Trioxide, CrO_3	0.05000	69897
Citral, $C_6H_{16}O$	0.1522	18241
Citric Acid, $C_6H_8O_7 \cdot H_2O$	0.07005	84541
Citric Acid, Anhydrous, $C_6H_8O_7$	0.06404	80645
Dichloracetic Acid, $CHCl_2CO_2H$	0.1099	04100
Dimethyl Phthalate, $C_6H_4(COOCH_3)$	0.09720	98767
Ethyl Acetate, $CH_3CO_2C_2H_5$	0.0881	94498
Ethyl Benzoate, $C_9H_{10}O_2$	0.1502	17667
Ethyl Bromide, C_2H_5Br	0.1090	00389
Ethyl Butyrate, $C_6H_{12}O_2$	0.1162	06483
Ethyl Chloride, CH_3CH_2Cl	0.06452	80956

One ml of normal alkali hydroxide
is equivalent to:

	Gram	Logarithm
Ethyl Citrate, $(C_2H_5)_3C_6H_5O_7$	0.09205	96402
Ethyl Formate, $C_3H_6O_2$	0.07405	86953
Ethyl Oxalate, $(C_2H_5)_2C_2O_4$	0.07306	86368
Ethyl Salicylate, $C_9H_{10}O_3$	0.1662	22063
Ethyl Tartrate $(C_2H_5)_2C_4H_4O_6$	0.1031	01326
Ethyl Valerate, $C_7H_{14}O_2$	0.1302	11461
Fluosilicic Acid — *see* Hydrofluosilicic Acid		
Formaldehyde, HCHO	0.03002	47741
Formic Acid, HCO_2H	0.04603	66295
Glycerol, $C_3H_8O_3$ (by oxidation with periodate)	0.09210	96426
Glyceryl Triacetate (triacetin), $(CH_4CO_2)_3C_3H_5$	0.07272	86165
Hexachlorophene, $C_{13}H_6Cl_6O_2$	0.4069	60949
Histidine Monohydrochloride, Anhydrous, $(C_6H_9N_3O_2 \cdot HCl$	0.09581	02036
Hydriodic Acid, HI	0.1279	10687
Hydrobromic Acid, HBr	0.08092	90806
Hydrochloric Acid, HCl	0.03646	56182
Hydrofluoric Acid, HF	0.02001	30125
Hydrofluosilicic Acid, H_2SIF_6	0.02401	38039
Hydroxylamine Hydrochloride, $NH_2OH \cdot HCl$	0.006950	84198
Hypophosphorous Acid, H_3PO_2	0.0660	81981
Indole Acetic Acid, $C_8H_6NCH_2COOH$	0.1752	24353
Indole Butyric Acid, $C_8H_6N(CH_2)_3COOH$	0.2032	30792
Indole Propionic Acid, $C_8H_6N(CH_2)_2COOH$	0.1890	27646
Lactic Acid, $CH_3CHOHCO_2H$	0.09008	95463
Lauric Acid, $CH_3(CH_2)_{10}COOH$	0.2003	30168
Levulinic Acid, $C_4H_7O \cdot CO_2H$	0.1161	06483
Maleic Acid, COOHHCC:HCOOH	0.05802	76358
Malic Acid, $COOHCH_2CHOHCOOH$	0.06704	82633
Malonic Acid, $COOHCH_2COOH$	0.05202	71617
Mandelic Acid, $C_6H_5CH(OH)COOH$	0.1522	18241
Menthol, $C_{10}H_{19}OH$	0.1562	19368
Menthyl Acetate, $C_{10}H_{19} \cdot C_2H_3OH$	0.1982	29710
Menthyl Salicylate, $C_{10}H_{19} \cdot C_7H_5O_3$	0.2802	44747
Methyl Oxalate, $(CH_3)_2C_2O_4$	0.05904	77115
Methyl Salicylate, $CH_3C_7H_5O_3$	0.1521	18213
Molybdic Acid, H_2MoO_4	0.08101	90854
Monochloracetic Acid, CH_2ClCO_2H	0.09448	97534
Mucic Acid, $COOH(CHOH)_4COOH$	0.1051	02160
Naphthalene Acetic Acid, $C_{10}H_7CH_2COOH$	0.1861	26975
Naphthalene Butyric Acid, $C_{10}H_7(CH_2)_3COOH$	0.2141	33062
Naphthalene Propionic Acid, $C_{10}H_7(CH_2)_2COOH$	0.2001	30125
Naphthoic Acid, $C_{10}H_7COOH$	0.1721	23578
Nicotinic Acid, $C_6H_5O_2N$	0.1231	09026
Nitric Acid, HNO_3	0.06302	79948
Oleic Acid, $C_{18}H_{34}O_2$	0.2825	45071
Oxalic Acid, $C_2H_2O_4 \cdot 2H_2O$	0.06303	79955

NORMAL ALKALI HYDROXIDE—*Continued*

One ml of normal alkali hydroxide
is equivalent to:

	Gram	Logarithm
Palmitic Acid, $C_{15}H_{31}CO_2H$	0.2565	40875
Paranitrobenzoylchloride, $NO_2C_6H_4COCl$	0.09275	96506
Paraformaldehyde, $(HCHO)_3$	0.03002	47741
Perchloric Acid, $HClO_4$	0.1005	00217
Phenolsulfonic Acid, $HOC_6H_4SO_3H_3$	0.1741	24080
Phenylacetic Acid, $C_6H_5CH_2COOH$	0.1361	13386
Phenylbutyric Acid, $C_6H_5(CH_2)_3COOH$	0.1641	21511
Phenylcinchoninic Acid (Cinchophen), $C_{16}H_{11}O_2N$	0.2493	39672
Phenylpropionic Acid, $C_6H_5(CH_2)_2COOH$	0.1401	14644
Phosphoric Acid, H_3PO_4, thymolphthalein, indicator	0.04902	69037
Phosphoric Anhydride, P_2O_5, thymolphthalein, indicator	0.03549	55035
Phosphoric Anhydride, P_2O_5 (as ammonium phosphomolybdate)	0.003088	48968
Phosphorous Acid, H_3PO_3	0.04103	61310
Phosphorous, P (as ammonium phosphomolybdate)	0.001349	13001
Phthalic Anhydride, $C_6H_4(CO)_2O$	0.07402	86935
Picric Acid, $C_6H_2OH(NO_2)_3$	0.2291	36003
Potassium Arsenate, Monobasic, KH_2AsO_4, phenolph. indicator	0.1801	25551
Potassium Binoxalate, $KHC_2O_4 \cdot H_2O$	0.1461	16465
Potassium Biphthalate, $KHC_8H_4O_4$	0.2042	30984
Potassium Biphosphate, KH_2PO_4	0.1361	13386
Potassium Bisulfate, $KHSO_4$	0.1362	13418
Potassium Bitartrate, $KHC_4H_4O_6$	0.1881	27439
Potassium Tetroxalate, $KHCO_2O_4 \cdot H_2C_2O_4 \cdot 2H_2O$	0.08472	92799
Propionic Acid, C_2H_5COOH	0.07408	86970
Saccharin, $C_7H_5NO_3S$	0.1832	26293
Saccharin Soluble, Anhydrous, $C_7H_4NO_3SNa$	0.2052	31218
Salicylic Acid, $HO \cdot C_6H_4CO_2 \cdot H$	0.1381	14019
Sodium Biphosphate, $NaH_2PO_4 \cdot H_2O$	0.1381	14019
Sodium Biphosphate, Anhydrous	0.1200	07918
Sodium Bisulfate, $NaHSO_4$	0.1201	07954
Sodium Bitartrate, $NaHC_4H_4O_6 \cdot H_2O$	0.1901	27898
Stearic Acid, $C_{18}H_{36}O_2$	0.2843	45378
Succinic Acid, $H_2C_4H_4O_4$	0.05903	77107
Sulfamic Acid, $H_2N \cdot SO_2 \cdot OH$	0.09710	98717
Sulfanilic Acid, $NH_2C_6H_4SO_3H \cdot H_2O$	0.1912	28149
Sulfanilic Acid, Anhydrous	0.1732	23855
Sulfosalicylic Acid, $SO_3H \cdot C_6H_3OHCO_2H \cdot 2H_2O$	0.1271	10415
Sulfosalicylic Acid, Anhydrous	0.1091	03782
Sulfuric Acid, H_2SO_4	0.04904	69055
Sulfurous Acid, H_2SO_3, phenolph. indicator	0.04104	61319
Sulfur Dioxide, SO_2, phenolph, indicator	0.03203	50556
Sulfur Trioxide, SO_3	0.04003	60239
Tartaric Acid, $C_4H_6O_6$	0.07505	87535
Theobromine, $C_7H_8N_4O_2$ (after treatment with $AgNO_3$)	0.1802	25575
Triacetin—*see* Glyceryl Triacetate		
Trichloracetic Acid, $CCl_3 \cdot COOH$	0.1634	21325
Uric Acid, $C_5H_4N_4O_3$	0.1681	22557
Valeric Acid, $C_5H_{10}O_2$	0.1021	00903
Vanillin, $HO \cdot C_6H_3 \cdot OCH_3 \cdot CHO$	0.1521	18213

TENTH-NORMAL AMMONIUM OR POTASSIUM THIOCYANATE

One ml of tenth-normal ammonium thiocyanate
is equivalent to:

	Gram	Logarithm
Ammonium Thiocyanate, NH_4SCN	0.007611	88144
Mercuric Acetate, $Hg(C_2H_3O_2)_2$	0.01593	20222
Mercuric Nitrate, Anhydrous	0.01623	21032
Mercuric Nitrate, $Hg(NO_3)_2 \cdot H_2O$	0.01713	23376
Mercuric Oxide, HgO	0.01083	03463
Mercuric Sulfate, $HgSO_4$	0.01484	17143
Mercurous Chloride, $HgCl$	0.02361	37310
Mercurous Nitrate, $HgNO_3 \cdot H_2O$	0.01403	14706
Mercurous Nitrate, Anhydrous	0.01313	11826
Mercury, Hg	0.01003	00130
Potassium Thiocyanate, $KSCN$	0.009716	98749
SCN	0.005808	
Silver, Ag	0.01079	03302
Silver Acetate, $AgC_2H_3O_2$	0.01669	22246
Silver Carbonate, Ag_2CO_3	0.01379	13956
Silver Lactate, $AgC_3H_5O_3$	0.01969	29425
Silver Nitrate, $AgNO_3$	0.01699	23019
Silver Oxide, Ag_2O	0.01159	06408
Silver Sulfate, Ag_2SO_4	0.01559	19285
Sodium Thiocyanate, $NaSCN$	0.008108	90891

TENTH-NORMAL BROMINE

One ml of tenth-normal bromine
is equivalent to:

	Gram	Logarithm
Acetanilide, C_8H_9ON	0.002252	35257
Aluminum, Al [from Aluminum Oxinate, $Al(C_9H_6NO)$]	0.002248	35180
Aluminum Chloride, $AlCl_3 \cdot 6H_2O$ [from Aluminum Oxinate, $Al(C_9H_6No)$]	0.02014	30406
Aluminum Oxide, Al_2O_3 [from Aluminum Oxinate, $Al (C_9H_6NO)$]	0.004248	62818
Aluminum Sulfate, $Al_2(SO_4)_3 \cdot 18H_2O$ [from Aluminum Oxinate, $Al(C_9H_6NO)$]	0.02777	44358
Ammonium Hypophosphite, $NH_4H_2PO_2$	0.002077	31744
Bromine, Br	0.007992	90266
Calcium Hypophosphite, $Ca(H_2PO_2)_2$	0.002127	32777
p-Chlorophenol, C_5H_5CO	0.003214	50705

TENTH-NORMAL BROMINE — *Continued*

One ml of tenth-normal bromine
is equivalent to:

	Gram	Logarithm
Hexylresorcinol, $C_{19}H_{18}O_2$	0.004857	68655
Hypophosphorous Acid, $H(H_2PO_2)$	0.001601	20439
8-Hydroxyquinoline, $HO \cdot C_9H_6N$	0.003627	55955
Magnesium, Mg [from Magnesium Oxinate, $Mg(C_9H_6NO)_2 \cdot 2H_2O$]	0.003040	48287
Magnesium Chloride, $MgCl_2 \cdot 6H_2O$ [from Magnesium Oxinate, $Mg(C_9H_6NO)_2 \cdot 2H_2O$]	0.02542	40518
Magnesium Oxide, MgO [from Magnesium Oxinate, $Mg(C_9H_6NO)_2 \cdot 2H_2O$]	0.005040	70672
Magnesium Sulfate, $MgSO_4 \cdot 6H_2O$ [from Magnesium Oxinate, $Mg(C_9H_6NO)_2 \cdot 2H_2O$]	0.03081	48869
Phenol, C_6H_5OH	0.001568	19535
Phenolsulfonphthalein, $C_{19}H_{14}O_5S$	0.004430	64640
Resorcinol, $C_6H_4(OH)_2$	0.001834	26340
Sodium Hypophosphite, $NaH_2PO_2 \cdot H_2O$	0.002651	42341
Sulfanilamide, $C_6H_8N_2O_2S$	0.04305	63397

TENTH-NORMAL CERIC SULFATE

One ml of tenth-normal ceric sulfate
is equivalent to:

	Gram	Logarithm
Ammonium Oxalate $(NH_4)_2C_2O_4 \cdot H_2O$	0.007106	85156
Arsenic, As, in arsenous compounds	0.003747	57368
Arsenic Trioxide, As_2O_3	0.004947	69434
Calcium, Ca (titrated as the oxalate)	0.002004	30190
Calcium Oxide, CaO (titrated as the oxalate)	0.002804	44778
Cobalt, Co [from $K_2NaCo(NO_2)_6$]	0.004912	69126
Ferric Oxide, Fe_2O_3 (after reduction)	0.007984	90222
Ferrous Ammonium Sulfate, $Fe(NH_4)_2(SO_4)_2 \cdot 6H_2O$	0.03921	59343
Ferrous Chloride, $FeCl_2 \cdot 4H_2O$	0.01988	29842
Ferrous Oxide, FeO	0.007184	85637
Ferrous Sulfate, $FeSO_4 \cdot 7H_2O$	0.02780	44404
Ferrous Sulfate, Anhydrous	0.01519	18156
2-Methyl-naphthoquinone (Menadione), $C_{11}H_8O_2$	0.001722	23603
Nitrous Acid Anhydride, N_2O_3	0.003801	57990
Oxalic Acid, $C_2H_2O_4 \cdot 2H_2O$	0.006303	79955
Potassium, K, [from $K_2NaCo(NO_2)_6$]	0.0006517	81405
Potassium Chloride, KCl, [from $K_2NaCo(NO_2)_6$]	0.001243	09447
Potassium Nitrite, KNO_2	0.004255	62890
Potassium Oxalate, $K_2C_2O_4 \cdot H_2O$	0.009211	96431
Potassium Oxide, K_2O	0.0007850	89487
Potassium Sulfate, K_2SO_4, [from $K_2NaCo(NO_2)_6$]	0.001452	16197
Sodium Nitrite, $NaNO_2$	0.003451	53794
Sodium Oxalate, $Na_2C_2O_4$	0.006700	82607

TENTH-MOLAR ETHYLENEDIAMINE TETRAACETATE, EDTA

One ml of tenth-molar EDTA
is equivalent to:

	Gram	Logarithm
Calcium, Ca	0.004008	60293
Calcium Carbonate, $CaCO_3$	0.01001	00043
Calcium Chloride, Anhydrous, $CaCl_2$	0.0111	04523
Calcium Hydroxide, $Ca(OH)_2$	0.007410	86982
Calcium Oxide, CaO	0.005608	74881
Magnesium, Mg	0.002403	38075
Mercury, Hg	0.02006	30233

TENTH-NORMAL IODINE

One ml of tenth-normal iodine
is equivalent to:

	Gram	Logarithm
Acetone, $(CH_3)_2CO$	0.000968	98565
Acetophenetidin, $C_{10}H_{13}O_2N$	0.00896	95231
Ammonium Sulfite, Anhydrous, $(NH_4)_2SO_3$	0.005813	76440
Ammonium Thiosulfate, $NH_4S_2O_3$	0.01482	17085
Antimony, Sb	0.004007	60282
Antimony, in Antimonous compounds	0.006088	78447
Antimony Chloride, $SbCl_3$	0.01141	05729
Antimony Potassium Tartrate, $K(SbO)C_4H_4O_6 \cdot \frac{1}{2}H_2O$	0.01670	22272
Antimony Potassium Tartrate, Anhydrous	0.01624	21059
Antimony Trioxide, Sb_2O_3	0.007210	85739
Antimony Trisulfide, Sb_2S_3	0.008415	92505
Arsenic, As (metal)	0.002499	39777
Arsenic, in Arsenous compounds	0.003747	57368
Arsenic Pentoxide, As_2O_5	0.005748	75852
Arsenic Trioxide, As_2O_3	0.004947	69434
Arsenous Bromide, $AsBr_3$	0.01574	19700
Arsenous Chloride, $AsCl_3$	0.009067	95746
Arsenous Iodide, AsI_3	0.02278	35755
Ascorbic Acid, $C_6H_8O_6$	0.008806	94463
Barium Sulfide, BaS	0.008472	92799
Barium Sulfite, $BaSO_3$	0.01087	03623
Bromine, Br	0.007992	90266
Calcium Bisulfite, $Ca(HSO_3)_2$	0.005056	70381
Calcium Sulfide, CaS	0.003607	55715
Calcium Sulfite, $CaSO_3 \cdot 2H_2O$	0.007809	89260
Calcium Sulfite, Anhydrous	0.006007	77866
Calcium Thiosulfate, CaS_2O_3	0.01522	18241
Chlorine, Cl	0.003547	54986
Cyanogen, CN	0.001301	11428
Ferrous Sulfide, FeS	0.004395	64296
Formaldehyde, HCHO	0.001501	17638
Hydrazine, H_2NNH_2	0.008010	90363
Hydrazine Dihydrochloride, $HCl \cdot NH_2 \cdot NH_2 \cdot HCl$	0.002629	41979

TENTH-NORMAL IODINE—*Continued*

One ml of tenth-normal iodine
is equivalent to:

	Gram	Logarithm
Hydrazine Sulfate, $(NH_2)_2 \cdot H_2SO_4$	0.003253	51228
Hydrocyanic Acid, HCN	0.001351	13066
Hydrogen Sulfide, H_2S	0.001704	23147
Iodine, I	0.01269	10353
Iron, Fe, in ferric salts	0.005584	74695
Iron, Metal, Fe	0.002792	44592
Isomiazide (Nicotinic Acid Hydrazide), $C_6H_7N_3O$	0.003420	53173
Mercurous Chloride, HgCl	0.02361	37310
Mercurous Iodide, HgI	0.03275	51521
Mercurous Nitrate, $HgNO_3 \cdot H_2O$	0.02806	44809
Mercurous Nitrate, Anhydrous	0.02626	41929
Mercury, Hg, metal	0.01003	00130
Mercury, in mercurous compounds	0.02006	30233
Methylthionine Chloride, Anhydrous, $C_{16}H_{18}N_3ClS$	0.00533	72673
Oxygen, O	0.00800	90309
Potassium Arsenite, $KAsO_2$	0.007303	86350
Potassium Bisulfite, $KHSO_3$	0.006009	77880
Potassium Cyanide, KCN	0.003255	51255
Potassium Metabisulfite, $K_2S_2O_5$	0.005558	74492
Potassium Sulfide, K_2S	0.005514	74147
Potassium Sulfite, $K_2SO_3 \cdot 2H_2O$	0.009715	98744
Potassium Sulfite, Anhydrous	0.007914	89840
Potassium Xanthate, $KS_2COC_2H_5$	0.01603	20493
Sodium Arsenate, $Na_2HAsO_4 \cdot 7H_2O$ (after reduction)	0.01560	19312
Sodium Arsenate, Anhydrous	0.009299	96844
Sodium Arsenite, $NaAsO_2$	0.006497	81271
Sodium Bisulfite, $NaHSO_3$	0.005203	71625
Sodium Cacodylate, Anhydrous, $(CH_3)_2AsO \cdot ONa$	0.007999	90304
Sodium Cyanide, NaCN	0.002450	38917
Sodium Formaldehyde Sulfoxylate, $NaHCH_2SO_3 \cdot 2H_2O$	0.003853	58580
Sodium Metabisulfite, $Na_2S_2O_5$	0.004754	67706
Sodium Sulfide, $Na_2S \cdot 9H_2O$	0.01201	07954
Sodium Sulfide, Anhydrous	0.003904	59151
Sodium Sulfite, $Na_2SO_3 \cdot 7H_2O$	0.01261	10072
Sodium Sulfite, Anhydrous	0.006303	79955
Sodium Thioglycollate, $HS \cdot CH_2 \cdot COONa$	0.01141	05729
Sodium Thiosulfate, $Na_2S_2O_3 \cdot 5H_2O$	0.02482	39480
Sodium Thiosulfate, Anhydrous	0.01581	19893
Stannous Chloride, $SnCl_2 \cdot 2H_2O$	0.01128	05231
Stannous Sulfate, $SnSO_4$	0.01084	03503
Strontium Sulfide, SrS	0.005985	77706
Strontium Sulfite, $SrSO_3$	0.008385	92350
Sulfur, Monosulfidic, S	0.001604	20520
Sulfur Dioxide, SO_2	0.003203	50556
Thioglycollic Acid, $C_2H_4O_25$	0.00921	96426
Tin, Sn, in stannous compounds	0.005935	77342

TENTH-NORMAL OXALIC ACID

One ml of tenth-normal oxalic acid
is equivalent to:

	Gram	Logarithm
Calcium, Ca....................................	0.002004	30190
Calcium Acetate, $Ca(C_2H_3O_2)_2 \cdot H_2O$.............................	0.008806	94478
Calcium Acetate, Anhydrous.....................................	0.007906	89796
Calcium Bromide, $CaBr_2 \cdot 2H_2O$.............................	0.01180	07188
Calcium Bromide, Anhydrous.....................................	0.00996	99983
Calcium Carbonate, $CaCO_3$....................................	0.005004	69932
Calcium Chloride, $CaCl_2 \cdot 2H_2O$.............................	0.007351	86635
Calcium Chloride, $CaCl_2 \cdot 6H_2O$.............................	0.01096	03981
Calcium Chloride, Anhydrous, $CaCl_2$.........................	0.005550	74429
Calcium Hydroxide, $Ca(OH)_2$.........................	0.003705	56879
Calcium Iodide, Anhydrous, CaI_2.............................	0.01470	16732
Calcium Nitrate, $Ca(NO_3)_2 \cdot 4H_2O$.............................	0.01181	07225
Calcium Nitrate, Anhydrous....................................	0.008205	91408
Calcium Oxide, CaO.....................................	0.002804	44778
Calcium Sulfate, $CaSO_4 \cdot 2H_2O$.............................	0.008609	93495
Calcium Sulfate, Anhydrous, $CaSO_4$.............................	0.006807	83296
Lead, Pb......................................	0.01036	01536
Lead Acetate, $Pb(C_2H_3O_2)_2 \cdot 3H_2O$.............................	0.01897	27807
Lead Acetate, Anhydrous.....................................	0.01626	21112
Lead Carbonate, $PbCO_3$....................................	0.01336	12581
Lead Carbonate, Basic, $(PbCO_3)_2 \cdot Pb(OH)_2$.....................	0.01292	11126
Lead Chloride, $PbCl_2$....................................	0.01391	14426
Lead Nitrate, $Pb(NO_3)_2$....................................	0.01656	21906
Lead Oxide, PbO.....................................	0.01116	04766
Lead Sulfate, $PbSO_4$....................................	0.01516	18070
Manganese Dioxide, MnO_2....................................	0.004347	63819
Oxalic Acid, $(CO \cdot OH)_2 \cdot 2H_2O$.............................	0.006303	79955
Oxalic Acid, Anhydrous.......................................	0.004501	65341
Potassium Permanganate, $KMnO_4$.............................	0.003161	49982
Thorium, Th...................................	0.005803	76365
Thorium Nitrate, $Th(NO_3)_4 \cdot 4H_2O$.............................	0.01371	13704
Thorium Nitrate, Anhydrous, $Th(NO_3)_4$.........................	0.01200	07918
Thorium Oxide, ThO_2.......................................	0.006603	81974

TENTH-NORMAL POTASSIUM DICHROMATE

One ml of tenth-normal potassium dichromate
is equivalent to:

	Gram	Logarithm
Barium, Ba..	0.004579	66077
Barium Oxide, BaO...	0.005112	70859
Ferric Oxide, Fe_2O_3..	0.007984	90222
Ferroso-ferric Oxide, Fe_3O_4....................................	0.007717	88745
Ferrous Iron, Fe^{++}..	0.005584	74695
Ferrous Ammonium Sulfate, $Fe(NH_4)_2(SO_4)_2 \cdot 6H_2O$................	0.03921	59340

TENTH-NORMAL POTASSIUM DICHROMATE — *Continued*

One ml of tenth-normal potassium dichromate
is equivalent to:

	Gram	Logarithm
Ferrous Carbonate, $FeCO_3$	0.01158	06371
Ferrous Chloride, $FeCl_2 \cdot 4H_2O$	0.01988	29842
Ferrous Chloride, Anhydrous	0.01268	10312
Ferrous Sulfate, $FeSO_4 \cdot 7H_2O$	0.02780	44404
Ferrous Sulfate, Anhydrous	0.01519	18156
Glycerol, $C_3H_5(OH)_3$	0.006578	81809
Lead, Pb	0.006907	83929
Lead Acetate, $Pb(C_2H_3O_2)_2 \cdot 3H_2O$	0.01264	10175
Lead Acetate, Anhydrous	0.01084	03503
Lead Acetate, Basic, $Pb(C_2H_3O_2)_2 \cdot Pb(OH)_2 \cdot H_2O$	0.009740	98856
Lead Carbonate, $PbCO_3$	0.008907	94973
Lead Carbonate, basic, $(PbCO_3)_2 \cdot Pb(OH)_2$	0.008618	93541
Lead Chloride, $PbCl_2$	0.009270	96708
Lead Nitrate, $Pb(NO_3)_2$	0.01104	04297
Lead Oxide, PbO	0.007441	87163
Sodium Thiosulfate, $Na_2S_2O_3 \cdot 5H_2O$	0.02482	39480
Sodium Thiosulfate, Anhydrous	0.01581	19893
Zinc, Zn	0.003269	51442

TWENTIETH-MOLAR POTASSIUM IODATE

One ml of twentieth-molar potassium iodate
is equivalent to:

	Gram	Logarithm
Ammonium Iodide, NH_4I	0.01450	16137
Arsenic Trioxide, As_2O_3	0.009894	99974
Barium Iodide, $BaI_2 \cdot 2H_2O$	0.02136	32960
Barium Iodide, Anhydrous	0.01956	29137
Cadmium Iodide, CdI_2	0.01831	26269
Calcium Iodide CaI_2	0.01470	16732
Hydriodic Acid, HI	0.01279	10687
Iodine, I	0.10269	10346
Mercuric Iodide, HgI_2	0.02272	35641
Phenylhydrazine, $C_6H_5NH \cdot NH_2$	0.005404	73272
Phenylhydrazine Hydrochloride, $C_6H_5NH \cdot NH_2 \cdot HCl$	0.007227	85896
Potassium Iodide, KI	0.01660	22011
Sodium Iodide, Anhydrous, NaI	0.01499	17580
Strontium Iodide, Anhydrous, SrI_2	0.01707	23223
Zinc Iodide, ZnI_2	0.01596	20303

TENTH-NORMAL POTASSIUM PERMANGANATE

One ml of tenth-normal potassium permanganate
is equivalent to:

	Gram	Logarithm
Ammonium Formate, NH_4CHO_2	0.003153	49872
Ammonium Oxalate, $(NH_4)_2C_2O_4 \cdot H_2O$	0.007105	85156
Ammonium Oxalate, Anhydrous	0.006204	79267
Ammonium Persulfate, $(NH_4)_2S_2O_8$	0.01141	05729
Ammonium Vanadate, NH_4VO_3	0.01170	06819
Barium Peroxide, BaO_2	0.008468	92778
Calcium, Ca	0.002004	30190
Calcium Acetate, $Ca(C_2H_3O_2)_2 \cdot H_2O$	0.008807	94483
Calcium Acetate, Anhydrous	0.01091	03782
Calcium Bromide, $CaBr_2 \cdot 2H_2O$	0.01180	07188
Calcium Carbonate, $CaCO_3$	0.005004	69932
Calcium Chloride, $CaCl_2 \cdot 2H_2O$	0.007352	86635
Calcium Chloride, $CaCl_2 \cdot 6H_2O$	0.01095	09941
Calcium Chloride, Anhydrous, $CaCl_2$	0.005550	74429
Calcium Formate, $Ca(HCO_2)_2$ (from the HCOOH)	0.003253	51228
Calcium Gluconate, $Ca(C_6H_{11}O_7)_2 \cdot H_2O$	0.02152	33284
Calcium Lactate, $Ca(C_3H_5O_2)_2 \cdot 5H_2O$	0.01541	18780
Calcium Lactate, Anhydrous	0.01091	03782
Calcium Levulinate, $Ca(C_5H_7O_3)_2 \cdot 2H_2O$	0.01531	18498
Calcium Mandelate, $Ca(C_8H_7O_3)_2$	0.01712	23350
Calcium Nitrate, $Ca(NO_3)_2 \cdot 4H_2O$	0.01181	07225
Calcium Nitrate, Anhydrous	0.008205	91408
Calcium Oxide, CaO	0.002804	44778
Calcium Peroxide, CaO_2	0.003604	55678
Calcium Sulfate, $CaSO_4 \cdot 2H_2O$	0.008609	93495
Calcium Sulfate, Anhydrous	0.006810	83296
Chromium, Cr	0.0008666	93780
Cobalt, Co, [from $K_2NaCo(NO_2)_6$]	0.0004912	69126
Cuprous Chloride, CuCl	0.009900	99567
Cuprous Oxide, Cu_2O	0.007157	85473
Ferric Ammonium Oxalate, $Fe(NH_4)_3(C_2O_4)_3 \cdot 3H_2O$	0.007133	85327
Ferric Oxide, Fe_2O_3	0.007984	90222
Ferric Oxalate, $Fe_2(C_2O_4) \cdot 6H_2O$	0.008064	90655
Ferroso-Ferric Oxide, Fe_3O_4	0.07717	88747
Ferrous Ammonium Sulfate, $Fe(NH_4)_2(SO_4)_2 \cdot 6H_2O$	0.03921	59343
Ferrous Carbonate, $FeCO_3$	0.01159	06408
Ferrous Chloride, $FeCl_2 \cdot 4H_2O$	0.01988	29842
Ferrous Chloride, Anhydrous	0.01268	10312
Ferrous Oxalate, $FeC_2O_4 \cdot 2H_2O$	0.005996	77786
Ferrous Oxide, FeO	0.007184	85637
Ferrous Sulfate, $FeSO_4 \cdot 7H_2O$	0.02780	44404
Ferrous Sulfate, Anhydrous	0.01519	18156
Formic Acid, HCO_2H	0.002301	36192
Hydrogen Peroxide, H_2O_2	0.001701	23070
Hydroxylamine Hydrochloride, $NH_2OH \cdot HCl$	0.003475	54095
Hydroxylamine Sulfate, $(NH_2OH)_2H_2SO_4$	0.004103	61310
Iron, Fe	0.005584	74695
Indigo, $C_{16}H_{10}N_2O_2$	0.006552	81637

TENTH-NORMAL POTASSIUM PERMANGANATE—*Continued*

One ml of tenth-normal potassium permanganate
is equivalent to:

	Gram	Logarithm
Indigo Carmine, $CC_{16}H_8O_2N_2(NaSO_3)_2$	0.01165	0663
Iodine, I	0.01269	10353
Lead Dioxide, PbO_2	0.01196	07773
Lead Oxide, Red, Pb_3O_4	0.03428	53504
Magnesium Peroxide, MgO_2	0.002816	44963
Manganese, Mn	0.001099	04100
Manganese Oxide, MnO	0.003547	54985
Manganese Dioxide, MnO_2	0.004347	63816
Mercury (Mercurous) Hg	0.002006	30233
Molybdenum Trioxide, MoO_3 (from yellow ppt. after reduction)	0.004800	68124
Nitrous Acid Anhydride, N_2O_3	0.003801	57990
Nitrogen Tetroxide, N_2O_4	0.003551	55035
Oxalic Acid, $H_2C_2O_4 \cdot 2H_2O$	0.006303	79955
Oxalic Acid, Anhydrous	0.004501	65330
Oxygen, O	0.0008000	90309
Phosphorus, P (yellow ppt. after reduction)	0.00008617	93536
Phosphorus Pentoxide, P_2O_5 (yellow ppt. after reduction)	0.0001972	29491
Potassium, K, [from $K_2NaCo(No_2)_6$]	0.0006517	81405
Potassium Chlorate, $KClO_3$	0.002043	31027
Potassium Chloride, KCl, [from $K_2NaCo(NO_2)_6$]	0.001243	09447
Potassium Ferricyanide, $K_3Fe(CN)_6$	0.03292	51746
Potassium Ferrocyanide, $K_4Fe(CN)_6 \cdot 3H_2O$	0.04223	62562
Potassium Ferrocyanide, Anhydrous	0.03683	56620
Potassium Nitrite, KNO_2	0.004255	62890
Potassium Oxalate, $K_2C_2O_4 \cdot H_2O$	0.009211	96431
Potassium Oxalate, Anhydrous	0.008310	91960
Potassium Oxide, K_2O, [from $K_2NaCo(NO_2)_6$]	0.0007850	89487
Potassium Nitrate, KNO_3, [from $K_2NaCO(NO_2)_6$]	0.001685	22660
Potassium Sulfate, K_2SO_4, [from $K_2NaCO(NO_2)_6$]	0.001452	16197
Potassium Persulfate, $K_2S_2O_8$	0.01352	13098
Potassium Tetroxalate, $KHC_2O_4 \cdot H_2C_2O_4 \cdot 2H_2O$	0.006354	80305
Sodium Bismuthate	0.01400	14613
Sodium Ferricyanide, $Na_3Fe(CN)_6$	0.02814	44932
Sodium Ferrocyanide, $Na_4Fe(CN)_6 \cdot 12H_2O$	0.05201	71609
Sodium Ferrocyanide, Anhydrous	0.03039	48273
Sodium Formate, HCOONa	0.003401	53161
Sodium Nitrite, $NaNO_2$	0.003451	53794
Sodium Oxalate, $Na_2C_2O_4$	0.006700	82607
Sodium Perborate, $NaBO_3 \cdot H_2O$	0.004992	69827
Sodium Perborate, $NaBO_3 \cdot 4H_2O$	0.007703	88649
Sodium Perborate, Anhydrous	0.004091	61183
Sodium Peroxide, Na_2O_2	0.003900	59106
Strontium Peroxide, SrO_2	0.005982	77685
Tin, Sn, in stannous compounds	0.005935	77342
Titanium, Ti	0.004790	68034
Titanium Dioxide, TiO_2	0.007990	90255

TENTH-NORMAL POTASSIUM PERMANGANATE—*Continued*

One ml of tenth-normal potassium permanganate
is equivalent to:

	Gram	Logarithm
Uranium, U	0.01190	07654
Uranium Oxide, UO$_2$	0.01350	13046
Vanadium, V	0.005095	70714
Vanadyl Sulfate, Anhydrous, VOSO$_4$	0.01630	21219
Zinc, Zn	0.003269	51441
Zinc Oxalate, Anhydrous, ZnC$_2$O$_4$	0.007669	88474
Zinc Peroxide, ZnO$_2$	0.004869	68744

TENTH-NORMAL SILVER NITRATE

One ml of tenth-normal silver nitrate
is equivalent to:

	Gram	Logarithm
Acetyl Bromide, C$_2$H$_3$OBr	0.01229	08955
Acetyl Chloride, C$_2$H$_3$OCl	0.007848	89476
Allyl Iso-thiocyanate, C$_3$H$_5$NCS	0.004956	69513
Aluminum Chloride, AlCl$_3 \cdot$6H$_2$O	0.008048	90569
Aluminum Chloride, Anhydrous	0.004445	64787
Ammonium Bromide, NH$_4$Br	0.009796	99105
Ammonium Chloride, NH$_4$Cl	0.005350	72835
Ammonium Cyanide, NH$_4$CN	0.004405	64395
Ammonium Iodide, NH$_4$I	0.01450	16137
Ammonium Phosphate, Dibasic (NH$_4$)$_2$HPO$_4$	0.004404	64384
Ammonium Phosphate, Monobasic, NH$_4$H$_2$PO$_4$	0.003837	58399
Ammonium Thiocyanate, NH$_4$SCN	0.007611	88144
Arsenous Bromide, AsBr$_3$	0.01049	02078
Amyl Nitrite, C$_5$H$_{11}$NO$_2$ (by reaction with KClO$_3$)	0.03515	54593
Arsenous Iodide, AsI$_3$	0.01519	18156
Barium Bromide, BaBr$_2 \cdot$2H$_2$O	0.01666	22167
Barium Bromide, Anhydrous	0.01481	17056
Barium Chloride, BaCl$_2 \cdot$2H$_2$O	0.01222	08707
Barium Chloride, Anhydrous	0.01041	01745
Barium Cyanide, Ba(CN)$_2$	0.009470	97635
Barium Iodide, BaI$_2 \cdot$2H$_2$O	0.02136	32960
Barium Iodide, Anhydrous	0.01222	29137
Bromoform, CHBr$_3$	0.008426	92562
Bromine, Br	0.007992	90266
Bromobenzene, Mono, C$_6$H$_5$Br	0.01570	19590
Benzoyl Chloride, C$_6$H$_5$COCl	0.01405	14768
Benzyl Chloride, C$_6$H$_5$CH$_2$Cl	0.01266	10243
Cadmium Bromide, CdBr$_2 \cdot$4H$_2$O	0.01722	23603
Cadmium Chloride, CdCl$_2 \cdot 2\frac{1}{2}$H$_2$O	0.01142	05767
Cadmium Chloride, Anhydrous, CdCl$_2$	0.009166	96218
Cadmium Cyanide, Cd(CN)$_2$	0.008221	91492
Cadmium Iodide, CdI$_2$	0.01831	26276
Calcium Bromide, CaBr$_2 \cdot$2H$_2$O	0.01180	07188
Calcium Bromide, Anhydrous	0.009996	99983

TENTH-NORMAL SILVER NITRATE — *Continued*

One ml of tenth-normal silver nitrate
is equivalent to:

	Gram	Logarithm
Calcium Chloride, Anhydrous, $CaCl_2$	0.005550	74429
Calcium Chloride, Dihydrate, $CaCl_2 \cdot 2H_2O$	0.007351	86635
Calcium Chloride, Hexahydrate, $CaCl_2 \cdot 6H_2O$	0.01095	03941
Calcium Cyanide, $Ca(CN)_2$	0.004605	66323
Calcium Iodide, $CaI_2 \cdot 6H_2O$	0.02010	30320
Calcium Iodide, Anhydrous	0.01470	16732
Chlorine, Cl	0.003547	54986
Chloroform, $CHCl_3$	0.003980	59988
Carbon Tetrachloride, CCl_4	0.003846	58501
Chlorobutanol, $C_4H_7OCl_3$	0.005931	77188
Choline Chloride, $C_5H_{14}ONCl$	0.01396	14489
Cuprous Cyanide, CuCN	0.008958	95221
Cyanogen, C_2N_2	0.005202	71617
Ethyl Bromide, C_2H_5Br	0.01090	03743
Ethyl Chloride, C_2H_5Cl	0.006450	80956
Ethyl Iodide, C_2H_5I	0.01560	19312
Ethylene Bromide, CH_2BrCH_2Br	0.009393	97280
Ethyl Nitrite, $C_2H_5NO_2$ (by reaction with $KClO_3$)	0.02252	35257
Ferric Chloride, $FeCl_3 \cdot 6H_2O$	0.009010	95472
Ferric Chloride, Anhydrous	0.005407	73296
Ferrous Bromide, Anhydrous, $FeBr_2$	0.01078	03262
Ferrous Chloride, Anhydrous	0.006338	80195
Ferrous Iodide, $FeI_2 \cdot 4H_2O$	0.01909	28081
Ferrous Iodide, Anhydrous	0.01548	81897
Gamma Benzenehexachloride, $C_6H_6Cl_2$	0.009695	98655
Hydriodic Acid, HI	0.01279	10687
Hydrobromic Acid, HBr	0.008093	90811
Hydrochloric Acid, HCl	0.003647	56194
Hydrocyanic Acid, HCN, to first formation of ppt.	0.005404	73272
Hydrocyanic Acid, HCN, K_2CrO_4, as indicator	0.002702	43169
Iodine, I	0.01269	10346
Iodoform, CHI_3	0.01313	11826
Lead Bromide, $PbBr_2$	0.01835	26364
Lead Chloride, $PbCl_2$	0.01390	14301
Lead Iodide, PbI_2	0.02305	36267
Lead Thiocyanate, $Pb(SCN)_2$	0.01616	20844
Lithium Bromide, Anhydrous, LiBr	0.008686	93882
Lithium Chloride, Anhydrous, LiCl	0.004240	62737
Lithium Iodide, Anhydrous, LiI	0.01339	12678
Magnesium Bromide, $MgBr_2 \cdot 6H_2O$	0.01461	16465
Magnesium Bromide, Anhydrous	0.009208	96417
Magnesium Chloride, $MgCl_2 \cdot 6H_2O$	0.01017	00732
Magnesium Chloride, Anhydrous, $MgCl_2$	0.004762	67779
Magnesium Iodide, $MgI_2 \cdot 8H_2O$	0.02111	32449
Manganese Bromide, $MnBr_2 \cdot 4H_2O$	0.01344	12840
Manganese Chloride, $MnCl_2 \cdot 4H_2O$	0.009895	99542

TENTH-NORMAL SILVER NITRATE—*Continued*

One ml of tenth-normal silver nitrate
is equivalent to:

	Gram	Logarithm
Manganese Chloride, Anhydrous, $MnCl_2$	0.006292	79879
Manganese Iodide, $MnI_2 \cdot 4H_2O$	0.01904	27967
Methyl Iodide, CH_3I	0.01419	15198
Methylene Iodide, CH_2I_2	0.01339	12678
Nickel Cyanide, Anhydrous, $Ni(CN)_2$	0.005540	74351
Nitrous Acid Anhydride, N_2O_3 (by reaction with $KClO_3$)	0.01140	05690
Phosphoric Acid, H_3PO_4	0.003269	51441
Phosphorus Pentoxide, P_2O_5	0.002368	37438
Potassium Bromide, KBr	0.01190	07555
Potassium Chloride, KCl	0.007456	87251
Potassium Cyanide, KCN	0.01302	11461
Potassium Iodide, KI	0.01660	22011
Potassium Nitrate, KNO_3	0.01011	00475
Potassium Perchlorate $KClO_4$ from the Cl	0.01386	14176
Potassium Phosphate, Dibasic, K_2HPO_4	0.005808	76403
Potassium Thiocyanate, KSCN	0.009717	98753
Reinecke Salt (or Ammonium Reineckate), $NH_4[Cr(NH_3)_2(SCN)_4] \cdot H_2O$	0.008862	94753
SCN	0.005808	76403
Sodium Bromide, Anhydrous, NaBr	0.01029	01242
Sodium Chloride, NaCl	0.005845	76678
Sodium Cyanide, NaCN	0.009801	99127
Sodium Iodide, NaI	0.01499	18580
Sodium Nitrite, $NaNO_2$	0.02070	31597
Sodium Nitroferricyanide, $Na_2Fe(CN)_5NO \cdot 2H_2O$	0.01489	17289
Sodium Perchlorate, $NaClO_4 \cdot H_2O$ from the Cl	0.01405	14768
Sodium Perchlorate, Anhydrous, $NaClO_4$ from the Cl	0.01225	08814
Sodium Phosphate, Dibasic, Anhydrous, Na_2HPO_4	0.004735	67532
Sodium Thiocyanate, NaSCN	0.008107	90886
Strontium Bromide, $SrBr_2 \cdot 6H_2O$	0.01778	24993
Strontium Bromide, Anhydrous	0.01237	09237
Strontium Chloride, $SrCl_2 \cdot 6H_2O$	0.01333	12483
Strontium Chloride, Anhydrous	0.007928	89916
Theophylline, $C_7H_8O_2 \cdot H_2O$	0.01982	29710
Zinc Bromide, $ZnBr_2$	0.01126	05154
Zinc Chloride, $ZnCl_2$	0.006815	83347
Zinc Cyanide, $Zn(CN)_2$	0.01174	06967
Zinc Iodide, ZnI_2	0.01596	20303

TENTH-NORMAL SODIUM NITRITE

One ml of tenth-normal sodium nitrite
is equivalent to:

	Gram	Logarithm
Aminobenzoic Acid, $C_7H_7O_2N$	0.01371	13704
Aminosalicylic Acid, $NH_2C_7H_5NO_3$	0.01531	18498
Ammonium Sulfamate, $NH_4SO_3NH_2$	0.01141	05729

TENTH-NORMAL SODIUM NITRITE—*Continued*

One ml of tenth-normal sodium nitrate
is equivalent to:

	Gram	Logarithm
Butacaine, $C_{18}H_{30}N_2O_2$	0.03064	48629
Butacaine Sulfate, $(C_{18}H_{30}N_2O_2)_2 \cdot H_2SO_4$	0.03555	55084
Calcium Aminosalicylate, $(NH_2C_7H_5NO_3)_2Ca$	0.01722	23603
Procaine, $C_{13}H_{20}N_2O_2$	0.02363	37346
Procaine Hydrochloride (Novocaine), $C_{13}H_{20}N_2O_2HCl$	0.02728	43584
Sodium Aminosalicylate, Anhydrous, $NH_2C_7H_5NO_3Na$	0.01751	24329
Succinylsulfathiazole, $C_{13}H_{13}N_3O_5S_2$	0.03554	55072
Sulfadiazine, $C_{10}H_{10}N_4O_2S$	0.02503	39846
Sulfadiazine Sodium, $C_{10}H_9N_4O_2SNa$	0.02723	43505
Sulfaguanidine, $C_7H_{10}N_4O_2S$	0.02142	33082
Sulfamic Acid, $HO \cdot SO_2NH_2$	0.00971	98717
Sulfanilamide, $C_6H_8N_2O_2S$	0.01722	23603
Sulfanilic Acid, $C_6H_5(NH_2)SO_3$	0.01732	23855
Sulfapyridine, $C_{11}H_{11}N_3O_2S$	0.02493	39672
Sulfapyridine Sodium, $C_{11}H_{10}N_3O_2SNa$	0.02713	43345
Sulfathiazole, $C_9H_8N_3O_2S_2$	0.02543	40535
Sulfathiazole Sodium, $C_9H_8N_3O_2S_2Na$	0.02733	44295

TENTH-NORMAL SODIUM THIOSULFATE

One ml of tenth-normal sodium thiosulfate
is equivalent to:

	Gram	Logarithm
Ammonium Chromate, $(NH_4)_2CrO_4$	0.005070	70501
Ammonium Dichromate, $(NH_4)_2Cr_2O_7$	0.004202	62346
Ammonium Persulfate, $(NH_4)_2S_2O_8$	0.01141	05729
Amyl Nitrite, $C_5H_{11}NO_2$	0.01171	06856
Antimony, Sb, in antimonic compounds	0.006088	78447
Antimony Pentachloride, $SbCl_5$	0.01495	17464
Antimony Pentasulfide, Sb_2S_5	0.01010	00432
Antimony Pentoxide, Sb_2O_5	0.008010	90363
Arsenic, As, in arsenic compounds	0.003747	57368
Arsenic Acid, H_3AsO_4	0.003548	54998
Arsenic Pentachloride, $AsCl_5$	0.01261	10072
Arsenic Pentoxide, As_2O_5	0.005748	75952
Barium Chlorate, $Ba(ClO_3)_2 \cdot H_2O$	0.002686	42911
Barium Chromate, $BaCrO_4$	0.008446	92665
Barium Iodate, $Ba(IO_3)_2$	0.004060	60853
Bromine, Br	0.07902	90266
Calcium Dichromate. $CaCr_2O_7 \cdot 3H_2O$	0.005169	71314
Calcium Dichromate, Anhydrous	0.004268	63022
Ceric Ammonium Sulfate, $Ce(NH_4)_4(SO_4)_4 \cdot 4H_2O$	0.06686	82518
Ceric Oxide, CeO_2	0.01723	23629
Ceric Sulfate, $Ce(SO_4)_2 \cdot 4H_2O$	0.04044	60681
Ceric Sulfate, Anhydrous	0.03323	52153

TENTH-NORMAL SODIUM THIOSULFATE—*Continued*

One ml of tenth-normal sodium thiosulfate
is equivalent to:

	Gram	Logarithm
Chloramine T, $C_7H_7ClNO_2SNa \cdot 3H_2O$	0.01408	14860
Chlorine, Cl	0.003546	54974
Chromium, Cr	0.001733	23880
Chromium Ammonium Sulfate, $CrNH_4(SO_4)_2 \cdot 12H_2O$	0.01595	20276
Chromium Chloride, $CrCl_3 \cdot 6H_2O$	0.008820	94547
Chromium Chloride, Anhydrous	0.005279	72255
Chromium Nitrate, $Cr(NO_3)_3$	0.007934	89949
Chromium Oxide, Cr_2O_3	0.002533	40364
Chromium Potassium Sulfate, $CrK(SO_4)_2 \cdot 12H_2O$	0.01665	22141
Chromium Sulfate, $Cr_2(SO_4)_3 \cdot 15H_2O$	0.01104	04297
Chromium Sulfate, Anhydrous	0.006536	81531
Chromium Trioxide, CrO_3	0.003333	52284
Cobalt, Co	0.005894	77041
Cobalt Acetate, $Co(CH_3 \cdot CO_2)_2 \cdot 4H_2O$	0.02491	39637
Cobalt Ammonium Sulfate, $CoSO_4(NH_4)_2SO_4 \cdot 6H_2O$	0.03952	59682
Cobalt Chloride, $CoCl_2 \cdot 6H_2O$	0.02380	37658
Cobalt Chloride, Anhydrous	0.01299	11361
Cobalt Nitrate, $Co(NO_3)_2 \cdot 6H_2O$	0.02911	46404
Cobalt Nitrate, Anhydrous	0.01830	26245
Cobalt Sulfate, $CoSO_4 \cdot 7H_2O$	0.02811	44886
Cobalt Sulfate, Anhydrous	0.01550	19033
Copper, Cu, in cupric salts	0.006357	80325
Cupric Acetate, $Cu(C_2H_3O_2)_2 \cdot H_2O$	0.01996	30016
Cupric Acetate, Anhydrous, $Cu(C_2H_3O_2)_2$	0.01816	25912
Cupric Ammonium Chloride, $CuCl_2 \cdot 2NH_4Cl \cdot 2H_2O$	0.02776	44326
Cupric-ammonio Sulfate, $Cu(NH_3)_4SO_4 \cdot H_2O$	0.02458	39058
Cupric Bromide, $CuBr_2$	0.02234	34908
Cupric Carbonate, Basic, $CuCO_3 \cdot Cu(OH)_2$	0.01106	04376
Cupric Chloride, $CuCl_2 \cdot 2H_2O$	0.01705	23172
Cupric Chloride, Anhydrous, $CuCl_2$	0.01345	12872
Cupric Nitrate, $Cu(NO_3)_2 \cdot 3H_2O$	0.02416	38310
Cupric Nitrate, Anhydrous, $Cu(NO_3)_2$	0.01878	27370
Cupric Oxide, CuO	0.007957	90075
Cupric Potassium Chloride, $CuCl_2 \cdot 2KCl \cdot 2H_2O$	0.03196	50461
Cupric Sulfate, $CuSO_4 \cdot 5H_2O$	0.02497	39742
Cupric Sulfate, Anhydrous	0.01596	20303
Cuprous Oxide, Cu_2O (from Cu)	0.007157	85473
Dichloramine T, $C_7H_7Cl_2NO_2S$	0.006003	77837
Ethyl Nitrite, $C_5H_5NO_2$	0.007507	87535
Ferric Acetate, $Fe(C_2H_3O_2)_3$	0.02329	36717
Ferric Ammonium Sulfate, $Fe(NH_4)(SO_4)_2 \cdot 12H_2O$	0.04822	68323
Ferric Ammonium Sulfate, Anhydrous, $Fe(NH_4)(SO_4)_2$	0.02660	42488
Ferric Chloride, $FeCl_3 \cdot 6H_2O$	0.02703	43185
Ferric Chloride, Anhydrous	0.01622	21005
Ferric Hydroxide, $Fe(OH)_3$	0.01069	02898
Ferric Nitrate, $Fe(NO_3)_3 \cdot 9H_2O$	0.04040	60638
Ferric Nitrate, Anhydrous	0.02419	38364
Ferric Oxide, Fe_2O_3	0.007984	90222
Ferric Phosphate, $FePO_4$	0.01509	17869

TENTH-NORMAL SODIUM THIOSULFATE—*Continued*

One ml of tenth-normal sodium thiosulfate
is equivalent to:

	Gram	Logarithm
Ferric Sulfate, Anhydrous, $Fe_2(SO_4)_3$	0.03999	60195
Ferrous Lactate, $Fe(C_3H_5O_3)_2 \cdot 3H_2O$, after oxidation	0.02880	45939
Glyceryl Trinitrate, $C_3H_5(NO_3)_3$	0.01150	06070
Iodic Acid, HIO_3	0.002932	46716
Iodine Pentoxide, I_2O_5	0.002782	44436
Iodine, I	0.01269	10346
Iron, Fe	0.005584	74695
Lead Chromate, $PnCrO_4$	0.01077	03222
Lead Dioxide, PbO_2	0.01196	07777
Lead Oxide, Red, Pb_3O_4	0.03428	53508
Lead Tetraacetate, $Pb(C_2H_3O_2)_4$	0.02217	37967
Osmium Tetroxide, OsO_4	0.006355	80312
Oxygen, O	0.000800	90309
Ozone, O_3	0.00240	38021
Potassium Biniodate, $KH(IO_3)_2$	0.003250	51188
Potassium Bromate, $KBrO_3$	0.002784	44467
Potassium Chlorate, $KClO_3$	0.002043	30027
Potassium Chromate, K_2CrO_4	0.006473	81111
Potassium Dichromate, $K_2Cr_2O_7$	0.004904	69055
Potassium Ferricyanide, $K_3Fe(CN)_6$	0.03292	51746
Potassium Iodate, KIO_3	0.003567	55230
Potassium Nitrite, KNO_2	0.004255	62890
Potassium Periodate, KIO_4	0.002125	32736
Potassium Permanganate, $KMnO_4$	0.003161	49982
Potassium Persulfate, $K_2S_2O_8$	0.01352	13098
Potassium Selenite, K_2SeO_3	0.005129	71003
Selenious Acid, H_2SeO_3	0.003225	50853
Selenium Dioxide, SeO_2	0.002780	44404
Sodium Arsenate, Dibasic, $Na_2HAsO_4 \cdot 7H_2O$	0.01560	19312
Sodium Arsenate, Dibasic, Anhydrous	0.009295	96825
Sodium Bromate, $NaBrO_3$	0.002515	40054
Sodium Chlorate, $NaClO_3$	0.001774	24895
Sodium Chromate, $Na_2CrO_4 \cdot 4H_2O$	0.007802	89221
Sodium Chromate, Anhydrous	0.005400	73239
Sodium Dichromate, $Na_2Cr_2O_7 \cdot 2H_2O$	0.004967	69609
Sodium Dichromate, Anhydrous	0.004367	63018
Sodium Ferricyanide, $Na_3Fe(CN)_6$	0.002809	44855
Sodium Hypochlorite, NaOCl	0.003723	57089
Sodium Iodate, $NaIO_3$	0.003299	51838
Sodium Nitrite, $NaNO_2$	0.003450	53786
Sodium Periodate (metaperiodate) $NaIO_4$	0.002674	42716
Sodium Permanganate, $NaMnO_4$	0.002839	45317
Sodium Peroxide, Na_2O_2	0.003900	59106
Sodium Selenate, Na_2SeO_4	0.003153	49872
Sodium Selenite, Na_2SeO_3	0.004330	63649
Sodium Thiosulfate, $Na_2S_2O_3 \cdot 5H_2O$	0.02482	39480
Sodium Thiosulfate, Anhydrous	0.01581	19896

GRAVIMETRIC AND OTHER FREQUENTLY REQUIRED
CONVERSION FACTORS

Found	Sought or to Convert into	Factor	Found	Sought or to Convert into	Factor
Ag	Br.	0.7408	BiPO$_4$	Bi.	0.6874
	Cl.	0.3287		Bi$_2$O$_3$.	0.7663
	CN.	0.2413		Bi$_2$S$_3$.	0.8458
	I.	1.177			
	AgNO$_3$.	1.576	Bi$_2$S$_3$	Bi.	0.8129
AgCl	Cl.	0.2474	B$_2$O$_3$	B.	0.3107
	HCl.	0.2544		BF$_3$.	1.948
	KCl.	0.5202			
	Ag.	0.7526	Cd	CdCl$_2$.	1.6300
	AgNO$_3$.	1.185		CdCl$_2$·2½H$_2$O.	2.031
	NaCl.	0.4078		Cd(NO$_3$)$_2$·4H$_2$O.	2.711
Al$_2$O$_3$	Al.	0.5291		CdO.	1.142
	AlNH$_4$(SO$_4$)$_2$·12H$_2$O	8.893		CdSO$_4$.	1.855
	AlK(SO$_4$)$_2$·12H$_2$O. . .	9.305		CdSO$_4$·2⅔H$_2$O.	2.282
	AlCl$_3$.	2.616		CdS.	1.285
	AlCl$_3$·6H$_2$O.	4.755			
	Al$_2$(SO$_4$)$_3$·18H$_2$O. . . .	6.536	CdO	Cd.	0.8754
Al(C$_9$H$_6$NO)$_3$	Al.	0.0587		CdCl$_2$.	1.428
Aluminum	AlCl$_3$.	0.2902		Cd(NO$_3$)$_2$·4H$_2$O.	2.403
oxinate	AlCl$_3$·6H$_2$O.	0.5255		CdSO$_4$2⅔H$_2$O.	1.998
(Hydroxy-	Al(NO$_3$)$_3$·9H$_2$O.	0.8165		CdS.	1.125
quinolate)	Al$_2$O$_3$.	0.1110			
	AlK(SO$_4$)$_2$·12H$_2$O. . .	0.9681	CdS	Cd.	0.7781
	Al$_2$(SO$_4$)$_3$·18H$_2$O. . . .	0.7253		CdO.	0.8889
Au	AuCl$_3$.	1.539		CdSO$_4$.	1.373
	HAuCl$_4$·4H$_2$O.	2.090	CaF$_2$	F.	0.4866
BaCO$_3$	C.	0.0609		HF.	0.5126
	CO$_2$.	0.2229		MgSiF$_6$·6H$_2$O.	1.180
	CO$_3$.	0.3040		KF.	1.489
				NaF.	1.076
BaCrO$_4$	Ba.	0.5422		Na$_2$SiF$_6$.	0.8038
	BaO.	0.6053		SiF$_4$.	0.6664
	Cr.	0.2052			
	Cr$_2$O$_3$.	0.3000	CaO	Ca.	0.7146
	CrO$_3$.	0.3947		CaCO$_3$.	1.785
				CO$_2$.	0.7874
BaSO$_4$	Ba.	0.5785			
	BaCO$_3$.	0.8456	CaSO$_4$	Ca.	0.2943
	BaCl$_2$.	0.8923		CaF$_2$.	0.5735
	BaCl$_2$·2H$_2$O.	1.047		CaO.	0.4120
	BaSO$_4$.	1.120		F.	0.2791
	BaO.	0.6570			
	BaS.	0.7258	CO$_2$	C.	0.2729
	S.	0.1374		CaCO$_3$.	2.2743
	SO$_2$.	0.2745		CaO.	1.291
	H$_2$SO$_4$.	0.4201		CO$_3$.	1.364
	SO$_3$.	0.3430		K$_2$CO$_3$.	3.140
	SO$_4$.	0.4115		Na$_2$CO$_3$.	2.409
				NaHCO$_3$.	1.906
Bi$_2$O$_3$	Bi.	0.8970			
	Bi(NO$_3$)$_3$·5H$_2$O.	2.087	CeO$_2$	Ce.	0.8141
	BiOCl.	1.1184		Ce$_2$O$_3$.	0.9541
	Bi$_2$S$_3$.	1.104			
			Cr$_2$O$_3$	Cr.	0.6842
BiOCl	Bi.	0.8024		CrK(SO$_4$)$_2$·12H$_2$O. . .	6.571
	Bi(NO$_3$)$_3$·5H$_2$O.	1.866		CrCl$_3$.	2.084
	Bi$_2$O$_3$.	0.8946		CrO$_3$.	1.316
			Co	CoCl$_2$·6H$_2$O.	4.036
				Co(NO$_3$)$_2$·6H$_2$O.	3.936
				CoO.	1.271
				Co$_3$O$_4$.	1.362
				CoSO$_4$·7H$_2$O.	4.168

Found	Sought or to Convert into	Factor	Found	Sought or to Convert into	Factor
Co_3O_4	Co	0.7343	$Mg_2P_2O_7$	Mg	0.21853
	$CoCl_2 \cdot 6H_2O$	2.964		$MgCl_2$	0.8553
	$Co(NO_3)_2 \cdot 6H_2O$	3.637		MgO	0.3623
	CoO	0.9336		$MgSO_4$	1.081
Cu	$CuCl_2 \cdot 2H_2O$	2.682		$MgSO_4 \cdot 7H_2O$	2.214
	$Cu(NO_3)_2 \cdot 3H_2O$			H_3PO_4	0.8805
	CuO	1.252		P	0.2784
	$CuSO_4 \cdot 5H_2O$	3.138		P_2O_5	0.6379
	$CuSO_4$	2.006		Na_2HPO_4	1.276
CuO	Cu	0.7989	Magnesium Sodium Uranyl Acetate $MgNa(C_2H_3O_2)_3$ $\cdot 3UO_2(C_2H_3O_2)_2$ $\cdot 6H_2O$	Na	0.0154
	$Cu(NO_3)_2 \cdot 3H_2O$	3.037		NaCl	0.0391
	$CuSO_4 \cdot 5H_2O$	3.138		Na_2O	0.0207
Fe_2O_3	Fe	0.6994		Na_2SO_4	0.0475
	$FeCl_3$	2.032			
	$FeCl_3 \cdot 6H_2O$	3.386	Mn_3O_4	Mn	0.7203
	FeO	0.9000		MnO	0.9301
	$FeSO_4$	1.903		$MnSO_4$	1.980
	$FeSO_4 \cdot 7H_2O$	3.482	$Mn_2P_2O_7$	Mn	0.3871
Hg	$HgCl_2$	1.354		MnO	0.4998
	HgCl	1.177		$MnSO_4$	1.064
HgCl	Hg	0.8498	$MnSO_4$	Mn	0.3638
	$HgCl_2$	1.150			
HgS	Hg	0.8622	MoO_3	Mo	0.6666
	$HgCl_2$	1.167	N	NH_3	1.216
	$Hg(NO_3)_2$	1.396		HNO_3	4.498
H_2O	H	0.1119	NaCl	Na	0.3934
	O	0.8881		Na_2CO_3	0.9068
$KClO_4$	K	0.2822	Na_2SO_4	Na	0.3238
	KCl	0.5381		NaCl	0.8230
	KNO_3	0.7293		Na_2O	0.4364
	K_2O	0.3400	NH_3	HN_4	1.059
	K_2SO_4	0.6289		NH_4Cl	3.141
K_2PtCl_6	Pt	0.4015		$(NH_4)_2SO_4$	3.880
	K	0.1609		N	0.8224
	KCl	0.3067	$Ni(C_4H_7N_2O_2)_2$ Nickel Dimethyl Glyoxime	Ni	0.2032
	KNO_3	0.4160		$Ni(NO_3)_2 \cdot 6H_2O$	1.007
	K_2O	0.0938		$NiSO_4 \cdot 6H_2O$	0.9098
	K_2SO_4	0.3588			
K_2SO_4	K	0.4488	$PbCrO_4$	Cr	0.1609
	KCl	0.8550		Cr_2O_3	0.2352
	KNO_3	1.160		CrO_3	0.3094
	K_2O	0.5405		Pb	0.6410
$K(C_6H_5)B$ Potassium Tetraphenylboron	K	0.1093		PbO	0.6905
	KCl	0.2106	$PbMoO_4$	Pb	0.5644
	KNO_3	0.2820		Mo	0.2613
	K_2O	0.1313		MoO_3	0.3922
	K_2SO_4	0.2430	$PbSO_4$	Pb	0.6833
Li_3PO_4	Li	0.1798		PbO	0.7359
	LiCl	1.098		PbS	0.7889
	Li_2O	0.3870	Pd	Iodine	2.379
Li_2SO_4	Li	0.1262	PdI_2	Iodine	0.7041
	LiCl	0.7713			
$Mg(C_9H_6NO)_2$ Magnesium Oxinate (Hydroxyquinolate)	$2H_2O$		Pt	$H_2PtCl_6 \cdot 6H_2O$	2.654
	Mg	0.06973		$PtCl_4$	1.727
	$MgCl_2$			K	0.4006
	$MgCl_2 \cdot 6H_2O$	0.5832		KCl	0.7640
	$Mg(NO_3)_2 \cdot 6H_2O$	0.7349		K_2O	0.4826
	MgO	0.1154		K_2SO_4	0.8926
	$MgSO_4 \cdot 7H_2O$	0.7070			

Found	Sought or to Convert into	Factor	Found	Sought or to Convert into	Factor
Sb_2S_3	Sb	0.7168	V_2O_5	V	0.5602
SiO_2	Si	0.4674	WO_3	W	0.7930
	SiF_4	1.732		$Na_2WO_4 \cdot 2H_2O$	1.422
SnO_2	Sn	0.7877		Na_2WO_4, Anhydrous	1.267
	$SnCl_4$	1.729	Zn	$Zn(C_2H_3O_2)_2 \cdot 2H_2O$	3.537
	$SnCl_2 \cdot 3H_2O$	1.497		$ZnCl_2$	2.085
SO_2	S	0.5005		ZnO	1.245
	SO_3	2.149		$ZnSO_4$	1.491
$SrSO_4$	Sr	0.4770		$ZnSO_4 \cdot 7H_2O$	4.399
	$SrCO_3$	0.8036	ZnO	Zn	0.8034
	$SrCl_2$	0.8631		$Zn(C_2H_3O_2)_2 \cdot 2H_2O$	2.697
	$Sr(NO_3)_2$	1.152		$ZnCl_2$	1.675
	SrO	0.5641		$ZnSO_4$	1.984
ThO_2	Th	0.8788		$ZnSO_4 \cdot 7H_2O$	3.534
	$Th(NO_3)_4 \cdot 6H_2O$	2.901	$Zn_2P_2O_7$	Zn	0.4289
TiO_2	Ti	0.5995		$ZnCl_2$	0.8924
$TlBr$	Tl	0.7182		ZnO	0.5339
	$TlNO_3$	0.8661		$ZnSO_4 \cdot 7H_2O$	1.886
Tl_2CrO_4	Tl	0.7788	ZnNa Uranyl	Na	0.0149
U_3O_8	U	0.8480	acetate ZnNa $(C_2H_3O_2)_3 \cdot$	NaCl	0.0380
	$UO(NO_3)_2 \cdot 6H_2O$	1.788	$3UO_2(C_2H_3O_2)_2$	Na_2O	0.0202
	UO_3	1.019	$\cdot 6H_2O$		
$(UO_2)_2P_2O_7$	U	0.6676	ZrO_2	Zr	0.7403
	$UO_2(NO_3)_2 \cdot 6H_2O$	1.406		$Zr(NO_4)_4 5H_2O$	3.482
	UO_3	0.8102			

INDEX